Traveller's Library

CONTAINING NOVELS, SHORT STORIES,
ESSAYS AND POEMS BY

Frank Swinnerton
Joseph Conrad
Max Beerbohm
Arthur Machen
H. G. Wells
E. M. Forster
Oliver Onions
Perceval Gibbon
A. Neil Lyons
C. S. Evans
D. H. Lawrence
Aldous Huxley
Edmund Gosse
John Galsworthy
Desmond MacCarthy
Virginia Woolf
H. W. Garrod
Roy Campbell
Siegfried Sassoon
Hilaire Belloc
Frances Cornford
W. J. Turner
Ralph Hodgson
William H. Davies
John Masefield

Joseph Plunkett
Sacheverell Sitwell
Arnold Bennett
Robert Bridges
Alice Meynell
Francis Thompson
Rupert Brooke
Walter de la Mare
James Elroy Flecker
William Butler Yeats
Lytton Strachey
Julian Huxley
J. B. S. Haldane
Bertrand Russell
Norah Hoult
Osbert Sitwell
Michael Arlen
Martin Armstrong
William Gerhardi
Katherine Mansfield
Harold Nicolson
David Garnett
Saki (H. H. Munro)
E. C. Bentley

Traveller's Library

COMPILED AND WITH NOTES BY

W. Somerset Maugham

Garden City, New York

DOUBLEDAY, DORAN & COMPANY, INC.

1933

Acknowledgments

THANKS are due to the following firms and individuals for permission to use material mentioned:

Martin Armstrong, for "Biography" and "The Poet and the Mandrill," from "The Puppet Show." (Published in America by Brentano's.) Burns, Oates & Washbourne, Ltd., for "The Hound of Heaven," and "The Kingdom of God" (In No Strange Land), from "The Selected Poems of Francis Thompson. Jonathan Cape, for "Leisure," by William H. Davies. The Dial Press, Inc., for "The Making of a Poet," "The Serf," "Horses on the Camargue," and "On Some South African Novelists," from "Adamastor, Poems by Roy Campbell," copyright, 1931, by The Dial Press, Inc. Gerald Duckworth & Co., Ltd., for "Tarantella," "Lines to a Don," "The Statue," "On a Dead Hostess," "On a Great Election," "Partly from the Greek," by Hilaire Belloc, from "Sonnets & Verse." (Robt. M. McBride & Co., publishers in America.) Dodd, Mead & Company, for "The Happy Hypocrite," by Max Beerbohm, copyright, 1896, 1924, by Dodd, Mead & Company; "The Soldier," "The Hill," "The Old Vicarage, Grantchester," and "Heaven," from "The Collected Poems of Rupert Brooke," copyright, 1915, by Dodd, Mead & Company; "Robert Louis Stevenson," from "Recollections of Stevenson," by Edmund Gosse. Doubleday, Doran & Company, Inc., for "Nocturne," by Frank Swinnerton, copyright, 1917, by Doubleday, Doran & Company, Inc.; "The Old Wives' Tale," by Arnold Bennett; "The Man With the Broken Nose," from "These Charming People" by Michael Arlen, copyright, 1924, by Doubleday,

v

Doran & Company, Inc.; "Wordsworth in the Tropics," from
"Do What You Will," by Aldous Huxley, copyright, 1929, by
Aldous Huxley; "An Outpost of Progress," from "Tales of
Unrest," by Joseph Conrad, copyright, 1898, by Doubleday,
Doran & Company, Inc.; "Youth," by Joseph Conrad, copy-
right, 1899, by S. S. McClure Company, 1903, by Doubleday,
Doran & Company, Inc.; "The Tillotson Banquet," from
"Mortal Coils," by Aldous Huxley, copyright, 1922, by Double-
day, Doran & Company, Inc.; "A Night at Pietramala," from
"Along the Road," by Aldous Huxley, copyright, 1925, by
Doubleday, Doran & Company, Inc.; "The Machine Breaks
Down," by Osbert Sitwell, from "Triple Fugue"; "The Rio
Grande," by Sacheverell Sitwell, from "The Thirteenth
Caesar"; "The Country of the Blind," from "Short Stories of
H. G. Wells," copyright, 1895, by H. G. Wells. Duffield & Com-
pany, for "The Big Drum," by William Gerhardi, from "Pretty
Creatures," copyright, 1927, by Duffield & Company. E. P.
Dutton Company, for "No. 2 The Pines," by Max Beerbohm,
from "And Even Now"; the following by Siegfried Sassoon:
"Base Details" from "Counter Attack and Other Poems,"
"Blighters" from "Picture Show," and "Idyll" from "Old
Huntsman and Other Poems." Perceval Gibbon, for "The
Second-Class Passenger." (First published by Methuen & Co.,
Ltd.) J. B. S. Haldane, for "The Last Judgment," copyright,
1927, by Harper & Brothers. Harcourt, Brace and Company,
Inc., for "Dr. Burney's Evening Party," by Virginia Woolf,
from "The Second Common Reader," copyright, 1932, by
Harcourt, Brace and Company, Inc. Harper & Brothers, for
"Mrs. Johnson," from "Poor Women," by Norah Hoult, copy-
right, 1929, by Harper & Brothers. A. M. Heath & Co., Ltd.,
on behalf of Mr. Norman Gullick, for "Swinburne," by Ed-
mund Gosse. William Heinemann, Ltd., for "Bringing a New
Boy," from "Nash and Some Others," by C. S. Evans; "Io"
from "Widdershins," by Oliver Onions. Henry Holt & Com-
pany, for "Arabia," "The Listeners," "The Three Strangers,"
"An Epitaph," "The Little Salamander," by Walter de la
Mare, from "Collected Poems," copyright, 1920, by Henry
Holt & Company. Houghton Mifflin Company, for "The
Marquis de Chaumont" and "Arketall," from "Some People,"
by Harold Nicolson. Alfred A. Knopf, Inc., for "Trent's Last
Case," by E. C. Bentley, copyright, 1913, 1930, by Alfred A.
Knopf, Inc.; "Religion and Science: Old Wine in New Bottles,"

from "Essays of a Biologist," by Julian Huxley, copyright, 1923, by Alfred A. Knopf, Inc.; the following poems from "The Collected Poems of James Elroy Flecker": "The Golden Journey to Samarkand—Prologue," "War Song of the Saracens," "The Old Ships," "Brumana," "Hyali"; "The Celestial Omnibus" from "The Celestial Omnibus and Other Stories" by E. M. Forster; "Enoch Soames" from "Seven Men" by Max Beerbohm, copyright, 1920, by Max Beerbohm; "The Inmost Light" from "The House of Souls," by Arthur Machen, copyright, 1922, by Alfred A. Knopf, Inc.; "Psychology" and "Pictures" from "Bliss and Other Stories," by Katherine Mansfield; "Miss Brill" from "The Garden Party," by Katherine Mansfield, copyright, 1922, by Alfred A. Knopf, Inc.; "Lady Into Fox" by David Garnett, copyright, 1923, by Alfred A. Knopf, Inc. A. Neil Lyons, for "The Ginger-Nut." The Macmillan Company, for "Sea-Fever" by John Masefield, from "Collected Poems," copyright; "Down by the Salley Gardens," "The Lake Isle of Innisfree," and "When You Are Old," by William Butler Yeats, from "Early Poems and Stories," also "To a Friend Whose Work Has Come to Nothing" and "That the Night Come," from "Later Poems," by William Butler Yeats, copyright; "The Bull," and "The Mystery," from "Poems" by Ralph Hodgson, copyright, 1917, by The Macmillan Company. Desmond MacCarthy, for "A Hermit's Day" from "Remnants." W. W. Norton & Company, Inc., for "Introduction: On the Value of Scepticism" and "Eastern and Western Ideals of Happiness," from "Sceptical Essays," copyright, 1928, by Bertrand Russell; "A Free Man's Worship" by Bertrand Russell, from "Mysticism and Logic," copyright, 1928, by W. W. Norton & Company, Inc. Oxford University Press, for "A Passer-By," "On a Dead Child," and "Nightingales" from "The Poetical Works of Robert Bridges"; "How to Know a Good Book from a Bad" from "The Profession of Poetry and other Lectures" by H. W. Garrod. The Poetry Bookshop, on behalf of Mrs. Cornford, the following: "Autumn Evening," and "To a Lady Seen from the Train," by Frances Cornford, from "Selections from Modern Poets—Made by J. C. Squire. G. P. Putnam's Sons for "Florence Nightingale" from "Eminent Victorians" by Lytton Strachey. Siegfried Sassoon, for "Everyone Sang," from "Selected Poems," published by William Heinemann, Ltd.; also other poems listed under E. P. Dutton Company and The Viking Press, Inc.

Charles Scribner's Sons, for "Renouncement" by Alice Meynell, from "The Poems of Alice Meynell," copyright, 1923, by Wilfrid Meynell; "Reminiscences of Conrad" by John Galsworthy, copyright, 1924, by Charles Scribner's Sons. The Talbot Press, Ltd., for "I See His Blood Upon the Rose," from "The Complete Poetical Works of Joseph Mary Plunkett. W. J. Turner, for "In the Caves of Auvergne." The Viking Press, Inc., for "Louise," "Tobermory," and "Esme," from "The Short Stories of 'Saki' (H. H. Munro)," copyright, 1930, by The Viking Press, Inc.; "Vision," by Siegfried Sassoon, from "Satirical Poems."

Contents

ESSAYS

SECTION I

POEMS

SECTION I

Contents

ESSAYS

SECTION II

SHORT STORIES

SECTION II

Contents

A NOVEL

Traveller's Library

THERE are people who have no head for cards. It is impossible not to be sorry for them, for what, one asks oneself, can the future have to offer them when the glow of youth has departed and advancing years force them, as they force all of us, to be spectators rather than actors in the comedy of life? Love is for the young and affection is but a frigid solace to a pining heart. Sport demands physical vigour and affairs a strenuous activity. To have learnt to play a good game of bridge is the safest insurance against the tedium of old age. Throughout life one may find in cards endless entertainment and an occupation for idle hours that rests the mind from care and pleasantly exercises the intelligence. For the people who say that only the stupid can play cards err; they do not know what decision, what quickness of apprehension, what judgment, what knowledge of character, are required to play a difficult hand perfectly. The good card-player trusts his intuition as implicitly as Monsieur Bergson, but he calls it a hunch; the brilliant card-player has a gift as specific as the poet's: he too is born not made. The student of human nature can find endless matter for observation in the behaviour of his fellow card-players. Meanness and generosity, prudence and audacity, courage and timidity, weakness and strength; all these men show at the card-table according to their natures, and because they are intent upon the game drop the mask they wear in the ordinary affairs of life. Few are so deep that you do not know the essential facts about them after a few rubbers of bridge. The card-table is a very good school for the study of mankind. The unhappy persons who have no card sense say that playing cards is a waste of time, but it is never waste of time to amuse oneself; and besides, the day has twenty-four hours and the week seven days, there is always a certain time to be wasted. In passing I may remark that even *they* generally own a greasy pack of cards, and when you come upon them unexpectedly you are just as likely to find them occupied in laying out a patience as in improving their minds with great literature or their souls with reflection. Of course when you ask them how leisure can be better employed they say, in conversation. For they are great talkers. They lament the decay of the art of conversation and ascribe it to the universal passion for bridge. It is obvious that this pastime has deprived many a light prattler of his audience and it is true that there are now few conversationalists in the grand style. I doubt whether the impatience of the present day would suffer their tyranny, for they seem to have indulged much in monologue and they were impatient of interruption. I have a notion that it is pleasanter to read Boswell's record of the conversations than it ever was to listen to Dr. Johnson. I have heard that when Mallarmé received his admirers on those Tuesdays which literary gossip has made famous, he stood in front of the fireplace and discoursed on some subject or other amid the silence of the company; and certainly the accounts one hears of the conversation of Anatole France do not lead one to suspect that there was much give and take. I should have thought that sort of thing must have been an interesting experience, and maybe an intellectual treat, but hardly a pleasant relaxation. It can indeed only have been supportable because the listeners were filled with awe of the speaker, and awe, happily, is not a feeling that we, English and Americans, particularly cherish for men of eminence. On the other hand ordinary conversation, the chit-chat of the drawing-room, is seldom in English-speaking countries witty or profound. Its staple is the foibles of our friends and the affairs of the day. We are shy of speaking in public of our souls, of God and Immortality, and we are rarely so interested in art and literature as to be willing to argue about them. The accompaniment of good music is needed to loosen our tongues. It is not often in a mixed gathering that conversation proceeds long without some of us hankering after the bridge-table, and if there is no sign of it glancing surreptitiously at our watches and wondering how soon we can decently take our leave. It is to meet this situation, I suppose, that in circles where cards are not played the games have been invented that add so much horror to social intercourse, such as Lights, Consequences and Anagrams. There are even people who have brought the torture of their fellows to such a pitch that they force you to invent rhymed couplets upon topics of their suggestion. Such diversions of course point to an abnormal pleasure in the infliction of boredom.

Perhaps the least intolerable of all these methods of passing time is to offer for discussion some point of behaviour. If, for instance, in some disaster you could only save one person and your choice lay between a small boy, a beautiful young woman and an eminent scientist, which would you choose? Another is, if you were going to spend the rest of your life on a desert island and could only take twelve books which would they be? This question occurred to me when I set about choosing the materials for the volume to which this is the introduction. It is of course no test of one's literary inclinations, for in such a case the amount of matter would have to be the first consideration. People very sensibly for the most part mention the Bible and the plays of Shakespeare. I have read the Bible twice through from cover to cover and have no great wish to read it again, but it certainly contains a lot of meat and I suppose would be a good book to take. The same may be said of Shakespeare. There are many of the plays which no one would in ordinary circumstances care to read a second time, but none that if you were pressed for reading matter you could not read at least once or twice a year. After these two the choice becomes more difficult and the answers vary; but the question of quantity is as important as that of quality and the whole of Wordsworth in one volume would evidently be preferred to the whole of Keats. And then you must consider that you will have to read the same thing twenty, fifty or a hundred times. There are a great many books that are worth reading once, a considerable number that are worth reading twice, but not many that are worth reading over and over again. I once knew a man who read *The Pickwick Papers* every year for thirty years, but he eventually died of cirrhosis of the liver.

In the collection of pieces that comprise this book I have not sought to provide a volume for anyone who looks forward to being cast away on a desert island. My object is modest. I have asked myself what I should like to take with me in a single volume of reasonable size if I could have but one book and were travelling from New York to San Francisco by train or across the Atlantic on a tramp steamer. I do not want to tire the reader of this preface with a long account of the reasons for which I have inserted this or that, but I should like him to have patience with me while I tell him exactly what I have been at. I am not a critic or a scholar. Either of these would doubtless have chosen very different things from what I have, but if the publishers of this volume had needed the taste of the one or the learning of the other I should certainly not have been invited to make the selection. I am a professional writer. I have read a great deal, sometimes for instruction and sometimes for pleasure, but never since I was a small boy without an inward eye on the relation between what I was reading and my professional interests. At one time I read omnivorously, but for a good many years I have read little but what immediately concerned me. I am sure that a great deal that was worth reading has thus escaped me. For this reason the reader will doubtless look in vain for much that he would have expected to find here. I am more interested in an author's personality than in the books he writes. I follow him in the attempts he makes to express himself, his experiments in this manner and that; but when he has produced the work in which he has at last said all he has to say about himself, when he has arrived at what perhaps for many years he has only approached, then I read him no longer. At least if I do it is out of politeness, because he has given me his book, or fear, in case he should be affronted if I didn't, and not from inclination. Sometimes I have to read many books by an author before my curiosity about him is satisfied and sometimes only his first or second. He may write half a hundred masterpieces after that, but life is short and there is a great deal I urgently want to read, and I am content to leave their enjoyment to others. I daresay some of the authors represented in this volume are not represented by their best things. I dare say they have written since much of greater merit, but I do not happen to have read it. These writers belong roughly to the same period. It is difficult to appreciate any generation but one's own. Few of the writers who were esteemed of importance when I was a young man excite me much now and even then I was doubtless more critical than became me. The young author may be forgiven if he is unfair to his elders. They occupy a place in the sun which he would gladly fill. But it is not only envy that leads him to depreciate them. For they deal with manners and customs that have constrained his youth; they represent an attitude towards life and deliver a philosophy which he is naturally in revolt against. They are realists and he is a romantic or the other way about. He cannot be expected to realise that his attitude and his philosophy will in a little while seem as dull and conventional as those that now outrage his sense of common decency. And it is easy to miss the merits of the writers who are pushing one into the background. I have always a sneaking sympathy with George Crabbe who read the poems of Byron, Walter Scott, Keats and Shelley, and thought them all stuff and nonsense. After all he might have been right. In the case of one of them he was, and perhaps of two. I would offer it as a test that an author can apply to himself; when he can see nothing at all in work that the best critical opinion of the day pronounces good, his hour has struck and nothing remains to him but to shut up shop and like Voltaire's Candide cultivate a garden. It is dangerous for an author to get too set in his own manner and I have always followed, though with circumspection, the productions of my fellow writers in order to see whether in technique or point of view they could teach me something that it behoved me to know. But during the forty years I have been studying my craft I have seen so many writers hailed as masters, enjoy their hour of glory, and sink into an oblivion which is always described as well-merited, that I have become sceptical; and now, when a new genius is discovered I wait a year or two before I concern myself with him. It is astonishing how many books I find there is no need for me to read at all. This volume then does not pretend to be a survey of English literature during the last thirty years or so, but merely a hap-hazard collection of pieces that I have read and thought I should like to read again. I have chosen them from the work of English writers partly because I know current English literature better than current American literature and because it seemed to me that by keeping to the authors of one country I obtained at least an illusion of unity, which is the only completeness such a miscellany can hope to have; but also because American literature during the last thirty years is so rich, especially in the short story, a form I am particularly attracted by, and in the light novel, a form not often successfully cultivated in England, that I should have been overwhelmed by the mass of matter. I could never have got into the limits of this book half the things I should have urgently wanted to put in. I have in point of fact read again all that is here offered to the reader and I think that it is good. When I was gathering the materials I made a list of a number of things that I thought I should like to include, but when I came to tackle them found that many of them did not bear a second reading. I made some unforeseen discoveries. Stories that I had thought profound now seemed to me pretentious and others that I had thought humorous, silly; verses that had moved me left me cold and essays I had found suggestive I now found trivial. I have thrown many old friends into the dustbin; but not without a sigh. Lest the kindly reader should think me heartless I hasten to add that I speak metaphorically; I have in fact put them in a large packing-case and sent them to the local hospital.

The ablest editor I know is accustomed to say: I am the average American and what interests me will interest my readers; the event has proved him right. Now I have most of my life been miserably conscious that I am not the average Englishman. Let no one think I say this with self-satisfaction, for I think that there is nothing better than to be like everybody else. It is the only way to be happy, and it is with but a wry face that one tells oneself that happiness is not everything. The best writers have been ordinary men and it is because they felt all the emotions of ordinary men that (with genius to help) they have been able to represent human beings with truth and sympathy. It is impossible to draw a complete picture of men unless you can think with their heads and feel with their hearts. There have of course been many excellent writers who in one way or another were abnormal and they have produced works that have a tang and an originality that make them sometimes more readable than the work of the greater writers, but I do not think they can be said ever to have reached those wonderful heights on which the Olympians dwell. I find *Wuthering Heights* more interesting than *David Copperfield*, but I have no doubt which is the greater novel. The accident of my birth in France, which enabled me to learn French and English simultaneously and thus instilled into me two modes of life, two liberties, two points of view, has prevented me from ever identifying myself completely with the instincts and prejudices of one people or the other, and it is in instinct and prejudice that sympathy is most deeply rooted; the accident of a physical infirmity, with its attendant nervousness, separated me to a greater extent than would be thought likely from the common life of others. In my communications with my fellows I have generally felt 'out of it'; in that uprush of emotion that sometimes seizes a crowd so that their hearts throb as one I have been lamentably aware that my own keeps its accustomed and normal rhythm. When 'Everybody suddenly burst out singing' as Siegfried Sassoon says in one of the most moving of the poems I have been allowed to reprint in this book, I have always felt exceedingly embarrassed. And when on New Year's Eve people join hands and swinging them up and down to the music, like a nurse rocking the baby, sing lustily *Should Auld Acquaintance be Forgot*, my shivering nerves whisper, yes, please. I cannot then offer this book as the choice of the average man and I cannot say that because these things please me they will please you. If you like me they will please you, and if you don't they won't. Though I do not share many of the prejudices that many people have, I naturally have prejudices of my own, and they will be obvious to anyone who reads this book through. I am a writer and I look at these things from my professional standpoint. This is the difference between the writer and the critic, that the critic, the good one, can look upon productions from the vantage-ground of the absolute and putting himself in the author's shoes can judge of the success of his efforts without the hindrance of predisposition. I do not think that many writers can do this. However good a book may be we can difficultly find merit in it if it is not the sort of thing we do, or think we can do ourselves. Mr E. M. Forster not very long ago wrote a book called *Aspects of the Novel*. In a novel of mine I ventured on a little gibe at its expense, but Mr Forster is a man of great disinterestedness, generous of soul, and with a delicate sense of humour; I think he forgave me my jest for he was good enough to write and tell me that he liked my book. His, nevertheless, is a good one, interesting not only to the novelist but also to the novel-reader; but I speak of it now to suggest that an acute reader could certainly divine from it what sort of novels Mr Forster would write. He makes much of just those characteristics in which no one now writing is richer than himself, but holds cheap that element of the novel, the story in which, I venture to think, his own weakness lies. My private opinion is that if Mr Forster, with his gift for beautiful English, his power of creating significant, interesting and living persons, his emotion and humour, his poetic feeling, could or would submit himself to the indignity of devising a good story he would write a novel that would make his eminent talent manifest to the whole world. But my opinion is neither here nor there. In this volume there is nothing that I would not have been glad to write myself. Of course I know that there is a great deal that I have not the gift to write. When I was young in moments of passion I used to beat my fists on the writing table and cry, by God, I wish I had more brains; but now, resigned though far from content, I am prepared to make do with what I have. Just as there are painters' pictures, there are writers' books. There are also readers' books. These are books that a reader enjoys but a writer, knowing the trick, finds intolerable. They are written to a formula. The author has set himself too easy a task. It is as if you expected a juggler to be amused by a child bouncing a ball. But they are sometimes very well done. They are often painstaking and sincere. When I start on a novel in which there is an elderly man, generally in the lower ranks of life, married to a young wife, and an adolescent, his son or a farm-hand, in the offing, my heart sinks. The course of the story, with its powerful scenes, is obvious to me. This kind of book is much praised for its 'strength.' But there may be as much 'strength' in a woman offering another a cup of tea as in a man kicking his wife to death with hob-nailed boots. The action is but a symbol. Dialect is the last straw. I do not like yokels who exchange wise cracks. Any workaday novelist knows that that sort of thing can be turned out by the yard and he laughs up his sleeve at the simplicity of the reading public that can find amusement in a form of humour so mechanical. Another kind that comes for me under the head of readers' books is the whimsical. These are much written by the literary sort of critics who think they will take a rest from serious work. They are often cultured and written with distinction. They have what is generally described as a charming fantasy. The formula here is simple. A middle-aged literary man takes a holiday in the country and on his walks meets a leprechaun and exchanges pleasantly philosophical remarks with him; or a young poet seeks lodgings in a London suburb where the maid-of-all-work is of an astonishing beauty; she converses with an ingenuousness that brings a lump to your throat, and there is certainly another lodger, a middle-aged literary man, who makes pleasantly philosophical remarks. Generally somebody dies in the end and it makes a very pathetic scene. There are very delicate descriptions of scenery. The reader will find nothing of the kind in these pages. He will find humour and he will find pathos. He will not find the namby pamby.

Nor will he find the didactic. Of late years the novel as everyone knows has widened its scope; it has become a platform for the exposition of the author's ideas. Novelists have become politicians, economists, social reformers and what not. They have used the novel to advocate this cause and that. They have been deeply concerned with the vital problems of the day. For this, I think, we may hold the Russians responsible. The Russian novelists brought something new to fiction, but by the circumstances of their civilisation they were inclined to subordinate art to social questions. Chekov, as we know, was much blamed for his indifference to them and his defenders were at pains to rebut the charge. They did not come out into the open and claim that he was an artist and that was enough, but sought chapter and verse to prove that his aim in describing the Russian peasant, for instance, was purely humanitarian. But the novelists who concern themselves with such things run a double danger. The first is that their views are unlikely to be sound (if they had the scientific instinct they would not be novelists) and the second is that the problems they deal with have seldom more than a temporary interest. What are you to say of a novel that becomes unreadable when an act of Parliament has changed a law? I forget what critic it was that said that the subject of great poetry was the common vicissitudes of humanity, birth and death, love and hatred, youth and old age. I venture to think that these are also the subjects of great fiction. I know it is out of fashion just now to think that the object of art is to entertain. I cannot help it. When I want instruction I go to philosophers, men of science and historians; I do not ask the novelist to give me anything but amusement. I am not in bad company, for Corneille (after Aristotle) thought that the pleasure of his audience was the poet's only aim, and the tender and perfect Racine contended, even with acrimony, that the first rule of the drama was to please and all the others were devised merely to achieve that end. And did not the philosophic Coleridge say that the object of poetry was delight? The unfortunate remark made by Terence in a play that few have read has had a disastrous effect on novelists. Of course it is very well that their sympathies should be universal, but that does not prove that their opinions are valuable. My uncle, a clergyman, told one of his curates who had a discordant voice and insisted on singing in church that it would be to the greater glory of God if he praised him only in his heart. I wonder if the writers of fiction who are so determined to teach us and improve us noticed that the other day a racing motorist who had driven a car faster than anyone else in the world was brought up on to a public platform to tell the free-born electors of a great constituency how they should vote on a question concerning the relations between the British Empire and India. There is a certain vulgarity in setting yourself up as an authority in matters on which your knowledge can be but superficial. I do not see why the story-teller should not be content to be a story-teller. He can be an artist and is that so little?

I read in the papers that rhetoric is coming into fashion again; and an eminent anthologist (but a less eminent novelist) is, I hear, bringing out a collection entirely devoted to purple passages. I shall not read it. In poetry, which is the happy avocation of youth, I do not mind, in moderation, a little rhetoric, but I do not like it in prose at all. I think the reader will find little in the following pages that is not written with simplicity. In my youth, influenced by the fashion of the day, I did my best to write in the grand manner. I studied the Bible, I sought phrases in the venerable Hooker and copied out passages of Jeremy Taylor. I ransacked the dictionary for unusual epithets. I went to the British Museum and made lists of the names of precious stones. But I had no bent that way and, resigning myself to writing not as I should have liked but as I could, I returned to the study of Swift. In passing I should like to suggest that the Bible has not had an altogether happy influence on English style. No one would deny that it is a great monument of the language, but after all it is a translation and its grandiloquent imagery is alien to our natures. For long I thought that Swift was the best model on which the modern English writer could form his style, and I still think there is something intoxicating in the order in which he places his words. But now I find in him a certain dryness and a dead level which is somewhat tiring. He is like a man who, whatever his emotion and however emphatic his words, never raises his voice. It is a little sinister. I think if I were starting over again I should devote myself to the study of Dryden. It was he who first gave English prose its form. He released the language from the ponderous eloquence that had overwhelmed it and made it the lovely, supple instrument which at its best it is. He had the straightforwardness and the limpidity of Swift; but a melodious variety and a conversational ease that Swift never attained. He had a happy charm of which the Dean was incapable. Swift's English flows like the water in a canal shaded by neat poplars, but Dryden's like a great river under the open sky. I know none more delightful. Of course a living language changes and it would be absurd for anyone to try to write like Dryden now. But his excellencies are still the excellencies of English prose. English is a very difficult language to write. Its grammar is so complicated that even the best writers often make gross mistakes. The various influences to which it has been subjected have made it a difficult medium to handle. Pedants have burdened it with pomposities. Clowns have jumped with it through paper hoops and juggled with its beauties as though they were the properties of the circus ring. Rhetoricians have floundered in the richness of its vocabulary. But its excellencies remain unimpaired. It is with joy and pride that I can point to them in many of the authors who grace this collection by their works.

W. S. M.

Frank Swinnerton

NOCTURNE

PART ONE
EVENING

CHAPTER I
SIX O'CLOCK

SIX o'clock was striking. The darkness by Westminster Bridge was intense; and as the tramcar turned the corner from the Embankment Jenny craned to look at the thickly running water below. The glistening of reflected lights which spotted the surface of the Thames gave its rapid current an air of such mysterious and especially sinister power that she was for an instant aware of almost uncontrollable terror. She could feel her heart beating, yet she could not withdraw her gaze. It was nothing: no danger threatened Jenny but the danger of uneventful life; and her sense of sudden yielding to unknown force was the merest fancy, to be quickly forgotten when the occasion had passed. None the less, for that instant her dread was breathless. It was the fear of one who walks in a wood, at an inexplicable rustle. The darkness and the sense of moving water continued to fascinate her, and she slightly shuddered, not at a thought, but at the sensation of the moment. At last she closed her eyes, still, however, to see mirrored as in some visual memory the picture she was trying to ignore. In a faint panic, hardly conscious to her fear, she stared at her neighbour's newspaper, spelling out the headings to some of the paragraphs, until the need of such protection was past.

As the car proceeded over the bridge, grinding its way through the still rolling echoes of the striking hour, it seemed part of an endless succession of such cars, all alike crowded with homeward-bound passengers, and all, to the curious mind, resembling ships that pass very slowly at night from safe harbourage to the unfathomable elements of the open sea. It was

such a cold still night that the sliding windows of the car were
almost closed, and the atmosphere of the covered upper deck
was heavy with tobacco smoke. It was so dark that one could
not see beyond the fringes of the lamplight upon the bridge.
The moon was in its last quarter, and would not rise for several hours; and while the glitter of the city lay behind, and the
sky was greyed with light from below, the surrounding blackness spread creeping fingers of night in every shadow.

The man sitting beside Jenny continued to puff steadfastly
at his pipe, lost in the news, holding mechanically in his further hand the return ticket which would presently be snatched
by the hurrying tram-conductor. He was a shabby middle-aged
clerk with a thin beard, and so he had not the least interest for
Jenny, whose eye was caught by other beauties than those of
assiduous labour. She had not even to look at him to be quite
sure that he did not matter to her. Almost, Jenny did not care
whether he had glanced sideways at herself or not. She presently gave a quiet sigh of relief as at length the river was left
behind and the curious nervous tension—no more lasting than
she might have felt at seeing a man balancing upon a high
window-sill—was relaxed. She breathed more deeply, perhaps,
for a few instants; and then, quite naturally, she looked at her
reflection in the sliding glass. That hat, as she could see in the
first sure speedless survey, had got the droops. "See about
you!" she said silently and threateningly, jerking her head.
The hat trembled at the motion, and was thereafter ignored.
Stealthily Jenny went back to her own reflection in the window, catching the clearly-chiselled profile of her face, bereft in
the dark mirror of all its colour. She could see her nose and
chin quite white, and her lips as part of the general colourless
gloom. A little white brooch at her neck stood boldly out; and
that was all that could be seen with any clearness, as the light
was not directly overhead. Her eyes were quite lost, apparently, in deep shadows. Yet she could not resist the delight
of continuing narrowly to examine herself. The face she saw
was hardly recognisable as her own; but it was bewitchingly
pale, a study in black and white, the kind of face which, in a
man, would at once have drawn her attention and stimulated
her curiosity. She had longed to be pale, but the pallor she was
achieving by millinery work in a stuffy room was not the marble whiteness which she had desired. Only in the sliding window
could she see her face ideally transfigured. There it had the

brooding dimness of strange poetic romance. You couldn't
know about that girl, she thought. You'd want to know about
her. You'd wonder all the time about her, as though she had a
secret. . . . The reflection became curiously distorted. Jenny
was smiling to herself.

As soon as the tramcar had passed the bridge, lighted windows above the shops broke the magic mirror and gave Jenny
a new interest, until, as they went onward, a shopping district,
ablaze with colour, crowded with loitering people, and alive
with din, turned all thoughts from herself into one absorbed
contemplation of what was beneath her eyes. So absorbed was
she, indeed, that the conductor had to prod her shoulder with
his two fingers before he could recover her ticket and exchange
it for another. " 'Arf asleep, some people!" he grumbled, shoving aside the projecting arms and elbows which prevented his
free passage between the seats. "Feyuss please!" Jenny
shrugged her shoulder, which seemed as though it had been irritated at the conductor's touch. It felt quite bruised. "Silly old
fool!" she thought, with a brusque glance. Then she went
silently back to the contemplation of all the life that gathered
upon the muddy and glistening pavements below.

ii

In a few minutes they were past the shops and once again in
darkness, grinding along, pitching from end to end, the driver's bell clanging every minute to warn carts and people off
the tramlines. Once, with an awful thunderous grating of the
brakes, the car was pulled up, and everybody tried to see what
had provoked the sense of accident. There was a little shouting, and Jenny, staring hard into the roadway, thought she
could see as its cause a small girl pushing a perambulator
loaded with bundles of washing. Her first impulse was pity—
"Poor little thing"; but the words were hardly in her mind before they were chased away by a faint indignation at the child
for getting in the tram's way. Everybody ought to look where
they were going. Ev-ry bo-dy ought to look where they were
go-ing, said the pitching tramcar. Ev-ry bo-dy. . . . Oh,
sickening! Jenny looked at her neighbour's paper—her refuge.
"Striking speech," she read. Whose? What did it matter?
Talk, talk. . . . Why didn't they do something? What were

they to do? The tram pitched to the refrain of a comic song: "Actions speak louder than words!" That kid who was wheeling the perambulator full of washing. . . . Jenny's attention drifted away like the speech of one who yawns, and she looked again at her reflection. The girl in the sliding glass wouldn't say much. She'd think the more. She'd say, when Sir Herbert pressed for his answer, "My thoughts are my own, Sir Herbert Mainwaring." What was it the girl in *One of the Best* said? "You may command an army of soldiers; but you cannot still the beating of a woman's heart!" Silly fool, she was. Jenny had felt the tears in her eyes, burning, and her throat very dry, when the words had been spoken in the play; but Jenny at the theatre and Jenny here and now were different persons. Different? Why, there were fifty Jennys. But the shrewd, romantic, honest, true Jenny was behind them all, not stupid, not sentimental, bold as a lion, destructively experienced in hardship and endurance, very quick indeed to single out and wither humbug that was within her range of knowledge, but innocent as a child before any other sort of humbug whatsoever. That was why she could now sneer at the stage-heroine, and could play with the mysterious beauties of her own reflection; but it was why she could also be led into quick indignation by something read in a newspaper.

Tum-ty tum-ty tum-ty tum, said the tram. There were some more shops. There were straggling shops and full-blazing rows of shops. There were stalls along the side of the road, women dancing to an organ outside a public-house. Shops, shops, houses, houses, houses . . . light, darkness. . . . Jenny gathered her skirt. This was where she got down. One glance at the tragic lady of the mirror, one glance at the rising smoke that went to join the general cloud; and she was upon the iron-shod stairs of the car and into the greasy roadway. Then darkness, as she turned along beside a big building into the side streets among rows and rows of the small houses of Kennington Park.

iii

It was painfully dark in these side streets. The lamps drew beams such a short distance that they were as useless as the hidden stars. Only down each street one saw mild spots starting out of the gloom, fascinating in their regularity, like shin-

ing beads set at prepared intervals in a body of jet. The houses
were all in darkness, because evening meals were laid in the
kitchens: the front rooms were all kept for Sunday use, ex-
cepting when the Emeralds and Edwins and Geralds and
Dorises were practising upon their mothers' pianos. Then you
could hear a din! But not now. Now all was as quiet as night,
and even doors were not slammed. Jenny crossed the street and
turned a corner. On the corner itself was a small chandler's
shop, with "Magnificent Tea, per 2/-lb."; "Excellent Tea,
per 1/8d. lb."; "Good Tea, per 1/4d. lb." advertised in great
bills upon its windows above a huge collection of unlikely goods
gathered together like a happy family in its tarnished abode.
Jenny passed the dully-lighted shop, and turned in at her own
gate. In a moment she was inside the house, sniffing at the warm
odour-laden air within doors. Her mouth drew down at the corners. Stew to-night! An amused gleam, lost upon the dowdy
passage, fled across her bright eyes. Emmy wouldn't have
thanked her for that! Emmy—sick to death herself of the smell
of cooking—would have slammed down the pot in despairing
rage.

In the kitchen a table was laid; and Emmy stretched her
head back to peer from the scullery, where she was busy at the
gas stove. She did not say a word. Jenny also was speechless;
and went as if without thinking to the kitchen cupboard. The
table was only half-laid as usual; but that fact did not make
her action the more palatable to Emmy. Emmy, who was older
than Jenny by a mysterious period—diminished by herself,
but kept at its normal term of three years by Jenny, except
in moments of some heat, when it grew for purposes of retort,
—was also less effective in many ways, such as in appearance
and in adroitness; and Jenny comprised in herself, as it were,
the good looks of the family. Emmy was the housekeeper, who
looked after Pa Blanchard; Jenny was the roving blade who
augmented Pa's pension by her own fluctuating wages. That
was another slight barrier between the sisters. Nevertheless,
Emmy was quite generous enough, and was long-suffering, so
that her resentment took the general form of silences and secret
broodings upon their different fortunes. There was a great
deal to be said about this difference, and the saying grew more
and more remote from explicit utterance as thought of it
ground into Emmy's mind through long hours and days and
weeks of solitude. Pa could not hear anything besides the bang-

ing of pots, and he was too used to sudden noises to take any notice of such a thing; but the pots themselves, occasionally dented in savage dashes against each other or against the taps, might have heard vicious apostrophes if they had listened intently to Emmy's ejaculations. As it was, with the endurance of pots, they mutely bore their scars and waited dumbly for superannuation. And every bruise stood to Emmy when she renewed acquaintance with it as mark of yet another grievance against Jenny. For Jenny enjoyed the liberties of this life while Emmy stayed at home. Jenny sported while Emmy was engaged upon the hideous routine of kitchen affairs, and upon the nursing of a comparatively helpless old man who could do hardly anything at all for himself.

Pa was in his bedroom,—the back room on the ground-floor, chosen because he could not walk up the stairs, but must have as little trouble in self-conveyance as possible,—staggeringly making his toilet for the meal to come, sitting patiently in front of his dressing-table by the light of a solitary candle. He would appear in due course, when he was fetched. He had been a strong man, a runner and cricketer in his youth, and rather obstreperously disposed; but that time was past, and his strength for such pursuits was as dead as the wife who had suffered because of its vagaries. He could no longer disappear on the Saturdays, as he had been used to do in the old days. His chair in the kitchen, the horse-hair sofa in the sitting-room, the bed in the bedroom, were the only changes he now had from one day's end to another. Emmy and Jenny, pledges of a real but not very delicate affection, were all that remained to call up the sorrowful thoughts of his old love, and those old times of virility, when Pa and his strength and his rough boisterousness had been the delight of perhaps a dozen regular companions. He sometimes looked at the two girls with a passionless scrutiny, as though he were trying to remember something buried in ancient neglect; and his eyes would thereafter, perhaps at the mere sense of helplessness, fill slowly with tears, until Emmy, smothering her own rough sympathy, would dab Pa's eyes with a harsh handkerchief and would rebuke him for his decay. Those were hard moments in the Blanchard home, for the two girls had grown almost manlike in abhorrence of tears, and with this masculine distaste had arisen a corresponding feeling of powerlessness in face of emotion which they could not share. It was as though Pa had become something

like an old and beloved dog, unable to speak, pitied and despised, yet claiming by his very dumbness something that they
could only give by means of pats and half-bullying kindness.
At such times it was Jenny who left her place at the table and
popped a morsel of food into Pa's mouth; but it was Emmy
who best understood the bitterness of his soul. It was Emmy,
therefore, who would snap at her sister and bid her get on with
her own food; while Pa Blanchard made trembling scrapes
with his knife and fork until the mood passed. But then it was
Emmy who was most with Pa; it was Emmy who hated him in
the middle of her love because he stood to her as the living symbol of her daily inescapable servitude in this household. Jenny
could never have felt that she would like to kill Pa. Emmy
sometimes felt that. She at times, when he had been provoking
or obtuse, so shook with hysterical anger, born of the inevitable days in his society and in the kitchen, that she could have
thrown at him the battered pot which she carried, or could
have pushed him passionately against the mantelpiece in her
fierce hatred of his helplessness and his occasional perverse
stupidity. He was rarely stupid with Jenny, but giggled at
her teasing.

Jenny was taller than Emmy by several inches. She was tall
and thin and dark, with an air of something like impudent
bravado that made her expression sometimes a little wicked.
Her nose was long and straight, almost sharp-pointed; her face
too thin to be a perfect oval. Her eyes were wide open, and so
full of power to show feeling that they seemed constantly alive
with changing and mocking lights and shadows. If she had been
stouter the excellent shape of her body, now almost too thick
in the waist, would have been emphasised. Happiness and comfort, a decrease in physical as in mental restlessness, would
have made her more than ordinarily beautiful. As it was she
drew the eye at once, as though she challenged a conflict of
will: and her movements were so swift and eager, so little
clumsy or jerking, that Jenny had a carriage to command
admiration. The resemblance between the sisters was ordinarily
not noticeable. It would have needed a photograph—because
photographs, besides flattening the features, also in some manner "compose" and distinguish them—to reveal the likenesses
in shape, in shadow, even in outline, which were momentarily
obscured by the natural differences of colouring and expression. Emmy was less dark, more temperamentally unadventur-

ous, stouter, and possessed of more colour. She was twenty-eight or possibly twenty-nine, and her mouth was rather too hard for pleasantness. It was not peevish, but the lips were set as though she had endured much. Her eyes, also, were hard; although if she cried one saw her face soften remarkably into the semblance of that of a little girl. From an involuntary defiance her expression changed to something really pathetic. One could not help loving her then, not with the free give and take of happy affection, but with a shamed hope that nobody could read the conflict of sympathy and contempt which made one's love frigid and self-conscious. Jenny rarely cried: her cheeks reddened and her eyes grew full of tears; but she did not cry. Her tongue was too ready and her brain too quick for that. Also, she kept her temper from flooding over into the self-abandonment of angry weeping and vituperation. Perhaps it was that she had too much pride—or that in general she saw life with too much self-complacency, or that she was not in the habit of yielding to disappointment. It may have been that Jenny belonged to that class of persons who are called, self-sufficient. She plunged through a crisis with her own zest, meeting attack with counter-attack, keeping her head, surveying with the instinctive irreverence and self-protective wariness of the London urchin the possibilities and swaying fortunes of the fight. Emmy, so much slower, so much less self-reliant, had no refuge but in scolding that grew shriller and more shrill until it ended in violent weeping, a withdrawal from the field entirely abject. She was not a born fighter. She was harder on the surface, but weaker in powers below the surface. Her long solitudes had made her build up grievances, and devastating thoughts, had given her a thousand bitter things to fling into the conflict; but they had not strengthened her character, and she could not stand the strain of prolonged argument. Sooner or later she would abandon everything, exhausted, and beaten into impotence. She could bear more, endure more, than Jenny; she could bear much, so that the story of her life might be read as one long scene of endurance of things which Jenny would have struggled madly to overcome or to escape. But having borne for so long, she could fight only like a cat, her head as it were turned aside, her fur upon end, stealthily moving paw by paw, always keeping her front to the foe, but seeking for escape—until the pride perilously supporting her temper gave way and she dissolved into incoherence and quivering sobs.

It might have been said roughly that Jenny more closely
resembled her father, whose temperament in her care-free,
happy-go-lucky way she understood very well (better than
Emmy did), and that while she carried into her affairs a necessarily more delicate refinement than his she had still the dare-
devil spirit that Pa's friends had so much admired. She had
more humour than Emmy—more power to laugh, to be detached, to be indifferent. Emmy had no such power. She could
laugh; but she could only laugh seriously, or at obviously
funny things. Otherwise, she felt everything too much. As
Jenny would have said, she "couldn't take a joke." It made her
angry, or puzzled, to be laughed at. Jenny laughed back, and
tried to score a point in return, not always scrupulously. Emmy
put a check on her tongue. She was sometimes virtuously silent.
Jenny rarely put a check on her tongue. She sometimes let it
say perfectly outrageous things, and was surprised at the consequences. For her it was enough that she had not meant to
hurt. She sometimes hurt very much. She frequently hurt
Emmy to the quick, darting in one of her sure careless stabs
that shattered Emmy's self-control. So while they loved each
other, Jenny also despised Emmy, while Emmy in return hated
and was jealous of Jenny, even to the point of actively wishing in moments of furtive and shamefaced savageness to harm
her. That was the outward difference between the sisters in
time of stress. Of their inner, truer, selves it would be more rash
to speak, for in times of peace Jenny had innumerable insights
and emotions that would be forever unknown to the elder girl.
The sense of rivalry, however, was acute: it coloured every
moment of their domestic life, unwinking and incessant. When
Emmy came from the scullery into the kitchen bearing her
precious dish of stew, and when Jenny, standing up, was measured against her, this rivalry could have been seen by any
skilled observer. It rayed and forked about them as lightning
might have done about two adjacent trees. Emmy put down
her dish.

"Fetch Pa, will you!" she said briefly. One could see who
gave orders in the kitchen.

iv

Jenny found her father in his bedroom, sitting before the
dressing-table upon which a tall candle stood in an equally tall

candlestick. He was looking intently at his reflection in the looking-glass, as one who encounters and examines a stranger. In the glass his face looked red and ugly, and the tossed grey hair and heavy beard were made to appear startlingly unkempt. His mouth was open, and his eyes shaded by lowered lids. In a rather trembling voice he addressed Jenny upon her entrance.

"Is supper ready?" he asked. "I heard you come in."

"Yes, Pa," said Jenny. "Aren't you going to brush your hair? Got a fancy for it like that, have you? My! What a man! With his shirt unbuttoned and his tie out. Come here! Let's have a look at you!" Although her words were unkind, her tone was not, and as she rectified his omissions and put her arm round him Jenny gave her father a light hug. "All right, are you? Been a good boy?"

"Yes . . . a good boy . . ." he feebly and waveringly responded. "What's the noos to-night, Jenny?"

Jenny considered. It made her frown, so concentrated was her effort to remember.

"Well, somebody's made a speech," she volunteered. "They can all do that, can't they! And somebody's paid five hundred pounds transfer for Jack Sutherdon . . . is it Barnsley or Burnley? . . . And—oh, a fire at Southwark. . . . Just the usual sort of news, Pa. No murders. . . ."

"Ah, they don't have the murders they used to have," grumbled the old man.

"That's the police, Pa." Jenny wanted to reassure him.

"I don't know how it is," he trembled, stiffening his body and rising from the chair.

"Perhaps they hush 'em up?" That was a shock to him. He could not move until the notion had sunk into his head. "Or perhaps people are more careful. . . . Don't get leaving themselves about like they used to."

Pa Blanchard had no suggestion. Such perilous ideas, so frequently started by Jenny for his mystification, joggled together in his brain and made there the subject of a thousand ruminations. They tantalised Pa's slowly revolving thoughts, and kept these moving through long hours of silence. Such notions preserved his interest in the world, and his senile belief in Magic, as nothing else could have done.

Together, their pace suited to his step, the two moved

slowly to the door. It took a long time to make the short journey, though Jenny supported her father on the one side and
he used a stick in his right hand. In the passage he waited
while she blew out his candle; and then they went forward to
the meal. At the approach Pa's eyes opened wider, and lumi-
nously glowed.

"Is there dumplings?" he quivered, seeming to tremble with
excitement.

"One for you, Pa!" cried Emmy from the kitchen. Pa gave
a small chuckle of joy. His progress was accelerated. They
reached the table, and Emmy took his right arm for the descent
into a substantial chair. Upon Pa's plate glistened a fair dumpling, a glorious mountain of paste amid the wreckage of meat
and gravy. "And now, perhaps," Emmy went on, smoothing
back from her forehead a little streamer of hair, "you'll close
the door, Jenny. . . ."

It was closed with a bang that made Pa jump and Emmy
look savagely up.

"Sorry!" cried Jenny. "How's that dumpling, Pa?" She sat
recklessly at the table.

v

To look at the three of them sitting there munching away
was a sight not altogether pleasing. Pa's veins stood out from
his forehead, and the two girls devoted themselves to the food
as if they needed it. There was none of the airy talk that goes
on in the houses of the rich while maids or menservants come
respectfully to right or left of the diners with decanters or
dishes. Here the food was the thing, and there was no speech.
Sometimes Pa's eyes rolled, sometimes Emmy glanced up with
unconscious malevolence at Jenny, sometimes Jenny almost
winked at the lithograph portrait of Edward the Seventh (as
Prince of Wales) which hung over the mantelpiece above the
one-and-tenpenny-ha'penny clock that ticked away so busily
there. Something had happened long ago to Edward the Seventh, and he had a stain across his Field Marshal's uniform.
Something had happened also to the clock, which lay upon its
side, as if kicking in a death agony. Something had happened
to almost everything in the kitchen. Even the plates on the

dresser, and the cups and saucers that hung or stood upon the shelves, bore the noble scars of service. Every time Emmy turned her glance upon a damaged plate, as sharp as a stalactite, she had the thought: "Jenny's doing." Every time she looked at the convulsive clock Emmy said to herself: "That was Miss Jenny's cleverness when she chucked the cosy at Alf." And when Emmy said in this reflective silence of animosity the name "Alf" she drew a deep breath and looked straight up at Jenny with inscrutable eyes of pain.

vi

The stew being finished, Emmy collected the plates, and retired once again to the scullery. Now did Jenny show afresh that curiosity whose first flush had been so ill-satisfied by the meat course. When, however, Emmy reappeared with that most domestic of sweets, a bread pudding, Jenny's face fell once more; for of all dishes she most abominated bread pudding. Under her breath she adversely commented.

"Oh lor!" she whispered. "Stew and b. p. What a life!"

Emmy, not hearing, but second sighted on such matters, shot a malevolent glance from her place. In an awful voice, intended to be a trifle arch, she addressed her father.

"Bready butter pudding, Pa?" she inquired. The old man whinnied with delight, and Emmy was appeased. She had one satisfied client, at any rate. She cut into the pudding with a knife, producing wedges with a dexterous hand.

"Hey ho!" observed Jenny to herself, tastelessly beginning the work of laborious demolition.

"Jenny thinks it's common. She ought to have the job of getting the meals!" cried Emmy, bitterly, obliquely attacking her sister by talking at her. "Something to talk about then!" she sneered with chagrin, up in arms at a criticism.

"Well, the truth is," drawled Jenny. . . . "If you want it . . . I don't like bread pudding." Somehow she had never said that before, in all the years; but it seemed to her that bread pudding was like ashes in the mouth. It was like duty, or funerals, or . . . stew.

"The stuff's *got* to be finished up!" flared Emmy defiantly, with a sense of being adjudged inferior because she had duti-fully habituated herself to the appreciation of bread pudding. "You might think of that! What else am I to do?"

"That's just it, old girl. Just why I don't like it. I just *hate* to feel I'm finishing it up. Same with stew. I know it's been something else first. It's not *fresh*. Same old thing, week in, week out. Finishing up the scraps!"

"Proud stomach!" A quick flush came into Emmy's cheeks; and tears started to her eyes.

"Perhaps it is. Oh, but Em! Don't you feel like that yourself. . . . Sometimes? O-o-h! . . ." She drawled the word wearily. "Oh for a bit more money! Then we could give stew to the cat's-meat man and bread to old Thompson's chickens. And then we could have nice things to eat. Nice birds and pastry . . . and trifle, and ices, and wine. . . . Not all this muck!"

"Muck!" cried Emmy, her lips seeming to thicken. "When I'm so hot. . . . And sick of it all! *You* go out; you do just exactly what you like. . . . And then you come home and . . . ." She began to gulp. "What about me?"

"Well, it's just as bad for both of us!" Jenny did not think so really; but she said it. She thought Emmy had the bread and butter pudding nature, and that she did not greatly care what she ate as long as it was not too fattening. Jenny thought of Emmy as born for housework and cooking—of stew and bread puddings. For herself she had dreamed a nobler destiny, a destiny of romance, of delicious unknown things, romantic and indescribably exciting. She was to have the adventures, because she needed them. Emmy didn't need them. It was all very well for Emmy to say "What about me?" It was no business of hers what happened to Emmy. They were different. Still, she repeated more confidently because there had been no immediate retort:

"Well, it's just as bad for both of us! *Just* as bad!"

"'Tisn't! You're out all day—doing what you like!"

"Oh!" Jenny's eyes opened with theatrical wideness at such a perversion of the facts. "Doing what I like! The millinery!"

"You are! You don't have to do all the scrapping to make things go round, like I have to. No, you don't! Here have I . . . . been in this . . . place, slaving! Hour after hour! I wish *you'd* try and manage better. I bet you'd be thankful to finish up the scraps some way—any old way! I'd like to see *you* do what I do!"

Momentarily Jenny's picture of Emmy's nature (drawn ac-

commodatingly by herself in order that her own might be differentiated and exalted by any comparison) was shattered.
Emmy's vehemence had thus the temporary effect of creating
a fresh reality out of a common idealisation of circumstance.
The legend would re-form later, perhaps, and would continue
so to re-form as persuasion flowed back upon Jenny's egotism,
until it crystallised hard and became unchallengeable; but at
any rate for this instant Jenny had had a glimmer of insight
into that tamer discontent and rebelliousness that encroached
like a canker upon Emmy's originally sweet nature. The shock
of impact with unpleasant conviction made Jenny hasten to
dissemble her real belief in Emmy's born inferiority. Her note
was changed from one of complaint into one of persuasive entreaty.

"It's not that. It's not that. Not at all. But wouldn't you
like a change from stew and bread pudding yourself? Sometimes, I mean. You *seem* to like it all right." At that ill-considered suggestion, made with unintentional savageness, Jenny so
worked upon herself that her own colour rose high. Her temper became suddenly unmanageable. "You talk about me being
out!" she breathlessly exclaimed. "When do I go out? When!
Tell me!"

"O-o-h! I *like* that! What about going to the pictures with
Alf Rylett?" Emmy's hands were jerking upon the table in
her anger. "You're always out with him!"

"Me? Well I never! I'm not. When——"

They were interrupted unexpectedly by a feeble and jubilant voice.

"More bready butter pudding!" said Pa Blanchard, tip-
ping his plate to show that he had finished.

"Yes, Pa!" For the moment Emmy was distracted from her
feud. In a mechanical way, as mothers sometimes, deep in conversation, attend to their children's needs, she put another
wedge of pudding upon the plate. "Well, I say you *are*," she
resumed in the same strained voice. "And tell me when *I* go out!
I go out shopping. That's all. But for that, I'm in the house
day and night. You don't care tuppence about Alf—you
wouldn't, not if he was walking the soles off his boots to come
to you. You never think about him. He's like dirt, to you. Yet
you go out with him time after time. . . ." Her lips as she
broke off were pursed into a trembling unhappy pout, sure
forerunner of tears. Her voice was weak with feeling. The

memory of lonely evenings surged into her mind, evenings when Jenny was out with Alf, while she, the drudge, stayed at home with Pa, until she was desperate with the sense of unutterable wrong. "Time after time, you go."

"Sorry, I'm sure!" flung back Jenny, fairly in the fray, too quick not to read the plain message of Emmy's tone and expression, too cruel to relinquish the sudden advantage. "I never guessed you wanted him. I wouldn't have done it for worlds. You never *said*, you know!" Satirically, she concluded, with a studiously careful accent, which she used when she wanted to indicate scorn or innuendo, "I'm sorry. I ought to have asked if I might!" Then, with a dash into grimmer satire: "Why doesn't he ask you to go with him? Funny his asking me, isn't it?"

Emmy grew violently crimson. Her voice had a roughness in it. She was mortally wounded.

"Anybody'd know you were a lady!" she said warmly.

"They're welcome!" retorted Jenny. Her eyes flashed, glittering in the paltry gaslight. "He's never . . . Emmy, I didn't know you were such a silly little fool. Fancy going on like that . . . about a man like him. At your age!"

Vehement glances flashed between them. All Emmy's jealousy was in her face, clear as day. Jenny drew a sharp breath. Then, obstinately, she closed her lips, looking for a moment like the girl in the sliding window, inscrutable. Emmy, also recovering herself, spoke again, trying to steady her voice.

"It's not what you think. But I can't bear to see you . . . playing about with him. It's not fair. He thinks you mean it. You don't!"

"Course I don't. I don't mean anything. A fellow like that!" Jenny laughed a little, woundingly.

"What's the matter with him?" Savagely, Emmy betrayed herself again. She was trembling from head to foot, her mind blundering hither and thither for help against a quicker-witted foe. "It's only *you* he's not good enough for," she said passionately. "What's the matter with him?"

Jenny considered, her pale face now deadly white, all the heat gone from her cheeks, though the hard glitter remained in her eyes, cruelly indicating the hunger within her bosom.

"Oh, he's all right in his way," she drawlingly admitted. "He's clean. That's in his favour. But he's quiet . . . he's got no devil in him. Sort of man who tells you what he likes for breakfast. I only go with him . . . well, you know why, as well as I do. He's all right enough, as far as he goes. But he's never on for a bit of fun. That's it: he's got no devil in him. I don't like that kind. Prefer the other sort."

During this speech Emmy had kept back bitter interruptions by an unparalleled effort. It had seemed as though her fury had flickered, blazing and dying away as thought and feeling struggled together for mastery. At the end of it, however, and at Jenny's declared preference for men of devil, Emmy's face hardened.

"You be careful, my girl," she prophesied with a warning glance of anger. "If that's the kind you're after. Take care you're not left!"

"Oh, I can take care," Jenny said, with cold nonchalance. "Trust me!"

vii

Later, when they were both in the chilly scullery, washing up the supper dishes, they were again constrained. Somehow when they were alone together they could not quarrel: it needed the presence of Pa Blanchard to stimulate them to retort. In his rambling silences they found the spur for their unkind eloquence, and too often Pa was used as a stalking-horse for their angers. He could hardly hear, and could not follow the talk; but by directing a remark to him, so that it cannoned off at the other, each obtained satisfaction for the rivalry that endured from day to day between them. Their hungry hearts, all the latent bitternesses in their natures, yearning for expression, found it in his presence. But alone, whatever their angers, they were generally silent. It may have been that their love was strong, or that their courage failed, or that the energy required for conflict was not aroused. That they deeply loved one another was sure; there was rivalry, jealousy, irritation between them, but it did not affect their love. The jealousy was a part of their general discontent—a jealousy that would grow more intense as each remained frustrate and unhappy. Neither understood the forces at work within herself; each saw these perversely illustrated in the other's faults. In each case the cause of unhappiness was unsatisfied love, unsatisfied craving for love. It was more acute in Emmy's case, because she was

older and because the love she needed was under her eyes being
wasted upon Jenny—if it were love, and not that mixture of
admiration and desire with self-esteem that goes to make the
common formula to which the name of love is generally attached. Jenny could not be jealous of Emmy as Emmy was
jealous of Jenny. She had no cause; Emmy was not her rival.
Jenny's rival was life itself, as will be shown hereafter: she had
her own pain.

It was thus only natural that the two girls, having pushed
Pa's chair to the side of the kitchen fire, and having loaded
and set light to Pa's pipe, should work together in silence for
a few minutes, clearing the table and washing the supper
dishes. They were distant, both aggrieved; Emmy with labouring breath and a sense of bitter animosity, Jenny with the
curled lip of one triumphant who does not need her triumph
and would abandon it at the first move of forgiveness. They
could not speak. The work was done, and Emmy was rinsing
the washing basin, before Jenny could bring herself to say
awkwardly what she had in her mind.

"Em," she began. "I didn't know you . . . you know." A
silence. Emmy continued to swirl the water round with the
small washing-mop, her face averted. Jenny's lip stiffened. She
made another attempt, to be the last, restraining her irritation with a great effort. "If you like I won't . . . I won't go
out with him any more."

"Oh, you needn't worry," Emmy doggedly said, with her
teeth almost clenched. "I'm not worrying about it." She tried
then to keep silent; but the words were forced from her
wounded heart. With uncontrollable sarcasm she said: "It's
very good of you, I'm sure!"

"Em!" It was coaxing. Jenny went nearer. Still there was
no reply. "Em . . . don't be a silly cat. If he'd only ask *you*
to go once or twice. He'd always want to. You needn't worry
about me being . . . See, I like somebody else—another fellow. He's on a ship. Nowhere near here. I only go with Alf
because . . . well, after all, he's a man; and they're scarce.
Suppose I leave off going with him. . . ."

Both knew she had nothing but kind intention, as in fact the
betrayal of her own secret proved; but as Jenny could not keep
out of her voice the slightest tinge of complacent pity, so
Emmy could not accept anything so intolerable as pity.

"Thanks," she said in perfunctory refusal; "but you can do

what you like. Just what you like." She was implacable. She was drying the basin, her face hidden. "I'm not going to take your leavings." At that her voice quivered and had again that thread of roughness in it which had been there earlier. "Not likely!"

"Well, I can't help it, can I!" cried Jenny, out of patience. "If he likes me best. If he *won't* come to you. I mean, if I say I won't go out with him—will that put him on to you or send him off altogether? Em, do be sensible. Really, I never knew. Never dreamt of it. I've never wanted him. It's not as though he'd whistled and I'd gone trotting after him. Em! You get so ratty about——"

"Superior!" cried Emmy, gaspingly. "Look down on me!" She was for an instant hysterical, speaking loudly and weepingly. Then she was close against Jenny; and they were holding each other tightly, while Emmy's dreadful quiet sobs shook both of them to the heart. And Jenny, above her sister's shoulder, could see through the window the darkness that lay without; and her eyes grew tender at an unbidden thought, which made her try to force herself to see through the darkness, as though she were sending a speechless message to the unknown. Then, feeling Emmy still sobbing in her arms, she looked down, laying her face against her sister's face. A little contemptuous smile appeared in her eyes, and her brow furrowed. Well, Emmy could cry. *She* couldn't. She didn't want to cry. She wanted to go out in the darkness that so pleasantly enwrapped the earth, back to the stir and glitter of life somewhere beyond. Abruptly Jenny sighed. Her vision had been far different from this scene. It had carried her over land and sea right into an unexplored realm where there was wild laughter and noise, where hearts broke tragically and women in the hour of ruin turned triumphant eyes to the glory of life, and where blinding streaming lights and scintillating colours made everything seem different, made it seem romantic, rapturous, indescribable. From that vision back to the cupboard-like house in Kennington Park, and stodgy Alf Rylett, and supper of stew and bread and butter pudding, and Pa, and this little sobbing figure in her arms, was an incongruous flight. It made Jenny's mouth twist in a smile so painful that it was almost a grimace.

"Oh lor!" she said again, under her breath, as she had said it earlier. "*What* a life!"

CHAPTER II

THE TREAT

GRADUALLY Emmy's tearless sobs diminished; she began to murmur broken, meaningless ejaculations of self-contempt; and to strain away from Jenny. At last she pushed Jenny from her, feverishly freeing herself, so that they stood apart, while Emmy blew her nose and wiped her eyes. All this time they did not speak to each other, and when Emmy turned blindly away Jenny mechanically took hold of the kettle, filled it, and set it to boil upon the gas. Emmy watched her curiously, feeling that her nose was cold and her eyes were burning. Little dry tremors seemed to shake her throat; dreariness had settled upon her, pressing her down; making her feel ashamed of such a display of the long secret so carefully hoarded away from prying glances.

"What's that for?" she miserably asked, indicating the kettle.

"Going to steam my hat," Jenny said. "The brim's all floppy." There was now only a practical note in her voice. She, too, was ashamed. "You'd better go up and lie down for a bit. I'll stay with Pa, in case he falls into the fire. Just the sort of thing he *would* do on a night like this. Just because you're upset."

"I shan't go up. It's too cold. I'll sit by the fire a bit."

They both went into the kitchen, where the old man was whistling under his breath.

"Was there any noos on the play-cards?" he inquired after a moment, becoming aware of their presence. "Emmy— Jenny."

"No, Pa. I told you. Have to wait till Sunday. Funny thing there's so much more news in the Sunday papers. I suppose people are all extra wicked on Saturdays. They get paid Friday night, I shouldn't wonder; and it goes to their heads."

"Silly!" Emmy said under her breath. "It's the week's news."

"That's all right, old girl," admonished Jenny. "I was only giving him something to think about. Poor old soul. Now,

about this hat: the girls all go on at me. . . . Say I dress like
a broker's-man. I'm going to smarten myself up. You never
know what might happen. Why, I might get off with a Duke!"
    Emmy was overtaken by an impulse of gratitude.
    "You can have mine, if you like," she said. "The one you
gave me . . . on my birthday." Jenny solemnly shook her
head. She did not thank her sister. Thanks were never given in
that household, because they were a part of "peliteness," and
were supposed to have no place in the domestic arena.
    "Not if I know it!" she humorously retorted. "I made it
for you, and it suits you. Not my style at all. I'll just get out
my box of bits. You'll see something that'll surprise you, my
girl."
    The box proved to contain a large number of "bits" of all
sizes and kinds—fragments of silk (plain and ribbed), of
plush, of ribbon both wide and narrow; small sprays of mar-
guerites, a rose or two, some poppies, and a bunch of violets; a
few made bows in velvet and silk; some elastic, some satin,
some feathers, a wing here and there . . . the miscellaneous
assortment of odds-and-ends always appropriated (or, in the
modern military slang, "won") by assistants in the millinery.
Some had been used, some were startlingly new. Jenny was
more modest in such acquirements than were most of her associates; but she was affected, as all such must be, by the prevailing wind. Strangely enough, it was not her habit to wear
very smart hats, for business or at any other time. She would
have told you, in the event of any such remark, that when you
had been fiddling about with hats all day you had other things
to do in the evenings. Yet she had good taste and very nimble
fingers when occasion arose. In bringing her box from the bedroom she brought also from the stand in the passage her drooping hat, against which she proceeded to lay various materials,
trying them with her sure eye, seeking to compose a picture,
with that instructive sense of cynosure which marks the crafty
expert. Fascinated, with her lips parted in an expression of
that stupidity which is so often the sequel to a fit of crying,
Emmy watched Jenny's proceedings, her eyes travelling from
the hat to the ever-growing heap of discarded ornaments. She
was dully impressed with the swift judgment of her sister in
consulting the secrets of her inner taste. It was a judgment
unlike anything in her own nature of which she was aware, ex-
cepting the measurement of ingredients for a pudding.

So they sat, all engrossed, while the kettle began to sing and the desired steam to pour from the spout, clouding the scullery. The only sound that arose was the gurgling of Pa Blanchard's pipe (for he was what is called in Kennington Park a wet smoker). He sat remembering something or pondering the insufficiency of news. Nobody ever knew what he thought about in his silences. It was a mystery over which the girls did not puzzle, because they were themselves in the habit of sitting for long periods without speech. Pa's broodings were as customary to them as the absorbed contemplativeness of a baby. "Give him his pipe," as Jenny said; "and he'll be quiet for hours—till it goes out. *Then* there's a fuss! My word, what a racket! Talk about a fire alarm!" And on such occasions she would mimic him ridiculingly, to diminish his complaints, while Emmy roughly relighted the hubble-bubble and patted her father once more into a contented silence. Pa was to them, although they did not know it, their bond of union. Without him, they would have fallen apart, like the outer pieces of a wooden boot-tree. For his sake, with all the apparent lack of sympathy shown in their behaviour to him, they endured a life which neither desired nor would have tolerated upon her own account. So it was that Pa's presence acted as a check and served them as company of a meagre kind, although he was less interesting or expansive than a little dog might have been.

When Jenny went out to the scullery carrying her hat, after sweeping the scraps she had declined back into the old draper's cardboard box which amply contained such treasures and preserved them from dust, Emmy, now quite quiet again, continued to sit by the fire, staring at the small glowing strip that showed under the door of the kitchen grate. Every now and then she would sigh, wearily closing her eyes; and her breast would rise as if with a sob. And she would sometimes look slowly up at the clock, with her head upon one side in order to see the hands in their proper aspect, as if she were calculating.

ii

From the scullery came the sound of Jenny's whistle as she cheerily held the hat over the steam. Pa heard it as something far away, like a distant salvationists' band, and pricked up his ears; Emmy heard it, and her brow was contracted. Her expression darkened. Jenny began to hum:

" 'Oh Liza, sweet Liza,
If you die an old maid you'll have only yourself to blame . . .' "

It was like a sudden noise in a forest at night, so poignant was the contrast of the radiating silences that succeeded. Jenny's voice stopped sharply. Perhaps it had occurred to her that her song would be overheard. Perhaps she had herself become affected by the meaning of the words she was so carelessly singing. There was once more an air of oblivion over all things. The old man sank back in his chair, puffing slowly, blue smoke from the bowl of the pipe, grey smoke from between his lips. Emmy looked again at the clock. She had the listening air of one who awaits a bewildering event. Once she shivered, and bent to the fire, raking among the red tumbling small coal with the bent kitchen poker. Jenny began to whistle again, and Emmy impatiently wriggled her shoulders, jarred by the noise. Suddenly she could bear no longer the whistle that pierced her thoughts and distracted her attention, but went out to the scullery.

"How are you getting on?" she asked with an effort.

"Fine. This gas leaks. Can't you whiff it? Don't know which one it is. Pa all right?"

"Yes, he's all right. Nearly finished?"

"Getting on. Tram nearly ran over a kid to-night. She was wheeling a pram full of washing on the line. There wasn't half a row about it—shouting and swearing. Anybody would have thought the kid had laid down on the line. I expect she was frightened out of her wits—all those men shouting at her. There, now I'll lay it on the plate rack over the gas for a bit. . . . Look smart, shan't I! With a red rose in it and a red ribbon. . . ."

"Not going to have those streamers, or any lace, are you?"

"Not likely. You see the kids round here wearing them; but the kids round here are always a season late. Same with their costumes. They don't know any better. I do!"

Jenny was cheerfully contemptuous. She knew what was being worn along Regent Street and in Bond Street, because she saw it with her own eyes. Then she came home and saw the girls of her own district swanking about like last year's patterns, as

she said. She couldn't help laughing at them. It made her think
of the tales of savages wearing top hats with strings of beads
and thinking they were all in the latest European fashion.
That is the constant amusement of the expert as she regards
the amateur. She has all the satisfaction of knowing better,
without the turmoil of competition, a fact which distinguishes
the superior spirit from the struggling helot. Jenny took full
advantage of her situation and her knowledge.

"Yes, you know a lot," Emmy said dryly.

"Ah, you've noticed it?" Jenny was not to be gibed at without retort. "I'm glad."

"So *you* think," Emmy added, as though she had not heard
the reply.

There came at this moment a knock at the front door. Emmy
swayed, grew pale, and then slowly reddened until the colour
spread to the very edges of her bodice. The two girls looked at
one another, a deliberate interchange of glances that was at
the same time, upon both sides, an intense scrutiny. Emmy was
breathing heavily; Jenny's nostrils were pinched.

"Well," at last said Jenny, drawlingly. "Didn't you hear
the knock? Aren't you going to answer it?" She reached as she
spoke to the hat lying upon the plate rack above the gas stove,
looking fixedly away from her sister. Her air of gravity was
unchanged. Emmy, hesitating, made as if to speak, to implore
something; but, being repelled, she turned, and went thoughtfully across the kitchen to the front door. Jenny carried her
hat into the kitchen and sat down at the table as before. The
half-contemptuous smile had reappeared in her eyes; but her
mouth was quite serious.

iii

Pa Blanchard had worked as a boy and man in a large iron
foundry. He had been a very capable workman, and had received as the years went on the maximum amount (with over-
time) to be earned by men doing his class of work. He had not
been abstemious, and so he had spent a good deal of his earn-
ings in what is in Kennington Park called "pleasure"; but he
had also possessed that common kind of sense which leads men
to pay money into sick and benefit clubs. Accordingly, his
wife's illness and burial had, as he had been in the habit of

saying, "cost him nothing." They were paid by his societies. Similarly, when he had himself been attacked by the paralytic seizure which had wrecked his life, the societies had paid; and now, in addition to the pension allowed by his old employers, he received a weekly dole from the societies which brought his income up to fifty shillings a week. The pension, of course, would cease upon his death; but so long as life was kept burning within him nothing could affect the amounts paid weekly into the Blanchard exchequer. Pa was fifty-seven, and normally would have had a respectable number of years before him; his wants were now few, and his days were carefully watched over by his daughters. He would continue to draw his pensions for several years yet, unless something unexpected happened to him. Meanwhile, therefore, his pipe was regularly filled and his old pewter tankard appeared at regular intervals, in order that Pa should feel as little as possible the change in his condition.

Mrs. Blanchard had been dead ten years. She had been very much as Emmy now was, but a great deal more cheerful. She had been plump and fresh-coloured, and in spite of Pa Blanchard's ways she had led a happy life. In the old days there had been friends and neighbours, now all lost in course of removals from one part of London to another, so that the girls were without friends and knew intimately no women older than themselves. Mrs. Blanchard, perhaps in accord with her cheerfulness, had been a complacent, selfish little woman, very neat and clean, and disposed to keep her daughters in their place. Jenny had been her favourite; and even so early had the rivalry between them been established. Besides this, Emmy had received all the rebuffs needed to check in her the same complacent selfishness that distinguished her mother. She had been frustrated all along, first by her mother, then by her mother's preference for Jenny, finally (after a period during which she dominated the household after her mother's death) by Jenny herself. It was thus not upon a pleasant record of personal success that Emmy could look back, but rather upon a series of chagrins of which each was the harder to bear because of the history of its precursors. Emmy, between eighteen and nineteen at the time of her mother's death, had grasped her opportunity, and had made the care of the household her lot. She still bore, what was a very different reading of her ambition, the cares of the household. Jenny, as she grew up, had proved unruly; Pa Blanchard's illness had made home service compulsory; and so matters were like to remain indefinitely. Is it any wonder that Emmy was restive and unhappy as she saw her youth going and her horizons closing upon her with the passing of each year? If she had been wholly selfish that fact would have been enough to sour her temper. But another, emotionally more potent, fact produced in Emmy feelings of still greater stress. To that fact she had this evening given involuntary expression. Now, how would she, how could she, handle her destiny? Jenny, shrewdly thinking as she sat with her father in the kitchen and heard Emmy open the front door, pondered deeply as to her sister's ability to turn to account her own sacrifice.

iv

Within a moment Alf Rylett appeared in the doorway of the kitchen, Emmy standing behind him until he moved forward, and then closing the door and leaning back against it. His first glance was in the direction of Jenny, who, however, did not rise as she would ordinarily have done. He glanced quickly at her face and from her face to her hands, so busily engaged in manipulating the materials from which she was to re-trim her hat. Then he looked at Pa Blanchard, whom he touched lightly and familiarly upon the shoulder. Alf was a rather squarely built young man of thirty, well under six feet, but not ungainly. He had a florid, reddish complexion, and his hair was of a common but unnamed colour, between brown and grey, curly and crisp. He was clean-shaven. Alf was obviously one who worked with his hands: in the little kitchen he appeared to stand upon the tips of his toes, in order that his walk might not be too noisy. That fact might have suggested either mere nervousness or a greater liking for life out of doors. When he walked it was as though he did it all of a piece, so that his shoulders moved as well as his legs. The habit was shown as he lunged forward to grip Jenny's hand. When he spoke he shouted, and he addressed Pa as a boy might have done who was not quite completely at his ease, but who thought it necessary to pretend that he was so.

"Good evening, Mr. Blanchard!" he cried boisterously. "Sitting by the fire, I see!"

Pa looked at him rather vacantly, apparently straining his

memory in order to recognise the new-comer. It was plain that as a personal matter he had no immediate use for Alf Rylett; but he presently nodded his head.

"Sitting by the fire," he confirmed. "Getting a bit warm. It's cold to-night. Is there any noos, Alf Rylett?"

"Lots of it!" roared Alf, speaking as if it had been to a deaf man or a foreigner. "They say this fire at Southwark means ten thousand pounds damage. Big factory there—gutted. Of course, no outside fire escapes. *As* usual. Fully insured, though. It'll cost them nothing. You can't help wondering what causes these fires when they're heavily insured. Eh? Blazing all night, it was. Twenty-five engines. Twenty-five, mind you! That shows it was pretty big, eh? I saw the red in the sky, myself. 'Well,' I thought to myself, 'there's somebody stands to lose something,' I thought. But the insurance companies are too wide to stand all the risk themselves. They share it out, you know. It's a mere flea-bite to them. And . . . a . . . well then there's a . . . See, then there's a bigamy case."

"Hey?" cried Pa sharply, brightening. "What's that about?"

"Nothing much. Only a couple of skivvies. About ten pound three and fourpence between the pair of them. That was all he got." Pa's interest visibly faded. He gurgled at his pipe and turned his face towards the mantelpiece. "And . . . a . . . let's see, what else is there?" Alf racked his brains, puffing a little and arching his brows at the two girls, who seemed both to be listening, Emmy intently, as though she were repeating his words to herself. He went on: "Tram smash in Newcastle. Car went off the points. Eleven injured. Nobody killed. . . ."

"I don't call *that* much," said Jenny, critically, with a pin in her mouth. "Not much more than I told him an hour ago. He wants a murder, or a divorce. All these little tin-pot accidents aren't worth printing at all. What he wants is the cross-examination of the man who found the bones."

It was comical to notice the change on Alf at Jenny's interruption. From the painful concentration upon memory which had brought his eyebrows together there appeared in his expression the most delighted ease, a sort of archness that made his face look healthy and honest.

"What's that you're doing?" he eagerly inquired, forsaking Pa, and obviously thankful at having an opportunity to address Jenny directly. He came over and stood by the table, in spite of the physical effort which Emmy involuntarily made to will that he should not do so. Emmy's eyes grew tragic at his intimate, possessive manner in speaking to Jenny. "I say!" continued Alf, admiringly. "A new hat, is it? Smart! Looks absolutely A1. Real West End style, isn't it? Going to have some chiffong?"

"Sit down, Alf." It was Emmy who spoke, motioning him to a chair opposite to Pa. He took it, his shoulder to Jenny, while Emmy sat by the table, looking at him, her hands in her lap.

"How is he?" Alf asked, jerking his head at Pa. "Perked up when I said 'bigamy,' didn't he!"

"He's been very good, I will say," answered Emmy. "Been quiet all day. And he ate his supper as good as gold." Jenny's smile and little amused crouching of the shoulders caught her eye. "Well, so he did!" she insisted. Jenny took no notice. "He's had his—mustn't say it, because he *always* hears that word, and it's not time for his evening . . . Eight o'clock he has it."

"What's that?" said Alf, incautiously. "Beer?"

"Beer!" cried Pa. "Beer!" It was the cry of one who had been malignantly defrauded, a piteous wail.

"There!" said both the girls, simultaneously. Jenny added: "Now you've done it!"

"All right, Pa! Not time yet!" But Emmy went to the kitchen cupboard as Pa continued to express the yearning that filled his aged heart.

"Sorry!" whispered Alf. "Hold me hand out, naughty boy!"

"He's like a baby with his titty bottle," explained Emmy. "Now he'll be quiet again."

Alf fidgeted a little. This contretemps had unnerved him. He was less sure of himself.

"Well," he said at last, darkly. "What I came in about . . . Quarter to eight, is it? By Jove, I'm late. That's telling Mr. Blanchard all the news. The fact is, I've got a couple of tickets for the theatre down the road—for this evening, I thought . . . . erum . . ."

"Oh, extravagance!" cried Jenny, gaily, dropping the pin from between her lips and looking in an amused flurry at Emmy's anguished face opposite. It was as though a chill had struck across the room, as though both Emmy's heart and her own had given a sharp twist at the shock.

"Ah, that's where you're wrong. That's what cleverness does

for you." Alf nodded his head deeply and reprovingly. "Given
to me, they were, by a pal o' mine who works at the theatre.
They're for to-night. I thought——"

Jenny, with her heart beating, was stricken for an instant
with panic. She bent her head lower, holding the rose against
the side of her hat, watching it with a zealous eye, once again
to test the effect. He thought she was coquetting, and leaned a
little towards her. He would have been ready to touch her face
teasingly with his forefinger.

"Oh," Jenny exclaimed, with a hurried assumption of matter of fact ease suddenly ousting her panic. "That's very good.
So you thought you'd take *Emmy!* That was a very good boy!"

"I thought . . ." heavily stammered Alf, his eyes opening
in a surprised way as he found himself thus headed off from his
true intention. He stared blankly at Jenny, until she thought
he looked like the bull on the hoardings who has "heard that
they want more." Emmy stared at her also, quite unguardedly,
a concentrated stare of agonised doubt and impatience. Emmy's face grew pinched and sallow at the unexpected strain
upon her nerves.

"That was what you thought, wasn't it?" Jenny went on
impudently, shooting a sideways glance at him that made Alf
tame with helplessness. "Poor old Em hasn't had a treat for ever
so long. Do her good to go. You did mean that, didn't you?"

"I . . ." said Alf. "I . . ." He was inclined for a moment
to bluster. He looked curiously at Jenny's profile, judicial in
its severity. Then some kind of tact got the better of his first
impulse. "Well, I thought *one* of you girls . . ." he said.
"Will you come, Em? Have to look sharp."

"Really?" Emmy jumped up, her face scarlet and tears of
joy in her eyes. She did not care how it had been arranged.
Her pride was unaroused; the other thought, the triumph of
the delicious moment, was overwhelming. Afterwards—ah, no,
no! She would not think. She was going. She was actually going. In a blur she saw their faces, their kind eyes . . .

"Good boy!" cried Jenny. "Buck up, Em, if you're going
to change your dress. Seats! My word! How splendid!" She
clapped her hands quickly, immediately again taking up her
work so as to continue it. Into her eyes had come once more
that strange expression of pitying contempt. Her white hands
flashed in the wan light as she quickly threaded her needle and
knotted the silk.

CHAPTER III
Rows

AFTER Emmy had hurried out of the room to change her dress, Alf stood, still apparently stupefied at the unscrupulous rush of Jenny's feminine tactics, rubbing his hand against the back of his head. He looked cautiously at Pa Blanchard, and from him back to the mysterious unknown who had so recently defeated his object. Alf may or may not have prepared some kind of set speech of invitation on his way to the house. Obviously it is a very difficult thing, where there are two girls in a family, to invite one of them and not the other to an evening's orgy. If it had not previously occurred to Alf to think of the difficulty quite as clearly as he was now being made to do, that must have been because he thought of Emmy as imbedded in domestic affairs. After all, damn it, as he was thinking; if you want one girl it is rotten luck to be fobbed off with another. Alf knew quite well the devastating phrase, at one time freely used as an irresistible quip (like "There's hair" or "That's all right, tell your mother; it'll be ninepence") by which one suggested disaster—"And that spoilt his evening." The phrase was in his mind, horrible to feel. Yet what could he have done in face of the direct assault? "*Must* be a gentleman." He could hardly have said, before Emmy: "No, it's *you* I want!" He began to think about Emmy. She was all right—a quiet little piece, and all that. But she hadn't got Jenny's cheek! That was it! Jenny had got the devil's own cheek, and this was an example of it. But this was an unwelcome example of it. He ruminated still further; until he found he was standing on one foot and rubbing the back of his head, just like any stage booby.

"Oh, damn!" he cried, putting his raised foot firmly on the ground and bringing his wandering fist down hard into the open palm of his other hand.

"Here, here!" protested Jenny, pretending to be scandalised. "That's not the sort of language to use before Pa! He's not used to it. We're *awfully* careful what we say when Pa's here!"

"You're making a fool of me!" spluttered Alf, glaring at her. "That's about the size of it!"

"What about your pa and ma?" she inquired, gibing at him. "I've done nothing. Why don't you sit down. Of course you feel a fool, standing. I always do, when the manager sends for me. Think I'm going to get the sack." She thought he was going to bellow at her: "I hear they want more!" The mere notion of it made her smile, and Alf imagined that she was still laughing at her own manœuvre or at her impertinent jest.

"What did you do it for?" he asked, coming to the table.

"Cause it was all floppy. What did you think? Why, the girls all talk about me wearing it so long."

"I'm not talking about that," he said, in a new voice of exasperated determination. "You know what I'm talking about. Oh, yes, you do! I'm talking about those tickets. And me. And you!"

Jenny's eyes contracted. She looked fixedly at her work. Her hands continued busy.

"Well, you're going to take Emmy, aren't you!" she prevaricated. "You asked her to go."

"No!" he said. "I'm going with her, because she's said she'll go. But it was you that asked her."

"Did I? How could I? They weren't mine. You're a man. You brought the tickets. You asked her yourself." Jenny shook her head. "Oh, no, Alf Rylett. You mustn't blame me. Take my advice, my boy. You be very glad Emmy's going. If you mean me, I should have said 'No,' because I've got to do this hat. Emmy's going to-night. You'll enjoy yourself far more."

"Oh——!" He did not use an oath, but it was implied. "What did you do it for? Didn't you want to come yourself? No, look here, Jenny: I want to know what's going on. You've always come with me before." He glared at her in perplexity, puzzled to the depths of his intelligence by a problem beyond its range. Women had always been reported to him as a mystery; but he had never heeded.

"It's Emmy's turn, then," Jenny went on. She could not resist the display of a sisterly magnanimity, although it was not the true magnanimity, and in fact had no relation to the truth. "Poor old Em gets stuck in here day after day," she pleaded. "She's always with Pa till he thinks she's a fixture. Well, why shouldn't she have a little pleasure? You get her some chocs . . . at that shop. . . . *You* know. It'll be the treat of her life. She'll be as grateful to you for it. . . . Oh, I'm very glad she's got the chance of going. It'll keep her happy for days!"

Jenny, trying with all her might to set the affair straight and
satisfy everybody, was appealing to his vanity to salve his vanity. Alf saw himself recorded as a public benefactor. He perceived the true sublimity of altruism.

"Yes," he said, doggedly, recovering himself and becoming
a man, becoming Alf Rylett, once again. "That's all bally fine.
Sounds well as you put it; but you knew as well as I did that I
came to take *you*. I say nothing against Em. She's a good sort;
but——"

Jenny suddenly kindled. He had never seen her so fine.

"She's the best sort!" she said, with animation. "And don't
you forget it, Alf. Me—why, I'm as selfish as . . . as *dirt* beside her. Look a little closer, my lad. You'll see Em's worth
two of me. Any day! You think yourself jolly lucky she's going with you. That's all I've got to say to you!"

She had pushed her work back, and was looking up at him
with an air of excitement. She had really been moved by a generous impulse. Her indifference to Alf no longer counted. It
was swept away by a feeling of loyalty to Emmy. The tale she
had told, the plea she had advanced upon Emmy's behalf, if
it had not influenced him, had sent a warm thrill of conviction
through her own heart. When she came thus to feel deeply she
knew as if by instinct that Emmy, irritable unsatisfied Emmy,
was as much superior to Alf as she herself was superior to him.
A wave of arrogance swept her. Because he was a man, and
therefore so delectable in the lives of two lonely girls, he was
basely sure of his power to choose from among them at will.
He had no such power at that moment, in Jenny's mind. He
was the clay, for Emmy or herself to mould to their own advantage.

"You can think yourself *jolly* lucky, my lad!" she repeated.
"I can tell you that much!"

ii

Jenny leant back in her chair exhausted by her excitement.
Alf reached round for the chair he had left, and brought it to
the table. He sat down, his elbows on the table and his hands
clasped; and he looked directly at Jenny as though he were
determined to explode this false bubble of misunderstanding
which she was sedulously creating. As he looked at her, with his

face made keen by the strength of his resolve, Jenny felt her heart turn to water. She was physically afraid of him, not because he had any power to move her, but because in sheer bullock-like strength he was too much for her, as in tenacity he had equally an advantage. As a skirmisher, or in guerrilla warfare, in which he might always retire to a hidden fastness, baffling pursuers by innumerable ruses and doublings, Jenny could hold her own. On the plain, in face of superior strength, she had not the solid force needed to resist strong will and clear issues. Alf looked steadily at her, his reddish cheeks more red, his obstinate mouth more obstinate, so that she could imagine the bones of his jaws cracking with his determination.

"It won't do, Jen," he said. "And you know it."

Jenny wavered. Her eyes flinched from the necessary task of facing him down. Where women of more breeding have immeasurable resources of tradition behind them, to quell any such inquisition, she was by training defenceless. She had plenty of pluck, plenty of adroitness; but she could only play the sex game with Alf very crudely because he was not fine enough to be diverted by such finesse as she could employ. All Jenny could do was to play for safety in the passage of time. If she could beat him off until Emmy returned she could be safe for to-night; and if she were safe now—anything might happen another day to bring about her liberation.

"Bullying won't do. I grant that," she retorted defiantly. "You needn't think it will." She jerked her head.

"We're going to have this out," Alf went on. Jenny darted a look of entreaty at the kicking clock which lay so helplessly upon its side. If only the clock would come to her aid, forgetting the episode of the tea-cosy!

"Take you all your time," she said swiftly. "Why, the theatre's all full by now. The people are all in. They're tuning up for the overture. Look at it!" She pointed a wavering finger at the clock.

"We're going to have this out—now!" repeated Alf. "You know why I brought the tickets here. It was because I wanted to take *you*. It's no good denying it. That's enough. Somehow —I don't know why—you don't want to go; and while I'm not looking you shove old Em on to me."

"That's what you say," Jenny protested. Alf took no notice of her interruption. He doggedly proceeded.

"As I say, Em's all right enough. No fault to find with her.

But she's not you. And it's you I wanted. Now, if I take her——"

"You'll enjoy it very much," she weakly asserted. "Ever so much. Besides, Alf,"—she began to appeal to him, in an attempt to wheedle—"Em's a real good sort. . . . You don't know half the things . . ."

"I know all about Em. I don't need you to tell me what she is. I can see for myself." Alf rocked a little with an ominous obstinacy. His eyes were fixed upon her with an unwinking stare. It was as though, having delivered a blow with the full weight of party bias, he were desiring her to take a common-sense view of a vehement political issue.

"What can you see?" With a feeble dash of spirit, Jenny had attempted tactical flight. The sense of it made her feel as she had done, as a little girl, in playing touch; when, with a swerve, she had striven to elude the pursuer. So tense were her nerves on such occasions that she turned what is called "goosey" with the feel of the evaded fingers.

Alf rolled his head again, slightly losing his temper at the inconvenient question, which, if he had tried to answer it, might have diverted him from the stern chase upon which he was engaged. The sense of that made him doubly resolved upon sticking to the point.

"Oh, never you mind," he said, stubbornly. "Quite enough of that. Now the question is—and it's a fair one,—why did you shove Em on to me?"

"I didn't! You did it yourself!"

"Well, that's a flat lie!" he cried, slapping the table in a sudden fury, and glaring at her. "That's what that is."

Jenny crimsoned. It made the words no better that Alf had spoken truly. She was deeply offended. They were both now sparkling with temper, restless with it, and Jenny's teeth showing.

"I'm a liar, am I!" she exclaimed. "Well, you can just lump it, then. I shan't say another word. Not if you call me a liar. You've come here . . ." Her breath caught, and for a second she could not speak. "You've come here *kindly* to let us lick your boots, I suppose. Is that it? Well, we're not going to do it. We never have, and we never will. Never! It's a drop for you, you think, to take Emmy out. A bit of kindness on your part. She's not up to West End style. That it? But you needn't think you're too good for her. There's no reason, I'm sure. You're not! . . . . All because you're a man. Auch! I'm sick of the men! You think you've only got to whistle. Yes, you do! You think if you crook your little finger . . . Oh no, my lad. That's where you're wrong. You're making a big mistake there. We can look after ourselves, thank you! No chasing after the men! Pa's taught us that. We're not quite alone. We haven't got to take—we've neither of us got to take—whatever's offered to us . . . as you think. We've got Pa still!"

Her voice had risen. An unexpected interruption stopped the argument for the merest fraction of time.

"Aye," said Pa. "They've got their old Pa!" He had taken his pipe out of his mouth and was looking towards the combatants with an eye that for one instant seemed the eye of perfect comprehension. It frightened Jenny as much as it disconcerted Alf. It was to both of them, but especially to Alf, like the shock of a cold sponge laid upon a heated brow.

"I never said you hadn't!" he sulkily said, and turned round to look amazedly at Pa. But Pa had subsided once more, and was drinking with mournful avidity from his tankard. Occupied with the tankard, Pa had neither eye nor thought for anything else. Alf resumed after the baffled pause. "Yes. You've got him all right enough. . . ." Then: "You're trying to turn it off with your monkey tricks!" he said suddenly. "But I see what it is. I was a fool not to spot it at once. You've got some other fellow in tow. I'm not good enough for you any longer. Got no use for me yourself; but you don't mind turning me over to old Em. . . ." He shook his head. "Well, I don't understand it," he concluded miserably. "I used to think you was straight, Jen."

"I am!" It was a desperate cry, from her heart. Alf sighed.

"You're not playing the game, Jen old girl," he said, more kindly, more thoughtfully. "That's what's the matter. I don't know what it is, or what you're driving at; but that's what's wrong. What's the matter with me? Anything? I know I'm not much of a one to shout the odds about. I don't expect you to do that. Never did. But I never played you a trick like this. What is it? What's the game you think you're playing?" When she did not answer his urgent and humble appeal he went on in another tone: "I shall find out, mind you. It's not going to stop here. I shall ask Emmy. I can trust her."

"You *can't* ask her!" Jenny cried. It was wrung from her. "You just dare to ask her. If she knew you hadn't meant to take her to-night, it ud break her heart. It would. There!" Her voice had now the ring of intense sincerity. She was not afraid, not defiant. She was a woman, defending another woman's pride.

Alf groaned. His cheeks became less ruddy. He looked quickly at the door, losing confidence.

"No: I don't know what it is," he said again. "I don't understand it." He sat, biting his under lip, miserably undetermined. His grim front had disappeared. He was, from the conquering hero, become a crestfallen young man. He could not be passionate with Pa there. He felt that if only she were in his arms she could not be untruthful, could not resist him at all; but with the table between them she was safe from any attack. He was powerless. And he could not say he loved her. He would never be able to bring himself to say that to any woman. A woman might ask him if he loved her, and he would awkwardly answer that of course he did; but it was not in his nature to proclaim the fact in so many words. He had not the fluency, the dramatic sense, the imaginative power to sink and to forget his own self-consciousness. And so Jenny had won that battle—not gloriously, but through the sheer mischance of circumstances. Alf was beaten, and Jenny understood it.

"Don't *think* about me," she whispered, in a quick pity. Alf still shook his head, reproachfully eyeing her with the old bull-like concern. "I'm not worth thinking about. I'm only a beast. And you say you can trust Emmy. . . . She's ever so . . ."

"Ah, but she can't make me mad like you do!" he said simply. "Jen, will you come another night . . . Do!" He was beseeching her, his hands stretched towards her across the table, as near to making love as he would ever be. It was his last faint hope for the changing of her heart towards him. But Jenny slowly shook her head from side to side, a judge refusing the prisoner's final desperate entreaties.

"No," she said. "It's no good, Alf. It'll never be any good as long as I live."

iii

Alf put out his hand and covered Jenny's hand with it; and the hand he held, after a swift movement, remained closely imprisoned. And just at that moment, when the two were striving for mastery, the door opened and Emmy came back into the

room. She was fully dressed for going out, her face charmingly
set off by the hat she had offered earlier to Jenny, her eyes
alight with happiness, her whole bearing unutterably changed.

"*Now* who's waiting!" she demanded; and at the extraordinary sight before her she drew a quick breath, paling. It did not
matter that the clinging hands were instantly apart, or that
Alf rose hurriedly to meet her. "What's that?" she asked, in a
trembling tone. "What are you doing?" As though she felt
sick and faint, she sat sharply down upon her old chair near
the door. Jenny rallied.

"Only a kid's game," she said. "Nothing at all." Alf said
nothing, looking at neither girl. Emmy tried to speak again;
but at first the words would not come. Finally she went on,
with dreadful understanding.

"Didn't you want to take me, Alf? Did you want her to go?"

It was as though her short absence, perhaps even the change
of costume, had worked a curious and cognate change in her
mind. Perhaps it was that in her flushed happiness she had
forgotten to be suspicious, or had blindly misread the meanings
of the earlier colloquy, as a result of which the invitation had
been given.

"Don't be so silly!" quickly cried Jenny. "Of course he
wanted you to go!"

"Alf!" Emmy's eyes were fixed upon him with a look of urgent entreaty. She looked at Alf with all the love, all the extraordinary intimate confidence with which women of her class
do so generally regard the men they love, ready to yield judgment itself to his decision. When he did not answer, but stood
still before them like a red-faced boy, staring down at the floor,
she seemed to shudder, and began despairingly to unfasten the
buttons of her thick coat. Jenny darted up and ran to check the
process.

"Don't be a fool!" she breathed. "Like that! You've got no
time for a scene." Turning to Alf, she motioned him with a
swift gesture to the door. "Look sharp!" she cried.

"I'm not going!" Emmy struggled with Jenny's restraining
hands. "It's no good fussing me, Jenny. . . . I'm not going.
He can take who he likes. But it's not me."

Alf and Jenny exchanged angry glances, each bitterly blaming the other.

"Em!" Jenny shouted. "You're mad!"

"No, I'm not. Let me go! Let me go! He didn't want me to

go. He wanted you. 'Oh, I knew it. I was a fool to think he wanted me." Then, looking with a sort of crazed disdain at Jenny, she said coolly, "Well, how is it you're not ready? Don't you see your *substitute's* waiting? Your *land* lover!"

"Land!" cried Alf. "Land! A sailor!" He flushed deeply, raising his arms a little as if to ward off some further revelation. Jenny, desperate, had her hands higher than her head, protestingly quelling the scene. In a loud voice she checked them.

"Do . . . not . . . be . . . fools!" she cried. "What's all the fuss about? Simply because Alf's a born booby, standing there like a fool! I can't go. I wouldn't go—even if he wanted me. But he wants you!" She again seized Emmy, delaying once more Emmy's mechanical unfastening of the big buttons of her coat. "Alf! Get your coat. Get her out of the house! I never heard such rubbish! Alf, say . . . tell her you meant her to go! Say it wasn't me!"

"I shouldn't believe him," Emmy said, clearly. "I know I saw him holding your hand."

Jenny laughed hysterically.

"What a fuss!" she exclaimed. "He's been doing palmistry —reading it. All about . . . what's going to happen to me. Wasn't it, Alf!"

Emmy disregarded her, watching Alf's too-transparent uneasiness.

"You always *were* a little lying beast," she said, venomously. "A trickster."

"You see?" Jenny said, defiantly to Alf. "What my own sister says?"

"So you were. With your *sailor*. . . . And playing the fool with Alf!" Emmy's voice rose. "You always were. . . . I wonder Alf's never seen it long ago. . . ."

At this moment, with electrifying suddenness, Pa put down his tankard.

"What, ain't you gone yet?" he trembled. "I thought you was going out!"

"How did he know?" They all looked sharply at one another, sobered. So, for one instant, they stood, incapable of giving any explanation to the meekly inquiring old man who had disturbed their quarrel. Alf, so helpless before the girls, was steeled by the interruption. He took two steps towards Emmy.

"We'll have this out later on," he said. "Meanwhile . . .

Come on, Em! It's just on eight. Come along, there's a good girl!" He stooped, took her hands, and drew her to her feet. Then, with uncommon tenderness, he re-buttoned her coat, and, with one arm about her, led Emmy to the door. She pressed back, but it was against him, within the magic circle of his arm, suddenly deliriously happy.

Jenny, still panting, stood as she had stood for the last few minutes, and watched their departure. She heard the front door close as they left the house; and with shaky steps went and slammed the door of the kitchen. Trembling violently, she leant against the door, as Emmy had done earlier. For a moment she could not speak, could not think or feel; and only as a clock in the neighbourhood solemnly recorded the eighth hour did she choke down a little sob, and say with the ghost of her bereaved irony:

"That's *done* it!"

CHAPTER IV
THE WISH

WAITING until she had a little recovered her self-control, Jenny presently moved from the door to the fireplace, and proceeded methodically to put coals on the fire. She was still shaking slightly, and the corners of her mouth were uncontrollably twitching with alternate smiles and other raiding emotions; so that she did not yet feel in a fit state to meet Pa's scrutiny. He might be the old fool he sometimes appeared to be, and, inconveniently, he might not. Just because she did not want him to be particularly bright it was quite probable that he would have a flourish of brilliance. That is as it occasionally happens, in the dullest of mortals. So Jenny was some time in attending to the fire, until she supposed that any undue redness of cheek might be imagined to have been occasioned by her strenuous activities. She then straightened herself and looked down at Pa with a curious mixture of protectiveness and anxiety.

"Pleased with yourself, aren't you?" she inquired, more to make conversation which might engage the ancient mind in ruminant pastime than to begin any series of inquiries into Pa's mental states.

"Eh, Jenny?" said Pa, staring back at her. "Ain't you gone

out? Is it Emmy that's gone out? What did that fool Alf Rylett want? He was shouting. . . . I heard him."

"Yes, Pa; but you shouldn't have listened," rebuked Jenny, with a fine colour.

Pa shook his shaggy head. He felt cunningly for his empty tankard, hoping that it had been refilled by his benevolent genius. It was not until the full measure of his disappointment had been revealed that he answered her.

"I wasn't listening," he quavered. "I didn't hear what he said. . . . Did Emmy go out with him?"

"Yes, Pa. To the theatre. Alf brought tickets. Tickets! Tickets for seats. . . . Oh, dear! *Why* can't you understand! Didn't have to pay at the door. . . ."

Pa suddenly understood.

"Oh ah!" he said. "Didn't have to pay. . . ." There was a pause. "That's like Alf Rylett," presently added Pa. Jenny sat looking at him in consternation at such an uncharitable remark.

"It's not!" she cried. "I never *knew* you were such a wicked old man!"

Pa gave an antediluvian chuckle that sounded like a magical and appalling rattle from the inner recesses of his person. He was getting brighter and brighter, as the stars appear to do when the darkness deepens.

"See," he proceeded. "Did Alf say there was any noos?" He admitted an uncertainty. Furtively he looked at her, suspecting all the time that memory had betrayed him; but in his ancient way continuing to trust to Magic.

"Well, you didn't seem to think much of what he *did* bring. But I'll tell you a bit of news, Pa. And that is, that you've got a pair of the rummiest daughters I ever struck!"

Pa looked out from beneath his bushy grey eyebrows, resembling a worn and dilapidated perversion of Whistler's portrait of Carlyle. His eyelids seemed to work as he brooded upon her announcement. It was as though, together, these two explored the Blanchard archives for confirmation of Jenny's sweeping statement. The Blanchards of several generations might have been imagined as flitting across a fantastic horizon, keening for their withered laurels, thrown into the shades by these more brighter eccentrics. It was, or it might have been, a fascinating speculation. But Pa did not indulge this antique vein for very long. The moment and its concrete images beguiled him back to the daughter before him and the daughter who was engaged in an unexpected emotional treat. He said:

"I know," and gave a wide grin that showed the gaps in his teeth as nothing else could have done—not even the profoundest yawn. Jenny was stunned by this evidence of brightness in her parent.

"Well, you're a caution!" she cried. "And to think of you sitting there saying it! And I reckon they've got a pretty rummy old Pa—if the truth was only known."

Pa's grin, if possible, stretched wider. Again that terrible chuckle, which suggested a derangement of his internal parts, or the running-down of an overwound clock, wheezed across the startled air.

"Maybe," Pa said, with some unpardonable complacency. "Maybe."

"Bless my soul!" exclaimed Jenny. She could not be sure, when his manner returned to one of vacancy, and when the kitchen was silent, whether Pa and she had really talked thus, or whether she had dreamed their talk. To her dying day she was never sure, for Pa certainly added nothing to the conversation thereafter. Was it real? Or had her too excited brain played her a trick? Jenny pinched herself. It was like a fairy tale, in which cats talk and little birds humanly sing, or the tiniest of fairies appear from behind clocks or from within flower-pots. She looked at Pa with fresh awe. There was no knowing where you had him! He had the interest, for her, of one returned by miracle from other regions, gifted with preposterous knowledges. . . . He became at this instant fabulous, like Rip Van Winkle, or the Sleeping Beauty . . . or the White Cat. . . .

In her perplexity Jenny fell once more into a kind of dream, an argumentative dream. She went back over the earlier rows, re-living them, exaggerating unconsciously the noble unselfishness of her own acts and the pointed effectiveness of her speeches, until the scenes were transformed. They now appeared in other hues, in other fashionings. This is what volatile minds are able to do with all recent happenings whatsoever, re-casting them in form altogether more exquisite than the crude realities. The chiaroscuro of their experiences is thus so constantly changing and recomposing that—whatever the apparent result of the scene in fact—the dreamer is in retrospect always victor, in the heroic limelight. With Jenny this was a mood, not a preoccupation; but when she had been moved or excited beyond the ordinary she often did tend to put matters in a fresh aspect, more palatable to her self-love, and more picturesque in detail than the actual happening. That is one of the advantages of the rapidly-working brain, that its power of improvisation is, in solitude, very constant and reassuring. It is as though such a grain, upon this more strictly personal side, were a common-wealth of little cell-building microbes. The chief microbe comes, like the engineer, to estimate the damage to one's *amour propre* and to devise means of repair. He then summons all his neces-sary workmen, who are tiny self-loves and ancient praises and habitual complacencies and the staircase words of which one thinks too late for use in the scene itself; and with their help he restores that proportion without which the human being cannot maintain his self-respect. Jenny was like the British type as recorded in legend; being beaten, she never admitted it; but even, five minutes later, through the adroitness of her special engineer and his handymen, would be able quite seri-ously to demonstrate a victory to herself.

Defeat? Never! How Alf and Emmy shrank now before her increasing skill in argument. How were they shattered! How inept were their feebleness! How splendid Jenny had been, in act, in motive, in speech, in performance!

"Er, yes!" Jenny said, beginning to ridicule her own highly coloured picture. "Well, it was *something* like that!" She had too much sense of the ridiculous to maintain for long unques-tioned the heroic vein as natural to her own actions. More justly, she resumed her consideration of the scenes, pondering over them in their nakedness and their meanings, trying to see how all these stupid little feelings had burst their way from overcharged hearts, and how each word counted as part of the mosaic of misunderstanding that had been composed.

"Oh, blow!" Jenny impatiently ejaculated, with a sinking heart at the thought of any sequel. A sequel there was bound to be—however muffled. It did not rest with her. There were Emmy and Alf, both alike burning with the wish to avenge themselves—upon her! If only she could disappear—just drop out altogether, like a man overboard at night in a storm; and leave Emmy and Alf to settle together their own trouble. She couldn't drop out; nobody could, without dying, though they might often wish to do so; and even then their bodies were the only things that were gone, because for a long time they stub-

bornly survived in memory. No: she couldn't drop out. There
was no chance of it. She was caught in the web of life; not
alone, but a single small thing caught in the general mix-up of
actions and inter-actions. She had just to go on as she was
doing, waking up each morning after the events and taking her
old place in the world; and in this instance she would have,
somehow, to smooth matters over when the excitements and
agitations of the evening were past. It would be terribly difficult. She could not yet see a clear course. If only Emmy didn't
live in the same house! If only, by throwing Alf over as far as
concerned herself, she could at the same time throw him into
Emmy's waiting arms. Why couldn't everybody be sensible?
If only they could all be sensible for half-an-hour everything
could be arranged and happiness could be made real for each of
them. No: misunderstandings were bound to come, angers and
jealousies, conflicting desires, stupid suspicions. . . . Jenny
fidgeted in her chair and eyed Pa with a sort of vicarious hostility. Why, even that old man was a complication! Nay, he
was the worst thing of all! But for him, she *could* drop out!
There was no getting away from him! He was as much permanently there as the chair upon which he was drowsing. She
saw him as an incubus. And then Emmy being so fussy! Standing on her dignity when she'd give her soul for happiness! And
then Alf being so . . . What was Alf? Well, Alf was stupid.
That was the word for Alf. He was stupid. As stupid as any
stupid member of his immeasurably stupid sex could be!
   "Great booby!" muttered Jenny. Why, look at the way he
had behaved when Emmy had come into the room. It wasn't
honesty, mind you; because he could tell any old lie when he
wanted to. It was just funk. He hadn't known where to look,
or what to say. Too slow, he was, to think of anything. What
could you do with a man like that? Oh, what stupids men were!
She expected that Alf would feel very fine and noble as he
walked old Em along to the theatre—and afterwards, when
the evening was over and he had gone off in a cloud of glory,
He would think it all over and come solemnly to the conclusion
that the reason for his mumbling stupidity, his toeing and
heeling, and all that idiotic speechlessness that set Emmy on
her hind legs, was sheer love of the truth. He couldn't tell a
lie—to a woman. That would be it. He would pretend that
Jenny had chivvied him into taking Em, that he was too noble
to refuse to take Em, or to let Em really see point-blank that

he didn't want to take her; but when it came to the pinch he hadn't been able to screw himself into the truly noble attitude needed for such an act of self-sacrifice. He had been speechless when a prompt lie, added to the promptitude and exactitude of Jenny's lie, would have saved the situation. Not Alf!

"I cannot tell a lie," sneered Jenny. "To a woman. George Washington. I *don't* think!"

Yes; but then, said her secret complacency, preening itself, and suggesting that possibly a moment or two of satisfied pity might be at this point in place, he'd really wanted to take Jenny. He had taken the tickets because he had wanted to be in Jenny's company for the evening. Not Emmy's. There was all the difference. If you wanted a cream bun and got fobbed off with a scone! There was something in that. Jenny was rather flattered by her happy figure. She even excitedly giggled at the comparison of Emmy with a scone. Jenny did not like scones. She thought them stodgy. She had also that astounding feminine love of cream buns which no true man could ever acknowledge or understand. So Emmy became a scone, with not too many currants in it. Jenny's fluent fancy was inclined to dwell upon this notion. She a little lost sight of Alf's grievance in her pleasure at the figures she had drawn. Her mind was recalled with a jerk. Now: what was it? Alf had wanted to take her—Jenny. Right! He had taken Emmy. Right! Because he had taken Emmy, he had a grievance. Right! But against whom? Against Emmy? Certainly not. Against himself? By no means. Against Jenny? A horribly exulting and yet nervously penitent little giggle shook Jenny at her inability to answer this point as she had answered the others. For Alf *had* a grievance against Jenny, and she knew it. No amount of ingenious thought could hoodwink her sense of honesty for more than a debater's five minutes. No: Alf had a grievance. Jenny could not, in strict privacy, deny the fact. She took refuge in a shameless piece of bluster.

"Well, after all!" she cried, "he had the tickets given to him. It's not as though they *cost* him anything! So what's all the row about?"

ii

Thereafter she began to think of Alf. He had taken her out several times—not as many times as Emmy imagined, because

Emmy had thought about these excursions a great deal and not only magnified but multiplied them. Nevertheless, Alf had taken Jenny out several times. To a music hall once or twice; to the pictures, where they had sat and thrilled in cushioned darkness while acrobatic humans and grey-faced tragic creatures jerked and darted at top speed in and out of the most amazingly telescoped accidents and difficulties. And Alf had paid more than once, for all Pa said. It is true that Jenny had paid on her birthday for both of them; and that she had occasionally paid for herself upon an impulse of sheer independence. But there had been other times when Alf had really paid for both of them. He had been very decent about it. He had not tried any nonsense, because he was not a flirtatious fellow. Well, it had been very nice; and now it was all spoilt. It was spoilt because of Emmy. Emmy had spoilt it by wanting Alf for herself. Ugh! thought Jenny. Em had always been a jealous cat: if she had just seen Alf somewhere she wouldn't have wanted him. That was it! Em saw that Alf preferred Jenny; she saw that Jenny went out with him. And because she always wanted to do what Jenny did, and always wanted what Jenny had got, Em wanted to be taken out by Alf. Jenny, with the cruel unerringness of an exasperated woman, was piercing to Emmy's heart with fierce lambent flashes of insight. And if Alf had taken Em once or twice, and Jenny once or twice, not wanting either one or the other, or not wanting one of them more than the other, Em would have been satisfied. It would have gone no further. It would still have been sensible, without nonsense. But it wouldn't do for Em. So long as Jenny was going out Emmy stayed at home. She had said to herself: "Why should Jenny go, and not me . . . having all this pleasure?" That had been the first stage—Jenny worked it all out. First of all, it had been envy of Jenny's going out. Then had come stage number two: "Why should Alf Rylett always take Jenny, and not me?" That had been the first stage of jealousy of Alf. And the next time Alf took Jenny, Em had stayed at home, and thought herself sick about it, supposing that Alf and Jenny were happy and that she was unhappy, supposing they had all the fun, envying them the fun, hating them for having what she had not got, hating Jenny for monopolising Alf, hating Alf for monopolising Jenny; then, as she was a woman, hating Jenny for being a more pleasing woman than herself, and having her wounded jealousy moved into a strong craving for

Alf, driven deeper and deeper into her heart by long-continued thought and frustrated desire. And so she had come to look upon herself as one defrauded by Jenny of pleasure—of happiness—of love—of Alf Rylett.

"And she calls it love!" thought Jenny bitterly. "If that's love, I've got no use for it. Love's giving, not getting. I know that much. Love's giving yourself; wanting to give all you've got. It's got nothing at all to do with envy, or hating people, or being jealous. . . ." Then a swift feeling of pity darted through her, changing her thoughts, changing every shade of the portrait of Emmy which she had been etching with her quick corrosive strokes of insight. "Poor old Em!" she murmured. "She's had a rotten time. I know she has. Let her have Alf if she wants. I don't want him. I don't want anybody . . . except . . ." She closed her eyes in the most fleeting vision. "Nobody except just Keith. . . ."

Slowly Jenny raised her hand and pressed the back of her wrist to her lips, not kissing the wrist, but holding it against her lips so that they were forced hard back upon her teeth. She drew, presently, a deep breath, releasing her arm again and clasping her hands over her knees as she bent lower, staring at the glowing heart of the fire. Her lips were closely, seriously, set now; her eyes sorrowful. Alf and Emmy had receded from her attention as if they had been fantastic shadows. Pa, sitting holding his exhausted hubble-bubble, was as though he had no existence at all. Jenny was lost in memory and the painful aspirations of her own heart.

iii

How the moments passed during her reverie she did not know. For her it seemed that time stood still while she recalled days that were beautified by distance, and imagined days that should be still to come, made to compensate for that long interval of dullness that pressed her each morning into acquiescence. She bent nearer to the fire, smiling to herself. The fire showing under the little door of the kitchener was a bright red glowing ash, the redness that came into her imagination when the words "fire" or "heat" were used—the red heart, burning and consuming itself in its passionate immolation. She loved the fire. It was to her the symbol of rapturous surrender, that feminine ideal that lay still deeper than her pride, locked in the most secret chamber of her nature.

And then, as the seconds ticked away, Jenny awoke from her dream and saw that the clock upon the mantelpiece said half-past eight. Half-past eight was what, in the Blanchard home, was called "time." When Pa was recalcitrant Jenny occasionally shouted very loud, with what might have appeared to some people an undesirable knowledge of customs, "Act of Parliament, gentlemen, please"—which is a phrase sometimes used in clearing a public-house. To-night there was no need for her to do that. She had only to look at Pa, to take from his hand the almost empty pipe, to knock out the ashes, and to say:

"Time, Pa!" Obediently Pa held out his right hand and clutched in the other his sturdy walking-stick. Together they tottered into the bedroom, stood a moment while Jenny lighted the peep of gas which was Pa's guardian angel during the night, and then made their way to the bed. Pa sat upon the bed, like a child. Jenny took off Pa's collar and tie, and his coat and waistcoat; she took off his boots and his socks; she laid beside him the extraordinary faded scarlet nightgown in which Pa slept away the darkness. Then she left him to struggle out of his clothes as well as he could, which Pa did with a skill worthy of his best days. The cunning which replaces competence had shown him how the braces may be made to do their own work, how the shirt may with one hand be so manipulated as to be drawn swiftly over the head. . . . Pa was adept at undressing. He was in bed within five minutes, after a panting, exhausted interval during which he sat in a kind of trance, and was then proudly as usual knocking upon the floor with his walking-stick for Jenny to come and tuck him in for the night.

Jenny came, gave him a big kiss, and went back to the kitchen, where she resumed work upon her hat. It had lost its interest for her. She stitched quickly and roughly, not as one interested in needlework or careful for its own sake of the regularity of the stitch. Ordinarily she was accurate: to-night her attention was elsewhere. It had come back to the rows, because there is nothing either good or bad but thinking makes it ever so much more important than it really is. Loneliness with happy thoughts is perhaps an ideal state; but no torment could be greater than loneliness with thoughts that wound. Jenny's thoughts wounded her. The mood of complacency was

gone: that of shame and discontent was upon her. Distress was
uppermost in her mind—not the petulant wriggling of a spoilt
child, but the sober consciousness of pain in herself and in
others. In vain did Jenny give little gasps of annoyance, intended by her humour to disperse the clouds. The gasps and
exclamations were unavailing. She was angry, chagrined, miserable. . . . At last she could bear the tension no longer, but
threw down her work, rose, and walked impatiently about the
kitchen.

"Oh, *do* shut up!" she cried to her insistent thoughts.
'Enough to drive anybody off their nut. And they're not
worth it, either of them. Em's as stupid as she can be, thinking
about herself. . . . And as for Alf—anybody'd think I'd
tricked him. I haven't. I've gone out with him; but what's that?
Lots of girls go out with fellows for months, and nobody expects them to marry. The girls may want it; but the fellows
don't. They don't want to get settled down. And I don't blame
them. Why is Alf different? I suppose it's me that's different.
I'm not like other girls. . . ." That notion cheered her. "No:
I'm not like other girls. I want my bit of fun. I've never had
any. And just because I don't want to settle down and have a
lot of kids that mess the place to bits, of course I get hold of
Alf! It's too bad! Why can't he choose the right sort of girl?
Why can't he choose old Em? She's the sort that *does* want to
get settled. She knows she'll have to buck up about it, too. She
said I should get left. That's what she's afraid of, herself; only
she's afraid of getting left on the shelf. . . . I wonder why it
is the marrying men don't get hold of the marrying girls!
They do, sometimes, I suppose. . . ." Jenny shrugged restlessly and stood looking at nothing. "Oh, it's sickening! You
can't do anything you like in this world. Nothing at all! You've
always got to do what you *don't* like. They say it's good for
you. It's your 'duty.' Who to? And who are 'they,' to say such
a thing? What are they after? Just to keep people like me in
their place—do as you're told. Well, I'm not going to do as
I'm told. They can lump it! That's what they can do. What
does it matter—what happens to me? I'm me, aren't I? Got a
right to live, haven't I? Why should I be somebody's servant
all my life? I *won't*! If Alf doesn't want to marry Emmy, he
can go and whistle somewhere else. There's plenty of girls
who'd jump at him. But just because I don't, he'll worry me to
death. If I was to be all over him—see Alf sheer off! He'd think

there was something funny about me. Well, there is! I'm Jenny Blanchard; and I'm going to keep Jenny Blanchard. If I've got no right to live, then nobody's got any right to keep me from living. If there's no rights, other people haven't got any more than I have. They can't make me do anything—by any right they've got. People—managing people—think that because there isn't a corner of the earth they haven't collared they can tell you what you've got to do. Give you a ticket and a number, get up at six, eat so much a day, have six children, do what you're told. That may do for some people; but it's slavery. And I'm not going to do it. See!" She began to shout in her excited indignation. "See!" she cried again. "Just because I'm poor, I'm to do what I'm told. They seem to think that because they like to do what they're told, everybody ought to be the same. They're afraid. They're afraid of themselves—afraid of being left alone in the dark. They think everybody ought to be afraid—in case anybody should find out that they're cowards! But I'm not afraid, and I'm not going to do what I'm told. . . . I won't!"

In a frenzy she walked about the room, her eyes glittering, her face flushed with tumultuous anger. This was her defiance to life. She had been made into a rebel through long years in which she had unconsciously measured herself with others. Because she was a human being, Jenny thought she had a right to govern her own actions. With a whole priesthood against her, Jenny was a rebel against the world as it appeared to her —a crushing, numerically overwhelming pressure that would rob her of her one spiritual reality—the sense of personal freedom.

"Oh, I can't stand it!" she said bitterly. "I shall go mad! And Em taking it all in, and ready to have Alf's foot on her neck for life. And Alf ready to have Em chained to his foot for life. The fools! Why, I wouldn't . . . not even to Keith. . . . No, I wouldn't. . . . Fancy being boxed up and pretending I liked it—just because other people say they like it. Do as you're told. Do like other people. All be the same—a sticky mass of silly fools doing as they're told! All for a bit of bread, because somebody's bagged the flour for ever! And what's the good of it? If it was any good—but it's no good at all! And they go on doing it because they're cowards! Cowards, that's what they all are. Well, I'm not like that!"

Exhausted, Jenny sat down again; but she could not keep

still. Her feet would not remain quietly in the place she, as the governing intelligence, commanded. They too were rebels, nervous rebels, controlled by forces still stronger than the governing intelligence. She felt trapped, impotent, as though her hands were tied; as though only her whirling thoughts were unfettered. Again she took up the hat, but her hands so trembled that she could not hold the needle steady. It made fierce jabs into the hat. Stormily unhappy, she once more threw the work down. Her lips trembled. She burst into bitter tears, sobbing as though her heart were breaking. Her whole body was shaken with the deep and passionate sobs that echoed her despair.

iv

Presently, when she grew calmer, Jenny wiped her eyes, her face quite pale and her hands still convulsively trembling. She was worn out by the stress of the evening, by the vehemence of her rebellious feelings. When she again spoke to herself it was in a shamed, giggling way that nobody but Emmy had heard from her since the days of childhood. She gave a long sigh, looking through the blur at that clear glow from beneath the iron door of the kitchen grate. Miserably she refused to think again. She was half sick of thoughts that tore at her nerves and lacerated her heart. To herself Jenny felt that it was no good—crying was no good, thinking was no good, loving and sympathising and giving kindness—all these things were in this mood as useless as one another. There was nothing in life but the endless sacrifice of human spirit.

"Oh!" she groaned passionately. "If only something would happen. I don't care *what!* But something . . . something new . . . exciting. Something with a bite in it!"

She stared at the kicking clock, which every now and again seemed to have a spasm of distaste for its steady record of the fleeting seconds. "Wound up to go all day!" she thought, comparing the clock with herself in an angry impatience.

And then, as if it came in answer to her poignant wish for some untoward happening, there was a quick double knock at the front door of the Blanchards' dwelling, and a sharp whirring ring at the push-bell below the knocker. The sounds seemed to go violently through and through the little house in rapid waves of vibrant noise.

PART TWO
NIGHT

CHAPTER V
THE ADVENTURE

So UNEXPECTED was this interruption of her loneliness that Jenny was for an instant stupefied. She took one step, and then paused, dread firmly in her mind, paralysing her. What could it be? She could not have been more frightened if the sound had been the turning of a key in the lock. Were they back already? Had her hope been spoiled by some accident? Surely not. It was twenty minutes to nine. They were safe in the theatre by now. Oh, she was afraid! She was alone in the house—worse than alone! Jenny cowered. She felt she could not answer the summons. Tick-tick-tick said the clock, striking across the silences. Again Jenny made a step forward. Then, terrifying her, the noise began once more—the thunderous knock, the ping-ping-ping-whir of the bell. . . .

Wrenching her mind away from apprehensiveness she moved quickly to the kitchen door and into the dimly-lighted dowdy passage-way. Somewhere beyond the gas flicker and the hat-stand lay—what? With all her determination she pushed forward, almost running to the door. Her hand hovered over the little knob of the lock: only horror of a renewal of that dreadful sound prompted her to open the door quickly. She peered into the darkness, faintly silhouetted against the wavering light of the gas. A man stood there.

"Evening, miss," said the man. "Miss Jenny Blanchard?"

She could see there something white. He was holding it out to her. A letter!

"For me?" she asked, her voice still unsteady. She took the letter, a large square envelope. Mechanically she thanked the man, puzzling at the letter. From whom could a letter be brought to her?

"There's an answer," she heard. It came from ever so far away, in the dim distance beyond her vague wonderings. Jenny was lost, submerged in the sensations through which she had passed during the evening. She was quite unlike herself, timid and fearful, a frightened girl alone in an unhappy house.

"Wait a bit!" she said. "Will you wait there?"

"Yes," answered the man, startlingly enough. "I've got the car here."

The car! What did it mean? She caught now, as her eyes were more used to the darkness, the sheen of light upon a peaked cap such as would be worn by a chauffeur. It filled her mind that this man was in uniform. But if so, why? From whom should the letter come? He had said "Miss Jenny Blanchard."

"You *did* say it was for me? I'll take it inside. . . ." She left the door unfastened, but the man pulled it right to, so that the catch clicked. Then Jenny held the letter up under the flame of the passage gas. She read there by this meagre light her own name, the address, written in a large hand, very bold, with a sharp, sweeping stroke under all, such as a man of impetuous strength might make. There was a blue seal fastening the flap—a great pool of solid wax. Trembling so that she was hardly able to tear the envelope, Jenny returned to the kitchen, again scanning the address, the writing, the blue seal with its Minerva head. Still, in her perplexity, it seemed as though her task was first to guess the identity of the sender. Who could have written to her? It was unheard of, a thing for wondering jest, if only her lips had been steady and her heart beating with normal pulsation. With a shrug, she turned back from the seal to the address. She felt that some curious mistake had been made, that the letter was not for her at all, but for some other Jenny Blanchard, of whom she had never until now heard. Then, casting such a fantastic thought aside with another impatient effort, she tore the envelope, past the seal, in a ragged dash. Her first glance was at the signature. "Yours always, KEITH."

Keith! Jenny gave a sob and moved swiftly to the light. Her eyes were quite blurred with shining mist. She could not read the words. Keith! She could only murmur his name, holding the letter close against her.

ii

"MY DEAR JENNY," said the letter. "Do you remember? I said I should write to you when I got back. Well, here I am. I can't come to you myself. I'm tied here by the leg, and mustn't

leave for a moment. But you said you'd come to me. Will you?
Do! If you can come, you'll be a most awful dear, and I shall
be out of my wits with joy. Not really out of my wits. *Do* come,
there's a dear good girl. It's my only chance, as I'm off again
in the morning. The man who brings this note will bring you
safely to me in the car, and will bring you quite safely home
again. *Do* come! I'm longing to see you. I trust you to come. I
will explain everything when we meet. Yours always, KEITH."

A long sigh broke from Jenny's lips as she finished reading.
She was transfigured. Gone was the defiant look, gone were the
sharpnesses that earlier had appeared upon her face. A soft
colour flooded her cheeks; her eyes shone. Come to him! She
would go to the end of the world. . . . Keith! She said it
aloud, in a voice that was rich with her deep feeling, magically
transformed.

"Come to you, my dear!" said Jenny. "As if you need ask!"

Then she remembered that Emmy was out, that she was left
at home to look after her father, that to desert him would be a
breach of trust. Quickly her face paled, and her eyes became
horror-laden. She was shaken by the conflict of love and love,
love that was pity and love that was the overwhelming call of
her nature. The letter fluttered from her fingers, swooping
like a wounded bird to the ground, and lay unheeded at her
feet.

iii

"What *shall* I do?" Nobody to turn to; no help from any
hand. To stay was to give up the chance of happiness. To go
—oh, she couldn't go! If Keith was tied, so was Jenny. Half
demented, she left the letter where it had fallen, a white square
upon the shabby rug. In a frenzy she wrung her hands. What
could she do? It was a cry of despair that broke from her heart.
She couldn't go, and Keith was waiting. That it should have
happened upon this evening of all others! It was bitter! To
send back a message, even though it be written with all her
love, which still she must not express to Keith in case he should
think her lightly won, would be to lose him for ever. He would
never stand it. She saw his quick irritation, the imperious
glance. . . . He was a king among men. She must go! Whatever the failure in trust, whatever the consequences, she must

go. She couldn't go! Whatever the loss to herself, her place was here. Emmy would not have gone to the theatre if she had not known that Jenny would stay loyally there. It was too hard! The months, the long months during which Keith had not written, were upon her mind like a weariness. She had had no word from him, and the little photograph that he had laughingly offered had been her only consolation. Yes, well, why hadn't he written? Quickly her love urged his excuse. She might accuse him of having forgotten her, but to herself she explained and pardoned all. That was not for this moment. Keith was not in fault. It was this dreadful difficulty of occasion, binding her here when her heart was with him. To sit moping here by the fire when Keith called to her! Duty—the word was a mockery. "They" would say she ought to stay. Hidden voices throbbed the same message into her consciousness. But every eager impulse, winged with love, bade her go. To whom was her heart given? To Pa? Pity . . . pity. . . . She pitied him, helpless at home. If anything happened to him? Nothing would happen. What could happen? Supposing she had gone to the chandler's shop: in those few minutes all might happen that could happen in all the hours she was away. Yet Emmy often ran out, leaving Pa alone. He was in bed, asleep; he would not awaken, and would continue to lie there at rest until morning. Supposing she had gone to bed—she would still be in the house; but in no position to look after Pa. He might die any night while they slept. It was only the idea of leaving him, the superstitious idea that just *because* she was not there something would happen. Suppose she didn't go; but sat in the kitchen for two hours and then went to bed. Would she ever forgive herself for letting slip the chance of happiness that had come direct from the clouds? Never! But if she went, and something *did* happen, would she ever in that event know self-content again in all the days of her life? Roughly she shouldered away her conscience, those throbbing urgencies that told her to stay. She was to give up everything for a fear? She was to let Keith go for ever? Jenny wrung her hands, drawing sobbing breaths in her distress.

Something made her pick the letter swiftly up and read it through a second time. So wild was the desire to go that she began to whimper, kissing the letter again and again, holding it softly to her cold cheek. Keith! What did it matter? What did anything matter but her love? Was she never to know any

happiness? Where, then, was her reward? A heavenly crown of
martyrdom? What was the good of that? Who was the better
for it? Passionately Jenny sobbed at such a mockery of her
overwhelming impulse. "They" hadn't such a problem to solve.
"They" didn't know what it was to have your whole nature
craving for the thing denied. "They" were cowards, enemies to
freedom because they liked the music of their manacles! They
could not understand what it was to love so that one adored
the beloved. Not blood, but water ran in their veins! They
didn't know. . . . They couldn't feel. Jenny knew, Jenny felt;
Jenny was racked with the sweet passion that blinds the eyes
to consequences. She *must* go! Wickedness might be her nature:
what then? It was a sweet wickedness. It was her choice!

Jenny's glance fell upon the trimmed hat which lay upon
the table. Nothing but a cry from her father could have prevented her from taking it up and setting it upon her head. The
act was her defiance. She was determined. As one deaf and
blind, she went out of the kitchen, and to the hall-stand, fumbling there for her hatpins. She pinned her hat as deliberately
as she might have done in leaving the house any morning. Her
pale face was set. She had flung the gage. There remained only
the acts consequential. And of those, since they lay behind the
veil of night, who could now speak? Not Jenny!

iv

There was still Pa. He was there like a secret, lying snug in
his warm bed, drowsily coaxing sleep while Jenny planned a
desertion. Even when she was in the room, her chin grimly set
and her lips quivering, a shudder seemed to still her heart. She
was afraid. She could not forget him. He lay there so quiet in
the semi-darkness, a long mound under the bedclothes; and she
was almost terrified at speaking to him because her imagination was heightened by the sight of his dim outline. He was so
helpless! Ah, if there had only been two Jennies, one to go, one
to stay. The force of uncontrollable desire grappled with her
pity. She still argued within herself, a weary echo of her earlier
struggle. He would need nothing, she was sure. It would be for
such a short time that she left him. He would hardly know she
was not there. He would think she was in the kitchen. But if he
needed her? If he called, if he knocked with his stick, and she

lid not come, he might be alarmed, or stubborn, and might try to find his way through the passage to the kitchen. If he fell! Her flesh crept as she imagined him helpless upon the floor, feebly struggling to rise. . . . It was of no use. She was bound to tell him. . . .

Jenny moved swiftly from the room, and returned with his nightly glass and jug of water. There could be nothing else that he would want during the night. It was all he ever had, and he would sleep so until morning. She approached the bed upon tiptoe.

"Pa," she whispered. "Are you awake?" He stirred, and looked out from the bedclothes, and she was fain to bend over him and kiss the tumbled hair. "Pa, dear . . . I want to go out. I've got to go out. Will you be all right if I leave you? Sure? You'll be a good boy, and not move! I shall be before Emmy, and you won't be lonely, or frightened—will you!" She exhorted him. "See, I've *got* to go out; and if I can't leave you . . . You *are* awake, Pa?"

"Yes," breathed Pa, half asleep. "A good boy. Night, Jenny, my dearie girl."

She drew back from the bed, deeply breathing, and stole to the door. One last glance she took, at the room and at the bed, closed the door and stood irresolute for a moment in the passage. Then she whipped her coat from the peg and put it on. She took her key and opened the front door. Everything was black, except that upon the roofs opposite the rising moon cast a glittering surface of light, and the chimney pots made slanting broad markings upon the silvered slates. The road was quite quiet but for the purring of a motor, and she could now, as her eyes were clearer, observe the outline of a large car drawn to the left of the door. As the lock clicked behind her and as she went forward the side lights of the motor blazed across her vision, blinding her again.

"Are you there?" she softly called.

"Yes, miss." The man's deep voice came sharply out of the darkness, and he jumped down from his seat to open the door of the car. The action startled Jenny. Why had the man done that?

"Did you know I was coming?" she suddenly asked, drawing back with a sort of chill.

"Yes, miss," said the man. Jenny caught her breath. She half turned away, like a shy horse that fears the friendly hand.

He had been sure of her, then. Oh, that was a wretched thought! She was shaken to the heart by such confidence. He had been sure of her! There was a flash of time in which she determined not to go; but it passed with dreadful speed. Too late, now, to draw back. Keith was waiting: he expected her! The tears were in her eyes. She was more unhappy than she had been yet, and her heart was like water.

The man still held open the door of the car. The inside was warm and inviting. His hand was upon her elbow; she was lost in the soft cushions, and drowned in the sweet scent of the great nosegay of flowers which hung before her in a shining holder. And the car was purring more loudly, and moving, moving as a ship moves when it glides so gently from the quay. Jenny covered her face with her hands, which cooled her burning cheeks as if they had been ice. Slowly the car nosed out of the road into the wider thoroughfare. Her adventure had begun in earnest. There was no drawing back now.

CHAPTER VI

THE YACHT

To LIE deep among cushions, and gently to ride out along streets and roads that she had so often tramped in every kind of weather, was enough to intoxicate Jenny. She heard the soft humming of the engine, and saw lamps and other vehicles flashing by, with a sense of effortless speed that was to her incomparable. If only she had been mentally at ease, and free from distraction, she would have enjoyed every instant of her journey. Even as it was, she could not restrain her eagerness as they overtook a tramcar, and the chauffeur honked his horn, and they glided nearer and nearer, and passed, and seemed to leave the tram standing. Each time this was in process of happening Jenny gave a small excited chuckle, thinking of the speed, and the ease, and of how the people in the tram must feel at being defeated in the race. Every such encounter became a race, in which she pressed physically forward as if to urge her steed to the final effort. Never had Jenny been so eager for victory, so elated when its certainty was confirmed. It was worth while to live for such experience. How she envied her driver! With his steady hands upon the steering wheel.

. . . Ah, he was like a sailor, like the sailor of romance, with the wind beating upon his face and his eyes ever-watchful. And under his hand the car rode splendidly to Keith.

Jenny closed her eyes. She could feel her heart beating fast, and the blood heating her cheeks, reddening them. The blood hurt her, and her mouth seemed to hurt, too, because she had smiled so much. She lay back, thinking of Keith and of their meetings—so few, so long ago, so indescribably happy and beautiful. She always remembered him as he had been when first he had caught her eye, when he had stood so erect among other men who lounged by the sea, smoking and lolling at ease. He was different, as she was different. And she was going to him. How happy she was! And why did her breath come quickly and her heart sink? She could not bother to decide that question. She was too excited to do so. In all her life she had never known a moment of such breathless anticipation, of excitement which she believed was all happiness.

There was one other thought that Jenny shirked, and that went on nevertheless in spite of her inattention, plying and moulding somewhere deep below her thrilling joy. The thought was, that she must not show Keith that she loved him, because while she knew—she felt sure—that he loved her, she must not be the smallest fraction of time before him in confession. She was too proud for that. He would tell her that he loved her; and the spell would be broken. Her shyness would be gone; her bravado immediately unnecessary. But until then she must beware. It was as necessary to Keith's pride as to her own that he should win her. The Keith she loved would not care for a love too easily won. The consciousness of this whole issue was at work below her thoughts; and her thoughts, from joy and dread, to the discomfort of doubt, raced faster than the car, speedless and headlong. Among them were two that bitterly corroded. They were of Pa and of Keith's confidence that she would come. Both were as poison in her mind.

ii

And then there came a curious sense that something had happened. The car stopped in darkness, and through the air there came in the huge tones of Big Ben the sound of a striking hour. It was nine o'clock. They were back at Westminster.

Before her was the bridge, and above was the lighted face of the clock, like some faded sun. And the strokes rolled out in swelling waves that made the whole atmosphere feel sound-laden. The chauffeur had opened the door of the car, and was offering his free hand to help Jenny to step down to the ground.

"Are we *there?*" she asked in a bewildered way, as if she had been dreaming. "How quick we've been!"

"Yes, miss. Mr. Redington's down the steps. You see them steps. Mr. Redington's down there in the dinghy. Mind how you go, miss. Hold tight to the rail. . . ." He closed the door of the car and pointed to the steps.

The dinghy! Those stone steps to the black water! Jenny was shaken by a shudder. The horror of the water which had come upon her earlier in the evening returned more intensely. The strokes of the clock were the same, the darkness, the feeling of the sinister water rolling there beneath the bridge, resistlessly carrying its burdens to the sea. If Keith had not been there she would have turned and run swiftly away, overcome by her fear. She timidly reached the steps, and stopped, peering down through the dimness. She put her foot forward so that it hung dubiously beyond the edge of the pavement.

"What a coward!" she thought, violently, with self-contempt. It drove her forward. And at that moment she could see below, at the edge of the lapping water, the outline of a small boat and of a man who sat in it using the oars against the force of the current so as to keep the boat always near the steps. She heard a dear familiar voice call out with a perfect shout of welcome:

"Jenny! Good girl! How are you! Come along; be careful how you come. That's it. . . . Six more, and then stop!" Jenny obeyed him—she desired nothing else, and her doubtings were driven away in a breath. She went quickly down. The back water lapped and wattled against the stone and the boat, and she saw Keith stand up, drawing the dinghy against the steps and offering her his hand. He had previously been holding up a small lantern that gilded the brown mud with a feeble colour and made the water look like oil. "Now!" he cried quickly. "Step!" The boat rocked, and Jenny crouched down upon the narrow seat, aflame with rapture, but terrified of the water. It was so near, so inescapably near. The sense of its smooth softness, its yieldingness, and the danger lurking be-

neath the flowing surface was acute. She tried more desperately to sit exactly in the middle of the boat, so that she should
not overbalance it. She closed her eyes, sitting very still, and
heard the water saying plup-plup-plup all round her, and she
was afraid. It meant soft death: she could not forget that.
Jenny could not swim. She was stricken between terror and joy
that overwhelmed her. Then:

"That's my boat," Keith said, pointing. "I say, you *are* a
sport to come!" Jenny saw lights shining from the middle of
the river, and could imagine that a yacht lay there stubbornly
resisting the current of the flowing Thames.

iii

Crouching still, she watched Keith bend to his oars, driving
the boat's nose beyond the shadowy yacht because he knew that
he must allow for the current. Her eyes devoured him, and her
heart sang. Plup-plup-plup-plup said the water. The oars
plashed gently. Jenny saw the blackness gliding beside her,
thick and swift. They might go down, down, down in that black
nothingness, and nobody would know of it. . . . The oars
ground against the edge of the dinghy—wood against wood,
grumbling and echoing upon the water. Behind everything she
heard the roaring of London, and was aware of lights, moving
and stationary, high above them. How low upon the water they
were! It seemed to be on a level with the boat's edges. And how
much alone they were, moving there in the darkness while the
life of the city went on so far above. If the boat sank! Jenny
shivered, for she knew that she would be drowned. She could
imagine a white face under the river's surface, lanterns flashing, and then—nothing. It would be all another secret happening, a mystery, the work of a tragic instant; and Jenny Blanchard would be forgotten for ever, as if she had never been. It
was a horrid sensation to her as she sat there, so near death.

And all the time that Jenny was mutely enduring these terrors they were slowly nearing the yacht, which grew taller as
they approached, and more clearly outlined against the sky.
The moon was beginning to catch all the buildings and to
lighten the heavens. Far above, and very pale, were stars; but
the sky was still murky, so that the river remained in darkness.
They came alongside the yacht. Keith shipped his oars, caught

hold of something which Jenny could not see; and the dinghy was borne round, away from the yacht's side. He half rose, catching with both his hands at an object projecting from the yacht, and hastily knotting a rope. Jenny saw a short ladder hanging over the side, and a lantern shining.

"There you are!" Keith cried. "Up you go! It's quite steady. Hold the brass rail. . . ."

After a second in which her knees were too weak to allow of her moving, Jenny conquered her tremors, rose unsteadily in the boat, and cast herself at the brass rail that Keith had indicated. To the hands that had been so tightly clasped together, steeling her, the rail was startlingly cold; but the touch of it nerved her, because it was firm. She felt the dinghy yield as she stepped from it, and she seemed for one instant to be hanging precariously in space above the terrifying waters. Then she was at the top of the ladder ready for Keith's warning shout about the descent to the deck. She jumped down. She was aboard the yacht; and as she glanced around Keith was upon the deck beside her, catching her arm. Jenny's triumphant complacency was so great that she gave a tiny nervous laugh. She had not spoken at all until this moment: Keith had not heard her voice.

"Well!" said Jenny. "*That's* over!" And she gave an audible sigh of relief. "Thank goodness!"

"And here you are!" Keith cried. "Aboard the *Minerva*."

iv

He led her to a door, and down three steps. And then it seemed to Jenny as if Paradise burst upon her. She had never before seen such a room as this cabin. It was a room such as she had dreamed about in those ambitious imaginings of a wondrous future which had always been so vaguely irritating to Emmy. It seemed, partly because the ceiling was low, to be very spacious; the walls and ceiling were of a kind of dusky amber hue; a golden brown was everywhere the prevailing tint. The tiny curtains, the long settees into which one sank, the chairs, the shades of the mellow lights—all were of some variety of this delicate golden brown. In the middle of the cabin stood a square table; and on the table, arrayed in an exquisitely white tablecloth, was laid a wondrous meal. The table was laid for two: candles with amber shades made silver shine and glasses glitter. Upon a fruit stand were peaches and nectarines; upon a tray she saw decanters; little dishes crowding the table bore mysterious things to eat such as Jenny had never before seen. Upon a side table stood other dishes, a tray bearing coffee cups and ingredients for the provision of coffee, curious silver boxes. Everywhere she saw flowers similar to those which had been in the motor car. Under her feet was a carpet so thick that she felt her shoes must be hidden in its pile. And over all was this air of quiet expectancy which suggested that everything awaited her coming. Jenny gave a deep sigh, glanced quickly at Keith, who was watching her, and turned away, her breath catching. The contrast was too great: it made her unhappy. She looked down at her skirt, at her hands; she thought of her hat and her hidden shoes. She thought of Emmy, the bread and butter pudding, of Alf Rylett . . . of Pa lying at home in bed, alone in the house.

v

Keith drew her forward slightly, until she came within the soft radiance of the cabin lights.

"I say, it *is* sporting of you to come!" he said. "Let's have a look at you—do!"

They stood facing one another. Keith saw Jenny, tall and pale, looking thin in her shabby dress, but indescribably attractive and beautiful even in her new shyness. And Jenny saw the man she loved: her eyes were veiled, but they were unfathomably those of one deeply in love. She did not know how to hide the emotions with which she was so painfully struggling. Pride and joy in him; shyness and a sort of dread; hunger and reserve—Keith might have read them all, so plainly were they written. Yet her first words were wounded and defiant.

"The man . . . that man . . . He *knew* I was coming," she said, in a voice of reproach. "You were pretty sure I should come, you know."

Keith said quietly:

"I *hoped* you would." And then he lowered his eyes. She was disarmed, and they both knew.

Keith Redington was nearly six feet in height. He was thin,

and even bony; but he was very toughly and strongly built, and his face was as clean and brown as that of any healthy man who travels far by sea. He was less dark than Jenny, and his hair was almost auburn, so rich a chestnut was it. His eyes were blue and heavily lashed; his hands were long and brown, with small freckles between the knuckles. He stood with incomparable ease, his hands and arms always ready, but in perfect repose. His lips, for he was clean-shaven, were keen and firm. His glance was fearless. As the phrase is, he looked every inch a sailor, born to challenge the winds and the waters. To Jenny, who knew only those men who show at once what they think or feel, his greater breeding made Keith appear inscrutable, as if he had belonged to a superior race. She could only smile at him, with parted lips, not at all the baffling lady of the mirror, or the contemptuous younger sister, or the daring franc-tireur of her little home at Kennington Park. Jenny Blanchard she remained, but the simple, eager Jenny to whom these other Jennies were but imperious moods.

"Well, I've come," she said. "But you needn't have been so sure."

Keith gave an irrepressible grin. He motioned her to the table, shaking his head at her tone.

"Come and have some grub," he said cheerfully. "I was about as sure as you were. You needn't worry about that, old sport. There's so little time. Come and sit down; there's a good girl. And presently I'll tell you all about it." He looked so charming as he spoke that Jenny obediently smiled in return, and the light came rushing into her eyes, chasing away the shadows, so that she felt for that time immeasurably happy and unsuspicious. She sat down at the laden table, smiling again at the marvels which it carried.

"My word, what a feast!" she said helplessly. "Talk about the Ritz!"

Keith busied himself with the dishes. The softly glowing cabin threw over Jenny its spell; the comfort, the faint slow rocking of the yacht, the sense of enclosed solitude, lulled her. Every small detail of ease, which might have made her nervous, merged with the others in a marvellous contentment because she was with Keith, cut off from the world, happy and at peace. If she sighed, it was because her heart was full. But she had forgotten the rest of the evening, her shabbiness, every care that troubled her normal days. She had cast these things off for the time, and was in a glow of pleasure. She smiled at Keith with a sudden mischievousness. They both smiled, without guilt, and without guile, like two children at a reconciliation.

vi

"Soup?" said Keith, and laid before her a steaming plate. "All done by kindness."

"Have you been cooking?" Some impulse made Jenny motherly. It seemed a strange reversal of the true order that he should cook for her. "It's like *The White Cat* to have it. . . ."

"It's a secret," Keith laughed. "Tell you later. Fire away!" He tasted the soup, while Jenny looked at five little letter biscuits in her own plate. She spelt them out E T K I H— KEITH. He watched her, enjoying the spectacle of the naïve mind in action as the light darted into her face. "I've got JENNY," he said, embarrassed. She craned, and read the letters with open eyes of marvel. They both beamed afresh at the primitive fancy.

"How did you do it?" Jenny asked inquisitively. "But it's nice." They supped the soup. Followed, whitebait: thousands of little fish. . . . Jenny hardly liked to crunch them. Keith whipped away the plates, and dived back into the cabin with a huge pie that made her gasp. "My gracious!" said Jenny. "I can never eat it!"

"Not *all* of it," Keith admitted. "Just a bit, eh?" He carved.

"Oh, thank goodness it's not stew and bread and butter pudding!" cried Jenny, as the first mouthful of the pie made her shut her eyes tightly. "It's like heaven!"

"If they have pies there." Jenny had not meant that: she had meant only that her sensations were those of supreme contentment. "Give me the old earth; and supper with Jenny!"

"Really?" Jenny was all brimming with delight.

"What will you have to drink? Claret? Burgundy?" Keith was again upon his feet. He poured out a large glass of red wine and laid it before her. Jenny saw with marvel the reflections of light on the wine and of the wine upon the tablecloth. She took a timid sip, and the wine ran tingling into her being.

"High life," she murmured. "Don't make me tipsy!" They exchanged overjoyed and intimate glances, laughing.

There followed trifle. Trifle had always been Jenny's dream;

and this trifle was her dream come true. It melted in the mouth; its flavours were those of innumerable spices. She was transported with happiness at the mere thought of such trifle. As her palate vainly tried to unravel the secrets of the dish, Keith, who was closely observant, saw that she was lost in a kind of fanatical adoration of trifle.

"You like it?" he asked.

"I shall never forget it!" cried Jenny. "Never as long as I live. When I'm an old . . . great-aunt . . ." She had hesitated at her destiny. "I shall bore all the kids with tales about it. I shall say 'That night on the yacht . . . when I first knew what trifle meant. . . .' They won't half get sick of it. But I shan't."

"You'll like to think about it?" asked Keith. "Like to remember to-night?"

"Will *you*?" parried Jenny. "The night you had Jenny Blanchard to supper?" Their eyes met, in a long and searching glance, in which candour was not unmixed with a kind of measuring distrust.

vii

Keith's face might have been carven for all the truth that Jenny got from it then. There darted across her mind the chauffeur's certainty that she was to be his passenger. She took another sip of wine.

"Yes," she said again, very slowly. "You *were* sure I was coming. You got it all ready. Been a bit of a sell if I hadn't come. You'd have had to set to and eat it yourself. . . . Or get somebody else to help you."

She meant "another girl," but she did not know she meant that until the words were spoken. Her own meaning stabbed her heart. That icy knowledge that Keith was sure of her was bitterest of all. It made her happiness defiant rather than secure. He was the only man for her. How did she know there were not other women for Keith! How could she ever know that? Rather, it sank into her consciousness that there must be other women. His very ease showed her that. The equanimity of his laughing expression brought her the unwelcome knowledge.

"I should have looked pretty small if I'd made no prepara-

ions, shouldn't I?" Keith inquired in a dry voice. "If you'd
ome here and found the place cold and nothing to eat you'd
ave made a bit of a shindy."

A reserve had fallen between them. Jenny knew she had been
inwise. It pressed down upon her heart the feeling that he was
omehow still a stranger to her. And all the time they had been
apart he had not seemed a stranger, but one to whom her most
leeting and intimate thoughts might freely have been given.
That had been the wonderful thought to her—that they had
met so seldom and understood each other so well. She had made
a thousand speeches to him in her dreams. Together, in these
same dreams, they had seen and done innumerable things, together, always in perfect confidence, in perfect understanding.
Yet now, when she saw him afresh, all was different. Keith was
different. He was browner, thinner, less warm in manner; and
more familiar, too, as though he were sure of her. His clothes
were different, and his carriage. He was not the same man. It
was still Keith, still the man Jenny loved; but as though he
were also somebody else whom she was meeting for the first
time. Her love, the love intensified by long broodings, was as
strong; but he was a stranger. All that intimacy which seemed
to have been established between them once and for ever was
broken by the new contact in unfamiliar surroundings. She
was shy, uncertain, hesitating; and in her shyness she had
blundered. She had been unwise, and he was offended when she
could least afford to have him so offended. It took much resolution upon Jenny's part to essay the recovery of lost ground.
But the tension was the worse for this mistake, and she suffered the more because of her anxious emotions.

"Oh, well," she said at last, as calmly as she could. "I daresay we should have managed. I mightn't have come. But I've
come, and you had all these beautiful things ready; and . . ."
Her courage to be severe abruptly failed; and lamely she concluded: "And it's simply like fairyland. . . . I'm ever so
happy."

Keith grinned again, showing perfect white teeth. For a moment he looked, Jenny thought, quite eager. Or was that only
her fancy because she so desired to see it? She shook her head;
and that drew Keith's eye.

"More trifle?" he suggested, with an arch glance. Jenny
noticed he wore a gold ring upon the little finger of his right
hand. It gleamed in the faint glow of the cabin. So, also, did

the fascinating golden hairs upon the back of his hand. Gentl
the cabin rose and fell, rocking so slowly that she could onl
occasionally be sure that the movement was true. She shook he
head in reply.

"I've had one solid meal to-night," she explained. "Wish .
hadn't! If I'd known I was coming out I'd have starved my
self all day. Then you'd have been shocked at me!"

Keith demurely answered, as if to reassure her:

"Takes a lot to shock me. Have a peach?"

"I must!" she breathed. "I can't let the chance slip. O-oh.
what a scent!" She reached the peach towards him. "Grand.
isn't it!" Jenny discovered for Keith's quizzical gaze an unexpected dimple in each pale cheek. He might have been Adam.
and she the original temptress.

"Shall I peel it?"

"Seems a shame to take it off!" Jenny watched his deft fingers as he stripped the peach. The glowing skin of the fruit
fell in lifeless peelings upon his plate, dying as it were under
her eyes. Keith had poured wine for her in another, smaller,
glass. She shook her head.

"I shall be drunk!" she protested. "Then I should sing!
Horrible, it would be!"

"Not with a little port . . . I'm not pressing you to a lot.
Am I?" He brought coffee to the table, and she began to admire first of all the pattern of the silver tray. Jenny had never
seen such a tray before, outside a shop, nor so delicately porcelain a coffee-service. It helped to give her the sense of strange,
unforgettable experience.

"You didn't say if you'd remember this evening," she slowly
reflected. Keith looked sharply up from the coffee, which he
was pouring, she saw, from a thermos flask.

"Didn't I?" he said. "Of course I shall remember it. I've
done better. I've looked forward to it. That's something you've
not done. I've looked forward to it for weeks. You don't think
of that. We've been in the Mediterranean, coasting about.
I've been planning what I'd do when we got back. Then Templecombe said he'd be coming right up to London; and I
planned to see you."

"Templecombe?" Jenny queried. "Who's he?"

"He's the lord who owns this yacht. Did you think it was my
yacht?"

"No . . . I hoped it wasn't . . ." Jenny said slowly.

viii

Keith's eyes were upon her; but she looked at her peach stone, her hand still lightly holding the fruit knife, and her fingers half caught by the beam of a candle which stood beside her. He persisted:

"Well, Templecombe took his valet, who does the cooking; and my hand—my sailorman—wanted to go and visit his wife . . . and that left me to see after the yacht. D'you see? I had the choice of keeping Tomkins aboard, or staying aboard myself."

"You might almost have given me longer notice," urged Jenny. "It seems to me."

"No. I'm under instructions. I'm not a free man," said Keith soberly. "I was once; but I'm not now. I'm captain of a yacht. I do what I'm told."

Jenny fingered her port-wine glass, and in looking at the light upon the wine her eyes became fixed.

"Will you ever do anything else?" she asked. Keith shrugged slightly.

"You want to know a lot," he said.

"I don't know very much, do I?" Jenny answered, in a little dead voice. "Just somewhere about nothing at all. I have to pretend the rest."

"D'you want to know it?"

Jenny gave a quick look at his hands which lay upon the table. She could not raise her eyes further. She was afraid to do so. Her heart seemed to be beating in her throat.

"It's funny me having to ask for it, isn't it!" she said, suddenly haggard.

CHAPTER VII

MORTALS

KEITH did not answer. That was the one certainty she had; and her heart sank. He did not answer. That meant that really she was nothing to him, that he neither wanted nor trusted her. And yet she had thought a moment before—only a moment before—that he was as moved as herself. They had seemed to be upon the brink of confidences; and now he had drawn back.

Each instant deepened her sense of failure. When Jenny stealthily looked sideways, Keith sat staring before him, his expression unchanged. She had failed.

"You don't trust me," she said, with her voice trembling. There was another silence. Then:

"Don't I?" Keith asked, indifferently. He reached his hand out and patted hers, even holding it lightly for an instant. "I think I do. You don't think so?"

"No." She merely framed the word, sighing.

"You're wrong, Jenny." Keith's voice changed. He deliberately looked round the table at the little dishes that still lay there untouched. "Have some of these sweets, will you. . . . No?" Jenny could only draw her breath sharply, shaking her head. "Almonds, then?" She moved impatiently, her face distorted with wretched exasperation. As if he could see that, and as if fear of the outcome hampered his resolution, Keith hurried on. "Well, look here: we'll clear the table together, if you like. Take the things through the other cabin—*that* one—to the galley; root up the table by its old legs—I'll show you how it's done;—and then we can have a talk. I'll . . . I'll tell you as much as I can about everything you want to know. That do?"

"I can't stay long. I've left Pa in bed." She could not keep the note of roughness from her pleading voice, although shame at being petulant was struggling with her deeper feeling.

"Well, he won't want to get up again yet, will he?" Keith answered composedly. Oh, he had nerves of steel! thought Jenny. "I mean, this *is* his bedtime, I suppose?" There was no answer. Jenny looked at the tablecloth, numbed by her sensations. "Do you have to look after him all the time? That's a bit rough. . . ."

"No," was forced from Jenny. "No, I don't . . . not generally. But to-night—but that's a long story, too. With rows in it." Which made Keith laugh. He laughed not quite naturally, forcing the last several jerks of his laughter, so that she shuddered at the thought of his possible contempt. It was as if everything she said was lost before ever it reached his heart— as if the words were like weak blows against an overwhelming strength. Discouragement followed and deepened after every blow—every useless and baffled word. There was again silence, while Jenny set her teeth, forcing back her bitterness and her chagrin, trying to behave as usual, and to check the throbbing

within her breast. He was trying to charm her, teasingly to
wheedle her back into kindness, altogether misunderstanding
her mood. He was guarded and considerate when she wanted
only passionate and abject abandonment of disguise.

"We'll toss up who shall begin first," Keith said in a jocu-
lar way. "How's that for an idea?"

Jenny felt her lips tremble. Frantically she shook her head,
compressing the unruly lips. Only by keeping in the same position, by making herself remain still, could she keep back the
tears. Her thought went on, that Keith was cruelly playing
with her, mercilessly watching the effect of his own coldness
upon her too sensitive heart. Eh, but it was a lesson to her!
What brutes men could be, at this game! And that thought
gave her, presently, an unnatural composure. If he were cruel,
she would never show her wounds. She would sooner die. But
her eyes, invisible to him, were dark with reproach, and her
face drawn with agony.

"Well, we'd better do *something*," she said, in a sharp voice;
and rose to her feet. "Where is it the things go?" Keith also
rose, and Jenny felt suddenly sick and faint at the relaxation
of her self-control.

ii

"Hullo, hullo!" Keith cried, and was at once by her side.
"Here; have a drink of water." Jenny, steadying herself by
the table, sipped a little of the water.

"Is it the wine that's made me stupid?" she asked. "I feel
as if my teeth were swollen, and my skin was too tight for my
bones. Beastly!"

"How horrid!" Keith said lightly, taking from her hand the
glass of water. "If it's the wine you won't feel the effects long.
Go on deck if you like. You'll feel all right in the air. I'll clear
away." Jenny would not leave him. She shook her head decidedly. "Wait a minute, then. I'll come too!"

They moved quickly about, leaving the fruit and little sweets
and almonds upon the side table, but carrying everything else
through a sleeping-cabin into the galley. It was this other
cabin that still further deepened Jenny's sense of pain—of inferiority. That was the feeling now most painful. She had just
realised it. She was a common girl; and Keith—ah, Keith was
secure enough, she thought.

In that moment Jenny deliberately gave him up. She felt it was impossible that he should love her. When she looked around it was with a sorrowfulness as of farewell. These things were the things that Keith knew and had known—that she would never again see but in the bitter memories of this night. The night would pass, but her sadness would remain. She would think of him here. She gave him up, quite humble in her perception of the disparity between them. And yet her own love would stay, and she must store her memory full of all that she would want to know when she thought of his every moment. Jenny ceased to desire him. She somehow—it may have been by mere exhausted cessation of feeling—wished only to understand his life and then never to see him again. It was a kind of numbness that seized her. Then she awoke once again, stirred by the bright light and by the luxury of her surroundings.

"This where you sleep?" With passionate interest in everything that concerned him, Jenny looked eagerly about the cabin. She now indicated a broad bunk, with a beautifully white counterpane and such an eiderdown quilt as she might optimistically have dreamed about. The tiny cabin was so compact, and so marvellously furnished with beautiful things that it seemed to Jenny a kind of suite in tabloid form. She did not understand how she had done without all these luxurious necessities for five-and-twenty years.

"Sometimes," Keith answered, having followed her marvelling eye from beauty to beauty. "When there's company I sleep forward with the others." He had been hurrying by with a cruet and the bread dish when her exclamation checked him.

"Is this lord a friend of yours, then?" Jenny asked.

"Sometimes," Keith dryly answered. "Understand?" Jenny frowned again at his tone.

"No," she said. Keith passed on.

Jenny stood surveying the sleeping-cabin. A whole nest of drawers attracted her eye, deep drawers that would hold innumerable things. Then she saw a hand-basin with taps for hot and cold water. Impulsively she tried the hot-water tap, and was both relieved and disappointed when it gasped and offered her cold water. There were monogrammed toilet appointments beautiful to see; a leather-cased carriage clock, a shelf full of books that looked fascinating; towels; tiny rugs; a light above the hand-basin, and another to switch on above the bunk. . . . It was wonderful! And there was a looking-glass before her in which she could see her own reflection as clear as day—too clearly for her pleasure!

The face she irresistibly saw in this genuine mirror looked pale and tired, although upon each white cheek there was a hard scarlet flush. Her eyes were liquid, the pupils dilated; her whole appearance was one of suppressed excitement. She had chagrin, not only because she felt that her appearance was unattractive, but because it seemed to her that her face kept no secrets. Had she seen it as that of another, Jenny would unerringly have read its painful message.

"Eh, dear," she said aloud. "You give yourself away, old sport! Don't you, now!" The mirrored head shook in disparaging admission of its own shortcoming. Jenny bent nearer, meeting the eyes with a clear stare. There were wretched lines about her mouth. For the first time in her life she had a horrified fear of growing older. It was as though, when she shut her eyes, she saw herself as an old woman. She felt a curious stab at her heart.

Keith, returning, found Jenny still before the mirror, engaged in this unsparing scrutiny; and, laughing gently, he caught her elbow with his fingers. In the mirror their glances met. At his touch Jenny thrilled, and unconsciously leaned towards him. From the mirrored glance she turned questioningly, to meet upon his face a beaming expression of tranquil enjoyment that stimulated her to candid remark. Somehow it restored some of her lost ease to be able to speak so.

"I look funny, don't I?" She appealed to his judgment. Keith bent nearer, as for more detailed examination, retaining hold upon her elbow. His face was tantalisingly close to hers, and Jenny involuntarily turned her head away, not coquettishly, but through embarrassment at a mingling of desire and timidity.

"Is that the word?" he asked. "You look all right, my dear." My dear! She knew that the words meant more to her than they did to him, so carelessly were they uttered; but they sent a shock through her. How Jenny wished that she might indeed be dear to Keith! He released her, and she followed him, laden, backwards and forwards until the table was cleared. Then he unscrewed the table legs, and the whole thing came gently away in his hands. There appeared four small brass sockets imbedded in the carpet's deep pile; and the centre of the room was clear. By the same dexterous use of his acquaintance with

the cabin's mechanism, Keith unfastened one of the settees, and
wheeled it forward so that it stood under the light, and in great
comfort for the time when they should sit to hear his story.

"Now!" he said. "We'll have a breather on deck to clear
your old head."

iii

By this time the moon was silvering the river, riding high
above the earth, serenely a thing of eternal mystery to her be-
holders. With the passing of clouds and the deepening of the
night, those stars not eclipsed by the moon shone like swarmed
throbbing points of silver. They seemed more remote, as though
the clearer air had driven them farther off. Jenny, her own
face and throat illumined, stared up at the moon, marvelling;
and then she turned, without speaking, to the black shadows
and the gliding, silent water. Upon every hand was the chequer
of contrast, beautiful to the eye, and haunting to the spirit. A
soft wind stirred her hair and made her bare her teeth in pleasure
at the sweet contact.

Keith led her to the wide wooden seat which ran by the side
of the deck, and they sat together there. The noise of the city
was dimmer; the lamps were yellowed in the moon's whiter
light; there were occasional movements upon the face of the
river. A long way away they heard a sharp panting as a motor
boat rushed through the water, sending out a great surging
wave that made all other craft rise and fall and sway as the
river's agitation subsided. The boat came nearer, a coloured
light showing; and presently it hastened past, a moving thing
with a muffled figure at its helm; and the *Minerva* rocked
gently almost until the sound of the motor boat's tuff-tuff had
been lost in the general noise of London. Nearer at hand, above
them, Jenny could hear the clanging of tram-gongs and the
clatter and slow boom of motor omnibuses; but these sounds
were mellowed by the evening, and although they were near
enough to be comforting they were too far away to interrupt
this pleasant solitude with Keith. The two of them sat in the
shadow, and Jenny craned to hear the chuckle of the water
against the yacht's sides. It was a beautiful moment in her life.
. . . She gave a little moan, and swayed against Keith, her
delight succeeded by deadly languor.

iv

So for a moment they sat, Keith's arm around her shoulders; and then Jenny moved so as to free herself. She was restless and unhappy again, her nerves on edge. The moon and the water, which had soothed her, were now an irritation. Keith heard her breath come and go, quickly, heavily.

"Sorry, Jenny," he said, in a tone of puzzled apology. She caught his fallen hand, pressing it eagerly.

"It's nothing. Only that minute. Like somebody walking on my grave."

"You're cold. We'll go down to the cabin again." He was again cool and unembarrassed. Together they stood upon the deck in the moonlight, while the water flowed rapidly beneath them and the night's mystery emphasised their remoteness from the rest of the world. They had no part, at this moment, in the general life; but were solitary, living only to themselves. . . .

Keith's arm was about her as they descended; but he let it drop as they stood once more in the golden-brown cabin. "Sit here!" He plumped a cushion for her, and Jenny sank into an enveloping softness that rose about her as water might have done, so that she might have been alarmed if Keith had not been there looking down with such an expression of concern.

"I'm really all right," she told him, reassuringly. "Miserable for a tick—that's all!"

"Sure?" He seemed genuinely alarmed, scanning her face. She had again turned sick and faint, so that her knees were without strength. Was he sincere? If only she could have been sure of him. It meant everything in the world to her. If only Keith would say he loved her: if only he would kiss her! He had never done that. The few short days of their earlier comradeship had been full of delight; he had taken her arm, he had even had her in his arms during a wild bluster of wind; but always the inevitable kiss had been delayed, had been averted; and only her eager afterthoughts had made romance of their meagre acquaintance. Yet now, when they were alone, together, when every nerve in her body seemed tense with desire for him, he was somehow aloof—not constrained (for then she would have been happy, at the profoundly affecting knowledge that she had carried the day), but unsympathetically and unlovingly at ease. She could not read his face: in his manner she read only a barren kindness that took all and gave nothing. If he didn't love her she need not have come. It would have been better to go on as she had been doing, dreaming of him until—until what? Jenny sighed at the grey vision. Only hunger had driven her to his side on this evening—the imperative hunger of her nature upon which Keith had counted. He had been sure she would come—that was unforgivable. He had welcomed her as he might have welcomed a man; but as he might also have welcomed any man or woman who would have relieved his loneliness upon the yacht. Not a loved friend. Jenny, with her brain restored by the gentle breeze to its normal quickness of action, seemed dartingly to seek in every direction for reassurance! and she found in everything no single tone or touch to feed her insatiable greed for tokens of his love. Oh, but she was miserable indeed—disappointed in her dearest and most secret aspirations. He was perhaps afraid that she wanted to attach herself to him? If that were so, why couldn't he be honest, and tell her so? That was all she wanted from him. She wanted only the truth. She felt she could bear anything but this kindness, this charming detached thought for her. He was giving her courtesy when all she needed was that his passion should approach her own. And when she should have been strong, mistress of herself, she was weak as water. Her strength was turned, her self-confidence mocked by his bearing. She trembled with the recurring vehemence of her love, that had been fed upon solitude, upon the dreariness in which she spent her mere calendared days. Her eyes were sombrely glowing, dark with pain; and Keith was leaning towards her as he might have leant towards any girl who was half fainting. She could have cried, but that she was too proud to cry. She was not Emmy, who cried. She was Jenny Blanchard, who had come upon this fool's trip because a force stronger than her pride had bidden her to forsake all but the impulse of her love. And Keith, secure and confident, was coolly, as it were, disentangling himself from the claim she had upon him by virtue of her love. It seemed to Jenny that he was holding her at a distance. Nothing could have hurt her more. It shamed her to think that Keith might suspect her honesty and her unselfishness. When she had thought of nothing but her love and the possibility of his own.

She read now, in this moment of descent into misery, a dreadful blunder made by her own overweening eagerness. She

saw Keith, alone, thinking that he would be at a loss to fill his
time, suddenly remembering her, thinking in a rather contemptuous way of their days together, and supposing that she would
do as well as another for an hour's talk to keep him from a
stagnant evening. If that were so, good-bye to her dreams.
If she were no more to him than that there was no hope left in
her life. For Keith might ply from port to port, seeing in her
only one girl for his amusement; but he had spoilt her for another man. No other man could escape the withering comparison with Keith. To Jenny he was a king among men, incomparable; and if he did not love her, then the proud Jenny
Blanchard, who unhesitatingly saw life and character with an
immovable reserve, was the merest trivial legend of Kennington Park. She was like every other girl, secure in her complacent belief that she could win love—until the years crept by,
and no love came, and she must eagerly seek to accept whatever travesty of love sidled within the radius of her attractiveness.

Suddenly Jenny looked at Keith.

"Better now," she said harshly. "You'll have to buck up
with your tale—won't you! If you're going to get it out before I have to toddle home again."

"Oh," said Keith, in a confident tone. "You're here now.
You'll stay until I've quite finished."

"What do you mean?" asked Jenny sharply. "Don't talk
rubbish!"

Keith held up a warning forefinger. He stretched his legs
and drew from his pocket a stout pipe.

"I mean what I say." He looked sideways at her. "Don't be
a fool, Jenny."

Her heart was chilled at the menace of his words no less than
by the hardness of his voice.

v

"I don't know what you're talking about, Keith; but you'll
take me back to the steps when I say," she said. Keith filled his
pipe. "I suppose you think it's funny to talk like that." Jenny
looked straight in front of her, and her heart was fluttering.
It was not her first tremor; but she was deeply agitated. Keith,
with a look that was almost a smile, finished loading the pipe

and struck a match. He then settled himself comfortably at her side.

"Don't be a juggins, Jenny," he remarked, in a dispassionate way that made her feel helpless.

"Sorry," she said quickly. "I've got the jumps. I've had awful rows to-night . . . before coming out."

"Tell me about them," Keith urged. "Get 'em off your chest." She shook her head. Oh no, she wanted something from him very different from such kindly sympathy.

"Only make it worse," she claimed. "Drives it in more. Besides, I don't want to. I want to hear about you."

"Oh, me!" he made a laughing noise. "There's nothing to tell."

"You said you would." Jenny was alarmed at his perverseness; but they were not estranged now.

Keith was smiling rather bitterly at his own thoughts, it seemed.

"I wonder why it is women want to know such a lot," he said, drowsily.

"All of them?" she sharply countered. "I suppose you ought to know."

"You look seedy still. . . . Are you really feeling better?" Jenny took no notice. "Well, yes: I suppose all of them. They all want to take possession of you. They're never satisfied with what they've got."

"Perhaps they haven't got anything," Jenny said. And after a painful pause: "Oh, well: I shall have to be going home." She wearily moved, in absolute despair, perhaps even with the notion of rising, though her mind was in turmoil.

"Jenny!" He held her wrist, preventing any further movement. He was looking at her with an urgent gaze. Then, violently, with a rapid motion, he came nearer, and forced his arm behind Jenny's waist, drawing her close against his breast, her face averted until their cheeks touched, when the life seemed to go out of Jenny's body and she moved her head quickly in resting it on his shoulder, Keith's face against her hair, and their two hearts beating quickly. It was done in a second, and they sat so, closely embraced, without speech. Still Jenny's hands were free, as if they had been lifeless. Time seemed to stand still, and every noise to stop, during that long moment. And in her heart Jenny was saying over and over, utterly hopeless, "It's no good; it's no good; it's no good. . . ." Wretchedly she attempted to press herself free, her elbow against Keith's breast. She could not get away; but each flying instant deepened her sense of bitter failure.

"It's no use," she said at last, in a dreadful murmur. "You don't want me a bit. Far better let me go."

Keith loosed his hold, and she sat away from him with a little sigh that was almost a shudder. Her hands went as if by instinct to her hair, smoothing it. Another instinct, perhaps, made her turn to him with the ghost of a reassuring smile.

"Silly, we've been," she said, huskily. "I've been thinking about you all this time; and this is the end of it. Well, I was a fool to come. . . ." She sat up straight, away from the back of the settee; but she did not look at Keith. She was looking at nothing. Only in her mind was going on the tumult of merciless self-judgment. Suddenly her composure gave way and she was again in his arms, not crying, but straining him to her. And Keith was kissing her, blessed kisses upon her soft lips, as if he truly loved her as she had all this time hoped. She clung to him in a stupor.

CHAPTER VIII
PENALTIES

"POOR old Jenny," Keith was saying, stroking her arm and holding his cheek against hers.

"You don't want me . . ." groaned Jenny.

"Yes."

"I can tell you don't. You don't mean it. D'you think I can't tell!"

Keith raised a finger and lightly touched her hair. He rubbed her cheek with his own, so that she could feel the soft bristles of his shaven beard. And he held her more closely within the circle of his arm.

"Because I'm clumsy?" he breathed. "You know too much, Jenny."

"No: I can tell. . . . It's all the difference in the world."

"Well, then; how many others have kissed you? . . . Eh?"

"Keith!" Jenny struggled a little. "Let me go now."

"How many?" Keith kissed her cheek. "Tell the whole dreadful truth."

"If I asked you how many girls . . . what would you say then?" Jenny's sombre eyes were steadily watching him, prying into the secrets of his own. He gave a flashing smile, that lighted up his brown face.

"We're both jealous," he told her. "Isn't that what's the matter?"

"You don't trust me. You don't want me. You're only teasing." With a vehement effort she recovered some of her self-control. Pride was again active, the dominant emotion. "So am I only teasing," she concluded. "You're too jolly pleased with yourself."

"How did you know I was clumsy?" Keith asked. "I shall bite your old face. I shall nibble it . . . as if I was a horse . . . and you were a bit of sugar. Fancy Jenny going home with half a face!" He laughed excitedly at his forced pleasantry, and the sound of his laugh was music to Jenny's ears. He was excited. He was moved. Quickly the melancholy pressed back upon her after this momentary surcease. He was excited because she was in his arms—not because he loved her.

"Why did you send for me?" she suddenly said. "In your letter you said you'd explain everything. Then you said you'd tell me about yourself. You've done nothing but tease all the time. . . . Are you afraid, or what? Keith, dear: you don't know what it means to me. If you don't want me—let me go. I oughtn't to have come. I was silly to come; but I had to. But if you only wanted somebody to tease . . . one of the others would have done quite as well."

Again the smile spread across Keith's face, brightening his eyes and making his teeth glisten.

"I said you were jealous," he murmured in her ear. "One of the others, indeed! Jenny, there's no other—nobody like you, my sweet. There couldn't be. Do you think there could be?"

"Nobody such a fool," Jenny said, miserably.

"Who's a fool? You?" He seemed to think for a moment; and then went on: "Well, I've told you I planned the supper. . . . That was true."

"Let me go. I'm getting cramped." Jenny drew away; but he followed, holding her less vigorously, but in no way releasing her. "No: really let me go." Keith shook his head.

"I shan't let you go," he said. "Make yourself comfortable."

"I only make myself miserable." Jenny felt her hair, which was loosened. Her cheeks were hot.

"Are you sorry you came?"

"Yes." Keith pressed closer to her, stifling her breath. She saw his brown cheeks for an instant before she was again enveloped in his strong embrace; and then she heard a single word breathed in her ear.

"Liar!" said Keith. In a moment he added: "Sorry be pole-axed."

ii

It was the second time in that evening that Jenny had been accused of lying; and when the charge had been brought by Alf she had flamed with anger. Now, however, she felt no anger. She felt through her unhappiness a dim motion of exulting joy. Half suffocated, she was yet thrilled with delight in Keith's strength, with belief in his love because it was ardently shown. Strength was her god. She worshipped strength as nearly all women worship it. And to Jenny strength, determination, manhood, were Keith's attributes. She loved him for being strong; she found in her own weakness the triumph of powerlessness, of humiliation.

"You're suffocating me," she warned him, panting.

"D'you love me a little?"

"Yes. A little."

"A lot? Say you love me a lot! And you're glad you came . . ."

Jenny held his face to hers, and kissed him passionately.

"Dear!" she fiercely whispered.

Keith slowly released her, and they both laughed breathlessly, with brimming, glowing eyes. He took her hand, still smiling and watching her face.

"Old silly," Keith murmured. "Aren't you an old silly! Eh?"

"So you say. You ought to know. . . . I suppose I am . . ."

"But a nice old silly . . . And a good old girl to come to-night."

"But then you *knew* I should come," urged Jenny, drily, frowningly regarding him.

"You can't forgive that, can you! You think I ought to have come grovelling to you. It's not proper to ask you to come to

me . . . to believe you might come . . . to have everything
ready in *case* you might come. Prude, Jenny! That's what you
are."

"A prude wouldn't have come."

"That's all you know," said Keith, teasingly. "She'd have
come—out of curiosity; but she'd have made a fuss. That's
what prudes are. That's what they do."

"Well, I expect you know," Jenny admitted, sarcastically.
The words wounded her more than they wounded him. Where
Keith laughed, Jenny quivered. "You don't know what it
means to me——" she began again, and checked her too unguarded tongue.

"To come?" He bent towards her. "Of course, it's marvellous to me! Was that what you meant?"

"No. To think . . . other girls . . ." She could not speak
distinctly.

"Other girls?" Keith appeared astonished. "Do you really
believe . . ." He too paused. "No other girls come on this
yacht to see me. I've known other girls. I've made love to other
girls—what man hasn't? You don't get to my age without . . ."

"Without what?" Jenny asked coolly.

"I'm not pretending anything to you. I'm thirty and a bit
over. A man doesn't get to my age . . . No man does, without having been made a fool of."

"Oh, I don't mind that," Jenny said sharply. "It's the girls
you've fooled."

"Don't you believe it, Jenny. They've always been wiser
than me. Say they've known a bit more. You're different . . ."
Jenny shook her head, sighing.

"I bet they've all been that," she slowly said. "Till the next
one." The old unhappiness had returned, gripping her heart.
She no longer looked at him, but stared away, straight in front
of her.

"Well, what if they had all been different?" Keith persisted.
"Supposing I were to tell you about them. Each one . . .
There's no time for it, Jenny. You'll have to take my word for
it. You'll do that if you want to. If you want to believe in me.
Do you?"

"Of course I do!" Jenny blazed. "I can't! Be different if I
was at home. But I'm here, and you knew I'd come. D'you see
what I mean?"

"You're not in a trap, old girl," said Keith. "You can go home this minute if you think you are." His colour also rose. "You make too much fuss. You want me to tell you good fat lies to save your face. Don't be a juggins, Jenny! Show your spirit! Jenny!"

Keith still held her hand. He drew it towards him, and Jenny was made to lean by his sudden movement. He slipped his arm again round her. Jenny did not yield herself. He was conscious of rebuff, although she did not struggle.

"You want me to trust you blindfold," she said in a dreary voice. "It's not good enough, Keith. Really it isn't! When you don't trust me. You sent for me, and I came. As soon as I was here you . . . you were as beastly as you could be . . ." Her voice trembled.

"Not really beastly . . ." Keith urged, and his coaxing tone and concerned expression shook her. "Nice beastly, eh?"

"You weren't nice. You weren't . . ." Jenny hesitated. "You didn't . . . you weren't nice."

"I didn't want to frighten you."

Jenny drew herself up, frantically angry.

"*Now* who's lying!" she savagely cried, and put her hands to disengage herself. "Oh Keith, I'm so sick of it!" He held her more tightly. All her efforts were unavailing against that slowly increased pressure from his strong arms.

"Listen, Jenny," Keith said. "I love you. That's that. I wanted to see you more than anything on earth. I wanted to kiss you. Good God, Jen. . . . D'you think you're the easiest person in the world to manage?"

iii

The bewilderment that succeeded clove the silence. Jenny gasped against her will.

"What do you mean?" she demanded.

"You think I'm looking on you as cheap . . . when I'm in an absolute funk of you!" Keith cried.

"Oh-oh!" Her exclamation was incredulity itself. Keith persisted warmly:

"I'm not lying. It's all true. And you're a termagant, Jenny. That's what you are. You want it all your own way! Anything that goes wrong is my fault—not yours! You don't think there's anything that's your fault. It's all mine. But, my good girl, that's ricidulous. What d'you think I know about *you?* Eh? Nothing whatever! Absolutely nothing! You think you're as clear as day! You're not. You're a dark horse. I'm afraid of you—afraid of your temper . . . your pride. You won't see that. You think it's my fault that . . ." Keith's excitement almost convinced Jenny.

"Shouting won't do any good," she said, deeply curious and overwhelmed by her bewilderment.

"Pull yourself together, Jenny!" he urged. "Look at it from my side if you can. Try! Imagine I've got a side, that is. And now I'll tell you something about myself . . . no lies; and you'll have to make the best of the truth. The Truth!" Laughing, he kissed her; and Jenny, puzzled but intrigued, withheld her indignation in order to listen to the promised account. Keith began. "Well, Jenny: I told you I was thirty. I'm thirty-one in a couple of months. I'll tell you the date, and you can work me a sampler. And I was born in a place you've never set eyes on—and I hope you never will set eyes on it. I was born in Glasgow. And there's a smelly old river there, called the Clyde, where they launch big ships . . . a bit bigger than the *Minerva.* The *Minerva* was built in Holland. Well, my old father was a tough old chap—not a Scotchman, though my mother was Scotch—with a big business in Glasgow. He was as rich as—well, richer than anybody you ever met. Work that out! And he was as tough as a Glasgow business man. They're a special kind. And I was his little boy. He had no other little boys. You interested?"

Jenny nodded sharply, her breast against his, so that she felt every breath he drew.

"Yes: well, my father was so keen that I should grow up into a Glasgow business man that he nearly killed me. He hated me. Simply because when I did anything it was always something away from the pattern—the plan. D'you see? And he'd nearly beat my head in each time. . . . Yes, wasn't it! . . . Well, when I was ten he and I had got into such a way that we were sworn enemies. He'd got a strong will; but so had I, even though I was such a kid. And I wouldn't—I couldn't—do what he told me to. And when I was thirteen, I ran away. I'd always loved the river, and boats, and so on; and I ran away from my old father. And he nearly went off his head . . . and he brought me back. Didn't take him long to find me! That was when I began to hate *him.* I'd only been afraid of him before; but I was growing up. Well, he put me to a school where they watched me all the time. I sulked, I worked, I did every blessed thing; and I grew older still, and more afraid of my father, and somehow less afraid of him, too. I got a sort of horror of him. I hated him. And when he said I'd got to go into the business I just told him I'd see him damned first. That was when he first saw that you can't make any man a slave—not even your own son—as long as he's got enough to eat. He couldn't starve me. It's starved men who are made slaves, Jenny. They've got no guts. Well, he threw me over. He thought I should starve myself and then go back to him, fawning. I didn't go. I was eighteen, and I went on a ship. I had two years of it; and my father died. I got nothing. All went to a cousin. I was nobody; but I was free. Freedom's the only thing that's worth while in this life. And I was twenty or so. It was then that I picked up a girl in London and tried to keep her—not honest, but straight to me. I looked after her for a year, working down by the river. But it was no good. She went off with other men because I got tired of her. I threw her over when I found that out. I mean, I told her she could stick to me or let me go. She wanted both. I went to sea again. It was then I met Templecombe. I met him in South America, and we got very pally. Then I came back to England. I got engaged to a girl—got married to her when I was twenty-three . . ."

"Married!" cried Jenny, pulling herself away. She had flushed deeply. Her heart was like lead.

"I'm not lying. You're hearing it all. And she's dead."

"What was her name?"

"Adela. . . . She was little and fair; and she was a little sport. But I only married her because I was curious. I didn't care for her. In a couple of months I knew I'd made a mistake. She told me herself. She knew much more than I did. She was older than I was; and she knew a lot for her age—about men. She'd been engaged to one and another since she was fifteen; and in ten years you get to know a good deal. I think she knew everything about men—and I was a boy. She died two years ago. Well, after I'd been with her for a year I broke away. She only wanted me to fetch and carry. . . . She 'took possession' of me, as they say. I went into partnership with a man who let me in badly; and Adela went back to her work and I went back to sea. And a year later I went to prison because a woman I was living with was a jealous cat and got the blame

thrown on to me for something I knew nothing about. D'you
see? Prison. Never mind the details. When I came out of prison
I was going downhill as fast as a barrel; and then I saw an
advertisement of Templecombe's for a skipper. I saw him, and
told him all about myself; and he agreed to overlook my little
time in prison if I signed on with him to look after this yacht.
Now you see I haven't got a very good record. I've been in
prison; and I've lived with three women; and I've got no prospects except that I'm a good sailor and know my job. But I
never did what I was sent to prison for; and, as I told you, the
three women all knew more than I did. I've never done a girl
any harm intentionally; and the last of them belongs to six
years ago. Since then I've met other girls, and some of them
have run after me because I was a sailor-man. They do, you
know. You're the girl I love; and I want you to remember that
I was a kid when I got married. That's the tale, Jenny; and
every word of it's true. And now what d'you think of it? Are
you afraid of me now? Don't you think I'm a bit of a fool?
Or d'you think I'm the sort of fellow that fools the girls?"

There was no reply to his question for a long time; until
Keith urged her afresh.

"What I'm wondering," said Jenny, in a slow and rather
puzzled way, "is, what you'd think of me if I'd lived with three
different men. Because I'm twenty-five, you know."

iv

It might have checked Keith in mid-career. His tone had
certainly not been one of apology. But along with a natural
complacency he had the honesty that sometimes accompanies
success in affairs.

"Well," he said frankly, "I shouldn't like it, Jen."

"How d'you think I like it?"

"D'you love me? Jenny, dear!"

"I don't know. I don't see why you should be different."

"Nor do I. I am, though. I wish I wasn't. Can you see that?
Have you ever wished you weren't yourself? Of course you
have. So have I. Have you had men running after you all the
time? Have you been free night and day, with time on your
hands, and temptations going? You haven't. You don't know
what it is. You've been at home. And what's more, you've been

tied up because . . . because people think girls are safer if they're tied up."

"*Men* do!" flashed Jenny. "They like to have it all to themselves."

"Well, if you'd ever been on your own for days together, and thinking as much about women as all young men do . . ."

"I wonder if I should boast of it," Jenny said drily. "To a girl I was pretending to love."

Keith let his arm drop from her waist. He withdrew it, and sighed. Then he moved forward upon the settee, half rising, with his hands upon his knees.

"Ah well, Jenny: perhaps I'd better be taking you ashore," he said in a constrained, exasperated tone.

"You don't care if you break my heart," Jenny whispered. "It's all one to you."

"That's simply not true. . . . But it's no good discussing it." He had lost his temper, and was full of impatience. He sat frowning, disliking her, with resentment and momentary aversion plainly to be seen in his bearing.

"Just because I don't agree that it's mighty kind of you to . . . condescend!" Jenny was choking. "You thought I should jump for joy because other women had had you. I don't know what sort of girl you thought I was."

"Well, I thought . . . I thought you were fond of me," Keith slowly said, making an effort to speak coldly. "That was what I thought."

"Thought I'd stand anything!" she corrected. "And fall on your neck into the bargain."

"Jenny, old girl . . . That's not true. But I thought you'd understand better than you've done. I thought you'd understand *why* I told you. You think I thought I was so sure of you. . . . I wish you'd try to see a bit further." He leaned back again, not touching her, but dejectedly frowning; his face pale beneath the tan. His anger had passed in a deeper feeling. "I told you because you wanted to know about me. If I'd been the sort of chap you're thinking I should have told a long George Washington yarn, pretending to be an innocent hero. Well, I didn't. I'm not an innocent hero. I'm a man who's knocked about for fifteen years. You've got the truth. Women don't like the truth. They want a yarn. A yappy, long, sugar-coated yarn, and lots of protestations. This is all because I haven't asked you to forgive me—because I haven't sworn not to do it again if only you'll forgive me. You want to see yourself forgiving me. On a pinnacle . . . Graciously forgiving me——"

"Oh, you're a beast!" cried Jenny. "Let me go home." She rose to her feet, and stood in deep thought. For a moment Keith remained seated: then he too rose. They did not look at one another, but with bent heads continued to reconsider all that had been said.

v

"I've all the time been trying to show you I'm not a beast," Keith urged at last. "But a human being. It takes a woman to be something above a human being." He was sneering, and the sneer chilled her.

"If you'd been thinking of somebody for months," she began in a trembling tone. "Thinking about them all the time, living on it day after day . . . just thinking about them and loving them with all your heart. . . . You don't know the way a woman does it. There's nothing else for them to think about. I've been thinking every minute of the day—about how you looked, and what you said; and telling myself—though I didn't believe it —that you were thinking about me just the same. And I've been planning how you'd look when I saw you again, and what we'd say and do. . . . You don't know what it's meant to me. You've never dreamed of it. And now to come to-night—when I ought to be at home looking after my dad. And to hear you talk about . . . about a lot of other girls as if I was to take them for granted. Why, how do I know there haven't been lots of others since you saw me?"

"Because I tell you it's not so," he interposed. "Because I've been thinking of you all the time."

"How many days at the seaside was it? Three?"

"It was enough for me. It was enough for you."

"And now one evening's enough for both of us," Jenny cried sharply. "Too much!"

"You'll cry your eyes out to-morrow," he warned.

"Oh, to-night!" she assured him recklessly.

"Because you don't love me. You throw all the blame on me; but it's your own pride that's the real trouble, Jenny. You want to come round gradually; and time's too short for it. Remember, I'm away again to-morrow. Did you forget that?"

Jenny shivered. She had forgotten everything but her grievance.

"How long will you be away?" she asked.

"Three months at least. Does it matter?" She reproached his bitterness by a glance. "Jenny, dear," he went on; "when time's so short, is it worth while to quarrel? You see what it is; if you don't try and love me you'll go home unhappy, and we shall both be unhappy. I told you I'm not a free man. I'm not. I want to be free. I want to be free all the time; and I'm tied . . ."

"You're still talking about yourself," said Jenny, scornfully, on the verge of tears.

vi

Well, they had both made their unwilling attempts at reconciliation; and they were still further estranged. They were not loving one another; they were just quarrelsome and unhappy at being able to find no safe road of compromise. Jenny had received a bitter shock; Keith, with the sense that she was judging him harshly, was sullen with his deeply wounded heart. They both felt bruised and wretched, and deeply ashamed and offended. And then they looked at each other, and Jenny gave a smothered sob. It was all that was needed; for Keith was beside her in an instant, holding her unyielding body, but murmuring gentle coaxing words into her ear. In an instant more Jenny was crying in real earnest, buried against him; and her tears were tears of relief as much as of pain.

CHAPTER IX

WHAT FOLLOWED

THE *Minerva* slowly and gently rocked with the motion of the current. The stars grew brighter. The sounds diminished. Upon the face of the river lights continued to twinkle, catching and mottling the wavelets. The cold air played with the water, and flickered upon the *Minerva's* deck; strong enough only to appear mischievous, too soft and wayward to make its presence known to those within. And in the *Minerva's* cabin, set as it were in that softly rayed room of old gold and golden brown, Jenny was clinging to Keith, snatching once again at precarious happiness. Far off, in her aspirations, love was desired as synonymous with peace and contentment; but in her heart Jenny had no such pretence. She knew that it was otherwise. She knew that passive domestic enjoyment would not bring her nature peace, and that such was not the love she needed. Keith alone could give her true love. And she was in Keith's arms, puzzled and lethargic with something that was only not despair because she could not fathom her own feelings.

"Keith," she said, presently. "I'm sorry to be a fool."

"You're *not* a fool, old dear," he assured her. "But I'm a beast."

"Yes, I think you are," Jenny acknowledged. There was a long pause. She tried to wipe her eyes, and·at last permitted Keith to do that for her, flinching at contact with the handkerchief, but aware all the time of some secret joy. When she could speak more calmly, she went on: "Suppose we don't talk any more about being . . . what we are . . . and forgiving and all that. We don't mean it. We only say it . . ."

"Well, I mean it—about being a beast," Keith said humbly. "That's because I made you cry."

"Well," said Jenny, agreeingly, "you can be a beast—I mean, think you are one. And if I'm miserable I shall think I've been a fool. But we'll cut out about forgiving. Because I shall never really forgive you. I couldn't. It'll always be there, till I'm an old woman——"

"Only till you're happy, dear," Keith told her. "That's all that means."

"I can't think like that. I feel it's in my bones. But you're going away. Where are you going? D'you know? Is it far?"

"We're going back to the South. Otherwise it's too cold for yachting. And Templecombe wants to keep out of England at the moment. He's safe on the yacht. He can't be got at. There's some wretched predatory woman of title pursuing him. . . ."

"Here . . . here!" cried Jenny. "I can't understand if you talk pidgin-English, Keith."

"Well . . . you know what ravenous means? Hungry. And a woman of title—you know what a lord is. . . . Well, and she's chasing about, dropping little scented notes at every street corner for him."

"Oh they are *awful!*" cried Jenny. "Countesses! Always in the divorce court, or something. Somebody ought to stop them. They don't have countesses in America, do they? Why don't we have a republic, and get rid of them all? If they'd got the floor to scrub they wouldn't have time to do anything wrong."

"True," said Keith. "True. D'you like scrubbing floors?"

"No. But I do it. And keep my hands nice, too." The hands were inspected and approved.

"But then you're more free than most people," Keith presently remarked, in a tone of envy.

"Free!" exclaimed Jenny. "Me! In the millinery! When I've got to be there every morning at nine sharp or get the sack, and often, busy times, stick at it till eight or later, for a few bob a week. And never have any time to myself except when I'm tired out! Who gets the fun? Why, it's *all* work, for people like me; all work for somebody else. What d'you call being free? Aren't they free?"

"Not one. They're all tied up. Templecombe's hawk couldn't come on this yacht without a troop of friends. They can't go anywhere they like unless it's 'the thing' to be done. They do everything because it's the right thing—because if they do something else people will think it's odd—think they're odd. And they can't stand that!"

"Well, but Keith! Who is it that's free?"

"Nobody," he said.

"I thought perhaps it was only poor people . . . just *because* they were poor."

"Well, Jenny . . . That's so. But when people needn't do what they're told they invent a system that turns them into slaves. They have a religion, or they run like the Gadarine swine into a fine old lather and pretend that everybody's got to do the same for some reason or other. They call it the herd instinct, and all sorts of names. But there's nobody who's really free. Most of them don't want to be. If they were free they wouldn't know what to do. If their chains were off they'd fall down and die. They wouldn't be happy if there wasn't a system grinding them as much like each other as it can."

"But why not? What's the good of being alive at all if you've got to do everything whether you want to do it or not? It's not sense!"

"It's fact, though. From the king to the miner—all a part of a big complicated machine that's grinding us slowly to bits, making us all more and more wretched."

"But who makes it like that, Keith?" cried Jenny. "Who says it's to be so?"

Keith laughed grimly.

"Don't let's talk about it," he urged. "No good talking about it. The only thing to do is to fight it—get out of the machine . . ."

"But there's nowhere to go, is there?" asked Jenny. "I was thinking about it this evening. 'They've' got every bit of the earth. Wherever you go 'they're' there . . . with laws and police and things all ready for you. You've *got* to give in."

"I'm not going to," said Keith. "I'll tell you that, Jenny."

"But Keith! Who is it that makes it so? There *must* be somebody to start it. Is it God?"

Keith laughed again, still more drily and grimly.

ii

Jenny was not yet satisfied. She still continued to revolve the matter in her mind.

"You said nobody was free, Keith. But then you said you were free—when you got married."

"*Till* I got married. Then I wasn't. I fell into the machine and got badly chawed then."

"Don't you want to get married?" Jenny asked. "Ever again?"

"Not that way." Keith's jaw was set. "I've been there; and to me that's what hell is."

How Jenny wished she could understand! She did not want to get married herself—that way. But she wanted to serve. She wanted Keith to be her husband; she wanted to make him happy, and to make his home comfortable. She felt that to work for the man she loved was the way to be truly happy. Did he not think that he could be happy in working for her? She *couldn't* understand. It was all so hard that she sometimes felt that her brain was clamped with iron bolts and chains.

"What way d'you want to get married?" Jenny asked.

"I want to marry *you*. Any old way. And I want to take you to the other end of the world—where there aren't any laws and neighbours and rates and duties and politicians and imitations of life. . . . And I want to set you down on virgin soil and make a real life for you. In Labrador or Alaska . . ." He glowed with enthusiasm. Jenny glowed too, infected by his enthusiasm.

"Sounds fine!" she said. Keith exclaimed eagerly. He was alive with joy at her welcome.

"Would you come?" he cried. "Really?"

"To the end of the world?" Jenny said. "Rather!"

They kissed passionately, carried away by their excitement, brimming with joy at their agreement in feeling and desire. The cabin seemed to expand into the virgin forest and the open plain. A new vision of life was opened to Jenny. Exultingly she pictured the future, bright, active, occupied—away from all the old cramping things. It was the life she had dreamed, away from men, away from stuffy rooms and endless millinery, away from regular hours and tedious meals, away from all that now made up her daily dullness. It was splendid! Her quick mind was at work, seeing, arranging, imagining as warm as life the changed days that would come in such a terrestrial Paradise. And then Keith, watching with triumph the mounting joy in her expression, saw the joy subside, the brilliance fade, the eagerness give place to doubt and then to dismay.

"What is it?" he begged. "Jenny, dear!"

"It's Pa!" Jenny said. "I couldn't leave him . . . not for anything!"

"Is that all? We'll take him with us!" cried Keith. Jenny sorrowfully shook her head.

"No. He's paralysed," she explained, and sighed deeply at the faded vision.

iii

"Well, I'm not going to give up the idea for that," Keith resumed, after a moment. Jenny shook her head, and a wry smile stole into her face, making it appear thinner than before.

"I didn't expect you would," she said quietly. "It's me that has to give it up."

"Jenny!" He was astonished by her tone. "D'you think I meant that? Never! We'll manage something. Something can be done. When I come back . . ."

"Ah, you're going away!" Jenny cried in agony. "I shan't
see you. I shall have every day to think of . . . day after day.
And you won't write. And I shan't see you. . . ." She held him
to her, her breast against his, desperate with the dread of being
separated from him. "It's easy for you, at sea, with the wind
and the sun; and something fresh to see, and something happening all the time. But me—in a dark room, poring over bits
of straw and velvet to make hats for soppy women, and then
going home to old Em and stew for dinner. There's not much
fun in it, Keith. . . . No, I didn't mean to worry you by griz-
zling. It's too bad of me! But seeing you, and hearing that
plan, it's made me remember how beastly I felt before your
letter came this evening. I was nearly mad with it. I'd been mad
before; but never as bad as this was. And then your letter came
—and I wanted to come to you; and I came, and we've wasted
such a lot of time not understanding each other. Even now,
I can't be sure you love me—not *sure!* I think you do; but you
only say so. How's anyone ever to be sure, unless they know
it in their bones? And I've been thinking about you every minute since we met. Because I never met anybody like you, or
loved anybody before . . ."

She broke off, her voice trembling, her face against his,
breathless and exhausted.

iv

"Now listen, Jenny," said Keith. "This is this. I love you,
and you love me. That's right, isn't it? Well. I don't care about
marriage—I mean, a ceremony; but you do. So we'll be married
when I come back in three months. That's all right, isn't it?
And when we're married, we'll either take your father with us,
whatever his health's like; or we'll do something with him that'll
do as well. I should be ready to put him in somebody's care;
but you wouldn't like that . . ."

"I love him," Jenny said. "I couldn't leave him to somebody
else for ever."

"Yes. Well, you see there's nothing to be miserable about.
It's all straightforward now. Nothing—except that we're going to be apart for three months. Now, Jen: don't let's waste
any more time being miserable; but let's sit down and be happy
for a bit. . . . How's that?"

Jenny smiled, and allowed him to bring her once again to the settee and to begin once more to describe their future life. "It's cold there, Jenny. Not warm at all. Snow and ice. And you won't see anybody for weeks and months—anybody but just me. And we shall have to do everything for ourselves—clothes, house-building, food catching and killing. . . . Trim your own hats. . . . Like the Swiss Family Robinson; only you won't have everything growing outside as they did. And we'll go out in canoes if we go on the water at all; and see Indians—'Heap big man bacca' sort of business—and perhaps hear wolves (I'm not quite sure of that); and go about on sledges . . . with dogs to draw them. But with all that we shall be free. There won't be any bureaucrats to tyrannise over us; no fashions, no regulations, no homemade laws to make dull boys of us. Just fancy, Jenny: nobody to *make* us do anything. Nothing but our own needs and wishes . . ."

"I expect we shall tyrannise—as you call it—over each other," Jenny said shrewdly. "It seems to me that's what people do."

"Little wretch!" cried Keith. "To interrupt with such a thing. When I was just getting busy and eloquent. I tell you: there'll be inconveniences. You'll find you'll want somebody besides me to talk to and look after. But then perhaps you'll have somebody!"

"Who?" asked Jenny, unsuspiciously. "Not Pa, I'm sure."

Keith held her away from him, and looked into her eyes. Then he crushed her against him, laughing. It took Jenny quite a minute to understand what he meant.

"Very dull, aren't you!" cried Keith. "Can't see beyond the end of your nose."

"I shouldn't think it was hardly the sort of place for babies," Jenny sighed. "From what you say."

v

Keith roared with laughter, so that the *Minerva* seemed to shake in sympathy with his mirth.

"You're priceless!" he said. "My bonny Jenny. I shouldn't think there was ever anybody like you in the world!"

"Lots of girls," Jenny reluctantly suggested, shaking a dolorous head at the ghost of a faded vanity. "I'm afraid." She revived even as she spoke; and encouragingly added: "Perhaps not exactly like."

"I don't believe it! You're unique. The one and only Jenny Redington!"

"Red——!" Jenny's colour flamed. "Sounds nice," she said; and was then silent.

"When we're married," went on Keith, watching her; "where shall we go for our honeymoon? I say! . . . how would you like it if I borrowed the yacht from Templecombe and ran you off somewhere in it? I expect he'd let me have the old *Minerva*. Not a bad idea, eh what!"

"*When* we're married," Jenny said breathlessly, very pale.

"What d'you mean?" Keith's eyes were so close to her own that she was forced to lower her lids. "When I come back from this trip. Templecombe says three months. It may be less."

"It may be more." Jenny had hardly the will to murmur her warning—her distrust.

"Very unlikely; unless the weather's bad. I'm reckoning on a mild winter. If it's cold and stormy then of course yachting's out of the question. But we'll be back before the winter, any way. And then—darling Jenny—we'll be married as soon as I can get the license. There's something for you to look forward to, my sweet. Will you like to look forward to it?"

Jenny could feel his breath upon her face; but she could not move or speak. Her breast was rising to quickened breathing; her eyes were burning; her mouth was dry. When she moistened her lips she seemed to hear a cracking in her mouth. It was as though fever were upon her, so moved was she by the expression in Keith's eyes. She was neither happy nor unhappy; but she was watching his face as if fascinated. She could feel his arm so gently about her shoulder, and his breast against hers; and she loved him with all her heart. She had at this time no thought of home; only the thought that they loved each other and that Keith would be away for three months; facing dangers indeed, but all the time loving her. She thought of the future, of that time when they both would be free, when they should no longer be checked and bounded by the fear of not having enough food. That was the thing, Jenny felt, that kept poor people in dread of the consequences of their own acts. And Jenny felt that if they might live apart from the busy world, enduring together whatever ills might come to them from their unsophisticated mode of life, they would be able to be happy.

She thought that Keith would have no temptations that she did not share; no other men drawing him by imitativeness this way and that, out of the true order of his own character; no employer exacting in return for the weekly wage a servitude that was far from the blessed ideal of service. Jenny thought these things very simply—impulsively—and not in a form to be intelligible if set down as they occurred to her; but the notions swam in her head along with her love for Keith and her joy in the love which he returned. She saw his dear face so close to her own, and heard her own heart thumping vehemently, quicker and quicker, so that it sounded thunderously in her ears. She could see Keith's eyes, so easily to be read, showing out the impulses that crossed and possessed his mind. Love for her she was sure she read, love and kindness for her, and mystification, and curiosity, and the hot slumbering desire for her that made his breathing short and heavy. In a dream she thought of these things, and in a dream she felt her own love for Keith rising and stifling her, so that she could not speak, but could only rest there in his arms, watching that beloved face and storing her memory with its precious betrayals.

Keith gently kissed her, and Jenny trembled. A thousand temptations were whirling in her mind—thoughts of his absence, their marriage, memory, her love. . . . With an effort she raised her lips again to his, kissing him in passion, so that when he as passionately responded it seemed as though she fainted in his arms and lost all consciousness but that of her love and confidence in him and the eager desire of her nature to yield itself where love was given.

CHAPTER X

Cinderella

Through the darkness, and into the brightness of the moon's light, the rolling notes of Big Ben were echoing and re-echoing, as each stroke followed and drove away the lingering waves of its predecessor and was in turn dispersed by the one that came after. The sounds made the street noises sharper, a mere rattle against the richness of the striking clock. It was an hour that struck; and the quarters were followed by twelve

single notes. Midnight. And Jenny Blanchard was still upon
the *Minerva*; and Emmy and Alf had left the theatre; and Pa
Blanchard was alone in the little house in Kennington Park.

The silvered blackness of the *Minerva* was disturbed. A long
streak of yellow light showed from the door leading into the
cabin while yet the sounds of the clock hung above the river.
It became ghostly against the moonlight that bleached the
deck, a long grey-yellow finger pointing the way to the yacht's
side.

Jenny and Keith made their way up the steps and to the
deck, and Jenny shivered a little in the strong light. Her face
was in shadow. She hurried, restored to sanity by the sounds
and the thought of her father. Horror and self-blame were
active in her mind—not from the fear of discovery; but from
shame at having for so long deserted him.

"Oh, hurry!" Jenny whispered, as Keith slipped over the
side of the yacht into the waiting dinghy. There was a silence,
and presently the heavy cludder of oars against the boat's side.

"Jenny! Come along!" called Keith from the water.

Not now did Jenny shrink from the running tide. Her one
thought was to get home; and she had no inclination to think
of what lay between her and Kennington Park. She hardly
understood what Keith said as he rowed to the steps. She saw
the bridge looming, its black shadow cutting the water that
sparkled so dully in the moonlight; and then she saw the steps
leading from the bridge to the river's edge. They were alongside; she was ashore; and Keith was pressing her hand in
parting. Still she could not look at him until she was at the top
of the steps, when she turned and raised her hand in farewell.

ii

She knew she had to walk for a little way down the road in
the direction of her home, and then up a side street, where she
had been told that she would find the motor car awaiting her.
And for some seconds she could not bear the idea of speaking
to the chauffeur, from the sense that he must know exactly how
long she had been on board the yacht. The hesitation caused
her to linger, as the cold air had caused her to think. It was
as though she feared that when he was found the man would be
impudent to her, and leer, behaving familiarly as he might

have done to a common woman. Because she was alone and un-
protected. It was terrible. Her secret filled her with the sense
of irremediable guilt. Already she was staled with the evening's
excitement. She stopped and wavered, her shadow, so black and
small, hesitating as she did. Could she walk home? She looked
at the black houses, and listened to the terrifying sinister roar
that continued faintly to fill the air. Could she go by tram? If
she did—whatever she did—the man might wait for her all
night, and Keith would know how cowardly she had been. It
might even come to the ears of Lord Templecombe, and disgrace Keith before him. To go or to stay was equally to bring
acute distress upon herself, the breathless shame of being
thought disgraced for ever. Already it seemed to her that the
shadows were peopled with observers ready to spy upon her,
to seize her, to bear her away into hidden places. . . .

At last, her mind resolved by her fears, which crowded upon
her in a tumult, Jenny stepped fearfully forward. The car was
there, dimly outlined, a single light visible to her eye. It was
drawn up at the side of the street; and the chauffeur was
fast asleep, his head upon his arms, and his arms spread upon
the steering-wheel.

"I say!" cried Jenny in a panic, her glance quickly over her
shoulder at unseen dangers. "Wake up! Wake up!"

She stepped into the car, and it began to quiver with life
as the engine was started. Then, as if drowned in the now
familiar scent of the hanging bouquet, Jenny lay back once
more in the soft cushions; bound for home, for Emmy and Alf
and Pa; her evening's excursion at an end, and only its sequel
to endure.

PART THREE
MORNING

CHAPTER XI
AFTER THE THEATRE

AFTER leaving the house Emmy and Alf pressed along in the darkness, Alf's arm still surrounding and supporting Emmy, Emmy still half jubilantly and half sorrowfully continuing to recognise her happiness and the smothered chagrin of her emotions. She was not able to feel either happy or miserable; but happiness was uppermost. Dislike of Jenny had its place, also; for she could account for every weakness of Alf's by reference to Jenny's baseness. But indeed Emmy could not think, and could only passively and excitedly endure the conflicting emotions of the moment. And Alf did not speak, but hurried her along as fast as his strong arm could secure her compliance with his own pace; and they walked through the night-ridden streets and full into the blaze of the theatre entrance without any words at all. Then, when the staring vehemence of the electric lights whitened and shadowed her face, Emmy drew away, casting down her eyes, alarmed at the disclosures which the brilliance might devastatingly make. She slipped from his arm, and stood rather forlornly while Alf fished in his pockets for the tickets. With docility she followed him, thrilled when he stepped aside in passing the commissionaire and took her arm. Together they went up the stairs, the heavy carpets with their drugget covers silencing every step, the gilded mirrors throwing their reflections backwards and forwards until the stairs seemed peopled with hosts of Emmys and Alfs. As they drew near the closed doors of the circle the hush filling the staircases and vestibules of the theatre was intensified. An aproned attendant seemed to Emmy's sensitiveness to look them up and down and superciliously to disapprove them. She moved with indignation. A dull murmur, as of single voices, disturbed the air somewhere behind the rustling attendant: and when the doors were quickly opened Emmy saw beyond the darkness and the intrusive flash of light caused by the opening doors a square of brilliance and a dashing figure upon the stage talk-

110

ing staccato. Those of the audience who were sitting near the doors turned angrily and with curiosity to view the new-comers; and the voice that Emmy had distinguished went more stridently on, with a strong American accent. In a flurry she found and crept into her seat, trying to understand the play, to touch Alf, to remove her hat, to discipline her excitements. And the staccato voice went on and on, detailing a plan of some sort which she could not understand because they had missed the first five minutes of the play. Emmy could not tell that the actor was only pretending to be an American; she could not understand why, having spoken twenty words, he must take six paces farther from the footlights until he had spoken thirteen more; but she could and did feel most overwhelmingly exuber-ant at being as it were alone in that half-silent multitude, sit-ting beside Alf, their arms touching, her head whirling, her heart beating, and a wholly exquisite warmth flushing her cheeks.

ii

The first interval found the play well advanced. A robbery had been planned—for it was a "crook" play—and the heroine had already received wild-eyed the advances of a fur-coated millionaire. When the lights of the theatre popped up, and members of the orchestra began once more unmercifully to tune their instruments, it was possible to look round at the not especially large audience. But in whichever direction Emmy looked she was always brought back as by a magnet to Alf, who sat ruminantly beside her. To Alf's sidelong eye Emmy was looking surprisingly lovely. The tired air and the slightly peevish mouth to which he was accustomed had given place to the flush and sparkle of an excited girl. Alf was aware of sur-prise. He blinked. He saw the lines smoothed away from round her mouth—the lines of weariness and dissatisfaction,—and was tempted by the softness of her cheek. As he looked quickly off again he thought how full Jenny would have been of com-ment upon the play, how he would have sat grinning with precious enjoyment at her merciless gibes during the whole of the interval. He had the sense of Jenny as all movement, as flashing and drawing him into quagmires of sensation, like a will-o'-the-wisp. Emmy was not like that. She sat tremulously smiling, humble before him, diffident, flattering. She was in-

telligent: that was it. Intelligent was the word. Not lively, but
restful. Critically he regarded her. Rather a nice girl,
Emmy. . . .

Alf roused himself, and looked around.

"Here, miss!" he called; and "S-s-s-s" when she did not hear
him. It was his way of summoning an attendant or a waitress.
"S-s-s-s." The attendant brought chocolates, which Alf handed
rather magnificently to his companion. He plunged into his
pockets—in his rough-and-ready, muscular way—for the
money, leaning far over the next seat, which was unoccupied.
"Like some lemon?" he said to Emmy. Together they inspected
the box of chocolates, which contained much imitation-lace
paper and a few sweets. "Not half a sell," grumbled Alf to himself, thinking of the shilling he had paid; but he looked with
gratification at Emmy's face as she enjoyingly ate the chocolates. As her excitement a little strained her nervous endurance
Emmy began to pale under the eyes; her eyes seemed to grow
larger; she lost the first air of sparkle, but she became more
pathetic. "Poor little thing," thought Alf, feeling masculine.
"Poor little thing: she's tired. Poor little thing."

iii

In the middle of this hot, excitedly-talking audience, they
seemed to bask as in a warm pool of brilliant light. The bril-
liants in the dome of the theatre intensified all the shadows,
heightened all the smiles, illumined all the silken blouses and
silver bangles, the flashing eyes, the general air of fête.

"All right?" Alf inquired protectively. Emmy looked in
gratitude towards him.

"Lovely," she said. "Have another?"

"I meant you," he persisted. "Yourself, I mean." Emmy
smiled, so happily that nobody could have been unmoved at the
knowledge of having given such pleasure.

"Oh, grand!" Emmy said. Then her eyes contracted. Memory came to her. The angry scene that had passed earlier
returned to her mind, hurting her, and injuring her happiness.
Alf hurried to engage her attention, to distract her from
thoughts that had in them such discomfort as she so quickly
showed.

"Like the play? I didn't quite follow what it was this old general had done to him. Did you?"

"Hadn't he kept him from marrying . . ." Emmy looked conscious for a moment. "Marrying the right girl? I didn't understand it either. It's only a play."

"Of course," Alf agreed. "See how that girl's eyes shone when old fur-coat went after her? Fair shone, they did. Like lamps. They'd got the limes on her. . . . You couldn't see them. My —er—my friend's the electrician here. He says it drives him nearly crazy, the way he has to follow her about in the third act. She . . . she's got some pluck, he says; the way she fights three of them single-handed. They've all got revolvers. She's got one; but it's not loaded. Lights a cigarette, too, with them all watching her, ready to rush at her."

"There!" said Emmy, admiringly. She was thinking: "It's only a play."

"She gets hold of his fur coat, and puts it on . . . Imitates his voice. . . . You can see it's her all the time, you know. So could they, if they looked a bit nearer. However, they don't. . . . I suppose there wouldn't be any play if they did. . . ."

Emmy was not listening to him: she was dreaming. She was as gauche and simple in his company as a young girl would have been; but her mind was different. It was practical in its dreams, and they had their disturbing unhappiness, as well, from the greater poignancy of her desire. She was not a young girl, to be agreeably fluttered and to pass on to the next admirer without a qualm. She loved him, blindly but painfully; without the ease of young love, but with all the sickness of first love. And she had jealousy, the feeling that she was not his first object, to poison her feelings. She could not think of Jenny without tremors of anger. And still, for pain, her thoughts went throbbing on about Jenny whenever, in happiness, she had seen a home and Alf and a baby and the other plain clear consequences of earning his love—of taking him from Jenny.

And then the curtain rose, the darkness fell, and the orchestra's tune slithered into nothing. The play went on, about the crook and the general and the millionaire and the heroine and all their curiously simple-minded friends. And every moment something happened upon the stage, from fights to thefts, from kisses (which those in the gallery, not wholly absorbed by the play, generously augmented) to telephone calls, plots, speeches

(many speeches, of irreproachable moral tone), shoutings, and
sudden wild appeals to the delighted occupants of the gallery.
And Emmy sat through it hardly heeding the uncommon events,
aware of them as she would have been aware of distant shouting. Her attention was preoccupied with other matters. She
had her own thoughts, serious enough in themselves. Above all,
she was enjoying the thought that she was with Alf, and that
their arms were touching; and she was wondering if he knew
that.

iv

Through another interval they sat with silent embarrassment, the irreplaceable chocolates, which had earlier been consumed, having served their turn as a means of devouring attention. Alf was tempted to fly to the bar for a drink and composure, but he did not like to leave Emmy; and he could not
think of anything which could safely be said to her in the
middle of this gathering of hot and radiant persons. "To
speak" in such uproar meant "to shout." He felt that every
word he uttered would go echoing in rolls and rolls of sound
out among the multitude. They were not familiar enough to
make that a matter of indifference to him. He was in the stage
of secretiveness. And Emmy, after trying once or twice to open
various small topics, had fallen back upon her own thoughts,
and could invent nothing to talk about until the difficulties that
lay between them had been removed. Her brow contracted. She
moved her shoulders, or sat pressed reservedly against the back
of her seat. Her voice, whenever she did not immediately hear
some word fall from Alf, became sharp and self-conscious—
almost "managing."

It was a relief to both of them, and in both the tension of
sincere feeling had perceptibly slackened, when the ignored
orchestra gave way before the rising curtain. Again the two
drew together in the darkness, as all other couples were doing,
comforted by proximity, and even by the unacknowledged
mutual pleasure of it; again they watched the extraordinary
happenings upon the stage. The fur coat was much used,
cigarettes were lighted and flung away with prodigal recklessness, pistols were revealed—one of them was even fired into the
air;—and jumping, trickling music heightened the effects of
a number of strong speeches about love, and incorruptibility,

and womanhood. . . . The climax was reached. In the middle of the climax, while yet the lover wooed and the villain died, the audience began to rustle, preparatory to going home. Even Emmy was influenced to the extent of discovering and beginning to adjust her hat. It was while she was pinning it, with her elbows raised, that the curtain fell. Both Emmy and Alf rose in the immediately successive re-illumination of the theatre; and Emmy looked so pretty with her arms up, and with the new hat so coquettishly askew upon her head, and with a long hatpin between her teeth, that Alf could not resist the impulse to put his arm affectionately round her in leading the way out.

v

And then, once in the street, he made no scruple about taking Emmy's arm within the crook of his as they moved from the staring whiteness of the theatre lamps out into the calmer moonshine. It was eleven o'clock. The night was fine, and the moon rode high above amid the twinkling stars. When Alf looked at Emmy's face it was transfigured in this beautiful light, and he drew her gently from the direct way back to the little house.

"Don't let's go straight back," he said. "Stroll u'll do us good."

Very readily Emmy obeyed his guidance. Her heart was throbbing; but her brain was clear. He wanted to be with her; and the knowledge of that made Emmy happier than she had been since early childhood.

"It's been lovely," she said, with real warmth of gratitude, looking away from him with shyness.

"Hm," growled Alf, in a voice of some confusion. "Er . . . you don't go much to the theatre, do you?"

"Not much," Emmy agreed. "See, there's Pa. He always looks to me . . ."

"Yes." Alf could not add anything to that for a long time. "Fine night," he presently recorded. "D'you like a walk? I mean . . . I'm very fond of it, a night like this. Mr. Blanchard's all right, I suppose?"

"Oh, yes. *She's* there." Emmy could not bring herself to name Jenny to him. Yet her mind was busy thinking of the earlier jar, recomposing the details, recalling the words that had passed. Memory brought tears into her eyes; but she would not allow Alf to see them, and soon she recovered her self-control. It had to be spoken of: the evening could not pass without reference to it; or it would spoil everything. Alf would think of her—he was bound to think of her—as a crying, petulant, jealous woman, to whom he had been merely kind. Patronising, even! Perhaps, even, the remembrance of it would prevent him from coming again to the house. Men like Alf were so funny in that respect. It took so little to displease them, to drive them away altogether. At last she ventured: "It was nice of you to take me."

Alf fidgeted, jerking his head, and looking recklessly about him.

"Not at all," he grumbled. "Not tired, are you?" Emmy reassured him. "What I mean, I'm very glad. . . . Now, look here, Em. May as well have it out. . . ." Emmy's heart gave a bound: she walked mechanically beside him, her head as stiffly held as though the muscles of her neck had been paralysed. "May as well, er . . . have it out," repeated Alf. "That's how I am—I like to be all shipshape from the start. When I came along this evening I *did* mean to ask young Jen to go with me. That was quite as you thought. I never thought you'd, you know, *care* to come with me. I don't know why; but there it is. I never meant to put it like I did . . . in that way . . . to have a fuss and upset anybody. I've . . . I mean, she's been out with me half-a-dozen times; and so I sort of naturally thought of her."

"Of course," agreed Emmy. "Of course."

"But I'm glad you came," Alf said. Something in his honesty, and the brusqueness of his rejoicing, touched Emmy, and healed her first wound—the thought that she might have been unwelcome to him. They went on a little way, more at ease; both ready for the next step in intimacy which was bound to be taken by one of them.

"I thought she might have said something to you—about me not *wanting* to come," Emmy proceeded, tentatively. "Made you think I never wanted to go out."

Alf shook his head. Emmy had there no opening for her resentment.

"No," he said, with stubborn loyalty. "She's always talked very nice about you."

"What does she say?" swiftly demanded Emmy.

"I forget. . . . Saying you had a rough time at home. Saying it was rough on you. That you're one of the best. . . ."

"*She* said that?" gasped Emmy. "It's not like her to say that. Did she really? She's so touchy about me, generally. Sometimes, the way she goes on, anybody'd think I was the miserablest creature in the world, and always on at her about something. I'm not, you know; only she thinks it. Well, I can't help it, can I? If you knew how I have to work in that house, you'd be . . . surprised. I'm always at it. The way the dirt comes in—you'd wonder where it all came from! And see, there's Pa and all. She doesn't take that into account. She gets on all right with him; but she isn't there all day, like I am. That makes a difference, you know. He's used to me. She's more of a change for him."

Alf was cordial in agreement. He was seeing all the difference between the sisters. In his heart there still lingered a sort of cherished enjoyment of Jenny's greater spirit. Secretly it delighted him, like a forbidden joke. He felt that Jenny—for all that he must not, at this moment, mention her name—kept him on the alert all the time, so that he was ever in hazardous pursuit. There was something fascinating in such excitement as she caused him. He never knew what she would do or say next; and while that disturbed and distressed him it also lacerated his vanity and provoked his admiration. He admired Jenny more than he could ever admire Emmy. But he also saw Emmy as different from his old idea of her. He had seen her trembling defiance early in the evening, and that had moved him and made him a little afraid of her; he had also seen her flushed cheeks at the theatre, and Emmy had grown in his eyes suddenly younger. He could not have imagined her so cordial, so youthful, so interested in everything that met her gaze. Finally, he found her quieter, more amenable, more truly wifely than her sister. It was an important point in Alf's eyes. You had to take into account—if you were a man of common sense —relative circumstances. Devil was all very well in courtship; but mischief in a girl became contrariness in a domestic termagant. That was an idea that was very much in Alf's thoughts during this walk, and it lingered there like acquired wisdom.

"Say she's going with a sailor?" he suddenly demanded.

"So she told me. I've never seen him. She doesn't tell lies, though."

"I thought you said she did!"

Emmy flinched: she had forgotten the words spoken in her wild anger, and would have been ashamed to account for them in a moment of greater coolness.

"I mean, if she says he's a sailor, that's true. She told me he was on a ship. I suppose she met him when she was away that time. She's been very funny ever since. Not funny—restless. Anything I've done for her she's made a fuss. I give her a thorough good meal; and oh! there's such a fuss about it. 'Why don't we have ice creams, and merangs, and wine, and grouse, and sturgeon——' "

"Ph! Silly talk!" said Alf, in contemptuous wonder. "I mean to say . . ."

"Oh, well: you know what flighty girls are. He's probably a swank-pot. A steward, or something of that sort. I expect he has what's left over, and talks big about it. But she's got ideas like that in her head, and she thinks she's too good for the likes of us. It's too much trouble to her to be pelite these days. I've got the fair sick of it, I can tell you. And then she's always out. . . . *Somebody's* got to be at home, just to look after Pa and keep the fire in. But Jenny—oh dear no! She's no sooner home than she's out again. Can't rest. Says it's stuffy indoors, and off she goes. I don't see her for hours. Well, I don't know . . . but if she doesn't quiet down a bit she'll only be making trouble for herself later on. She can't keep house, you know! She can scrub; but she can't cook so very well, or keep the place nice. She hasn't got the patience. You think she's doing the dusting; and you find her groaning about what she'd do if she was rich. 'Yes,' I tell her; 'it's all very well to do that; but you'd far better be doing something *useful*,' I say. 'Instead of wasting your time on idle fancies.' "

"Very sensible," agreed Alf, completely absorbed in such a discourse.

"She's trying, you know. You can't leave her for a minute. She says I'm stodgy; but I say it's better to be practical than flighty. Don't you think so, Alf?"

"Exackly!" said Alf, in a tone of the gravest assent. "Exackly."

vi

"I mean," pursued Emmy, "you must have a *little* common-sense. But she's been spoilt—she's the youngest. I'm a little

older than she is . . . *wiser*, I say; but she won't have it. . . .
And Pa's always made a fuss of her. Really, sometimes, you'd
have thought she was a boy. Racing about! My word, such a
commotion! And then going out to the millinery, and getting
among a lot of other girls. You don't know *who* they are—if
they're ladies or not. It's not a good influence for her . . ."

"She ought to get out of it," Alf said. To Emmy it was a
ghastly moment.

"She'll never give it up," she hurriedly said. "You know,
it's in her blood. Off she goes! And they make a fuss of her.
She mimics everybody, and they laugh at it—they think it's
funny to mimic people who can't help themselves—if they *are*
a bit comic. So she goes; and when she does come home Pa's
so glad to see a fresh face that he makes a fuss of her, too. And
she stuffs him up with all sorts of tales—things that never
happened—to keep him quiet. She says it gives him something
to think about. . . . Well, I suppose it does. I expect you
think I'm very unkind to say such things about my own sister;
but really I can't help seeing what's under my nose; and I
sometimes get so—you know, worked up, that I don't know
how to hold myself. She doesn't understand what it is to be
cooped up indoors all day long, like I am; and it never occurs
to her to say 'Go along, Em; you run out for a bit.' I have to
say to her: 'You be in for a bit, Jen?' and then she p'tends
she's always in. And then there's a rumpus. . . ."

Alf was altogether subdued by this account: it had that
degree of intimacy which, when one is in a sentimental mood,
will always be absorbing. He felt that he really was getting to
the bottom of the mystery known to him as Jenny Blanchard.
The picture had verisimilitude. He could see Jenny as he
listened. He was seeing her with the close and searching eye of
a sister, as nearly true, he thought, as any vision could be.
Once the thought, "I expect there's another story" came sidling
into his head; but it was quickly drowned in further reminiscence from Emmy, so that it was clearly a dying desire that
he felt for Jenny. Had Jenny been there, to fling her gage into
the field, Alf might gapingly have followed her, lost again in
admiration of her more sparkling tongue and equipments. But
in such circumstances the arraigned party is never present.
If Jenny had been there the tale could not have been told.
Emmy's virtuous and destructive monologue would not merely
have been interrupted: it would have been impossible. Jenny

would have done all the talking. The others, all amaze, would have listened with feelings appropriate to each, though with feelings in common unpleasant to be borne.

"I bet there's a rumpus," Alf agreed. "Old Jen's not one to take a blow. She ups and gets in the first one." He couldn't help admiring Jenny, even yet. So he hastened to pretend that he did not admire her; out of a kind of tact. "But of course . . . that's all very well for a bit of sport, but it gets wearisome after a time. I know what you mean. . . ."

"Don't think I've been complaining about her," Emmy said. "I wouldn't. Really, I wouldn't. Only I do think sometimes it's not quite fair that she should have all the fun, and me none of it. I don't want a lot. My tastes are very simple. But when it comes to none at all—well, Alf, what do *you* think?"

"It's a bit thick," admitted Alf. "And that's a fact."

"See, she's always having her own way. Does just what she likes. There's no holding her."

"Wants a man to do that," ruminated Alf, with a half chuckle. "Eh?"

"Well," said Emmy, a little brusquely. "I pity the man who tries it on."

vii

Emmy was not deliberately trying to secure from Alf a proposal of marriage. She was trying to show him the contrast between Jenny and herself, and to readjust the balances as he appeared to have been holding them. She wanted to impress him. She was as innocent of any other intention as any girl could have been. It was jealousy that spoke; not scheme. And she was perfectly sincere in her depreciation of Jenny. She could not understand what it was that made the admiring look come into the faces of those who spoke to Jenny, nor why the unwilling admiration that started into her own heart should ever find a place there. She was baffled by character, and she was engaged in the common task of rearranging life to suit her own temperament.

They had been walking for some little distance now along deserted streets, the moon shining upon them, their steps softly echoing, and Emmy's arm as warm as toast. It was like a real lover's walk, she could not help thinking, half in the shadow and wholly in the stillness of the quiet streets. She felt very contented; and with her long account of Jenny already uttered, and her tough body already reanimated by the walk, Emmy was at leisure to let her mind wander among sweeter things. There was love, for example, to think about; and when she glanced sideways Alf's shoulder seemed such a little distance from her cheek. And his hand was lightly clasping her wrist. A strong hand, was Alf's, with a broad thumb and big capable fingers. She could see it in the moonlight, and she had suddenly an extraordinary longing to press her cheek against the back of Alf's hand. She did not want any silly nonsense, she told herself; and the tears came into her eyes, and her nose seemed pinched and tickling with the cold at the mere idea of any nonsense; but she could not help longing with the most intense longing to press her cheek against the back of Alf's hand. That was all. She wanted nothing more. But that desire thrilled her. She felt that if it might be granted she would be content, altogether happy. She wanted so little!

And as if Alf too had been thinking of somebody nearer to him than Jenny, he began:

"I don't know if you've ever thought at all about me, Em. But your saying what you've done . . . about yourself . . . it's made me think a bit. I'm all on my own now—have been for years; but the way I live isn't good for anyone. It's a fact it's not. I mean to say, my rooms that I've got . . . they're not big enough to swing a cat in; and the way the old girl at my place serves up the meals is a fair knock-out, if you notice things like I do. If I think of her, and then about the way you do things, it gives me the hump. Everything you do's so nice. But with her—the plates have still got bits of yesterday's mustard on them, and all fluffy from the dishcloth . . ."

"Not washed prop'ly," Emmy interestedly remarked: "that's what that is."

"Exackly. And the meat's raw inside. Cooks it too quickly. And when I have a bloater for my breakfast—I'm partial to a bloater—it's black outside, as if it was done in the cinders; and then inside—well, I like them done all through, like any other man. Then I can't get her to get me gammon rashers. She will get these little tiddy rashers, with little white bones in them. Why, while you're cutting them out the bacon gets cold. You may think I'm fussy . . . fiddly with my food. I'm not, really; only I like it . . ."

"Of course you do," Emmy said. "She's not interested, that's

what it is. She thinks anything's food; and some people don't
mind at all what they eat. They don't notice."

"No. I *do*. If you go to a restaurant you get it different.
You get more of it, too. Well, what with one thing and another
I've got very fed up with Madame Bucks. It's all dirty and half
baked. There's great holes in the carpet of my sitting-room—
holes you could put your foot through. And I've done that,
as a matter of fact. Put my foot through and nearly gone
over. *Should* have done, only for the table. Well, I meant to
say . . . you can't help being fed up with it. But she knows
where I work, and I know she's hard up; so I don't like to go
anywhere else, because if anybody asked me if he should go
there, I couldn't honestly recommend him to; and yet, you see
how it is, I shouldn't like to leave her in the lurch, if she knew
I was just gone somewhere else down the street."

"No," sympathetically agreed Emmy. "I quite see. It's very
awkward for you. Though it's no use being too kind-hearted
with these people; because they *don't* appreciate it; and if you
don't say anything they just go on in the same way, never
troubling themselves about you. They think, as long as you
don't say anything you're all right; and it's not their place
to make any alteration. They're quite satisfied. Look at Jenny
and me."

"Is she satisfied?" asked Alf.

"With herself, she is. She's never satisfied with me. She never
tries to see it from my point of view."

"No," Alf nodded his head wisely. "That's what it is. They
don't." He nodded again.

"Isn't it a lovely night," ventured Emmy. "See the moon
over there."

They looked up at the moon and the stars and the unfathomable sky. It took them at once away from the streets and the
subject of their talk. Both sighed as they stared upwards, lost
in the beauty before them. And when at last their eyes dropped,
the street lamps had become so yellow and tawdry that they
were like stupid spangles in contrast with the stars. Alf still
held Emmy's arm so snugly within his own, and her wrist was
within the clasp of his fingers. It was so little a thing to slide
his fingers into a firm clasp of her hand, and they drew closer.

"Lovely, eh!" Alf ejaculated, with a further upward lift of
his eyes. Emmy sighed again.

"Not like down here," she soberly said.

"No, it's different. Down here's all right, though," Alf
assured her. "Don't you think it is?" He gave a rather nervous
little half laugh. "Don't you think it is?"

"Grand!" Emmy agreed, with the slightest hint of dryness.

"I say, it was awfully good of you to come to-night," said
Alf. "I've . . . you've enjoyed it, haven't you?" He was looking sharply at her, and Emmy's face was illumined. He saw
her soft cheeks, her thin, soft little neck; he felt her warm
gloved hand within his own. "D'you mind?" he asked, and bent
abruptly so that their faces were close together. For a moment,
feeling so daring that his breath caught, Alf could not carry
out his threat. Then, roughly, he pushed his face against hers,
kissing her. Quickly he released Emmy's arm, so that his own
might be more protectingly employed; and they stood embraced in the moonlight.

viii

It was only for a minute, for Emmy, with instinctive secrecy,
drew away into the shadow. At first Alf did not understand,
and thought himself repelled; but Emmy's hands were invit-
ingly raised. The first delight was broken. One more sensitive
might have found it hard to recapture; but Alf stepped quickly
to her side in the shadow, and they kissed again. He was surprised at her passion. He had not expected it, and the flattery
was welcome. He grinned a little in the safe darkness, consciously and even sheepishly, but with eagerness. They were
both clumsy and a little trembling, not very practised lovers,
but curious and excited. Emmy felt her hat knocked a little
sideways upon her head.

It was Emmy who moved first, drawing herself away from
him, she knew not why.

"Where you going?" asked Alf, detaining her. "What is it?
Too rough, am I?" He could not see Emmy's shaken head, and
was for a moment puzzled at the ways of woman—so far from
his grasp.

"No," Emmy said. "It's wonderful."

Peering closely, Alf could see her eyes shining.

"D'you think you're fond enough of me, Emmy?" She
demurred.

"That's a nice thing to say! As if it was for me to tell you!"
she whispered archly back.

"What ought I to say? I'm not . . . mean to say, I don't know how to say things, Emmy. You'll have to put up with my rough ways. Give us a kiss, old sport."

"How many more! You *are* a one!" Emmy was not pliant enough. In her voice there was the faintest touch of—something that was not self-consciousness, that was perhaps a sense of failure. Perhaps she was back again suddenly into her maturity, finding it somehow ridiculous to be kissed and to kiss with such abandon. Alf was not baffled, however. As she withdrew he advanced, so that his knuckle rubbed against the brick wall to which Emmy had retreated.

"I say," he cried sharply. "Here's the wall."

"Hurt yourself?" Emmy quickly caught his hand and raised it, examining the knuckle. The skin might have been roughened; but no blood was drawn. Painfully, exultingly, her dream realized, she pressed her cheek against the back of his hand.

ix

"What's that for?" demanded Alf.

"Nothing. Never you mind. I wanted to do it." Emmy's cheeks were hot as she spoke; but Alf marvelled at the action, and at her confession of such an impulse.

"How long had you . . . wanted to do it?"

"Mind your own business. The idea! Don't you know better than that?" Emmy asked. It made him chuckle delightedly to have such a retort from her. And it stimulated his curiosity.

"I believe you're a bit fond of me," he said. "I don't see why. There's nothing about me to write home about, I shouldn't think. But there it is: love's a wonderful thing."

"Is it?" asked Emmy, distantly. Why couldn't he say he loved her? Too proud, was he? Or was he shy? He had only used the word "love" once, and that was in this general sense— as though there *was* such a thing. Emmy was shy of the word, too; but not as shy as that. She was for a moment anxious, because she wanted him to say the word, or some equivalent. If it was not said, she was dependent upon his charity later, and would cry sleeplessly at night for want of sureness of him.

"D'you love me?" she suddenly said. Alf whistled. He seemed for that instant to be quite taken aback by her inquiry. "There's no harm in me asking, I suppose." Into Emmy's voice there came a thread of roughness.

"No harm at all," Alf politely said. "Not at all." He continued to hesitate.

"Well?" Emmy waited, still in his arms, her ears alert.

"We're engaged, aren't we?" Alf muttered shamefacedly. "Erum . . . what sort of ring would you like? I don't say you'll get it . . . and it's too late to go and choose one to-night."

Emmy flushed again: he felt her tremble.

"You *are* in a hurry," she said, too much moved for her archness to take effect.

"Yes, I am." Alf's quick answer was reassuring enough. Emmy's heart was eased. She drew him nearer with her arms about his neck, and they kissed again.

"I wish you'd say you love me," she whispered. "Mean such a lot to me."

"No!" cried Alf incredulously. "Really?"

"Do you?"

"I'll think about it. Do you—me?"

"Yes. I don't mind saying it if you will."

Alf gave a little whistle to himself, half under his breath. He looked carefully to right and left, and up at the house-wall against which they were standing. Nobody seemed to be in danger of making him feel an abject fool by overhearing such a confession as he was invited to make; and yet it was such a terrible matter. He was confronted with a difficulty of difficulties. He looked at Emmy, and knew that she was waiting, entreating him with her shining eyes.

"Er," said Alf, reluctantly and with misgiving. "Er . . . well, I . . . a . . . suppose I do . . ."

Emmy gave a little cry, that was half a smothered laugh of happiness at her triumph. It was not bad! She had made him admit it on the first evening. Later, when she was more at ease, he should be more explicit.

x

"Well," said Alf, instantly regretting his admission, and inclined to bluster. "Now I suppose you're satisfied?"

"Awfully!" breathed Emmy. "You're a dear good soul. You're splendid, Alf!"

For a few minutes more they remained in that benign, unforgettable shadow; and then, very slowly, with Alf's arm about Emmy's waist, and Emmy's shoulder so confidingly against his breast, they began to return homewards. Both spoke very subduedly, and tried to keep their shoes from too loudly striking the pavement as they walked; and the wandering wind came upon them in glee round every corner and rustled like a busybody among all the consumptive bushes in the front gardens they passed. Sounds carried far. A long way away they heard the tramcars grinding along the main road. But here all was hush, and to the beating of two hearts in unison; and to both of them happiness lay ahead. Their aims were similar, in no point jarring or divergent. Both wanted a home, and loving labour, and quiet evenings of pleasant occupation. To both the daily work came with regularity, not as an intrusion or a wrong to manhood and womanhood; it was inevitable, and was regarded as inevitable. Neither Emmy nor Alf ever wondered why they should be working hard when the sun shone and the day was fine. Neither compared the lot accorded by station with an ideal fortune of blessed ease. They were not temperamentally restless. They both thought, with a practical sense that is as convenient as it is generally accepted, "somebody must do the work: may as well be me." No discontent would be theirs. And Alf was a good worker at the bench, a sober and honest man; and Emmy could make a pound go as far as any other woman in Kennington Park. They had before them a faithful future of work in common, of ideals (workaday ideals) in common; and at this instant they were both marvellously content with the immediate outlook. Not for them to change the order of the world.

"I feel it's so suitable," Emmy startlingly said, in a hushed tone, as they walked. "Your . . . you know . . . 'supposing you do' . . . me; and me . . . doing the same for you."

Alf looked solemnly round at her. His Emmy skittish? It was not what he had thought. Still, it diverted him; and he ambled in pursuit.

"Yes," he darkly said. "What do you 'suppose you do' for me?"

"Why, love you," Emmy hurried to explain, trapping herself by speed into the use of the tabooed word. "Didn't you know? Though it seems funny to say it like that. It's so new. I've never dared to . . . you know . . . say it. I mean, we're both of us quiet, and reliable . . . we're not either of us flighty, I mean. That's why I think we suit each other—better than if we'd been different. Not like we are."

"I'm sure we do," Alf said.

"Not like some people. You can't help wondering to yourself however they came to get married. They seem so unlike.
Don't they! It's funny. Ah well, love's a wonderful thing—as
you say!" She turned archly to him, encouragingly.

"You seem happy," remarked Alf, in a critical tone. But he
was not offended; only tingled into desire for her by the strange
gleam of merriment crossing her natural seriousness, the jubilant note of happy consciousness that the evening's love-making
had bred. Alf drew her more closely to his side, increasingly
sure that he had done well. She was beginning to intrigue him.
With an emotion that startled himself as much as it delighted
Emmy, he said thickly in her ear, "D'you love me . . . like
this?"

xi

They neared the road in which the Blanchards lived: Emmy
began to press forward as Alf seemed inclined to loiter. In the
neighbourhood the church that had struck eight as they left
the house began once again to record an hour.

"By George!" cried Alf. "Twelve. . . . Midnight!" They
could feel the day pass.

They were at the corner, beside the little chandler's shop
which advertised to the moon its varieties of tea; and Alf
paused once again.

"Half a tick," he said. "No hurry, is there?"

"You'll come in for a bit of supper," Emmy urged. Then,
plumbing his hesitation, she went on, in a voice that had steel
somewhere in its depths. "They'll both be gone to bed. She
won't be there."

"Oh, I wasn't thinking of that," Alf declared, with uncon-
vincing nonchalance.

"I'll give you a drop of Pa's beer," Emmy said drily.

She took out a key, and held it up for his inspection.

"I say!" Alf pretended to be surprised at the sight of a key.

"Quite a big girl, aren't I! Well, you see: there are two, and
Pa never goes out. So we have one each. Saves a lot of bother."
As she spoke Emmy was unlocking the door and entering the
house. "See, you can have supper with me, and then it won't
seem so far to walk home. And you can throw Madame Buck's
rinds at the back of the fire. You'll like that; and so will she."

Alf, now perfectly docile, and even thrilled with pleasure at the idea of being with her for a little while longer, followed Emmy into the passage, where the flickering gas showed too feeble a light to be of any service to them. Between the two walls they felt their way into the house, and Alf softly closed the door.

"Hang your hat and coat on the stand," whispered Emmy, and went tiptoeing forward to the kitchen. It was in darkness. "Oo, she is a monkey! She's let the fire out," Emmy continued, in the same whisper. "Have you got a match? The gas is out." She opened the kitchen door wide, and stood there taking off her hat, while Alf fumbled his way along the passage. "Be quick," she said.

Alf pretended not to be able to find the matches, so that he might give her a hearty kiss in the darkness. He was laughing to himself because he had only succeeded, in his random venture, in kissing her chin; and then, when she broke away with a smothered protest and a half laugh, he put his hand in his pocket again for the match-box. The first match fizzed along the box as it was struck, and immediately went out.

"Oh, *do* hurry up!" cried Emmy in a whisper, thinking he was still sporting with her. "Don't keep on larking about, Alf!"

"I'm not!" indignantly answered the delinquent. "It wouldn't strike. Half a tick!"

He moved forward in the darkness, to be nearer the gas; and as he took the step his foot caught against something upon the floor. He exclaimed.

"Now what is it?" demanded Emmy. For answer Alf struck his match, and they both looked at the floor by Alf's feet. Emmy gave a startled cry and dropped to her knees.

"Hul-lo!" said Alf; and with his lighted match raised he moved to the gas, stepping, as he did so, over the body of Pa Blanchard, which was lying at full length across the kitchen floor.

CHAPTER XII

CONSEQUENCES

IN THE succeeding quietness, Emmy fumbled at the old man's hands; then quickly at his breast, near the heart. Trembling violently, she looked up at Alf, as if beseeching his aid. He too knelt, and Emmy took Pa's lolling head into her lap, as though by her caress she thought to restore colour and life to the features. The two discoverers did not speak nor reason: they were wholly occupied with the moment's horror. At last Alf said, almost in a whisper:

"I think it's all right. He's hit his head. Feel his head, and see if it's bleeding."

Emmy withdrew one hand. A finger was faintly smeared with blood. She shuddered, looking in horror at the colour against her hand; and Alf nodded sharply at seeing his supposition verified. His eye wandered from the insensible body, to a chair, to the open cupboard, to the topmost shelf of the cupboard. Emmy followed his glance point by point, and in conclusion they looked straight into each other's eyes, with perfect understanding. Alf's brows arched.

"Get some water—quick!" Emmy cried sharply. She drew her handkerchief from her breast as Alf returned with a jugful of water; and, having folded it, she dangled the kerchief in the jug.

"Slap it on!" urged Alf. "He can't feel it, you know."

So instructed, Emmy first of all turned Pa's head to discover the wound, and saw that her skirt was already slightly stained by the oozing blood. With her wetted handkerchief she gently wiped the blood from Pa's hair. It was still quite moist, and more blood flowed at the touch. That fact made her realise instinctively that the accident, the stages of which had been indicated by Alf's wandering glances, had happened within a few minutes of their arrival. When Alf took the jug and threw some of its contents upon the old man's grey face, splashing her, she made an impatient gesture of protest.

"No, no!" she cried. "It's all over *me!*"

"Been after his beer, he has," Alf unnecessarily explained. "That's what it is. Got up on the chair, and fell off it, trying to get at it. Bad boy!"

As she did not answer, from the irritation caused by nervous apprehensiveness, he soaked his own handkerchief and began to slap it across Pa's face, until the jug was empty. Alf thoughtfully sprinkled the last drops from it so that they fell cascading about Pa. He was turning away to refill the jug, when a notion occurred to him.

"Any brandy in the house?" he asked. "Ought to have thought of it before. Pubs are all closed now."

"See if there's any . . . up there." Emmy pointed vaguely upwards. She was bent over Pa, gently wiping the trickles of water from his ghastly face, caressing with her wet handkerchief the closed eyes and the furrowed brow.

Alf climbed upon the chair from which Pa had fallen, and reached his hand round to the back of the high shelf, feeling for whatever was there. With her face upturned, Emmy watched and listened. She heard a very faint clink, as if two small bottles had been knocked together, and then a little dump, as if one of them had fallen over.

"Glory!" said Alf, still in the low voice that he had used earlier. "Believe I've got it!"

"Got it? Is there any in it?" Emmy at the same instant was asking.

Alf was sniffing at the little bottle which he had withdrawn from the cupboard. He then descended carefully from the chair, and held the uncorked bottle under her nose, for a corroborative sniff. It was about half full of brandy. Satisfied, he knelt as before, now trying, however, to force Pa's teeth apart, and rubbing some of the brandy upon the parted lips.

"This'll do it!" Alf cheerfully and reassuringly cried. "Half a tick. I'll get some water to wet his head again." He stumbled once more out into the scullery, and the careful Emmy unconsciously flinched as she heard the jug struck hard in the darkness against the tap. Her eye was fixed upon the jug as it was borne brimming and splashing back to her side. She could not help feeling such housewifely anxiety even amid the tremors of her other acute concern. As Alf knelt he lavishly sprinkled some more water upon Pa's face, and set the jug ready to Emmy's hand, working with a quiet deftness that aroused her watchful admiration. He was here neither clumsy nor rough: if his methods were as primitive as the means at hand his gentle treatment of the senseless body showed him to be adaptable to an emergency. How she loved him! Pride gleamed in Emmy's eyes. She could see in him the eternal handy-man of her delight, made for husband-hood and as clearly without nonsense as any working wife could have wished.

Pa's nightshirt was blackened with great splashes of water, and the soaked parts clung tightly to his breast. At the neck it was already open, and they both thought they could see at this moment a quick contraction of the throat. An additional augury was found in the fact that Alf simultaneously had succeeded in dribbling some of the brandy between Pa's teeth, and although some of it ran out at the corners of his mouth and out on to his cheeks, some also was retained and would help to revive him. Alf gave another quick nod, this time one of satisfaction.

"Feel his heart!" Emmy whispered. He did so. "Can you feel it?"

"It's all right. Famous!"

Pa gave a little groan. He seemed to stir. Emmy felt his shoulders move against her knees; and she looked quickly up, a faint relieved smile crossing her anxious face. Then, as Alf returned her glance, his eyes became fixed, and he looked beyond her and up over her head. Jenny stood in the doorway, fully dressed, but without either hat or coat, her face blanched at the picture before her.

ii

To Jenny, coming with every precautionary quietness into the house, the sight came as the greatest shock. She found the kitchen door ajar, heard voices, and then burst upon the three feebly illumined figures. Emmy, still in her out-of-doors coat, knelt beside Alf upon the floor; and between them, with a face terribly grey, lay Pa, still in his old red nightshirt, with one of his bare feet showing. The stained shirt, upon which the marks of water, looking in this light perfectly black, might have been those of blood, filled Jenny with horror. It was only when she saw both Emmy and Alf staring mutely at her that she struggled against the deadly faintness that was thickening a veil of darkness before her eyes. It was a dreadful moment.

"Hullo, Jen!" Alf said. "Look here!"

"I thought you must be in bed," Emmy murmured. "Isn't it awful!"

Not a suspicion! Her heart felt as if somebody had sharply pinched it. They did not know she had been out! It made her tremble in a sudden flurry of excited relief. She quickly came forward, bending over Pa. Into his cheeks there had come the faintest wash of colour. His eyelids fluttered. Jenny stooped and took his hand, quite mechanically, pressing it between hers and against her heart. And at that moment Pa's eyes opened wide, and he stared up at her. With Alf at his side and Emmy behind him, supporting his head upon her lap, Pa could see only Jenny, and a twitching grin fled across his face—a grin of loving recognition. It was succeeded by another sign of recovery, a peculiar fumbling suggestion of remembered cunning.

"Jenny, my dearie," whispered Pa, gaspingly. "A good . . . . boy!" His eyes closed again.

Emmy looked in quick challenge at Alf, as if to say "You see how it is! She comes in last, and it's her luck that he should see her. . . . *Always* the same!" And Jenny was saying, very low:

"It looks to me as if you'd been a bad boy!"

"Can't be with him *all* the time!" Emmy put in, having reached a point of general self-defence in the course of her mental explorations. She was recovering from her shock and her first horrible fears.

"Shall we get him to bed? Carry him back in there?" Jenny asked. "The floor's soaking wet." She had not to receive any rebuke: Emmy, although shaken, was reviving in happiness and in graciousness with each second's diminution of her dread. She now agreed to Pa's removal; and they all stumbled into his bedroom and laid him upon his own bed. Alf went quickly back again to the kitchen for the brandy; and presently a good dose of this was sending its thrilling and reviving fire through Pa's person. Emmy had busied herself in making a bandage for his wounded head; and Jenny had arranged him more comfortably, drying his chest and laying a little towel between his body and the nightshirt lest he should take cold. Pa was very complacently aware of these ministrations, and by the time they were in full order completed he was fast asleep, having expressed no sort of contrition for his naughtiness or for the alarm he had given them all.

Reassured, the party returned to the kitchen.

iii

Alf could not now wait to sit down to supper; but he drank a glass of beer, after getting it down for himself and rather humorously illustrating how Pa's designs must have been frustrated. He then, with a quick handshake with Jenny, hurried away.

"I'll let you out," Emmy said. There were quick exchanged glances. Jenny was left alone in the kitchen for two or three

minutes until Emmy returned, humming a little self-consciously, and no longer pale.

"Quite a commotion," said Emmy, with assumed ease.

Jenny was looking at her, and Jenny's heart felt as though
it were bursting. She had never in her life known such a sensation of guilt—guilt at the suppression of a vital fact. Yet
above that sense of guilt, which throbbed within all her consciousness, was a more superficial concern with the happenings
of the moment.

"Yes," Jenny said. "And . . . Had you been in long?" she
asked quickly.

"Only a minute. We found him like that. We didn't come
straight home."

"Oh," said Jenny, significantly, though her heart was thudding. "You didn't come straight home." Emmy's colour rose
still higher. She faltered slightly, and tears appeared in her
eyes. She could not explain. Some return of her jealousy, some
feeling of what Jenny would "think," checked her. The communication must be made by other means than words. The two
sisters eyed each other. They were very near, and Emmy's lids
were the first to fall. Jenny stepped forward, and put a protective arm round her; and as if Emmy had been waiting for
that she began smiling and crying at one and the same moment.

"Looks to me as if . . ." Jenny went on after this exchange.

"I'm sorry I was a beast," Emmy said. "I'm as different as
anything now."

"You're a dear!" Jenny assured her. "Never mind about
what you said."

It was an expansive moment. Their hearts were charged. To
both the evening had been the one poignant moment of their
lives, an evening to provide reflections for a thousand other
evenings. And Emmy was happy, for the first time for many
days, with the thought of happy life before her. She described
in detail the events of the theatre and the walk. She did not
give an exactly true story. It was not to be expected that she
would do so. Jenny did not expect it. She gave indications of
her happiness, which was her main object; and she gave further indications, less intentional, of her character, as no author
can avoid doing. And Jenny, immediately discounting, and in
the light of her own temperament re-shaping and re-propor-
tioning the form of Emmy's narrative, was like the eternal
critic—apprehending only what she could personally recog-

nise. But both took pleasure in the tale, and both saw forward
into the future a very satisfactory ending to Emmy's romance.

"And we got back just as twelve was striking," Emmy concluded.

A deep flush overspread Jenny's face. She turned away
quickly in order that it might not be seen. Emmy still continued busy with her thoughts. It occurred to her to be surprised
that Jenny should be fully dressed. The surprise pressed her
further onward with the narrative.

"And then, of course, we found Pa. Wasn't it strange of him
to do it? He couldn't have been there long. . . . He must have
waited for you to go up. He must have listened. I must find another place to keep it, though he's never done such a thing before in his life. He must have listened for you going up, and
then come creeping out here. . . . Why, there's his candle on
the floor! Fancy that! Might have set fire to the whole house!
See, you couldn't have been upstairs long. . . . I thought you
must have been, seeing the fire was black out. Did you go to
sleep in front of it? I thought you might have laid a bit of supper for us. I thought you *would* have. But if you were asleep, I
don't wonder. I thought you'd have been in bed hours. Did you
hear anything? He must have made a racket falling off the
chair. What made you come down again? Pa must have listened
like anything."

"I didn't come down," Jenny said, in a slow, passionless
voice. "I hadn't gone to bed. I was out. I'd been out all the evening . . . since quarter-to-nine."

iv

At first Emmy could not understand. She stood, puzzled, unable to collect her thoughts.

"Jenny!" at last she said, unbelievingly. Accusing impulses
showed in her face. The softer mood, just passing, was replaced by one of anger. "Well, I must say it's like you," Emmy
concluded. "I'm not to have a *moment* out of the house. I can't
even leave you . . ."

"Half-an-hour after you'd gone," urged Jenny, "I got a
note from Keith."

"Keith!" It was Emmy's sign that she had noted the name.

"I told you. . . . He'd only got the one evening in London."

"Couldn't he have come here?"

"He mustn't leave his ship. I didn't know what to do. At first I thought I *couldn't* go. But the man was waiting——"

"Man!" cried Emmy. "What man?"

"The chauffeur."

Emmy's face changed. Her whole manner changed. She was outraged.

"Jenny! Is he *that* sort! Oh, I warned you. . . . There's never any good in it. He'll do you no good."

"He's a captain of a little yacht. He's not what you think," Jenny protested, very pale, her heart sinking under such a rebuke, under such knowledge as she alone possessed.

"Still, to go to him!" Emmy was returned to that aspect of the affair. "And leave Pa!"

"I know. I know," Jenny cried. She was no longer protective. She was herself in need of comfort. "But I *had* to go. You'd have gone yourself!" She met Emmy's gaze steadily, but without defiance.

"No I shouldn't!" It was Emmy who became defiant. Emmy's jealousy was again awake. "However much I wanted to go. I should have stayed."

"And lost him!" Jenny cried.

"Are you sure of him now?" asked Emmy swiftly. "If he's gone again."

With her cheeks crimson, Jenny turned upon her sister.

"Yes, I'm sure of him. And I love him. I love him as much as you love Alf." She had the impulse, almost irresistible, to add "More!" but she restrained her tongue just in time. That was a possibility Emmy could never admit. It was only that they were different.

"But to leave Pa!" Emmy's bewildered mind went back to what was the real difficulty. Jenny protested.

"He was in bed. I thought he'd be safe. He was tucked up. Supposing I hadn't gone. Supposing I'd gone up to bed an hour ago. Still he'd have done the same."

"You know he wouldn't," Emmy said, very quietly. Jenny felt a wave of hysteria pass through her. It died down. She held herself very firmly. It was true. She knew that she was only defending herself.

"I don't know," she said, in a false, aggrieved voice. "How do I know?"

"You do. He knew you were out. He very likely woke up and felt frightened."

"Felt thirsty, more like it!" Jenny exclaimed.

"Well, you did wrong," Emmy said. "However you like to put it to yourself, you did wrong."

"I always manage to. Don't I!" Jenny's speech still was without defiance. She was humble. "It's a funny thing; but it's true . . ."

"You always want to go your own way," Emmy reproved.

"Oh, I don't think *that's* wrong!" hastily said Jenny. "Why should you go anybody else's way?"

"I don't know," admitted Emmy. "But it's safer."

"Whose way do you go?" Jenny had stumbled upon a question so unanswerable that she was at liberty to answer it for herself. "I don't know whose way you go now; but I do know whose way you'll go soon. You'll go Alf's way."

"Well?" demanded Emmy. "If it's a good way?"

"Well, I go Keith's way!" Jenny answered, in a fine glow. "And he goes mine."

Emmy looked at her, shaking her head in a kind of narrow wisdom.

"Not if he sends a chauffeur," she said slowly. "Not that sort of man."

v

For a moment Jenny's heart burned with indignation. Then it turned cold. If Emmy were right! Supposing—just supposing . . . Savagely she thrust doubt of Keith from her: her trust in him was forced by dread into still warmer and louder proclamation.

"You don't understand!" she cried. "You *couldn't*. You've never seen him. Wait a minute!" She went quickly out of the kitchen and up to her bedroom. There, secretly kept from every eye, was the little photograph of Keith. She brought it down. In anxious triumph she showed it to Emmy. Emmy's three years' seniority had never been of so much account. "There," Jenny said. "That's Keith. Look at him!"

Emmy held the photograph under the meagre light. She was astonished, although she kept outwardly calm; because Keith

—besides being obviously what is called a gentleman—looked honest and candid. She could not find fault with the face.

"He's very good-looking," she admitted, in a critical tone. "Very."

"Not the sort of man you thought," emphasised Jenny, keenly elated at Emmy's dilemma.

"Is he . . . has he got any money?"

"Never asked him. No—I don't think he has. It wasn't *his* chauffeur. A lord's."

"There! He knows lords. . . . Oh, Jenny!" Emmy's tone was still one of warning. "He won't marry you. I'm sure he won't."

"Yes he will," Jenny said confidently. But the excitement had shaken her, and she was not the firm Jenny of custom. She looked imploringly at Emmy. "*Say* you believe it!" she begged. Emmy returned her urgent gaze, and felt Jenny's arm round her. Their two faces were very close. "You'd have done the same," Jenny urged.

Something in her tone awakened a suspicion in Emmy's mind. She tried to see what lay behind those glowing mysteries that were so close to hers. Her own eyes were shining as if from an inner brightness. The sisters, so unlike, so inexpressibly contrary in every phase of their outlook, in every small detail of their history, had this in common—that each, in her own manner, and with the consequences drawn from differences of character and aim, had spent happy hours with the man she loved. What was to follow remained undetermined. But Emmy's heart was warmed with happiness: she was for the first time filled only with impulses of kindness and love for Jenny. She would blame no more for Jenny's desertion. It was just enough, since the consequences of that desertion had been remedied, to enhance Emmy's sense of her own superiority. There remained only the journey taken by Jenny. She again took from her sister's hand the little photograph. Alf's face seemed to come between the photograph and her careful, por-ing scrutiny, more the jealous scrutiny of a mother than that of a sister.

"He's rather *thin*," Emmy ventured, dubiously. "What colour are his eyes?"

"Blue. And his hair's brown. . . . He's lovely."

"He *looks* nice," Emmy said, relenting.

"He *is* nice. Em, dear . . . Say you'd have done the same!"

Emmy gave Jenny a great hug, kissing her as if Jenny had been her little girl. To Emmy the moment was without alloy. Her own future assured, all else fell into the orderly picture which made up her view of life. But she was not quite calm, and it even surprised her to feel so much warmth of love for Jenny. Still holding her sister, she was conscious of a quick impulse that was both exulting and pathetically shy.

"It's funny us both being happy at once. Isn't it!" she whispered, all sparkling.

vi

To herself Jenny groaned a sufficient retort.

"I don't know that I'm feeling so tremendously happy my own self," she thought. For the reaction had set in. She was glad enough to bring about by various movements their long-delayed bedward journey. She was beginning to feel that her head and her heart were both aching, and that any more confidences from Emmy would be unbearable. And where Emmy had grown communicative—since Emmy had nothing to conceal—Jenny had felt more and more that her happiness was staled as thought corroded it. By the time they turned out the kitchen gas the clock pointed to twenty minutes past two, and the darkest hour was already recorded. In three more hours the sun would rise, and Jenny knew that long before then she would see the sky greying as though the successive veils of the transformation were to reveal the crystal grotto. She preceded Emmy up the stairs, carrying a candle and lighting the way. At the top of the staircase Emmy would find her own candle, and they would part. They were now equally eager for the separation, Emmy because she wanted to think over and over again the details of her happiness, and to make plans for a kind of life that was to open afresh in days that lay ahead. Arrived at the landing the sisters did not pause or kiss, but each looked and smiled seriously as she entered her bedroom. With the closing of the doors noise seemed to depart from the little house, though Jenny heard Emmy moving in her room. The house was in darkness. Emmy was gone; Pa lay asleep in the dim light, his head bandaged and the water slowly soaking into the towel protectively laid upon his chest; in the kitchen the ailing clock ticked away the night. Everything seemed at peace but Jenny, who, when she had closed the door and set her candle down, went quickly to the bed, sitting upon its edge and looking straight before her with dark and sober eyes. She had much to think of. She would never forgive herself now for leaving Pa. It might have been a more serious accident that had happened during her absence; she could even plead, to Emmy, that the accident might have happened if she had not left the house at all; but nothing her quick brain could urge had really satisfied Jenny. The stark fact remained that she had been there under promise to tend Pa; and that she had failed in her acknowledged trust. He might have died. If he had died, she would have been to blame. Not Pa! He couldn't help himself! He was driven by inner necessity to do things which he must not be allowed to do. Jenny might have pleaded the same justification. She had done so before this. It had been a necessity to her to go to Keith. As far as that went she did not question the paramount power of impulse. Not will, but the strongest craving, had led her. Jenny could perhaps hardly discourse learnedly upon such things: she must follow the dictates of her nature. But she never accused Pa of responsibility. He was an irresponsible. She had been left to look after him. She had not stayed; and ill had befallen. A bitter smile curved Jenny's lips.

"I suppose they'd say it was a punishment," she whispered. "They'd like to think it was."

After that she stayed a long time silent, swaying gently while her candle flickered, her head full of a kind of formless musing. Then she rose from the bed and took her candle so that she could see her face in the small mirror upon the dressing-table. The candle flickered still more in the draught from the open window; and Jenny saw her breath hang like a cloud before her. In the mirror her face looked deadly pale; and her lips were slightly drawn as if she were about to cry. Dark shadows were upon her face, whether real or the work of the feeble light she did not think to question. She was looking straight at her own eyes, black with the dilation of pupil, and somehow struck with the horror which was her deepest emotion. Jenny was speaking to the girl in the glass.

"I shouldn't have thought it of you," she was saying. "You come out of a respectable home and you do things like this. Silly little fool, you are. Silly little fool. Because you can't stand his not loving you . . . you go and do that." For a mo-

ment she stopped, turning away, her lip bitten, her eyes veiled.
"Oh, but he does love me!" she breathed. *"Quite* as much . . .
quite as much . . . nearly . . . nearly as much . . ." She
sighed deeply, standing lone in the centre of the room, her long,
thin shadow thrown upon the wall in front of her. "And to
leave Pa!" she was thinking, and shaking her head. *"That* was
wrong, when I'd promised. I shall always know it was wrong.
I shall never be able to forget it as long as I live. Not as long
as I live. And if I hadn't gone, I'd never have seen Keith again
—never! He'd have gone off; and my heart would have broken.
I should have got older and older, and hated everybody. Hated
Pa, most likely. And now I just hate myself. . . . Oh, it's so
difficult!" She moved impatiently, and at last went back to the
mirror, not to look into it but to remove the candle, to blow it
out, and to leave the room in darkness. This done, Jenny drew
up the blind, so that she could see the outlines of the roofs opposite. It seemed to her that for a long distance there was no
sound at all: only there, all the time, far behind all houses,
somewhere buried in the heart of London, there was the same
unintermittent low growl. It was always in her ears, even at
night, like a sleepless pulse, beating steadily through the silences.

Jenny was not happy. Her heart was cold. She continued to
look from the window, her face full of gravity. She was hearing again Keith's voice as he planned their future; but she was
not sanguine now. It all seemed too far away, and so much had
happened. So much had happened that seemed as though it
could never be realised, never be a part of memory at all, so
blank and sheer did it now stand, pressing upon her like overwhelming darkness. She thought again of the bridge, and the
striking hours; the knock, the letter, the hurried ride; she remembered her supper and the argument with Emmy; the argument with Alf; and her fleeting moods, so many, so painful,
during her time with Keith. To love, to be loved: that was her
sole commandment of life—how learned she knew not. To love
and to work she knew was the theory of Emmy. But how different they were, how altogether unlike! Emmy with Alf;
Jenny with Keith. . . .

"Yes, but she's got what she wants," Jenny whispered in the
darkness. "That's what she wants. It wouldn't do for me. Only
in this world you've all got to have one pattern, whether it
suits you or not. Else you're not 'right.' 'They' don't like it.

And I'm outside . . . I'm a misfit. Eh, well: it's no good whimpering about it. What must be, must; as they say!"

Soberly she moved from the window and began to undress in the darkness, stopping every now and then as if she were listening to that low humming far beyond the houses, when the thought of unresting life made her heart beat more quickly. Away there upon the black running current of the river was Keith, on that tiny yacht so open upon the treacherous sea to every kind of danger. And nothing between Keith and sudden, horrible death but that wooden hulk and his own seamanship. She was Keith's: she belonged to him; but he did not belong to her. To Keith she might, she would give all, as she had done; but he would still be apart from her. He might give his love, his care: but she knew that her pride and her love must be the love and pride to submit—not Keith's. Away from him, released from the spell, Jenny knew that she had yielded to him the freedom she so cherished as her inalienable right. She had given him her freedom. It was in his power. For her real freedom was her innocence and her desire to do right. It was not that she wanted to defy, so much as that she could bear no shackles, and that she had no respect for the belief that things should be done only because they were always done, and for no other reason but that of tradition. And she feared nothing but her own merciless judgment.

It was not now that she dreaded Emmy's powerlessness to forgive her, or the opinion of anybody else in the world. It was that she could not forgive herself. Those who are strong enough to live alone in the world, so long as they are young and vigorous, have this rare faculty of self-judgment. It is only when they are exhausted that they turn elsewhere for judgment and pardon.

Jenny sat once again upon the bed.

"Oh Keith, my dearest . . ." she began. "My Keith . . ." Her thoughts flew swiftly to the yacht, to Keith. With unforgettable pain she heard his voice ringing in her ears, saw his clear eyes, as honest as the day, looking straight into her own. Pain mingled with love and pride; and battled there within her heart, making a fine tumult of sensation; and Jenny felt herself smiling in the darkness at such a conflict. She even began very softly to laugh. But as if the sound checked her and awoke the secret sadness that the tumultuous sensations were trying to hide, her courage suddenly gave way.

"Keith!" she gently called, her voice barely audible. Only silence was there. Keith was far away—unreachable. Jenny pressed her hands to her lips, that were trembling uncontrollably. She rose, struggling for composure, struggling to get back to the old way of looking at everything. It seemed imperative that she should do so. In a forlorn, quivering voice she ventured:

"What a life! Golly, what a life!"

But the effort to pretend that she could still make fun of the events of the evening was too great for Jenny. She threw herself upon the bed, burying her face in the pillow.

"Keith . . . oh Keith! . . ."

SHORT STORIES

SECTION I

I wish I knew some book on the art and theory of the short story, so that I could read it and give the reader an authoritative view on the question; I do not, and so must content myself with offering him my own reflections. I do not set them down with confidence. I have written a good many short stories myself, but no writer writes what he wants to, he writes what he can, and it is natural enough that he should think the best way to do a thing is the way he does it. One would like to make up one's mind exactly what a short story is. One would like to be certain how it differs from the novel. Of course you can say that a short story is a piece of fiction of not more than so many pages and a novel is a piece of fiction of so many more. That is easy. It would be difficult to fix the number. The French now seem to write novels that are shorter and shorter. What are you to say of François Mauriac, perhaps the most interesting of the younger French novelists, who describes as a novel a book of two hundred pages of large print? It is shorter than many a piece of fiction that its author has published as a short story. I suggest first of all that length has nothing to do with the case. There is no reason why you should not have a novel in five pages and a short story in three hundred. I think the short story is something very different from the novel, but it is a difference that many celebrated authors have not realised; or if they have, it may be that they have not cared. For example take a celebrated story by Chekov called *The Lady with the Dog*. Well, to my mind that is not a short story, but a short novel: on the other hand the same author's *Peasants*, which is about as long, very well fulfills the demands I make of a short story. Some writers write short stories of the length of a novel, and there may not be a word too much in

143

them; but they remain short stories. The best example I know of this is Frank Swinnerton's *Nocturne*.

It may be that the element of time is important. I am never comfortably at home with a short story the action of which takes place during many months or years. The passing of time and the changes it effects have been much studied in fiction of late, and the subject is fascinating, especially now that we have become as perhaps never before conscious of change, but it does not seem proper to the short story. I think it possible that the short story should occupy itself with a single moment of time. I was interested to see how Aldous Huxley, than whom no writer is more aware of what he is about, in a story called *Chawdron*, in which he related events that had occurred during many years, used the device of making the narrator tell the story to a friend in the interval between breakfast and luncheon. In this ingenious way he used the materials of a novel for a very well constructed short story. There is something static in the short story; the novel is dynamic. In the latter one thing leads to another; in the former it stays put. One of the most interesting things in modern fiction has been the discovery that it is possible to show the change in personality that the events of life occasion. It is because there is nothing of this in the older novels that they seem to us so unreal. Take *La Cousine Bette*, for instance, one of the best novels, by, take it all in all, the greatest novelist that ever lived. You are told all about Madame Marneffe the first time she is described, she is given you in all her horror, and she remains throughout what she was at the beginning. She neither changes nor developes. Then there is Harold Skimpole. A full length portrait of him is drawn on his first appearance and the reader knows no more about him at the end of a long book than he knew then. Dickens had told all he knew at once and there was nothing more to add. It is on this account perhaps that these novelists were driven to melodramatic incident. When the characters are frozen (like German credits) the story is the only way in which the author can hold his reader's attention. The short story does not aim at the developement of character; nor does it aim at the discovery of character. I mean by this the process by which an author presents you with an enigmatic creature whose personality is gradually divulged; he confronts you with a mystery and its solution may have all the excitement of a detective story. The short-story writer can only

show what his people are at the moment he chooses to interfere
in their fates. He has no space to show any change in them and
no time to be secret about them. So far as he uses incident to
portray character his intrigue must be simple. If, however, he is
not interested in character, but only in the story, I do not see
why this should not be as complicated as he likes. You have a
very good example of this in *The Second-Class Passenger* by
Perceval Gibbons. The shortness of time occupied by the events
related gives the author the unity necessary to the form. I seem
forced by what I have said to the following definition: the short
story is a piece of fiction, of any length you choose, which
deals with a single situation, but this situation may be a mood,
a character or an event. It is only the fashion of the moment
that decrees that the delineation of a mood is of more consequence than the other two. Indeed, looking back on the past, it
is possible to argue that the narration of an event has more
chance of enduring than the description of a mood or the analysis
of a character. But they say that example is better than pre-
cept and so I point to the following stories as, in their several
ways, excellent specimens of the form.

W. S. M.

Joseph Conrad

YOUTH

This could have occurred nowhere but in England, where men and sea interpenetrate, so to speak—the sea entering into the life of most men, and the men knowing something or everything about the sea, in the way of amusement, of travel, or of 'bread-winning.

We were sitting round a mahogany table that reflected the bottle, the claret-glasses, and our faces as we leaned on our elbows. There was a director of companies, an accountant, a lawyer, Marlow, and myself. The director had been a *Conway* boy, the accountant had served four years at sea, the lawyer—a fine crusted Tory, High Churchman, the best of old fellows, the soul of honour—had been chief officer in the P. & O. service in the good old days when mail-boats were square-rigged at least on two masts, and used to come down the China Sea before a fair monsoon with stun'sails set alow and aloft. We all began life in the merchant service. Between the five of us there was the strong bond of the sea, and also the fellowship of the craft, which no amount of enthusiasm for yachting, cruising, and so on can give, since one is only the amusement of life and the other is life itself.

Marlow (at least I think that is how he spelt his name) told the story, or rather the chronicle, of a voyage:—

"Yes, I have seen a little of the Eastern seas; but what I remember best is my first voyage there. You fellows know there are those voyages that seem ordered for the illustration of life, that might stand for a symbol of existence. You fight, work, sweat, nearly kill yourself, sometimes do kill yourself, trying to accomplish something—and you can't. Not from any fault of yours. You simply can do nothing, neither great nor little—not a thing in the world—not even marry an old maid, or get a wretched 600-ton cargo of coal to its port of destination.

"It was altogether a memorable affair. It was my first voyage to the East, and my first voyage as second mate; it was also my skipper's first command. You'll admit it was time. He was sixty if a day; a little man, with a broad, not very straight back, with bowed shoulders and one leg more bandy than the other, he had that queer twisted-about appearance you see so often in men who work in the fields. He had a nut-cracker face —chin and nose trying to come together over a sunken mouth —and it was framed in iron-gray fluffy hair, that looked like a chin-strap of cotton-wool sprinkled with coal-dust. And he had blue eyes in that old face of his, which were amazingly like a boy's, with that candid expression some quite common men preserve to the end of their days by a rare internal gift of simplicity of heart and rectitude of soul. What induced him to accept me was a wonder. I had come out of a crack Australian clipper, where I had been third officer, and he seemed to have a prejudice against crack clippers as aristocratic and high-toned. He said to me, 'You know, in this ship you will have to work.' I said I had to work in every ship I had ever been in. 'Ah, but this is different, and you gentlemen out of them big ships; . . . . but there! I dare say you will do. Join to-morrow.'

"I joined to-morrow. It was twenty-two years ago; and I was just twenty. How time passes! It was one of the happiest days of my life. Fancy! Second mate for the first time—a really responsible officer! I wouldn't have thrown up my new billet for a fortune. The mate looked me over carefully. He was also an old chap, but of another stamp. He had a Roman nose, a snow-white, long beard, and his name was Mahon, but he insisted that it should be pronounced Mann. He was well connected; yet there was something wrong with his luck, and he had never got on.

"As to the captain, he had been for years in coasters, then in the Mediterranean, and last in the West Indian trade. He had never been round the Capes. He could just write a kind of sketchy hand, and didn't care for writing at all. Both were thorough good seamen of course, and between those two old chaps I felt like a small boy between two grandfathers.

"The ship also was old. Her name was the *Judea.* Queer name, isn't it? She belonged to a man Wilmer, Wilcox—some name like that; but he has been bankrupt and dead these twenty years or more, and his name don't matter. She had been laid up in Shadwell basin for ever so long. You may imagine her state. She was all rust, dust, grime—soot aloft, dirt on deck. To me it was like coming out of a palace into a ruined cottage. She was about 400 tons, had a primitive windlass, wooden latches to the doors, not a bit of brass about her, and a big square stern. There was on it, below her name in big letters, a lot of scrollwork, with the gilt off, and some sort of a coat of arms, with the motto 'Do or Die' underneath. I remember it took my fancy immensely. There was a touch of romance in it, something that made me love the old thing—something that appealed to my youth!

"We left London in ballast—sand ballast—to load a cargo of coal in a northern port of Bankok. Bankok! I thrilled. I had been six years at sea, but had only seen Melbourne and Sydney, very good places, charming places in their way—but Bankok!

"We worked out of the Thames under canvas, with a North Sea pilot on board. His name was Jermyn, and he dodged all day long about the galley drying his handkerchief before the stove. Apparently he never slept. He was a dismal man, with a perpetual tear sparkling at the end of his nose, who either had been in trouble, or was in trouble, or expected to be in trouble—couldn't be happy unless something went wrong. He mistrusted my youth, my common-sense, and my seamanship, and made a point of showing it in a hundred little ways. I dare say he was right. It seems to me I knew very little then, and I know not much more now; but I cherish a hate for that Jermyn to this day.

"We were a week working up as far as Yarmouth Roads, and then we got into a gale—the famous October gale of twenty-two years ago. It was wind, lightning, sleet, snow, and a terrific sea. We were flying light, and you may imagine how bad it was when I tell you we had smashed bulwarks and a flooded deck. On the second night she shifted her ballast into the lee bow, and by that time we had been blown off somewhere on the Dogger Bank. There was nothing for it but go below with shovels and try to right her, and there we were in that vast hold, gloomy like a cavern, the tallow dips stuck and flickering on the beams, the gale howling above, the ship tossing about like mad on her side; there we all were, Jermyn, the captain, every one, hardly able to keep our feet, engaged on that

gravedigger's work, and trying to toss shovelfuls of wet sand
up to windward. At every tumble of the ship you could see
vaguely in the dim light men falling down with a great flourish
of shovels. One of the ship's boys (we had two), impressed by
the weirdness of the scene, wept as if his heart would break. We
could hear him blubbering somewhere in the shadows.

"On the third day the gale died out, and by and by a north-
country tug picked us up. We took sixteen days in all to get
from London to the Tyne! When we got into dock we had lost
our turn for loading, and they hauled us off to a tier where
we remained for a month. Mrs. Beard (the captain's name was
Beard) came from Colchester to see the old man. She lived on
board. The crew of runners had left, and there remained only
the officers, one boy and the steward, a mulatto who answered
to the name of Abraham. Mrs. Beard was an old woman, with a
face all wrinkled and ruddy like a winter apple, and the figure
of a young girl. She caught sight of me once, sewing on a button, and insisted on having my shirts to repair. This was something different from the captains' wives I had known on board
crack clippers. When I brought her the shirts, she said: 'And
the socks? They want mending, I am sure, and John's—Captain Beard's—things are all in order now. I would be glad of
something to do.' Bless the old woman. She overhauled my outfit for me, and meantime I read for the first time *Sartor
Resartus* and Burnaby's *Ride to Khiva*. I didn't understand
much of the first then; but I remember I preferred the soldier
to the philosopher at the time; a preference which life has only
confirmed. One was a man, and the other was either more—or
less. However, they are both dead and Mrs. Beard is dead, and
youth, strength, genius, thoughts, achievements, simple hearts
—all die. . . . No matter.

"They loaded us at last. We shipped a crew. Eight able
seamen and two boys. We hauled off one evening to the buoys
at the dock-gates, ready to go out, and with a fair prospect of
beginning the voyage next day. Mrs. Beard was to start for
home by a late train. When the ship was fast we went to tea.
We sat rather silent through the meal—Mahon, the old couple,
and I. I finished first, and slipped away for a smoke, my
cabin being in a deck-house just against the poop. It was high
water, blowing fresh with a drizzle; the double dock-gates were
opened, and the steam-colliers were going in and out in the
darkness with their lights burning bright, a great plashing of

propellers, rattling of winches, and a lot of hailing on the pier-
heads. I watched the procession of head-lights gliding high and
of green lights gliding low in the night, when suddenly a red
gleam flashed at me, vanished, came into view again, and remained. The fore-end of a steamer loomed up close. I shouted
down the cabin, 'Come up, quick!' and then heard a startled
voice saying afar in the dark, 'Stop her, sir.' A bell jingled.
Another voice cried warningly, 'We are going right into that
barque, sir.' The answer to this was a gruff 'All right,' and
the next thing was a heavy crash as the steamer struck a glancing blow with the bluff of her bow about our fore-rigging.
There was a moment of confusion, yelling, and running about.
Steam roared. Then somebody was heard saying, 'All clear,
sir.' . . . 'Are you all right?' asked the gruff voice. I had
jumped forward to see the damage, and hailed back, 'I think
so.' 'Easy astern,' said the gruff voice. A bell jingled. 'What
steamer is that?' screamed Mahon. By that time she was no
more to us than a bulky shadow manœuvring a little way off.
They shouted at us some name—a woman's name, Miranda or
Melissa—or some such thing. 'This means another month in
this beastly hole,' said Mahon to me, as we peered with lamps
about the splintered bulwarks and broken braces. 'But where's
the captain?'

"We had not heard or seen anything of him all that time.
We went aft to look. A doleful voice arose hailing somewhere
in the middle of the dock, '*Judea* ahoy!' . . . How the devil did
he get there? . . . 'Hallo!' we shouted. 'I am adrift in our
boat without oars,' he cried. A belated water-man offered his
services, and Mahon struck a bargain with him for half-a-
crown to tow our skipper alongside; but it was Mrs. Beard
that came up the ladder first. They had been floating about
the dock in that mizzly cold rain for nearly an hour. I was
never so surprised in my life.

"It appears that when he heard my shout 'Come up' he
understood at once what was the matter, caught up his wife,
ran on deck, and across, and down into our boat, which was
fast to the ladder. Not bad for a sixty-year-old. Just imagine
that old fellow saving heroically in his arms that old woman—
the woman of his life. He set her down on a thwart, and was
ready to climb back on board when the painter came adrift
somehow, and away they went together. Of course in the confusion we did not hear him shouting. He looked abashed. She

said cheerfully, 'I suppose it does not matter my losing the train now?' 'No, Jenny—you go below and get warm,' he growled. Then to us: 'A sailor has no business with a wife— I say. There I was, out of the ship. Well, no harm done this time. Let's go and look at what that fool of a steamer smashed.'

"It wasn't much, but it delayed us three weeks. At the end of that time, the captain being engaged with his agents, I carried Mrs. Beard's bag to the railway-station and put her all comfy into a third-class carriage. She lowered the window to say, 'You are a good young man. If you see John—Captain Beard—without his muffler at night, just remind him from me to keep his throat well wrapped up.' 'Certainly, Mrs. Beard,' I said. 'You are a good young man; I noticed how attentive you are to John—to Captain——' The train pulled out suddenly; I took my cap off to the old woman: I never saw her again. . . . Pass the bottle.

"We went to sea next day. When we made that start for Bankok we had been already three months out of London. We had expected to be a fortnight or so—at the outside.

"It was January, and the weather was beautiful—the beautiful sunny winter weather that has more charm than in the summer-time, because it is unexpected, and crisp, and you know it won't, it can't, last long. It's like a windfall, like a godsend, like an unexpected piece of luck.

"It lasted all down the North Sea, all down Channel; and it lasted till we were three hundred miles or so to the westward of the Lizards: then the wind went round to the sou'west and began to pipe up. In two days it blew a gale. The *Judea*, hove to, wallowed on the Atlantic like an old candle-box. It blew day after day: it blew with spite, without interval, without mercy, without rest. The world was nothing but an immensity of great foaming waves rushing at us, under a sky low enough to touch with the hand and dirty like a smoked ceiling. In the stormy space surrounding us there was as much flying spray as air. Day after day and night after night there was nothing round the ship but the howl of the wind, the tumult of the sea, the noise of water pouring over her deck. There was no rest for her and no rest for us. She tossed, she pitched, she stood on her head, she sat on her tail, she rolled, she groaned, and we had to hold on while on deck and cling to our bunks when below, in a constant effort of body and worry of mind.

"One night Mahon spoke through the small window of my berth. It opened right into my very bed, and I was lying there sleepless, in my boots, feeling as though I had not slept for years, and could not if I tried. He said excitedly—

" 'You got the sounding-rod in here, Marlow? I can't get the pumps to suck. By God! it's no child's play.'

"I gave him the sounding-rod and lay down again, trying to think of various things—but I thought only of the pumps. When I came on deck they were still at it, and my watch relieved at the pumps. By the light of the lantern brought on deck to examine the sounding-rod I caught a glimpse of their weary, serious faces. We pumped all the four hours. We pumped all night, all day, all the week—watch and watch. She was working herself loose, and leaked badly—not enough to drown us at once, but enough to kill us with the work at the pumps. And while we pumped the ship was going from us piecemeal: the bulwarks went, the stanchions were torn out, the ventilators smashed, the cabin-door burst in. There was not a dry spot in the ship. She was being gutted bit by bit. The long-boat changed, as if by magic, into matchwood where she stood in her gripes. I had lashed her myself, and was rather proud of my handiwork, which had withstood so long the malice of the sea. And we pumped. And there was no break in the weather. The sea was white like a sheet of foam, like a caldron of boiling milk; there was not a break in the clouds, no—not the size of a man's hand—no, not for so much as ten seconds. There was for us no sky, there were for us no stars, no sun, no universe—nothing but angry clouds and an infuriated sea. We pumped watch and watch, for dear life; and it seemed to last for months, for years, for all eternity, as though we had been dead and gone to a hell for sailors. We forgot the day of the week, the name of the month, what year it was, and whether we had ever been ashore. The sails blew away, she lay broadside on under a weather-cloth, the ocean poured over her, and we did not care. We turned those handles, and had the eyes of idiots. As soon as we had crawled on deck I used to take a round turn with a rope about the men, the pumps, and the mainmast, and we turned, we turned incessantly, with the water to our waists, to our necks, over our heads. It was all one. We had forgotten how it felt to be dry.

"And there was somewhere in me the thought: By Jove! this is the deuce of an adventure—something you read about;

and it is my first voyage as second mate—and I am only twenty—and here I am lasting it out as well as any of these men, and keeping my chaps up to the mark. I was pleased. I would not have given up the experience for worlds. I had moments of exultation. Whenever the old dismantled craft pitched heavily with her counter high in the air, she seemed to me to throw up, like an appeal, like a defiance, like a cry to the clouds without mercy, the words written on her stern: '*Judea*, London. Do or Die.'

"O youth! The strength of it, the faith of it, the imagination of it! To me she was not an old rattle-trap carting about the world a lot of coal for a freight—to me she was the endeavour, the test, the trial of life. I think of her with pleasure, with affection, with regret—as you would think of someone dead you have loved. I shall never forget her. . . . Pass the bottle.

"One night when tied to the mast, as I explained, we were pumping on, deafened with the wind, and without spirit enough in us to wish ourselves dead, a heavy sea crashed aboard and swept clean over us. As soon as I got my breath I shouted, as in duty bound, 'Keep on, boys!' when suddenly I felt something hard floating on deck strike the calf of my leg. I made a grab at it and missed. It was so dark we could not see each other's faces within a foot—you understand.

"After that thump the ship kept quiet for a while, and the thing, whatever it was, struck my leg again. This time I caught it—and it was a saucepan. At first, being stupid with fatigue and thinking of nothing but the pumps, I did not understand what I had in my hand. Suddenly it dawned upon me, and I shouted, 'Boys, the house on deck is gone. Leave this, and let's look for the cook.'

"There was a deck-house forward, which contained the galley, the cook's berth, and the quarters of the crew. As we had expected for days to see it swept away, the hands had been ordered to sleep in the cabin—the only safe place in the ship. The steward, Abraham, however, persisted in clinging to his berth, stupidly, like a mule—from sheer fright I believe, like an animal that won't leave a stable falling in an earthquake. So we went to look for him. It was chancing death, since once out of our lashings we were as exposed as if on a raft. But we went. The house was shattered as if a shell had exploded inside. Most of it had gone overboard—stove, men's quarters, and their property, all was gone; but two posts, holding a portion of the bulkhead to which Abraham's bunk was attached, remained as if by a miracle. We groped in the ruins and came upon this, and there he was, sitting in his bunk, surrounded by foam and wreckage, jabbering cheerfully to himself. He was out of his mind; completely and for ever mad, with this sudden shock coming upon the fag-end of his endurance. We snatched him up, lugged him aft, and pitched him head-first down the cabin companion. You understand there was no time to carry him down with infinite precautions and wait to see how he got on. Those below would pick him up at the bottom of the stairs all right. We were in a hurry to go back to the pumps. That business could not wait. A bad leak is an inhuman thing.

"One would think that the sole purpose of that fiendish gale had been to make a lunatic of that poor devil of a mulatto. It eased before morning, and next day the sky cleared, and as the sea went down the leak took up. When it came to bending a fresh set of sails the crew demanded to put back—and really there was nothing else to do. Boats gone, decks swept clean, cabin gutted, men without a stitch but what they stood in, stores spoiled, ship strained. We put her head for home, and —would you believe it? The wind came east right in our teeth. It blew fresh, it blew continuously. We had to beat up every inch of the way, but she did not leak so badly, the water keeping comparatively smooth. Two hours' pumping in every four is no joke—but it kept her afloat as far as Falmouth.

"The good people there live on casualties of the sea, and no doubt were glad to see us. A hungry crowd of shipwrights sharpened their chisels at the sight of that carcass of a ship. And, by Jove! they had pretty pickings off us before they were done. I fancy the owner was already in a tight place. There were delays. Then it was decided to take part of the cargo out and caulk her topsides. This was done, the repairs finished, cargo reshipped; a new crew came on board, and we went out—for Bankok. At the end of a week we were back again. The crew said they weren't going to Bankok—a hundred and fifty days' passage—in a something hooker that wanted pumping eight hours out of the twenty-four; and the nautical papers inserted again the little paragraph: '*Judea*. Barque. Tyne to Bankok; coals; put back to Falmouth leaky and with crew refusing duty.'

"There were more delays—more tinkering. The owner came down for a day, and said she was as right as a little fiddle. Poor old Captain Beard looked like the ghost of a Geordie skipper—through the worry and humiliation of it. Remember he was sixty, and it was his first command. Mahon said it was a foolish business, and would end badly. I loved the ship more than ever, and wanted awfully to get to Bankok. To Bankok! Magic name, blessed name. Mesopotamia wasn't a patch on it. Remember I was twenty, and it was my first second-mate's billet, and the East was waiting for me.

"We went out and anchored in the outer roads with a fresh crew—the third. She leaked worse than ever. It was as if those confounded shipwrights had actually made a hole in her. This time we did not even go outside. The crew simply refused to man the windlass.

"They towed us back to the inner harbour, and we became a fixture, a feature, an institution of the place. People pointed us out to visitors as 'That 'ere barque that's going to Bankok —has been here six months—put back three times.' On holidays the small boys pulling about in boats would hail, '*Judea*, ahoy!' and if a head showed above the rail shouted, 'Where you bound to?—Bankok?' and jeered. We were only three on board. The poor old skipper mooned in the cabin. Mahon undertook the cooking, and unexpectedly developed all a Frenchman's genius for preparing nice little messes. I looked languidly after the rigging. We became citizens of Falmouth. Every shopkeeper knew us. At the barber's or tobacconist's they asked familiarly, 'Do you think you will ever get to Bankok?' Meantime the owner, the underwriters, and the charterers squabbled amongst themselves in London, and our pay went on. . . . Pass the bottle.

"It was horrid. Morally it was worse than pumping for life. It seemed as though we had been forgotten by the world, belonged to nobody, would get nowhere; it seemed that, as if bewitched, we would have to live for ever and ever in that inner harbour, a derision and a byword to generations of long-shore loafers and dishonest boatmen. I obtained three months' pay and a five days' leave, and made a rush for London. It took me a day to get there and pretty well another to come back— but three months' pay went all the same. I don't know what I did with it. I went to a music-hall, I believe, lunched, dined, and supped in a swell place in Regent Street, and was back to

time, with nothing but a complete set of Byron's works and a
new railway rug to show for three months' work. The boat-
man who pulled me off to the ship said: 'Hallo! I thought you
had left the old thing. *She* will never get to Bankok.' 'That's
all *you* know about it,' I said scornfully—but I didn't like
that prophecy at all.

"Suddenly a man, some kind of agent to somebody, appeared
with full powers. He had grog-blossoms all over his face, an
indomitable energy, and was a jolly soul. We leaped into life
again. A hulk came alongside, took our cargo, and then we
went into dry dock to get our copper stripped. No wonder
she leaked. The poor thing, strained beyond endurance by the
gale, had, as if in disgust, spat out all the oakum of her lower
seams. She was recaulked, new coppered, and made as tight
as a bottle. We went back to the hulk and reshipped our cargo.

"Then, on a fine moonlight night, all the rats left the ship.

"We had been infested with them. They had destroyed our
sails, consumed more stores than the crew, affably shared our
beds and our dangers, and now, when the ship was made sea-
worthy, concluded to clear out. I called Mahon to enjoy the
spectacle. Rat after rat appeared on our rail, took a last
look over his shoulder, and leaped with a hollow thud into the
empty hulk. We tried to count them, but soon lost the tale.
Mahon said: 'Well, well! don't talk to me about the intelligence
of rats. They ought to have left before, when we had that
narrow squeak from foundering. There you have the proof
how silly is the superstition about them. They leave a good ship
for an old rotten hulk, where there is nothing to eat, too, the
fools! . . . I don't believe they know what is safe or what is
good for them, any more than you or I.'

"And after some more talk we agreed that the wisdom of
rats had been grossly overrated, being in fact no greater than
that of men.

"The story of the ship was known, by this, all up the
Channel from Land's End to the Forelands, and we could get
no crew on the south coast. They sent us one all complete
from Liverpool, and we left once more—for Bankok.

"We had fair breezes, smooth water right into the tropics,
and the old *Judea* lumbered along in the sunshine. When she
went eight knots everything cracked aloft, and we tied our
caps to our heads; but mostly she strolled on at the rate of
three miles an hour. What could you expect? She was tired—

that old ship. Her youth was where mine is—where yours is—
you fellows who listen to this yarn; and what friend would
throw your years and your weariness in your face? We didn't
grumble at her. To us aft, at least, it seemed as though we
had been born in her, reared in her, had lived in her for ages,
had never known any other ship. I would just as soon have
abused the old village church at home for not being a cathedral.

"And for me there was also my youth to make me patient.
There was all the East before me, and all life, and the thought
that I had been tried in that ship and had come out pretty
well. And I thought of men of old who, centuries ago, went
that road in ships that sailed no better, to the land of
palms, and spices, and yellow sands, and of brown nations
ruled by kings more cruel than Nero the Roman, and more
splendid than Solomon the Jew. The old bark lumbered on,
heavy with her age and the burden of her cargo, while I lived
the life of youth in ignorance and hope. She lumbered on
through an interminable procession of days; and the fresh
gilding flashed back at the setting sun, seemed to cry out over
the darkening sea the words painted on her stern, '*Judea*,
London. Do or Die.'

"Then we entered the Indian Ocean and steered northerly
for Java Head. The winds were light. Weeks slipped by. She
crawled on, do or die, and people at home began to think of
posting us as overdue.

"One Saturday evening, I being off duty, the men asked
me to give them an extra bucket of water or so—for washing
clothes. As I did not wish to screw on the fresh-water pump
so late, I went forward whistling, and with a key in my hand
to unlock the forepeak scuttle, intending to serve the water
out of a spare tank we kept there.

"The smell down below was as unexpected as it was frightful. One would have thought hundreds of paraffin-lamps had
been flaring and smoking in that hole for days. I was glad to
get out. The man with me coughed and said, 'Funny smell,
sir.' I answered negligently, 'It's good for the health they
say,' and walked aft.

"The first thing I did was to put my head down the square
of the midship ventilator. As I lifted the lid a visible breath,
something like a thin fog, a puff of faint haze, rose from the
opening. The ascending air was hot, and had a heavy, sooty,

paraffiny smell. I gave one sniff, and put down the lid gently. It was no use choking myself. The cargo was on fire.

"Next day she began to smoke in earnest. You see it was to be expected, for though the coal was of a safe kind, that cargo had been so handled, so broken up with handling, that it looked more like smithy coal than anything else. Then it had been wetted—more than once. It rained all the time we were taking it back from the hulk, and now with this long passage it got heated, and there was another case of spontaneous combustion.

"The captain called us into the cabin. He had a chart spread on the table, and looked unhappy. He said, 'The coast of West Australia is near, but I mean to proceed to our destination. It is the hurricane month, too; but we will just keep her head for Bankok, and fight the fire. No more putting back anywhere, if we all get roasted. We will try first to stifle this 'ere damned combustion by want of air.'

"We tried. We battened down everything, and still she smoked. The smoke kept coming out through imperceptible crevices; it forced itself through bulkheads and covers; it oozed here and there and everywhere in slender threads, in an invisible film, in an incomprehensible manner. It made its way into the cabin, into the forecastle; it poisoned the sheltered places on the deck, it could be sniffed as high as the mainyard. It was clear that if the smoke came out the air came in. This was disheartening. This combustion refused to be stifled.

"We resolved to try water, and took the hatches off. Enormous volumes of smoke, whitish, yellowish, thick, greasy, misty, choking, ascended as high as the trucks. All hands cleared out aft. Then the poisonous cloud blew away, and we went back to work in a smoke that was no thicker now than that of an ordinary factory chimney.

"We rigged the force-pump, got the hose along, and by and by it burst. Well, it was as old as the ship—a prehistoric hose, and past repair. Then we pumped with the feeble head-pump, drew water with buckets, and in this way managed in time to pour lots of Indian Ocean into the main hatch. The bright stream flashed in sunshine, fell into a layer of white crawling smoke, and vanished on the black surface of coal. Steam ascended mingling with the smoke. We poured salt water as into a barrel without a bottom. It was our fate to pump in that

ship, to pump out of her, to pump into her; and after keeping
water out of her to save ourselves from being drowned, we
frantically poured water into her to save ourselves from being
burnt.

"And she crawled on, do or die, in the serene weather. The
sky was a miracle of purity, a miracle of azure. The sea was
polished, was blue, was pellucid, was sparkling like a precious
stone, extending on all sides, all round to the horizon—as if
the whole terrestrial globe had been one jewel, one colossal
sapphire, a single gem fashioned into a planet. And on the
lustre of the great calm waters the *Judea* glided imperceptibly,
enveloped in languid and unclean vapours, in a lazy cloud that
drifted to leeward, light and slow; a pestiferous cloud defiling
the splendour of sea and sky.

"All this time of course we saw no fire. The cargo smoul-
dered at the bottom somewhere. Once Mahon, as we were working side by side, said to me with a queer smile: 'Now, if she
only would spring a tidy leak—like that time when we first
left the Channel—it would put a stopper on this fire. Wouldn't
it?' I remarked irrelevantly, 'Do you remember the rats?'

"We fought the fire and sailed the ship too as carefully as
though nothing had been the matter. The steward cooked and
attended on us. Of the other twelve men, eight worked while
four rested. Everyone took his turn, captain included. There
was equality, and if not exactly fraternity, then a deal of
good feeling. Sometimes a man, as he dashed a bucketful of
water down the hatchway, would yell out, 'Hurrah for
Bankok!' and the rest laughed. But generally we were taciturn
and serious—and thirsty. Oh! how thirsty! And we had to be
careful with the water. Strict allowance. The ship smoked, the
sun blazed. . . . Pass the bottle.

"We tried everything. We even made an attempt to dig
down to the fire. No good, of course. No man could remain
more than a minute below. Mahon, who went first, fainted
there, and the man who went to fetch him out did likewise.
We lugged them out on deck. Then I leaped down to show
how easily it could be done. They had learned wisdom by that
time, and contented themselves by fishing for me with a chain-
hook tied to a broom-handle, I believe. I did not offer to go
and fetch up my shovel, which was left down below.

"Things began to look bad. We put the long-boat into the
water. The second boat was ready to swing out. We had also

another, a 14-foot thing, on davits aft, where it was quite safe.
"Then, behold, the smoke suddenly decreased. We redoubled
our efforts to flood the bottom of the ship. In two days there
was no smoke at all. Everybody was on the broad grin. This
was on a Friday. On Saturday no work, but sailing the ship
of course, was done. The men washed their clothes and their
faces for the first time in a fortnight, and had a special dinner
given them. They spoke of spontaneous combustion with contempt, and implied *they* were the boys to put out combustions.
Somehow we all felt as though we each had inherited a large
fortune. But a beastly smell of burning hung about the ship.
Captain Beard had hollow eyes and sunken cheeks. I had never
noticed so much before how twisted and bowed he was. He and
Mahon prowled soberly about hatches and ventilators, sniffing.
It struck me suddenly poor Mahon was a very, very old chap.
As to me, I was as pleased and proud as though I had helped
to win a great naval battle. O! Youth!

"The night was fine. In the morning a homeward-bound
ship passed us hull down—the first we had seen for months;
but we were nearing the land at last, Java Head being about
190 miles off, and nearly due north.

"Next day it was my watch on deck from eight to twelve.
At breakfast the captain observed, 'It's wonderful how that
smell hangs about the cabin.' About ten, the mate being on the
poop, I stepped down on the main-deck for a moment. The
carpenter's bench stood abaft the mainmast: I leaned against
it sucking at my pipe, and the carpenter, a young chap, came
to talk to me. He remarked, 'I think we have done very well,
haven't we?' and then I perceived with annoyance the fool
was trying to tilt the bench. I said curtly, 'Don't, Chips,' and
immediately became aware of a queer sensation, of an absurd
delusion,—I seemed somehow to be in the air. I heard all round
me like a pent-up breath released—as if a thousand giants
simultaneously had said Phoo!—and felt a dull concussion
which made my ribs ache suddenly. No doubt about it—I was
in the air, and my body was describing a short parabola. But
short as it was, I had the time to think several thoughts in, as
far as I can remember, the following order: 'This can't be the
carpenter—What is it?—Some accident—Submarine volcano?
—Coals, gas!—By Jove! we are being blown up—Everybody's
dead—I am falling into the after-hatch—I see fire in it.'

"The coal-dust suspended in the air of the hold had glowed

dull-red at the moment of the explosion. In the twinkling of an eye, in an infinitesimal fraction of a second since the first tilt of the bench, I was sprawling full length on the cargo. I picked myself up and scrambled out. It was quick like a rebound. The deck was a wilderness of smashed timber, lying crosswise like trees in a wood after a hurricane; an immense curtain of soiled rags waved gently before me—it was the mainsail blown to strips. I thought, The masts will be toppling over directly; and to get out of the way bolted on all-fours towards the poop-ladder. The first person I saw was Mahon, with eyes like saucers, his mouth open, and the long white hair standing straight on end round his head like a silver halo. He was just about to go down when the sight of the main-deck stirring, heaving up, and changing into splinters before his eyes, petrified him on the top step. I stared at him in unbelief, and he stared at me with a queer kind of shocked curiosity. I did not know that I had no hair, no eyebrows, no eyelashes, that my young moustache was burnt off, that my face was black, one cheek laid open, my nose cut, and my chin bleeding. I had lost my cap, one of my slippers, and my shirt was torn to rags. Of all this I was not aware. I was amazed to see the ship still afloat, the poop-deck whole—and, most of all, to see anybody alive. Also the peace of the sky and the serenity of the sea were distinctly surprising. I suppose I expected to see them convulsed with horror. . . . Pass the bottle.

"There was a voice hailing the ship from somewhere—in the air, in the sky—I couldn't tell. Presently I saw the captain—and he was mad. He asked me eagerly, 'Where's the cabin-table?' and to hear such a question was a frightful shock. I had just been blown up, you understand, and vibrated with that experience,—I wasn't quite sure whether I was alive. Mahon began to stamp with both feet and yelled at him, 'Good God! don't you see the deck's blown out of her?' I found my voice, and stammered out as if conscious of some gross neglect of duty, 'I don't know where the cabin-table is.' It was like an absurd dream.

"Do you know what he wanted next? Well, he wanted to trim the yards. Very placidly, and as if lost in thought, he insisted on having the foreyard squared. 'I don't know if there's anybody alive,' said Mahon, almost tearfully. 'Surely,' he said, gently, 'there will be enough left to square the foreyard.'

"The old chap, it seems, was in his own berth winding up he chronometers, when the shock sent him spinning. Immediately it occurred to him—as he said afterwards—that the ship had struck something, and he ran out into the cabin. There, he saw, the cabin-table had vanished somewhere. The deck being blown up, it had fallen down into the lazarette of course. Where we had our breakfast that morning he saw only a great hole in the floor. This appeared to him so awfully mysterious, and impressed him so immensely, that what he saw and heard after he got on deck were mere trifles in comparison. And, mark, he noticed directly the wheel deserted and his barque off her course—and his only thought was to get that miserable, stripped, undecked, smouldering shell of a ship back again with her head pointing at her port of destination. Bankok! That's what he was after. I tell you this quiet, bowed, bandy-legged, almost deformed little man was immense in the singleness of his idea and in his placid ignorance of our agitation. He motioned us forward with a commanding gesture, and went to take the wheel himself.

"Yes; that was the first thing we did—trim the yards of that wreck! No one was killed, or even disabled, but everyone was more or less hurt. You should have seen them! Some were in rags, with black faces, like coal-heavers, like sweeps, and had bullet heads that seemed closely cropped, but were in fact singed to the skin. Others, of the watch below, awakened by being shot out from their collapsing bunks, shivered incessantly, and kept on groaning even as we went about our work. But they all worked. That crew of Liverpool hard cases had in them the right stuff. It's my experience they always have. It is the sea that gives it—the vastness, the loneliness surrounding their dark stolid souls. Ah! Well! we stumbled, we crept, we fell, we barked our shins on the wreckage, we hauled. The masts stood, but we did not know how much they might be charred down below. It was nearly calm, but a long swell ran from the west and made her roll. They might go at any moment. We looked at them with apprehension. One could not foresee which way they would fall.

"Then we retreated aft and looked about us. The deck was a tangle of planks on edge, of planks on end, of splinters, of ruined woodwork. The masts rose from that chaos like big trees above a matted undergrowth. The interstices of that mass of wreckage were full of something whitish, sluggish, stirring—

of something that was like a greasy fog. The smoke of the invisible fire was coming up again, was trailing, like a poisonous thick mist in some valley choked with dead wood. Already lazy wisps were beginning to curl upwards amongst the mass of splinters. Here and there a piece of timber, stuck upright, resembled a post. Half of a fife-rail had been shot through the foresail, and the sky made a patch of glorious blue in the ignobly soiled canvas. A portion of several boards holding together had fallen across the rail, and one end protruded overboard, like a gangway leading upon nothing, like a gangway leading over the deep sea, leading to death—as if inviting us to walk the plank at once and be done with our ridiculous troubles. And still the air, the sky—a ghost, something invisible was hailing the ship.

"Someone had the sense to look over, and there was the helmsman, who had impulsively jumped overboard, anxious to come back. He yelled and swam lustily like a merman, keeping up with the ship. We threw him a rope, and presently he stood amongst us streaming with water and very crestfallen. The captain had surrendered the wheel, and apart, elbow on rail and chin in hand, gazed at the sea wistfully. We asked ourselves, What next? I thought, Now, this is something like. This is great. I wonder what will happen. O youth!

"Suddenly Mahon sighted a steamer far astern. Captain Beard said, 'We may do something with her yet.' We hoisted two flags, which said in the international language of the sea, 'On fire. Want immediate assistance.' The steamer grew bigger rapidly, and by and by spoke with two flags on her foremast, 'I am coming to your assistance.'

"In half an hour she was abreast, to windward, within hail, and rolling slightly, with her engines stopped. We lost our composure, and yelled all together with excitement, 'We've been blown up.' A man in a white helmet, on the bridge, cried, 'Yes! All right! all right!' and he nodded his head, and smiled, and made soothing motions with his hand as though at a lot of frightened children. One of the boats dropped in the water, and walked towards us upon the sea with her long oars. Four Calashes pulled a swinging stroke. This was my first sight of Malay seamen. I've known them since, but what struck me then was their unconcern: they came alongside, and even the bowman standing up and holding to our main-chains with the boat-hook did not deign to lift his head for a glance. I thought people who had been blown up deserved more attention.

"A little man, dry like a chip and agile like a monkey, clambered up. It was the mate of the steamer. He gave one look, and cried, 'O boys—you had better quit.'

"We were silent. He talked apart with the captain for a time,—seemed to argue with him. Then they went away together to the steamer.

"When our skipper came back we learned that the steamer was the *Somerville*, Captain Nash, from West Australia to Singapore via Batavia with mails, and that the agreement was she should tow us to Anjer or Batavia, if possible, where we could extinguish the fire by scuttling, and then proceed on our voyage—to Bankok! The old man seemed excited. 'We will do it yet,' he said to Mahon, fiercely. He shook his fist at the sky. Nobody else said a word.

"At noon the steamer began to tow. She went ahead slim and high, and what was left of the *Judea* followed at the end of seventy fathom of tow-rope,—followed her swiftly like a cloud of smoke with mast-heads protruding above. We went aloft to furl the sails. We coughed on the yards, and were careful about the bunts. Do you see the lot of us there, putting a neat furl on the sails of that ship doomed to arrive nowhere? There was not a man who didn't think that at any moment the masts would topple over. From aloft we could not see the ship for smoke, and they worked carefully, passing the gaskets with even turns. 'Harbour furl—aloft there!' cried Mahon from below.

"You understand this? I don't think one of those chaps expected to get down in the usual way. When we did I heard them saying to each other, 'Well, I thought we would come down overboard, in a lump—sticks and all—blame me if I didn't.' 'That's what I was thinking to myself,' would answer wearily another battered and bandaged scarecrow. And, mind, these were men without the drilled-in habit of obedience. To an onlooker they would be a lot of profane scallywags without a redeeming point. What made them do it—what made them obey me when I, thinking consciously how fine it was, made them drop the bunt of the foresail twice to try and do it better? What? They had no professional reputation—no examples, no praise. It wasn't a sense of duty; they all knew well enough how to shirk, and laze, and dodge—when they

had a mind to it—and mostly they had. Was it the two pounds
ten a-month that sent them there? They didn't think their
pay half good enough. No; it was something in them, something inborn and subtle and everlasting. I don't say positively
that the crew of a French or German merchantman wouldn't
have done it, but I doubt whether it would have been done in
the same way. There was a completeness in it, something solid
like a principle, and masterful like an instinct—a disclosure
of something secret—of that hidden something, that gift of
good or evil that makes racial difference, that shapes the fate
of nations.

"It was that night at ten that, for the first time since we
had been fighting it, we saw the fire. The speed of the towing
had fanned the smouldering destruction. A blue gleam appeared forward, shining below the wreck of the deck. It wavered in patches, it seemed to stir and creep like the light of a
glowworm. I saw it first, and told Mahon. 'Then the game's
up,' he said. 'We had better stop this towing, or she will burst
out suddenly fore and aft before we can clear out.' We set up
a yell; rang bells to attract their attention; they towed on.
At last Mahon and I had to crawl forward and cut the rope
with an axe. There was no time to cast off the lashings. Red
tongues could be seen licking the wilderness of splinters under
our feet as we made our way back to the poop.

"Of course they very soon found out in the steamer that
the rope was gone. She gave a loud blast of her whistle, her
lights were seen sweeping in a wide circle, she came up ranging
close along-side, and stopped. We were all in a tight group on
the poop looking at her. Every man had saved a little bundle
or a bag. Suddenly a conical flame with a twisted top shot up
forward and threw upon the black sea a circle of light, with the
two vessels side by side and heaving gently in its centre. Captain Beard had been sitting on the gratings still and mute for
hours, but now he rose slowly and advanced in front of us, to
the mizzen-shrouds. Captain Nash hailed: 'Come along! Look
sharp. I have mail-bags on board. I will take you and your
boats to Singapore.'

" 'Thank you! No!' said our skipper. 'We must see the last
of the ship.'

" 'I can't stand by any longer,' shouted the other. 'Mails—
you know.'

" 'Ay, ay! We are all right.'

" 'Very well! I'll report you in Singapore. . . . Good-bye!'

"He waved his hand. Our men dropped their bundles quietly. The steamer moved ahead, and passing out of the circle of light, vanished at once from our sight, dazzled by the fire which burned fiercely. And then I knew that I would see the East first as commander of a small boat. I thought it fine; and the fidelity to the old ship was fine. We should see the last of her. Oh, the glamour of youth! Oh, the fire of it, more dazzling than the flames of the burning ship, throwing a magic light on the wide earth, leaping audaciously to the sky, pres-ently to be quenched by time, more cruel, more pitiless, more bitter than the sea—and like the flames of the burning ship surrounded by an impenetrable night.

*   *   *   *   *   *

"The old man warned us in his gentle and inflexible way that it was part of our duty to save for the underwriters as much as we could of the ship's gear. Accordingly we went to work aft, while she blazed forward to give us plenty of light. We lugged out a lot of rubbish. What didn't we save? An old barometer fixed with an absurd quantity of screws nearly cost me my life: a sudden rush of smoke came upon me, and I just got away in time. There were various stores, bolts of canvas, coils of rope; the poop looked like a marine bazaar, and the boats were lumbered to the gunwales. One would have thought the old man wanted to take as much as he could of his first command with him. He was very, very quiet, but off his balance evidently. Would you believe it? He wanted to take a length of old stream-cable and a kedge-anchor with him in the long-boat. We said, 'Ay, ay, sir,' deferentially, and on the quiet let the things slip overboard. The heavy medicine-chest went that way, two bags of green coffee, tins of paint—fancy, paint! —a whole lot of things. Then I was ordered with two hands into the boats to make a stowage and get them ready against the time it would be proper for us to leave the ship.

"We put everything straight, stepped the long-boat's mast for our skipper, who was to take charge of her, and I was not sorry to sit down for a moment. My face felt raw, every limb ached as if broken, I was aware of all my ribs, and would have sworn to a twist in the backbone. The boats, fast astern, lay in a deep shadow, and all around I could see the circle of the sea lighted by the fire. A gigantic flame arose forward straight and clear. It flared fierce, with noises like the whirr of wings, with rumbles as of thunder. There were cracks, detonations, and from the cone of flame the sparks flew upwards, as man is born to trouble, to leaky ships, and to ships that burn.

"What bothered me was that the ship, lying broadside to the swell and to such wind as there was—a mere breath—the boats would not keep astern where they were safe, but persisted, in a pig-headed way boats have, in getting under the counter and then swinging alongside. They were knocking about dangerously and coming near the flame, while the ship rolled on them, and, of course, there was always the danger of the masts going over the side at any moment. I and my two boat-keepers kept them off as best we could, with oars and boat-hooks; but to be constantly at it became exasperating, since there was no reason why we should not leave at once. We could not see those on board, nor could we imagine what caused the delay. The boat-keepers were swearing feebly, and I had not only my share of the work but also had to keep at it two men who showed a constant inclination to lay themselves down and let things slide.

"At last I hailed, 'On deck there,' and someone looked over. 'We're ready here,' I said. The head disappeared, and very soon popped up again. 'The captain says, All right, sir, and to keep the boats well clear of the ship.'

"Half an hour passed. Suddenly there was a frightful racket, rattle, clanking of chain, hiss of water, and millions of sparks flew up into the shivering column of smoke that stood leaning slightly above the ship. The cat-heads had burned away, and the two red-hot anchors had gone to the bottom, tearing out after them two hundred fathom of red-hot chain. The ship trembled, the mass of flame swayed as if ready to collapse, and the fore top-gallant-mast fell. It darted down like an arrow of fire, shot under, and instantly leaping up within an oar's-length of the boats, floated quietly, very black on the luminous sea. I hailed the deck again. After some time a man in an unexpectedly cheerful but also muffled tone, as though he had been trying to speak with his mouth shut, informed me, 'Coming directly, sir,' and vanished. For a long time I heard nothing but the whirr and roar of the fire. There were also whistling sounds. The boats jumped, tugged at the painters, ran at each other playfully, knocked their sides together, or, do what we would, swung in a bunch against the ship's side. I couldn't stand it any longer, and swarming up a rope, clambered aboard over the stern.

"It was as bright as day. Coming up like this, the sheet of fire facing me was a terrifying sight, and the heat seemed hardly bearable at first. On a settee cushion dragged out of the cabin Captain Beard, his legs drawn up and one arm under his head, slept with the light playing on him. Do you know what the rest were busy about? They were sitting on deck right aft, round an open case, eating bread and cheese and drinking bottled stout.

"On the background of flames twisting in fierce tongues above their heads they seemed at home like salamanders, and looked like a band of desperate pirates. The fire sparkled in the whites of their eyes, gleamed on patches of white skin seen through the torn shirts. Each had the marks as of a battle about him—bandaged heads, tied-up arms, a strip of dirty rag round a knee—and each man had a bottle between his legs and a chunk of cheese in his hand. Mahon got up. With his handsome and disreputable head, his hooked profile, his long white beard, and with an uncorked bottle in his hand, he resembled one of those reckless sea-robbers of old making merry amidst violence and disaster. 'The last meal on board,' he explained solemnly. 'We had nothing to eat all day, and it was no use leaving all this.' He flourished the bottle and indicated the sleeping skipper. 'He said he couldn't swallow anything, so I got him to lie down,' he went on; and as I stared, 'I don't know whether you are aware, young fellow, the man had no sleep to speak of for days—and there will be dam' little sleep in the boats.' 'There will be no boats by-and-by if you fool about much longer,' I said, indignantly. I walked up to the skipper and shook him by the shoulder. At last he opened his eyes, but did not move. 'Time to leave her, sir,' I said quietly.

"He got up painfully, looked at the flames, at the sea sparkling round the ship, and black, black as ink farther away; he looked at the stars shining dim through a thin veil of smoke in a sky black, black as Erebus.

" 'Youngest first,' he said.

"And the ordinary seaman, wiping his mouth with the back of his hand, got up, clambered over the taffrail, and vanished. Others followed. One, on the point of going over, stopped short to drain his bottle, and with a great swing of his arm flung it at the fire. 'Take this!' he cried.

"The skipper lingered disconsolately, and we left him to commune alone for a while with his first command. Then I went up again and brought him away at last. It was time. The ironwork on the poop was hot to the touch.

"Then the painter of the long-boat was cut, and the three boats, tied together, drifted clear of the ship. It was just sixteen hours after the explosion when we abandoned her. Mahon had charge of the second boat, and I had the smallest —the 14-foot thing. The long-boat would have taken the lot of us; but the skipper said we must save as much property as we could—for the underwriters—and so I got my first command. I had two men with me, a bag of biscuits, a few tins of meat, and a breaker of water. I was ordered to keep close to the long-boat, that in case of bad weather we might be taken into her.

"And do you know what I thought? I thought I would part company as soon as I could. I wanted to have my first command all to myself. I wasn't going to sail in a squadron if there were a chance for independent cruising. I would make land by myself. I would beat the other boats. Youth! All youth! The silly, charming, beautiful youth.

"But we did not make a start at once. We must see the last of the ship. And so the boats drifted about that night, heaving and setting on the swell. The men dozed, waked, sighed, groaned. I looked at the burning ship.

"Between the darkness of earth and heaven she was burning fiercely upon a disc of purple sea shot by the blood-red play of gleams; upon a disc of water glittering and sinister. A high, clear flame, an immense and lonely flame, ascended from the ocean, and from its summit the black smoke poured continuously at the sky. She burned furiously; mournful and imposing like a funeral pile kindled in the night, surrounded by the sea, watched over by the stars. A magnificent death had come like a grace, like a gift, like a reward to that old ship at the end of her laborious days. The surrender of her weary ghost to the keeping of stars and sea was stirring like the sight of a glorious triumph. The masts fell just before daybreak, and for a moment there was a burst and turmoil of sparks that seemed to fill with flying fire the night patient and watchful, the vast night lying silent upon the sea. At daylight she was only a charred shell, floating still under a cloud of smoke and bearing a glowing mass of coal within.

"Then the oars were got out, and the boats forming in a line moved round her remains as if in procession—the long-boat leading. As we pulled across her stern a slim dart of fire shot out viciously at us, and suddenly she went down, head first, in a great hiss of steam. The unconsumed stern was the last to sink; but the paint had gone, had cracked, had peeled off, and there were no letters, there was no word, no stubborn device that was like her soul, to flash at the rising sun her creed and her name.

"We made our way north. A breeze sprang up, and about noon all the boats came together for the last time. I had no mast or sail in mine, but I made a mast out of a spare oar and hoisted a boat-awning for a sail, with a boat-hook for a yard. She was certainly over-masted, but I had the satisfaction of knowing that with the wind aft I could beat the other two. I had to wait for them. Then we all had a look at the captain's chart, and, after a sociable meal of hard bread and water, got our last instructions. These were simple: steer north, and keep together as much as possible. 'Be careful with that jury-rig, Marlow,' said the captain; and Mahon, as I sailed proudly past his boat, wrinkled his curved nose and hailed, 'You will sail that ship of yours under water, if you don't look out, young fellow.' He was a malicious old man—and may the deep sea where he sleeps now rock him gently, rock him tenderly to the end of time!

"Before sunset a thick rain-squall passed over the two boats, which were far astern, and that was the last I saw of them for a time. Next day I sat steering my cockle-shell—my first com-mand—with nothing but water and sky around me. I did sight in the afternoon the upper sails of a ship far away, but said nothing, and my men did not notice her. You see I was afraid she might be homeward bound, and I had no mind to turn back from the portals of the East. I was steering for Java—another blessed name—like Bankok, you know. I steered many days.

"I need not tell you what it is to be knocking about in an open boat. I remember nights and days of calm, and we pulled, we pulled, and the boat seemed to stand still, as if bewitched within the circle of the sea horizon. I remember the heat, the deluge of rain-squalls that kept us baling for dear life (but filled our water-cask), and I remember sixteen hours on end

with a mouth dry as a cinder and a steering-oar over the stern
to keep my first command head on to a breaking sea. I did
not know how good a man I was till then. I remember the
drawn faces, the dejected figures of my two men, and I remember my youth and the feeling that will never come back
any more—the feeling that I could last for ever, outlast the
sea, the earth, and all men; the deceitful feeling that lures us on
to joys, to perils, to love, to vain effort—to death; the
triumphant conviction of strength, the heat of life in the
handful of dust, the glow in the heart that with every year
grows dim, grows cold, grows small, and expires—and expires,
too soon, too soon—before life itself.

"And this is how I see the East. I have seen its secret places
and have looked into its very soul; but now I see it always from
a small boat, a high outline of mountains, blue and afar in
the morning; like faint mist at noon; a jagged wall of purple
at sunset. I have the feel of the oar in my hand, the vision of
a scorching blue sea in my eyes. And I see a bay, a wide bay,
smooth as glass and polished like ice, shimmering in the dark.
A red light burns far off upon the gloom of the land, and the
night is soft and warm. We drag at the oars with aching arms,
and suddenly a puff of wind, a puff faint and tepid and
laden with strange odours of blossoms, of aromatic wood, comes
out of the still night—the first sigh of the East on my face.
That I can never forget. It was impalpable and enslaving, like
a charm, like a whispered promise of mysterious delight.

"We had been pulling this finishing spell for eleven hours.
Two pulled, and he whose turn it was to rest sat at the tiller.
We had made out the red light in that bay and steered for it,
guessing it must mark some small coasting port. We passed
two vessels, outlandish and high-sterned, sleeping at anchor,
and, approaching the light, now very dim, ran the boat's nose
against the end of a jutting wharf. We were blind with fatigue.
My men dropped the oars and fell off the thwarts as if dead.
I made fast to a pile. A current rippled softly. The scented
obscurity of the shore was grouped into vast masses, a density
of colossal clumps of vegetation, probably—mute and fantastic
shapes. And at their foot the semicircle of a beach gleamed
faintly, like an illusion. There was not a light, not a stir, not
a sound. The mysterious East faced me, perfumed like a
flower, silent like death, dark like a grave.

"And I sat weary beyond expression, exulting like a conqueror, sleepless and entranced as if before a profound, a fateful enigma.

"A splashing of oars, a measured dip reverberating on the level of water, intensified by the silence of the shore into loud claps, made me jump up. A boat, a European boat, was coming in. I invoked the name of the dead; I hailed: *Judea* ahoy! A thin shout answered.

"It was the captain. I had beaten the flagship by three hours, and I was glad to hear the old man's voice again, tremulous and tired. 'Is it you, Marlow?' 'Mind the end of that jetty, sir,' I cried.

"He approached cautiously, and brought up with the deep-sea lead-line which we had saved—for the underwriters. I eased my painter and fell alongside. He sat, a broken figure at the stern, wet with dew, his hands clasped in his lap. His men were asleep already. 'I had a terrible time of it,' he murmured. 'Mahon is behind—not very far.' We conversed in whispers, in low whispers, as if afraid to wake up the land. Guns, thunder, earthquakes would not have awakened the men just then.

"Looking round as we talked, I saw away at sea a bright light travelling in the night. 'There's a steamer passing the bay,' I said. She was not passing, she was entering, and she even came close and anchored. 'I wish,' said the old man, 'you would find out whether she is English. Perhaps they could give us a passage somewhere.' He seemed nervously anxious. So by dint of punching and kicking I started one of my men into a state of somnambulism, and giving him an oar, took another and pulled towards the lights of the steamer.

"There was a murmur of voices in her, metallic hollow clangs of the engine-room, footsteps on the deck. Her ports shone, round like dilated eyes. Shapes moved about, and there was a shadowy man high up on the bridge. He heard my oars.

"And then, before I could open my lips, the East spoke to me, but it was in a Western voice. A torrent of words was poured into the enigmatical, the fateful silence; outlandish, angry words, mixed with words and even whole sentences of good English, less strange but even more surprising. The voice swore and cursed violently; it riddled the solemn peace of the bay by a volley of abuse. It began by calling me Pig, and from that went crescendo into unmentionable adjectives—in English. The man up there raged aloud in two languages, and

with a sincerity in his fury that almost convinced me I had, in
some way, sinned against the harmony of the universe. I could
hardly see him, but began to think he would work himself into
a fit.

"Suddenly he ceased, and I could hear him snorting and
blowing like a porpoise. I said—

" 'What steamer is this, pray?'.

" 'Eh? What's this? And who are you?'

" 'Castaway crew of an English barque burnt at sea. We
came here to-night. I am the second mate. The captain is in
the long-boat, and wishes to know if you would give us a passage somewhere.'

" 'Oh, my goodness! I say. . . . This is the *Celestial* from
Singapore on her return trip. I'll arrange with your captain
in the morning, . . . and, . . . I say, . . . did you hear me
just now?'

" 'I should think the whole bay heard you.'

" 'I thought you were a shore-boat. Now, look here—this
infernal lazy scoundrel of a caretaker has gone to sleep again
—curse him. The light is out, and I nearly ran foul of the end
of this damned jetty. This is the third time he plays me this
trick. Now, I ask you, can anybody stand this kind of thing?
It's enough to drive a man out of his mind. I'll report him.
. . . I'll get the Assistant Resident to give him the sack,
by . . . ! See—there's no light. It's out, isn't it! I take you
to witness the light's out. There should be a light, you know.
A red light on the——'

" 'There was a light,' I said, mildly.

" 'But it's out, man! What's the use of talking like this?
You can see for yourself it's out—don't you? If you had to
take a valuable steamer along this God-forsaken coast you
would want a light, too. I'll kick him from end to end of his
miserable wharf. You'll see if I don't. I will——'

" 'So I may tell my captain you'll take us?' I broke in.

" 'Yes, I'll take you. Good-night,' he said, brusquely.

"I pulled back, made fast again to the jetty, and then went
to sleep at last. I had faced the silence of the East. I had
heard some of its language. But when I opened my eyes again
the silence was as complete as though it had never been
broken. I was lying in a flood of light, and the sky had never
looked so far, so high, before. I opened my eyes and lay without moving.

"And then I saw the men of the East—they were looking at me. The whole length of the jetty was full of people. I saw brown, bronze, yellow faces, the black eyes, the glitter, the colour of an Eastern crowd. And all these beings stared without a murmur, without a sigh, without a movement. They stared down at the boats, at the sleeping men who at night had come to them from the sea. Nothing moved. The fronds of palms stood still against the sky. Not a branch stirred along the shore, and the brown roofs of hidden houses peeped through the green foliage, through the big leaves that hung shining and still like leaves forged of heavy metal. This was the East of the ancient navigators, so old, so mysterious, resplendent and sombre, living and unchanged, full of danger and promise. And these were the men. I sat up suddenly. A wave of movement passed through the crowd from end to end, passed along the heads, swayed the bodies, ran along the jetty like a ripple on the water, like a breath of wind on a field—and all was still again. I see it now—the wide sweep of the bay, the glittering sands, the wealth of green infinite and varied, the sea blue like the sea of a dream, the crowd of attentive faces, the blaze of vivid colour—the water reflecting it all, the curve of the shore, the jetty, the high-sterned outlandish craft floating still, and the three boats with the tired men from the West sleeping, unconscious of the land and the people and of the violence of sunshine. They slept thrown across the thwarts, curled on bottom-boards, in the careless attitudes of death. The head of the old skipper, leaning back in the stern of the long-boat, had fallen on his breast, and he looked as though he would never wake. Farther out old Mahon's face was upturned to the sky, with the long white beard spread out on his breast, as though he had been shot where he sat at the tiller; and a man, all in a heap in the bows of the boat, slept with both arms embracing the stem-head and with his cheek laid on the gunwale. The East looked at them without a sound.

"I have known its fascination since; I have seen the mysterious shores, the still water, the lands of brown nations, where a stealthy Nemesis lies in wait, pursues, overtakes so many of the conquering race, who are proud of their wisdom, of their knowledge, of their strength. But for me all the East is contained in that vision of my youth. It is all in that moment when I opened my young eyes on it. I came upon it from a tussle with the sea—and I was young—and I saw it looking at me. And this is all that is left of it! Only a moment; a moment of strength, of romance, of glamour—of youth! . . . . A flick of sunshine upon a strange shore, the time to remember, the time for a sigh, and—good-bye!—Night—Good-bye . . . !"

He drank.

"Ah! The good old time—the good old time. Youth and the sea. Glamour and the sea! The good, strong sea, the salt, bitter sea, that could whisper to you and roar at you and knock your breath out of you."

He drank again.

"By all that's wonderful it is the sea, I believe, the sea itself—or is it youth alone? Who can tell? But you here—you all had something out of life: money, love—whatever one gets on shore—and, tell me, wasn't that the best time, that time when we were young at sea; young and had nothing, on the sea that gives nothing, except hard knocks—and sometimes a chance to feel your strength—that only—what you all regret?"

And we all nodded at him: the man of finance, the man of accounts, the man of law, we all nodded at him over the polished table that like a still sheet of brown water reflected our faces, lined, wrinkled; our faces marked by toil, by deceptions, by success, by love; our weary eyes looking still, looking always, looking anxiously for something out of life, that while it is expected is already gone—has passed unseen, in a sigh, in a flash—together with the youth, with the strength, with the romance of illusions.

Joseph Conrad

AN OUTPOST OF PROGRESS

THERE were two white men in charge of the trading station. Kayerts, the chief, was short and fat; Carlier, the assistant, was tall, with a large head and a very broad trunk perched upon a long pair of thin legs. The third man on the staff was a Sierra Leone nigger, who maintained that his name was Henry Price. However, for some reason or other, the natives down the river had given him the name of Makola, and it stuck to him through all his wanderings about the country. He spoke English and French with a warbling accent, wrote a beautiful hand, understood bookkeeping, and cherished in his innermost heart the worship of evil spirits. His wife was a negress from Loanda, very large and very noisy. Three children rolled about in sunshine before the door of his low, shed-like dwelling. Makola, taciturn and impenetrable, despised the two white men. He had charge of a small clay storehouse with a dried-grass roof, and pretended to keep a correct account of beads, cotton cloth, red kerchiefs, brass wire, and other trade goods it contained. Besides the storehouse and Makola's hut, there was only one large building in the cleared ground of the station. It was built neatly of reeds, with a verandah on all the four sides. There were three rooms in it. The one in the middle was the living-room, and had two rough tables and a few stools in it. The other two were the bedrooms for the white men. Each had a bedstead and a mosquito net for all furniture. The plank floor was littered with the belongings of the white men; open half-empty boxes, torn wearing apparel, old boots; all the things dirty, and all the things broken, that accumulate mysteriously round untidy men. There was also another dwelling-place some distance away from the buildings. In it, under a tall cross much out of the perpendicular,

177

slept the man who had seen the beginning of all this; who had
planned and had watched the construction of this outpost
of progress. He had been, at home, an unsuccessful painter
who, weary of pursuing fame on an empty stomach, had gone
out there through high protections. He had been the first
chief of that station. Makola had watched the energetic artist
die of fever in the just finished house with his usual kind of
"I told you so" indifference. Then, for a time, he dwelt alone
with his family, his account books, and the Evil Spirit that
rules the lands under the equator. He got on very well with
his god. Perhaps he had propitiated him by a promise of
more white men to play with, by and by. At any rate the
director of the Great Trading Company, coming up in a
steamer that resembled an enormous sardine box with a flat-
roofed shed erected on it, found the station in good order, and
Makola as usual quietly diligent. The director had the cross
put up over the first agent's grave, and appointed Kayerts to
the post. Carlier was told off as second in charge. The director
was a man ruthless and efficient, who at times, but very imperceptibly, indulged in grim humour. He made a speech to
Kayerts and Carlier, pointing out to them the promising
aspect of their station. The nearest trading-post was about
three hundred miles away. It was an exceptional opportunity
for them to distinguish themselves and to earn percentages on
the trade. This appointment was a favour done to beginners.
Kayerts was moved almost to tears by his director's kindness.
He would, he said, by doing his best, try to justify the flattering confidence, &c., &c. Kayerts had been in the Administration of the Telegraphs, and knew how to express himself
correctly. Carlier, an ex-non-commissioned officer of cavalry
in an army guaranteed from harm by several European
Powers, was less impressed. If there were commissions to get,
so much the better; and, trailing a sulky glance over the river,
the forests, the impenetrable bush that seemed to cut off the
station from the rest of the world, he muttered between his
teeth, "We shall see, very soon."

Next day, some bales of cotton goods and a few cases of
provisions having been thrown on shore, the sardine-box
steamer went off, not to return for another six months. On
the deck the director touched his cap to the two agents, who
stood on the bank waving their hats, and turning to an old
servant of the Company on his passage to headquarters, said,

"Look at those two imbeciles. They must be mad at home to send me such specimens. I told those fellows to plant a vegetable garden, build new storehouses and fences, and construct a landing-stage. I bet nothing will be done! They won't know how to begin. I always thought the station on this river useless, and they just fit the station!"

"They will form themselves there," said the old stager with a quiet smile.

"At any rate, I am rid of them for six months," retorted the director.

The two men watched the steamer round the bend, then, ascending arm in arm the slope of the bank, returned to the station. They had been in this vast and dark country only a very short time, and as yet always in the midst of other white men, under the eye and guidance of their superiors. And now, dull as they were to the subtle influences of surroundings, they felt themselves very much alone, when suddenly left unassisted to face the wilderness; a wilderness rendered more strange, more incomprehensible by the mysterious glimpses of the vigorous life it contained. They were two perfectly insignificant and incapable individuals, whose existence is only rendered possible through the high organization of civilized crowds. Few men realize that their life, the very essence of their character, their capabilities and their audacities, are only the expression of their belief in the safety of their surroundings. The courage, the composure, the confidence; the emotions and principles; every great and every insignificant thought belongs not to the individual but to the crowd: to the crowd that believes blindly in the irresistible force of its institutions and of its morals, in the power of its police and of its opinion. But the contact with pure unmitigated savagery, with primitive nature and primitive man, brings sudden and profound trouble into the heart. To the sentiment of being alone of one's kind, to the clear perception of the loneliness of one's thoughts, of one's sensations—to the negation of the habitual, which is safe, there is added the affirmation of the unusual, which is dangerous; a suggestion of things vague, uncontrollable, and repulsive, whose discomposing intrusion excites the imagination and tries the civilized nerves of the foolish and the wise alike.

Kayerts and Carlier walked arm in arm, drawing close to one another as children do in the dark; and they had the same,

not altogether unpleasant, sense of danger which one half
suspects to be imaginary. They chatted persistently in familiar
tones. "Our station is prettily situated," said one. The other
assented with enthusiasm, enlarging volubly on the beauties
of the situation. Then they passed near the grave. "Poor
devil!" said Kayerts. "He died of fever, didn't he?" muttered
Carlier, stopping short. "Why," retorted Kayerts, with indignation, "I've been told that the fellow exposed himself
recklessly to the sun. The climate here, everybody says, is not
at all worse than at home, as long as you keep out of the sun.
Do you hear that, Carlier? I am chief here, and my orders are
that you should not expose yourself to the sun!" He assumed
his superiority jocularly, but his meaning was serious. The
idea that he would, perhaps, have to bury Carlier and remain
alone, gave him an inward shiver. He felt suddenly that this
Carlier was more precious to him here, in the centre of Africa,
than a brother could be anywhere else. Carlier, entering into
the spirit of the thing, made a military salute and answered
in a brisk tone, "Your orders shall be attended to, chief!"
Then he burst out laughing, slapped Kayerts on the back and
shouted, "We shall let life run easily here! Just sit still and
gather in the ivory those savages will bring. This country
has its good points, after all!" They both laughed loudly
while Carlier thought: "That poor Kayerts; he is so fat and
unhealthy. It would be awful if I had to bury him here. He is
a man I respect." . . . Before they reached the verandah
of their house they called one another "my dear fellow."

The first day they were very active, pottering about with
hammers and nails and red calico, to put up curtains, make
their house habitable and pretty; resolved to settle down comfortably to their new life. For them an impossible task. To
grapple effectually with even purely material problems requires more serenity of mind and more lofty courage than
people generally imagine. No two beings could have been
more unfitted for such a struggle. Society, not from any
tenderness, but because of its strange needs, had taken care of
those two men, forbidding them all independent thought, all
initiative, all departure from routine; and forbidding it under
pain of death. They could only live on condition of being
machines. And now, released from the fostering care of men
with pens behind the ears, or of men with gold lace on the

sleeves, they were like those lifelong prisoners who, liberated after many years, do not know what use to make of their freedom. They did not know what use to make of their faculties, being both, through want of practice, incapable of independent thought.

At the end of two months Kayerts often would say, "If it was not for my Melie, you wouldn't catch me here." Melie was his daughter. He had thrown up his post in the Administration of the Telegraphs, though he had been for seventeen years perfectly happy there, to earn a dowry for his girl. His wife was dead, and the child was being brought up by his sisters. He regretted the streets, the pavements, the cafés, his friends of many years; all the things he used to see, day after day; all the thoughts suggested by familiar things— the thoughts effortless, monotonous, and soothing of a Government clerk; he regretted all the gossip, the small enmities, the mild venom, and the little jokes of Government offices. "If I had had a decent brother-in-law," Carlier would remark, "a fellow with a heart, I would not be here." He had left the army and had made himself so obnoxious to his family by his laziness and impudence, that an exasperated brother-in-law had made superhuman efforts to procure him an appointment in the Company as a second-class agent. Having not a penny in the world he was compelled to accept this means of livelihood as soon as it became quite clear to him that there was nothing more to squeeze out of his relations. He, like Kayerts, regretted his old life. He regretted the clink of sabre and spurs on a fine afternoon, the barrack-room witticisms, the girls of garrison towns; but, besides, he had also a sense of grievance. He was evidently a much ill-used man. This made him moody, at times. But the two men got on well together in the fellowship of their stupidity and laziness. Together they did nothing, absolutely nothing, and enjoyed the sense of the idleness for which they were paid. And in time they came to feel something resembling affection for one another.

They lived like blind men in a large room, aware only of what came in contact with them (and of that only imperfectly), but unable to see the general aspect of things. The river, the forest, all the great land throbbing with life, were like a great emptiness. Even the brilliant sunshine disclosed nothing intelligible. Things appeared and disappeared before their eyes

in an unconnected and aimless kind of way. The river seemed
to come from nowhere and flow nowhither. It flowed through a
void. Out of that void, at times, came canoes, and men with
spears in their hands would suddenly crowd the yard of the
station. They were naked, glossy black, ornamented with
snowy shells and glistening brass wire, perfect of limb. They
made an uncouth babbling noise when they spoke, moved in a
stately manner, and sent quick, wild glances out of their
startled, never-resting eyes. Those warriors would squat in
long rows, four or more deep, before the verandah, while their
chiefs bargained for hours with Makola over an elephant tusk.
Kayerts sat on his chair and looked down on the proceedings,
understanding nothing. He stared at them with his round blue
eyes, called out to Carlier, "Here, look! look at that fellow
there—and that other one, to the left. Did you ever see such
a face? Oh, the funny brute!"

Carlier, smoking native tobacco in a short wooden pipe,
would swagger up twirling his moustaches, and surveying the
warriors with haughty indulgence, would say—

"Fine animals. Brought any bone? Yes? It's not any too
soon. Look at the muscles of that fellow—third from the end.
I wouldn't care to get a punch on the nose from him. Fine
arms, but legs no good below the knee. Couldn't make cavalry
men of them." And after glancing down complacently at his
own shanks, he always concluded: "Pah! Don't they stink!
You, Makola! Take that herd over to the fetish" (the storehouse was in every station called the fetish, perhaps because
of the spirit of civilization it contained) "and give them up
some of the rubbish you keep there. I'd rather see it full of
bone than full of rags."

Kayerts approved.

"Yes, yes! Go and finish that palaver over there, Mr.
Makola. I will come round when you are ready, to weigh the
tusk. We must be careful." Then turning to his companion:
"This is the tribe that lives down the river; they are rather
aromatic. I remember, they had been once before here. D'ye
hear that row? What a fellow has got to put up with in this
dog of a country! My head is split."

Such profitable visits were rare. For days the two pioneers
of trade and progress would look on their empty courtyard
in the vibrating brilliance of vertical sunshine. Below the high
bank, the silent river flowed on glittering and steady. On

the sands in the middle of the stream, hippos and alligators sunned themselves side by side. And stretching away in all directions, surrounding the insignificant cleared spot of the trading post, immense forests, hiding fateful complications of fantastic life, lay in the eloquent silence of mute greatness. The two men understood nothing, cared for nothing but for the passage of days that separated them from the steamer's return. Their predecessor had left some torn books. They took up these wrecks of novels, and, as they had never read anything of the kind before, they were surprised and amused. Then during long days there were interminable and silly discussions about plots and personages. In the centre of Africa they made acquaintance of Richelieu and of d'Artagnan, of Hawk's Eye and of Father Goriot, and of many other people. All these imaginary personages became subjects for gossip as if they had been living friends. They discounted their virtues, suspected their motives, decried their successes; were scandalized at their duplicity or were doubtful about their courage. The accounts of crimes filled them with indignation, while tender or pathetic passages moved them deeply. Carlier cleared his throat and said in a soldierly voice, "What nonsense!" Kayerts, his round eyes suffused with tears, his fat cheeks quivering, rubbed his bald head, and declared, "This is a splendid book. I had no idea there were such clever fellows in the world." They also found some old copies of a home paper. That print discussed what it was pleased to call "Our Colonial Expansion" in high-flown language. It spoke much of the rights and duties of civilization, of the sacredness of the civilizing work, and extolled the merits of those who went about bringing light, and faith and commerce to the dark places of the earth. Carlier and Kayerts read, wondered, and began to think better of themselves. Carlier said one evening, waving his hand about, "In a hundred years, there will be perhaps a town here. Quays, and warehouses, and barracks, and—and—billiard-rooms. Civilization, my boy, and virtue—and all. And then, chaps will read that two good fellows, Kayerts and Carlier, were the first civilized men to live in this very spot!" Kayerts nodded, "Yes, it is a consolation to think of that." They seemed to forget their dead predecessor; but, early one day, Carlier went out and replanted the cross firmly. "It used to make me squint whenever I walked that way," he explained to Kayerts over the morning coffee.

"It made me squint, leaning over so much. So I just planted
it upright. And solid, I promise you! I suspended myself
with both hands to the cross-piece. Not a move. Oh, I did that
properly."

At times Gobila came to see them. Gobila was the chief of
the neighbouring villages. He was a gray-headed savage, thin
and black, with a white cloth round his loins and a mangy
panther skin hanging over his back. He came up with long
strides of his skeleton legs, swinging a staff as tall as himself,
and, entering the common room of the station, would squat on
his heels to the left of the door. There he sat, watching Kayerts,
and now and then making a speech which the other did not
understand. Kayerts, without interrupting his occupation,
would from time to time say in a friendly manner: "How goes
it, you old image?" and they would smile at one another. The
two whites had a liking for that old and incomprehensible creature, and called him Father Gobila. Gobila's manner was pater-
nal, and he seemed really to love all white men. They all
appeared to him very young, indistinguishably alike (except
for stature), and he knew that they were all brothers, and also
immortal. The death of the artist, who was the first white man
whom he knew intimately, did not disturb this belief, because
he was firmly convinced that the white stranger had pretended
to die and got himself buried for some mysterious purpose of
his own, into which it was useless to inquire. Perhaps it was his
way of going home to his own country? At any rate, these were
his brothers, and he transferred his absurd affection to them.
They returned it in a way. Carlier slapped him on the back,
and recklessly struck off matches for his amusement. Kayerts
was always ready to let him have a sniff at the ammonia bottle.
In short, they behaved just like that other white creature that
had hidden itself in a hole in the ground. Gobila considered
them attentively. Perhaps they were the same being with the
other—or one of them was. He couldn't decide—clear up that
mystery; but he remained always very friendly. In consequence
of that friendship the women of Gobila's village walked in
single file through the reedy grass, bringing every morning
to the station, fowls, and sweet potatoes, and palm wine, and
sometimes a goat. The Company never provisions the stations
fully, and the agents required those local supplies to live. They
had them through the good-will of Gobila, and lived well. Now
and then one of them had a bout of fever, and the other nursed

him with gentle devotion. They did not think much of it. It left them weaker, and their appearance changed for the worse. Carlier was hollow-eyed and irritable. Kayerts showed a drawn, flabby face above the rotundity of his stomach, which gave him a weird aspect. But being constantly together, they did not notice the change that took place gradually in their appearance, and also in their dispositions. Five months passed in that way.

Then, one morning, as Kayerts and Carlier, lounging in their chairs under the verandah, talked about the approaching visit of the steamer, a knot of armed men came out of the forest and advanced towards the station. They were strangers to that part of the country. They were tall, slight, draped classically from neck to heel in blue fringed cloths, and carried percussion muskets over their bare right shoulders. Makola showed signs of excitement, and ran out of the storehouse (where he spent all his days) to meet these visitors. They came into the courtyard and looked about them with steady, scornful glances. Their leader, a powerful and determined-looking negro with bloodshot eyes, stood in front of the verandah and made a long speech. He gesticulated much, and ceased very suddenly.

There was something in his intonation, in the sounds of the long sentences he used, that startled the two whites. It was like a reminiscence of something not exactly familiar, and yet resembling the speech of civilized men. It sounded like one of those impossible languages which sometimes we hear in our dreams.

"What lingo is that?" said the amazed Carlier. "In the first moment I fancied the fellow was going to speak French. Anyway, it is a different kind of gibberish to what we ever heard."

"Yes," replied Kayerts. "Hey, Makola, what does he say? Where do they come from? Who are they?"

But Makola, who seemed to be standing on hot bricks, answered hurriedly, "I don't know. They come from very far. Perhaps Mrs. Price will understand. They are perhaps bad men."

The leader, after waiting for a while, said something sharply to Makola, who shook his head. Then the man, after looking round, noticed Makola's hut and walked over there. The next moment Mrs. Makola was heard speaking with great volubility. The other strangers—they were six in all—strolled about with an air of ease, put their heads through the door of the store room, congregated round the grave, pointed understandingly at the cross, and generally made themselves at home.

"I don't like those chaps—and, I say, Kayerts, they must be from the coast; they've got firearms," observed the sagacious Carlier.

Kayerts also did not like those chaps. They both, for the first time, became aware that they lived in conditions where the unusual may be dangerous, and that there was no power on earth outside of themselves to stand between them and the unusual. They became uneasy, went in and loaded their revolvers. Kayerts said, "We must order Makola to tell them to go away before dark."

The strangers left in the afternoon, after eating a meal prepared for them by Mrs. Makola. The immense woman was excited, and talked much with the visitors. She rattled away shrilly, pointing here and there at the forests and at the river. Makola sat apart and watched. At times he got up and whispered to his wife. He accompanied the strangers across the ravine at the back of the station-ground, and returned slowly looking very thoughtful. When questioned by the white men he was very strange, seemed not to understand, seemed to have forgotten French—seemed to have forgotten how to speak altogether. Kayerts and Carlier agreed that the nigger had had too much palm wine.

There was some talk about keeping a watch in turn, but in the evening everything seemed so quiet and peaceful that they retired as usual. All night they were disturbed by a lot of drumming in the villages. A deep, rapid roll near by would be followed by another far off—then all ceased. Soon short appeals would rattle out here and there, then all mingle together, increase, become vigorous and sustained, would spread out over the forest, roll through the night, unbroken and ceaseless, near and far, as if the whole land had been one immerse drum booming out steadily an appeal to heaven. And through the deep and tremendous noise sudden yells that resembled snatches of songs from a madhouse darted shrill and high in discordant jets of sound which seemed to rush far above the earth and drive all peace from under the stars.

Carlier and Kayerts slept badly. They both thought they had heard shots fired during the night—but they could not agree as to the direction. In the morning Makola was gone somewhere. He returned about noon with one of yesterday's strangers, and eluded all Kayerts' attempts to close with him: had become deaf apparently. Kayerts wondered. Carlier, who had been fishing off the bank, came back and remarked while he showed his catch, "The niggers seem to be in a deuce of a stir; I wonder what's up. I saw about fifteen canoes cross the river during the two hours I was there fishing." Kayerts, worried, said, "Isn't this Makola very queer to-day?" Carlier advised, "Keep all our men together in case of some trouble."

II

THERE were ten station men who had been left by the Director. Those fellows, having engaged themselves to the Company for six months (without having any idea of a month in particular and only a very faint notion of time in general), had been serving the cause of progress for upwards of two years. Belonging to a tribe from a very distant part of the land of darkness and sorrow, they did not run away, naturally supposing that as wandering strangers they would be killed by the inhabitants of the country; in which they were right. They lived in straw huts on the slope of a ravine overgrown with reedy grass, just behind the station buildings. They were not happy, regretting the festive incantations, the sorceries, the human sacrifices of their own land; where they also had parents, brothers, sisters, admired chiefs, respected magicians, loved friends, and other ties supposed generally to be human. Besides, the rice rations served out by the Company did not agree with them, being a food unknown to their land, and to which they could not get used. Consequently they were unhealthy and miserable. Had they been of any other tribe they would have made up their minds to die—for nothing is easier to certain savages than suicide—and so have escaped from the puzzling difficulties of existence. But belonging, as they did, to a warlike tribe with filed teeth, they had more grit, and went on stupidly living through disease and sorrow. They did very little work, and had lost their splendid physique. Carlier and Kayerts doctored them assiduously without being able to bring them back into condition again. They were mustered every morning and told off to different tasks—grass-cutting, fence-building, tree-felling, &c., &c., which no power on earth could induce them to execute efficiently. The two whites had practically very little control over them.

In the afternoon Makola came over to the big house and found Kayerts watching three heavy columns of smoke rising above the forests. "What is that?" asked Kayerts. "Some villages burn," answered Makola, who seemed to have regained his wits. Then he said abruptly: "We have got very little ivory; bad six months' trading. Do you like get a little more ivory?"

"Yes," said Kayerts, eagerly. He thought of percentages which were low.

"Those men who came yesterday are traders from Loanda who have got more ivory than they can carry home. Shall I buy? I know their camp."

"Certainly," said Kayerts. "What are those traders?"

"Bad fellows," said Makola, indifferently. "They fight with people, and catch women and children. They are bad men, and got guns. There is a great disturbance in the country. Do you want ivory?"

"Yes," said Kayerts. Makola said nothing for a while. Then: "Those workmen of ours are no good at all," he muttered, looking round. "Station in very bad order, sir. Director will growl. Better get a fine lot of ivory, then he say nothing."

"I can't help it; the men won't work," said Kayerts. "When will you get that ivory?"

"Very soon," said Makola. "Perhaps to-night. You leave it to me, and keep indoors, sir. I think you had better give some palm wine to our men to make a dance this evening. Enjoy themselves. Work better to-morrow. There's plenty palm wine —gone a little sour."

Kayerts said "yes," and Makola, with his own hands, carried big calabashes to the door of his hut. They stood there till the evening, and Mrs. Makola looked into every one. The men got them at sunset. When Kayerts and Carlier retired, a big bonfire was flaring before the men's huts. They could hear their shouts and drumming. Some men from Gobila's village had joined the station hands, and the entertainment was a great success.

In the middle of the night, Carlier waking suddenly, heard a man shout loudly; then a shot was fired. Only one. Carlier ran out and met Kayerts on the verandah. They were both startled. As they went across the yard to call Makola, they saw shadows moving in the night. One of them cried, "Don't shoot! It's me, Price." Then Makola appeared close to them. "Go back, go back, please," he urged, "you spoil all." "There are strange men about," said Carlier. "Never mind; I know," said Makola. Then he whispered, "All right. Bring ivory. Say nothing! I know my business." The two white men reluctantly went back to the house, but did not sleep. They heard footsteps, whispers, some groans. It seemed as if a lot of men came in, dumped heavy things on the ground, squabbled a long time, then went away. They lay on their hard beds and thought: "This Makola is invaluable." In the morning Carlier came out, very sleepy, and pulled at the cord of the big bell. The station hands mustered every morning to the sound of the bell. That morning nobody came. Kayerts turned out also, yawning. Across the yard they saw Makola come out of his hut, a tin basin of soapy water in his hand. Makola, a civilized nigger, was very neat in his person. He threw the soapsuds skilfully over a wretched little yellow cur he had, then turning his face to the agent's house, he shouted from the distance, "All the men gone last night!"

They heard him plainly, but in their surprise they both yelled out together: "What!" Then they stared at one another. "We are in a proper fix now," growled Carlier. "It's incredible!" muttered Kayerts. "I will go to the huts and see," said Carlier, striding off. Makola coming up found Kayerts standing alone.

"I can hardly believe it," said Kayerts, tearfully. "We took care of them as if they had been our children."

"They went with the coast people," said Makola after a moment of hesitation.

"What do I care with whom they went—the ungrateful brutes!" exclaimed the other. Then with sudden suspicion, and looking hard at Makola, he added: "What do you know about it?"

Makola moved his shoulders, looking down on the ground. "What do I know? I think only. Will you come and look at the ivory I've got there? It is a fine lot. You never saw such."

He moved towards the store. Kayerts followed him mechanically, thinking about the incredible desertion of the men. On the ground before the door of the fetish lay six splendid tusks. "What did you give for it?" asked Kayerts, after surveying the lot with satisfaction.

"No regular trade," said Makola. "They brought the ivory and gave it to me. I told them to take what they most wanted in the station. It is a beautiful lot. No station can show such tusks. Those traders wanted carriers badly, and our men were no good here. No trade, no entry in books; all correct."

Kayerts nearly burst with indignation. "Why!" he shouted, "I believe you have sold our men for these tusks!" Makola stood impassive and silent. "I—I—will—I," stuttered Kayerts. "You fiend!" he yelled out.

"I did the best for you and the Company," said Makola, imperturbably. "Why you shout so much? Look at this tusk."

"I dismiss you! I will report you—I won't look at the tusk. I forbid you to touch them. I order you to throw them into the river. You—you!"

"You very red, Mr. Kayerts. If you are so irritable in the sun, you will get fever and die—like the first chief!" pronounced Makola impressively.

They stood still, contemplating one another with intense eyes, as if they had been looking with effort across immense distances. Kayerts shivered. Makola had meant no more than he said, but his words seemed to Kayerts full of ominous menace! He turned sharply and went away to the house. Makola retired into the bosom of his family; and the tusks, left lying before the store, looked very large and valuable in the sunshine.

Carlier came back on the verandah. "They're all gone, hey?" asked Kayerts from the far end of the common room in a muffled voice. "You did not find anybody?"

"Oh, yes," said Carlier, "I found one of Gobila's people lying dead before the huts—shot through the body. We heard that shot last night."

Kayerts came out quickly. He found his companion staring grimly over the yard at the tusks, away by the store. They both sat in silence for a while. Then Kayerts related his conversation with Makola. Carlier said nothing. At the midday meal they ate very little. They hardly exchanged a word that day. A great silence seemed to lie heavily over the station and press on their lips. Makola did not open the store; he spent the day playing with his children. He lay full-length on a mat outside his door, and the youngsters sat on his chest and clambered all over him. It was a touching picture. Mrs. Makola was busy cooking all day as usual. The white men made a somewhat better meal in the evening. Afterwards, Carlier smoking his pipe strolled over to the store; he stood for a long time over the tusks, touched one or two with his foot, even tried to lift the largest one by its small end. He came back to his chief, who had not stirred from the verandah, threw himself in the chair and said—

"I can see it! They were pounced upon while they slept heavily after drinking all that palm wine you've allowed Makolo to give them. A put-up job! See? The worst is, some of Gobila's people were there, and got carried off too, no doubt. The least drunk woke up, and got shot for his sobriety. This is a funny country. What will you do now?"

"We can't touch it, of course," said Kayerts.

"Of course not," assented Carlier.

"Slavery is an awful thing," stammered out Kayerts in an unsteady voice.

"Frightful—the sufferings," grunted Carlier with conviction.

They believed their words. Everybody shows a respectful deference to certain sounds that he and his fellows can make. But about feelings people really know nothing. We talk with indignation or enthusiasm; we talk about oppression, cruelty, crime, devotion, self-sacrifice, virtue, and we know nothing real beyond the words. Nobody knows what suffering or sacrifice means—except, perhaps the victims of the mysterious purpose of these illusions.

Next morning they saw Makola very busy setting up in the yard the big scales used for weighing ivory. By and by Carlier said: "What's that filthy scoundrel up to?" and lounged out into the yard. Kayerts followed. They stood watching. Makola took no notice. When the balance was swung true, he tried to lift a tusk into the scale. It was too heavy. He looked up helplessly without a word, and for a minute they stood round that balance as mute and still as three statues. Suddenly Carlier said: "Catch hold of the other end, Makola—you beast!" and together they swung the tusk up. Kayerts trembled in every limb. He muttered, "I say! O! I say!" and putting his hand in his pocket found there a dirty bit of paper and the stump of a pencil. He turned his back on the others, as if about to do

something tricky, and noted stealthily the weights which
Carlier shouted out to him with unnecessary loudness. When
all was over Makola whispered to himself: "The sun's very
strong here for the tusks." Carlier said to Kayerts in a careless tone: "I say, chief, I might just as well give him a lift
with this lot into the store."

As they were going back to the house Kayerts observed with
a sigh: "It had to be done." And Carlier said: "It's deplorable,
but, the men being Company's men the ivory is Company's
ivory. We must look after it." "I will report to the Director, of
course," said Kayerts. "Of course; let him decide," approved
Carlier.

At midday they made a hearty meal. Kayerts sighed from
time to time. Whenever they mentioned Makola's name they
always added to it an opprobrious epithet. It eased their conscience. Makola gave himself a half-holiday, and bathed his
children in the river. No one from Gobila's villages came near
the station that day. No one came the next day, and the
next, nor for a whole week. Gobila's people might have been
dead and buried for any sign of life they gave. But they were
only mourning for those they had lost by the witchcraft of
white men, who had brought wicked people into their country.
The wicked people were gone, but fear remained. Fear always
remains. A man may destroy everything within himself, love
and hate and belief, and even doubt; but as long as he clings
to life he cannot destroy fear: the fear, subtle, indestructible,
and terrible, that pervades his being; that tinges his thoughts;
that lurks in his heart; that watches on his lips the struggle
of his last breath. In his fear, the mild old Gobila offered extra
human sacrifices to all the Evil Spirits that had taken possession of his white friends. His heart was heavy. Some warriors
spoke about burning and killing, but the cautious old savage
dissuaded them. Who could foresee the woe those mysterious
creatures, if irritated, might bring? They should be left alone.
Perhaps in time they would disappear into the earth as the first
one had disappeared. His people must keep away from them,
and hope for the best.

Kayerts and Carlier did not disappear, but remained above
on this earth, that, somehow, they fancied had become bigger
and very empty. It was not the absolute and dumb solitude of
the post that impressed them so much as an inarticulate feeling
that something from within them was gone, something that

vorked for their safety, and had kept the wilderness from interfering with their hearts. The images of home; the memory of
people like them, of men that thought and felt as they used to
think and feel, receded into distances made indistinct by the
glare of unclouded sunshine. And out of the great silence of
the surrounding wilderness, its very hopelessness and savagery
seemed to approach them nearer, to draw them gently, to look
upon them, to envelop them with a solicitude irresistible,
familiar, and disgusting.

Days lengthened into weeks, then into months. Gobila's
people drummed and yelled to every new moon, as of yore, but
kept away from the station. Makola and Carlier tried once in
a canoe to open communications, but were received with a
shower of arrows, and had to fly back to the station for dear
life. That attempt set the country up and down the river into
an uproar that could be very distinctly heard for days. The
steamer was late. At first they spoke of delay jauntily, then
anxiously, then gloomily. The matter was becoming serious.
Stores were running short. Carlier cast his lines off the bank,
but the river was low, and the fish kept out in the stream.
They dared not stroll far away from the station to shoot.
Moreover, there was no game in the impenetrable forest. Once
Carlier shot a hippo in the river. They had no boat to secure it,
and it sank. When it floated up it drifted away, and Gobila's
people secured the carcase. It was the occasion for a national
holiday, but Carlier had a fit of rage over it and talked about
the necessity of exterminating all the niggers before the country could be made habitable. Kayerts mooned about silently;
spent hours looking at the portrait of his Melie. It represented
a little girl with long bleached tresses and a rather sour face.
His legs were much swollen, and he could hardly walk. Carlier,
undermined by fever, could not swagger any more, but kept
tottering about, still with a devil-may-care air, as became a
man who remembered his crack regiment. He had become
hoarse, sarcastic, and inclined to say unpleasant things. He
called it "being frank with you." They had long ago reckoned
their percentages on trade, including in them that last deal of
"this infamous Makola." They had also concluded not to say
anything about it. Kayerts hesitated at first—was afraid of
the Director.

"He has seen worse things done on the quiet," maintained
Carlier, with a hoarse laugh. "Trust him! He won't thank you

if you blab. He is no better than you or me. Who will talk if we hold our tongues? There is nobody here."

That was the root of the trouble! There was nobody there; and being left there alone with their weakness, they became daily more like a pair of accomplices than like a couple of devoted friends. They had heard nothing from home for eight months. Every evening they said, "To-morrow we shall see the steamer." But one of the Company's steamers had been wrecked, and the Director was busy with the other, relieving very distant and important stations on the main river. He thought that the useless station, and the useless men, could wait. Meantime Kayerts and Carlier lived on rice boiled without salt, and cursed the Company, all Africa, and the day they were born. One must have lived on such diet to discover what ghastly trouble the necessity of swallowing one's food may become. There was literally nothing else in the station but rice and coffee; they drank the coffee without sugar. The last fifteen lumps Kayerts had solemnly locked away in his box, together with a half-bottle of Cognâc, "in case of sickness," he explained. Carlier approved. "When one is sick," he said, "any little extra like that is cheering."

They waited. Rank grass began to sprout over the courtyard. The bell never rang now. Days passed, silent, exasperating, and slow. When the two men spoke, they snarled; and their silences were bitter, as if tinged by the bitterness of their thoughts.

One day after a lunch of boiled rice, Carlier put down his cup untasted, and said: "Hang it all! Let's have a decent cup of coffee for once. Bring out that sugar, Kayerts!"

"For the sick," muttered Kayerts, without looking up.

"For the sick," mocked Carlier. "Bosh! . . . Well! I am sick."

"You are no more sick than I am, and I go without," said Kayerts in a peaceful tone.

"Come! out with that sugar, you stingy old slave-dealer."

Kayerts looked up quickly. Carlier was smiling with marked insolence. And suddenly it seemed to Kayerts that he had never seen that man before. Who was he? He knew nothing about him. What was he capable of? There was a surprising flash of violent emotion within him, as if in the presence of something undreamt-of, dangerous, and final. But he managed to pronounce with composure—

"That joke is in very bad taste. Don't repeat it."

"Joke!" said Carlier, hitching himself forward on his seat. "I am hungry—I am sick—I don't joke! I hate hypocrites. You are a hypocrite. You are a slave-dealer. I am a slave-dealer. There's nothing but slave-dealers in this cursed country. I mean to have sugar in my coffee to-day, anyhow!"

"I forbid you to speak to me in that way," said Kayerts with a fair show of resolution.

"You!—What?" shouted Carlier, jumping up.

Kayerts stood up also. "I am your chief," he began, trying to master the shakiness of his voice.

"What?" yelled the other. "Who's chief? There's no chief here. There's nothing here: there's nothing but you and I. Fetch the sugar—you pot-bellied ass."

"Hold your tongue. Go out of this room," screamed Kayerts. "I dismiss you—you scoundrel!"

Carlier swung a stool. All at once he looked dangerously in earnest. "You flabby, good-for-nothing civilian—take that!" he howled.

Kayerts dropped under the table, and the stool struck the grass inner wall of the room. Then, as Carlier was trying to upset the table, Kayerts in desperation made a blind rush, head low, like a cornered pig would do, and over-turning his friend, bolted along the verandah, and into his room. He locked the door, snatched his revolver, and stood panting. In less than a minute Carlier was kicking at the door furiously, howling, "If you don't bring out that sugar, I will shoot you at sight, like a dog. Now then—one—two—three. You won't? I will show you who's the master."

Kayerts thought the door would fall in, and scrambled through the square hole that served for a window in his room. There was then the whole breadth of the house between them. But the other was apparently not strong enough to break in the door, and Kayerts heard him running round. Then he also began to run laboriously on his swollen legs. He ran as quickly as he could, grasping the revolver, and unable yet to understand what was happening to him. He saw in succession Makola's house, the store, the river, the ravine, and the low bushes; and he saw all those things again as he ran for the second time round the house. Then again they flashed past him. That morning he could not have walked a yard without a groan.

And now he ran. He ran fast enough to keep out of sight of
the other man.

Then as, weak and desperate, he thought, "Before I finish
the next round I shall die," he heard the other man stumble
heavily, then stop. He stopped also. He had the back and
Carlier the front of the house, as before. He heard him drop
into a chair cursing, and suddenly his own legs gave way, and
he slid down into a sitting posture with his back to the wall.
His mouth was as dry as a cinder, and his face was wet with
perspiration—and tears. What was it all about? He thought it
must be a horrible illusion; he thought he was dreaming; he
thought he was going mad! After a while he collected his
senses. What did they quarrel about? That sugar! How absurd!
He would give it to him—didn't want it himself. And he began
scrambling to his feet with a sudden feeling of security. But
before he had fairly stood upright, a commonsense reflection
occurred to him and drove him back into despair. He thought:
"If I give way now to that brute of a soldier, he will begin this
horror again to-morrow—and the day after—every day—raise
other pretensions, trample on me, torture me, make me his
slave—and I will be lost! Lost! The steamer may not come for
days—may never come." He shook so that he had to sit down
on the floor again. He shivered forlornly. He felt he could not,
would not move any more. He was completely distracted by
the sudden perception that the position was without issue—
that death and life had in a moment become equally difficult
and terrible.

All at once he heard the other push his chair back; and he
leaped to his feet with extreme facility. He listened and got
confused. Must run again! Right or left? He heard footsteps.
He darted to the left, grasping his revolver, and at the very
same instant, as it seemed to him, they came into violent collision. Both shouted with surprise. A loud explosion took place
between them; a roar of red fire, thick smoke; and Kayerts,
deafened and blinded, rushed back thinking: "I am hit—it's
all over." He expected the other to come round—to gloat over
his agony. He caught hold of an upright of the roof—"All
over!" Then he heard a crashing fall on the other side of the
house, as if somebody had tumbled headlong over a chair—
then silence. Nothing more happened. He did not die. Only
his shoulder felt as if it had been badly wrenched, and he
had lost his revolver. He was disarmed and helpless! He waited

for his fate. The other man made no sound. It was a stratagem. He was stalking him now! Along what side? Perhaps he was taking aim this very minute!

After a few moments of an agony frightful and absurd, he decided to go and meet his doom. He was prepared for every surrender. He turned the corner, steadying himself with one hand on the wall; made a few paces, and nearly swooned. He had seen on the floor, protruding past the other corner, a pair of turned-up feet. A pair of white naked feet in red slippers. He felt deadly sick, and stood for a time in profound darkness. Then Makola appeared before him, saying quietly: "Come along, Mr. Kayerts. He is dead." He burst into tears of gratitude; a loud, sobbing fit of crying. After a time he found himself sitting in a chair and looking at Carlier, who lay stretched on his back. Makola was kneeling over the body.

"Is this your revolver?" asked Makola, getting up.

"Yes," said Kayerts; then he added very quickly, "He ran after me to shoot me—you saw!"

"Yes, I saw," said Makola. "There is only one revolver; where's his?"

"Don't know," whispered Kayerts in a voice that had become suddenly very faint.

"I will go and look for it," said the other, gently. He made the round along the verandah, while Kayerts sat still and looked at the corpse. Makola came back empty-handed, stood in deep thought, then stepped quietly into the dead man's room, and came out directly with a revolver, which he held up before Kayerts. Kayerts shut his eyes. Everything was going round. He found life more terrible and difficult than death. He had shot an unarmed man.

After meditating for a while, Makola said softly, pointing at the dead man who lay there with his right eye blown out—

"He died of fever." Kayerts looked at him with a stony stare. "Yes," repeated Makola, thoughtfully, stepping over the corpse, "I think he died of fever. Bury him to-morrow."

And he went away slowly to his expectant wife, leaving the two white men alone on the verandah.

Night came, and Kayerts sat unmoving on his chair. He sat quiet as if he had taken a dose of opium. The violence of the emotions he had passed through produced a feeling of exhausted serenity. He had plumbed in one short afternoon the depths of horror and despair, and now found repose in the

conviction that life had no more secrets for him: neither had
death! He sat by the corpse thinking; thinking very actively,
thinking very new thoughts. He seemed to have broken loose
from himself altogether. His old thoughts, convictions, likes
and dislikes, things he respected and things he abhorred, appeared in their true light at last! Appeared contemptible and
childish, false and ridiculous. He revelled in his new wisdom
while he sat by the man he had killed. He argued with himself
about all things under heaven with that kind of wrong-headed
lucidity which may be observed in some lunatics. Incidentally
he reflected that the fellow dead there had been a noxious beast
anyway; that men died every day in thousands; perhaps in
hundreds of thousands—who could tell?—and that in the number, that one death could not possibly make any difference;
couldn't have any importance, at least to a thinking creature.
He, Kayerts, was a thinking creature. He had been all his life,
till that moment, a believer in a lot of nonsense like the rest of
mankind—who are fools; but now he thought! He knew! He
was at peace; he was familiar with the highest wisdom! Then he
tried to imagine himself dead, and Carlier sitting in his chair
watching him; and his attempt met with such unexpected success, that in a very few moments he became not at all sure who
was dead and who was alive. This extraordinary achievement
of his fancy startled him, however, and by a clever and timely
effort of mind he saved himself just in time from becoming
Carlier. His heart thumped, and he felt hot all over at the
thought of that danger. Carlier! What a beastly thing! To
compose his now disturbed nerves—and no wonder!—he tried
to whistle a little. Then, suddenly, he fell asleep, or thought he
had slept; but at any rate there was a fog, and somebody had
whistled in the fog.

He stood up. The day had come, and a heavy mist had descended upon the land: the mist penetrating, enveloping, and
silent; the morning mist of tropical lands; the mist that clings
and kills; the mist white and deadly, immaculate and
poisonous. He stood up, saw the body, and threw his arms
above his head with a cry like that of a man who, waking from
a trance, finds himself immured forever in a tomb. "*Help!*
. . . . *My God!*"

A shriek inhuman, vibrating and sudden, pierced like a
sharp dart the white shroud of that land of sorrow. Three
short, impatient screeches followed, and then, for a time, the

fog-wreaths rolled on, undisturbed, through a formidable silence. Then many more shrieks, rapid and piercing, like the yells of some exasperated and ruthless creature, rent the air. Progress was calling to Kayerts from the river. Progress and civilization and all the virtues. Society was calling to its accomplished child to come, to be taken care of, to be instructed, to be judged, to be condemned; it called him to return to that rubbish heap from which he had wandered away, so that justice could be done.

Kayerts heard and understood. He stumbled out of the verandah, leaving the other man quite alone for the first time since they had been thrown there together. He groped his way through the fog, calling in his ignorance upon the invisible heaven to undo its work. Makola flitted by in the mist, shouting as he ran—

"Steamer! Steamer! They can't see. They whistle for the station. I go ring the bell. Go down to the landing, sir. I ring."

He disappeared. Kayerts stood still. He looked upwards; the fog rolled low over his head. He looked round like a man who has lost his way; and he saw a dark smudge, a cross-shaped stain, upon the shifting purity of the mist. As he began to stumble towards it, the station bell rang in a tumultuous peal its answer to the impatient clamour of the steamer.

The Managing Director of the Great Civilizing Company (since we know that civilization follows trade) landed first, and incontinently lost sight of the steamer. The fog down by the river was exceedingly dense; above, at the station, the bell rang unceasing and brazen.

The Director shouted loudly to the steamer:

"There is nobody down to meet us; there may be something wrong, though they are ringing. You had better come, too!"

And he began to toil up the steep bank. The captain and the engine-driver of the boat followed behind. As they scrambled up the fog thinned, and they could see their Director a good way ahead. Suddenly they saw him start forward, calling to them over his shoulder:—"Run! Run to the house! I've found one of them. Run, look for the other!"

He had found one of them! And even he, the man of varied and startling experience, was somewhat discomposed by the manner of this finding. He stood and fumbled in his pockets (for a knife) while he faced Kayerts, who was hanging by a leather strap from the cross. He had evidently climbed the grave, which was high and narrow, and after tying the end of the strap to the arm, had swung himself off. His toes were only a couple of inches above the ground; his arms hung stiffly down; he seemed to be standing rigidly at attention, but with one purple cheek playfully posed on the shoulder. And, irreverently, he was putting out a swollen tongue at his Managing Director.

Max Beerbohm

THE HAPPY HYPOCRITE

NONE, it is said, of all who revelled with the Regent, was half
so wicked as Lord George Hell. I will not trouble my little
readers with a long recital of his great naughtiness. But it
were well they should know that he was greedy, destructive,
and disobedient. I am afraid there is no doubt that he often
sat up at Carlton House until long after bed-time, playing at
games, and that he generally ate and drank more than was
good for him. His fondness for fine clothes was such that he
used to dress on week-days quite as gorgeously as good people
dress on Sundays. He was thirty-five years old and a great
grief to his parents.

And the worst of it was that he set such a bad example to
others. Never, never did he try to conceal his wrong-doing;
so that, in time, every one knew how horrid he was. In fact,
I think he was proud of being horrid. Captain Tarleton, in his
account of *Contemporary Bucks*, suggested that his lordship's great Candour was a virtue and should incline us to
forgive some of his abominable faults. But, painful as it is to
me to dissent from any opinion expressed by one who is now
dead, I hold that Candour is good only when it reveals good
actions or good sentiments, and that, when it reveals evil, itself
is evil, even also.

Lord George Hell did, at last, atone for all his faults, in a
way that was never revealed to the world during his life-time.
The reason of his strange and sudden disappearance from that
social sphere, in which he had so long moved and never moved
again, I will unfold. My little readers will then, I think, acknowledge that any angry judgment they may have passed
upon him must be reconsidered and, it may be, withdrawn. I
will leave his lordship in their hands. But my plea for him will
not be based upon that Candour of his, which some of his

friends so much admired. There were, yes! some so weak and so wayward as to think it a fine thing to have an historic title and no scruples. "Here comes George Hell," they would say, "How wicked my lord is looking!" *Noblesse oblige*, you see, and so an aristocrat should be very careful of his good name. Anonymous naughtiness does little harm.

It is pleasant to record that many persons were inobnoxious to the magic of his title and disapproved of him so strongly that, whenever he entered a room where they happened to be, they would make straight for the door and watch him very severely through the key-hole. Every morning when he strolled up Piccadilly they crossed over to the other side in a compact body, leaving him to the companionship of his bad companions on that which is still called the "shady" side. Lord George— σχετλιος—was quite indifferent to this demonstration. Indeed, he seemed wholly hardened, and when ladies gathered up their skirts as they passed him he would lightly appraise their ankles.

I am glad I never saw his lordship. They say he was rather like Caligula, with a dash of Sir John Falstaff, and that sometimes on wintry mornings in St. James's Street young children would hush their prattle and cling in disconsolate terror to their nurses' skirts as they saw him come (that vast and fearful gentleman!) with the east wind ruffling the rotund surface of his beaver, ruffling the fur about his neck and wrists, and striking the purple complexion of his cheeks to a still deeper purple. "King Bogey" they called him in the nurseries. In the hours when they too were naughty, their nurses would predict his advent down the chimney or from the linen-press, and then they always "behaved." So that, you see, even the unrighteous are a power for good, in the hands of nurses.

It is true that his lordship was a non-smoker—a negative virtue, certainly, and due, even that, I fear, to the fashion of the day—but there the list of his good qualities comes to an abrupt conclusion. He loved with an insatiable love the town and the pleasures of the town, whilst the ennobling influences of our English lakes were quite unknown to him. He used to boast that he had not seen a buttercup for twenty years, and once he called the country "a Fool's Paradise." London was the only place marked on the map of his mind. London gave him all he wished for. Is it not extraordinary to think that he had never spent a happy day nor a day of any kind in Follard Chase, that desirable mansion in Herts, which he had won from Sir Follard Follard, by a chuck of the dice, at Boodle's, on his seventeenth birthday? Always cynical and unkind, he had refused to give the broken baronet his "revenge." Always unkind and insolent, he had offered to instal him in the lodge —an offer which was, after a little hesitation, accepted. "On my soul, the man's place is a sinecure," Lord George would say; "he never has to open the gate for me."[1] So rust had covered the great iron gates of Follard Chase, and moss had covered its paths. The deer browsed upon its terraces. There were only wild flowers anywhere. Deep down among the weeds and water-lilies of the little stone-rimmed pond he had looked down upon, lay the marble faun, as he had fallen.

Of all the sins of his lordship's life surely not one was more wanton than his neglect of Follard Chase. Some whispered (nor did he ever trouble to deny) that he had won it by foul means, by loaded dice. Indeed no card-player in St. James's cheated more persistently than he. As he was rich and had no wife and family to support, and as his luck was always capital, I can offer no excuse for his conduct. At Carlton House, in the presence of many bishops and cabinet ministers, he once dunned the Regent most arrogantly for 5000 guineas out of which he had cheated him some months before, and went so far as to declare that he would not leave the house till he got it; whereupon His Royal Highness, with that unfailing tact for which he was ever famous, invited him to stay there as a guest, which, in fact, Lord George did, for several months. After this, we can hardly be surprised when we read that he "seldom sat down to the fashionable game of Limbo with less than four, and sometimes with *as many as seven aces* up his sleeve."[2] We can only wonder that he was tolerated at all.

At Garble's, that nightly resort of titled rips and roysterers, he usually spent the early part of his evenings. Round the illuminated garden, with La Gambogi, the dancer, on his arm and a Bacchic retinue at his heels, he would amble leisurely, clad in Georgian costume, which was not then, of course, fancy dress, as it is now.[3] Now and again, in the midst of his noisy

[1] *Lord Coleraine's Correspondence*, page 101.

[2] *Contemporary Bucks*, vol. 1, page 73.

[3] It would seem, however, that, on special occasions, his lordship indulged in odd costumes. "I have seen him," says Captain Tarleton (vol. 1, p. 69), "attired as a French clown, as a sailor, or in the crimson hose of a Sicilian grandee—*peu beau spectacle*. He never disguised his face, whatever his costume, however."

talk, he would crack a joke of the period, or break into a sentimental ballad, dance a little or pick a quarrel. When he tired of such fooling, he would proceed to his box in the tiny *al fresco* theatre and patronise the jugglers, pugilists, play-actors and whatever eccentric persons happened to be performing there.

The stars were splendid and the moon as beautiful as a great camellia one night in May, as his lordship laid his arms upon the cushioned ledge of his box and watched the antics of the Merry Dwarf, a little, curly-headed creature, whose *début* it was. Certainly Garble had found a novelty. Lord George led the applause, and the Dwarf finished his frisking with a pretty song about lovers. Nor was this all. Feats of archery were to follow. In a moment the Dwarf reappeared with a small, gilded bow in his hand and a quiverful of arrows slung at his shoulder. Hither and thither he shot these vibrant arrows, very precisely, several into the bark of the acacias that grew about the overt stage, several into the fluted columns of the boxes, two or three to the stars. The audience was delighted. *"Bravo! Bravo Saggitaro!"* murmured Lord George, in the language of La Gambogi, who was at his side. Finally, the waxen figure of a man was carried on by an assistant and propped against the trunk of a tree. A scarf was tied across the eyes of the Merry Dwarf, who stood in a remote corner of the stage. *Bravo* indeed! For the shaft had pierced the waxen figure through the heart or just where the heart would have been, if the figure had been human and not waxen.

Lord George called for port and champagne and beckoned the bowing homuncle to his box, that he might compliment him on his skill and pledge him in a bumper of the grape.

"On my soul, you have a genius for the bow," his lordship cried with florid condescension. "Come and sit by me, but first let me present you to my divine companion the Signora Gambogi—Virgo and Sagittarius, egad! You may have met on the Zodiac."

"Indeed, I met the Signora many years ago," the Dwarf replied, with a low bow. "But not on the Zodiac, and the Signora perhaps forgets me."

At this speech the Signora flushed angrily, for she was indeed no longer young, and the Dwarf had a childish face. She thought he mocked her; her eyes flashed. Lord George's twinkled rather maliciously.

"Great is the experience of youth," he laughed. "Pray, are you stricken with more than twenty summers?" "With more than I can count," said the Dwarf. "To the health of your lordship!" and he drained his long glass of wine. Lord George replenished it, and asked by what means or miracle he had acquired his mastery of the bow.

"By long practice," the little thing rejoined; "long practice on human creatures." And he nodded his curls mysteriously.

"On my heart, you are a dangerous box-mate."

"Your lordship were certainly a good target."

Little liking this joke at his bulk, which really rivalled the Regent's, Lord George turned brusquely in his chair and fixed his eyes upon the stage. This time it was the Gambogi who laughed.

A new operette, *The Fair Captive of Samarcand*, was being enacted, and the frequenters of Garble's were all curious to behold the new *débutante*, Jenny Mere, who was said to be both pretty and talented. These predictions were surely fulfilled, when the captive peeped from the window of her wooden turret. She looked so pale under her blue turban. Her eyes were dark with fear; her parted lips did not seem capable of speech. "Is it that she is frightened of us?" the audience wondered. "Or of the flashing scimitar of Aphoschaz, the cruel father who holds her captive?" So they gave her loud applause, and when at length she jumped down, to be caught in the arms of her gallant lover, Nissarah, and, throwing aside her Eastern draperies, did a simple dance, in the convention of Columbine, their delight was quite unbounded. She was very young and did not dance very well, it is true, but they forgave her that. And when she turned in the dance and saw her father with his scimitar, their hearts beat swiftly for her. Nor were all eyes tearless when she pleaded with him for her life.

Strangely absorbed, quite callous of his two companions, Lord George gazed over the footlights. He seemed as one who was in a trance. Of a sudden, something shot sharp into his heart. In pain he sprang to his feet and, as he turned, he seemed to see a winged and laughing child, in whose hand was a bow, fly swiftly away into the darkness. At his side was the Dwarf's chair. It was empty. Only La Gambogi was with him, and her dark face was like the face of a fury.

Presently he sank back into his chair, holding one hand to

his heart, that still throbbed from the strange transfixion. H
breathed very painfully and seemed scarce conscious of hi
surroundings. But La Gambogi knew he would pay no mor
homage to her now, for that the love of Jenny Mere had com
into his heart.

When the operette was over, his love-sick lordship snatchec
up his cloak and went away without one word to the lady a*
his side. Rudely he brushed aside Count Karoloff and Mr. Fitz
Clarence, with whom he had arranged to play hazard. Of hi*
comrades, his cynicism, his reckless scorn—of all the materia
of his existence—he was oblivious now. He had no time for
penitence or diffident delay. He only knew that he must kneel
at the feet of Jenny Mere and asked her to be his wife.

"Miss Mere," said Garble, "is in her room, resuming her
ordinary attire. If your lordship deign to await the conclusion
of her humble toilet, it shall be my privilege to present her to
your lordship. Even now, indeed, I hear her footfall on the
stair."

Lord George uncovered his head and with one hand nervously smoothed his rebellious wig.

"Miss Mere, come hither," said Garble. "This is my Lord
George Hell, that you have pleased whom by your poor efforts
this night will ever be the prime gratification of your passage
through the roseate realms of art."

Little Miss Mere who had never seen a lord, except in fancy
or in dreams, curtseyed shyly and hung her head. With a
loud crash Lord George fell on his knees. The manager was
greatly surprised, the girl greatly embarrassed. Yet neither of
them laughed, for sincerity dignified his posture and sent eloquence from its lips.

"Miss Mere," he cried, "give ear, I pray you, to my poor
words, nor spurn me in misprision from the pedestal of your
beauty, genius, and virtue. All too conscious, alas! of my pre-
sumption in the same, I yet abase myself before you as a
suitor for your adorable hand. I grope under the shadow of
your raven locks. I am dazzled in the light of those trans-
lucent orbs, your eyes. In the intolerable whirlwind of your
fame I faint and am afraid."

"Sir——" the girl began, simply.

"Say 'My lord,' " said Garble, solemnly.

"My lord, I thank you for your words. They are beautiful. But indeed, indeed, I can never be your bride."

Lord George hid his face in his hands.

"Child," said Mr. Garble, "let not the sun rise e'er you have retracted those wicked words."

"My wealth, my rank, my irremediable love for you, I throw them at your feet," Lord George cried, piteously. "I would wait an hour, a week, a lustre, even a decade, did you but bid me hope!"

"I can never be your wife," she said, slowly. "I can never be the wife of any man whose face is not saintly. Your face, my lord, mirrors, it may be, true love for me, but it is even as a mirror long tarnished by the reflection of this world's vanity. It is even as a tarnished mirror. Do not kneel to me, for I am poor and humble. I was not made for such impetuous wooing. Kneel, if you please, to some greater, gayer lady. As for my love, it is my own, nor can it ever be torn from me, but given, as true love needs be given, freely. Ah, rise from your knees. That man, whose face is wonderful as the faces of the saints, to him I will give my true love."

Miss Mere, though visibly affected, had spoken this speech with a gesture and elocution so superb, that Mr. Garble could not help applauding, deeply though he regretted her attitude towards his honoured patron. As for Lord George, he was immobile, a stricken oak. With a sweet look of pity, Miss Mere went her way, and Mr. Garble, with some solicitude, helped his lordship to rise from his knees. Out into the night, without a word, his lordship went. Above him the stars were still splendid. They seemed to mock the festoons of little lamps, dim now and guttering in the garden of Garble's. What should he do? No thoughts came; only his heart burnt hotly. He stood on the brim of Garble's lake, shallow and artificial as his past life had been. Two swans slept on its surface. The moon shone strangely upon their white, twisted necks. Should he drown himself? There was no one in the garden to prevent him, and in the morning they would find him floating there, one of the noblest of love's victims. The garden would be closed in the evening. There would be no performance in the little theatre. It might be that Jenny Mere would mourn him. "Life is a prison, without bars," he murmured, as he walked away.

All night long he strode, knowing not whither, through the mysterious streets and squares of London. The watchmen, to whom his figure was most familiar, gripped their staves at his approach, for they had old reason to fear his wild and

riotous habits. He did not heed them. Through that dim conflict between darkness and day, which is ever waged silentl
over our sleep, Lord George strode on in the deep absorptio
of his love and of his despair. At dawn he found himself on th
outskirts of a little wood in Kensington. A rabbit rushed pas
him through the dew. Birds were fluttering in the branches
The leaves were tremulous with the presage of day, and the ai
was full of the sweet scent of hyacinths.

How cool the country was! It seemed to cure the feverisl
maladies of his soul and consecrate his love. In the fai
light of the dawn he began to shape the means of winning
Jenny Mere, that he had conceived in the desperate hours o
the night. Soon an old woodman passed by, and, with rough
courtesy, showed him the path that would lead him quickest to
the town. He was loth to leave the wood. With Jenny, he
thought, he would live always in the country. And he picked a
posy of wild flowers for her.

His *rentrée* into the still silent town strengthened his
Arcadian resolves. He, who had seen the town so often in its
hours of sleep, had never noticed how sinister its whole aspect
was. In its narrow streets the white houses rose on either side
of him like cliffs of chalk. He hurried swiftly along the unswept pavement. How had he loved this city of evil secrets?

At last he came to St. James's Square, to the hateful door of
his own house. Shadows lay like memories in every corner of
the dim hall. Through the window of his room a sunbeam
slanted across his smooth, white bed, and fell ghastly on the
ashen grate.

. . . .

It was a bright morning in Old Bond Street, and fat little
Mr. Aeneas, the fashionable mask-maker, was sunning himself
at the door of his shop. His window was lined as usual with all
kinds of masks—beautiful masks with pink cheeks, and absurd
masks with protuberant chins; curious πρόσωπα copied from old
tragic models; masks of paper for children, of fine silk for
ladies, and of leather for working men; bearded or beardless,
gilded or waxen (most of them, indeed were waxen), big or
little masks. And in the middle of this vain galaxy hung the
presentment of a Cyclop's face, carved cunningly of gold, with
a great sapphire in its brow.

The sun gleamed brightly on the window and on the bald

head and varnished shoes of fat little Mr. Aeneas. It was too early for any customers to come and Mr. Aeneas seemed to be greatly enjoying his leisure in the fresh air. He smiled complacently as he stood there, and well he might, for he was a great artist, and was patronized by several crowned heads and not a few of the nobility. Only the evening before, Mr. Brummell had come into his shop and ordered a light summer mask, wishing to evade for a time the jealous vigilance of Lady Otterton. It pleased Mr. Aeneas to think that his art made him the recipient of so many high secrets. He smiled as he thought of the titled spendthrifts, who, at this moment, *perdus* behind his masterpieces, passed unscathed among their creditors. He was the secular confessor of his day, always able to give absolution. An unique position!

The street was as quiet as a village street. At an open window over the way, a handsome lady, wrapped in a muslin *peignoir*, sat sipping her cup of chocolate. It was La Signora Gambogi, and Mr. Aeneas made her many elaborate bows. This morning, however, her thoughts seemed far away, and she did not notice the little man's polite efforts. Nettled at her negligence, Mr. Aeneas was on the point of retiring into his shop, when he saw Lord George Hell hastening up the street, with a posy of wild flowers in his hand.

"His lordship is up betimes!" he said to himself. "An early visit to La Signora, I suppose."

Not so, however. His lordship came straight towards the mask-shop. Once he glanced up at the Signora's window and looked deeply annoyed when he saw her sitting there. He came quickly into the shop.

"I want the mask of a saint," he said.

"Mask of a saint, my lord? Certainly!" said Mr. Aeneas, briskly. "With or without halo? His Grace the Bishop of St. Aldreds always wears his with a halo. Your lordship does not wish for a halo? Certainly! If your lordship will allow me to take the measurement——"

"I must have the mask to-day," Lord George said. "Have you none ready-made?"

"Ah, I see. Required for immediate wear," murmured Mr. Aeneas, dubiously. "You see, your lordship takes a rather large size." And he looked at the floor.

"Julius!" he cried suddenly to his assistant, who was putting finishing touches to a mask of Barbarossa which the young king of Zürremburg was to wear at his coronation the following week. "Julius! Do you remember the saint's mask we made for Mr. Ripsby, a couple of years ago?"

"Yes, sir," said the boy. "It's stored upstairs."

"I thought so," replied Mr. Aeneas. "Mr. Ripsby only had it on hire. Step upstairs, Julius, and bring it down. I fancy it is just what your lordship would wish. Spiritual, yet handsome."

"Is it a mask that is even as a mirror of true love?" Lord George asked gravely.

"It was made precisely as such," the mask-maker answered. "In fact it was made for Mr. Ripsby to wear at his silver wedding, and was very highly praised by the relatives of Mrs. Ripsby. Will your lordship step into my little room?"

So Mr. Aeneas led the way to his parlour behind the shop. He was elated by the distinguished acquisition to his *clientèle,* for hitherto Lord George had never patronized his business. He bustled round his parlour and insisted that his lordship should take a chair and a pinch from his snuff-box, while the saint's mask was being found.

Lord George's eye travelled along the rows of framed letters from great personages, which lined the walls. He did not see them though, for he was calculating the chances that La Gambogi had not observed him, as he entered the mask-shop. He had come down so early that he thought she would be still abed. That sinister old proverb, *La jalouse se lève de bonne heure,* rose in his memory. His eye fell unconsciously on a large, round mask made of dull silver, with the features of a human face traced over its surface in faint filigree.

"Your lordship wonders what mask that is!" chirped Mr. Aeneas, tapping the thing with one of his little finger nails.

"What is that mask?" Lord George murmured, absently.

"I ought not to divulge, my lord," said the mask-maker. "But I know your lordship would respect a professional secret, a secret of which I am pardonably proud. This," he said, "is a mask for the sun-god, Apollo, whom heaven bless!"

"You astound me," said Lord George.

"Of no less a person, I do assure you. When Jupiter, his father, made him lord of the day, Apollo craved that he might sometimes see the doings of mankind in the hours of night time. Jupiter granted so reasonable a request, and when next Apollo had passed over the sky and hidden in the sea, and darkness had fallen on all the world, he raised his head above the waters that he might watch the doings of mankind in the hours of night time. But," Mr. Aeneas added, with a smile, "his bright countenance made light all the darkness. Men rose from their couches or from their revels, wondering that day was so soon come, and went to their work. And Apollo sank weeping into the sea. 'Surely,' he cried, 'it is a bitter thing that I alone, of all the gods, may not watch the world in the hours of night time. For in those hours, as I am told, men are even as gods are. They spill the wine and are wreathed with roses. Their daughters dance in the light of torches. They laugh to the sound of flutes. On their long couches they lie down at last and sleep comes to kiss their eyelids. None of these things may I see. Wherefore the brightness of my beauty is even as a curse to me and I would put it from me.' And as he wept, Vulcan said to him, 'I am not the least cunning of the gods, nor the least pitiful. Do not weep, for I will give you that which shall end your sorrow. Nor need you put from you the brightness of your beauty.' And Vulcan made a mask of dull silver and fastened it across his brother's face. And that night, thus masked, the sun-god rose from the sea and watched the doings of mankind in the night time. Nor any longer were men abashed by his bright beauty, for it was hidden by the mask of silver. Those whom he had so often seen haggard over their daily tasks, he saw feasting now and wreathed with red roses. He heard them laugh to the sound of flutes, as their daughters danced in the red light of torches. And when at length they lay down upon their soft couches and sleep kissed their eyelids, he sank back into the sea and hid his mask under a little rock in the bed of the sea. Nor have men ever known that Apollo watches them often in the night time, but fancied it to be some pale goddess."

"I myself have always thought it was Diana," said Lord George Hell.

"An error, my lord!" said Mr. Aeneas, with a smile. "*Ecce signum!*" And he tapped the mask of dull silver.

"Strange!" said his lordship. "And pray how comes it that Apollo has ordered of *you* this new mask?"

"He has always worn twelve new masks every year, inasmuch as no mask can endure for many nights the near brightness of his face, before which even a mask of the best and purest silver soon tarnishes, and wears away. Centuries ago,

Vulcan tired of making so very many masks. And so Apollo
sent Mercury down to Athens, to the shop of Phoron, a
Phoenician mask-maker of great skill. Phoron made Apollo's
masks for many years, and every month Mercury came to his
shop for a new one. When Phoron died, another artist was
chosen, and, when he died, another, and so on through all the
ages of the world. Conceive, my lord, my pride and pleasure
when Mercury flew into my shop, one night last year, and made
me Apollo's warrant-holder. It is the highest privilege that
any mask-maker can desire. And when I die," said Mr. Aeneas,
with some emotion, "Mercury will confer my post upon another."

"And do they pay you for your labour?" Lord George
asked.

Mr. Aeneas drew himself up to his full height, such as it
was. "In Olympus, my lord," he said, "they have no currency.
For any mask-maker, so high a privilege is its own reward.
Yet the sun-god is generous. He shines more brightly into my
shop than into any other. Nor does he suffer his rays to melt
any waxen mask made by me, until its wearer doff it and
it be done with." At this moment Julius came in with the Ripsby mask. "I must ask your lordship's pardon, for having kept
you so long," pleaded Mr. Aeneas. "But I have a large store of
old masks and they are imperfectly catalogued."

It certainly was a beautiful mask, with its smooth, pink
cheeks and devotional brows. It was made of the finest wax.
Lord George took it gingerly in his hands and tried it on his
face. It fitted à merveille.

"Is the expression exactly as your lordship would wish?"
asked Mr. Aeneas.

Lord George laid it on the table and studied it intently. "I
wish it were more as a perfect mirror of true love," he said at
length. "It is too calm, too contemplative."

"Easily remedied!" said Mr. Aeneas. Selecting a fine pencil,
he deftly drew the eyebrows closer to each other. With a brush
steeped in some scarlet pigment, he put a fuller curve upon the
lips. And, behold! it was the mask of a saint who loves dearly.
Lord George's heart throbbed with pleasure.

"And for how long does your lordship wish to wear it?"
asked Mr. Aeneas.

"I must wear it until I die," replied Lord George.

"Kindly be seated then, I pray," rejoined the little man.

"For I must apply the mask with great care. Julius, you will assist me!"

So, while Julius heated the inner side of the waxen mask over a little lamp, Mr. Aeneas stood over Lord George gently smearing his features with some sweet-scented pomade. Then he took the mask and powdered its inner side, quite soft and warm now, with a fluffy puff. "Keep quite still, for one instant," he said, and clapped the mask firmly on his lordship's upturned face. So soon as he was sure of its perfect adhesion, he took from his assistant's hand a silver file and a little wooden spatula, with which he proceeded to pare down the edge of the mask, where it joined the neck and ears. At length, all traces of the "join" were obliterated. It remained only to arrange the curls of the lordly wig over the waxen brow.

The disguise was done. When Lord George looked through the eyelets of his mask into the mirror that was placed in his hand, he saw a face that was saintly, itself a mirror of true love. How wonderful it was! He felt his past was a dream. He felt he was a new man indeed. His voice went strangely through the mask's parted lips, as he thanked Mr. Aeneas.

"Proud to have served your lordship," said that little worthy, pocketing his fee of fifty guineas, while he bowed his customer out.

When he reached the street, Lord George nearly uttered a curse through those sainted lips of his. For there, right in his way, stood La Gambogi, with a small, pink parasol. She laid her hand upon his sleeve and called him softly by his name. He passed her by without a word. Again she confronted him.

"I cannot let go so handsome a lover," she laughed, "even though he spurn me! Do not spurn me, George. Give me your posy of wild flowers. Why, you never looked so lovingly at me in all your life!"

"Madam," said Lord George, sternly, "I have not the honour to know you." And he passed on.

The lady gazed after her lost lover with the blackest hatred in her eyes. Presently she beckoned across the road to a certain spy.

And the spy followed him.

Lord George, greatly agitated, had turned into Piccadilly. It was horrible to have met this garish embodiment of his past on the very threshold of his fair future. The mask-maker's elevating talk about the gods, followed by the initiative ceremony of his saintly mask, had driven all discordant memories from his love-thoughts of Jenny Mere. And then to be met by La Gambogi! It might be that, after his stern words, she would not seek to cross his path again. Surely she would not seek to mar his sacred love. Yet, he knew her dark, Italian nature, her passion of revenge. What was the line in Virgil? *Spretaeque*—something. Who knew but that somehow, sooner or later, she might come between him and his love?

He was about to pass Lord Barrymore's mansion. Count Karoloff and Mr. FitzClarence were lounging in one of the lower windows. Would they know him under his mask? Thank God! they did not. They merely laughed as he went by, and Mr. FitzClarence cried in a mocking voice, "Sing us a hymn, Mr. What-ever-your-saint's-name-is!" The mask, then, at least, was perfect. Jenny Mere would not know him. He need fear no one but La Gambogi. But would not she betray his secret? He sighed.

That night he was going to visit Garble's and to declare his love to the little actress. He never doubted that she would love him for his saintly face. Had she not said, "That man whose face is wonderful as are the faces of the saints, to him I will give my true love"? She could not say now that his face was as a tarnished mirror of love. She would smile on him. She would be his bride. But would La Gambogi be at Garble's?

The operette would not be over before ten that night. The clock in Hyde Park Gate told him it was not yet ten—ten of the morning. Twelve whole hours to wait, before he could fall at Jenny's feet! "I cannot spend that time in this place of memories," he thought. So he hailed a yellow cabriolet and bade the jarvey drive him out to the village of Kensington.

When they came to the little wood where he had been but a few hours ago, Lord George dismissed the jarvey. The sun, that had risen as he stood there thinking of Jenny, shone down on his altered face, but, though it shone very fiercely, it did not melt his waxen features. The old woodman, who had shown him his way, passed by under a load of faggots and did not know him. He wandered among the trees. It was a lovely wood. Presently he came to the bank of that tiny stream, the Ken, which still flowed there in those days. On the moss of its bank he lay down and let its water ripple over his hand. Some bright pebble glistened under the surface, and, as he peered down at it, he saw in the stream the reflection of his mask.

A great shame filled him that he should so cheat the girl he loved. Behind that fair mask there would still be the evil face that had repelled her. Could he be so base as to decoy her into love of that most ingenious deception? He was filled with a great pity for her, with a hatred of himself. And yet, he argued, was the mask indeed a mean trick? Surely it was a secret symbol of his true repentance and of his true love. His face was evil, because his life had been evil. He had seen a gracious girl, and of a sudden his very soul had changed. His face alone was the same as it had been. It was not just that his face should be evil still.

There was the faint sound of some one sighing. Lord George looked up, and there, on the further bank, stood Jenny Mere, watching him. As their eyes met, she blushed and hung her head. She looked like nothing but a tall child, as she stood there, with her straight, limp frock of lilac cotton and her sunburnt straw bonnet. He dared not speak; he could only gaze at her. Suddenly there perched astride the bough of a tree, at her side, that winged and laughing child, in whose hand was a bow. Before Lord George could warn her, an arrow had flashed down and vanished in her heart, and Cupid had flown away.

No cry of pain did she utter, but stretched out her arms to her lover, with a glad smile. He leapt quite lightly over the little stream and knelt at her feet. It seemed more fitting that he should kneel before the gracious thing he was unworthy of. But she, knowing only that his face was as the face of a great saint, bent over him and touched him with her hand.

"Surely," she said, "you are that good man for whom I have waited. Therefore do not kneel to me, but rise and suffer me to kiss your hand. For my love of you is lowly, and my heart is all yours."

But he answered, looking up into her fond eyes, "Nay, you are a queen, and I must needs kneel in your presence."

And she shook her head wistfully, and she knelt down, also, in her tremulous ecstasy, before him. And as they knelt, the one to the other, the tears came into her eyes, and he kissed her. Though the lips that he pressed to her lips were only waxen, he thrilled with happiness, in that mimic kiss. He held her close to him in his arms, and they were silent in the sacredness of their love.

From his breast he took the posy of wild flowers that he had gathered.

"They are for you," he whispered, "I gathered them for you, hours ago, in this wood. See! They are not withered."

But she was perplexed by his words and said to him, blushing, "How was it for me that you gathered them, though you had never seen me?"

"I gathered them for you," he answered, "knowing I should soon see you. How was it that you, who had never seen me, yet waited for me?"

"I waited, knowing I should see you at last." And she kissed the posy and put it at her breast.

And they rose from their knees and went into the wood, walking hand in hand. As they went, he asked the names of the flowers that grew under their feet. "These are primroses," she would say. "Did you not know? And these are ladies' feet, and these forget-me-nots. And that white flower, climbing up the trunks of the trees and trailing down so prettily from the branches, is called Astyanax. These little yellow things are buttercups. Did you not know?" And she laughed.

"I know the names of none of the flowers," he said.

She looked up into his face and said timidly, "Is it worldly and wrong of me to have loved the flowers? Ought I to have thought more of those higher things that are unseen?"

His heart smote him. He could not answer her simplicity.

"Surely the flowers are good, and did not you gather this posy for me?" she pleaded. "But if you do not love them, I must not. And I will try to forget their names. For I must try to be like you in all things."

"Love the flowers always," he said. "And teach me to love them."

So she told him all about the flowers, how some grew very slowly and others bloomed in a night; how clever the convolvulus was at climbing, and how shy violets were, and why honeycups had folded petals. She told him of the birds, too, that sang in the wood, how she knew them all by their voices. "That is a chaffinch singing. Listen!" she said. And she tried to imitate its note, that her lover might remember. All the birds, according to her, were good, except the cuckoo, and whenever she heard him sing she would stop her ears, lest she should forgive him for robbing the nests. "Every day," she said, "I have come to the wood, because I was lonely, and it seemed to pity me. But now I have you. And it is glad."

She clung closer to his arm, and he kissed her. She pushed back her straw bonnet, so that it dangled from her neck by its ribands, and laid her little head against his shoulder. For a while he forgot his treachery to her, thinking only of his love and her love. Suddenly she said to him, "Will you try not to be angry with me, if I tell you something? It is something that will seem dreadful to you."

"*Pauvrette*," he answered, "you cannot have anything very dreadful to tell."

"I am very poor," she said, "and every night I dance in a theatre. It is the only thing I can do to earn my bread. Do you despise me because I dance?" She looked up shyly at him and saw that his face was full of love for her and not angry.

"Do you like dancing?" he asked.

"I hate it," she answered, quickly. "I hate it indeed. Yet— to-night, alas! I must dance again in the theatre."

"You need never dance again," said her lover. "I am rich and I will pay them to release you. You shall dance only for me. Sweetheart, it cannot be much more than noon. Let us go into the town, while there is time, and you shall be made my bride, and I your bridegroom, this very day. Why should you and I be lonely?"

"I do not know," she said.

So they walked back through the wood, taking a narrow path which Jenny said would lead them quickest to the village. And, as they went, they came to a tiny cottage, with a garden that was full of flowers. The old woodman was leaning over its paling, and he nodded to them as they passed.

"I often used to envy the woodman," said Jenny, "living in that dear little cottage."

"Let us live there, then," said Lord George. And he went back and asked the old man if he were not unhappy, living there alone.

"'Tis a poor life here for me," the old man answered. "No folk come to the wood, except little children, now and again, to play, or lovers like you. But they seldom notice me. And in winter I am alone with Jack Frost. Old men love merrier company than that. Oh! I shall die in the snow with my faggots on my back. A poor life here!"

"I will give you gold for your cottage and whatever is in it, and then you can go and live happily in the town," Lord George said. And he took from his coat a note for two hundred guineas, and held it across the palings.

"Lovers are poor, foolish derry-docks," the old man muttered. "But I thank you kindly, sir. This little sum will keep me cosy, as long as I last. Come into the cottage as soon as can be. It's a lonely place and does my heart good to depart from it."

"We are going to be married this afternoon, in the town," said Lord George. "We will come straight back to our home."

"May you be happy!" replied the woodman. "You'll find me gone when you come."

And the lovers thanked him and went their way.

"Are you very rich?" Jenny asked. "Ought you to have bought the cottage for that great price?"

"Would you love me as much if I were quite poor, little Jenny?" he asked her after a pause.

"I did not know you were rich when I saw you across the stream," she said.

And in his heart Lord George made a good resolve. He would put away from him all his worldly possessions. All the money that he had won at the clubs, fairly or foully, all that hideous accretion of gold guineas, he would distribute among the comrades he had impoverished. As he walked, with the sweet and trustful girl at his side, the vague record of his infamy assailed him, and a look of pain shot behind his smooth mask. He would atone. He would shun no sacrifice that might cleanse his soul. All his fortune he would put from him. Follard Chase he would give back to Sir Follard. He would sell his house in St. James's Square. He would keep some little part of his patrimony, enough for him in the wood, with Jenny, but no more.

"I shall be quite poor, Jenny," he said.

And they talked of the things that lovers love to talk of, how happy they would be together and how economical. As they were passing Herbert's pastry shop, which as my little readers know, still stands in Kensington, Jenny looked up rather wistfully into her lover's ascetic face.

"Should you think me greedy," she asked him, "if I wanted a bun? They have beautiful buns here!"

Buns! The simple word started latent memories of his childhood. Jenny was only a child, after all. Buns! He had forgotten what they were like. And as they looked at the piles of variegated cakes in the window, he said to her, "Which are buns, Jenny? I should like to have one, too."

"I am almost afraid of you," she said. "You must despise me so. Are you so good that you deny yourself all the vanity and pleasure that most people love? It is wonderful not to know what buns are! The round, brown, shiny cakes, with little raisins in them, are buns."

So he bought two beautiful buns, and they sat together in the shop, eating them. Jenny bit hers rather diffidently, but was reassured when he said that they must have buns very often in the cottage. Yes! he, the famous toper and *gourmet* of St. James's, relished this homely fare, as it passed through the insensible lips of his mask to his palate. He seemed to rise, from the consumption of his bun, a better man.

But there was no time to lose now. It was already past two o'clock. So he got a chaise from the inn opposite the pastry-shop, and they were swiftly driven to Doctors' Commons. There he purchased a special license. When the clerk asked him to write his name upon it, he hesitated. What name should be assume? Under a mask he had wooed this girl, under an unreal name he must make her his bride. He loathed himself for a trickster. He had vilely stolen from her the love she would not give him. Even now, should he not confess himself the man whose face had frightened her, and go his way? And yet, surely, it was not just that he, whose soul was transfigured, should bear his old name. Surely George Hell was dead, and his name had died with him. So he dipped a pen in the ink and wrote "George Heaven," for want of a better name. And Jenny wrote "Jenny Mere" beneath it.

An hour later they were married according to the simple rites of a dear little registry office in Covent Garden.

And in the cool evening they went home.

.   .   .   .

In the cottage that had been the woodman's they had a wonderful honeymoon. No king and queen in any palace of gold were happier than they. For them their tiny cottage was a palace, and the flowers that filled the garden were their couriers. Long and careless and full of kisses were the days of their reign.

Sometimes, indeed, strange dreams troubled Lord George's

sleep. Once he dreamt that he stood knocking and knocking
at the great door of a castle. It was a bitter night. The frost
enveloped him. No one came. Presently he heard a footstep in
the hall beyond, and a pair of frightened eyes peered at him
through the grill. Jenny was scanning his face. She would not
open to him. With tears and wild words be beseeched her, but
she would not open to him. Then, very stealthily, he crept
round the castle and found a small casement in the wall. It was
open. He climbed swiftly, quietly through it. In the darkness
of the room some one ran to him and kissed him gladly. It was
Jenny. With a cry of joy and shame he awoke. By his side lay
Jenny, sleeping like a little child.

After all, what was a dream to him? It could not mar the
reality of his daily happiness. He cherished his true penitence
for the evil he had done in the past. The past! That was indeed
the only unreal thing that lingered in his life. Every day its
substance dwindled, grew fainter yet, as he lived his rustic
honeymoon. Had he not utterly put it from him? Had he not,
a few hours after his marriage, written to his lawyer, declaring solemnly that he, Lord George Hell, had forsworn the
world, that he was where no man would find him, that he desired
all his worldly goods to be distributed, thus and thus, among
these and those of his companions? By this testament he had
verily atoned for the wrong he had done, had made himself
dead indeed to the world.

No address had he written upon this document. Though
its injunctions were final and binding, it could betray no clue
of his hiding-place. For the rest, no one would care to seek
him out. He, who had done no good to human creature, would
pass unmourned out of memory. The clubs, doubtless, would
laugh and puzzle over his strange recantations, envious of
whomever he enriched. They would say 'twas a good riddance
of a rogue and soon forget him.[1] But she, whose prime patron

[1] I would refer my little readers once more to the pages of *Contemporary
Bucks,* where Captain Tarleton speculates upon the sudden disappearance of
Lord George Hell and describes its effect on the town. "Not even the
shrewdest," says he, "even gave a guess that would throw a ray of revealing
light on the *disparition* of this profligate man. It was supposed that he carried off with him a little dancer from Garble's, at which *haunt of pleasantry*
he was certainly on the night he vanished, and whither the young lady never
returned again. Garble declared he had been compensated for her perfidy, but
that he was sure she had not succumbed to his lordship, having in fact rejected him soundly. Did his lordship, say the cronies, take his life—and hers?
Il n'y a pas d'épreuve.
"The most astonishing matter is that the runaway should have written out

he had been, who had loved him in her vile fashion, La Gambogi, would she forget him easily, like the rest? As the sweet days went by, her spectre, also, grew fainter and less formidable. She knew his mask indeed, but how should she find him in the cottage near Kensington? *Devia dulcedo latebrarum!* He was safe hidden with his bride. As for the Italian, she might search and search—or had forgotten him, in the arms of another lover.

Yes! Few and faint became the blemishes of his honeymoon. At first, he had felt that his waxen mask, though it had been the means of his happiness, was rather a barrier 'twixt him and his bride. Though it was sweet to kiss her through it, to look at her through it with loving eyes, yet there were times when it incommoded him with its mockery. Could he but put it from him! yet, that, of course, could not be. He must wear it all his life. And so, as days went by he grew reconciled to his mask. No longer did he feel it jarring on his face. It seemed to become an integral part of him, and, for all its rigid material, it did forsooth express the one emotion that filled him, true love. The face, for whose sake Jenny gave him her heart, could not but be dear to this George Heaven, also.

Every day chastened him with its joy. They lived a very simple life, he and Jenny. They rose betimes, like the birds, for whose goodness they both had so sincere a love. Bread and honey and little strawberries were their morning fare, and in the evening they had seed cake and dewberry wine. Jenny herself made the wine and her husband drank it, in strict moderation, never more than two glasses. He thought it tasted far better than the Regent's cherry brandy, or the Tokay at Brooks's. Of these treasured topes he had, indeed, nearly forgotten the taste. The wine made from wild berries by his little bride was august enough for his palate. Sometimes, after they

a complete will, restoring all money he had won at cards, etc., etc. This certainly corroborates the opinion that he was seized with a sudden repentance and fled over the seas to a foreign monastery, where he died at last in *religious silence*. That's as it may, but many a spendthrift found his pocket clinking with guineas, a not unpleasant sound, I declare. The Regent himself was benefited by the odd will, and old Sir Follard Follard found himself once more in the ancestral home he had forfeited. As for Lord George's mansion in St. James's Square, that was sold with all its appurtenances, and the money fetched by the sale, no bagatelle, was given to various good objects, according to my lord's stated wishes. Well, many of us blessed his name—we had cursed it often enough. Peace to his ashes, in whatever urn they may be resting, on the billows of whatever ocean they float!"

had dined thus, he would play the flute to her upon the moonlit lawn, or tell her of the great daisy-chain he was going to make for her on the morrow, or sit silently by her side, listening to the nightingale, till bedtime. So admirably simple were their days.

One morning, as he was helping Jenny to water the flowers, he said to her suddenly, "Sweetheart, we had forgotten!"

"What was there we should forget?" asked Jenny, looking up from her task.

" 'Tis the mensiversary of our wedding," her husband answered gravely. "We must not let it pass without some celebration."

"No, indeed," she said, "we must not. What shall we do?"

Between them they decided upon an unusual feast. They would go into the village and buy a bag of beautiful buns and eat them in the afternoon. So soon, then, as all the flowers were watered, they set forth to Herbert's shop, bought the buns and returned home in very high spirits, George bearing a paper bag that held no less than twelve of the wholesome delicacies. Under the plane tree on the lawn Jenny sat her down, and George stretched himself at her feet. They were loth to enjoy their feast too soon. They dallied in childish anticipation. On the little rustic table Jenny built up the buns, one above the other, till they looked like a tall pagoda. When, very gingerly, she had crowned the structure with the twelfth bun, her husband looking on with admiration, she clapped her hands and danced about it. She laughed so loudly (for, though she was only sixteen years old, she had a great sense of humour), that the table shook, and alas! the pagoda tottered and fell to the lawn. Swift as a kitten, Jenny chased the buns, as they rolled, hither and thither, over the grass, catching them deftly with her hand. Then she came back, flushed and merry under her tumbled hair, with her arm full of buns. She began to put them back in the paper bag.

"Dear husband," she said, looking down to him, "why do not you smile too at my folly? Your grave face rebukes me. Smile, or I shall think I vex you. Please smile a little."

But the mask could not smile, of course. It was made for a mirror of true love, and it was grave and immobile. "I am very much amused, dear," he said, "at the fall of the buns, but my lips will not curve to a smile. Love of you has bound them in spell."

"But I can laugh, though I love you. I do not understand."
And she wondered. He took her hand in his and stroked it
gently, wishing it were possible to smile. Some day, perhaps,
she would tire of this monotonous gravity, this rigid sweetness. It was not strange that she should long for a little facile
expression. They sat silently.

"Jenny, what is it?" he whispered suddenly. For Jenny,
with wide-open eyes, was gazing over his head, across the lawn.
"Why do you look frightened?"

"There is a strange woman smiling at me across the palings," she said. "I do not know her."

Her husband's heart sank. Somehow, he dared not turn his
head to the intruder. He dreaded who she might be.

"She is nodding to me," said Jenny. "I think she is foreign,
for she has an evil face."

"Do not notice her," he whispered. "Does she look evil?"

"Very evil and very dark. She has a pink parasol. Her
teeth are like ivory."

"Do not notice her. Think! It is the mensiversary of our
wedding, dear!"

"I wish she would not smile at me. Her eyes are like bright
blots of ink."

"Let us eat our beautiful buns!"

"Oh, she is coming in!" George heard the latch of the gate
jar. "Forbid her to come in!" whispered Jenny, "I am afraid!"
He heard the jar of heels on the gravel path. Yet he dared
not turn. Only he clasped Jenny's hand more tightly, as he
waited for the voice. It was La Gambogi's.

"Pray, pray, pardon me! I could not mistake the back of so
old a friend."

With the courage of despair, George turned and faced the
woman.

"Even," she smiled, "though his face has changed marvellously."

"Madam," he said, rising to his full height and stepping
between her and his bride, "begone, I command you, from
the garden. I do not see what good is to be served by the
renewal of our acquaintance."

"Acquaintance!" murmured La Gambogi, with an arch of
her beetle-brows. "Surely we were friends, rather, nor is my
esteem for you so dead that I would crave estrangement."

"Madam," rejoined Lord George, with a tremor in his

voice, "you see me happy, living very peacefully with my bride——"

"To whom, I beseech you, old friend, present me."

"I would not," he said hotly, "desecrate her sweet name by speaking it with so infamous a name as yours."

"Your choler hurts me, old friend," said La Gambogi, sinking composedly upon the garden-seat and smoothing the silk of her skirts.

"Jenny," said George, "then do you retire, pending this lady's departure, to the cottage." But Jenny clung to his arm. "I were less frightened at your side," she whispered. "Do not send me away!"

"Suffer her pretty presence," said La Gambogi. "Indeed I am come this long way from the heart of the town, that I may see her, no less than you, George. My wish is only to befriend her. Why should she not set you a mannerly example, giving me welcome? Come and sit by me, little bride, for I have things to tell you. Though you reject my friendship, give me, at least, the slight courtesy of audience. I will not detain you overlong, will be gone very soon. Are you expecting guests, George? On dirait une masque champêtre!" She eyed the couple critically. "Your wife's mask," she said, "is even better than yours."

"What does she mean?" whispered Jenny. "Oh, send her away!"

"Serpent," was all George could say, "crawl from our Eden, ere you poison with your venom its fairest denizen."

La Gambogi rose. "Even my pride," she cried passionately, "knows certain bounds. I have been forbearing, but even in my zeal for friendship I will not be called 'serpent.' I will indeed begone from this rude place. Yet, ere I go, there is a boon I will deign to beg. Show me, oh show me but once again, the dear face I have so often caressed, the lips that were dear to me!"

George started back.

"What does she mean?" whispered Jenny.

"In memory of our old friendship," continued La Gambogi, "grant me this piteous favour. Show me your own face but for one instant, and I vow I will never again remind you that I live. Intercede for me, little bride. Bid him unmask for me. You have more authority over him than I. Doff his mask with your own uxorious fingers."

"What does she mean?" was the refrain of poor Jenny.

"If," said George, gazing sternly at his traitress, "you do not go now, of your own will, I must drive you, man though I am, violently from the garden."

"Doff your mask and I am gone."

George made a step of menace towards her.

"False saint!" she shrieked, "then *I* will unmask you."

Like a panther she sprang upon him and clawed at his waxen cheeks. Jenny fell back, mute with terror. Vainly did George try to free himself from the hideous assailant, who writhed round and round him, clawing, clawing at what Jenny fancied to be his face. With a wild cry, Jenny fell upon the furious creature and tried, with all her childish strength, to release her dear one. The combatives swayed to and fro, a revulsive trinity. There was a loud pop, as though some great cork had been withdrawn, and La Gambogi recoiled. She had torn away the mask. It lay before her upon the lawn, upturned to the sky.

George stood motionless. La Gambogi stared up into his face, and her dark flush died swiftly away. For there, staring back at her, was the man she had unmasked, but, lo! his face was even as his mask had been. Line for line, feature for feature, it was the same. 'Twas a saint's face.

"Madam," he said, in the calm voice of despair, "your cheek may well blanch, when you regard the ruin you have brought upon me. Nevertheless do I pardon you. The gods have avenged, through you, the imposture I wrought upon one who was dear to me. For that unpardonable sin I am punished. As for my poor bride, whose love I stole by the means of that waxen semblance, of her I cannot ask pardon. Ah, Jenny, Jenny, do not look at me. Turn your eyes from the foul reality that I dissembled." He shuddered and hid his face in his hands. "Do not look at me. I will go from the garden. Nor will I ever curse you with the odious spectacle of my face. Forget me, forget me."

But, as he turned to go, Jenny laid her hands upon his wrists and besought him that he would look at her. "For indeed," she said, "I am bewildered by your strange words. Why did you woo me under a mask? And why do you imagine I could love you less dearly, seeing your own face?"

He looked into her eyes. On their violet surface he saw the

tiny reflection of his own face. He was filled with joy and wonder.

"Surely," said Jenny, "your face is even dearer to me, even fairer, than the semblance that hid it and deceived me. I am not angry. 'Twas well that you veiled from me the full glory of your face, for indeed I was not worthy to behold it too soon. But I am your wife now. Let me look always at your own face. Let the time of my probation be over. Kiss me with your own lips."

So he took her in his arms, as though she had been a little child, and kissed her with his own lips. She put her arms round his neck, and he was happier than he had ever been. They were alone in the garden now. Nor lay the mask any longer upon the lawn, for the sun had melted it.

ENOCH SOAMES

WHEN a book about the literature of the eighteen-nineties was given by Mr. Holbrook Jackson to the world, I looked eagerly in the index for SOAMES, ENOCH. I had feared he would not be there. He was not there. But everybody else was. Many writers whom I had quite forgotten, or remembered but faintly, lived again for me, they and their work, in Mr. Holbrook Jackson's pages. The book was as thorough as it was brilliantly written. And thus the omission found by me was an all the deadlier record of poor Soames' failure to impress himself on his decade.

I daresay I am the only person who noticed the omission. Soames had failed so piteously as all that! Nor is there a counterpoise in the thought that if he had had some measure of success he might have passed, like those others, out of my mind, to return only at the historian's beck. It is true that had his gifts, such as they were, been acknowledged in his lifetime, he would never have made the bargain I saw him make —that strange bargain whose results have kept him always in the foreground of my memory. But it is from those very results that the full piteousness of him glares out.

Not my compassion, however, impels me to write of him. For his sake, poor fellow, I should be inclined to keep my pen out of the ink. It is ill to deride the dead. And how can I write about Enoch Soames without making him ridiculous? Or rather, how am I to hush up the horrid fact that he *was* ridiculous? I shall not be able to do that. Yet, sooner or later, write about him I must. You will see, in due course, that I have no option. And I may as well get the thing done now.

In the Summer Term of '93 a bolt from the blue flashed down on Oxford. It drove deep, it hurtlingly embedded itself in the soil. Dons and undergraduates stood around, rather pale, discussing nothing but it. Whence came it, this meteorite? From Paris. Its name? Will Rothenstein. Its aim? To do a series of twenty-four portraits in lithograph. These were to be published from the Bodley Head, London. The matter was urgent. Already the Warden of A, and the Master of B, and the Regius Professor of C, had meekly "sat." Dignified and doddering old men, who had never consented to sit to any one, could not withstand this dynamic little stranger. He did not sue: he invited; he did not invite: he commanded. He was twenty-one years old. He wore spectacles that flashed more than any other pair ever seen. He was a wit. He was brimful of ideas. He knew Whistler. He knew Edmond de Goncourt. He knew every one in Paris. He knew them all by heart. He was Paris in Oxford. It was whispered that, so soon as he had polished off his selection of dons, he was going to include a few undergraduates. It was a proud day for me when I—I was included. I liked Rothenstein not less than I feared him; and there arose between us a friendship that has grown ever warmer, and been more and more valued by me, with every passing year.

At the end of Term he settled in—or rather, meteoritically into—London. It was to him I owed my first knowledge of that forever enchanting little world-in-itself, Chelsea, and my first acquaintance with Walter Sickert and other august elders who dwelt there. It was Rothenstein that took me to see, in Cambridge Street, Pimlico, a young man whose drawings were already famous among the few—Aubrey Beardsley, by name. With Rothenstein I paid my first visit to the Bodley Head. By him I was inducted into another haunt of intellect and daring, the domino room of the Café Royal.

There, on that October evening—there, in that exuberant vista of gilding and crimson velvet set amidst all those opposing mirrors and upholding caryatids, with fumes of tobacco ever rising to the painted and pagan ceiling, and with the hum of presumably cynical conversation broken into so sharply now and again by the clatter of dominoes shuffled on marble tables, I drew a deep breath, and "This indeed," said I to myself, "is life."

It was the hour before dinner. We drank vermouth. Those who knew Rothenstein were pointing him out to those who knew him only by name. Men were constantly coming in through the swing-doors and wandering slowly up and down in search of vacant tables, or of tables occupied by friends. One of these rovers interested me because I was sure he wanted to catch Rothenstein's eye. He had twice passed our table, with a hesitating look; but Rothenstein, in the thick of a disquisition on Puvis de Chavannes, had not seen him. He was a stooping, shambling person, rather tall, very pale, with longish and brownish hair. He had a thin vague beard—or rather, he had a chin on which a large number of hairs weakly curled and clustered to cover its retreat. He was an odd-looking person; but in the 'nineties odd apparitions were more frequent, I think, than they are now. The young writers of that era—and I was sure this man was a writer—strove earnestly to be distinct in aspect. This man had striven unsuccessfully. He wore a soft black hat of clerical kind but of Bohemian intention, and a grey waterproof cape which, perhaps because it was waterproof, failed to be romantic. I decided that "dim" was the *mot juste* for him. I had already essayed to write, and was immensely keen on the *mot juste*, that Holy Grail of the period.

The dim man was now again approaching our table, and this time he made up his mind to pause in front of it. "You don't remember me," he said in a toneless voice.

Rothenstein brightly focussed him. "Yes, I do," he replied after a moment, with pride rather than effusion—pride in a retentive memory. "Edwin Soames."

"Enoch Soames," said Enoch.

"Enoch Soames," repeated Rothenstein in a tone implying that it was enough to have hit on the surname. "We met in Paris two or three times when you were living there. We met at the Café Groche."

"And I came to your studio once."

"Oh yes; I was sorry I was out."

"But you were in. You showed me some of your paintings, you know. . . . I hear you're in Chelsea now."

"Yes."

I almost wondered that Mr. Soames did not, after this monosyllable, pass along. He stood patiently there, rather like a dumb animal, rather like a donkey looking over a gate. A sad figure, his. It occurred to me that "hungry" was perhaps the *mot juste* for him; but—hungry for what? He looked as if he had little appetite for anything. I was sorry for him; and Rothenstein, though he had not invited him to Chelsea, did ask him to sit down and have something to drink.

Seated, he was more self-assertive. He flung back the wings of his cape with a gesture which—had not those wings been waterproof—might have seemed to hurl defiance at things in general. And he ordered an absinthe. "*Je me tiens toujours fidèle,*" he told Rothenstein, "*á la sorcière glauque.*"

"It is bad for you," said Rothenstein dryly.

"Nothing is bad for one," answered Soames. "*Dans ce monde il n'y a ni de bien ni de mal.*"

"Nothing good and nothing bad? How do you mean?"

"I explained it all in the preface to 'Negations.' "

" 'Negations'?"

"Yes; I gave you a copy of it."

"Oh, yes, of course. But did you explain—for instance—that there was no such thing as bad or good grammar?"

"N-no," said Soames. "Of course in Art there is the good and the evil. But in Life—no." He was rolling a cigarette. He had weak white hands, not well washed, and with finger-tips much stained by nicotine. "In Life there are illusions of good and evil, but"—his voice trailed away to a murmur in which the words "vieux jeu" and "rococo" were faintly audible. I think he felt he was not doing himself justice, and feared that Rothenstein was going to point out fallacies. Anyhow, he cleared his throat and said "*Parlons d'autre chose.*"

It occurs to you that he was a fool? It didn't to me. I was young, and had not the clarity of judgment that Rothenstein already had. Soames was quite five or six years older than either of us. Also, he had written a book.

It was wonderful to have written a book.

If Rothenstein had not been there, I should have revered

Soames. Even as it was, I respected him. And I was very near indeed to reverence when he said he had another book coming out soon. I asked if I might ask what kind of book it was to be. "My poems," he answered. Rothenstein asked if this was to be the title of the book. The poet meditated on this suggestion, but said he rather thought of giving the book no title at all. "If a book is good in itself—" he murmured, waving his cigarette.

Rothenstein objected that absence of title might be bad for the sale of a book. "If," he urged, "I went into a bookseller's and said simply 'Have you got?' or 'Have you a copy of?' how would they know what I wanted?"

"Oh, of course I should have my name on the cover," Soames answered earnestly. "And I rather want," he added, looking hard at Rothenstein, "to have a drawing of myself as frontispiece." Rothenstein admitted that this was a capital idea, and mentioned that he was going into the country and would be there for some time. He then looked at his watch, exclaimed at the hour, paid the waiter, and went away with me to dinner. Soames remained at his post of fidelity to the glaucous witch.

"Why were you so determined not to draw him?" I asked.

"Draw him? Him? How can one draw a man who doesn't exist?"

"He is dim," I admitted. But my *mot juste* fell flat. Rothenstein repeated that Soames was non-existent.

Still, Soames had written a book. I asked if Rothenstein had read "Negations." He said he had looked into it, "but," he added crisply, "I don't profess to know anything about writing." A reservation very characteristic of the period! Painters would not then allow that any one outside their own order had a right to any opinion about painting. This law (graven on the tablets brought down by Whistler from the summit of Fujiyama) imposed certain limitations. If other arts than painting were not utterly unintelligible to all but the men who practised them, the law tottered—the Monroe Doctrine, as it were, did not hold good. Therefore no painter would offer an opinion of a book without warning you at any rate that his opinion was worthless. No one is a better judge of literature than Rothenstein; but it wouldn't have done to tell him so in those days; and I knew that I must form an unaided judgment on "Negations."

Not to buy a book of which I had met the author face to face would have been for me in those days an impossible act of self-denial. When I returned to Oxford for the Christmas Term I had duly secured "Negations." I used to keep it lying carelessly on the table in my room, and whenever a friend took it up and asked what it was about I would say "Oh, it's rather a remarkable book. It's by a man whom I know." Just "what it was about" I never was able to say. Head or tail was just what I hadn't made of that slim green volume. I found in the preface no clue to the exiguous labyrinth of contents, and in that labyrinth nothing to explain the preface.

"Lean near to life. Lean very near—nearer.

"Life is web, and therein nor warp nor woof is, but web only.

"It is for this I am Catholick in church and in thought, yet do let swift Mood weave there what the shuttle of Mood wills."

These were the opening phrases of the preface, but those which followed were less easy to understand. Then came "Stark: *A Conte,*" about a midinette who, so far as I could gather, murdered, or was about to murder, a mannequin. It was rather like a story by Catulle Mendès in which the translator had either skipped or cut out every alternate sentence. Next, a dialogue between Pan and St. Ursula—lacking, I felt, in "snap." Next, some aphorisms (entitled ἀφορίσματα). Throughout, in fact, there was a great variety of form; and the forms had evidently been wrought with much care. It was rather the substance that eluded me. Was there, I wondered, any substance at all? It did now occur to me: suppose Enoch Soames was a fool! Up cropped a rival hypothesis: suppose *I* was! I inclined to give Soames the benefit of the doubt. I had read "L'Après-midi d'un Faune" without extracting a glimmer of meaning. Yet Mallarmé—of course—was a Master. How was I to know that Soames wasn't another? There was a sort of music in his prose, not indeed arresting, but perhaps, I thought, haunting, and laden perhaps with meanings as deep as Mallarmé's own. I awaited his poems with an open mind.

And I looked forward to them with positive impatience after I had had a second meeting with him. This was on an evening in January. Going into the aforesaid domino room, I passed a table at which sat a pale man with an open book before him.

He looked from his book to me, and I looked back over my shoulder with a vague sense that I ought to have recognised him. I returned to pay my respects. After exchanging a few words, I said with a glance to the open book, "I see I am interrupting you," and was about to pass on, but "I prefer," Soames replied in his toneless voice, "to be interrupted," and I obeyed his gesture that I should sit down.

I asked him if he often read here. "Yes; things of this kind I read here," he answered, indicating the title of his book—"The Poems of Shelley."

"Anything that you really"—and I was going to say "admire?" But I cautiously left my sentence unfinished, and was glad that I had done so, for he said, with unwonted emphasis, "Anything second-rate."

I had read little of Shelley, but "Of course," I murmured, "he's very uneven."

"I should have thought evenness was just what was wrong with him. A deadly evenness. That's why I read him here. The noise of this place breaks the rhythm. He's tolerable here." Soames took up the book and glanced through the pages. He laughed. Soames' laugh was a short, single and mirthless sound from the throat, unaccompanied by any movement of the face or brightening of the eyes. "What a period!" he uttered, laying the book down. And "What a country!" he added.

I asked rather nervously if he didn't think Keats had more or less held his own against the drawbacks of time and place. He admitted that there were "passages in Keats," but did not specify them. Of "the older men," as he called them, he seemed to like only Milton. "Milton," he said, "wasn't sentimental." Also, "Milton had a dark insight." And again, "I can always read Milton in the reading-room."

"The reading-room?"

"Of the British Museum. I go there every day."

"You do? I've only been there once. I'm afraid I found it rather a depressing place. It—it seemed to sap one's vitality."

"It does. That's why I go there. The lower one's vitality, the more sensitive one is to great art. I live near the Museum. I have rooms in Dyott Street."

"And you go round to the reading-room to read Milton?"

"Usually Milton." He looked at me. "It was Milton," he certificatively added, "who converted me to Diabolism."

"Diabolism? Oh yes? Really?" said I, with that vague dis-

comfort and that intense desire to be polite which one feels
when a man speaks of his own religion. "You—worship the
Devil?"

Soames shook his head. "It's not exactly worship," he qualified, sipping his absinthe. "It's more a matter of trusting and
encouraging."

"Ah, yes . . . But I had rather gathered from the preface
to 'Negations' that you were a—a Catholic."

"*Je l'étais à cette époque.* Perhaps I still am. Yes, I'm a
Catholic diabolist."

This profession he made in an almost cursory tone. I could
see that what was upmost in his mind was the fact that I had
read "Negations." His pale eyes had for the first time gleamed.
I felt as one who is about to be examined, *viva voce*, on the
very subject in which he is shakiest. I hastily asked him how
soon his poems were to be published. "Next week," he told me.

"And are they to be published without a title?"

"No. I found a title, at last. But I shan't tell you what it
is," as though I had been so impertinent as to inquire. "I am
not sure that it wholly satisfies me. But it is the best I can find.
It suggests something of the quality of the poems. . . Strange
growths, natural and wild, yet exquisite," he added, "and
many-hued, and full of poisons."

I asked him what he thought of Baudelaire. He uttered the
snort that was his laugh, and "Baudelaire," he said, "was a
bourgeois malgré lui." France had only one poet: Villon; "and
two-thirds of Villon were sheer journalism." Verlaine was "an
épicier malgré lui." Altogether, rather to my surprise, he rated
French literature lower than English. There were "passages"
in Villiers de l'Isle-Adam. But "I," he summed up, "owe nothing to France." He nodded at me. "You'll see," he predicted.

I did not, when the time came, quite see that. I thought the
author of "Fungoids" did—unconsciously, of course—owe
something to the young Parisian décadents, or to the young
English ones who owed something to *them*. I still think so. The
little book—bought by me in Oxford—lies before me as I
write. Its pale grey buckram cover and silver lettering have
not worn well. Nor have its contents. Through these, with a
melancholy interest, I have again been looking. They are not
much. But at the time of their publication I had a vague suspicion that they *might* be. I suppose it is my capacity for faith,
not poor Soames' work, that is weaker than it once was. . .

To a Young Woman

Thou art, who hast not been!
Pale tunes irresolute
And traceries of old sounds
Blown from a rotted flute
Mingle with noise of cymbals rouged with rust,
Nor not strange forms and epicene
Lie bleeding in the dust,
Being wounded with wounds.

For this it is
That in thy counterpart
Of age-long mockeries
Thou hast not been nor art!

There seemed to me a certain inconsistency as between the
first and last lines of this. I tried, with bent brows, to resolve
the discord. But I did not take my failure as wholly incom-
patible with a meaning in Soames' mind. Might it not rather
indicate the depth of his meaning? As for the craftsmanship,
"rouged with rust" seemed to me a fine stroke, and "nor not"
instead of "and" had a curious felicity. I wondered who the
Young Woman was, and what she had made of it all. I sadly
suspect that Soames could not have made more of it than she.
Yet, even now, if one doesn't try to make any sense at all of
the poem, and reads it just for the sound, there is a certain
grace of cadence. Soames was an artist—in so far as he was
anything, poor fellow!

It seemed to me, when first I read "Fungoids," that, oddly
enough, the Diabolistic side of him was the best. Diabolism
seemed to be a cheerful, even a wholesome, influence in his life.

Nocturne

Round and round the shutter'd Square
I stroll'd with the Devil's arm in mine.
No sound but the scrape of his hoofs was there
And the ring of his laughter and mine.
We had drunk black wine.

I scream'd, "I will race you, Master!"
"What matter," he shriek'd, "to-night
Which of us runs the faster?
There is nothing to fear to-night
In the foul moon's light!"

Then I look'd him in the eyes,
And I laugh'd full shrill at the lie he told
And the gnawing fear he would fain disguise.
It was true, what I'd time and again been told:
    He was old—old.

There was, I felt, quite a swing about that first stanza—a
joyous and rollicking note of comradeship. The second was
slightly hysterical perhaps. But I liked the third: it was so
bracingly unorthodox, even according to the tenets of Soames'
peculiar sect in the faith. Not much "trusting and encouraging" here! Soames triumphantly exposing the Devil as a liar,
and laughing "full shrill," cut a quite heartening figure, I
thought—then! Now, in the light of what befell, none of his
poems depresses me so much as "Nocturne."

I looked out for what the metropolitan reviewers would have
to say. They seemed to fall into two classes: those who had
little to say and those who had nothing. The second class was
the larger, and the words of the first were cold; insomuch that

Strikes a note of modernity throughout. . . . These tripping numbers.—*Preston Telegraph.*

was the only lure offered in advertisements by Soames' publisher. I had hopes that when next I met the poet I could congratulate him on having made a stir; for I fancied he was not
so sure of his intrinsic greatness as he seemed. I was but able
to say, rather coarsely, when next I did see him, that I hoped
"Fungoids" was "selling splendidly." He looked at me across
his glass of absinthe and asked if I had bought a copy. His
publisher had told him that three had been sold. I laughed, as
at a jest.

"You don't suppose I *care*, do you?" he said, with something
like a snarl. I disclaimed the notion. He added that he was
not a tradesman. I said mildly that I wasn't, either, and mur-

mured that an artist who gave truly new and great things to the world had always to wait long for recognition. He said he cared not a sou for recognition. I agreed that the act of creation was its own reward.

His moroseness might have alienated me if I had regarded myself as a nobody. But ah! hadn't both John Lane and Aubrey Beardsley suggested that I should write an essay for the great new venture that was afoot—"The Yellow Book"? And hadn't Henry Harland, as editor, accepted my essay? And wasn't it to be in the very first number? At Oxford I was still *in statu pupillari*. In London I regarded myself as very much indeed a graduate now—one whom no Soames could ruffle. Partly to show off, partly in sheer good-will, I told Soames he ought to contribute to "The Yellow Book." He uttered from the throat a sound of scorn for that publication.

Nevertheless, I did, a day or two later, tentatively ask Harland if he knew anything of the work of a man called Enoch Soames. Harland paused in the midst of his characteristic stride around the room, threw up his hands towards the ceiling, and groaned aloud: he had often met "that absurd creature" in Paris, and this very morning had received some poems in manuscript from him.

"Has he *no* talent?" I asked.

"He has an income. He's all right." Harland was the most joyous of men and most generous of critics, and he hated to talk of anything about which he couldn't be enthusiastic. So I dropped the subject of Soames. The news that Soames had an income did take the edge off solicitude. I learned afterwards that he was the son of an unsuccessful and deceased bookseller in Preston, but had inherited an annuity of £300 from a married aunt, and had no surviving relatives of any kind. Materially, then, he was "all right." But there was still a spiritual pathos about him, sharpened for me now by the possibility that even the praises of *The Preston Telegraph* might not have been forthcoming had he not been the son of a Preston man. He had a sort of weak doggedness which I could not but admire. Neither he nor his work received the slightest encouragement; but he persisted in behaving as a personage: always he kept his dingy little flag flying. Wherever congregated the *jeunes féroces* of the arts, in whatever Soho restaurant they had just discovered, in whatever music-hall they were most frequenting, there was Soames in the midst of them, or rather

on the fringe of them, a dim but inevitable figure. He never
sought to propitiate his fellow-writers, never bated a jot of
his arrogance about his own work or of his contempt for theirs.
To the painters he was respectful, even humble; but for the
poets and prosaists of "The Yellow Book," and later of "The
Savoy," he had never a word but of scorn. He wasn't resented.
It didn't occur to anybody that he or his Catholic Diabolism
mattered. When, in the autumn of '96, he brought out (at his
own expense, this time) a third book, his last book, nobody
said a word for or against it. I meant, but forgot, to buy it.
I never saw it, and am ashamed to say I don't even remember
what it was called. But I did, at the time of its publication, say
to Rothenstein that I thought poor old Soames was really a
rather tragic figure, and that I believed he would literally die
for want of recognition. Rothenstein scoffed. He said I was
trying to get credit for a kind heart which I didn't possess;
and perhaps this was so. But at the private view of the New
English Art Club, a few weeks later, I beheld a pastel portrait
of "Enoch Soames, Esq." It was very like him, and very like
Rothenstein to have done it. Soames was standing near it, in
his soft hat and his waterproof cape, all through the afternoon. Anybody who knew him would have recognised the portrait at a glance, but nobody who didn't know him would have
recognised the portrait from its bystander: it "existed" so
much more than he; it was bound to. Also, it had not that expression of faint happiness which on this day was discernible,
yes, in Soames' countenance. Fame had breathed on him. Twice
again in the course of the month I went to the New English,
and on both occasions Soames himself was on view there. Looking back, I regard the close of that exhibition as having been
virtually the close of his career. He had felt the breath of
Fame against his cheek—so late, for such a little while; and
at its withdrawal he gave in, gave up, gave out. He, who had
never looked strong or well, looked ghastly now—a shadow of
the shade he had once been. He still frequented the domino
room, but, having lost all wish to excite curiosity, he no longer
read books there. "You read only at the Museum now?" asked
I, with attempted cheerfulness. He said he never went there
now. "No absinthe there," he muttered. It was the sort of
thing that in the old days he would have said for effect; but it
carried conviction now. Absinthe, erst but a point in the "personality" he had striven so hard to build up, was solace and

necessity now. He no longer called it "la sorcière glauque." He had shed away all his French phrases. He had become a plain, unvarnished, Preston man.

Failure, if it be a plain, unvarnished, complete failure, and even though it be a squalid failure, has always a certain dignity. I avoided Soames because he made me feel rather vulgar. John Lane had published, by this time, two little books of mine, and they had had a pleasant little success of esteem. I was a—slight but definite—"personality." Frank Harris had engaged me to kick up my heels in *The Saturday Review*, Alfred Harmsworth was letting me do likewise in *The Daily Mail.* I was just what Soames wasn't. And he shamed my gloss. Had I known that he really and firmly believed in the greatness of what he as an artist had achieved, I might not have shunned him. No man who hasn't lost his vanity can be held to have altogether failed. Soames' dignity was an illusion of mine. One day in the first week of June, 1897, that illusion went. But on the evening of that day Soames went too.

I had been out most of the morning, and, as it was too late to reach home in time for luncheon, I sought "the Vingtième." This little place—Restaurant du Vingtième Siècle, to give it its full title—had been discovered in '96 by the poets and prosaists, but had now been more or less abandoned in favour of some later find. I don't think it lived long enough to justify its name; but at that time there it still was, in Greek Street, a few doors from Soho Square, and almost opposite to that house where, in the first years of the century, a little girl, and with her a boy named De Quincey, made nightly encampment in darkness and hunger among dust and rats and old legal parchments. The Vingtième was but a small whitewashed room, leading out into the street at one end and into a kitchen at the other. The proprietor and cook was a Frenchman, known to us as Monsieur Vingtième; the waiters were his two daughters, Rose and Berthe; and the food, according to faith, was good. The tables were so narrow, and were set so close together, that there was space for twelve of them, six jutting from either wall.

Only the two nearest to the door, as I went in, were occupied. On one side sat a tall, flashy, rather Mephistophelian man whom I had seen from time to time in the domino room and elsewhere. On the other side sat Soames. They made a queer contrast in that sunlit room—Soames sitting haggard in that

hat and cape which nowhere at any season had I seen him doff, and this other, this keenly vital man, at sight of whom I more than ever wondered whether he were a diamond merchant, a conjurer, or the head of a private detective agency. I was sure Soames didn't want my company; but I asked, as it would have seemed brutal not to, whether I might join him, and took the chair opposite to his. He was smoking a cigarette, with an untasted salmi of something on his plate and a half-empty bottle of Sauterne before him; and he was quite silent. I said that the preparations for the Jubilee made London impossible. (I rather liked them, really.) I professed a wish to go right away till the whole thing was over. In vain did I attune myself to his gloom. He seemed not to hear me nor even to see me. I felt that his behaviour made me ridiculous in the eyes of the other man. The gangway between the two rows of tables at the Vingtième was hardly more than two feet wide (Rose and Berthe, in their ministrations, had always to edge past each other, quarrelling in whispers as they did so), and any one at the table abreast of yours was practically at yours. I thought our neighbour was amused at my failure to interest Soames, and so, as I could not explain to him that my insistence was merely charitable, I became silent. Without turning my head, I had him well within my range of vision. I hoped I looked less vulgar than he in contrast with Soames. I was sure he was not an Englishman, but what *was* his nationality? Though his jet-black hair was *enbrosse*, I did not think he was French. To Berthe, who waited on him, he spoke French fluently, but with a hardly native idiom and accent. I gathered that this was his first visit to the Vingtième; but Berthe was offhand in her manner to him: he had not made a good impression. His eyes were handsome, but —like the Vingtième's tables—too narrow and set too close together. His nose was predatory, and the points of his moustache, waxed up beyond his nostrils, gave a fixity to his smile. Decidedly, he was sinister. And my sense of discomfort in his presence was intensified by the scarlet waistcoat which tightly, and so unseasonably in June, sheathed his ample chest. This waistcoat wasn't wrong merely because of the heat, either. It was somehow all wrong in itself. It wouldn't have done on Christmas morning. It would have struck a jarring note at the first night of "Hernani." I was trying to account for its wrongness when Soames suddenly and strangely broke silence. "A hundred years hence!" he murmured, as in a trance.

"We shall not be here!" I briskly but fatuously added.
"We shall not be here. No," he droned, "but the Museum
will still be just where it is. And the reading-room, just where
it is. And people will be able to go and read there." He inhaled
sharply, and a spasm as of actual pain contorted his features.

I wondered what train of thought poor Soames had been
following. He did not enlighten me when he said, after a long
pause, "You think I haven't minded."

"Minded what, Soames?"

"Neglect. Failure."

"*Failure?*" I said heartily. "Failure?" I repeated vaguely.
"Neglect—yes, perhaps; but that's quite another matter. Of
course you haven't been—appreciated. But what then? Any
artist who—who gives—" What I wanted to say was, "Any
artist who gives truly new and great things to the world has
always to wait long for recognition"; but the flattery would
not out: in the face of his misery, a misery so genuine and
so unmasked, my lips would not say the words.

And then—he said them for me. I flushed. "That's what you
were going to say, isn't it?" he asked.

"How did you know?"

"It's what you said to me three years ago, when 'Fungoids'
was published." I flushed the more. I need not have done so
at all, for "It's the only important thing I ever heard you
say," he continued. "And I've never forgotten it. It's a true
thing. It's a horrible truth. But—d'you remember what I answered? I said 'I don't care a sou for recognition.' And you
believed me. You've gone on believing I'm above that sort of
thing. You're shallow. What should *you* know of the feelings
of a man like me? You imagine that a great artist's faith in
himself and in the verdict of posterity is enough to keep him
happy. . . You've never guessed at the bitterness and loneliness, the"—his voice broke; but presently he resumed, speaking with a force that I had never known in him. "Posterity!
What use is it to *me?* A dead man doesn't know that people
are visiting his grave—visiting his birthplace—putting up
tablets to him—unveiling statues of him. A dead man can't
read the books that are written about him. A hundred years
hence! Think of it! If I could come back to life *then*—just
for a few hours—and go to the reading-room, and *read!* Or
better still: if I could be projected, now, at this moment, into
that future, into that reading-room, just for this one after-

noon! I'd sell myself body and soul to the devil, for that! Think of the pages and pages in the catalogue: 'SOAMES, ENOCH' endlessly—endless editions, commentaries, prolegomena, biographies"—but here he was interrupted by a sudden loud creak of the chair at the next table. Our neighbour had half risen from his place. He was leaning towards us, apologetically intrusive.

"Excuse—permit me," he said softly. "I have been unable not to hear. Might I take a liberty? In this little restaurant-sans-façon"—he spread wide his hands—"might I, as the phrase is, 'cut in'?"

I could but signify our acquiescence. Berthe had appeared at the kitchen door, thinking the stranger wanted his bill. He waved her away with his cigar, and in another moment had seated himself beside me, commanding a full view of Soames.

"Though not an Englishman," he explained, "I know my London well, Mr. Soames. Your name and fame—Mr. Beerbohm's too—very known to me. Your point is: who am *I?*" He glanced quickly over his shoulder, and in a lowered voice said "I am the Devil."

I couldn't help it: I laughed. I tried not to, I knew there was nothing to laugh at, my rudeness shamed me, but—I laughed with increasing volume. The Devil's quiet dignity, the surprise and disgust of his raised eyebrows, did but the more dissolve me. I rocked to and fro, I lay back aching. I behaved deplorably.

"I am a gentleman, and," he said with intense emphasis, "I thought I was in the company of *gentlemen.*"

"Don't!" I gasped faintly. "Oh, don't!"

"Curious, *nicht wahr?*" I heard him say to Soames. "There is a type of person to whom the very mention of my name is—oh so-awfully-funny! In your theatres the dullest comédien needs only to say 'The Devil!' and right away they give him 'the loud laugh that speaks the vacant mind.' Is it not so?"

I had now just breath enough to offer my apologies. He accepted them, but coldly, and re-addressed himself to Soames.

"I am a man of business," he said, "and always I would put things through 'right now,' as they say in the States. You are a poet. *Les affaires*—you detest them. So be it. But with me you will deal, eh? What you have said just now gives me furiously to hope."

Soames had not moved, except to light a fresh cigarette. He

sat crouched forward, with his elbows squared on the table, and his head just above the level of his hands, staring up at the Devil. "Go on," he nodded. I had no remnant of laughter in me now.

"It will be the more pleasant, our little deal," the Devil went on, "because you are—I mistake not?—a Diabolist."

"A Catholic Diabolist," said Soames.

The Devil accepted the reservation genially. "You wish," he resumed, "to visit now—this afternoon as-ever-is—the reading-room of the British Museum, yes? but of a hundred years hence, yes? *Parfaitement.* Time—an illusion. Past and future—they are as ever-present as the present, or at any rate only what you call 'just-round-the-corner.' I switch you on to any date. I project you—pouf! You wish to be in the reading-room just as it will be on the afternoon of June 3, 1997? You wish to find yourself standing in that room, just past the swing-doors, this very minute, yes? and to stay there till closing time? Am I right?"

Soames nodded.

The Devil looked at his watch. "Ten past two," he said. "Closing time in summer same then as now: seven o'clock. That will give you almost five hours. At seven o'clock—pouf!—you find yourself again here, sitting at this table. I am dining to-night *dans le monde—dans le higlif.* That concludes my present visit to your great city. I come and fetch you here, Mr. Soames, on my way home."

"Home?" I echoed.

"Be it never so humble!" said the Devil lightly.

"All right," said Soames.

"Soames!" I entreated. But my friend moved not a muscle.

The Devil had made as though to stretch forth his hand across the table and touch Soames' forearm; but he paused in his gesture.

"A hundred years hence, as now," he smiled, "no smoking allowed in the reading-room. You would better therefore——"

Soames removed the cigarette from his mouth and dropped it into his glass of Sauterne.

"Soames!" again I cried. "Can't you"—but the Devil had now stretched forth his hand across the table. He brought it slowly down on—the table-cloth. Soames' chair was empty. His cigarette floated sodden in his wine-glass. There was no other trace of him.

For a few moments the Devil let his hand rest where it lay, gazing at me out of the corners of his eyes, vulgarly triumphant.

A shudder shook me. With an effort I controlled myself and rose from my chair. "Very clever," I said condescendingly. "But—'The Time Machine' is a delightful book, don't you think? So entirely original!"

"You are pleased to sneer," said the Devil, who had also risen, "but it is one thing to write about an impossible machine; it is a quite other thing to be a Supernatural Power." All the same, I had scored.

Berthe had come forth at the sound of our rising. I explained to her that Mr. Soames had been called away, and that both he and I would be dining here. It was not until I was out in the open air that I began to feel giddy. I have but the haziest recollection of what I did, where I wandered, in the glaring sunshine of that endless afternoon. I remember the sound of carpenters' hammers all along Piccadilly, and the bare chaotic look of the half-erected "stands." Was it in the Green Park, or in Kensington Gardens, or *where* was it that I sat on a chair beneath a tree, trying to read an evening paper? There was a phrase in the leading article that went on repeating itself in my fagged mind—"Little is hidden from this august Lady full of the garnered wisdom of sixty years of Sovereignty." I remember wildly conceiving a letter (to reach Windsor by express messenger told to await answer):

MADAM,—Well knowing that your Majesty is full of the garnered wisdom of sixty years of Sovereignty, I venture to ask your advice in the following delicate matter. Mr. Enoch Soames, whose poems you may or may not know, . . .

Was there *no* way of helping him—saving him? A bargain was a bargain, and I was the last man to aid or abet any one in wriggling out of a reasonable obligation. I wouldn't have lifted a little finger to save Faust. But poor Soames!— doomed to pay without respite an eternal price for nothing but a fruitless search and a bitter disillusioning. . . .

Odd and uncanny it seemed to me that he, Soames, in the flesh, in the waterproof cape, was at this moment living in the last decade of the next century, poring over books not yet written, and seeing and seen by men not yet born. Uncannier and odder still, that to-night and evermore he would be in Hell. Assuredly, truth was stranger than fiction.

Endless that afternoon was. Almost I wished I had gone with Soames—not indeed to stay in the reading-room, but to sally forth for a brisk sight-seeing walk around a new London. I wandered restlessly out of the Park I had sat in. Vainly I tried to imagine myself an ardent tourist from the eighteenth century. Intolerable was the strain of the slow-passing and empty minutes. Long before seven o'clock I was back at the Vingtième.

I sat there just where I had sat for luncheon. Air came in listlessly through the open door behind me. Now and again Rose or Berthe appeared for a moment. I had told them I would not order any dinner till Mr. Soames came. A hurdy-gurdy began to play, abruptly drowning the noise of a quarrel between some Frenchmen further up the street. Whenever the tune was changed I heard the quarrel still raging. I had bought another evening paper on my way. I unfolded it. My eyes gazed ever away from it to the clock over the kitchen door. . . .

Five minutes, now, to the hour! I remembered that clocks in restaurants are kept five minutes fast. I concentrated my eyes on the paper. I vowed I would not look away from it again. I held it upright, at its full width, close to my face, so that I had no view of anything but it. . . . Rather a tremulous sheet? Only because of the draught, I told myself.

My arms gradually became stiff; they ached; but I could not drop them—now. I had a suspicion, I had a certainty. Well, what then? . . . What else had I come for? Yet I held tight that barrier of newspaper. Only the sound of Berthe's brisk footstep from the kitchen enabled me, forced me, to drop it, and to utter:

"What shall we have to eat, Soames?"

"*Il est souffrant, ce pauvre Monsieur Soames?*" asked Berthe.

"He's only—tired." I asked her to get some wine—Burgundy—and whatever food might be ready. Soames sat crouched forward against the table, exactly as when last I had seen him. It was as though he had never moved—he who had moved so unimaginably far. Once or twice in the afternoon it had for an instant occurred to me that perhaps his journey was not to be fruitless—that perhaps we had all been wrong

ı our estimate of the works of Enoch Soames. That we had
een horribly right was horribly clear from the look of him.
ut "Don't be discouraged," I falteringly said. "Perhaps it's
nly that you—didn't leave enough time. Two, three centuries
ence, perhaps——"
"Yes," his voice came. "I've thought of that."
"And now—now for the more immediate future! Where are
ou going to hide? How would it be if you caught the Paris
xpress from Charing Cross? Almost an hour to spare. Don't
o on to Paris. Stop at Calais. Live in Calais. He'd never
hink of looking for you in Calais."
"It's like my luck," he said, "to spend my last hours on
arth with an ass." But I was not offended. "And a treacher-
us ass," he strangely added, tossing across to me a crumpled
it of paper which he had been holding in his hand. I glanced
t the writing on it—some sort of gibberish, apparently. I
aid it impatiently aside.
"Come, Soames! pull yourself together! This isn't a mere
natter of life and death. It's a question of eternal torment,
nind you! You don't mean to say you're going to wait limply
ere till the Devil comes to fetch you?"
"I can't do anything else. I've no choice."
"Come! This is 'trusting and encouraging' with a vengeance! This is Diabolism run mad!" I filled his glass with
ine. "Surely, now that you've *seen* the brute——"
"It's no good abusing him."
"You must admit there's nothing Miltonic about him,
Soames."
"I don't say he's not rather different from what I ex-
pected."
"He's a vulgarian, he's a swell-mobsman, he's the sort of
nan who hangs about the corridors of trains going to the
Riviera and steals ladies' jewel-cases. Imagine eternal torment
presided over by *him!*"
"You don't suppose I look forward to it, do you?"
"Then why not slip quietly out of the way?"
Again and again I filled his glass, and always, mechanically,
ne emptied it; but the wine kindled no spark of enterprise in
him. He did not eat, and I myself ate hardly at all. I did not
n my heart believe that any dash for freedom could save him.
The chase would be swift, the capture certain. But better any-
hing than this passive, meek, miserable waiting. I told

Soames that for the honour of the human race he ought t
make some show of resistance. He asked what the human rac
had ever done for him. "Besides," he said, "can't you unde
stand that I'm in his power? You saw him touch me, didn'
you? There's an end of it. I've no will. I'm sealed."

I made a gesture of despair. He went on repeating the wor
"sealed." I began to realise that the wine had clouded hi
brain. No wonder! Foodless he had gone into futurity, fooc
less he still was. I urged him to eat at any rate some bread. I
was maddening to think that he, who had so much to tel
might tell nothing. "How was it all," I asked, "yonder
Come! Tell me your adventures."

"They'd make first-rate 'copy,' wouldn't they?"

"I'm awfully sorry for you, Soames, and I make all possibl
allowances; but what earthly right have you to insinuate tha
I should make 'copy,' as you call it, out of you?"

The poor fellow pressed his hands to his forehead. "I don'
know," he said. "I had some reason, I know. . . . I'll try t
remember."

"That's right. Try to remember everything. Eat a littl
more bread. What did the reading-room look like?"

"Much as usual," he at length muttered.

"Many people there?"

"Usual sort of number."

"What did they look like?"

Soames tried to visualise them. "They all," he presentl
remembered, "looked very like one another."

My mind took a fearsome leap. "All dressed in Jaeger?"

"Yes. I think so. Greyish-yellowish stuff."

"A sort of uniform?" He nodded. "With a number on it
perhaps?—a number on a large disc of metal sewn on to th
left sleeve? DKF 78,910—that sort of thing?" It was even so
"And all of them—men and women alike—looking very well
cared-for? very Utopian? and smelling rather strongly o
carbolic? and all of them quite hairless?" I was right ever
time. Soames was only not sure whether the men and wome
were hairless or shorn. "I hadn't time to look at them ver
closely," he explained.

"No, of course not. But——"

"They stared at *me*, I can tell you. I attracted a great dea
of attention." At last he had done that! "I think I rathe
scared them. They moved away whenever I came near. The

ollowed me about at a distance, wherever I went. The men at he round disk in the middle seemed to have a sort of panic whenever I went to make inquiries."

"What did you do when you arrived?"

Well, he had gone straight to the catalogue, of course—to he S volumes, and had stood long before SN–SOF, unable o take this volume out of the shelf, because his heart was beating so. . . . At first, he said, he wasn't disappointed—he only hought there was some new arrangement. He went to the niddle desk and asked where the catalogue of *twentieth*-entury books was kept. He gathered that there was still only ne catalogue. Again he looked up his name, stared at the hree little pasted slips he had known so well. Then he went nd sat down for a long time. . . .

"And then," he droned, "I looked up the 'Dictionary of National Biography' and some encyclopædias. . . . I went back o the middle desk and asked what was the best modern book n late nineteenth-century literature. They told me Mr. T. K. Nupton's book was considered the best. I looked it up in the catalogue and filled in a form for it. It was brought to me. My name wasn't in the index, but—Yes!" he said with a sudden change of tone. "That's what I'd forgotten. Where's that bit of paper? Give it me back."

I, too, had forgotten that cryptic screed. I found it fallen on the floor, and handed it to him.

He smoothed it out, nodding and smiling at me disagreeably. "I found myself glancing through Nupton's book," he resumed. "Not very easy reading. Some sort of phonetic spelling. . . . All the modern books I saw were phonetic."

"Then I don't want to hear any more, Soames, please."

"The proper names seemed all to be spelt in the old way. But for that, I mightn't have noticed my own name."

"Your own name? Really? Soames, I'm *very* glad."

"And yours."

"No!"

"I thought I should find you waiting here to-night. So I took the trouble to copy out the passage. Read it."

I snatched the paper. Soames' handwriting was characteristically dim. It, and the noisome spelling, and my excitement, made me all the slower to grasp what T. K. Nupton was driving at.

The document lies before me at this moment. Strange that

the words I here copy out for you were copied out for me b
poor Soames just seventy-eight years hence. . . .

From p. 234 of "Inglish Littracher 1890–1900" bi T. K
Nupton, publishd bi th Stait, 1992:

"Fr egzarmpl, a riter ov th time, naimd Max Beerbohn
hoo woz stil alive in th twentieth cenchri, rote a stauri in wic
e pautraid an immajnari karrakter kauld 'Enoch Soames'—
a thurd-rait poit hoo beleevz imself a grate jeneus an maix
bargin with th Devvl in auder ter no wot posterriti thinx o
im! It iz a sumwot labud sattire but not without vallu a
showing hou seriusli the yung men ov th aiteen-ninetiz too
themselvz. Nou that the littreri profeshn haz bin auganized a
a departmnt of publik servis, our riters hav found their levv
an hav lernt ter doo their duti without thort ov th morrc
'Th laibrer iz werthi ov hiz hire,' an that iz aul. Thank hevv;
we hav no Enoch Soameses amung us to-dai!"

I found that by murmuring the words aloud (a device whic
I commend to my reader) I was able to master them, little b
little. The clearer they became, the greater was my bewilder
ment, my distress and horror. The whole thing was a night
mare. Afar, the great grisly background of what was in stor
for the poor dear art of letters; here, at the table, fixing o
me a gaze that made me hot all over, the poor fellow whom—
whom evidently . . . but no: whatever down-grade my char
acter might take in coming years, I should never be such a
brute as to——

Again I examined the screed. "Immajnari"—but her
Soames was, no more imaginary, alas! than I. And "labud"—
what on earth was that? (To this day, I have never made ou
that word.) "It's all very—baffling," I at length stammered

Soames said nothing, but cruelly did not cease to look a
me.

"Are you sure," I temporised, "quite sure you copied th
thing out correctly?"

"Quite."

"Well, then it's this wretched Nupton who must have mad
—must be going to make—some idiotic mistake. . . . Lool
here, Soames! you know me better than to suppose that I . .
After all, the name 'Max Beerbohm' is not at all an uncommor
one, and there must be several Enoch Soameses running
around—or rather, 'Enoch Soames' is a name that migh

ccur to any one writing a story. And I don't write stories:
'm an essayist, an observer, a recorder. . . . I admit that
t's an extraordinary coincidence. But you must see——"

"I see the whole thing," said Soames quietly. And he added,
vith a touch of his old manner, but with more dignity than I
aad ever known in him, "*Parlons d'autre chose.*"

I accepted that suggestion very promptly. I returned
traight to the more immediate future. I spent most of the
ong evening in renewed appeals to Soames to slip away and
eek refuge somewhere. I remember saying at last that if in-
leed I was destined to write about him, the supposed "stauri"
aad better have at least a happy ending. Soames repeated
hose last three words in a tone of intense scorn. "In Life and
n Art," he said, "all that matters is an *inevitable* ending."

"But," I urged, more hopeful than I felt, "an ending that
:an be avoided *isn't* inevitable."

"You aren't an artist," he rasped. "And you're so hope-
essly not an artist that, so far from being able to imagine a
hing and make it seem true, you're going to make even a true
hing seem as if you'd made it up. You're a miserable bungler.
And it's like my luck."

I protested that the miserable bungler was not I—was not
;oing to be I—but T. K. Nupton; and we had a rather heated
argument, in the thick of which it suddenly seemed to me that
Soames saw he was in the wrong: he had quite physically
:owered. But I wondered why—and now I guessed with a cold
hrob just why—he stared so, past me. The bringer of that
'inevitable ending" filled the doorway.

I managed to turn in my chair and to say, not without a
emblance of lightness, "Aha, come in!" Dread was indeed
ather blunted in me by his looking so absurdly like a villain
n a melodrama. The sheen of his tilted hat and of his shirt-
:ront, the repeated twists he was giving to his moustache, and
nost of all the magnificence of his sneer, gave token that he
vas there only to be foiled.

He was at our table in a stride. "I am sorry," he sneered
vitheringly, "to break up your pleasant party, but——"

"You don't: you complete it," I assured him. "Mr. Soames
and I want to have a little talk with you. Won't you sit? Mr.
Soames got nothing—frankly nothing—by his journey this
afternoon. We don't wish to say that the whole thing was a
swindle—a common swindle. On the contrary, we believe you

meant well. But of course the bargain, such as it was, is off.'

The Devil gave no verbal answer. He merely looked at Soames and pointed with rigid forefinger to the door. Soames was wretchedly rising from his chair when, with a desperate quick gesture, I swept together two dinner-knives that were on the table, and laid their blades across each other. The Devil stepped sharp back against the table behind him, averting his face and shuddering.

"You are not superstitious!" he hissed.

"Not at all," I smiled.

"Soames!" he said as to an underling, but without turning his face, "put those knives straight!"

With an inhibitive gesture to my friend, "Mr. Soames," I said emphatically to the Devil, "is a *Catholic Diabolist*"; but my poor friend did the Devil's bidding, not mine; and now with his master's eyes again fixed on him, he arose, he shuffled past me. I tried to speak. It was he that spoke. "Try," was the prayer he threw back at me as the Devil pushed him roughly out through the door, "*try* to make them know that I did exist!"

In another instant I too was through that door. I stood staring all ways—up the street, across it, down it. There was moonlight and lamplight, but there was not Soames nor that other.

Dazed, I stood there. Dazed, I turned back, at length, into the little room; and I suppose I paid Berthe or Rose for my dinner and luncheon, and for Soames': I hope so, for I never went to the Vingtième again. Ever since that night I have avoided Greek Street altogether. And for years I did not set foot even in Soho Square, because on that same night it was there that I paced and loitered, long and long, with some such dull sense of hope as a man has in not straying far from the place where he has lost something. . . . "Round and round the shutter'd Square"—that line came back to me on my lonely beat, and with it the whole stanza, ringing in my brain and bearing in on me how tragically different from the happy scene imagined by him was the poet's actual experience of that prince in whom of all princes we should put not our trust.

But—strange how the mind of an essayist, be it never so stricken, roves and ranges!—I remember pausing before a wide doorstep and wondering if perchance it was on this very one that the young De Quincey lay ill and faint while poor Ann

lew as fast as her feet would carry her to Oxford Street, the
'stony-hearted step-mother" of them both, and came back
)earing that "glass of port wine and spices" but for which he
might, so he thought, actually have died. Was this the very
loorstep that the old De Quincey used to revisit in homage? I
)ondered Ann's fate, the cause of her sudden vanishing from
the ken of her boy-friend; and presently I blamed myself for
letting the past override the present. Poor vanished Soames!

And for myself, too, I began to be troubled. What had I
better do? Would there be a hue and cry—Mysterious Disappearance of an Author, and all that? He had last been seen
lunching and dining in my company. Hadn't I better get a
hansom and drive straight to Scotland Yard? . . . They
would think I was a lunatic. After all, I reassured myself,
London was a very large place, and one very dim figure might
easily drop out of it unobserved—now especially, in the blinding glare of the near Jubilee. Better say nothing at all, I
thought.

And I was right. Soames' disappearance made no stir at all.
He was utterly forgotten before any one, so far as I am aware,
noticed that he was no longer hanging around. Now and again
some poet or prosaist may have said to another, "What has
become of that man Soames?" but I never heard any such
question asked. The solicitor through whom he was paid his
annuity may be presumed to have made inquiries, but no echo
of these resounded. There was something rather ghastly to me
in the general unconsciousness that Soames had existed, and
more than once I caught myself wondering whether Nupton,
that babe unborn, were going to be right in thinking him a
figment of my brain.

In that extract from Nupton's repulsive book there is one
point which perhaps puzzles you. How is it that the author,
though I have here mentioned him by name and have quoted
the exact words he is going to write, is not going to grasp the
obvious corollary that I have invented nothing? The answer
can be only this: Nupton will not have read the later passages
of this memoir. Such lack of thoroughness is a serious fault in
any one who undertakes to do scholar's work. And I hope these
words will meet the eye of some contemporary rival to Nupton
and be the undoing of Nupton.

I like to think that some time between 1992 and 1997 somebody will have looked up this memoir, and will have forced on

the world his inevitable and startling conclusions. And I have
reasons for believing that this will be so. You realise that the
reading-room into which Soames was projected by the Devil
was in all respects precisely as it will be on the afternoon of
June 3, 1997. You realise, therefore, that on that afternoon
when it comes round, there the self-same crowd will be, and
there Soames too will be, punctually, he and they doing precisely what they did before. Recall now Soames' account of the
sensation he made. You may say that the mere difference of his
costume was enough to make him sensational in that uniformed crowd. You wouldn't say so if you had ever seen him.
I assure you that in no period could Soames be anything but
dim. The fact that people are going to stare at him, and follow
him around, and seem afraid of him, can be explained only on
the hypothesis that they will somehow have been prepared for
his ghostly visitation. They will have been awfully waiting to
see whether he really would come. And when he does come the
effect will of course be—awful.

An authentic, guaranteed, proven ghost, but—only a ghost,
alas! Only that. In his first visit, Soames was a creature of
flesh and blood, whereas the creatures into whose midst he was
projected were but ghosts, I take it—solid, palpable, vocal,
but unconscious and automatic ghosts, in a building that was
itself an illusion. Next time, that building and those creatures
will be real. It is of Soames that there will be but the semblance. I wish I could think him destined to revisit the world
actually, physically, consciously. I wish he had this one brief
escape, this one small treat, to look forward to. I never forget
him for long. He is where he is, and forever. The more rigid
moralists among you may say he has only himself to blame.
For my part, I think he has been very hardly used. It is well
that vanity should be chastened; and Enoch Soames' vanity
was, I admit, above the average, and called for special treatment. But there was no need for vindictiveness. You say he
contracted to pay the price he is paying; yes; but I maintain
that he was induced to do so by fraud. Well-informed in all
things, the Devil must have known that my friend would gain
nothing by his visit to futurity. The whole thing was a very
shabby trick. The more I think of it, the more detestable the
Devil seems to me.

Of him I have caught sight several times, here and there,
since that day at the Vingtième. Only once, however, have I

seen him at close quarters. This was in Paris. I was walking, one afternoon, along the Rue d'Antin, when I saw him advancing from the opposite direction—over-dressed as ever, and swinging an ebony cane, and altogether behaving as though the whole pavement belonged to him. At thought of Enoch Soames and the myriads of other sufferers eternally in this brute's dominion, a great cold wrath filled me, and I drew myself up to my full height. But—well, one is so used to nodding and smiling in the street to any body whom one knows that the action becomes almost independent of oneself: to prevent it requires a very sharp effort and great presence of mind. I was miserably aware, as I passed the Devil, that I nodded and smiled to him. And my shame was the deeper and hotter because he, if you please, stared straight at me with the utmost haughtiness.

To be cut—deliberately cut—by *him!* I was, I still am, furious at having had that happen to me.

THE INMOST LIGHT

One evening in autumn, when the deformities of London were veiled in faint blue mist, and its vistas and far-reaching streets seemed splendid, Mr. Charles Salisbury was slowly pacing down Rupert Street, drawing nearer to his favourite restaurant by slow degrees. His eyes were downcast in study of the pavement, and thus it was that as he passed in at the narrow door a man who had come up from the lower end of the street jostled against him.

"I beg your pardon—wasn't looking where I was going. Why, it's Dyson!"

"Yes, quite so. How are you, Salisbury?"

"Quite well. But where have you been, Dyson? I don't think I can have seen you for the last five years?"

"No; I dare say not. You remember I was getting rather hard up when you came to my place at Charlotte Street?"

"Perfectly. I think I remember your telling me that you owed five weeks' rent, and that you had parted with your watch for a comparatively small sum."

"My dear Salisbury, your memory is admirable. Yes, I was hard up. But the curious thing is that soon after you saw me I became harder up. My financial state was described by a friend as 'stone broke.' I don't approve of slang, mind you, but such was my condition. But suppose we go in; there might be other people who would like to dine—it's human weakness, Salisbury."

"Certainly; come along. I was wondering as I walked down whether the corner table were taken. It has a velvet back you know."

"I know the spot; it's vacant. Yes, as I was saying, I became even harder up."

"What did you do then?" asked Salisbury, disposing of his hat, and settling down in the corner of the seat, with a glance of fond anticipation at the *menu*.

"What did I do? Why, I sat down and reflected. I had a good classical education, and a positive distaste for business of any kind: that was the capital with which I faced the world. Do you know, I have heard people describe olives as nasty! What lamentable Philistinism! I have often thought, Salisbury, that I could write genuine poetry under the influence of olives and red wine. Let us have Chianti; it may not be very good, but the flasks are simply charming."

"It is pretty good here. We may as well have a big flask."

"Very good. I reflected, then, on my want of prospects, and I determined to embark in literature."

"Really; that was strange. You seem in pretty comfortable circumstances, though."

"Though! What a satire upon a noble profession. I am afraid, Salisbury, you haven't a proper idea of the dignity of an artist. You see me sitting at my desk—or at least you can see me if you care to call—with pen and ink, and simple nothingness before me, and if you come again in a few hours you will (in all probability) find a creation!"

"Yes, quite so. I had an idea that literature was not remunerative."

"You are mistaken; its rewards are great. I may mention, by the way, that shortly after you saw me I succeeded to a small income. An uncle died, and proved unexpectedly generous."

"Ah, I see. That must have been convenient."

"It was pleasant—undeniably pleasant. I have always considered it in the light of an endowment of my researches. I told you I was a man of letters; it would, perhaps, be more correct to describe myself as a man of science."

"Dear me, Dyson, you have really changed very much in the last few years. I had a notion, don't you know, that you were a sort of idler about town, the kind of man one might meet on the north side of Piccadilly every day from May to July."

"Exactly. I was even then forming myself, though all unconsciously. You know my poor father could not afford to send me to the University. I used to grumble in my ignorance at not having completed my education. That was the folly of youth,

Salisbury; my University was Piccadilly. There I began to study the great science which still occupies me."

"What science do you mean?"

"The science of the great city; the physiology of London; literally and metaphysically the greatest subject that the mind of man can conceive. What an admirable *salmi* this is; undoubtedly the final end of the pheasant. Yet I feel sometimes positively overwhelmed with the thought of the vastness and complexity of London. Paris a man may get to understand thoroughly with a reasonable amount of study; but London is always a mystery. In Paris you may say: 'Here live the actresses, here the Bohemians, and the *Ratés*'; but it is different in London. You may point out a street, correctly enough, as the abode of washerwomen; but, in that second floor, a man may be studying Chaldee roots, and in the garret over the way a forgotten artist is dying by inches."

"I see you are Dyson, unchanged and unchangeable," said Salisbury, slowly sipping his Chianti. "I think you are misled by a too fervid imagination; the mystery of London exists only in your fancy. It seems to me a dull place enough. We seldom hear of a really artistic crime in London, whereas I believe Paris abounds in that sort of thing."

"Give me some more wine. Thanks. You are mistaken, my dear fellow, you are really mistaken. London has nothing to be ashamed of in the way of crime. Where we fail is for want of Homers, not Agamemnons. *Carent quia vate sacro*, you know."

"I recall the quotation. But I don't think I quite follow you."

"Well, in plain language, we have no good writers in London who make a specialty of that kind of thing. Our common reporter is a dull dog; every story that he has to tell is spoilt in the telling. His idea of horror and of what excites horror is so lamentably deficient. Nothing will content the fellow but blood, vulgar red blood, and when he can get it he lays it on thick, and considers that he has produced a telling article. It's a poor notion. And, by some curious fatality, it is the most commonplace and brutal murders which always attract the most attention and get written up the most. For instance, I dare say that you never heard of the Harlesden case?"

"No; no, I don't remember anything about it."

"Of course not. And yet the story is a curious one. I will

ell it you over our coffee. Harlesden, you know, or I expect ou don't know, is quite on the out-quarters of London; something curiously different from your fine old crusted suburb ike Norwood or Hampstead, different as each of these is from he other. Hampstead, I mean, is where you look for the head of your great China house with his three acres of land and pine-houses, though of late there is the artistic substratum; while Norwood is the home of the prosperous middle-class family who took the house 'because it was near the Palace,' and sickened of the Palace six months afterwards; but Harlesden is a place of no character. It's too new to have any character as yet. There are the rows of red houses and the rows of white houses and the bright green Venetians, and the blistering doorways, and the little backyards they call gardens, and a few feeble shops, and then, just as you think you're going to grasp the physiognomy of the settlement, it all melts away."

"How the dickens is that? the houses don't tumble down before one's eyes, I suppose!"

"Well, no, not exactly that. But Harlesden as an entity disappears. Your street turns into a quiet lane, and your staring houses into elm trees, and the back-gardens into green meadows. You pass instantly from town to country; there is no transition as in a small country town, no soft gradations of wider lawns and orchards, with houses gradually becoming less dense, but a dead stop. I believe the people who live there mostly go into the City. I have seen once or twice a laden 'bus bound thitherwards. But however that may be, I can't conceive a greater loneliness in a desert at midnight than there is there at mid-day. It is like a city of the dead; the streets are glaring and desolate, and as you pass it suddenly strikes you that this too is part of London. Well, a year or two ago there was a doctor living there; he had set up his brass plate and his red lamp at the very end of one of those shining streets, and from the back of the house, the fields stretched away to the north. I don't know what his reason was in settling down in such an out-of-the-way place, perhaps Dr. Black, as we will call him, was a far-seeing man and looked ahead. His relations, so it appeared afterwards, had lost sight of him for many years and didn't even know he was a doctor, much less where he lived. However, there he was settled in Harlesden, with some fragments of a practice, and an uncommonly pretty wife. People used to see them walking out together in the summer

evenings soon after they came to Harlesden, and, so far as
could be observed, they seemed a very affectionate couple.
These walks went on through the autumn, and then ceased,
but, of course, as the days grew dark and the weather cold, the
lanes near Harlesden might be expected to lose many of their
attractions. All through the winter nobody saw anything of
Mrs. Black, the doctor used to reply to his patients' inquiries
that she was a 'little out of sorts, would be better, no doubt, in
the spring.' But the spring came, and the summer, and no
Mrs. Black appeared, and at last people began to rumour
and talk amongst themselves, and all sorts of queer things
were said at 'high teas,' which you may possibly have heard
are the only form of entertainment known in such suburbs.
Dr. Black began to surprise some very odd looks cast in his
derection, and the practice, such as it was, fell off before his
eyes. In short, when the neighbours whispered about the matter, they whispered that Mrs. Black was dead, and that the
doctor had made away with her. But this wasn't the case;
Mrs. Black was seen alive in June. It was a Sunday afternoon, one of those few exquisite days that an English climate
offers, and half London had strayed out into the fields, north,
south, east, and west to smell the scent of the white May, and
to see if the wild roses were yet in blossom in the hedges. I
had gone out myself early in the morning, and had had a long
ramble, and somehow or other as I was steering homeward I
found myself in this very Harlesden we have been talking
about. To be exact, I had a glass of beer in the 'General Gordon,' the most flourishing house in the neighbourhood, and as
I was wandering rather aimlessly about, I saw an uncommonly
tempting gap in a hedgerow, and resolved to explore the
meadow beyond. Soft grass is very grateful to the feet after
the infernal grit strewn on suburban sidewalks, and after
walking about for some time I thought I should like to sit
down on a bank and have a smoke. While I was getting out
my pouch, I looked up in the direction of the houses, and as I
looked I felt my breath caught back, and my teeth began to
chatter, and the stick I had in one hand snapped in two with
the grip I gave it. It was as if I had had an electric current
down my spine, and yet for some moment of time which seemed
long, but which must have been very short, I caught myself
wondering what on earth was the matter. Then I knew what
had made my very heart shudder and my bones grind together

n an agony. As I glanced up I had looked straight towards
the last house in the row before me, and in an upper window
of that house I had seen for some short fraction of a second a
face. It was the face of a woman, and yet it was not human.
You and I, Salisbury, have heard in our time, as we sat in our
seats in church in sober English fashion, of a lust that cannot
be satiated and of a fire that is unquenchable, but few of us
have any notion what these words mean. I hope you never
may, for as I saw that face at the window, with the blue sky
above me and the warm air playing in gusts about me, I knew
I had looked into another world—looked through the window of a commonplace, brand-new house, and seen hell open
before me. When the first shock was over, I thought once or
twice that I should have fainted; my face streamed with a cold
sweat, and my breath came and went in sobs, as if I had been
half drowned. I managed to get up at last, and walk round
to the street, and there I saw the name 'Dr. Black' on the post
by the front gate. As fate or my luck would have it, the door
opened and a man came down the steps as I passed by. I had
no doubt it was the doctor himself. He was of a type rather
common in London; long and thin, with a pasty face and a
dull black moustache. He gave me a look as we passed each
other on the pavement, and though it was merely the casual
glance which one foot-passenger bestows on another, I felt
convinced in my mind that here was an ugly customer to deal
with. As you may imagine, I went my way a good deal puzzled
and horrified too by what I had seen; for I had paid another
visit to the 'General Gordon,' and had got together a good
deal of the common gossip of the place about the Blacks. I
didn't mention the fact that I had seen a woman's face in the
window; but I heard that Mrs. Black had been much admired
for her beautiful golden hair, and round what had struck me
with such a nameless terror, there was a mist of flowing yellow hair, as it was an aureole of glory round the visage of
a satyr. The whole thing bothered me in an indescribable manner; and when I got home I tried my best to think of the
impression I had received as an illusion, but it was no use.
I knew very well I had seen what I have tried to describe to
you, and I was morally certain that I had seen Mrs. Black.
And then there was the gossip of the place, the suspicion of
foul play, which I knew to be false, and my own conviction
that there was some deadly mischief or other going on in that

bright red house at the corner of Devon Road: how to con
struct a theory of a reasonable kind out of these two elements.
In short, I found myself in a world of mystery; I puzzled my
head over it and filled up my leisure moments by gathering
together odd threads of speculation, but I never moved a step
towards any real solution, and as the summer days went on
the matter seemed to grow misty and indistinct, shadowing
some vague terror, like a nightmare of last month. I suppose
it would before long have faded into the background of my
brain—I should not have forgotten it, for such a thing could
never be forgotten—but one morning as I was looking over
the paper my eye was caught by a heading over some two
dozen lines of small type. The words I had seen were simply
'The Harlesden Case,' and I knew what I was going to read.
Mrs. Black was dead. Black had called in another medical
man to certify as to cause of death, and something or other
had aroused the strange doctor's suspicions and there had
been an inquest and *post-mortem*. And the result? That, I
will confess, did astonish me considerably; it was the triumph
of the unexpected. The two doctors who made the autopsy
were obliged to confess that they could not discover the faintest trace of any kind of foul play; their most exquisite tests
and reagents failed to detect the presence of poison in the
most infinitesimal quantity. Death, they found, had been
caused by a somewhat obscure and scientifically interesting
form of brain disease. The tissue of the brain and the molecules of the grey matter had undergone a most extraordinary
series of changes; and the younger of the two doctors, who
has some reputation, I believe, as a specialist in brain trouble,
made some remarks in giving his evidence which struck me
deeply at the time, though I did not then grasp their full significance. He said: 'At the commencement of the examination
I was astonished to find appearances of a character entirely
new to me, notwithstanding my somewhat large experience.
I need not specify these appearances at present, it will be sufficient for me to state that as I proceeded in my task I could
scarcely believe that the brain before me was that of a human
being at all.' There was some surprise at this statement, as
you may imagine, and the coroner asked the doctor if he meant
to say that the brain resembled that of an animal. 'No,' he
replied, 'I should not put it in that way. Some of the appearances I noticed seemed to point in that direction, but others,

and these were the more surprising, indicated a nervous organization of a wholly different character from that either of
man or the lower animals.' It was a curious thing to say, but
of course the jury brought in a verdict of death from natural
causes, and, so far as the public was concerned, the case came
to an end. But after I had read what the doctor said I made
up my mind that I should like to know a good deal more, and
I set to work on what seemed likely to prove an interesting
investigation. I had really a good deal of trouble, but I was
successful in a measure. Though why—my dear fellow, I had
no notion at the time. Are you aware that we have been here
nearly four hours? The waiters are staring at us. Let's have
the bill and be gone."

The two men went out in silence, and stood a moment in the
cool air, watching the hurrying traffic of Coventry Street pass
before them to the accompaniment of the ringing bells of
hansoms and the cries of the newsboys; the deep far murmur
of London surging up ever and again from beneath these
louder noises.

"It is a strange case, isn't it?" said Dyson at length. "What
do you think of it?"

"My dear fellow, I haven't heard the end, so I will reserve
my opinion. When will you give me the sequel?"

"Come to my rooms some evening; say next Thursday.
Here's the address. Good-night; I want to get down to the
Strand." Dyson hailed a passing hansom, and Salisbury
turned northward to walk home to his lodgings.

ii

Mr. Salisbury, as may have been gathered from the few
remarks which he had found it possible to introduce in the
course of the evening, was a young gentleman of a peculiarly
solid form of intellect, coy and retiring before the mysterious
and the uncommon, with a constitutional dislike of paradox.
During the restaurant dinner he had been forced to listen in
almost absolute silence to a strange tissue of improbabilities
strung together with the ingenuity of a born meddler in plots
and mysteries, and it was with a feeling of weariness that he
crossed Shaftesbury Avenue, and dived into the recesses of
Soho, for his lodgings were in a modest neighbourhood to the

north of Oxford Street. As he walked he speculated on the probable fate of Dyson, relying on literature, unbefriended by a thoughtful relative, and could not help concluding that so much subtlety united to a too vivid imagination would in all likelihood have been rewarded with a pair of sandwich-boards or a super's banner. Absorbed in this train of thought, and admiring the perverse dexterity which could transmute the face of a sickly woman and a case of brain disease into the crude elements of romance, Salisbury strayed on through the dimly-lighted streets, not noticing the gusty wind which drove sharply round corners and whirled the stray rubbish of the pavement into the air in eddies, while black clouds gathered over the sickly yellow moon. Even a stray drop or two of rain blown into his face did not rouse him from his meditations, and it was only when with a sudden rush the storm tore down upon the street that he began to consider the expediency of finding some shelter. The rain, driven by the wind, pelted down with the violence of a thunderstorm, dashing up from the stones and hissing through the air, and soon a perfect torrent of water coursed along the kennels and accumulated in pools over the choked-up drains. The few stray passengers who had been loafing rather than walking about the street had scuttered away, like frightened rabbits, to some invisible places of ref-uge, and though Salisbury whistled loud and long for a han-som, no hansom appeared. He looked about him, as if to discover how far he might be from the haven of Oxford Street, but strolling carelessly along, he had turned out of his way, and found himself in an unknown region, and one to all ap-pearance devoid even of a public-house where shelter could be bought for the modest sum of two pence. The street lamps were few and at long intervals, and burned behind grimy glasses with the sickly light of oil, and by this wavering glim-mer Salisbury could make out the shadowy and vast old houses of which the street was composed. As he passed along, hurry-ing, and shrinking from the full sweep of the rain, he noticed the innumerable bell-handles, with names that seemed about to vanish of old age graven on brass plates beneath them, and here and there a richly carved pent-house overhung the door, blackening with the grime of fifty years. The storm seemed to grow more and more furious; he was wet through, and a new hat had become a ruin, and still Oxford Street seemed as far off as ever; it was with deep relief that the dripping man

caught sight of a dark archway which seemed to promise
shelter from the rain if not from the wind. Salisbury took up
his position in the driest corner and looked about him; he
was standing in a kind of passage contrived under part of a
house, and behind him stretched a narrow footway leading
between blank walls to regions unknown. He had stood there
for some time, vainly endeavouring to rid himself of some of
his superfluous moisture, and listening for the passing wheel
of a hansom, when his attention was aroused by a loud noise
coming from the direction of the passage behind, and growing
louder as it drew nearer. In a couple of minutes he could make
out the shrill, raucous voice of a woman, threatening and re-
nouncing and making the very stones echo with her accents,
while now and then a man grumbled and expostulated. Though
to all appearance devoid of romance, Salisbury had some relish for street rows, and was, indeed, somewhat of an amateur
in the more amusing phases of drunkenness; he therefore
composed himself to listen and observe with something of the
air of a subscriber to grand opera. To his annoyance, however,
the tempest seemed suddenly to be composed, and he could
hear nothing but the impatient steps of the woman and the
slow lurch of the man as they came towards him. Keeping
back in the shadow of the wall, he could see the two drawing
nearer; the man was evidently drunk, and had much ado to
avoid frequent collision with the wall as he tacked across from
one side to the other, like some bark beating up against a wind.
The woman was looking straight in front of her, with tears
streaming from her blazing eyes, but suddenly as they went
by the flame blazed up again, and she burst forth into a torrent of abuse, facing round upon her companion.

"You low rascal, you mean, contemptible cur," she went on,
after an incoherent storm of curses, "you think I'm to work
and slave for you always, I suppose, while you're after that
Green Street girl and drinking every penny you've got? But
you're mistaken, Sam—indeed, I'll bear it no longer. Damn
you, you dirty thief, I've done with you and your master too,
so you can go your own errands, and I only hope they'll get
you into trouble."

The woman tore at the bosom of her dress, and taking something out that looked like paper, crumpled it up and flung it
away. It fell at Salisbury's feet. She ran out and disappeared
in the darkness, while the man lurched slowly into the street,

grumbling indistinctly to himself in a perplexed tone of voice. Salisbury looked out after him, and saw him maundering along the pavement, halting now and then and swaying indecisively, and then starting off at some fresh tangent. The sky had cleared, and white fleecy clouds were fleeting across the moon, high in the heaven. The light came and went by turns, as the clouds passed by, and, turning round as the clear, white rays shone into the passage, Salisbury saw the little ball of crumpled paper which the woman had cast down. Oddly curious to know what it might contain, he picked it up and put it in his pocket, and set out afresh on his journey.

iii

Salisbury was a man of habit. When he got home, drenched to the skin, his clothes hanging lank about him, and a ghastly dew besmearing his hat, his only thought was of his health, of which he took studious care. So, after changing his clothes and encasing himself in a warm dressing-gown, he proceeded to prepare a sudorific in the shape of hot gin and water, warming the latter over one of those spirit-lamps which mitigate the austerities of the modern hermit's life. By the time this preparation had been exhibited, and Salisbury's disturbed feelings had been soothed by a pipe of tobacco, he was able to get into bed in a happy state of vacancy, without a thought of his adventure in the dark archway, or of the weird fancies with which Dyson had seasoned his dinner. It was the same at breakfast the next morning, for Salisbury made a point of not thinking of any thing until that meal was over; but when the cup and saucer were cleared away, and the morning pipe was lit, he remembered the little ball of paper, and began fumbling in the pockets of his wet coat. He did not remember into which pocket he had put it, and as he dived now into one and now into another, he experienced a strange feeling of apprehension lest it should not be there at all, though he could not for the life of him have explained the importance he attached to what was in all probability mere rubbish. But he sighed with relief when his fingers touched the crumpled surface in an inside pocket, and he drew it out gently and laid it on the little desk by his easy-chair with as much care as if it had been some rare jewel. Salisbury sat smoking and staring at his find for a few minutes, an odd temptation to throw the thing in the fire and have done with it struggling with as odd a speculation as to its possible contents, and as to the reason why the infuriated woman should have flung a bit of paper from her with such vehemence. As might be expected, it was the latter feeling that conquered in the end, and yet it was with something like repugnance that he at last took the paper and unrolled it, and laid it out before him. It was a piece of common dirty paper, to all appearance torn out of a cheap exercise-book, and in the middle were a few lines written in a queer cramped hand. Salisbury bent his head and stared eagerly at it for a moment, drawing a long breath, and then fell back in his chair gazing blankly before him, till at last with a sudden revulsion he burst into a peal of laughter, so long and loud and uproarious that the landlady's baby in the floor below awoke from sleep and echoed his mirth with hideous yells. But he laughed again and again, and took the paper up to read a second time what seemed such meaningless nonsense.

"Q. has had to go and see his friends in Paris," it began. "Traverse Handel S. 'Once around the grass, and twice around the lass, and thrice around the maple tree.'"

Salisbury took up the paper and crumpled it as the angry woman had done, and aimed it at the fire. He did not throw it there, however, but tossed it carelessly into the well of the desk, and laughed again. The sheer folly of the thing offended him, and he was ashamed of his own eager speculation, as one who pores over the high-sounding announcements in the agony column of the daily paper, and finds nothing but advertisement and triviality. He walked to the window, and stared out at the languid morning life of his quarter; the maids in slatternly print dresses washing door-steps, the fish-monger and the butcher on their rounds, and the tradesmen standing at the doors of their small shops, drooping for lack of trade and excitement. In the distance a blue haze gave some grandeur to the prospect, but the view as a whole was depressing, and would only have interested a student of the life of London, who finds something rare and choice in its every aspect. Salisbury turned away in disgust, and settled himself in the easy-chair, upholstered in a bright shade of green, and decked with yellow gimp, which was the pride and attraction of the apart-

ments. Here he composed himself to his morning's occupation
—the perusal of a novel that dealt with sport and love in a
manner that suggested the collaboration of a stud-groom and
a ladies' college. In an ordinary way, however, Salisbury
would have been carried on by the interest of the story up to
lunch-time, but this morning he fidgeted in and out of his
chair, took the book up and laid it down again, and swore at
last to himself and at himself in mere irritation. In point of
fact the jingle of the paper found in the archway had "got
into his head," and do what he would he could not help muttering over and over, "Once around the grass, and twice around
the lass, and thrice around the maple tree." It became a positive pain, like the foolish burden of a music-hall song, everlastingly quoted, and sung at all hours of the day and night,
and treasured by the street boys as an unfailing resource for
six months together. He went out into the streets, and tried to
forget his enemy in the jostling of the crowds and the roar and
clatter of the traffic, but presently he would find himself stealing quietly aside, and pacing some deserted byway, vainly
puzzling his brains, and trying to fix some meaning to phrases
that were meaningless. It was a positive relief when Thursday
came, and he remembered that he had made an appointment
to go and see Dyson; the flimsy reveries of the self-styled man
of letters appeared entertaining when compared with this
ceaseless iteration, this maze of thought from which there
seemed no possibility of escape. Dyson's abode was in one of
the quietest of the quiet streets that lead down from the Strand
to the river, and when Salisbury passed from the narrow stairway into his friend's room, he saw that the uncle had been
beneficent indeed. The floor glowed and flamed with all the
colours of the East; it was, as Dyson pompously remarked, "a
sunset in a dream," and the lamplight, the twilight of London
streets, was shut out with strangely worked curtains, glittering here and there with threads of gold. In the shelves of an
oak *armoire* stood jars and plates of old French china, and
the black and white of etchings not to be found in the Hay-
market or in Bond Street, stood out against the splendour of a
Japanese paper. Salisbury sat down on the settle by the
hearth, and sniffed and mingled fumes of incense and tobacco, wondering and dumb before all this splendour after the
green rep and the oleographs, the gilt-framed mirror, and the
lustres of his own apartment.

"I am glad you have come," said Dyson. "Comfortable little room, isn't it? But you don't look very well, Salisbury. Nothing disagreed with you, has it?"

"No; but I have been a good deal bothered for the last few days. The fact is I had an odd kind of—of—adventure, I suppose I may call it, that night I saw you, and it has worried me a good deal. And the provoking part of it is that it's the merest nonsense—but, however, I will tell you all about it, by and by. You were going to let me have the rest of that odd story you began at the restaurant."

"Yes. But I am afraid, Salisbury, you are incorrigible. You are a slave to what you call matter of fact. You know perfectly well that in your heart you think the oddness in that case is of my making, and that it is all really as plain as the police reports. However, as I have begun, I will go on. But first we will have something to drink, and you may as well light your pipe."

Dyson went up to the oak cupboard, and drew from its depths a rotund bottle and two little glasses, quaintly gilded. "It's Benedictine," he said. "You'll have some, won't you?"

Salisbury assented, and the two men sat sipping and smoking reflectively for some minutes before Dyson began.

"Let me see," he said at last, "we were at the inquest, weren't we? No, we had done with that. Ah, I remember. I was telling you that on the whole I had been successful in my inquiries, investigation, or whatever you like to call it, into the matter. Wasn't that where I left off?"

"Yes, that was it. To be precise, I think 'though' was the last word you said on the matter."

"Exactly. I have been thinking it all over since the other night, and I have come to the conclusion that that 'though' is a very big 'though' indeed. Not to put too fine a point on it, I have had to confess that what I found out, or thought I found out, amounts in reality to nothing. I am as far away from the heart of the case as ever. However, I may as well tell you what I do know. You may remember my saying that I was impressed a good deal by some remarks of one of the doctors who gave evidence at the inquest. Well, I determined that my first step must be to try if I could get something more definite and intelligible out of that doctor. Somehow or other I managed to get an introduction to the man, and he gave me an appointment to come and see him. He turned out to be a pleasant, genial fellow; rather young and not in the least like the typical medical man, and he began the conference by offering me whisky and cigars. I didn't think it worth while to beat about the bush, so I began by saying that part of his evidence at the Harlesden Inquest struck me as very peculiar, and I gave him the printed report, with the sentences in question underlined. He just glanced at the slip, and gave me a queer look. 'It struck you as peculiar, did it?' said he. 'Well, you must remember that the Harlesden case was very peculiar. In fact, I think I may safely say that in some features it was unique—quite unique.' 'Quite so,' I replied, 'and that's exactly why it interests me, and why I want to know more about it. And I thought that if anybody could give me any information it would be you. What is your opinion of the matter?'

"It was a pretty downright sort of question, and my doctor looked rather taken aback.

"'Well,' he said, 'as I fancy your motive in inquiring into the question must be mere curiosity, I think I may tell you my opinion with tolerable freedom. So, Mr., Mr. Dyson? if you want to know my theory, it is this: I believe that Dr. Black killed his wife.'

"'But the verdict,' I answered, 'the verdict was given from your own evidence.'

"'Quite so; the verdict was given in accordance with the evidence of my colleague and myself, and, under the circumstances, I think the jury acted very sensibly. In fact, I don't see what else they could have done. But I stick to my opinion, mind you, and I say this also. I don't wonder at Black's doing what I firmly believe he did. I think he was justified.'

"'Justified! How could that be?' I asked. I was astonished, as you may imagine, at the answer I had got. The doctor wheeled round his chair and looked steadily at me for a moment before he answered.

"'I suppose you are not a man of science yourself? No; then it would be of no use my going into detail. I have always been firmly opposed myself to any partnership between physiology and psychology. I believe that both are bound to suffer. No one recognizes more decidedly than I do the impassable gulf, the fathomless abyss that separates the world of consciousness from the sphere of matter. We know that every change of consciousness is accompanied by a rearrangement of the molecules in the grey matter; and that is all. What the

nk between them is, or why they occur together, we do not
now, and most authorities believe that we never can know.
et, I will tell you that as I did my work, the knife in my
and, I felt convinced, in spite of all theories, that what lay
efore me was not the brain of a dead woman—not the brain
f a human being at all. Of course I saw the face; but it was
uite placid, devoid of all expression. It must have been a
eautiful face, no doubt, but I can honestly say that I would
ot have looked in that face when there was life behind it for
thousand guineas, no, nor for twice that sum.'

"'My dear sir,' I said, 'you surprise me extremely. You say
hat it was not the brain of a human being. What was it,
hen?''

"'The brain of a devil.' He spoke quite coolly, and never
noved a muscle. 'The brain of a devil,'' he repeated, 'and I
ave no doubt that Black found some way of putting an end
o it. I don't blame him if he did. Whatever Mrs. Black was,
he was not fit to stay in this world. Will you have anything
nore? No? Good-night, good-night.'

"It was a queer sort of opinion to get from a man of science,
wasn't it? When he was saying that he would not have looked
on that face when alive for a thousand guineas, or two thousand guineas, I was thinking of the face I had seen, but I said
nothing. I went again to Harlesden, and passed from one shop
to another, making small purchases, and trying to find out
whether there was anything about the Blacks which was not
already common property, but there was very little to hear.
One of the tradesmen to whom I spoke said he had known the
dead woman well; she used to buy of him such quantities of
grocery as were required for their small household, for they
never kept a servant, but had a charwoman in occasionally,
and she had not seen Mrs. Black for months before she died.
According to this man Mrs. Black was 'a nice lady,' always
kind and considerate, and so fond of her husband and he of
her, as every one thought. And yet, to put the doctor's opinion
on one side, I knew what I had seen. And then after thinking
it all over, and putting one thing with another, it seemed to
me that the only person likely to give me much assistance
would be Black himself, and I made up my mind to find him.
Of course he wasn't to be found in Harlesden; he had left, I
was told, directly after the funeral. Everything in the house
had been sold, and one fine day Black got into the train with a

small portmanteau, and went, nobody knew where. It was
chance if he were ever heard of again, and it was by a mer
chance that I came across him at last. I was walking one da
along Gray's Inn Road, not bound for anywhere in particular
but looking about me, as usual, and holding on to my hat, fo
it was a gusty day in early March, and the wind was makin§
the treetops in the Inn rock and quiver. I had come up fron
the Holborn end, and I had almost got to Theobald's Road
when I noticed a man walking in front of me, leaning on ε
stick, and to all appearance very feeble. There was something
about his look that made me curious, I don't know why, and .
began to walk briskly with the idea of overtaking him, when o:
a sudden his hat blew off and came bounding along the pave
ment to my feet. Of course I rescued the hat, and gave it ε
glance as I went towards its owner. It was a biography in it
self; a Piccadilly maker's name in the inside, but I don't think
a beggar would have picked it out of the gutter. Then I looked
up and saw Dr. Black of Harlesden waiting for me. A queer
thing, wasn't it? But, Salisbury, what a change! When I saw
Dr. Black come down the steps of his house at Harlesden he
was an upright man, walking firmly with well-built limbs; a
man, I should say, in the prime of his life. And now before me
there crouched this wretched creature, bent and feeble, with
shrunken cheeks, and hair that was whitening fast, and limbs
that trembled and shook together, and misery in his eyes. He
thanked me for bringing him his hat, saying, 'I don't think I
should ever have got it, I can't run much now. A gusty day,
sir, isn't it?' and with this he was turning away, but by little
and little I contrived to draw him into the current of conversation, and we walked together eastward. I think the man
would have been glad to get rid of me; but I didn't intend to
let him go, and he stopped at last in front of a miserable house
in a miserable street. It was, I verily believe, one of the most
wretched quarters I have ever seen: houses that must have been
sordid and hideous enough when new, that had gathered foulness with every year, and now seemed to lean and totter to
their fall. 'I live up there,' said Black, pointing to the tiles,
'not in the front—in the back. I am very quiet there. I won't
ask you to come in now, but perhaps some other day——' I
caught him up at that, and told him I should be only too glad
to come and see him. He gave me an odd sort of glance, as if
he were wondering what on earth I or anybody else could care

about him, and I left him fumbling with his latch-key. I think
you will say I did pretty well when I tell you that within a
few weeks I had made myself an intimate friend of Black's. I
shall never forget the first time I went to his room; I hope I
shall never see such abject, squalid misery again. The foul
paper, from which all pattern or trace of a pattern had long
vanished, subdued and penetrated with the grime of the evil
street, was hanging in mouldering pennons from the wall.
Only at the end of the room was it possible to stand upright,
and the sight of the wretched bed and the odour of corruption
that pervaded the place made me turn faint and sick. Here
I found him munching a piece of bread; he seemed surprised
to find that I had kept my promise, but he gave me his chair
and sat on the bed while we talked. I used to go to see him
often, and we had long conversations together, but he never
mentioned Harlesden or his wife. I fancy that he supposed me
ignorant of the matter, or thought that if I had heard of it,
I should never connect the respectable Dr. Black of Harlesden
with a poor garreteer in the backwoods of London. He was a
strange man, and as we sat together smoking, I often wondered whether he were mad or sane, for I think the wildest
dreams of Paracelsus and the Rosicrucians would appear plain
and sober fact compared with the theories I have heard him
earnestly advance in that grimy den of his. I once ventured
to hint something of the sort to him. I suggested that something he had said was in flat contradiction to all science and
all experience. 'No,' he answered, 'not all experience, for mine
counts for something. I am no dealer in unproved theories;
what I say I have proved for myself, and at a terrible cost.
There is a region of knowledge which you will never know,
which wise men seeing from afar off shun like the plague, as
well they may, but into that region I have gone. If you knew,
if you could even dream of what may be done, of what one or
two men have done in this quiet world of ours, your very soul
would shudder and faint within you. What you have heard
from me has been but the merest husk and outer covering of
true science—that science which means death, and that which
is more awful than death, to those who gain it. No, when men
say that there are strange things in the world, they little know
the awe and the terror that dwell always with them and about
them.' There was a sort of fascination about the man that drew
me to him, and I was quite sorry to have to leave London for a

month or two; I missed his odd talk. A few days after I came
back to town I thought I would look him up, but when I gave
the two rings at the bell that used to summon him, there was
no answer. I rang and rang again, and was just turning to go
away, when the door opened and a dirty woman asked me what
I wanted. From her look I fancy she took me for a plain
clothes officer after one of her lodgers, but when I inquired
if Mr. Black were in, she gave me a stare of another kind.
'There's no Mr. Black lives here,' she said. 'He's gone. He's
dead this six weeks. I always thought he was a bit queer in his
head, or else had been and got into some trouble or other. He
used to go out every morning from ten till one, and one Monday morning we heard him come in, and go into his room and
shut the door, and a few minutes after, just as we was a-sitting
down to our dinner, there was such a scream that I thought I
should have gone right off. And then we heard a stamping
and down he came, raging and cursing most dreadful, swearing he had been robbed of something that was worth millions.
And then he just dropped down in the passage, and we
thought he was dead. We got him up to his room, and put him
on his bed, and I just sat there and waited, while my 'usband
he went for the doctor. And there was the winder wide open,
and a little tin box he had lying on the floor open and empty,
but of course nobody could possible have got in at the winder,
and as for him having anything that was worth anything, it's
nonsense, for he was often weeks and weeks behind with his
rent, and my 'usband he threatened often and often to turn
him into the street, for, as he said, we've got a living to myke
like other people—and, of course, that's true; but, somehow,
I didn't like to do it, though he was an odd kind of a man, and
I fancy had been better off. And then the doctor came and
looked at him, and said as he couldn't do nothing, and that
night he died as I was a-sitting by his bed; and I can tell you
that, with one thing and another, we lost money by him, for
the few bits of clothes as he had were worth next to nothing
when they came to be sold.' I gave the woman half a sovereign
for her trouble, and went home thinking of Dr. Black and the
epitaph she had made him, and wondering at his strange fancy
that he had been robbed. I take it that he had very little to
fear on that score, poor fellow; but I suppose that he was
really mad, and died in a sudden access of his mania. His landlady said that once or twice when she had had occasion to go

into his room (to dun the poor wretch for his rent, most likely), he would keep her at the door for about a minute, and that when she came in she would find him putting away his tin box in the corner by the window; I suppose he had become possessed with the idea of some great treasure, and fancied himself a wealthy man in the midst of all his misery. *Explicit*, my tale is ended, and you see that though I knew Black, I know nothing of his wife or of the history of her death.—— That's the Harlesden case, Salisbury, and I think it interests me all the more deeply because there does not seem the shadow of a possibility that I or any one else will ever know more about it. What do you think of it?"

"Well, Dyson, I must say that I think you have contrived to surround the whole thing with a mystery of your own making. I go for the doctor's solution: Black murdered his wife, being himself in all probability an undeveloped lunatic."

"What? Do you believe, then, that this woman was something too awful, too terrible to be allowed to remain on the earth? You will remember that the doctor said it was the brain of a devil?"

"Yes, yes, but he was speaking, of course, metaphorically. It's really quite a simple matter if you only look at it like that."

"Ah, well, you may be right; but yet I am sure you are not. Well, well, it's no good discussing it any more. A little more Benedictine? That's right; try some of this tobacco. Didn't you say that you had been bothered by something—something which happened that night we dined together?"

"Yes, I have been worried, Dyson, worried a great deal. I—— But it's such a trivial matter—indeed, such an absurdity—that I feel ashamed to trouble you with it."

"Never mind, let's have it, absurd or not."

With many hesitations, and with much inward resentment of the folly of the thing, Salisbury told his tale, and repeated reluctantly the absurd intelligence and the absurder doggerel of the scrap of paper, expecting to hear Dyson burst out into a roar of laughter.

"Isn't it too bad that I should let myself be bothered by such stuff as that?" he asked, when he had stuttered out the jingle of once, and twice, and thrice.

Dyson had listened to it all gravely, even to the end, and meditated for a few minutes in silence.

"Yes," he said at length, "it was a curious chance, your taking shelter in that archway just as those two went by. But I don't know that I should call what was written on the paper nonsense; it is bizarre certainly, but I expect it has a meaning for somebody. Just repeat it again, will you, and I will write it down. Perhaps we might find a cipher of some sort, though I hardly think we shall."

Again had the reluctant lips of Salisbury slowly to stammer out the rubbish that he abhorred, while Dyson jotted it down on a slip of paper.

"Look over it, will you?" he said, when it was done; "it may be important that I should have every word in its place. Is that all right?"

"Yes; that is an accurate copy. But I don't think you will get much out of it. Depend upon it, it is mere nonsense, a wanton scribble. I must be going now, Dyson. No, no more; that stuff of yours is pretty strong. Good-night."

"I suppose you would like to hear from me, if I did find out anything?"

"No, not I; I don't want to hear about the thing again. You may regard the discovery, if it is one, as your own."

"Very well.. Good-night."

iv

A good many hours after Salisbury had returned to the company of the green rep chairs, Dyson still sat at his desk, itself a Japanese romance, smoking many pipes, and meditating over his friend's story. The bizarre quality of the inscription which had annoyed Salisbury was to him an attraction, and now and again he took it up and scanned thoughtfully what he had written, especially the quaint jingle at the end. It was a token, a symbol, he decided, and not a cipher, and the woman who had flung it away was in all probability entirely ignorant of its meaning; she was but the agent of the "Sam" she had abused and discarded, and he too was again the agent of some one unknown; possibly of the individual styled Q, who had been forced to visit his French friends. But what to make of "Traverse Handel S." Here was the root and source of the enigma, and not all the tobacco of Virginia seemed likely to suggest any clue here. It seemed almost hopeless, but Dyson regarded himself as the Wellington of mysteries, and went to bed feeling assured that sooner or later he would hit upon the right track. For the next few days he was deeply engaged in his literary labours, labours which were a profound mystery even to the most intimate of his friends, who searched the railway bookstalls in vain for the result of so many hours spent at the Japanese bureau in company with strong tobacco and black tea. On this occasion Dyson confined himself to his room for four days, and it was with genuine relief that he laid down his pen and went out into the streets in quest of relaxation and fresh air. The gas-lamps were being lighted, and the fifth edition of the evening papers was being howled through the streets, and Dyson, feeling that he wanted quiet, turned away from the clamorous Strand, and began to trend away to the north-west. Soon he found himself in streets that echoed to his footsteps, and crossing a broad new thoroughfare, and verging still to the west, Dyson discovered that he had penetrated to the depths of Soho. Here again was life; rare vintages of France and Italy, at prices which seemed contemptibly small, allured the passer-by; here were cheeses, vast and rich, here olive oil, and here a grove of Rabelaisian sausages; while in a neighbouring shop the whole Press of Paris appeared to be on sale. In the middle of the roadway a strange miscellany of nations sauntered to and fro, for there cab and hansom rarely ventured; and from window over window the inhabitants looked forth in pleased contemplation of the scene. Dyson made his way slowly along, mingling with the crowd on the cobble-stones, listening to the queer babel of French and German, and Italian and English, glancing now and again at the shop-windows with their levelled batteries of bottles, and had almost gained the end of the street, when his attention was arrested by a small shop at the corner, a vivid contrast to its neighbours. It was the typical shop of the poor quarter; a shop entirely English. Here were vended tobacco and sweets, cheap pipes of clay and cherry-wood; penny exercise-books and pen-holders jostled for precedence with comic songs, and story papers with appalling cuts showed that romance claimed its place beside the actualities of the evening paper, the bills of which fluttered at the doorway. Dyson glanced up at the name above the door, and stood by the kennel trembling, for a sharp pang, the pang of one who has made a discovery, had for a moment left him incapable of motion. The name over the shop was Travers. Dyson looked up again, this time at the corner of the wall above the lamp-post, and read in white letters on a blue ground the words "Handel Street, W. C." and the legend was repeated in fainter letters just below. He gave a little sigh of satisfaction, and without more ado walked boldly into the shop, and stared full in the face of the fat man who was sitting behind the counter. The fellow rose to his feet, and returned the stare a little curiously, and then began in stereotyped phrase—

"What can I do for you, sir?"

Dyson enjoyed the situation and a dawning perplexity on the man's face. He propped his stick carefully against the counter and leaning over it, said slowly and impressively—

"Once around the grass, and twice around the lass, and thrice around the maple-tree."

Dyson had calculated on his words producing an effect, and he was not disappointed. The vendor of the miscellanies gasped, open-mouthed like a fish, and steadied himself against the counter. When he spoke, after a short interval, it was in a hoarse mutter, tremulous and unsteady.

"Would you mind saying that again, sir? I didn't quite catch it."

"My good man, I shall most certainly do nothing of the kind. You heard what I said perfectly well. You have got a clock in your shop, I see; an admirable timekeeper, I have no doubt. Well, I give you a minute by your own clock."

The man looked about him in a perplexed indecision, and Dyson felt that it was time to be bold.

"Look here, Travers, the time is nearly up. You have heard of Q, I think. Remember, I hold your life in my hands. Now!"

Dyson was shocked at the result of his own audacity. The man shrank and shrivelled in terror, the sweat poured down a face of ashy white, and he held up his hands before him.

"Mr. Davies, Mr. Davies, don't say that—don't for Heaven's sake. I didn't know you at first, I didn't indeed. Good God! Mr. Davies, you wouldn't ruin me? I'll get it in a moment."

"You had better not lose any more time."

The man slunk piteously out of his own shop, and went into a back parlour. Dyson heard his trembling fingers fumbling with a bunch of keys, and the creak of an opening box. He came back presently with a small package neatly tied up in brown paper in his hands, and still, full of terror, handed it to Dyson.

"I'm glad to be rid of it," he said, "I'll take no more jobs of this sort."

Dyson took the parcel and his stick, and walked out of the shop with a nod, turning round as he passed the door. Travers had sunk into his seat, his face still white with terror, with one hand over his eyes, and Dyson speculated a good deal as he walked rapidly away as to what queer chords those could be on which he had played so roughly. He hailed the first hansom he could see and drove home, and when he had lit his hanging lamp, and laid his parcel on the table, he paused for a moment, wondering on what strange thing the lamp-light would soon shine. He locked his door, and cut the strings, and unfolded the paper layer after layer, and came at last to a small wooden box, simply but solidly made. There was no lock, and Dyson had simply to raise the lid, and as he did so he drew a long breath and started back. The lamp seemed to glimmer feebly like a single candle, but the whole room blazed with light—and not with light alone, but with a thousand colours, with all the glories of some painted window; and upon the walls of his room and on the familiar furniture, the glow flamed back and seemed to flow again to its source, the little wooden box. For there upon a bed of soft wool lay the most splendid jewel, a jewel such as Dyson had never dreamed of, and within it shone the blue of far skies, and the green of the sea by the shore, and the red of the ruby, and deep violet rays, and in the middle of all it seemed aflame as if a fountain of fire rose up, and fell, and rose again with sparks like stars for drops. Dyson gave a long deep sigh, and dropped into his chair, and put his hands over his eyes to think. The jewel was like an opal, but from a long experience of the shop-windows he knew there was no such thing as an opal one-quarter or one-eighth of its size. He looked at the stone again, with a feeling that was almost awe, and placed it gently on the table under the lamp, and watched the wonderful flame that shone and sparkled in its centre, and then turned to the box, curious to know whether it might contain other marvels. He lifted the bed of wool on which the opal had reclined, and saw beneath, no more jewels, but a little old pocket-book, worn and shabby

with use. Dyson opened it at the first leaf, and dropped th
book again appalled. He had read the name of the owner
neatly written in blue ink:

STEVEN BLACK, M. D.,
Oranmore,
Devon Road,
Harlesden.

It was several minutes before Dyson could bring himself t
open the book a second time; he remembered the wretched exil
in his garret; and his strange talk, and the memory too of th
face he had seen at the window, and of what the specialist ha
said, surged up in his mind, and as he held his finger on th
cover, he shivered, dreading what might be written within
When at last he held it in his hand, and turned the pages, h
found that the first two leaves were blank, but the third wa
covered with clear, minute writing, and Dyson began to rea
with the light of the opal flaming in his eyes.

v

"Ever since I was a young man"—the record began—"I de
voted all my leisure and a good deal of time that ought to hav
been given to other studies to the investigation of curious an
obscure branches of knowledge. What are commonly called th
pleasures of life had never any attractions for me, and I live
alone in London, avoiding my fellow-students, and in my turr
avoided by them as a man self-absorbed and unsympathetic
So long as I could gratify my desire of knowledge of a pe
culiar kind, knowledge of which the very existence is a pro
found secret to most men, I was intensely happy, and I hav
often spent whole nights sitting in the darkness of my room
and thinking of the strange world on the brink of which I trod
My professional studies, however, and the necessity of obtaining a degree, for some time forced my more obscure employ
ment into the background, and soon after I had qualified I
met Agnes, who became my wife. We took a new house in thi
remote suburb, and I began the regular routine of a sobe
practice, and for some months lived happily enough, sharing
in the life about me, and only thinking at odd intervals of tha

occult science which had once fascinated my whole being. I had
learnt enough of the paths I had begun to tread to know that
they were beyond all expression difficult and dangerous, that
to persevere meant in all probability the wreck of a life, and
that they led to regions so terrible, that the mind of man
shrinks appalled at the very thought. Moreover, the quiet and
the peace I had enjoyed since my marriage had wiled me away
to a great extent from places where I knew no peace could
dwell. But suddenly—I think indeed it was the work of a
single night, as I lay awake on my bed gazing into the darkness—suddenly, I say, the old desire, the former longing, returned, and returned with a force that had been intensified ten
times by its absence; and when the day dawned and I looked out
of the window, and saw with haggard eyes the sunrise in the
east, I knew that my doom had been pronounced; that as I had
gone far, so now I must go farther with unfaltering steps. I
turned to the bed where my wife was sleeping peacefully, and
lay down again, weeping bitter tears, for the sun had set on our
happy life and had risen with a dawn of terror to us both. I
will not set down here in minute detail what followed; outwardly I went about the day's labour as before, saying nothing to my wife. But she soon saw that I had changed; I spent
my spare time in a room which I had fitted up as a laboratory,
and often I crept upstairs in the grey dawn of the morning,
when the light of many lamps still glowed over London; and
each night I had stolen a step nearer to that great abyss which
I was to bridge over, the gulf between the world of consciousness and the world of matter. My experiments were many and
complicated in their nature, and it was some months before I
realized whither they all pointed, and when this was borne in
upon me in a moment's time, I felt my face whiten and my
heart still within me. But the power to draw back, the power
to stand before the doors that now opened wide before me and
not to enter in, had long ago been absent; the way was closed,
and I could only pass onward. My position was as utterly
hopeless as that of the prisoner in an utter dungeon, whose
only light is that of the dungeon above him; the doors were
shut and escape was impossible. Experiment after experiment
gave the same result, and I knew, and shrank even as the
thought passed through my mind, that in the work I had to
do there must be elements which no laboratory could furnish,
which no scales could ever measure. In that work, from which

even I doubted to escape with life, life itself must enter; from
some human being there must be drawn that essence which
men call the soul, and in its place (for in the scheme of the
world there is no vacant chamber)—in its place would enter
in what the lips can hardly utter, what the mind cannot conceive without a horror more awful than the horror of death
itself. And when I knew this, I knew also on whom this fate
would fall; I looked into my wife's eyes. Even at that hour
if I had gone out and taken a rope and hanged myself, I might
have escaped, and she also, but in no other way. At last I told
her all. She shuddered, and wept, and called on her dead
mother for help, and asked me if I had no mercy, and I could
only sigh. I concealed nothing from her; I told her what she
would become, and what would enter in where her life had
been; I told her of all the shame and of all the horror. You
who will read this when I am dead—if indeed I allow this record to survive,—you who have opened the box and have seen
what lies there, if you could understand what lies hidden in
that opal! For one night my wife consented to what I asked
of her, consented with the tears running down her beautiful
face, and hot shame flushing red over her neck and breast, consented to undergo this for me. I threw open the window, and
we looked together at the sky and the dark earth for the last
time; it was a fine star-light night, and there was a pleasant
breeze blowing, and I kissed her on her lips, and her tears ran
down upon my face. That night she came down to my laboratory, and there, with shutters bolted and barred down, with
curtains drawn thick and close, so that the very stars might
be shut out from the sight of that room, while the crucible
hissed and boiled over the lamp, I did what had to be done,
and led out what was no longer a woman. But on the table the
opal flamed and sparkled with such light as no eyes of man
have ever gazed on, and the rays of the flame that was within
it flashed and glittered, and shone even to my heart. My wife
had only asked one thing of me; that when there came at
last what I had told her, I would kill her. I have kept that
promise."

There was nothing more. Dyson let the little pocketbook
fall, and turned and looked again at the opal with its flaming
inmost light, and then with unutterable irresistible horror
surging up in his heart, grasped the jewel, and flung it on the

ground, and trampled it beneath his heel. His face was white with terror as he turned away, and for a moment stood sick and trembling, and then with a start he leapt across the room and steadied himself against the door. There was an angry hiss, as of steam escaping under great pressure, and as he gazed, motionless, a volume of heavy yellow smoke was slowly issuing from the very centre of the jewel, and wreathing itself in snakelike coils above it. And then a thin white flame burst forth from the smoke, and shot up into the air and vanished; and on the ground there lay a thing like a cinder, black and crumbling to the touch.

H. G. Wells

THE COUNTRY
OF THE BLIND

THREE hundred miles and more from Chimborazo, one hundred
from the snows of Cotopaxi, in the wildest wastes of Ecuador's
Andes, there lies that mysterious mountain valley, cut off from
the world of men, the Country of the Blind. Long years ago
that valley lay so far open to the world that men might come
at last through frightful gorges and over an icy pass into its
equable meadows; and thither indeed men came, a family or so
of Peruvian half-breeds fleeing from the lust and tyranny of
an evil Spanish ruler. Then came the stupendous outbreak of
Mindobamba, when it was night in Quito for seventeen days,
and the water was boiling at Yaguachi and all the fish floating
dying even as far as Guayaquil; everywhere along the Pacific
slopes there were landslips and swift thawings and sudden
floods, and one whole side of the old Arauca crest slipped and
came down in thunder, and cut off the Country of the Blind
for ever from the exploring feet of men. But one of these
early settlers had chanced to be on the hither side of the
gorges when the world had so terribly shaken itself, and he
perforce had to forget his wife and his child and all the
friends and possessions he had left up there, and start life
over again in the lower world. He started it again but ill, blindness overtook him, and he died of punishment in the mines; but
the story he told begot a legend that lingers along the length
of the Cordilleras of the Andes to this day.

He told of his reason for venturing back from that fastness,
into which he had first been carried lashed to a llama, beside
a vast bale of gear, when he was a child. The valley, he said,
had in it all that the heart of man could desire—sweet water,
pasture, an even climate, slopes of rich brown soil with tangles
of a shrub that bore an excellent fruit, and on one side great

anging forests of pine that held the avalanches high. Far
verhead, on three sides, vast cliffs of grey-green rock were
apped by cliffs of ice; but the glacier stream came not to
hem but flowed away by the farther slopes, and only now and
hen huge ice masses fell on the valley side. In this valley it
either rained nor snowed, but the abundant springs gave a
ich green pasture, that irrigation would spread over all the
alley space. The settlers did well indeed there. Their beasts
lid well and multiplied, and but one thing marred their happi-
less. Yet it was enough to mar it greatly. A strange disease
ad come upon them, and had made all the children born to
hem there—and indeed, several older children also—blind.
t was to seek some charm or antidote against this plague of
lindness that he had with fatigue and danger and difficulty
eturned down the gorge. In those days, in such cases, men did
ot think of germs and infections but of sins; and it seemed
o him that the reason of this affliction must lie in the negligence
of these priestless immigrants to set up a shrine so soon as they
entered the valley. He wanted a shrine—a handsome, cheap,
effectual shrine—to be erected in the valley; he wanted relics
and such-like potent things of faith, blessed objects and mysterious medals and prayers. In his wallet he had a bar of
native silver for which he would not account; he insisted there
was none in the valley with something of the insistence of an
inexpert liar. They had all clubbed their money and ornaments
together, having little need for such treasure up there, he said,
to buy them holy help against their ill. I figure this dim-eyed
young mountaineer, sunburnt, gaunt, and anxious, hat-brim
clutched feverishly, a man all unused to the ways of the lower
world, telling this story to some keen-eyed, attentive priest
before the great convulsion; I can picture him presently seeking to return with pious and infallible remedies against that
trouble, and the infinite dismay with which he must have faced
the tumbled vastness where the gorge had once come out. But
the rest of his story of mischances is lost to me, save that I
know of his evil death after several years. Poor stray from
that remoteness! The stream that had once made the gorge
now bursts from the mouth of a rocky cave, and the legend
his poor, ill-told story set going developed into the legend of
a race of blind men somewhere "over there" one may still
hear to-day.

And amidst the little population of that now isolated and

forgotten valley the disease ran its course. The old became
groping and purblind, the young saw but dimly, and the children that were born to them saw never at all. But life was very
easy in that snow-rimmed basin, lost to all the world, with
neither thorns nor briars, with no evil insects nor any beasts
save the gentle breed of llamas they had lugged and thrust
and followed up the beds of the shrunken rivers in the gorges
up which they had come. The seeing had become purblind so
gradually that they scarcely noted their loss. They guided the
sightless youngsters hither and thither until they knew the
whole valley marvellously, and when at last sight died out
among them the race lived on. They had even time to adapt
themselves to the blind control of fire, which they made carefully in stoves of stone. They were a simple strain of people at
the first, unlettered, only slightly touched with the Spanish
civilisation, but with something of a tradition of the arts of
old Peru and of its lost philosophy. Generation followed generation. They forgot many things; they devised many things.
Their tradition of the greater world they came from became
mythical in colour and uncertain. In all things save sight they
were strong and able; and presently the chance of birth and
heredity sent one who had an original mind and who could
talk and persuade among them, and then afterwards another.
These two passed, leaving their effects, and the little community grew in numbers and in understanding, and met and
settled social and economic problems that arose. Generation
followed generation. There came a time when a child was born
who was fifteen generations from that ancestor who went out
of the valley with a bar of silver to seek God's aid, and who
never returned. Thereabouts it chanced that a man came
into this community from the outer world. And this is the story
of that man.

He was a mountaineer from the country near Quito, a man
who had been down to the sea and had seen the world, a reader
of books in an original way, an acute and enterprising man,
and he was taken on by a party of Englishmen who had come
out to Ecuador to climb mountains, to replace one of their
three Swiss guides who had fallen ill. He climbed here and he
climbed there, and then came the attempt on Parascotopetl,
the Matterhorn of the Andes, in which he was lost to the outer
world. The story of the accident has been written a dozen
times. Pointer's narrative is the best. He tells how the party

worked their difficult and almost vertical way up to the very foot of the last and greatest precipice, and how they built a night shelter amidst the snow upon a little shelf of rock, and, with a touch of real dramatic power, how presently they found Núñez had gone from them. They shouted, and there was no reply; shouted and whistled, and for the rest of that night they slept no more.

As the morning broke they saw the traces of his fall. It seems impossible he could have uttered a sound. He had slipped eastward towards the unknown side of the mountain; far below he had struck a steep slope of snow, and ploughed his way down it in the midst of a snow avalanche. His track went straight to the edge of a frightful precipice, and beyond that everything was hidden. Far, far below, and hazy with distance, they could see trees rising out of a narrow, shut-in valley— the lost Country of the Blind. But they did not know it was the lost Country of the Blind, nor distinguish it in any way from any other narrow streak of upland valley. Unnerved by this disaster, they abandoned their attempt in the afternoon, and Pointer was called away to the war before he could make another attack. To this day Parascotopetl lifts an unconquered crest, and Pointer's shelter crumbles unvisited amidst the snows.

And the man who fell survived.

At the end of the slope he fell a thousand feet, and came down in the midst of a cloud of snow upon a snow slope even steeper than the one above. Down this he was whirled, stunned and insensible, but without a bone broken in his body; and then at last came to gentler slopes, and at last rolled out and lay still, buried amidst a softening heap of the white masses that had accompanied and saved him. He came to himself with a dim fancy that he was ill in bed; then realised his position with a mountaineer's intelligence, and worked himself loose, and after a rest or so, out until he saw the stars. He rested flat upon his chest for a space, wondering where he was and what had happened to him. He explored his limbs, and discovered that several of his buttons were gone and his coat turned over his head. His knife had gone from his pocket and his hat was lost, though he had tied it under his chin. He recalled that he had been looking for loose stones to raise his piece of the shelter wall. His ice-axe had disappeared.

He decided he must have fallen, and looked up to see, exaggerated by the ghastly light of the rising moon, the tremendous flight he had taken. For a while he lay, gazing blankly at that vast pale cliff towering above, rising moment by moment out of a subsiding tide of darkness. Its phantasmal mysterious beauty held him for a space, and then he was seized with a paroxysm of sobbing laughter. . . .

After a great interval of time he became aware that he was near the lower edge of the snow. Below, down what was now a moonlit and practicable slope, he saw the dark and broken appearance of rock-strewn turf. He struggled to his feet, aching in every joint and limb, got down painfully from the heaped loose snow about him, went downward until he was on the turf, and there dropped rather than lay beside a boulder, drank deep from the flask in his inner pocket, and instantly fell asleep. . . .

He was awakened by the singing of birds in the trees far below.

He sat up and perceived he was on a little alp at the foot of a vast precipice, that was grooved by the gully down which he and his snow had come. Over against him another wall of rock reared itself against the sky. The gorge between these precipices ran east and west and was full of the morning sunlight, which lit to the westward the mass of fallen mountain that closed the descending gorge. Below him it seemed there was a precipice equally steep, but behind the snow in the gully he found a sort of chimney-cleft dripping with snow-water which a desperate man might venture. He found it easier than it seemed, and came at last to another desolate alp, and then after a rock climb of no particular difficulty to a steep slope of trees. He took his bearings and turned his face up the gorge, for he saw it opened out above upon green meadows, among which he now glimpsed quite distinctly a cluster of stone huts of unfamiliar fashion. At times his progress was like clambering along the face of a wall, and after a time the rising sun ceased to strike along the gorge, the voices of the singing birds died away, and the air grew cold and dark about him. But the distant valley with its houses was all the brighter for that. He came presently to talus, and among the rocks he noted—for he was an observant man—an unfamiliar fern that seemed to clutch out of the crevices with intense green hands. He picked a frond or so and gnawed its stalk and found it helpful.

About midday he came at last out of the throat of the gorge into the plain and the sunlight. He was stiff and weary; he sat down in the shadow of a rock, filled up his flask with water from a spring and drank it down, and remained for a time resting before he went on to the houses.

They were very strange to his eyes, and indeed the whole aspect of that valley became, as he regarded it, queerer and more unfamiliar. The greater part of its surface was lush green meadow, starred with many beautiful flowers, irrigated with extraordinary care, and bearing evidence of systematic cropping piece by piece. High up and ringing the valley about was a wall, and what appeared to be a circumferential water-channel, from which the little trickles of water that fed the meadow plants came, and on the higher slopes above this flocks of llamas cropped the scanty herbage. Sheds, apparently shelters or feeding-places for the llamas, stood against the boundary wall here and there. The irrigation streams ran together into a main channel down the centre of the valley, and this was enclosed on either side by a wall breast high. This gave a singularly urban quality to this secluded place, a quality that was greatly enhanced by the fact that a number of paths paved with black and white stones, and each with a curious little kerb at the side, ran hither and thither in an orderly manner. The houses of the central village were quite unlike the casual and higgledy-piggledy agglomeration of the mountain villages he knew; they stood in a continuous row on either side of a central street of astonishing cleanness; here and there their parti-coloured façade was pierced by a door, and not a solitary window broke their even frontage. They were parti-coloured with extraordinary irregularity; smeared with a sort of plaster that was sometimes grey, sometimes drab, sometimes slate-coloured or dark brown; and it was the sight of this wild plastering first brought the word "blind" into the thoughts of the explorer. "The good man who did that," he thought, "must have been as blind as a bat."

He descended a steep place, and so came to the wall and channel that ran about the valley, near where the latter spouted out its surplus contents into the deeps of the gorge in a thin and wavering thread of cascade. He could now see a number of men and women resting on piled heaps of grass, as if taking a siesta, in the remoter part of the meadow, and nearer the village a number of recumbent children, and then nearer at hand three men carrying pails on yokes along a little path that ran from the encircling wall towards the houses. These latter were clad in garments of llama cloth and boots and belts of leather, and they wore caps of cloth with back and ear flaps. They followed one another in single file, walking slowly and yawning as they walked, like men who have been up all night. There was something so reassuringly prosperous and respectable in their bearing that after a moment's hesitation Núñez stood forward as conspicuously as possible upon his rock, and gave vent to a mighty shout that echoed round the valley.

The three men stopped, and moved their heads as though they were looking about them. They turned their faces this way and that, and Núñez gesticulated with freedom. But they did not appear to see him for all his gestures, and after a time, directing themselves towards the mountains far away to the right, they shouted as if in answer. Núñez bawled again, and then once more, and as he gestured ineffectually the word "blind" came up to the top of his thoughts. "The fools must be blind," he said.

When at last, after much shouting and wrath, Núñez crossed the stream by a little bridge, came through a gate in the wall, and approached them, he was sure that they were blind. He was sure that this was the Country of the Blind of which the legends told. Conviction had sprung upon him, and a sense of great and rather enviable adventure. The three stood side by side, not looking at him, but with their ears directed towards him, judging him by his unfamiliar steps. They stood close together like men a little afraid, and he could see their eyelids closed and sunken, as though the very balls beneath had shrunken away. There was an expression near awe on their faces.

"A man," one said, in hardly recognisable Spanish—"a man it is—a man or a spirit—coming down from the rocks."

But Núñez advanced with the confident steps of a youth who enters upon life. All the old stories of the lost valley and the Country of the Blind had come back to his mind, and through his thoughts ran this old proverb, as if it were a refrain—

"In the Country of the Blind the One-eyed Man is King."

"In the Country of the Blind the One-eyed Man is King."

And very civilly he gave them greeting. He talked to them and used his eyes.

"Where does he come from, brother Pedro?" asked one.

"Down out of the rocks."

"Over the mountains I come," said Núñcz, "out of the country beyond there—where men can see. From near Bogotá, where there are a hundred thousands of people, and where the city passes out of sight."

"Sight?" muttered Pedro. "Sight?"

"He comes," said the second blind man, "out of the rocks."

The cloth of their coats Núñez saw was curiously fashioned, each with a different sort of stitching.

They startled him by a simultaneous movement towards him, each with a hand outstretched. He stepped back from the advance of these spread fingers.

"Come hither," said the third blind man, following his motion and clutching him neatly.

And they held Núñez and felt him over, saying no word further until they had done so.

"Carefully," he cried, with a finger in his eye, and found they thought that organ, with its fluttering lids, a queer thing in him. They went over it again.

"A strange creature, Correa," said the one called Pedro. "Feel the coarseness of his hair. Like a llama's hair."

"Rough he is as the rocks that begot him," said Correa, investigating Núñez's unshaven chin with a soft and slightly moist hand. "Perhaps he will grow finer." Núñez struggled a little under their examination, but they gripped him firm.

"Carefully," he said again.

"He speaks," said the third man. "Certainly he is a man."

"Ugh!" said Pedro, at the roughness of his coat.

"And you have come into the world?" asked Pedro.

"*Out* of the world. Over mountains and glaciers; right over above there, halfway to the sun. Out of the great big world that goes down, twelve days' journey to the sea."

They scarcely seemed to heed him. "Our fathers have told us men may be made by the forces of Nature," said Correa. "It is the warmth of things and moisture, and rottenness—rottenness."

"Let us lead him to the elders," said Pedro.

"Shout first," said Correa, "lest the children be afraid. This is a marvellous occasion."

So they shouted, and Pedro went first and took Núñez by the hand to lead him to the houses.

He drew his hand away. "I can see," he said.

"See?" said Correa.

"Yes, see," said Núñez, turning towards him, and stumbled against Pedro's pail.

"His senses are still imperfect," said the third blind man. "He stumbles, and talks unmeaning words. Lead him by the hand."

"As you will," said Núñez, and was led along, laughing.

It seemed they knew nothing of sight.

Well, all in good time he would teach them.

He heard people shouting, and saw a number of figures gathering together in the middle roadway of the village.

He found it taxed his nerve and patience more than he had anticipated, that first encounter with the population of the Country of the Blind. The place seemed larger as he drew near to it, and the smeared plasterings queerer, and a crowd of children and men and women (the women and girls, he was pleased to note, had some of them quite sweet faces, for all that their eyes were shut and sunken) came about him, holding on to him, touching him with soft, sensitive hands, smelling at him, and listening at every word he spoke. Some of the maidens and children, however, kept aloof as if afraid, and indeed his voice seemed coarse and rude beside their softer notes. They mobbed him. His three guides kept close to him with an effect of proprietorship, and said again and again, "A wild man out of the rocks."

"Bogotá," he said. "Bogotá. Over the mountain crests."

"A wild man—using wild words," said Pedro. "Did you hear that—*Bogotá?* His mind is hardly formed yet. He has only the beginnings of speech."

A little boy nipped his hand. "Bogotá!" he said mockingly.

"Ay! A city to your village, I come from the great world—where men have eyes and see."

"His name's Bogotá," they said.

"He stumbled," said Correa, "stumbled twice as we came hither."

"Bring him to the elders."

And they thrust him suddenly through a doorway into a room as black as pitch, save at the end there faintly glowed a fire. The crowd closed in behind him and shut out all but the faintest glimmer of day, and before he could arrest himself he had fallen headlong over the feet of a seated man. His arm, out-flung, struck the face of someone else as he went down; he felt the soft impact of features and heard a cry of anger, and for a moment he struggled against a number of hands that clutched him. It was a one-sided fight. An inkling of the situation came to him, and he lay quiet.

"I fell down," he said; "I couldn't see in this pitchy darkness."

There was a pause as if the unseen persons about him tried to understand his words. Then the voice of Correa said: "He is but newly formed. He stumbles as he walks and mingles words that mean nothing with his speech."

Others also said things about him that he heard or understood imperfectly.

"May I sit up?" he asked, in a pause. "I will not struggle against you again."

They consulted and let him rise.

The voice of an older man began to question him, and Núñez found himself trying to explain the great world out of which he had fallen, and the sky and mountains and sight and such-like marvels, to these elders who sat in darkness in the Country of the Blind. And they would believe and understand nothing whatever he told them, a thing quite outside his expectation. They would not even understand many of his words. For fourteen generations these people had been blind and cut off from all the seeing world; the names for all the things of sight had faded and changed; the story of the outer world was faded and changed to a child's story; and they had ceased to concern themselves with anything beyond the rocky slopes above their circling wall. Blind men of genius had arisen among them and questioned the shreds of belief and tradition they had brought with them from their seeing days, and had dismissed all these things as idle fancies, and replaced them with new and saner explanations. Much of their imagination had shrivelled with their eyes, and they had made for themselves new imaginations with their ever more sensitive ears and finger-tips. Slowly Núñez realised this; that his expectation of wonder and reverence at his origin and his gifts was not to be borne out; and after his poor attempt to explain sight to them had been set aside as the confused version of a new-made being describing the marvels of his incoherent sensations, he subsided, a little dashed, into listening to their instruction. And the eldest of the blind men explained to him life and philosophy and religion, how that the world (meaning their valley) had been first an empty hollow in the rocks, and then had come, first, inanimate things without the gift of touch, and llamas and a few other creatures that had little sense, and then men, and at last angels, whom one could hear singing and making fluttering sounds, but whom no one could touch at all, which puzzled Núñez greatly until he thought of the birds.

He went on to tell Núñez how this time had been divided into the warm and the cold, which are the blind equivalents of day and night, and how it was good to sleep in the warm and work during the cold, so that now, but for his advent, the whole town of the blind would have been asleep. He said Núñez must have been specially created to learn and serve the wisdom they had acquired, and for that all his mental incoherency and stumbling behaviour he must have courage and do his best to learn, and at that all the people in the doorway murmured encouragingly. He said the night—for the blind call their day night—was now far gone, and it behooved everyone to go back to sleep. He asked Núñez if he knew how to sleep, and Núñez said he did, but that before sleep he wanted food.

They brought him food—llama's milk in a bowl, and rough salted bread—and led him into a lonely place to eat out of their hearing, and afterwards to slumber until the chill of the mountain evening roused them to begin their day again. But Núñez slumbered not at all.

Instead, he sat up in the place where they had left him, resting his limbs and turning the unanticipated circumstances of his arrival over and over in his mind.

Every now and then he laughed, sometimes with amusement, and sometimes with indignation.

"Unformed mind!" he said. "Got no senses yet! They little know they've been insulting their heaven-sent king and master. I see I must bring them to reason. Let me think—let me think."

He was still thinking when the sun set.

Núñez had an eye for all beautiful things, and it seemed to him that the glow upon the snowfields and glaciers that rose about the valley on every side was the most beautiful thing he had ever seen. His eyes went from that inaccessible glory to the village and irrigated fields, fast sinking into the twilight, and suddenly a wave of emotion took him, and he thanked God from the bottom of his heart that the power of sight had been given him.

He heard a voice calling to him from out of the village.

"Ya ho there, Bogotá! Come hither!"

At that he stood up smiling. He would show these people once and for all what sight would do for a man. They would seek him, but not find him.

"You move not, Bogotá," said the voice.

He laughed noiselessly, and made two stealthy steps aside from the path.

"Trample not on the grass, Bogotá; that is not allowed."

Núñez had scarcely heard the sound he made himself. He stopped, amazed.

The owner of the voice came running up the piebald path towards him.

He stepped back into the pathway. "Here I am," he said.

"Why did you not come when I called you?" said the blind man. "Must you be led like a child? Cannot you hear the path as you walk?"

Núñez laughed. "I can see it," he said.

"There is no such word as *see*," said the blind man, after a pause. "Cease this folly, and follow the sound of my feet."

Núñez followed, a little annoyed.

"My time will come," he said.

"You'll learn," the blind man answered. "There is much to learn in the world."

"Has no one told you, 'In the Country of the Blind the One-eyed Man is King'?"

"What is blind?" asked the blind man carelessly over his shoulder.

Four days passed, and the fifth found the King of the Blind still incognito, as a clumsy and useless stranger among his subjects.

It was, he found, much more difficult to proclaim himself than he had supposed, and in the meantime, while he meditated his *coup d'état*, he did what he was told and learned the manners and customs of the Country of the Blind. He found working and going about at night a particularly irksome thing, and he decided that that should be the first thing he would change.

They led a simple, laborious life, these people, with all the elements of virtue and happiness, as these things can be understood by men. They toiled, but not oppressively; they had food and clothing sufficient for their needs; they had days and seasons of rest; they made much of music and singing, and there was love among them, and little children.

It was marvellous with what confidence and precision they went about their ordered world. Everything, you see, had been made to fit their needs; each of the radiating paths of the valley area had a constant angle to the others, and was distinguished by a special notch upon its kerbing; all obstacles and irregularities of path or meadow had long since been cleared away; all their methods and procedure arose naturally from their special needs. Their senses had become marvellously acute; they could hear and judge the slightest gesture of a man a dozen paces away—could hear the very beating of his heart. Intonation had long replaced expression with them, and touches gesture, and their work with hoe and spade and fork was as free and confident as garden work can be. Their sense of smell was extraordinarily fine; they could distinguish individual differences as readily as a dog can, and they went about the tending of the llamas, who lived among the rocks above and came to the wall for food and shelter, with ease and confidence. It was only when at last Núñez sought to assert himself that he found how easy and confident their movements could be.

He rebelled only after he had tried persuasion.

He tried at first on several occasions to tell them of sight. "Look you here, you people," he said. "There are things you do not understand in me."

Once or twice one or two of them attended to him; they sat with faces downcast and ears turned intelligently towards him, and he did his best to tell them what it was to see. Among his hearers was a girl, with eyelids less red and sunken than the others, so that one could almost fancy she was hiding eyes, whom especially he hoped to persuade. He spoke of the beauties of sight, of watching the mountains, of the sky and the sunrise, and they heard him with amused incredulity that presently became condemnatory. They told him there were indeed no mountains at all, but that the end of the rocks where the llamas grazed was indeed the end of the world; thence sprang a cavernous roof of the universe, from which the dew and the avalanches fell; and when he maintained stoutly the world had neither end nor roof such as they supposed, they said his thoughts were wicked. So far as he could describe sky and clouds and stars to them it seemed to them a hideous void, a terrible blankness in the place of the smooth roof to things in which they believed—it was an article of faith with them that the cavern roof was exquisitely smooth to the touch. He saw that in some manner he shocked them, and gave up that aspect of the matter altogether, and tried to show them the practical value of sight. One morning he saw Pedro in the path called Seventeen and coming towards the central houses, but still too far off for hearing or scent, and he told them as much. "In a little while," he prophesied, "Pedro will be here." An old man remarked that Pedro had no business on Path Seventeen, and then, as if in confirmation, that individual as he drew near turned and went transversely into Path Ten, and so back with nimble paces towards the outer wall. They mocked Núñez when Pedro did not arrive, and afterwards, when he asked Pedro questions to clear his character, Pedro denied and outfaced him, and was afterwards hostile to him.

Then he induced them to let him go a long way up the sloping meadows towards the wall with one complacent individual, and to him he promised to describe all that happened among the houses. He noted certain goings and comings, but the things that really seemed to signify to these people happened inside of or behind the windowless houses—the only things they took note of to test him by—and of these he could see or tell nothing; and it was after the failure of this attempt, and the ridicule they could not repress, that he resorted to force. He thought of seizing a spade and suddenly smiting one or two of them to earth, and so in fair combat showing the advantage of eyes. He went so far with that resolution as to seize his spade, and then he discovered a new thing about himself, and that was that it was impossible for him to hit a blind man in cold blood.

He hesitated, and found them all aware that he snatched up the spade. They stood alert, with their heads on one side, and bent ears towards him for what he would do next.

"Put that spade down," said one, and he felt a sort of helpless horror. He came near obedience.

Then he thrust one backwards against a house wall, and fled past him and out of the village.

He went athwart one of their meadows, leaving a track of trampled grass behind his feet, and presently sat down by the side of one of their ways. He felt something of the buoyancy that comes to all men in the beginning of a fight, but more perplexity. He began to realise that you cannot even fight happily with creatures who stand upon a different mental basis to yourself. Far away he saw a number of men carrying spades and sticks come out of the street of houses, and advance in a spreading line along the several paths towards him. They advanced slowly, speaking frequently to one another, and ever and again the whole cordon would halt and sniff the air and listen.

The first time they did this Núñez laughed. But afterwards he did not laugh.

One struck his trail in the meadow grass, and came stooping and feeling his way along it.

For five minutes he watched the slow extension of the cordon, and then his vague disposition to do something forthwith became frantic. He stood up, went a pace or so towards the circumferential wall, turned, and went back a little way. There they all stood in a crescent, still and listening.

He also stood still, gripping his spade very tightly in both hands. Should he charge them?

The pulse in his ears ran into the rhythm of "In the Country of the Blind the One-eyed Man is King!"

Should he charge them?

He looked back at the high and unclimbable wall behind— unclimbable because of its smooth plastering, but withal pierced with many little doors, and at the approaching line of seekers. Behind these, others were now coming out of the street of houses.

Should he charge them?

"Bogotá!" called one. "Bogotá! where are you?"

He gripped his spade still tighter, and advanced down the meadows towards the place of habitations, and directly he moved they converged upon him. "I'll hit them if they touch me," he swore; "by Heaven, I will. I'll hit." He called aloud, "Look here, I'm going to do what I like in this valley. Do you hear? I'm going to do what I like and go where I like!"

They were moving in upon him quickly, groping, yet moving rapidly. It was like playing blind man's buff, with everyone blindfolded except one. "Get hold of him!" cried one. He found himself in the arc of a loose curve of pursuers. He felt suddenly he must be active and resolute.

"You don't understand," he cried in a voice that was meant to be great and resolute, and which broke. "You are blind, and I can see. Leave me alone!"

"Bogotá! Put down that spade, and come off the grass!"

The last order, grotesque in its urban familiarity, produced a gust of anger.

"I'll hurt you," he said, sobbing with emotion. "By Heaven, I'll hurt you. Leave me alone!"

He began to run, not knowing clearly where to run. He ran from the nearest blind man, because it was a horror to hit him. He stopped, and then made a dash to escape from their closing ranks. He made for where a gap was wide, and the men on either side, with a quick perception of the approach of his paces, rushed in on one another. He sprang forward, and then saw he must be caught, and *swish!* the spade had struck. He felt the soft thud of hand and arm, and the man was down with a yell of pain, and he was through.

Through! And then he was close to the street of houses again, and blind men, whirling spades and stakes, were running with a sort of reasoned swiftness hither and thither.

He heard steps behind him just in time, and found a tall man rushing forward and swiping at the sound of him. He lost his nerve, hurled his spade a yard wide at his antagonist, and whirled about and fled, fairly yelling as he dodged another.

He was panic-stricken. He ran furiously to and fro, dodging when there was no need to dodge, and in his anxiety to see on every side of him at once, stumbling. For a moment he was down and they heard his fall. Far away in the circumferential wall a little doorway looked like heaven, and he set off in a wild rush for it. He did not even look round at his pursuers until it was gained, and he had stumbled across the bridge, clambered a little way among the rocks, to the surprise and dismay of a young llama, who went leaping out of sight, and lay down sobbing for breath.

And so his *coup d'état* came to an end.

He stayed outside the wall of the valley of the Blind for two nights and days without food or shelter, and meditated upon the unexpected. During these meditations he repeated very frequently and always with a profounder note of derision the exploded proverb: "In the Country of the Blind the One-Eyed Man is King." He thought chiefly of ways of fighting and conquering these people, and it grew clear that for him no practicable way was possible. He had no weapons, and now it would be hard to get one.

The canker of civilisation had got to him even in Bogotá, and he could not find it in himself to go down and assassinate a blind man. Of course, if he did that, he might then dictate terms on the threat of assassinating them all. But—sooner or later he must sleep! . . .

He tried also to find food among the pine trees, to be comfortable under pine boughs while the frost fell at night, and—with less confidence—to catch a llama by artifice in order to try to kill it—perhaps by hammering it with a stone—and so finally, perhaps, to eat some of it. But the llamas had a doubt of him and regarded him with distrustful brown eyes, and spat when he drew near. Fear came on him the second day and fits of shivering. Finally he crawled down to the wall of the Country of the Blind and tried to make terms. He crawled along by the stream, shouting, until two blind men came out to the gate and talked to him.

"I was mad," he said. "But I was only newly made."

They said that was better.

He told them he was wiser now, and repented of all he had done.

Then he wept without intention, for he was very weak and ill now, and they took that as a favourable sign.

They asked him if he still thought he could "*see*."

"No," he said. "That was folly. The word means nothing—less than nothing!"

They asked him what was overhead.

"About ten times ten the height of a man there is a roof above the world—of rock—and very, very smooth." . . . He burst again into hysterical tears. "Before you ask me any more, give me some food or I shall die."

He expected dire punishments, but these blind people were capable of toleration. They regarded his rebellion as but one more proof of his general idiocy and inferiority; and after they had whipped him they appointed him to do the simplest and heaviest work they had for anyone to do, and he, seeing no other way of living, did submissively what he was told.

He was ill for some days, and they nursed him kindly. That refined his submission. But they insisted on his lying in the dark, and that was a great misery. And blind philosophers came and talked to him of the wicked levity of his mind, and reproved him so impressively for his doubts about the lid of rock that covered their cosmic casserole that he almost doubted whether indeed he was not the victim of hallucination in not seeing it overhead.

So Núñez became a citizen of the Country of the Blind, and these people ceased to be a generalised people and became individualities and familiar to him, while the world beyond the mountains became more and more remote and unreal. There was Yacob, his master, a kindly man when not annoyed; there was Pedro, Yacob's nephew; and there was Medina-saroté, who was the youngest daughter of Yacob. She was little esteemed in the world of the Blind, because she had a clear-cut face, and lacked that satisfying, glossy smoothness that is the blind man's ideal of feminine beauty; but Núñez thought her beautiful at first, and presently the most beautiful thing in the whole creation. Her closed eyelids were not sunken and red after the common way of the valley, but lay as though they might open again at any moment; and she had long eyelashes, which were considered a grave disfigurement. And her voice was strong, and did not satisfy the acute hearing of the valley swains. So that she had no lover.

There came a time when Núñez thought that, could he win her, he would be resigned to live in the valley for all the rest of his days.

He watched her; he sought opportunities of doing her little services, and presently he found that she observed him. Once at a rest-day gathering they sat side by side in the dim star-light, and the music was sweet. His hand came upon hers and he dared to clasp it. Then very tenderly she returned his pressure. And one day, as they were at their meal in the dark-ness, he felt her hand very softly seeking him, and as it chanced the fire leaped then and he saw the tenderness of her face.

He sought to speak to her.

He went to her one day when she was sitting in the summer moonlight spinning. The light made her a thing of silver and mystery. He sat down at her feet and told her he loved her, and told her how beautiful she seemed to him. He had a lover's voice, he spoke with a tender reverence that came near to awe, and she had never before been touched by adoration. She made him no definite answer, but it was clear his words pleased her.

After that he talked to her whenever he could take an op-portunity. The valley became the world for him, and the world beyond the mountains where men lived in sunlight seemed no more than a fairy tale he would some day pour into her ears. Very tentatively and timidly he spoke to her of sight.

Sight seemed to her the most poetical of fancies, and she listened to his description of the stars and the mountains and her own sweet white-lit beauty as though it was a guilty indulgence. She did not believe, she could only half understand, but she was mysteriously delighted, and it seemed to him that she completely understood.

His love lost its awe and took courage. Presently he was for demanding her of Yacob and the elders in marriage, but she became fearful and delayed. And it was one of the elder sisters who first told Yacob that Medina-saroté and Núñez were in love.

There was from the first very great opposition to the marriage of Núñez and Medina-saroté; not so much because they valued her as because they held him as a being apart, an idiot, incompetent thing below the permissible level of a man. Her sisters opposed it bitterly as bringing discredit on them all; and old Yacob, though he had formed a sort of liking for his clumsy, obedient serf, shook his head and said the thing could not be. The young men were all angry at the idea of corrupting the race, and one went so far as to revile and strike Núñez. He struck back. Then for the first time he found an advantage in seeing, even by twilight, and after that fight was over no one was disposed to raise a hand against him. But they still found his marriage impossible.

Old Yacob had a tenderness for his last little daughter, and was grieved to have her weep upon his shoulder.

"You see, my dear, he's an idiot. He has delusions; he can't do anything right."

"I know," wept Medina-saroté. "But he's better than he was. He's getting better. And he's strong, dear father, and kind—stronger and kinder than any other man in the world. And he loves me—and, Father, I love him."

Old Yacob was greatly distressed to find her inconsolable, and, besides—what made it more distressing—he liked Núñez for many things. So he went and sat in the windowless council-chamber with the other elders and watched the trend of the talk, and said, at the proper time, "He's better than he was. Very likely, some day, we shall find him as sane as ourselves."

Then afterwards one of the elders, who thought deeply,

had an idea. He was the great doctor among these people, their medicine-man, and he had a very philosophical and inventive mind, and the idea of curing Núñez of his peculiarities appealed to him. One day when Yacob was present he returned to the topic of Núñez.

"I have examined Bogotá," he said, "and the case is clearer to me. I think very probably he might be cured."

"That is what I have always hoped," said old Yacob.

"His brain is affected," said the blind doctor.

The elders murmured assent.

"Now, *what* affects it?"

"Ah!" said old Yacob.

"*This*," said the doctor, answering his own question. "Those queer things that are called the eyes, and which exist to make an agreeable soft depression in the face, are diseased, in the case of Bogotá, in such a way as to affect his brain. They are greatly distended, he has eyelashes, and his eyelids move, and consequently his brain is in a state of constant irritation and distraction."

"Yes?" said old Yacob. "Yes?"

"And I think I may say with reasonable certainty that, in order to cure him completely, all that we need do is a simple and easy surgical operation—namely, to remove these irritant bodies."

"And then he will be sane?"

"Then he will be perfectly sane, and a quite admirable citizen."

"Thank Heaven for science!" said old Yacob, and went forth at once to tell Núñez of his happy hopes.

But Núñez's manner of receiving the good news struck him as being cold and disappointing.

"One might think," he said, "from the tone you take, that you did not care for my daughter."

It was Medina-saroté who persuaded Núñez to face the blind surgeons.

"*You* do not want me," he said, "to lose my gift of sight?"

She shook her head.

"My world is sight."

Her head drooped lower.

"There are the beautiful things, the beautiful little things—the flowers, the lichens among the rocks, the lightness and softness on a piece of fur, the far sky with its drifting down or clouds, the sunsets and the stars. And there is *you*. For you alone it is good to have sight, to see your sweet, serene face, your kindly lips, your dear, beautiful hands folded together . . . It is these eyes of mine you won, these eyes that hold me to you, that these idiots seek. Instead, I must touch you, hear you, and never see you again. I must come under that roof of rock and stone and darkness, that horrible roof under which your imagination stoops. . . . No; you would not have me do that?"

A disagreeable doubt had arisen in him. He stopped, and left the thing a question.

"I wish," she said, "sometimes——" She paused.

"Yes?" said he, a little apprehensively.

"I wish sometimes—you would not talk like that."

"Like what?"

"I know it's pretty—it's your imagination. I love it, but *now*——"

He felt cold. "*Now?*" he said faintly.

She sat still.

"You mean—you think—I should be better, better perhaps——"

He was realising things very swiftly. He felt anger, indeed, anger at the dull course of fate, but also sympathy for her lack of understanding—a sympathy near akin to pity.

"*Dear,*" he said, and he could see by her whiteness how intensely her spirit pressed against the things she could not say. He put his arms about her, he kissed her ear, and they sat for a time in silence.

"If I were to consent to this?" he said at last, in a voice that was very gentle.

She flung her arms about him, weeping wildly. "Oh, if you would," she sobbed, "if only you would!"

For a week before the operation that was to raise him from his servitude and inferiority to the level of a blind citizen, Núñez knew nothing of sleep, and all through the warm sunlit hours, while the others slumbered happily, he sat brooding or wandered aimlessly, trying to bring his mind to bear on his dilemma. He had given his answer, he had given his consent, and still he was not sure. And at last work-time was over, the sun rose in splendour over the golden crests, and his last

lay of vision began for him. He had a few minutes with
Medina-saroté before she went apart to sleep.

"To-morrow," he said, "I shall see no more."

"Dear heart!" she answered, and pressed his hands with all
her strength.

"They will hurt you but little," she said; "and you are
going through this pain—you are going through it, dear
lover, for *me*. . . . Dear, if a woman's heart and life can do
it, I will repay you. My dearest one, my dearest with the
tender voice, I will repay."

He was drenched in pity for himself and her.

He held her in his arms, and pressed his lips to hers, and
looked on her sweet face for the last time. "Good-bye!" he
whispered at that dear sight, "good-bye!"

And then in silence he turned away from her.

She could hear his slow retreating footsteps, and somthing
in the rhythm of them threw her into a passion of weeping.

He had fully meant to go to a lonely place where the
meadows were beautiful with white narcissus, and there remain until the hour of his sacrifice should come, but as he
went he lifted up his eyes and saw the morning, the morning
like an angel in golden armour, marching down the steeps. . . .

It seemed to him that before this splendour he, and this blind
world in the valley, and his love, and all, were no more than
a pit of sin.

He did not turn aside as he had meant to do, but went on,
and passed through the wall of the circumference and out
upon the rocks, and his eyes were always upon the sunlit ice
and snow.

He saw their infinite beauty, and his imagination soared
over them to the things beyond he was now to resign for ever.

He thought of that great free world he was parted from,
the world that was his own, and he had a vision of those
further slopes, distance beyond distance, with Bogotá, a place
of multitudinous stirring beauty, a glory by day, a luminous
mystery by night, a place of palaces and fountains and statues
and white houses, lying beautifully in the middle distance.
He thought how for a day or so one might come down through
passes, drawing ever nearer and nearer to its busy streets and
ways. He thought of the river journey, day by day, from great
Bogotá to the still vaster world beyond, through towns and
villages, forest and desert places, the rushing river day by

day, until its banks receded and the big steamers came splash
ing by, and one had reached the sea—the limitless sea, with
its thousand islands, its thousands of islands, and its ships
seen dimly far away in their incessant journeyings round and
about that greater world. And there, unpent by mountains
one saw the sky—the sky, not such a disc as one saw it here
but an arch of immeasurable blue, a deep of deeps in which
the circling stars were floating. . . .

His eyes scrutinised the great curtain of the mountains
with a keener inquiry.

For example, if one went so, up that gully and to that
chimney there, then one might come out high among those
stunted pines that ran round in a sort of shelf and rose still
higher and higher as it passed above the gorge. And then?
That talus might be managed. Thence perhaps a climb might
be found to take him up to the precipice that came below the
snow; and if that chimney failed, then another farther to the
east might serve his purpose better. And then? Then one
would be out upon the amber-lit snow there, and halfway up
to the crest of those beautiful desolations.

He glanced back at the village, then turned right round and
regarded it steadfastly.

He thought of Medina-saroté, and she had become small and
remote.

He turned again towards the mountain wall, down which
the day had come to him.

Then very circumspectly he began to climb.

When sunset came he was no longer climbing, but he was
far and high. He had been higher, but he was still very high.
His clothes were torn, his limbs were blood-stained, he was
bruised in many places, but he lay as if he were at his ease, and
there was a smile on his face.

From where he rested the valley seemed as if it were in a
pit and nearly a mile below. Already it was dim with haze
and shadow, though the mountain summits around him were
things of light and fire. The mountain summits around him
were things of light and fire, and the little details of the rocks
near at hand were drenched with subtle beauty—a vein of
green mineral piercing the grey, the flash of crystal faces here
and there, a minute, minutely beautiful orange lichen close

beside his face. There were deep mysterious shadows in the gorge, blue deepening into purple, and purple into a luminous darkness, and overhead was the illimitable vastness of the sky. But he heeded these things no longer, but lay quite inactive there, smiling as if he were satisfied merely to have escaped from the valley of the Blind in which he had thought to be King.

The glow of the sunset passed, and the night came, and still he lay peacefully contented under the cold stars.

E. M. Forster

THE CELESTIAL OMNIBUS

The boy who resided at Agathox Lodge, 28, Buckingham Park Road, Surbiton, had often been puzzled by the old sign-post that stood almost opposite. He asked his mother about it, and she replied that it was a joke, and not a very nice one, which had been made many years back by some naughty young men, and that the police ought to remove it. For there were two strange things about this sign-post: firstly, it pointed up a blank alley, and, secondly, it had painted on it, in faded characters, the words, "To Heaven."

"What kind of young men were they?" he asked.

"I think your father told me that one of them wrote verses, and was expelled from the University and came to grief in other ways. Still, it was a long time ago. You must ask your father about it. He will say the same as I do, that it was put up as a joke."

"So it doesn't mean anything at all?"

She sent him up-stairs to put on his best things, for the Bonses were coming to tea, and he was to hand the cake-stand.

It struck him, as he wrenched on his tightening trousers, that he might do worse than ask Mr. Bons about the sign-post. His father, though very kind, always laughed at him—shrieked with laughter whenever he or any other child asked a question or spoke. But Mr. Bons was serious as well as kind. He had a beautiful house and lent one books, he was a churchwarden, and a candidate for the County Council; he had donated to the Free Library enormously, he presided over the Literary Society, and had Members of Parliament to stop with him—in short, he was probably the wisest person alive.

Yet even Mr. Bons could only say that the sign-post was a joke—the joke of a person named Shelley.

"Of course!" cried the mother; "I told you so, dear. That was the name."

"Had you never heard of Shelley?" asked Mr. Bons.

"No," said the boy, and hung his head.

"But is there no Shelley in the house?"

"Why, yes!" exclaimed the lady, in much agitation. "Dear Mr. Bons, we aren't such Philistines as that. Two at the least. One a wedding present, and the other, smaller print, in one of the spare rooms."

"I believe we have seven Shelleys," said Mr. Bons, with a slow smile. Then he brushed the cake crumbs off his stomach, and, together with his daughter, rose to go.

The boy, obeying a wink from his mother, saw them all the way to the garden gate, and when they had gone he did not at once return to the house, but gazed for a little up and down Buckingham Park Road.

His parents lived at the right end of it. After No. 39 the quality of the houses dropped very suddenly, and 64 had not even a separate servants' entrance. But at the present moment the whole road looked rather pretty, for the sun had just set in splendour, and the inequalities of rent were drowned in a saffron afterglow. Small birds twittered, and the breadwinners' train shrieked musically down through the cutting—that wonderful cutting which has drawn to itself the whole beauty out of Surbiton, and clad itself, like any Alpine valley, with the glory of the fir and the silver birch and the primrose. It was this cutting that had first stirred desires within the boy —desires for something just a little different, he knew not what, desires that would return whenever things were sunlit, as they were this evening, running up and down inside him, up and down, up and down, till he would feel quite unusual all over, and as likely as not would want to cry. This evening he was even sillier, for he slipped across the road towards the sign-post and began to run up the blank alley.

The alley runs between high walls—the walls of the gardens of "Ivanhoe" and "Belle Vista" respectively. It smells a little all the way, and is scarcely twenty yards long, including the turn at the end. So not unnaturally the boy soon came to a standstill. "I'd like to kick that Shelley," he exclaimed, and glanced idly at a piece of paper which was pasted on the wall.

Rather an odd piece of paper, and he read it carefully before
he turned back. This is what he read:

S. AND C. R. C. C.

Alteration in Service.

Owing to lack of patronage the Company are regretfully
compelled to suspend the hourly service, and to retain only the

Sunrise and Sunset Omnibuses,

which will run as usual. It is to be hoped that the public will
patronize an arrangement which is intended for their convenience. As an extra inducement, the Company will, for the first
time, now issue

Return Tickets!

(available one day only), which may be obtained of the driver.
Passengers are again reminded that *no tickets are issued at
the other end*, and that no complaints in this connection will
receive consideration from the Company. Nor will the Company be responsible for any negligence or stupidity on the
part of Passengers, nor for Hailstorms, Lightning, Loss of
Tickets, nor for any Act of God.

For the Direction.

Now he had never seen this notice before, nor could he
imagine where the omnibus went to. S. of course was for Surbiton, and R.C.C. meant Road Car Company. But what was
the meaning of the other C.? Coombe and Malden, perhaps,
or possibly "City." Yet it could not hope to compete with the
South-Western. The whole thing, the boy reflected, was run
on hopelessly unbusiness-like lines. Why no tickets from the
other end? And what an hour to start! Then he realized that
unless the notice was a hoax, an omnibus must have been starting just as he was wishing the Bonses good-bye. He peered at
the ground through the gathering dusk, and there he saw
what might or might not be the marks of wheels. Yet nothing
had come out of the alley. And he had never seen an omnibus
at any time in the Buckingham Park Road. No: it must be a
hoax, like the sign-posts, like the fairy tales, like the dreams
upon which he would wake suddenly in the night. And with a

igh he stepped from the alley—right into the arms of his ather.

Oh, how his father laughed! "Poor, poor Popsey!" he cried. Diddums! Diddums! Diddums think he'd walky-palky up to ivvink!" And his mother, also convulsed with laughter, appeared on the steps of Agathox Lodge. "Don't, Bob!" she asped. "Don't be so naughty! Oh, you'll kill me! Oh, leave the oy alone!"

But all that evening the joke was kept up. The father implored to be taken too. Was it a very tiring walk? Need one ipe one's shoes on the door-mat? And the boy went to bed eeling faint and sore, and thankful for only one thing—that e had not said a word about the omnibus. It was a hoax, yet hrough his dreams it grew more and more real, and the streets f Surbiton, through which he saw it driving, seemed instead o become hoaxes and shadows. And very early in the morning he woke with a cry, for he had had a glimpse of its destiation.

He struck a match, and its light fell not only on his watch ut also on his calendar, so that he knew it to be half-an-hour o sunrise. It was pitch dark, for the fog had come down from London in the night, and all Surbiton was wrapped in its emraces. Yet he sprang out and dressed himself, for he was determined to settle once for all which was real: the omnibus r the streets. "I shall be a fool one way or the other," he hought, "until I know." Soon he was shivering in the road under the gas lamp that guarded the entrance to the alley.

To enter the alley itself required some courage. Not only vas it horribly dark, but he now realized that it was an impossible terminus for an omnibus. If it had not been for a policeman, whom he heard approaching through the fog, he vould never have made the attempt. The next moment he had made the attempt and failed. Nothing. Nothing but a blank alley and a very silly boy gaping at its dirty floor. It *was* a hoax. "I'll tell papa and mamma," he decided. "I deserve it. I deserve that they should know. I am too silly to be alive." And he went back to the gate of Agathox Lodge.

There he remembered that his watch was fast. The sun was not risen; it would not rise for two minutes. "Give the bus every chance," he thought cynically, and returned into the alley.

But the omnibus was there.

ii

It had two horses, whose sides were still smoking from thei journey, and its two great lamps shone through the fog agains the alley's walls, changing their cobwebs and moss into tissue of fairyland. The driver was huddled up in a cape. He face the blank wall, and how he had managed to drive in so neatl and so silently was one of the many things that the boy neve discovered. Nor could he imagine how ever he would drive out

"Please," his voice quavered through the foul brown air "Please, is that an omnibus?"

"Omnibus est," said the driver, without turning round There was a moment's silence. The policeman passed, cough ing, by the entrance of the alley. The boy crouched in th shadow, for he did not want to be found out. He was prett sure, too, that it was a Pirate; nothing else, he reasoned, woulc go from such odd places and at such odd hours.

"About when do you start?" He tried to sound nonchalant

"At sunrise."

"How far do you go?"

"The whole way."

"And can I have a return ticket which will bring me all th way back?"

"You can."

"Do you know, I half think I'll come." The driver made no answer. The sun must have risen, for he unhitched the brake And scarcely had the boy jumped in before the omnibus wa: off.

How? Did it turn? There was no room. Did it go forward: There was a blank wall. Yet it was moving—moving at s stately pace through the fog, which had turned from brown to yellow. The thought of warm bed and warmer breakfast made the boy feel faint. He wished he had not come. His parent: would not have approved. He would have gone back to them i the weather had not made it impossible. The solitude was ter rible; he was the only passenger. And the omnibus, thougl well-built, was cold and somewhat musty. He drew his coal round him, and in so doing chanced to feel his pocket. It wa: empty. He had forgotten his purse.

"Stop!" he shouted. "Stop!" And then, being of a polite disposition, he glanced up at the painted notice-board so that

e might call the driver by name. "Mr. Browne! stop; O, do
lease stop!"

Mr. Browne did not stop, but he opened a little window and
ooked in at the boy. His face was a surprise, so kind it was
nd modest.

"Mr. Browne, I've left my purse behind. I've not got a
enny. I can't pay for the ticket. Will you take my watch,
lease? I am in the most awful hole."

"Tickets on this line," said the driver, "whether single or
eturn, can be purchased by coinage from no terrene mint.
And a chronometer, though it had solaced the vigils of Charle-
nagne, or measured the slumbers of Laura, can acquire by no
nutation the double-cake that charms the fangless Cerberus
f Heaven!" So saying, he handed in the necessary ticket, and,
vhile the boy said "Thank you," continued: "Titular preten-
ions, I know it well, are vanity. Yet they merit no censure
vhen uttered on a laughing lip, and in an homonymous world
re in some sort useful, since they do serve to distinguish one
ack from his fellow. Remember me, therefore, as Sir Thomas
Browne."

"Are you a Sir? Oh, sorry!" He had heard of these gentle-
nen drivers. "It *is* good of you about the ticket. But if you go
n at this rate, however does your bus pay?"

"It does not pay. It was not intended to pay. Many are the
aults of my equipage; it is compounded too curiously of for-
ign woods; its cushions tickle erudition rather than promote
epose; and my horses are nourished not on the evergreen pas-
ures of the moment, but on the dried bents and clovers of
atinity. But that it pays!—that error at all events was never
ntended and never attained."

"Sorry again," said the boy rather hopelessly. Sir Thomas
ooked sad, fearing that, even for a moment, he had been the
ause of sadness. He invited the boy to come up and sit beside
im on the box, and together they journeyed on through the
og, which was now changing from yellow to white. There were
10 houses by the road; so it must be either Putney Heath or
Vimbledon Common.

"Have you been a driver always?"

"I was a physician once."

"But why did you stop? Weren't you good?"

"As a healer of bodies I had scant success, and several score
f my patients preceded me. But as a healer of the spirit I

have succeeded beyond my hopes and my deserts. For though
my draughts were not better nor subtler than those of other
men, yet, by reason of the cunning goblets wherein I offered
them, the queasy soul was ofttimes tempted to sip and be re
freshed."

"The queasy soul," he murmured; "if the sun sets with trees
in front of it, and you suddenly come strange all over, is that
a queasy soul?"

"Have you felt that?"

"Why yes."

After a pause he told the boy a little, a very little, about the
journey's end. But they did not chatter much, for the boy
when he liked a person, would as soon sit silent in his company
as speak, and this, he discovered, was also the mind of Sir
Thomas Browne and of many others with whom he was to be
acquainted. He heard, however, about the young man Shelley
who was now quite a famous person, with a carriage of his
own, and about some of the other drivers who are in the service
of the Company. Meanwhile the light grew stronger, though
the fog did not disperse. It was now more like mist than fog
and at times would travel quickly across them, as if it was part
of a cloud. They had been ascending, too, in a most puzzling
way; for over two hours the horses had been pulling against
the collar, and even if it were Richmond Hill they ought to
have been at the top long ago. Perhaps it was Epsom, or even
the North Downs; yet the air seemed keener than that which
blows on either. And as to the name of their destination, Sir
Thomas Browne was silent.

Crash!

"Thunder, by Jove!" said the boy, "and not so far off
either. Listen to the echoes! It's more like mountains."

He thought, not very vividly, of his father and mother. He
saw them sitting down to sausages and listening to the storm
He saw his own empty place. Then there would be questions
alarms, theories, jokes, consolations. They would expect him
back at lunch. To lunch he would not come, nor to tea, but he
would be in for dinner, and so his day's truancy would be
over. If he had had his purse he would have bought them presents—not that he should have known what to get them.

Crash!

The peal and the lightning came together. The cloud quivred as if it were alive, and torn streamers of mist rushed past. Are you afraid?" asked Sir Thomas Browne.

"What is there to be afraid of? Is it much farther?"

The horses of the omnibus stopped just as a ball of fire burst up and exploded with a ringing noise that was deafening but clear, like the noise of a blacksmith's forge. All the cloud was shattered.

"Oh, listen, Sir Thomas Browne! No, I mean look; we shall get a view at last. No, I mean listen; that sounds like a rainbow!"

The noise had died into the faintest murmur, beneath which another murmur grew, spreading stealthily, steadily, in a curve that widened but did not vary. And in widening curves a rainbow was spreading from the horses' feet into the dissolving mists.

"But how beautiful! What colours! Where will it stop? It is more like the rainbows you can tread on. More like dreams."

The colour and the sound grew together. The rainbow spanned an enormous gulf. Clouds rushed under it and were pierced by it, and still it grew, reaching forward, conquering the darkness, until it touched something that seemed more solid than a cloud.

The boy stood up. "What is that out there?" he called. "What does it rest on, out at that other end?"

In the morning sunshine a precipice shone forth beyond the gulf. A precipice—or was it a castle? The horses moved. They set their feet upon the rainbow.

"Oh, look!" the boy shouted. "Oh, listen! Those caves—or are they gateways? Oh, look between those cliffs at those ledges. I see people! I see trees!"

"Look also below," whispered Sir Thomas. "Neglect not the diviner Acheron."

The boy looked below, past the flames of the rainbow that licked against their wheels. The gulf also had cleared, and in its depths there flowed an everlasting river. One sunbeam entered and struck a green pool, and as they passed over he saw three maidens rise to the surface of the pool, singing, and playing with something that glistened like a ring.

"You down in the water——" he called.

They answered, "You up on the bridge——" There was a burst of music. "You up on the bridge, good luck to you. Truth in the depth, truth on the height."

"You down in the water, what are you doing?"

Sir Thomas Browne replied: "They sport in the mancipiar possession of their gold"; and the omnibus arrived.

iii

The boy was in disgrace. He sat locked up in the nursery c Agathox Lodge, learning poetry for a punishment. His fathe had said, "My boy! I can pardon anything but untruthfu ness," and had caned him, saying at each stroke, "There is *n* omnibus, *no* driver, *no* bridge, *no* mountain; you are a *truan* a *gutter snipe*, a *liar*." His father could be very stern at time: His mother had begged him to say he was sorry. But he coul not say that. It was the greatest day of his life, in spite of th caning and the poetry at the end of it.

He had returned punctually at sunset—driven not by Si Thomas Browne, but by a maiden lady who was full of quie fun. They had talked of omnibuses and also of barouche lan daus. How far away her gentle voice seemed now! Yet it wa scarcely three hours since he had left her up the alley.

His mother called through the door. "Dear, you are to come down and to bring your poetry with you."

He came down, and found that Mr. Bons was in the smok ing-room with his father. It had been a dinner party.

"Here is the great traveller!" said his father grimly. "Here is the young gentleman who drives in an omnibus over rain bows, while young ladies sing to him." Pleased with his wit, he laughed.

"After all," said Mr. Bons, smiling, "there is something a little like it in Wagner. It is odd how, in quite illiterate minds you will find glimmers of Artistic Truth. The case interests me. Let me plead for the culprit. We have all romanced in our time, haven't we?"

"Hear how kind Mr. Bons is," said his mother, while his father said, "Very well. Let him say his Poem, and that will do. He is going away to my sister on Tuesday, and *she* will cure him of this alley-slopering." (Laughter.) "Say your Poem."

The boy began. "'Standing aloof in giant ignorance.'"

His father laughed again—roared. "One for you, my son! 'Standing aloof in giant ignorance!' I never knew these poets talked sense. Just describes you. Here, Bons, you go in for poetry. Put him through it, will you, while I fetch up the whisky?"

"Yes, give me the Keats," said Mr. Bons. "Let him say his Keats to me."

So for a few moments the wise man and the ignorant boy were left alone in the smoking-room.

" 'Standing aloof in giant ignorance, of thee I dream and of the Cyclades, as one who sits ashore and longs perchance to visit——' "

"Quite right. To visit what?"

" 'To visit dolphin coral in deep seas,' " said the boy, and burst into tears

"Come, come! why do you cry?"

"Because—because all these words that only rhymed before, now that I've come back they're me."

Mr. Bons laid the Keats down. The case was more interesting than he had expected. "*You?*" he exclaimed. "This sonnet, *you?*"

"Yes—and look further on: 'Aye, on the shores of darkness there is light, and precipices show untrodden green.' It *is* so, sir. All these things are true."

"I never doubted it," said Mr. Bons, with closed eyes.

"You—then you believe me? You believe in the omnibus and the driver and the storm and that return ticket I got for nothing and——"

"Tut, tut! No more of your yarns, my boy. I meant that I never doubted the essential truth of Poetry. Some day, when you have read more, you will understand what I mean."

"But Mr. Bons, it *is* so. There *is* light upon the shores of darkness. I have seen it coming. Light and a wind."

"Nonsense," said Mr. Bons.

"If I had stopped! They tempted me. They told me to give up my ticket—for you cannot come back if you lose your ticket. They called from the river for it, and indeed I was tempted, for I have never been so happy as among those precipices. But I thought of my mother and father, and that I must fetch them. Yet they will not come, though the road starts opposite our house. It has all happened as the people up there warned me, and Mr. Bons has disbelieved me like every one else. I have been caned. I shall never see that mountain again."

"What's that about me?" said Mr. Bons, sitting up in his

chair very suddenly.

"I told them about you, and how clever you were, and how many books you had, and they said, 'Mr. Bons will certainly disbelieve you.'"

"Stuff and nonsense, my young friend. You grow impertinent. I—well—I will settle the matter. Not a word to your father. I will cure you. To-morrow evening I will myself call here to take you for a walk, and at sunset we will go up this alley opposite and hunt for your omnibus, you silly little boy."

His face grew serious, for the boy was not disconcerted, but leapt about the room singing, "Joy! joy! I told them you would believe me. We will drive together over the rainbow. I told them that you would come." After all, could there be anything in the story? Wagner? Keats? Shelley? Sir Thomas Browne? Certainly the case was interesting.

And on the morrow evening, though it was pouring with rain, Mr. Bons did not omit to call at Agathox Lodge.

The boy was ready, bubbling with excitement, and skipping about in a way that rather vexed the President of the Literary Society. They took a turn down Buckingham Park Road, and then—having seen that no one was watching them—slipped up the alley. Naturally enough (for the sun was setting) they ran straight against the omnibus.

"Good heavens!" exclaimed Mr. Bons. "Good gracious heavens!"

It was not the omnibus in which the boy had driven first, nor yet that in which he had returned. There were three horses —black, gray, and white, the gray being the finest. The driver, who turned round at the mention of goodness and of heaven, was a sallow man with terrifying jaws and sunken eyes. Mr. Bons, on seeing him, gave a cry as if of recognition, and began to tremble violently.

The boy jumped in.

"Is it possible?" cried Mr. Bons. "Is the impossible possible?"

"Sir; come in, sir. It is such a fine omnibus. Oh, here is his name—Dan some one."

Mr. Bons sprang in too. A blast of wind immediately slammed the omnibus door, and the shock jerked down all the omnibus blinds, which were very weak on their springs.

"Dan . . . Show me. Good gracious heavens! we're moving."

"Hooray!" said the boy.

Mr. Bons became flustered. He had not intended to be kidnapped. He could not find the door-handle, nor push up the blinds. The omnibus was quite dark, and by the time he had struck a match, night had come on outside also. They were moving rapidly.

"A strange, a memorable adventure," he said, surveying the interior of the omnibus, which was large, roomy, and constucted with extreme regularity, every part exactly answering to every other part. Over the door (the handle of which was outside) was written, "Lasciate ogni baldanza voi che entrate" —at least, that was what was written, but Mr. Bons said that it was Lashy arty something, and that baldanza was a mistake for speranza. His voice sounded as if he was in church. Meanwhile, the boy called to the cadaverous driver for two return tickets. They were handed in without a word. Mr. Bons covered his face with his hand and again trembled. "Do you know who that is!" he whispered, when the little window had shut upon them. "It is the impossible."

"Well, I don't like him as much as Sir Thomas Browne, though I shouldn't be surprised if he had even more in him."

"More in him?" He stamped irritably. "By accident you have made the greatest discovery of the century, and all you can say is that there is more in this man. Do you remember those vellum books in my library, stamped with red lilies? This —sit still, I bring you stupendous news!—*this is the man who wrote them.*"

The boy sat quite still. "I wonder if we shall see Mrs. Gamp?" he asked, after a civil pause.

"Mrs.——?"

"Mrs. Gamp and Mrs. Harris. I like Mrs. Harris. I came upon them quite suddenly. Mrs. Gamp's bandboxes have moved over the rainbow so badly. All the bottoms have fallen out, and two of the pippins off her bedstead tumbled into the stream."

"Out there sits the man who wrote my vellum books!" thundered Mr. Bons, "and you talk to me of Dickens and of Mrs. Gamp?"

"I know Mrs. Gamp so well," he apologized. "I could not help being glad to see her. I recognized her voice. She was telling Mrs. Harris about Mrs. Prig."

"Did you spend the whole day in her elevating company?"

"Oh, no. I raced. I met a man who took me out beyond to a race-course. You run, and there are dolphins out at sea."

"Indeed. Do you remember the man's name?"

"Achilles. No; he was later. Tom Jones."

Mr. Bons sighed heavily. "Well, my lad, you have made a miserable mess of it. Think of a cultured person with your opportunities! A cultured person would have known all these characters and known what to have said to each. He would not have wasted his time with a Mrs. Gamp or a Tom Jones. The creations of Homer, of Shakespeare, and of Him who drives us now, would alone have contented him. He would not have raced. He would have asked intelligent questions."

"But, Mr. Bons," said the boy humbly, "you will be a cultured person. I told them so."

"True, true, and I beg you not to disgrace me when we arrive. No gossiping. No running. Keep close to my side, and never speak to these Immortals unless they speak to you. Yes, and give me the return tickets. You will be losing them."

The boy surrendered the tickets, but felt a little sore. After all, he had found the way to this place. It was hard first to be disbelieved and then to be lectured. Meanwhile, the rain had stopped, and moonlight crept into the omnibus through the cracks in the blinds.

"But how is there to be a rainbow?" cried the boy.

"You distract me," snapped Mr. Bons. "I wish to meditate on beauty. I wish to goodness I was with a reverent and sympathetic person."

The lad bit his lip. He made a hundred good resolutions. He would imitate Mr. Bons all the visit. He would not laugh, or run, or sing, or do any of the vulgar things that must have disgusted his new friends last time. He would be very careful to pronounce their names properly, and to remember who knew whom. Achilles did not know Tom Jones—at least, so Mr. Bons said. The Duchess of Malfi was older than Mrs. Gamp—at least, so Mr. Bons said. He would be self-conscious, reticent, and prim. He would never say he liked any one. Yet, when the blind flew up at a chance touch of his head, all these good resolutions went to the winds, for the omnibus had reached the summit of a moonlit hill, and there was the chasm, and there, across it, stood the old precipices, dreaming, with their feet in the everlasting river. He exclaimed, "The mountain! Listen to the new tune in the water! Look at the camp fires in the ravines," and Mr. Bons, after a hasty glance, retorted, "Water? Camp fires? Ridiculous rubbish. Hold your tongue. There is nothing at all."

Yet, under his eyes, a rainbow formed, compounded not of sunlight and storm, but of moonlight and the spray of the river. The three horses put their feet upon it. He thought it the finest rainbow he had seen, but did not dare to say so, since Mr. Bons said that nothing was there. He leant out—the window had opened—and sang the tune that rose from the sleeping waters.

"The prelude to Rhinegold?" said Mr. Bons suddenly. "Who taught you these *leit motifs?*" He, too, looked out of the window. Then he behaved very oddly. He gave a choking cry, and fell back on to the omnibus floor. He writhed and kicked. His face was green.

"Does the bridge make you dizzy?" the boy asked.

"Dizzy!" gasped Mr. Bons. "I want to go back. Tell the driver."

But the driver shook his head.

"We are nearly there," said the boy. "They are asleep. Shall I call? They will be so pleased to see you, for I have prepared them."

Mr. Bons moaned. They moved over the lunar rainbow, which ever and ever broke away behind their wheels. How still the night was! Who would be sentry at the Gate?

"I am coming," he shouted, again forgetting the hundred resolutions. "I am returning—I, the boy."

"The boy is returning," cried a voice to other voices, who repeated, "The boy is returning."

"I am bringing Mr. Bons with me."

Silence.

"I should have said Mr. Bons is bringing me with him."

Profound silence.

"Who stands sentry?"

"Achilles."

And on the rocky causeway, close to the springing of the rainbow bridge, he saw a young man who carried a wonderful shield.

"Mr. Bons, it is Achilles, armed."

"I want to go back," said Mr. Bons.

The last fragment of the rainbow melted, the wheels sang upon the living rock, the door of the omnibus burst open. Out leapt the boy—he could not resist—and sprang to meet the warrior, who, stooping suddenly, caught him on his shield.

"Achilles!" he cried, "let me get down, for I am ignorant and vulgar, and I must wait for that Mr. Bons of whom I told you yesterday."

But Achilles raised him aloft. He crouched on the wonderful shield, on heroes and burning cities, on vineyards graven in gold, on every dear passion, every joy, on the entire image of the Mountain that he had discovered, encircled, like it, with an everlasting stream. "No, no," he protested, "I am not worthy. It is Mr. Bons who must be up here."

But Mr. Bons was whimpering, and Achilles trumpeted and cried, "Stand upright upon my shield!"

"Sir, I did not mean to stand! something made me stand. Sir, why do you delay? Here is only the great Achilles, whom you knew."

Mr. Bons screamed, "I see no one. I see nothing. I want to go back." Then he cried to the driver, "Save me! Let me stop in your chariot. I have honoured you. I have quoted you. I have bound you in vellum. Take me back to my world."

The driver replied, "I am the means and not the end. I am the food and not the life. Stand by yourself, as that boy has stood. I cannot save you. For poetry is a spirit; and they that would worship it must worship in spirit and in truth."

Mr. Bons—he could not resist—crawled out of the beautiful omnibus. His face appeared, gaping horribly. His hands followed, one gripping the step, the other beating the air. Now his shoulders emerged, his chest, his stomach. With a shriek of "I see London," he fell—fell against the hard, moonlit rock, fell into it as if it were water, fell through it, vanished, and was seen by the boy no more.

"Where have you fallen to, Mr. Bons? Here is a procession arriving to honour you with music and torches. Here come the men and women whose names you know. The mountain is awake, the river is awake, over the race-course the sea is awaking those dolphins, and it is all for you. They want you——"

There was the touch of fresh leaves on his forehead. Some one had crowned him.

ΤΕΛΟΣ

From the *Kingston Gazette, Surbiton Times,* and *Raynes Park Observer.*

The body of Mr. Septimus Bons has been found in a shockingly mutilated condition in the vicinity of the Bermondsey gas-works. The deceased's pockets contained a sovereign-purse, a silver cigar-case, a bijou pronouncing dictionary, and a couple of omnibus tickets. The unfortunate gentleman had apparently been hurled from a considerable height. Foul play is suspected, and a thorough investigation is pending by the authorities.

Oliver Onions

IO

As THE young man put his hand to the uppermost of the four brass bell-knobs to the right of the fanlighted door he paused, withdrew the hand again, and then pulled at the lowest knob. The sawing of bell-wire answered him, and he waited for a moment, uncertain whether the bell had rung, before pulling again. Then there came from the basement a single cracked stroke; the head of a maid appeared in the whitewashed area below; and the head was withdrawn as apparently the maid recognised him. Steps were heard along the hall; the door was opened; and the maid stood aside to let him enter, the apron with which she had slipped the latch still crumpled in her greasy hand.

"Sorry, Daisy," the young man apologised, "but I didn't want to bring her down all those stairs. How is she? Has she been out to-day?"

The maid replied that the person spoken of had been out; and the young man walked along the wide carpeted passage.

It was cumbered like an antique-shop with alabaster busts on pedestals, dusty palms in faience vases, and trophies of spears and shields and assegais. At the foot of the stairs was a rustling portière of strung beads, and beyond it the carpet was continued up the broad, easy flight, secured at each step by a brass rod. Where the stairs made a turn, the fading light of the December afternoon, made still dimmer by a window of decalcomanied glass, shone on a cloudy green aquarium with sallow goldfish, a number of cacti on a shabby console table, and a large and dirty white sheepskin rug. Passing along a short landing, the young man began the ascent of the second flight. This also was carpeted, but with a carpet that had done duty in some dining- or bed-room before being cut up into strips of the width of the narrow space between the wall and the hand-rail. Then, as he still mounted, the young man's feet sounded loud on oilcloth; and when he finally paused and knocked at a door it was on a small landing of naked boards beneath the cold gleam of the skylgiht above the well of the stairs.

"Come in," a girl's voice called.

The room he entered had a low sagging ceiling on which shone a low glow of firelight, making colder still the patch of eastern sky beyond the roofs and the cowls and hoods of chimneys framed by the square of the single window. The glow on the ceiling was reflected dully in the old dark mirror over the mantelpiece. An open door in the farther corner, hampered with skirts and blouses, allowed a glimpse of the girl's bed-room.

The young man set the paper bag he carried down on the littered round table and advanced to the girl who sat in an old wicker chair before the fire. The girl did not turn her head as he kissed her cheek, and he looked down at something that had muffled the sound of his steps as he had approached her.

"Hallo, that's new, isn't it, Bessie? Where did that come from?" he asked cheerfully.

The middle of the floor was covered with a common jute matting, but on the hearth was a magnificent leopard-skin rug.

"Mrs. Hepburn sent it up. There was a draught from under the door. It's much warmer for my feet."

"Very kind of Mrs. Hepburn. Well, how are you feeling to-day, old girl?"

"Better, thanks, Ed."

"That's the style. You'll be yourself again soon. Daisy says you've been out to-day?"

"Yes, I went for a walk. But not far; I went to the Museum and then sat down. You're early, aren't you?"

He turned away to get a chair, from which he had to move a mass of tissue-paper patterns and buckram linings. He brought it to the rug.

"Yes. I stopped last night late to cash up for Vedder, so he's staying to-night. Turn and turn about. Well, tell us all about it, Bess."

Their faces were red in the firelight. Hers had the prettiness that the first glance almost exhausts, the prettiness, amazing in its quantity, that one sees for a moment under the light of the street lamps when shops and offices close for the day.

She was short-nosed, pulpy-mouthed and faunish-eyed, and
only the rather remarkable smallness of the head on the splendid thick throat saved her from ordinariness. He, too, might
have been seen in his thousands at the close of any day, hurrying home to Catford or Walham Green or Tufnell Park to tea
and an evening with a girl or in a billiard-room, or else dining
cheaply "up West" preparatory to smoking cigarettes from
yellow packets in the upper circle of a music-hall. Four inches
of white up-and-down collar encased his neck; and as he lifted
his trousers at the knee to clear his purple socks, the pair of
paper covers showed, that had protected his cuffs during the
day at the office. He removed them, crumpled them up and
threw them on the fire; and the momentary addition to the
light of the upper chamber showed how curd-white was that
superb neck of hers and how moody and tired her eyes.

From his face only one would have guessed, and guessed
wrongly, that his preferences were for billiard-rooms and
music-halls. His conversation showed them to be otherwise. It
was of Polytechnic classes that he spoke, and of the course
of lectures in English literature that had just begun. And, as
if somebody had asserted that the pursuit of such studies was
not compatible with a certain measure of physical development
also, he announced that he was not sure that he should not
devote, say, half an evening a week, on Wednesdays, to training in the gymnasium.

"*Mens sana in corpore sano*, Bessie," he said; "a sound
mind in a sound body, you know. That's tremendously important, especially when a fellow spends the day in a stuffy
office. Yes, I think I shall give it half Wednesdays, from eight-
thirty to nine-thirty; sends you home in a glow. But I was
going to tell you about the Literature Class. The second
lecture's to-night. The first was splendid, all about the languages of Europe and Asia—what they call the Indo-Germanic
languages, you know. Aryans. I can't tell you exactly without
my notes, but the Hindoos and Persians, I think it was, they
crossed the Himalaya Mountains and spread westward somehow, as far as Europe. That was the way it all began. It was
splendid, the way the lecturer put it. English is a Germanic
language, you know. Then came the Celts. I wish I'd brought
my notes. I see you've been reading; let's look——"

A book lay on her knees, its back warped by the heat of the
fire. He took it and opened it.

"Ah, Keats! Glad you like Keats, Bessie. We needn't be great readers, but it's important that what we do read should be all right. I don't know him, not *really* know him, that is. But he's quite all right—A1 in fact. And he's an example of what I've always maintained, that knowledge should be brought within the reach of all. It just shows. He was the son of a livery-stable keeper, you know, so what he'd have been if he'd really had chances, been to universities and so on, there's no knowing. But, of course, it's more from the historical stand-point that I'm studying these things. Let's have a look——"

He opened the book where a hairpin between the leaves marked a place. The firelight glowed on the page, and he read, monotonously and inelastically:

> *"And as I sat, over the light blue hills*
> *There came a noise of revellers; the rills*
> *Into the wide stream came of purple hue—*
> *'Twas Bacchus and his crew!*
>
> *The earnest trumpet spake, and silver thrills*
> *From kissing cymbals made a merry din—*
> *'Twas Bacchus and his kin!*
>
> *Like to a moving vintage down they came,*
> *Crowned with green leaves, and faces all on flame*
> *All madly dancing through the pleasant valley*
> *To scare thee, Melancholy!"*

It was the wondrous passage from *Endymion*, of the descent of the wild inspired rabble into India. Ed plucked for a moment at his lower lip, and then, with a "Hm! What's it all about, Bessie?" continued:

> *"Within his car, aloft, young Bacchus stood,*
> *Trifling his ivy-dart, in dancing mood,*
> *With sidelong laughing;*
> *And little rills of crimson wine imbrued*
> *His plump white arms and shoulders, enough white*
> *For Venus' pearly bite;*
> *And near him rode Silenus on his ass,*
> *Pelted with flowers as he on did pass,*
> *Tipsily quaffing."*

"Hm! I see. Mythology. That's made up of tales, and myths, you know. Like Odin and Thor and those, only those were Scandinavian Mythology. So it would be absurd to take it too seriously. But I think, in a way, things like that do harm. You see," he explained, "the more beautiful they are the more harm they might do. We ought always to show virtue and vice in their true colours, and if you look at it from that point of view this is just drunkenness. That's rotten; destroys your body and intellect; as I heard a chap say once, it's an insult to the beasts to call it beastly. I joined the Blue Ribbon when I was fourteen and I haven't been sorry for it yet. No. Now there's Vedder; he 'went off on a bend,' as he calls it, last night, and even he says this morning it wasn't worth it. But let's read on."

Again he read, with unresilient movement:

> "*I saw Osirian Egypt kneel adown*
>   *Before the vine wreath crown!*
>   *I saw parched Abyssinia rouse and sing*
>   *To the silver cymbals' ring!*
> *I saw the whelming vintage hotly pierce*
>   *Old Tartary the fierce!*
> *Great Brahma from his mystic heaven groans. . . .*"

"Hm! He was a Buddhist god, Brahma was; mythology again. As I say, if you take it seriously, it's just glorifying intoxication.—But I say; I can hardly see. Better light the lamp. We'll have tea first, then read. No, you sit still; I'll get it ready; I know where things are——"

He rose, crossed to a little cupboard with a sink in it, filled the kettle at the tap, and brought it to the fire. Then he struck a match and lighted the lamp.

The cheap glass shade was of a foolish corolla shape, clear glass below, shading to pink, and deepening to red at the crimped edge. It gave a false warmth to the spaces of the room above the level of the mantelpiece, and Ed's figure, as he turned the regulator, looked from the waist upwards as if he stood within that portion of a spectrum screen that deepens to the band of red. The bright concentric circles that spread in rings of red on the ceiling were more dimly reduplicated in the old mirror over the mantelpiece; and the wintry eastern light beyond the chimney-hoods seemed suddenly almost to die out.

Bessie, her white neck below the level of the lamp-shade, had taken up the book again; but she was not reading. She was looking over it at the upper part of the grate. Presently she spoke.

"I was looking at some of those things this afternoon, at the Museum."

He was clearing from the table more buckram linings and patterns of paper, numbers of *Myra's Journal* and *The Delineator*. Already on his way to the cupboard he had put aside a red-bodiced dressmaker's "shape" of wood and wire.

"What things?" he asked.

"Those you were reading about. Greek, aren't they?"

"Oh, the Greek room! . . . But those people, Bacchus and those, weren't people in the ordinary sense. Gods and goddesses, most of 'em; Bacchus was a god. That's what mythology means. I wish sometimes our course took in Greek literature, but it's a dead language after all. German's more good in modern life. It would be nice to know everything, but one has to select, you know. Hallo, I clean forgot; I brought you some grapes, Bessie; here they are, in this bag; we'll have 'em after tea, what?"

"But," she said again after a pause, still looking at the grate, "they had their priests and priestesses, and followers and people, hadn't they? It was their things I was looking at —combs and brooches and hairpins, and things to cut their nails with. They're all in a glass case there. And they had safety-pins, exactly like ours."

"Oh, they were a civilised people," said Ed cheerfully. "It all gives you an idea. I only hope you didn't tire yourself out. You'll soon be all right, of course, but you have to be careful yet. We'll have a clean tablecloth, shall we?"

She had been seriously ill; her life had been despaired of; and somehow the young Polytechnic student seemed anxious to assure her that she was now all right again, or soon would be. They were to be married "as soon as things brightened up a bit," and he was very much in love with her. He watched her head and neck as he continued to lay the table, and then, as he crossed once more to the cupboard, he put his hand lightly in passing on her hair.

She gave so quick a start that he too started. She must

have been very deep in her reverie to have been so taken by
surprise.

"I say, Bessie, don't jump like that!" he cried with involuntary quickness. Indeed, had his hand been red-hot, or ice-
cold, or taloned, she could not have turned a more startled,
even frightened, face to him.

"It was your touching me," she muttered, resuming her
gaze into the grate.

He stood looking anxiously down on her. It would have been
better not to discuss her state, and he knew it; but in his
anxiety he forgot it.

"That jumpiness is the effect of your illness, you know. I
shall be glad when it's all over. It's made you so odd."

She was not pleased that he should speak of her "oddness."
For that matter, she, too, found him "odd"—at any rate,
found it difficult to realise that he was as he always had been.
He had begun to irritate her a little. His club-footed reading
of the verses had irritated her, and she had tried hard to hide
from him that his cocksure opinions and the tone in which they
were pronounced jarred on her. It was not that she was
"better" than he, "knew" any more than he did, didn't (she
supposed) love him still the same; these moods, that dated
from her illness, had nothing to do with those things; she
reproached herself sometimes that she was subject to such
doldrums.

"It's all right, Ed, but please don't touch me just now,"
she said.

He was in the act of leaning over her chair, but he saw
her shrink, and refrained.

"Poor old girl!" he said sympathetically. "What's the
matter?"

"I don't know. It's awfully stupid of me to be like this, but
I can't help it. I shall be better soon if you leave me alone."

"Nothing's happened, has it?"

"Only those silly dreams I told you about."

"Bother the dreams!" muttered the Polytechnic student.

During her illness she had had dreams, and had come to
herself at intervals to find Ed or the doctor, Mrs. Hepburn
or her aunt, bending over her. These kind, solicitous faces
had been no more than a glimpse, and then she had gone off
into the dreams again. The curious thing had been that the
dreams had seemed to be her vivid waking life, and the other

things—the anxious faces, the details of her dingy bedroom, the thermometer under her tongue—had been the dream. And, though she had come back to actuality, the dreams had never quite vanished. She could remember no more of them than that they had seemed to hold a high singing and jocundity, issuing from some region of haze and golden light; and they seemed to hover, ever on the point of being recaptured, yet ever eluding all her mental efforts. She was living now between reality and a vision.

She had fewer words than sensations, and it was a little pitiful to hear her vainly striving to make clear what she meant.

"It's so queer," she said. "It's like being on the edge of something—a sort of tiptoe—I can't describe it. Sometimes I could almost touch it with my hand, and then it goes away, but never *quite* away. It's like something just past the corner of my eye, over my shoulder, and I sit very still sometimes, trying to take it off its guard. But the moment I move my head it moves too—like this——"

Again he gave a quick start at the suddenness of her action. Very stealthily her faunish eyes had stolen sideways, and then she had swiftly turned her head.

"Here, I say, don't, Bessie!" he cried nervously. "You look awfully uncanny when you do that! You're brooding," he continued, "that's what you're doing, brooding. You're getting into a low state. You want bucking up. I don't think I shall go up to the Polytec. to-night; I shall stay and cheer you up. You know, I really don't think you're making an effort, darling."

His last words seemed to strike her. They seemed to fit in with something of which she too was conscious. "Not making an effort . . ." she wondered how he knew that. She felt in some vague way that it was important that she *should* make an effort.

For, while her dream ever evaded her, and yet never ceased to call her with such a voice as he who reads on a magic page of the calling of elves hears stilly in his brain, yet somehow behind the seduction was another and a sterner voice. There was warning as well as fascination. Beyond that edge at which she strained on tiptoe, mingled with the jocund calls to Hasten, Hasten, were deeper calls that bade her Beware. They puzzled her. Beware of what? Of what danger? And to whom? . . .

"How do you mean, I'm not making an effort, Ed?" she asked slowly, again looking into the fire, where the kettle now made a gnat-like singing.

"Why, an effort to get all right again. To be as you used to be—as, of course, you will be soon."

"As I *used* to be?" The words came with a little check in her breathing.

"Yes, before all this. To be yourself, you know."

"Myself?"

"All jolly, and without these jerks and jumps. I wish you could get away. A fortnight by the sea would do you all the good in the world."

She knew not what it was in the words "the sea" that caused her suddenly to breathe more deeply. The sea! . . . It was as if, by the mere uttering of them, he had touched some secret spring, brought to fulfilment some spell. What had he meant by speaking of the sea? . . . A fortnight before, had somebody spoken to her of the sea it would have been the sea of Margate, of Brighton, of Southend, that, supplying the image that a word calls up as if by conjuration, she would have seen before her; and what other image could she supply, could she *possibly* supply, now? . . . Yet she did, or almost did, supply one. What new experience had she had, or what old, old one had been released in her? With that confused, joyous dinning just beyond the range of physical hearing there had suddenly mingled a new illusion of sound—a vague, vast pash and rustle, silky and harsh both at once, its tireless voice holding meanings of stillness and solitude compared with which the silence that is mere absence of sound was vacancy. It was part of her dream, invisible, intangible, inaudible, yet there. As if he had been an enchanter, it had come into being at the word upon his lips. Had he other such words? Had he the Master Word that—(ah, she knew what the Master Word would do!)— would make the Vision the Reality and the Reality the Vision? Deep within her she felt something—her soul, herself, she knew not what—thrill and turn over and settle again. . . .

"The sea," she repeated in a low voice.

"Yes, that's what you want to set you up—rather! Do you remember that fortnight at Littlehampton, you and me and your Aunt? Jolly that was! I like Littlehampton. It isn't flash like Brighton, and Margate's always so beastly crowded.

And do you remember that afternoon by the windmill? I did love you that afternoon, Bessie!"

He continued to talk, but she was not listening. She was wondering why the words "the sea" were somehow part of it all—the pins and brooches of the Museum, the book on her knees, the dream. She remembered a game of hide-and-seek she had played as a child, in which cries of "Warm, warm, warmer!" had announced the approach to the hidden object. Oh, she was getting warm—positively hot. . . .

He had ceased to talk, and was watching her. Perhaps it was the thought of how he had loved her that afternoon by the windmill that had brought him close to her chair again. She was aware of his nearness, and closed her eyes for a moment as if she dreaded something. Then she said quickly, "Is tea nearly ready, Ed?" and, as he turned to the table, took up the book again.

She felt that even to touch that book brought her "warmer." It fell open at a page. She did not hear the clatter Ed made at the table, nor yet the babble his words had evoked, of the pierrots and banjos and minstrels of Margate and Littlehampton. It was to hear a gladder, wilder tumult that she sat once more so still, so achingly listening. . . .

> "*The earnest trumpet spake, and silver thrills*
> *From kissing cymbals made a merry din——*"

The words seemed to move on the page. In her eyes another light than the firelight seemed to play. Her breast rose, and in her thick white throat a little inarticulate sound twanged.

"Eh? Did you speak, Bessie?" Ed asked, stopping in his buttering of bread.

"Eh? . . . No."

In answering, her head had turned for a moment, and she had seen him. Suddenly it struck her with force: what a shaving of a man he was! Desk-chested, weak-necked, conscious of his little "important" lip and chin—yes, he needed a Polytechnic gymnastic course! Then she remarked how once, at Margate, she had seen him in the distance, as in a hired baggy bathing-dress he had bathed from a machine, in muddy water, one of a hundred others, all rather cold, flinging a polo-ball about and shouting stridently. "A sound mind in a sound body!" . . . He was rather vain of his neat shoes, too, and doubtless stunted his feet; and she had seen the little spot on his neck caused by the chafing of his collar-stud. . . . No, she did not want him to touch her, just now at any rate. His touch would be too like a betrayal of another touch . . . somewhere, sometime, somehow . . . in that tantalising dream that refused to allow itself either to be fully remembered or quite forgotten. What *was* that dream? *What* was it? . . .

She continued to gaze into the fire.

Of a sudden she sprang to her feet with a choked cry of almost animal fury. The fool *had* touched her. Carried away doubtless by the memory of that afternoon by the windmill, he had, in passing once more to the kettle, crept softly behind her and put a swift burning kiss on the side of her neck.

Then he had retreated before her, stumbling against the table and causing the cups and saucers to jingle.

The basket-chair tilted up, but righted itself again.

"I told you—I told you—" she choked, her stockish figure shaking with rage, "I told you—you——"

He put up his elbow as if to ward off a blow.

"You touch me—*you!*—*you!*" the words broke from her.

He had put himself farther round the table. He stammered.

"Here—dash it all, Bessie—what *is* the matter?"

"*You* touch me!"

"All right," he said sullenly. "I won't touch you again—no fear. I didn't know you were such a firebrand. All right, drop it now. I won't again. Good Lord!"

Slowly the white fist she had drawn back sank to her side again.

"All right now," he continued to grumble resentfully. "You needn't take on so. It's said—I won't touch you again." Then, as if he remembered that after all she was ill and must be humoured, he began, while her bosom still rose and fell rapidly, to talk with an assumption that nothing much had happened. "Come, sit down again, Bessie. The tea's in the pot and I'll have it ready in a couple of jiffs. What a ridiculous little girl you are, to take on like that! . . . And I say, listen! That's a muffin-bell, and there's a grand fire for toast! You sit down while I run out and get 'em. Give me your key, so I can let myself in again——"

He took her key from her bag, caught up his hat, and hastened out.

But she did not sit down again. She was no calmer for his quick disappearance. In that moment when he had recoiled from her she had had the expression of some handsome and angered snake, its hood puffed, ready to strike. She stood dazed; one would have supposed that that ill-advised kiss of his had indeed been the Master Word she sought, the Word she felt approaching, the Word to which the objects of the Museum, the book, that rustle of a sea she had never seen, had been but the ever "warming" stages. Some merest trifle stood between her and those elfin cries, between her and that thin golden mist in which faintly seen shapes seemed to move— shapes almost of tossed arms, waving, brandishing objects strangely all but familiar. That roaring of the sea was *not* the rushing of her own blood in her ears, that rosy flush *not* the artificial glow of the cheap red lamp-shade. The shapes were almost as plain as if she saw them in some clear but black mirror, the sounds almost as audible as if she heard them through some not very thick muffling. . . .

"Quick—the book," she muttered.

But even as she stretched out her hand for it, again came that solemn sound of warning. As if something sought to stay it, she had deliberately to thrust her hand forward. Again the high dinning calls of "Hasten! Hasten!" were mingled with that deeper "Beware!" She knew in her soul that, once over that terrible edge, the Dream would become the Reality and the Reality the Dream. She knew nothing of the fluidity of the thing called Personality—not a thing at all, but a state, a balance, a relation, a resultant of forces so delicately in equilibrium that a touch, and—*pff!*—the horror of Formlessness rushed over all.

As she hesitated a new light appeared in the chamber. Within the frame of the small square window, beyond the ragged line of the chimney-cowls, an edge of orange brightness showed. She leaned forward. It was the full moon, rusty and bloated and flattened by the earth-mist.

The next moment her hand had clutched at the book.

"Whence came ye, merry damsels! Whence came ye
So many, and so many, and such glee?
Why have ye left your bowers desolate,
Your lutes, and gentler fate?

> *'We follow Bacchus, Bacchus on the wing*
> *A-conquering!*
> *Bacchus, young Bacchus! Good or ill betide*
> *We dance before him through kingdoms wide!*
> *Come hither, Lady fair, and joinèd be*
> *To our wild minstrelsy!'"*

There was an instant in which darkness seemed to blot out all else; then it rolled aside, and in a blaze of brightness was gone. It was gone, and she stood face to face with her Dream, that for two thousand years had slumbered in the blood of her and her line. She stood, with mouth agape and eyes that hailed, her thick throat full of suppressed clamour. The other was the Dream now, and *these!* . . . they came down, mad and noisy and bright—Mænades, Thyades, satyrs, fauns—naked, in hides of beasts, ungirdled, dishevelled, wreathed and garlanded, dancing, singing, shouting. The thudding of their hooves shook the ground, and the clash of their timbrels and the rustling of their thyrsi filled the air. They brandished frontal bones, the dismembered quarters of kids and goats; they struck the bronze cantharus, they tossed the silver obba up aloft. Down a cleft of rocks and woods they came, trooping to a wide seashore with the red of the sunset behind them. She saw the evening light on the sleek and dappled hides, the gilded ivory and rich brown of their legs and shoulders, the white of inner arms held up on high, their wide red mouths, the quivering of the twin flesh-gouts on the necks of the leaping fauns. And, shutting out the glimpse of sky at the head of the deep ravine, the god himself descended, with his car full of drunken girls who slept with the serpents coiled about them.

Shouting and moaning and frenzied, leaping upon one another with libidinous laughter and beating one another with the half-stripped thyrsi, they poured down to the yellow sands and the anemonied pools of the shore. They raced to the water, that gleamed pale as nacre in the deepening twilight in the eye of the evening star. They ran along its edge over their images in the wet sands, calling their lost companion.

"Hasten, hasten!" they cried; and one of them, a young man with a torso noble as the dawn and shoulder-lines strong as those of the eternal hills, ran here and there calling her name.

"Louder, louder!" she called back in an ecstasy.

Something dropped and tinkled against the fender. It was

one of her hairpins. One side of her hair was in a loose tumble; she threw up the small head on the superb thick neck.

"Louder!—I cannot hear! Once more——"

The throwing up of her head that had brought down the rest of her hair had given her a glimpse of herself in the glass over the mantelpiece. For the last time that formidable "Beware!" sounded like thunder in her ears; the next moment she had snapped with her fingers the ribbon that was cutting into her throbbing throat. He with the torso and those shoulders was seeking her . . . how should he know her in that dreary garret, in those joyless habiliments? He would as soon know his own in that crimson-bodiced, wire-framed dummy by the window yonder! . . .

Her fingers clutched at the tawdry mercerised silk of her blouse. There was a rip, and her arms and throat were free. She panted as she tugged at something that gave with a short "click-click," as of steel fastenings; something fell against the fender. . . . These also. . . . She tore at them, and kicked them as they lay about her feet as leaves lie about the trunk of a tree in autumn. . . .

"*Ah!*"

And as she stood there, as if within the screen of a spectrum that deepened to the band of red, her eyes fell on the leopard-skin at her feet. She caught it up, and in doing so saw purple grapes—purple grapes that issued from the mouth of a paper bag on the table. With the dappled pelt about her she sprang forward. The juice spurted through them into the mass of her loosened hair. Down her body there was a spilth of seeds and pulp. She cried hoarsely aloud.

"Once more—oh, answer me! Tell me my name!"

Ed's steps were heard on the oilclothed portion of the staircase.

"My name—oh, my name!" she cried in an agony of suspense. . . . "Oh, they will not wait for me! They have lighted the torches—they run up and down the shore with torches—oh, cannot you see me? . . ."

Suddenly she dashed to the chair on which the litter of linings and tissue-paper lay. She caught up a double handful and crammed them on the fire. They caught and flared. There was a call upon the stairs, and the sound of somebody mounting in haste.

"Once—once only—my name!"

The soul of the Bacchante rioted, struggled to escape from her eyes. Then as the door was flung open, she heard, and gave a terrifying shout of recognition.

"I hear—I almost hear—but once more. . . . IO! *Io Io, Io!*"

Ed, in the doorway, stood for one moment agape; the next, ignorant of the full purport of his own words—ignorant that though man may come westwards he may yet bring his worship with him—ignorant that to make the Dream the Reality and the Reality the Dream is Heaven's dreadfullest favour—and ignorant that, that Edge once crossed, there is no return to the sanity and sweetness and light that are only seen clearly in the moment when they are lost for ever—he had dashed down the stairs crying in a voice hoarse and high with terror·

"She's mad! She's mad!"

Perceval Gibbon

THE SECOND-CLASS PASSENGER

THE party from the big German mail-boat had nearly completed their inspection of Mozambique. They had walked up and down the main street, admired the palms, lunched at the costly table of Lazarus, and purchased "curios"—Indian silks, Javanese knives, Birmingham metal-work, and what not—as mementoes of their explorations. In particular, Miss Paterson had invested in a heavy bronze image—apparently Japanese —concerning which she entertained the thrilling delusion that it was an object of local worship. It was a grotesque thing, massive and bulky, weighing not much less than ten or twelve pounds. Hence it was confided to the careful porterage of Dawson, an assiduous and favoured courtier of Miss Paterson; and he, having lunched, was fated to leave it behind at Lazarus' Hotel.

Miss Paterson shook her fluffy curls at him. They were drawing towards dinner, and the afternoon was wearing stale.

"I did so want that idol," she said plaintively. She had the childish quality of voice, the insipidity of intonation, which is best appreciated in steamboat saloons. "Oh, Mr. Dawson, don't you think you could get it back for me?"

"I'm frightfully sorry," said the contrite Dawson. "I'll go back at once. You don't know when the ship goes, do you?"

Another of Miss Paterson's cavaliers assured him that he had some hours yet. "The steward told me so," he added authoritatively.

"Then I'll go at once," said Dawson, hating him.

"Mind, don't lose the boat," Miss Paterson called after him.

He went swiftly back up the wide main street in which they had spent the day. Lamps were beginning to shine everywhere, and the dull peace of the place was broken by a new life. Those that dwell in darkness were going abroad now, and the small saloons were filling. Dawson noted casually that evening was evidently the lively time of Mozambique. He passed men of a type he had missed during the day, men of all nationalities, by their faces, and every shade of colour. They were lounging on the sidewalk in knots of two or three, sitting at the little tables outside the saloons, or lurking at the entrances of narrow alleys that ran aside from the main street every few paces. All were clad in thin white suits, and some wore knives in full sight, while there was that about them that would lead even the most innocent and conventional second-class passenger to guess at a weapon concealed somewhere. Some of them looked keenly at Dawson as he passed along; and although he met their eyes impassively, he—even he—was conscious of an implied estimate in their glance, as though they classified him with a look. Once he stepped aside to let a woman pass. She was large, flamboyantly southern and calm. She lounged along, a cloak over her left arm, her head thrown back, a cigarette between her wide, red lips. She, too, looked at Dawson—looked down at him with a superb lazy nonchalance, laughed a little, and walked on. The loungers on the sidewalk laughed too, but rather with her than at Dawson.

"I seem rather out of it here," he told himself patiently, and was glad to enter the wide portals of Lazarus' Hotel. A grand, swarthy Greek, magnificent in a scarlet jacket and gold braid, pulled open the door for him, and heard his mission smilingly.

"A brass-a image," he repeated. "Sir, you wait-a in the bar, an' I tell-a the boy go look."

"You must be quick, then," said Dawson, "'cause I'm in a hurry to get back."

"Yais," smiled the Greek. "Bimeby he rain-a bad."

"Rain?" queried Dawson incredulously. The air was like balm.

"You see," the Greek nodded. "This-a way, sir. I go look-a quick."

Dawson waited in the bar, where a dark, sallow barman stared him out of countenance for twenty minutes. At the end of that time the image was forthcoming. The ugly thing had burst the paper in which it was wrapped, and its grinning bullet-head projected handily. The paper was wisped about its middle like a petticoat. Dawson took it thankfully from the Greek, and made suitable remuneration in small silver.

"Bimeby rain," repeated the Greek, as he opened a door for him again.

"Well, I'm not made of sugar," replied Dawson, and set off.

It was night now, for in Mozambique evening is but a brief hiatus between darkness and day. It lasts only while the sun is dipping; once the upper limb is under the horizon it is night, full and absolute. As Dawson retraced his steps the sky over him was velvet-black, barely punctured by faint stars, and a breeze rustled faintly from the sea. He had not gone two hundred yards when a large, warm drop of rain splashed on his back. Another pattered on his hat, and it was raining, leisurely, ominously.

Dawson pulled up and took thought. At the end of the main street he would have to turn to the left to the sea-front, and then to the left again to reach the landing-stage. If, now, there were any nearer turning to the left—if any of the dark alleys that opened continually beside him were passable—he might get aboard the steamer to his dinner in the second-class saloon with a less emphatic drenching than if he went round by the way he had come. Mozambique, he reflected, could not have only one street—it was too big for that. From the steamer, as it came to anchor, he had seen acre upon acre of flat roofs, and one of the gloomy alleys beside him must surely debouch upon the sea-front. He elected to try one, anyhow, and accordingly turned aside into the next.

With ten paces he entered such a darkness as he had never known. The alley was barely ten feet wide: it lay like a crevasse between high, windowless walls of houses. The warm, leisurely rain dropped perpendicularly upon him from an invisible sky, and presently, hugging the wall, he butted against a corner, and found, or guessed, that his way was no longer straight. Underfoot there was mud and garbage that once gulfed him to the knee, and nowhere in all those terrible, silent walls on each side of him was there a light or a door, nor any sight of life near at hand. He might have been in a catacomb, companioned by the dead. The stillness and the loneliness scared and disturbed him. He turned on a sudden impulse to make his way back to the lights of the street.

But this was to reckon without the map of Mozambique— which does not exist. Ten minutes sufficed to overwhelm him in an intricacy of blind ways. He groped by a wall to a turning, fared cautiously to pass it, found a blank wall opposite him, and was lost. His sense of direction left him, and he had no longer any idea of where the street lay and where the sea. He floundered in gross darkness, inept and persistent. It took some time, many turnings, and a tumble in the mud to convince him that he was lost. And then the rain came down in earnest.

It roared, it pelted, it stamped on him. It was no rain, as he knew it: it was a cascade, a vehement and malignant assault by all the wetness in heaven. It whipped, it stung, it thrashed; he was drenched in a moment as though by a trick. He could see nothing, but groped blind and frightened under it, feeling along the wall with one hand, still carrying the bronze image by the head with the other. Once he dropped it, and would have left it, but with an impulse like an effort of self-respect, he searched for it, groping elbow-deep in the slush and water, found it, and stumbled on. Another corner presented itself; he came round it, and almost at once a light showed itself.

It was a slit of brightness, below a door, and without a question the drenched and bewildered Dawson lifted the image and hammered on the door with it. A hum of voices within abated as he knocked, and there was silence. He hammered again, and he heard bolts being withdrawn inside. The door opened slowly, and a man looked out.

"I've lost my way," flustered Dawson pitifully. "I'm wet through, and I don't know where I am." Even as he spoke the rain was cutting through his clothes like blades. "Please let me in," he concluded, "Please let me in."

The man was backed by the light, and Dawson could see nothing of him save that he was tall and stoutly made. But he laughed, and opened the door a foot farther to let him pass in.

"Come in," he bade him. His voice was foreign and high. "Come in. All may come in to-night."

Dawson entered, leading a trail of water over a floor of bare boards. His face was running wet, and he was newly dazzled with the light. But when he had wiped his eyes, he drew a deep breath of relief and looked about him. The room was unfurnished save for a littered table and some chairs, and a gaudy picture of the Virgin that hung on the wall. On each

ide of it was a sconce, in which a slovenly candle guttered.
A woman was perched on a corner of the table, a heavy shawl
ver her head. Under it the dark face, propped in the fork
f her hand, glowed sullenly, and her bare, white arm was like
a menacing thing. Dawson bowed to her with an instinct of
politeness. In a chair near her a grossly fat man was huddled,
scowling heavily under thick, fair brows, while the other man,
he who had opened the door, stood smiling.

The woman laughed softly as Dawson ducked to her, scan-
ing him with an amusement that he felt as ignominy. But she
pointed to the image dangling in his hand.

"What is that?" she asked.

Dawson laid it on the floor carefully. "It's a curio," he explained. "I was fetching it for a lady. An idol, you know."

The fat man burst into a hoarse laugh, and the other man
spoke to Dawson.

"An' you?" he queried. "What you doing 'ere, so late an' so
wet?"

"I was trying to take a short cut to the landing-stage,"
Dawson replied. "Like a silly fool, I thought I could find my
way through here. But I got lost somehow."

The fat man laughed again.

"You come off the German steamer?" suggested the woman.

Dawson nodded. "I came ashore with some friends," he
answered, "from the second-class. But I left them to go back
and fetch this idol, and here I am."

The tall man who had opened the door turned to the woman.

"So we must wait a leetle longer for your frien's," he said.

She tossed her head sharply.

"Friends!" she exclaimed. "Mother of God! Would you
walk about with your knives for ever? When every day other
men are taken, can you ask me to go free? Am I the wife of the
Intendente?"

"No, nod the vife!" barked the stout man violently. "But
f you gan't tell us noding better than to stop for der police
to dake us, vot's der good of you?"

The woman shrugged her shoulders, and the shawl slipped,
and showed them bare and white above her bodice.

"I have done all that one could do," she answered sullenly,
with defiant eyes. "Seven months you have done as you would,
untouched. That was through me. Now, fools, you must take
your turn—one month, three months, six months—who knows?

—in prison. One carries a knife—one goes to prison! Wha
would you have?"

"Gif der yong man a chair, Tonio," said the fat man, an
his companion reached Dawson a seat. His sat on it in the mid
dle of the floor, while they wrangled around him. He gathere
that the two men anticipated a visit from the police ver
shortly, and that they blamed it on the woman, who migh
have averted it. Both the men accused her of their misfor
tune, and she faced them dauntlessly. She tried to bring them
it seemed to accept it as inevitable, as a thing properly at
tendant on them; to show that she, after all, could not chang
the conditions of existence.

"You stabbed the Greek," she argued once, turning sharpl
on the tall man.

"Well," he began, and she flourished her hand as an *ergo*.

"Life is not spending money," she even philosophised. "On
pays for living, my friend, with work, with pain, with jail
Here you have to pay. I have paid for you, seven month
nearly, with smiles and love. But the price is risen. It is you
turn now."

Dawson gazed at her fascinated. She spoke and gesticulate
with a captivating spirit. Life brimmed in her. As she spoke
her motions were arguments in themselves. She put a case an
demolished it with a smile; presented the alternative, left
final word unspoken, and the thing was irresistible. Dawson
perched lonely on his chair, experienced a desire to enter th
conversation.

The men were beyond conviction. "Why didn't you"—d
this or that? the tall man kept asking, and his fat comrade ex
ploded, "Yes, vy?" They seemed to demand of her that sh
should accept blame without question; and to her answers
clear and ready, the fat man retorted with a gross oath.

"Excuse me, sir," began Dawson, shocked. He was aching t
be on the woman's side.

"Vot?" demanded the fat man.

"That's hardly the way to speak to a lady," said Dawso
gravely.

The tall man burst into a clear laugh, and the fat ma
glared at Dawson. He flinched somewhat, but caught th
woman's eye and found comfort and reinforcement there. She
too, was smiling, but gratefully, and she gave him a courteou
little nod of thanks.

"I don't like to hear such language used to a lady," he .id, speaking manfully enough, and giving the fat man eyes s steady as his own. "No gentleman would do it, I'm sure."

"Vot der hell you got to do mit it?" demanded the other rociously, while his companion laughed. The woman held up hand. "Do not quarrel," she said. "There is trouble enough ready. Besides, *they* may be here any moment. Is there any- ing to get ready?"

"But vot der hell," cried the fat man again. She turned on im.

"Fool! fool! Will you shout and curse all night, till the alge- as are on you?"

"Yes; an' you put dem on us," the tall man interrupted.

She turned swiftly on him, poising her small head over her are breasts with a superb scorn.

"Why do you lie?" she demanded hotly. "Why do you lie? Iust you hide even from your own blame behind my skirts? Iother of God!"—an outstretched hand called the tawdry irgin on the wall to witness—"you are neither man nor good east—just——"

The tall man interrupted. "Don' go on!" he said quietly. Don' go on!" His eyes were shining, and he carried one hand eneath his coat. "Don' dare to go on!"

"Dare!" The woman lifted her face insolently, brought up er bare arm with a slow sweep, and puffed once at an im- ginary cigarette. There was so much of defiance in the action hat Dawson, watching her, breathless, started to his feet with omething hard and heavy in his hand. It was the image.

"Thief!" said the woman slowly, gazing under languorous yelids at the white, venomous face of the tall man. "Thief nd——" she leaned forward and said the word, the ultimate nd supreme insult of the coast.

It was barely said when there flashed something in the man's and. He was poised on his toes, leaning forward a little, his rm swinging beside him. The woman flung both arms before er face and cried out; then leaned rapidly aside as a pointed nife whizzed past her head and struck twanging in the wall ehind her. The man sprang forward, and the next instant the oom was chaos, for Dawson, tingling to his extremities, tepped in and spread him out with a crashing blow on the ead. The "idol" was his weapon.

The stout German thundered an oath and heaved to h
feet, fumbling at his hip and babbling broken profanity.

Dawson swung the image and stepped towards him.

"Keep still," he cried, "or I'll brain you!"

"Der hell!" vociferated the German, and fired swiftly
him. The room filled with smoke, and Dawson, staggering u
hurt, but with his face stung with powder, did not see th
man fall. As the German drew the revolver clear, the woma
knifed him in the neck, and he collapsed on his face, belchin
blood upon the boards of the floor. The woman stood over hin
the knife still in her hand, looking at Dawson with a smile

"My God!" he said as he glanced about him. The tall ma
was lying at his feet, huddled hideously on the floor. The roo
stank of violence and passion. "My God!" and he stooped t
the body.

The woman touched him on the shoulder. "Come," she sai
"It's no good. It was a grand blow, a king's blow. You car
not help him."

"But—but——" he flustered as he rose. The emergency wa
beyond him. He had only half a strong man's equipment—th
mere brawn. "Two men killed. I must get back to the ship."

He saw the woman smiling, and caught at his calmnes
There was comprehension in her eyes, and to be understoo
is so often to be despised. "You must come too," he added, o
an impulse, and stopped, appalled by the idea.

"To the ship?" she cried and laughed. "Oh, la la! But no
Still, we must go from here. The police will be here any min
ute, and if they find you——" She left it unsaid, and the ga
was ominous.

The police! To mention them was to touch all that was con
ventional, suburban, and second-class in Dawson. He itched t
be gone. A picture of Vine Street police-court and a curtl
aloof magistrate flashed across his mind, and a reminiscence o
evening paper headlines, and his mind fermented hysterically

The woman put back her knife in some secret recess of he
clothes, and opened the door cautiously. "Now!" she said, bu
paused, and came back. She went to the picture of the Virgi
and turned its face to the wall. "One should not forget re
spect," she observed apologetically. "These things are remem
bered. Now come."

No sooner were they in the gloomy alley outside than th
neighbourhood of others was known to them. There was a

und of many feet ploughing in the mud, and a suppressed
oice gave a short order. The woman stopped and caught
awson's arm.

"Hush!" she whispered. "It is the police. They have come
or the men. They will be on both sides of us. Wait and lis-
en."

Dawson stood rigid, his heart thumping. The darkness
eemed to surge around him with menaces and dangers. The
olashing feet were nearer, coming up on their right, and once
ome metal gear clinked as its wearer scraped against the wall.
Ie could *smell* men, as he remembered afterwards. The woman
eside him retained her hold on his arm, and remained mo-
onless till it seemed that the advancing men must run into
hem.

"Come quietly," she whispered at length, putting warm lips
o his ear. Her hand dropped along his arm till she grasped
is fingers. She led him swiftly away from the place, having
aited till the police should be so near that the noise they made
ould drown their own retreat.

On they went, then, as before, swishing through the foul-
ess underfoot, and without speaking. Only at times the
oman's hold on his hand would tighten, and, meeting with
o response, would slacken again, and she would draw him
n ever more quickly.

"Where are we going?" he ventured to ask.

"We are escaping," she answered, with a brief tinkle of
aughter. "If you knew from what we are escaping, you would
ot care where. But hurry, always!"

Soon, however, she paused, still holding his hand. Again
ney heard footsteps, and this time the woman turned to him
esperately.

"There is a door near by," she breathed. "We must find it,
r——" again the unspoken word. "Feel always along the wall
here. Farther, go farther. It should be here."

They sprang on, with hands to the rough plaster on the
all, till Dawson encountered the door, set level with the wall,
or which they sought.

"Push," panted the woman, heaving at it with futile hands.
Even in the darkness he could see the gleam of her naked
rms and shoulders. "Push it in."

Dawson laid his shoulder to it, his arms folded, and shoved

desperately till his head buzzed. As he eased up he heard th
near feet of the menacing police again.

"You must push it in!" cried the woman. "It is the onl
way. If not——"

"Here, catch hold of this," said Dawson, and she found th
bronze image in her hands. "Let me come," she said, an
standing back a little, he flung his twelve stone of bone an
muscle heavily on the door. It creaked, and some fastenin,
within broke and fell to the ground.

Once again he assaulted it, and it was open. They passe
rapidly within, and closed it behind them, and with th
woman's hand guiding, Dawson stumbled up a long, narrow
sloppy stair that gave on to the flat roof of the building
Above them was sky again. The rain had passed, and th
frosty stars of Mozambique shone faintly. He took a dee
breath as he received the image from the hands of the woman

"You hear them?" she said, and he listened with a shudde
to the passing of the men below.

"But we must go on," she said. "We are not safe yet. Ove
the wall to the next roof. Come!"

They clambered over a low parapet, and dropped six feet t
another level. Dawson helped the woman up the opposite wall
and she sat reconnoitering on the top.

"Come quietly," she warned him, and he clambered up be
side her and looked down at the roof before them. In a kind o
tent persons appeared to be sleeping; their breath was plainl
to be heard.

"You must walk like a rat," she whispered, smiling, and low
ered herself. He followed. She was crouching in the shadow o
the wall, and drew him down beside her. Somebody had cease
to sleep in the tent, and was gabbling drowsily, in a monoto
nous sing-song.

"If they see us," she whispered to him, "they will think yo
have come here after the women."

"But we could say——" he began.

"There will be nothing to say," she interrupted. "Hush
There he comes."

Out of the tent crawled a man, lean and black and bearded
with a sheet wrapped around him. He stood up and looked
around, yawning. The woman nestled closer to Dawson, wh
gripped instinctively on the bronze image. The man walked t
the parapet on their left and looked over, and then walked

ack to the tent and stood irresolutely, muttering to himself.
Squatted under the wall, Dawson found room amid the race
of his disordered thoughts to wonder that he did not instantly
ee them.

He was coming towards them, and Dawson felt the bare
shoulder that pressed against his arm shrug slightly. The
man was ten paces away, walking right on to them, and look-
ng to the sky, when, with throbbing temples and tense lips,
Dawson rose, ran at him, and gripped him. He had the throat
in the crutch of his right hand, and strangled the man's yell
as it was conceived. They went down together, writhing and
clutching, Dawson uppermost, the man under him scratching
and slapping at him with open hands. He drew up a knee and
found a lean chest under it, drove it in, and choked his man
to silence and unconsciousness.

"Take this, take this," urged the woman, bending beside
him. She pressed her slender-bladed knife on him. "Just a
prick, and he is quite safe!"

Dawson rose. "No," he said. "He's still enough now. No
need to kill him." He looked at the body and from it to the
woman. "Didn't I get him to rights?" he asked exultantly.

She raised her face to his.

"It was splendid," she said. "With only the bare hands to
take an armed man——"

"Armed!" repeated Dawson.

"Surely," she answered. "That, at least, is always sure.
See," she pulled the man's sheet wide. Girt into a loin-cloth below was an ugly, broad blade. "Yes, it was magnificent. You
are a man, my friend."

"And you," he said, thrilled by her adulation and the proximity of her bare, gleaming bosom, "are a woman."

"Then——" she began spiritedly; but in a heat of cordial
impulse he took her to him and kissed her hotly on the lips.

"I was wondering when it could come," she said slowly, as
he released her. "When you spoke to the German about the
bad word, I began to wonder. I knew it would come. Kiss me
again, my friend, and we will go on."

"Are we getting towards the landing-stage?" he asked her,
as the next roof was crossed. "I mustn't miss my boat, you
know."

"Oh, that!" she answered. "You want to go back?"

"Well, of course," he replied, in some surprise. "That's

what I was trying to do when I knocked at your door. I've missed my dinner as it is."

"Missed your dinner!" she repeated, with a bubble of mirth. "Ye-es; you have lost that, but,"—she came to him and laid a hand on his shoulder, speaking softly—"but you have seen *me*. Is it nothing, friend, that you have saved me?"

He had stopped, and she was looking up to him, half-smiling, half-entreating, wholly alluring. He looked down into her dark face, with a sudden quickening about the heart.

"And all this fighting," she continued, as though he were to be convinced of something. "You conquer men as though you were bred on the roofs of Mozambique. You fight like—like a hero. It is a rush, a blow, a tumble, and you have them lying at your feet. And when you remember all this, will you not be glad, friend—will you not be glad that it was for me?"

He nodded, clearing his throat huskily. Her hand on his shoulder was a thing to charm him to fire.

"I'd fight—I'd fight for you," he replied uneasily, "as long as—as long as there was any one to fight."

He was feeling his way in speech, as best he could, past conventionalities. There had dawned on him, duskily and half-seen, the unfitness of little proprieties and verbose frills while he went to war across the roofs with this woman of passion.

"You would," she said fervently with half-closed eyes. "I know you would."

She dropped her hand, and stood beside him in silence. There was a long pause. He guessed she was waiting for the next move from him, and he nerved himself to be adequate to her unspoken demand.

"You lead on," he said at last unsteadily.

"Where?" she asked breathlessly.

He did not speak, but waved an open hand that gave her the freedom of choice. It was his surrender to the wild spirit of the Coast, and he grasped the head of the brass image the tighter when he had done it. She and Fate must guide now: it rested with him only to break opposing heads.

She smiled and shivered. "Come on, then," she said, and started before him.

They traversed perhaps a score of roofs enclosed with high parapets, on to each of which he lifted her, hands in her armpits, swinging her cleanly to the level of his face and planting her easily and squarely on the coping. He welcomed each opportunity to take hold of her and put out the strength of his muscles, and she sat where he placed her, smiling and silent, while he clambered up and dropped down on the other side.

At length a creaking wooden stair that hung precariously on the sheer side of a house brought them again to the ground level. It was another gloomy alley into which they descended, and the darkness about him and the mud underfoot struck Dawson with a sense of being again in familiar surroundings. The woman's hand slid into his as he stood, and they started along again together.

The alley seemed to be better frequented than that of which he already had experience. More than once dark, sheeted figures passed them by, noiseless save for the underfoot swish in the mud, and presently the alley widened into a little square, at one side of which there was a fresh rustle of green things. At the side of it a dim light showed through a big open door, from which came a musical murmur of voices, and Dawson recognised a church.

"The Little Garden of St. Sebastian," murmured the woman, and led him on to cross the square. A figure that had been hidden in the shadow now lounged forth, and revealed itself to them as a man in uniform. He stood across their way, and accosted the woman briefly in Portuguese.

Dawson stood fidgeting while she spoke with him. He seemed to be repeating a brief phrase over and over again, harshly and irritably; but she was cajoling, remonstrating, arguing, as he had seen her argue in that ill-fated room an hour back.

"What's the matter with him?" demanded Dawson impatiently.

"He says he won't let me go," answered the woman, with a tone of despair in her voice.

"The devil he won't! What's he got to do with it?"

"Oh, these little policemen, they always arrest me when they can," she replied, with a smile.

"Here, you!" cried Dawson, addressing himself to the man in uniform—"you go away. *Voetsaak*, see! You mind your own business, and get out."

The officer drawled something in his own tongue, which was, of course, unintelligible to Dawson, but it had the effect of annoying him strangely.

"You little beast!" he said, and knocked the man down with his fist.

"Run," hissed the woman at his elbow—"run before he can get up. No, not that way. To the church, and out by another way!"

She caught his hand, and together they raced across the square and in through the big door.

There were a few people within, most sleeping on the benches and along the floor by the walls. In the chancel there were others, masked by the lights, busy with some offices. A wave of sudden song issued from among them as Dawson and the woman entered, and gave way again to the high, nervous voice of a man that stood before the altar. All along the sides of the church was shadow, and the woman speedily found a little arched door.

"Come through the middle of it," she whispered urgently to Dawson, as she packed her loose skirts together in her hand—"cleanly through the middle; do not rub the wall as you come."

He obeyed and followed her, and they were once more in the darkness of an alley.

"It was the door of the lepers," she explained, as she let her skirts swish down again. "See, there is the light by the sea!"

The wind came cleanly up the alley, and soon they were at its mouth, where a lamp flickered in the breeze. Dawson drew a deep breath, and tucked the image under his arm. His palm was sore with the roughness of its head.

"Some one is passing," said the woman in a low tone. "Wait here till they are by."

Footsteps were approaching along the front, and very soon Dawson heard words and started.

"What is it?" whispered the woman, her breath on his neck.

"Listen!" he answered curtly.

The others came within the circle of the lamp—a girl and two men.

"I do hope he's found my idol," the girl was saying.

Dawson stepped into the light, and they turned and saw him.

"Why, here he is," exclaimed Miss Paterson shrilly.

He raised his hat to the woman who stood at the entrance to the alley—raised it as he would have raised it to a waitress in a bun-shop, and went over to the people from the second-class saloon.

"I found it," he said, lifting the image forward, and brushing with his hand at the foulness of blood and hair upon it. "But I was almost thinking I should miss the boat."

A. Neil Lyons

THE GINGER-NUT

When Maria Tute suddenly banged down the shutters of her little shop in the thick of a hot sunshine, she added another offence to the many which were written down for her damnation in the alien city of Soho.

This faded virgin, with her stock of Berlin wools and beaded mittens, was the most flagrantly English fact in Burke Street. Being herself a tea-drinker and addicted—something unduly—to brown bread and marmalade, she did not realise the importance attached by persons of more emotional appetite to the question of undisturbed siesta. She was *always* dashing out into the sunshine on warm afternoons and banging things. On this occasion she had banged such bangs as seemed beyond all decency.

Certain limp waiters and some fine old crusted cooks tumbled out of all the adjacent doorways to glare Latin adjectives at the woman and her sign.

Miss Tute, perhaps a little conscious of offence, stood at her threshold grasping the shutter-pole in an attitude faintly suggestive of defiance. She was not a young woman, nor beautiful, and the tea had evidently left its traces upon her temper. Her general demeanour, however, suggested an indulgent conscience and a kind heart. She was stately and dignified too —in a reminiscent sort of way—like Burke Street itself.

And the figure of Miss Tute stood almost solitary. But for a purring harmony of distant traffic, one might suppose oneself spirited into some complacent burgess city of the South.

Presently some boys came up the street.

They were not English boys. Their curls were thick and dark, and they wore them long about the ears, after the detestable manner of cheap labour. Their gait, too, betrayed them, being bold yet leisurely—not unsuggestive of a thoughtful "cake-walk." These youths came to a halt before Miss Tute and spoke loudly and with gesture. They were discussing the character and appearance of Miss Tute.

Maria was no linguist, but she probably guessed the voluble iteration of these visitors to possess the character of invective. Her normal procedure in such circumstances (which were of frequent occurrence) was to rush blindly forth with the shutter-pole, and to cry "Porco Macaroni" in a loud and penetrating voice.

To-day, however, this effective demonstration was not forthcoming. Miss Tute had an even better retort on hand.

To the dismay and discomfiture of her would-be tormentors, there suddenly manifested himself Mr. W., the blue-coated garrison of England. The boys departed hurriedly, and in comparative silence. Miss Tute approached her fellow-alien.

"What's the matter *now*, then?" demanded Mr. W., with an air of boredom.

"Nothing unusual," replied Miss Tute, in a kind voice. "Nothing unusual for this street—like a policeman in a hurry, for instance. I wanted you to take a tallergram, or mind the shop while I take it."

"Certainly," replied Policeman W. brightly, touching his helmet. "Clean yer doorstep, too?"

"Might do worse than that," was the lady's response. "A little stooping exercise is what they want in the police. . . . I tried to get a boy when I heard as you was out o' town. But you know what sort o' boy they grow round Burke Street. Little Eyetalian imps—all salad oil and 'Ebrew. If they found a tin o' metal polish in the place they'd eat it."

Constable W. gnawed his chin-strap, and something in his throat whirred faintly. These acts testified to his appreciation of Miss Tute's geniality.

"Well, well," he murmured, "I'll take yer tallegram."

"Thank you for nothing," replied Miss Tute. "I've shut me shop up now."

Mr. W. looked searchingly at the emporium in question. "The stores will be pleased," he said, and with that cryptic utterance, turned on his heel. This action brought Mr. W. face to face with two strangers, whom he regarded with irresolute displeasure.

ii

The strangers evidently did not belong to Soho, being neither of the curly-headed race which cooks, nor of the dignified
race which dines. One of the strangers, a young man, was a
young man of the type which is trousered in flannel; the other
stranger, a woman, wore yellow boots and an ostrich feather,
and was upholstered in a purple stuff of almost audible intensity. She carried a basket containing sweet peas and soaps in
multichromatic variety.

Policeman W., having directed his trained intelligence to
the science of probabilities, decided that the presence of the
strangers in Burke Street was probably undesirable. He therefore uttered, without any trace of his former indecision, the
time-honoured formula of distrust:

"Now then, pass along there! This ain't any business o'
yours."

"If you please, sergeant," replied the female stranger, "I
want to talk to the lady. The lady knows me, inspector. I want
to talk to the lady."

"What about that lad there?" demanded Mr. W., employing a tone of increased authority, in keeping with his so recent
advancement of rank.

"This *gentleman*," responded the woman, "is along o' me.
He wants to talk to the lady, too."

Policeman W. again applied his heel to the pavement, and
repeating, with a high degree of accomplishment, the most attractive of all constabulary movements, now faced Miss Tute.

"The woman says you know 'er," proclaimed Mr. W. "Says
she wants to talk to you."

Miss Tute, still grasping her shutter-pole, put a hand to
her forehead and peered at "the woman" from beneath its
shade.

"Why, it's Clara!" exclaimed Miss Tute. "In trouble
again?"

"No, miss," answered Clara, approaching the lady, as Mr.
W., with a sweep of his arm, indicated that she might regard
herself as a bus, and come on. "No, miss; I ain't in no trouble.
I come to wish you luck—you and your pore nephew."

Miss Tute's complexion warmed to a flesh tint. "You've got
a good heart, Clara," she said.

"I've got a 'usband on Dartmoor," answered Clara. "I don'
a month in 'Olloway meself. I know what Trouble is."

"You've got a good heart," repeated Miss Tute. She fum
bled ineffectively at the shutter with her pole.

"Will ya give the pore young gentleman these 'ere blooms,'
continued Clara. "They're fresh this mornin'—straight out o'
Covent Gardin. They ain't bin slept on. Strike me dead, they
ain't."

"Constable," said Miss Tute, "would you have the good
ness for to draw up this shutter?"

Constable W. was a pleasant and amenable young fellow at
heart, though superficially hardened by the weight of public
office. Soured as he was by contact with a thankless public
cynical inspectors, and a regulation helmet, he still was not
the man to act unhandsomely towards the aged or infirm or
weak of mind—in which last category it was his custom to
place all persons of the female sex. He held out an arm for the
shutter-pole.

Clara, assuming an air of inefficiency and refinement, stood
by the side of Mr. W., and watched his efforts to "effect an
entrance" with an expression of wonder and gratification.

"My word!" she exclaimed, in a hoarse whisper: "My word
—if I catch 'im bendin'!

"I brought me friend along," continued Clara, still whispering, but addressing herself particularly to Miss Tute, "because I thought your pore young gentleman might feel better,
like, if he knowed that a educated young feller like my friend
was wishful to shake 'ands with 'im. I thought it would cheer
the pore lad up like, to walk up Wardour Street along of a
proper young Nut, same's 'isself. A young gentleman what's
found Trouble, arter the style o' your nephew, 'e might get
the idea into 'is 'ead as some o' the Boys would want to turn
agin' 'im, arter this trouble o' his. But my friend here, he'd
like to go out along of your nephew and show him the sights
—the Zoological Gardins and the White City, and so on. Nothing rash, you understand. No port wine or cabs. Just a 'arm-
less look round and a bit o' dinner in the quiet end of 'Olborn.
You needn't think nothing about the expense o' it. 'E's well-
to-do, this young fellah is. 'E's got a regular position in the
noospaper world."

I offered Miss Tute a gracious bow in confirmation of this
statement.

Miss Tute returned the bow, and touching Clara's hand, she said, "You've got a good heart, Clara."

By this time Mr. W. had partly raised the shutter, and, to the all but irresistible temptation of Clara, he now stooped down, assuming an unconstabulary posture, for the purpose of completing his work.

"Mind how you go," Miss Tute admonished him. "There's a beer-bottle or two inside there!"

With a mighty heave of his mighty shoulders, Mr. W. accomplished the uplifting of the shutter.

"Come inside, dear," said Miss Tute to Clara.

Mr. W., standing clear of the entrance, removed his helmet, and blew on it. "Beer, eh?" he remarked.

Miss Tute, pausing on her threshold, looked undecidedly at the constable. "Well," she remarked at last, "if—if: it's against my principles, but if it's not against your regulations——"

"Oh, it ain't against my regulations," said Mr. W.

"I haven't changed me ideas," pursued Miss Tute. "That beer is for a friend—an *old* friend."

"I see: for a friend," mused Mr. W., again bending.

"Constable," inquired the lady suddenly, "did any of your brothers ever get put to gaol?"

"Certainly *not*," responded the constable.

"R!" exclaimed Miss Tute. "Well, mine did. Me *only* brother. He's coming out this afternoon. That's what the beer is for."

Policeman W. paused in the act of unscrewing the stopper from a bottle. "'Ow long?" he inquired.

"Ten years," replied Miss Tute.

Mr. W. screwed the stopper in again and replaced the bottle amongst its fellows. "We'll leave it at that!" he said. "Your brother'll want all this."

iii

With these words, Mr. W., averting his head from the row of bottles, walked manfully away.

"It isn't ten years, really—not since he went away," the exact Miss Tute explained to Clara. "They called it ten years. But they take off bits—a month here and a month there, you know—for gentlemanly behaviour. It won't be more than eight years, really, since he went away."

"Eight years is time enough to raise a thirst in," reflected Clara.

"Perhaps," said Miss Tute, "you and your friend'll sit in the room behind there, and keep an eye on the place while I go out and send this tallergram and do a bit o' shoppin'. Perhaps you'll stay this evening, and help to give the boy a welcome. It's to his Catford cousins, this tallergram. I think they ought to know. They won't be very cheerful comp'ny; but, thinking it all over, I think they ought to know. If any of them nasty little foreigners show their faces here, perhaps your young gentleman friend'll be so kind as to fetch 'em a flip behind the ear."

Clara surveyed the retreating figure of Miss Tute with reverent eyes. "That's a lady, that is," she said. "She don't 'arf look after some of us girls. When anybody belongin' to us gits into trouble, you know. Same as mine. She's very tender-'earted in that way, she is, along of this brother of 'ers bein' put away. It's give 'er a fondness for us girls: a flesh and blood sort o' fondness.

"No; I dunno what 'e done to git put away. Some bit o' trouble, same's anybody might run up against. On'y it comes 'ard on a gentleman—a Nib, like what he was. Oh, he was a reg'lar gentleman; a clerk in the Meat Market, they tell me.

"She don't 'arf look arter some of us gals, I tell ya. None o' your Scripture Teas, ya know, no bloomin' 'ymn work. Just a good friend, she is, same as yar aunt might be. Baby clothes and bloater paste, and 'am and 'arf dollars, and God knows what all."

Miss Tute presently returned, and having stayed herself with jam, and sponge-cake, told us, in fragmentary monologue, about the brother.

"Manslaughter!" she explained.

"R!" echoed Clara. "Manslaughter!"

"Knocked a man down in the Meat Market. 'Ad the misfortune to break three ribs and the neck bone."

"R!" exclaimed Clara; "the Meat Market."

"Quarrel over a girl," added Miss Tute.

"R!" cried Clara sagely; "a girl!"

"Yes," Miss Tute assented, "a girl. As good-for-nothing a parcel o' wickedness as ever anybody could wish to see. Never went near my brother all through his trouble, and directly he —directly they—directly his back was turned, she went off and married a job-master! I'd give her job-master; I'd—but there! Let us forgive. He's comin' out this afternoon; we won't think no evil of anybody. He's comin' out this afternoon, and I'll forget my principles and let him have his beer. A person can't help being fond of their own brother, even though he *is* a Ginger-nut. That's what my father called him—a Ginger-nut!"

"What is a Ginger-nut?" demanded Clara.

"Oh," replied Miss Tute, "it's a word what my father made up. It means a lot of things. Stands for bein' larky, you know, and borrowin' money, you know, and bettin', and goin' to music-'alls, and—and—fallin' in love a lot. Stands for havin' a lot of cheek and independence. In fact, if I was to give you the proper definition o' Ginger-nut, I should say it means anybody what's young and good lookin', the same as our George, with the Devil in their eyes, the same as our George's.

"You'll notice George's eyes this evenin'. My word, he's got the Devil in them!

"My father said I spoilt George. But father got to be very hard on George. I could see George's wilfulness as well as anybody; but what with his looks and his way of laughin', and those eyes of his, people got into the way of *lettin'* him be wilful. He's a good lad, really, on'y wilful, with a Devil in his eyes. He's a Ginger-nut. When he was a little self-willed chap of seven, he used to sleep in bed along of me, and sometimes I'd get drowsy and forgetful, and I'd push his little head from off my neck, and then, my word—wouldn't he half kick out. I tell you, he was a Ginger-nut!

"*I* didn't spoil him. I on'y made allowances. Father wouldn't. I'm not going to spoil him now. That beer there is simply a medicine. My medical man tells me that the change from Portland will very likely weaken him.

"There are the Catford cousins, too. They'll weaken him.

"But I thought it all over, and I came to the conclusion as they ought to know. They'll be here before six."

"And the lad, miss?" inquired Clara.

"He'll be coming later—eight o'clock or so. His uncle Fred —my father's brother, the sailor that was—he's gone to the prison to fetch him. Ugh—prison! think of it. Our George in prison. Eight years!"

"And yet, do you know, sir," reflected Miss Tute, addressing your servant, "if you was to *know* a Ginger-nut, I believe you'd agree with me that it's a paltry business to send a man to prison for."

iv

An unexpected blessing awaited Miss Tute, in the bifurcation of the Catford cousins. Only one Catford cousin—Cousin Maggie—came to welcome home the Ginger-nut. Providence had been pleased to render the other cousin immobile by reason of having afflicted that lady's mule canary with a complaint called croup.

Cousin Maggie was a pink, full-bosomed person, the cast of whose somewhat homely countenance testified to her possession of what is called "a responsive nature."

"Begun already, 'ave you?" Miss Tute remarked, when Cousin Maggie had recourse to an armchair and the stimulus of tears. "It's perhaps as well for you to start early. It'll get you nice and dry for the agony of shakin' 'ands with him."

"I—I'm silly; I know I am," admitted Cousin Maggie. "But it seems so wonderful to think o' seein' 'im again, after all these years; and to think of 'is pore 'air all cut short!"

"Think o' something sensible!" urged Miss Tute, with a sniff. "Hair soon grows again when you are a boy of his age."

"Boy!" the cousin echoed, sitting suddenly upright, and removing the handkerchief from her eyes. "Boy? Twenty-four and eight makes thirty-two, Maria! I call that a funny sort o' age for a boy."

"Of course," said Miss Tute, averting her head, "he'll be older. I hadn't thought of that."

"Bin thinking all this time of the wilful young Ginger-nut he used to be, hey, Maria?" suggested the cousin, beginning to brighten. "Ah! he'll be a grown man now: thirty-two, and a good age too!" added Cousin Maggie, with generosity. "My word, Maria, 'e wasn't 'arf a Ginger-nut, George wasn't, was 'e? Lord, 'ow 'e did slosh into that conductor for callin' out about my 'at. I'd 'a' given George me 'ead in them days. Such a 'andsome young fellar he was; so wilful, so well-mannered; and, my word—what eyes!"

Then came eight o'clock, and Maria and her cousin began

to make little visits to the front doorsteps, and to speculate upon the likelihood of train accidents. The drinking habits of Uncle Fred were also discussed. A tendency was exhibited to anticipate disaster. When the clock struck half-past eight and still there was no sign of Uncle Fred, no sign of the Ginger-nut, the tendency developed into a settled conviction. Suddenly Cousin Maggie, situated on the doorstep, uttered a triumphant cry.

"There he is," shrilled Maggie: "I see him! I see him!"

"Who?" called Miss Tute, making for the doorway.

"Why, Uncle Fred," answered Maggie. " 'E's turned the corner by the public house, and—and—why, yes—'e's brought some man along with him."

"Brought George along with him, you mean," Maria answered.

"That!" cried Cousin Maggie, shrinking back, with a curious movement.

v

Why Cousin Maggie did this I do not know, for the man who followed Uncle Fred was a perfectly sober and respectable-looking person.

He stooped slightly, and his walk was awkward and stiff. He walked with his eyes cast down upon the ground, his head bowed rigidly. His arms were held close into his side, as though he were a man accustomed much to walking in a press. This deliberate walk of his was certainly a little strange. So exact it was, so measured, as to suggest an invisible company marching with him, some on this side, some on that, others at his heels and before him. But should a man's cousin shrink back from him because his walk is strange?

Uncle Fred and his companion came on towards the shop, and I perceived that the Ginger-nut was dressed in a neat blue suit. When they had reached the nearest lamp-post but one, Miss Tute and her cousin went out to meet them.

"You've brought him then," said Miss Tute to Uncle Fred, to which that gentleman responded:

"Aye, I've *brought* 'im."

"Well, George dear. How are you, George dear?" Maria touched her brother's arm.

The Ginger-nut looked up, and offered her an undecided

grin. He fidgeted with his hands, and, presently, releasing one of them, jerked it hastily in the direction of Uncle Fred.

"He *is* a beggar," he said.

"Here's your Cousin Maggie," Miss Tute then stated. "Come all the way from Cartford to welcome you."

Maggie, her pocket handkerchief rather indifferently concealed, pressed toward him. He looked up as before, and grinned as before, and jerked his arm as before, but this time in the direction of Maria.

"She *is* a beggar," he said.

They crowded into the parlour, and Clara and your servant were in turn permitted to hold the Ginger-nut's hand. Maria then produced grilled chops, potatoes, apple dumplings, cheese, and other articles of diet.

Uncle Fred, the sailor that was, sat blithely down before these viands. The Ginger-nut seemed hesitant; required, as it were, to be coaxed into his seat, and, once there, seemed not capable of the effort required to fill his plate from the dishes before him.

"Feed baby, someone," cried the sailor, in a loud, impatient voice. "It needs a bit o' nursin', I can tell ya."

Maria heaped her brother's plate, and then he proceeded to eat, slowly, steadily, mechanically, but with devastating thoroughness. When he had emptied the plate, he laid down knife and fork and folded his arms, looking expectantly towards his sister, much in the way that terriers look at people.

She filled his plate again, and slowly, thoroughly, he cleared it again, and repeated the look of dumb expectancy. Again she filled his plate with meat; again he emptied it, and then she offered him pudding, which he declined with a shake of the head, but ate largely from the cheese, unabated by bread, and drank heavily of beer. When at last he seemed to be satisfied, Maria began to clear the table, while the Ginger-nut, folding his arms, looked steadily at the floor.

" 'Ave a pipe," roared Uncle Fred, the sailor that was, wiping his mouth. George looked up and nodded, rather furtively, with a cunning look in his eye.

"Then 'ave one, you great booby, you!" shouted Uncle Fred. "Ain't there two ounce o' baccy and a pipe and some matches in yer pocket?"

The Ginger-nut fumbled, and brought forth these articles; but, after looking at them curiously, he dropped them with a little, listless sigh into his lap, and refolded his arms. It was Maria who eventually filled his pipe, and applied the match. Then he smoked feverishly.

Uncle Fred, the sailor that was, then rose up from his seat and delivered himself of certain ideographic utterances.

"When a man," said he, "is passed off on you as a Terror, a Devil, a Ginger-nut, and what not, you don't expect to find 'im 'avin spasms, like a schoolgirl. When a man 'as got the name for wickedness, you do expect to find a flip more vice in 'im what you'd find in a dumb 'air-dresser. I like a beggar what is a beggar of a beggar, I do, 'avin' been to sea; but what I says is, if any beggar sets up to be a beggar, let 'im be no end of a fore-doomed son of a beast of a beggar, and no 'arf larks. The sort o' beggar what this silly beggar is would be used aboard a British vessel for shellin' peas. I'll bid you all good-night."

So Maria and Maggie were left alone with the responsibility of the Ginger-nut. They tried unceasingly, and with the zealous aid of Clara, to engage him in conversation. But the Ginger-nut had lost his relish for motiveless discourse. News and gossip of a public character moved him not. He sat always with his arms folded and his head down, and looked at you, when you spoke to him, with a queer, half-questioning expression, as though he suspected you of quizzing him.

Twice I beckoned to Clara, and twice we tried to go; but Miss Tute always laid her hand on Clara's arm.

"You make 'im laugh again, dear," Miss Tute would say.

Presently the Ginger-nut woke to an enthusiasm. Some brasswork caught his eye about the fireguard. The brass-work was dull, and he rubbed it with the sleeve of his coat. Then he drank beer and stared at the fender, after which he repolished the fender and drank more beer, and stared at his knees and fell asleep.

Maria lighted a candle and touched his shoulder. The Ginger-nut woke instantly, with a start, and stood upright, his hands held tight to his sides, in the attitude of attention. She led him to his chamber. The cousin, lighting another candle, bade us both good-night.

Presently Miss Tute came back into the room, and Clara left off crying. Maria sat down on a little hard stool, and thanked us gravely for having helped to entertain the Ginger-nut. Maria told us that the Ginger-nut was sleeping, and how well he was sleeping—so different from the little boy who used to kick and bite in wilful anger, because Maria moved her neck, which was his pillow.

"He's a more gentle fellow now," said Maria.

"Not 'arf, miss," assented Clara heartily, sitting at Maria's feet, stroking Maria's hand.

"But, my God!" exclaimed Maria, her drab cheeks warming: "What have they done to his eyes?"

C. S. Evans

BRINGING A NEW BOY

SHE came to the school one sunshiny Monday morning, dragging a reluctant boy along with a stiff arm. To the polite assistant-master who handed her a chair she nodded affably, fixing him with a wandering eye.

"Mornin', young man! Yes, I want to see the 'ead master, along o' my Johnny, who 'is father says 'as got to go to school, not as I 'olds with it myself, there wasn't none o' this 'ere eddication when I was a girl, and I got on well enough without it. I suppose you're one of the school-teachers! Ah, well, we must get a livin' somehow, live and let live 's wot I say, not but what school teachin' ain't all right in its way, mind you, though I 'ave seen some upstarts in my time. My sister Amelie's youngest girl, what was very clever at her lessons, bein' in Standard Seven when she was only twelve, and the top in all the examinations, though the smallest child in the class, and a-knowin' everything what her teacher could teach 'er, exceptin' arithmetic, which she never could abide, and I don't blame 'er, poor thing, for the way she used to worry at 'er sums, a-sittin' up all hours a-workin' at 'em, and 'er so thin as you could 'ave broke 'er in 'alf—— Want to see the 'ead master? Course I want to see the 'ead master. Don't I keep on tellin' yer. Anybody'd think you was deaf. Well, as I was a-saying, my sister Amelie's——

"Excuse you, O *certainly*. I come to see the *'ead* master, along o' my Johnny 'ere—(to Johnny)—take yer fist out of yer eyes, and stand up straight—if you make that face you'll get struck like it, and 'ow many times must I tell yer to wipe yer nose on yer 'ankercher. Ain't got a 'ankercher? No! course you ain't, you never 'as. Now don't you tell me I didn't give yer a 'ankercher! Don't you contradik me, my boy, or I'll tan yer when I get you 'ome——

363

"Mornin', sir. Yes, I wants to see the 'ead master. Are you the 'ead master? Well, now, I declare. I shouldn't aknown it if you 'adn't a-told me. I seen you in the playground, an' thought you was the caretaker. I did, *'struth*. Well, it only shows yer as yer never knows, as my sister Amelie used to say afore 'er 'usband run away from 'er and left 'er with a large family of ten, course 'e couldn't bear 'er *jaw*, which she did used to nag and no mistake, though not so bad as some of these 'ere suffragists which 'eaven 'elp their 'usbands is what I say——

"Wot's my business? Don't I tell yer I come to see the 'ead master along o' gettin' my Johnny in the school. You are the 'ead master! Well, you've tole me so about a *dozen* times, and I don't doubt yer word, though, as I said before——

"My name? Name of Gubbins. *Two* 'b's,' if you please. As my sister Amelie used ter say, there's more 'b's' in Gubbins than made a pot of Walker's 'oney, which is nasty un'ealthy stuff, though sweet and fillin', an' never seen a bee I'll warrant——

" 'Usband's name? Well 'is pals call 'im Bully, an' wot I call 'im depends on what I feel like, see? But 'is christened name is Joshyer, and it ain't 'is own fault, so don't you say a word about 'is name, young man. 'E's very techy about 'is name is Joshyer——

"Profession or occypation? Wot do yer mean? Don't you say a word about my 'usband, *if* you please, young man. Oh! wot does 'e do? *Now* you've arst me something. I'm sure I dunno. 'E dunno. Nobody dunno. When 'e works 'e's a French polisher. But 'e can polish off a pot of four-alf better'n anything else. But don't you say a word about my 'usband, young man. I come to see the 'ead master.

"Well, you needn't take anybody up so quick. I know you're the 'ead master. 'Aven't you tole me so about a 'undred times? 'E's ten. 'E don't look it, do 'e? But 'e's ten, you take it from me, young man, 'as ought to know. 'E's small, because 'e's delikit. When 'e was a baby 'e *lived* at the 'orsepittle. And don't you get a-pressin' 'im to learn, cause 'e's delikit——

"I *'ope* you don't use corpril punishment. I don't 'old with it myself. Lead, but don't drive's what I say. I shall 'ave to take 'im away if you corpril punishment 'im. 'E's delikit. As my sister Amelie used to say——

"*Wot!* You ain't got no room? School full? Wot d'yer mean by wasting my time? My time's money, young man, with a family of six to look arter. I come to see the 'ead master. Course, it don't matter to you whose time you waste 'avin' nothin' to do, but talk. I never seen such a man for talking and a-wastin' time. Why couldn't you say so at first, when I tole yer I come to see the 'ead master? Yes, I'm a-goin' now. If you'll stop talkin' and let me. (To Johnny.) Are you or are you not goin' to use your 'ankercher, when I tell yer? I'll tan yer when I get 'ome, disgracin' yer mother. You ain't got a 'ankercher? (To the world in general.) Now did yer ever 'ear the like o' that? 'Ere I come to see the 'ead——" (Voice lost in the distance.)

D. H. Lawrence

THE PRUSSIAN OFFICER

THEY had marched more than thirty kilometers since dawn,
along the white, hot road where occasional thickets of trees
threw a moment of shade, then out into the glare again. On
either hand, the valley, wide and shallow, glittered with heat;
dark green patches of rye, pale young corn, fallow and
meadow and black pine woods spread in a dull, hot diagram
under a glistening sky. But right in front the mountains
ranged across, pale blue and very still, snow gleaming gently
out of the deep atmosphere. And towards the mountains, on
and on, the regiment marched between the rye fields and the
meadows, between the scraggy fruit trees set regularly on
either side the high road. The burnished, dark green rye
threw off a suffocating heat, the mountains drew gradually
nearer and more distinct. While the feet of the soldiers grew
hotter, sweat ran through their hair under their helmets, and
their knapsacks could burn no more in contact with their
shoulders, but seemed instead to give off a cold, prickly sensation.

He walked on and on in silence, staring at the mountains
ahead, that rose sheer out of the land, and stood fold behind
fold, half earth, half heaven, the heaven, the barrier with slits
of soft snow, in the pale, bluish peaks.

He could now walk almost without pain. At the start, he had
determined not to limp. It had made him sick to take the first
steps, and during the first mile or so, he had compressed his
breath, and the cold drops of sweat had stood on his forehead.
But he had walked it off. What were they after all but bruises!
He had looked at them, as he was getting up: deep bruises
on the backs of his thighs. And since he had made his first
step in the morning, he had been conscious of them, till now he

ad a tight, hot place in his chest, with suppressing the pain, nd holding himself in. There seemed no air when he breathed. But he walked almost lightly.

The Captain's hand had trembled at taking his coffee at dawn: his orderly saw it again. And he saw the fine figure of the Captain wheeling on horseback at the farmhouse ahead, a handsome figure in pale blue uniform with facings of scarlet, and the metal gleaming on the black helmet and the sword-scabbard, and dark streaks of sweat coming on the silky bay horse. The orderly felt he was connected with that figure moving so suddenly on horseback: he followed it like a shadow, mute and inevitable and damned by it. And the officer was always aware of the tramp of the company behind, the march of his orderly among the men.

The Captain was a tall man of about forty, gray at the temples. He had a handsome, finely knit figure, and was one of the best horsemen in the West. His orderly, having to rub him down, admired the amazing riding muscles of his loins.

For the rest, the orderly scarcely noticed the officer any more than he noticed himself. It was rarely he saw his master's face: he did not look at it. The Captain had reddish-brown, stiff hair, that he wore short upon his skull. His mustache was also cut short and bristly over a full, brutal mouth. His face was rather rugged, the cheeks thin. Perhaps the man was the more handsome for the deep lines in his face, the irritable tension of his brow, which gave him the look of a man who fights with life. His fair eyebrows stood bushy over light blue eyes that were always flashing with cold fire.

He was a Prussian aristocrat, haughty and overbearing. But his mother had been a Polish Countess. Having made too many gambling debts when he was young, he had ruined his prospects in the Army, and remained an infantry captain. He had never married: his position did not allow of it, and no woman had ever moved him to it. His time he spent riding— occasionally he rode one of his own horses at the races—and at the officers' club. Now and then he took himself a mistress. But after such an event, he returned to duty with his brow still more tense, his eyes still more hostile and irritable. With the men, however, he was merely impersonal, though a devil when roused; so that, on the whole, they feared him, but had no great aversion from him. They accepted him as the inevitable.

To his orderly he was at first cold and just and indifferent he did not fuss over trifles. So that his servant knew practicall nothing about him, except just what orders he would give, an how he wanted them obeyed. That was quite simple. Then th change gradually came.

The orderly was a youth of about twenty-two, of mediun height, and well built. He had strong, heavy limbs, was swarthy with a soft, black, young mustache. There was somethin; altogether warm and young about him. He had firmly marke(eyebrows over dark, expressionless eyes, that seemed never t have thought, only to have received life direct through hi: senses, and acted straight from instinct.

Gradually the officer had become aware of his servant': young, vigorous, unconscious presence about him. He could no get away from the sense of the youth's person, while he wa: in attendance. It was like a warm flame upon the older man': tense, rigid body, that had become almost unliving, fixed There was something so free and self-contained about him, and something in the young fellow's movement, that made the officei aware of him. And this irritated the Prussian. He did not choose to be touched into life by his servant. He might easily have changed his man, but he did not. He now very rarely looked direct at his orderly, but kept his face averted, as if to avoid seeing him. And yet as the young soldier moved unthinking about the apartment, the elder watched him, and would notice the movement of his strong young shoulders under the blue cloth, the bend of his neck. And it irritated him. To see the soldier's young, brown, shapely peasant's hand grasp the loaf or the wine-bottle sent a flash of hate or of anger through the elder man's blood. It was not that the youth was clumsy: it was rather the blind, instinctive sureness of movement of an unhampered young animal that irritated the officer to such a degree.

Once, when a bottle of wine had gone over, and the red gushed out on to the tablecloth, the officer had started up with an oath, and his eyes, bluey like fire, had held those of the confused youth for a moment. It was a shock for the young soldier. He felt something sink deeper, deeper into his soul, where nothing had ever gone before. It left him rather blank and wondering. Some of his natural completeness in himself was gone, a little uneasiness took its place. And from that time an undiscovered feeling had held between the two men.

Henceforward the orderly was afraid of really meeting his master. His subconsciousness remembered those steely blue eyes and the harsh brows, and did not intend to meet them again. So he always stared past his master, and avoided him. Also, in a little anxiety, he waited for the three months to have gone, when his time would be up. He began to feel a constraint in the Captain's presence, and the soldier even more than the officer wanted to be left alone, in his neutrality as servant.

He had served the Captain for more than a year, and knew his duty. This he performed easily, as if it were natural to him. The officer and his commands he took for granted, as he took the sun and the rain, and he served as a matter of course. It did not implicate him personally.

But now if he were going to be forced into a personal interchange with his master he would be like a wild thing caught; he felt he must get away.

But the influence of the young soldier's being had penetrated through the officer's stiffened discipline, and perturbed the man in him. He, however, was a gentleman, with long, fine hands and cultivated movements, and was not going to allow such a thing as the stirring of his innate self. He was a man of passionate temper, who had always kept himself suppressed. Occasionally there had been a duel, an outburst before the soldiers. He knew himself to be always on the point of breaking out. But he kept himself hard to the idea of the Service. Whereas the young soldier seemed to live out his warm, full nature, to give it off in his very movements, which had a certain zest, such as wild animals have in free movement. And this irritated the officer more and more.

In spite of himself, the Captain could not regain his neutrality of feeling towards his orderly. Nor could he leave the man alone. In spite of himself, he watched him, gave him sharp orders, tried to take up as much of his time as possible. Sometimes he flew into a rage with the young soldier, and bullied him. Then the orderly shut himself off, as it were out of earshot, and waited, with sullen, flushed face, for the end of the noise. The words never pierced to his intelligence. He made himself, protectively, impervious to the feelings of his master.

He had a scar on his left thumb, a deep seam going across the knuckle. The officer had long suffered from it, and wanted to do something to it. Still it was there, ugly and brutal on the young, brown hand. At last the Captain's reserve gave way.

One day, as the orderly was smoothing out the tablecloth, the officer pinned down his thumb with a pencil, asking:

"How did you come by that?"

The young man winced and drew back at attention.

"A wood ax, Herr Hauptmann," he answered.

The officer waited for further explanation. None came. The orderly went about his duties. The elder man was sullenly angry. His servant avoided him. And the next day he had to use all his will power to avoid seeing the scarred thumb. He wanted to get hold of it and— A hot flame ran in his blood.

He knew his servant would soon be free, and would be glad. As yet, the soldier had held himself off from the elder man. The Captain grew madly irritable. He could not rest when the soldier was away, and when he was present, he glared at him with tormented eyes. He hated those fine, black brows over the unmeaning, dark eyes, he was infuriated by the free movement of the handsome limbs, which no military discipline could make stiff. And he became harsh and cruelly bullying, using contempt and satire. The young soldier only grew more mute and expressionless.

"What cattle were you bred by, that you can't keep straight eyes? Look me in the eyes when I speak to you."

And the soldier turned his dark eyes to the other's face, but there was no sight in them: he stared with the slightest possible cast, holding back his sight, perceiving the blue of his master's eyes, but receiving no look from them. And the elder man went pale, and his reddish eyebrows twitched. He gave his order, barrenly.

Once he flung a heavy military glove into the young soldier's face. Then he had the satisfaction of seeing the black eyes flare up into his own, like a blaze when straw is thrown on a fire. And he had laughed with a little tremor and a sneer.

But there were only two months more. The youth instinctively tried to keep himself intact: he tried to serve the officer as if the latter were an abstract authority and not a man. All his instinct was to avoid personal contact, even definite hate. But in spite of himself the hate grew, responsive to the officer's passion. However, he put it in the background. When he had left the Army he could dare acknowledge it. By nature he was active, and had many friends. He thought what amazing good fellows they were. But, without knowing it, he was alone. Now this solitariness was intensified. It would carry him through his term. But the officer seemed to be going irritably insane, and the youth was deeply frightened.

The soldier had a sweetheart, a girl from the mountains, independent and primitive. The two walked together, rather silently. He went with her, not to talk, but to have his arm round her, and for the physical contact. This eased him, made it easier for him to ignore the Captain; for he could rest with her held fast against his chest. And she, in some unspoken fashion, was there for him. They loved each other.

The Captain perceived it, and was mad with irritation. He kept the young man engaged all the evenings long, and took pleasure in the dark look that came on his face. Occasionally, the eyes of the two men met, those of the younger sullen and dark, doggedly unalterable, those of the elder sneering with restless contempt.

The officer tried hard not to admit the passion that had got hold of him. He would not know that his feeling for his orderly was anything but that of a man incensed by his stupid, perverse servant. So, keeping quite justified and conventional in his consciousness, he let the other thing run on. His nerves, however, were suffering. At last he slung the end of a belt in his servant's face. When he saw the youth start back, the pain-tears in his eyes and the blood on his mouth, he had felt at once a thrill of deep pleasure and of shame.

But this, he acknowledged to himself, was a thing he had never done before. The fellow was too exasperating. His own nerves must be going to pieces. He went away for some days with a woman.

It was a mockery of pleasure. He simply did not want the woman. But he stayed on for his time. At the end of it, he came back in an agony of irritation, torment, and misery. He rode all the evening, then came straight in to supper. His orderly was out. The officer sat with his long, fine hands lying on the table, perfectly still, and all his blood seemed to be corroding.

At last his servant entered. He watched the strong, easy young figure, the fine eyebrows, the thick black hair. In a week's time the youth had got back his old well-being. The hands of the officer twitched and seemed to be full of mad flame. The young man stood at attention, unmoving, shut off.

The meal went in silence. But the orderly seemed eager. He made a clatter with the dishes.

"Are you in a hurry?" asked the officer, watching the intent, warm face of his servant. The other did not reply.

"Will you answer my question?" said the Captain.

"Yes, sir," replied the orderly, standing with his pile of deep Army plates. The Captain waited, looked at him, then asked again:

"Are you in a hurry?"

"Yes, sir," came the answer, that sent a flash through the listener.

"For what?"

"I was going out, sir."

"I want you this evening."

There was a moment's hesitation. The officer had a curious stiffness of countenance.

"Yes, sir," replied the servant, in his throat.

"I want you to-morrow evening also—in fact, you may consider your evenings occupied, unless I give you leave."

The mouth with the young mustache set close.

"Yes, sir," answered the orderly, loosening his lips for a moment.

He again turned to the door.

"And why have you a piece of pencil in your ear?"

The orderly hesitated, then continued on his way without answering. He set the plates in a pile outside the door, took the stump of pencil from his ear, and put it in his pocket. He had been copying a verse for his sweetheart's birthday card. He returned to finish clearing the table. The officer's eyes were dancing, he had a little, eager smile.

"Why have you a piece of pencil in your ear?" he asked.

The orderly took his hands full of dishes. His master was standing near the great green stove, a little smile on his face, his chin thrust forward. When the young soldier saw him his heart suddenly ran hot. He felt blind. Instead of answering, he turned dazedly to the door. As he was crouching to set down the dishes, he was pitched forward by a kick from behind. The pots went in a stream down the stairs, he clung to the pillar of the banisters. And as he was rising he was kicked heavily again, and again, so that he clung sickly to the post for some moments. His master had gone swiftly into the room and closed the door. The maid-servant downstairs looked up the staircase and made a mocking face at the crockery disaster.

The officer's heart was plunging. He poured himself a glass

of wine, part of which he spilled on the floor, and gulped the remainder, leaning against the cool, green stove. He heard his man collecting the dishes from the stairs. Pale, as if intoxicated, he waited. The servant entered again. The Captain's heart gave a pang, as of pleasure, seeing the young fellow bewildered and uncertain on his feet, with pain.

"Schöner!" he said.

The soldier was a little slower in coming to attention.

"Yes, sir!"

The youth stood before him, with pathetic young mustache, and fine eyebrows very distinct on his forehead of dark marble.

"I asked you a question."

"Yes, sir."

The officer's tone bit like acid.

"Why had you a pencil in your ear?"

Again the servant's heart ran hot, and he could not breathe. With dark, strained eyes, he looked at the officer, as if fascinated. And he stood there sturdily planted, unconscious. The withering smile came into the Captain's eyes, and he lifted his foot.

"I—I forgot it—sir," panted the soldier, his dark eyes fixed on the other man's dancing blue ones.

"What was it doing there?"

He saw the young man's breast heaving as he made an effort for words.

"I had been writing."

"Writing what?"

Again the soldier looked him up and down. The officer could hear him panting. The smile came into the blue eyes. The soldier worked his dry throat, but could not speak. Suddenly the smile lit like a flame on the officer's face, and a kick came heavily against the orderly's thigh. The youth moved a pace sideways. His face went dead, with two black, staring eyes.

"Well?" said the officer.

The orderly's mouth had gone dry, and his tongue rubbed in it as on dry brown-paper. He worked his throat. The officer raised his foot. The servant went stiff.

"Some poetry, sir," came the crackling, unrecognizable sound of his voice.

"Poetry, what poetry?" asked the Captain with a sickly smile.

Again there was the working in the throat. The Captain's

heart had suddenly gone down heavily, and he stood sick and tired.

"For my girl, sir," he heard the dry, inhuman sound.

"Oh!" he said, turning away. "Clear the table."

"Click!" went the soldier's throat; then again, "click!" and then the half-articulate:

"Yes, sir."

The young soldier was gone, looking old, and walking heavily.

The officer, left alone, held himself rigid, to prevent himself from thinking. His instinct warned him that he must not think. Deep inside him was the intense gratification of his passion, still working powerfully. Then there was a counter-action, a horrible breaking down of something inside him, a whole agony of reaction. He stood there for an hour motionless, a chaos of sensations, but rigid with a will to keep blank his consciousness, to prevent his mind grasping. And he held himself so until the worst of the stress had passed, when he began to drink, drank himself to an intoxication, till he slept obliterated. When he woke in the morning he was shaken to the base of his nature. But he had fought off the realization of what he had done. He had prevented his mind from taking it in, had suppressed it along with his instincts, and the conscious man had nothing to do with it. He felt only as after a bout of intoxication, weak, but the affair itself all dim and not to be recovered. Of the drunkenness of his passion he successfully refused remembrance. And when his orderly appeared with coffee, the officer assumed the same self he had had the morning before. He refused the event of the past night—denied it had ever been—and was successful in his denial. He had not done any such thing—not he himself. Whatever there might be lay at the door of a stupid, insubordinate servant.

The orderly had gone about in a stupor all the evening. He drank some beer because he was parched, but not much, the alcohol made his feeling come back, and he could not bear it. He was dulled, as if nine-tenths of the ordinary man in him were inert. He crawled about disfigured. Still, when he thought of the kicks, he went sick, and when he thought of the threat of more kicking, in the room afterwards, his heart went hot and faint, and he panted, remembered the one that had come. He had been forced to say, "For my girl." He was much too done even to want to cry. His mouth hung slightly open, like an idiot's. He felt vacant, and wasted. So, he wandered at his work, painfully, and very slowly and clumsily, fumbling blindly with the brushes, and finding it difficult, when he sat down, to summon the energy to move again. His limbs, his jaw, were slack and nerveless. But he was very tired. He got to bed at last, and slept inert, relaxed, in a sleep that was rather stupor than slumber, a dead night of stupefaction shot through with gleams of anguish.

In the morning were the maneuvers. But he woke even before the bugle sounded. The painful ache in his chest, the dryness of his throat, the awful steady feeling of misery made his eyes come awake and dreary at once. He knew, without thinking, what had happened. And he knew that the day had come again, when he must go on with his round. The last bit of darkness was being pushed out of the room. He would have to move his inert body and go on. He was so young, and had known so little trouble, that he was bewildered. He only wished it would stay night, so that he could lie still, covered up by the darkness. And yet nothing would prevent the day from coming, nothing would save him from having to get up and saddle the Captain's horse, and make the Captain's coffee. It was there, inevitable. And then, he thought, it was impossible. Yet they would not leave him free. He must go and take the coffee to the Captain. He was too stunned to understand it. He only knew it was inevitable—inevitable, however long he lay inert.

At last, after heaving at himself, for he seemed to be a mass of inertia, he got up. But he had to force every one of his movements from behind, with his will. He felt lost, and dazed, and helpless. Then he clutched hold of the bed, the pain was so keen. And looking at his thighs, he saw the darker bruises on his swarthy flesh and he knew that, if he pressed one of his fingers on one of the bruises, he should faint. But he did not want to faint—he did not want anybody to know. No one should ever know. It was between him and the Captain. There were only the two people in the world now—himself and the Captain.

Slowly, economically, he got dressed and forced himself to walk. Everything was obscure, except just what he had his hands on. But he managed to get through his work. The very pain revived his dull senses. The worst remained yet. He took the tray and went up to the Captain's room. The officer, pale and heavy, sat at the table. The orderly, as he saluted, felt himself put out of existence. He stood still for a moment submitting to his own nullification—then he gathered himself, seemed to regain himself, and then the Captain began to grow vague, unreal, and the younger soldier's heart beat up. He clung to this situation—that the Captain did not exist—so that he himself might live. But when he saw his officer's hand tremble as he took the coffee, he felt everything falling shattered. And he went away, feeling as if he himself were coming to pieces, disintegrated. And when the Captain was there on horseback, giving orders, while he himself stood, with rifle and knapsack, sick with pain, he felt as if he must shut his eyes— as if he must shut his eyes on everything. It was only the long agony of marching with a parched throat that filled him with one single, sleep-heavy intention: to save himself.

ii

He was getting used even to his parched throat. That the snowy peaks were radiant among the sky, that the whity-green glacier-river twisted through its pale shoals, in the valley below, seemed almost supernatural. But he was going mad with fever and thirst. He plodded on uncomplaining. He did not want to speak, not to anybody. There were two gulls, like flakes of water and snow, over the river. The scent of green rye soaked in sunshine came like a sickness. And the march continued, monotonously, almost like a bad sleep.

At the next farmhouse, which stood low and broad near the high road, tubs of water had been put out. The soldiers clustered round to drink. They took off their helmets, and the steam mounted from their wet hair. The Captain sat on horseback, watching. He needed to see his orderly. His helmet threw a dark shadow over his light, fierce eyes, but his mustache and mouth and chin were distinct in the sunshine. The orderly must move under the presence of the figure of the horseman. It was not that he was afraid, or cowed. It was as if he were disemboweled, made empty, like an empty shell. He felt himself as nothing, a shadow creeping under the sunshine. And, thirsty as he was, he could scarcely drink, feeling the Captain near him. He would not take off his helmet to wipe his wet hair. He wanted to stay in shadow, not to be forced into consciousness. Starting, he saw the light heel of the officer prick the belly of the horse; the Captain cantered away, and he himself could relapse into vacancy.

Nothing, however, could give him back his living place in the hot, bright morning. He felt like a gap among it all. Whereas the Captain was prouder, overriding. A hot flash went through the young servant's body. The Captain was firmer and prouder with life, he himself was empty as a shadow. Again the flash went through him, dazing him out. But his heart ran a little firmer.

The company turned up the hill, to make a loop for the return. Below, from among the trees, the farm-bell clanged. He saw the laborers, mowing barefoot at the thick grass, leave off their work and go downhill, their scythes hanging over their shoulders, like long, bright claws curving down behind them. They seemed like dream-people, as if they had no relation to himself. He felt as in a blackish dream: as if all the other things were there and had form, but he himself was only a consciousness, a gap that could think and perceive.

The soldiers were tramping silently up the glaring hillside. Gradually his head began to revolve, slowly, rhythmically. Sometimes it was dark before his eyes, as if he saw this world through a smoked glass, frail shadows and unreal. It gave him a pain in his head to walk.

The air was too scented, it gave no breath. All the lush green-stuff seemed to be issuing its sap, till the air was deathly, sickly with the smell of greenness. There was the perfume of clover, like pure honey and bees. Then there grew a faint acrid tang—they were near the beeches; and then a queer clattering noise, and a suffocating, hideous smell; they were passing a flock of sheep, a shepherd in a black smock, holding his crook. Why should the sheep huddle together under this fierce sun? He felt that the shepherd would not see him, though he could see the shepherd.

At last there was the halt. They stacked rifles in a conical stack, put down their kit in a scattered circle around it, and dispersed a little, sitting on a small knoll high on the hillside. The chatter began. The soldiers were steaming with heat, but were lively. He sat still, seeing the blue mountains rising upon the land, twenty kilometers away. There was a blue fold in the ranges, then out of that, at the foot, the broad, pale bed of the river, stretches of whity-green water between pinkish-gray shoals among the dark pine woods. There it was, spread out a long way off. And it seemed to come downhill, the river. There was a raft being steered, a mile away. It was a strange country. Nearer, a red-roofed, broad farm with white base and square dots of windows crouched beside the wall of beech foliage on the wood's edge. There were long strips of rye and clover and pale green corn. And just at his feet, below the knoll, was a darkish bog, where globe flowers stood breathless still on their slim stalks. And some of the pale gold bubbles were burst, and a broken fragment hung in the air. He thought he was going to sleep.

Suddenly something moved into this colored mirage before his eyes. The Captain, a small, light-blue and scarlet figure, was trotting evenly between the strips of corn, along the level brow of the hill. And the man making flag-signals was coming on. Proud and sure moved the horseman's figure, the quick, bright thing, in which was concentrated all the light of this morning, which for the rest lay a fragile, shining shadow. Submissive, apathetic, the young soldier sat and stared. But as the horse slowed to a walk, coming up the last steep path, the great flash flared over the body and soul of the orderly. He sat waiting. The back of his head felt as if it were weighted with a heavy piece of fire. He did not want to eat. His hands trembled slightly as he moved them. Meanwhile the officer on horseback was approaching slowly and proudly. The tension grew in the orderly's soul. Then again, seeing the Captain ease himself on the saddle, the flash blazed through him.

The Captain looked at the patch of light blue and scarlet, and dark heads, scattered closely on the hillside. It pleased him. The command pleased him. And he was feeling proud. His orderly was among them in common subjection. The officer rose a little on his stirrups to look. The young soldier sat with averted, dumb face. The Captain relaxed on his seat. His slim-legged, beautiful horse, brown as a beech nut, walked proudly uphill. The Captain passed into the zone of the company's atmosphere: a hot smell of men, of sweat, of leather. He knew it very well. After a word with the lieutenant, he went a few paces higher, and sat there, a dominant figure, his sweat-marked horse swishing its tail, while he looked down on his men, on his orderly, a nonentity among the crowd.

The young soldier's heart was like fire in his chest, and he breathed with difficulty. The officer, looking downhill, saw three of the young soldiers, two pails of water between them, staggering across a sunny green field. A table had been set up under a tree, and there the slim lieutenant stood, importantly busy. Then the Captain summoned himself to an act of courage. He called his orderly.

The flame leapt into the young soldier's throat as he heard the command, and he rose blindly, stifled. He saluted, standing below the officer. He did not look up. But there was the flicker in the Captain's voice.

"Go to the inn and fetch me . . ." the officer gave his commands. "Quick!" he added.

At the last word, the heart of the servant leapt with a flash, and he felt the strength come over his body. But he turned in mechanical obedience, and set off at a heavy run downhill, looking almost like a bear, his trousers bagging over his military boots. And the officer watched this blind, plunging run all the way.

But it was only the outside of the orderly's body that was obeying so humbly and mechanically. Inside had gradually accumulated a core into which all the energy of that young life was compact and concentrated. He executed his commission, and plodded quickly back uphill. There was a pain in his head, as he walked, that made him twist his features unknowingly. But hard there in the center of his chest was himself, himself, firm, and not to be plucked to pieces.

The Captain had gone up into the wood. The orderly plodded through the hot, powerfully smelling zone of the company's atmosphere. He had a curious mass of energy inside him now. The Captain was less real than himself. He approached the green entrance to the wood. There, in the half-shade, he saw the horse standing, the sunshine and the flickering shadow of leaves dancing over his brown body. There was a clearing where timber had lately been felled. Here, in the gold-green shade beside the brilliant cup of sunshine, stood two figures, blue and pink, the bits of pink showing out plainly. The Captain was talking to his lieutenant.

The orderly stood on the edge of the bright clearing, where great trunks of trees, stripped and glistening, lay stretched like naked, brown-skinned bodies. Chips of wood littered the trampled floor, like splashed light, and the bases of the felled trees stood here and there, with their raw, level tops. Beyond was the brilliant, sunlit green of a beech.

"Then I will ride forward," the orderly heard his Captain say. The lieutenant saluted and strode away. He himself went forward. A hot flash passed through his belly, as he tramped towards his officer.

The Captain watched the rather heavy figure of the young soldier stumble forward, and his veins, too, ran hot. This was to be man to man between them. He yielded before the solid stumbling figure with bent head. The orderly stooped and put the food on a level-sawn tree-base. The Captain watched the glistening, sun-inflamed, naked hands. He wanted to speak to the young soldier, but could not. The servant propped a bottle against his thigh, pressed open the cork, and poured out the beer into the mug. He kept his head bent. The Captain accepted the mug.

"Hot!" he said, as if amiably.

The flame sprang out of the orderly's heart, nearly suffocating him.

"Yes, sir," he replied, between shut teeth.

And he heard the sound of the Captain's drinking, and he clenched his fists, such a strong torment came into his wrists. Then came the faint clang of the closing of the pot-lid. He looked up. The Captain was watching him. He glanced swiftly away. Then he saw the officer stoop and take a piece of bread from the tree-base. Again the flash of flame went through the young soldier, seeing the stiff body stoop beneath him, and his hands jerked. He looked away. He could feel the officer was nervous. The bread fell as it was being broken. The officer ate the other piece. The two men stood tense and still, the master laboriously chewing his bread, the servant staring with averted face, his fist clenched.

Then the young soldier started. The officer had pressed open the lid of the mug again. The orderly watched the lid of the mug, and the white hand that clenched the handle, as if he were fascinated. It was raised. The youth followed it with his eyes. And then he saw the thin, strong throat of the elder man moving up and down as he drank, the strong jaw working. And the instinct which had been jerking at the young man's wrist suddenly jerked free. He jumped, feeling as if it were rent in two by a strong flame.

The spur of the officer caught in a tree-root, he went down backwards with a crash, the middle of his back thudding sickeningly against a sharp-edged tree-base, the pot flying away. And in a second the orderly, with serious, earnest young face, and underlip between his teeth, had got his knee in the officer's chest and was pressing the chin backward over the farther edge of the tree-stump, pressing, with all his heart behind in a passion of relief, the tension of his wrists exquisite with relief. And with the base of his palms he shoved at the chin, with all his might. And it was pleasant, too, to have that chin, that hard jaw already slightly rough with beard, in his hands. He did not relax one hair's breadth, but, all the force of all his blood exulting in his thrust, he shoved back the head of the other man, till there was a little "cluck" and a crunching sensation. Then he felt as if his head went to vapor. Heavy convulsions shook the body of the officer, frightening and horrifying the young soldier. Yet it pleased him, too, to repress them. It pleased him to keep his hands pressing back the chin, to feel the chest of the other man yield in expiration to the weight of his strong, young knees, to feel the hard twitchings of the prostrate body jerking his own whole frame, which was pressed down on it.

But it went still. He could look into the nostrils of the other man, the eyes he could scarcely see. How curiously the mouth was pushed out, exaggerating the full lips, and the mustache bristling up from them. Then, with a start, he noticed the nostrils gradually filled with blood. The red brimmed, hesitated, ran over, and went in a thin trickle down the face to the eyes.

It shocked and distressed him. Slowly, he got up. The body twitched and sprawled there, inert. He stood and looked at it in silence. It was a pity *it* was broken. It represented more than the thing which had kicked and bullied him. He was afraid to look at the eyes. They were hideous now, only the whites showing, and the blood running to them. The face of the orderly was drawn with horror at the sight. Well, it was so. In his heart he was satisfied. He had hated the face of the Captain. It was extinguished now. There was a heavy relief in the orderly's soul. That was as it should be. But he could not bear to see the long, military body lying broken over the tree-base, the fine fingers crisped. He wanted to hide it away.

Quickly, busily, he gathered it up and pushed it under the felled tree-trunks, which rested their beautiful, smooth length either end on logs. The face was horrible with blood. He covered it with the helmet. Then he pushed the limbs straight

and decent, and brushed the dead leaves off the fine cloth of
the uniform. So, it lay quite still in the shadow under there.
A little strip of sunshine ran along the breast, from a chink
between the logs. The orderly sat by it for a few moments.
Here his own life also ended.

Then, through his daze, he heard the lieutenant, in a loud
voice, explaining to the men outside the wood, that they were
to suppose the bridge on the river below was held by the
enemy. Now they were to march to the attack in such and
such a manner. The lieutenant had no gift of expression. The
orderly, listening from habit, got muddled. And when the
lieutenant began it all again he ceased to hear.

He knew he must go. He stood up. It surprised him that
the leaves were glittering in the sun, and the chips of wood
reflecting white from the ground. For him a change had come
over the world. But for the rest it had not—all seemed the
same. Only he had left it. And he could not go back. It was
his duty to return with the beer-pot and the bottle. He could
not. He had left all that. The lieutenant was still hoarsely
explaining. He must go, or they would overtake him. And
he could not bear contact with any one now.

He drew his fingers over his eyes, trying to find out where
he was. Then he turned away. He saw the horse standing in
the path. He went up to it and mounted. It hurt him to sit in
the saddle. The pain of keeping his seat occupied him as they
cantered through the wood. He would not have minded anything, but he could not get away from the sense of being
divided from the others. The path led out of the trees. On the
edge of the wood he pulled up and stood watching. There in
the spacious sunshine of the valley soldiers were moving in a
little swarm. Every now and then, a man harrowing on a strip
of fallow shouted to his oxen, at the turn. The village and the
white-towered church was small in the sunshine. And he no
longer belonged to it—he sat there, beyond, like a man outside in the dark. He had gone out from everyday life into the
unknown, and he could not, he even did not want to go back.

Turning from the sun-blazing valley, he rode deep into the
wood. Tree-trunks, like people standing gray and still, took
no notice as he went. A doe, herself a moving bit of sunshine
and shadow, went running through the flecked shade. There
were bright green rents in the foliage. Then it was all pine
wood, dark and cool. And he was sick with pain, he had an

intolerable great pulse in his head, and he was sick. He had never been ill in his life. He felt lost, quite dazed with all this.

Trying to get down from the horse, he fell, astonished at the pain and his lack of balance. The horse shifted uneasily. He jerked its bridle and sent it cantering jerkily away. It was his last connection with the rest of things.

But he only wanted to lie down and not be disturbed. Stumbling through the trees, he came on a quiet place where beeches and pine trees grew on a slope. Immediately he had lain down and closed his eyes, his consciousness went racing on without him. A big pulse of sickness beat in him as if it throbbed through the whole earth. He was burning with dry heat. But he was too busy, too tearingly active in the incoherent race of delirium to observe.

iii

He came to with a start. His mouth was dry and hard, his heart beat heavily, but he had not the energy to get up. His heart beat heavily. Where was he?—the barracks—at home? There was something knocking. And, making an effort, he looked round—trees, and litter of greenery, and reddish, bright, still pieces of sunshine on the floor. He did not believe he was himself, he did not believe what he saw. Something was knocking. He made a struggle towards consciousness, but relapsed. Then he struggled again. And gradually his surroundings fell into relationship with himself. He knew, and a great pang of fear went through his heart. Somebody was knocking. He could see the heavy, black rags of a fir tree overhead. Then everything went black. Yet he did not believe he had closed his eyes. He had not. Out of the blackness sight slowly emerged again. And some one was knocking. Quickly, he saw the blood-disfigured face of his Captain, which he hated. And he held himself still with horror. Yet, deep inside him, he knew that it was so, the Captain should be dead. But the physical delirium got hold of him. Some one was knocking. He lay perfectly still, as if dead, with fear. And he went unconscious.

When he opened his eyes again, he started, seeing something creeping swiftly up a tree-trunk. It was a little bird. And the bird was whistling overhead. Tap-tap-tap—it was the

small, quick bird rapping the tree-trunk with its beak, as if its
head were a little round hammer. He watched it curiously.
It shifted sharply, in its creeping fashion. Then, like a mouse,
it slid down the bare trunk. Its swift creeping sent a flash of
revulsion through him. He raised his head. It felt a great
weight. Then, the little bird ran out of the shadow across a
still patch of sunshine, its little head bobbing swiftly, its white
legs twinkling brightly for a moment. How neat it was in its
build, so compact, with pieces of white on its wings. There
were several of them. They were so pretty—but they crept
like swift, erratic mice, running here and there among the
beech-mast.

He lay down again exhausted, and his consciousness lapsed.
He had a horror of the little creeping birds. All his blood
seemed to be darting and creeping in his head. And yet he
could not move.

He came to with a further ache of exhaustion. There was the
pain in his head, and the horrible sickness, and his inability
to move. He had never been ill in his life. He did not know
where he was or what he was. Probably he had got sunstroke.
Or what else?—he had silenced the Captain forever—some
time ago—oh, a long time ago. There had been blood on his
face, and his eyes had turned upwards. It was all right, somehow. It was peace. But now he had got beyond himself. He
had never been here before. Was it life, or not life? He was
by himself. They were in a big, bright place, those others,
and he was outside. The town, all the country, a big bright
place of light: and he was outside, here, in the darkened open
beyond, where each thing existed alone. But they would all
have to come out there sometime, those others. Little, and left
behind him, they all were. There had been father and mother
and sweetheart. What did they all matter? This was the open
land.

He sat up. Something scuffled. It was a little, brown squirrel
running in lovely, undulating bounds over the floor, its red
tail completing the undulation of its body—and then, as it
sat up, furling and unfurling. He watched it, pleased. It ran
on again, friskily, enjoying itself. It flew wildly at another
squirrel, and they were chasing each other, and making little
scolding, chattering noises. The soldier wanted to speak to
them. But only a hoarse sound came out of his throat. The
squirrels burst away—they flew up the trees. And then he saw

the one peeping round at him, halfway up a tree-trunk. A start of fear went through him, though, in so far as he was conscious, he was amused. It still stayed, its little, keen face staring at him halfway up the tree-trunk, its little ears pricked up, its clawy little hands clinging to the bark, its white breast reared. He started from it in panic.

Struggling to his feet, he lurched away. He went on walking, walking, looking for something—for a drink. His brain felt hot and inflamed for want of water. He stumbled on. Then he did not know anything. He went unconscious as he walked. Yet he stumbled on, his mouth open.

When, to his dumb wonder, he opened his eyes on the world again, he no longer tried to remember what it was. There was thick, golden light behind golden-green glitterings, and tall gray-purple shafts, and darknesses further off, surrounding him, growing deeper. He was conscious of a sense of arrival. He was amid the reality, on the real, dark bottom. But there was the thirst burning in his brain. He felt lighter, not so heavy. He supposed it was newness. The air was muttering with thunder. He thought he was walking wonderfully swiftly and was coming straight to relief—or was it to water?

Suddenly he stood still with fear. There was a tremendous flare of gold, immense—just a few dark trunks like bars between him and it. All the young level wheat was burnished gold glaring on its silky green. A woman, full-skirted, a black cloth on her head for head-dress, was passing like a block of shadow through the glistening, green corn, into the full glare. There was a farm, too, pale blue in shadow, and the timber black. And there was a church spire, nearly fused away in the gold. The woman moved on, away from him. He had no language with which to speak to her. She was the bright, solid unreality. She would make a noise of words that would confuse him, and her eyes would look at him without seeing him. She was crossing there to the other side. He stood against a tree.

When at last he turned, looking down the long, bare grove whose flat bed was already filling dark, he saw the mountains in a wonder-light, not far away, and radiant. Behind the soft, gray ridge of the nearest range the further mountains stood golden and pale gray, the snow all radiant like pure, soft gold. So still, gleaming in the sky, fashioned pure out of the ore of the sky, they shone in their silence. He stood and looked at them, his face illuminated. And like the golden, lustrous gleaming of the snow he felt his own thirst bright in him. He stood and gazed, leaning against a tree. And then everything slid away into space.

During the night the lightning fluttered perpetually, making the whole sky white. He must have walked again. The world hung livid round him for moments, fields a level sheen of gray-green light, trees in dark bulk, and the range of clouds black across a white sky. Then the darkness fell like a shutter, and the night was whole. A faint flutter of a half-revealed world, that could not quite leap out of the darkness! —Then there again stood a sweep of pallor for the land, dark shapes looming, a range of clouds hanging overhead. The world was a ghostly shadow, thrown for a moment upon the pure darkness, which returned ever whole and complete.

And the mere delirium of sickness and fever went on inside him—his brain opening and shutting like the night—then sometimes convulsions of terror from something with great eyes that stared round a tree—then the long agony of the march, and the sun decomposing his blood—then the pang of hate for the Captain, followed by a pang of tenderness and ease. But everything was distorted, born of an ache and resolving into an ache.

In the morning he came definitely awake. Then his brain flamed with the sole horror of thirstiness! The sun was on his face, the dew was steaming from his wet clothes. Like one possessed, he got up. There, straight in front of him, blue and cool and tender, the mountains ranged across the pale edge of the morning sky. He wanted them—he wanted them alone—he wanted to leave himself and be identified with them. They did not move, they were still and soft, with white, gentle markings of snow. He stood still, mad with suffering, his hands crisping and clutching. Then he was twisting in a paroxysm on the grass.

He lay still, in a kind of dream of anguish. His thirst seemed to have separated itself from him, and to stand apart, a single demand. Then the pain he felt was another single self. Then there was the clog of his body, another separate thing. He was divided among all kinds of separate beings. There was some strange, agonized connection between them, but they were drawing further apart. Then they would all split. The sun, drilling down on him, was drilling through the bond. Then they would all fall, fall through the everlasting lapse

f space. Then again, his consciousness reasserted itself. He
oused on to his elbow and stared at the gleaming mountains.
There they ranked, all still and wonderful between earth and
heaven. He stared till his eyes went black, and the mountains,
as they stood in their beauty, so clean and cool, seemed to have
t, that which was lost in him.

iv

When the soldiers found him, three hours later, he was lying
with his face over his arm, his black hair giving off heat under
the sun. But he was still alive. Seeing the open, black mouth
the young soldiers dropped him in horror.

He died in the hospital at night, without having seen again.
The doctors saw the bruises on his legs, behind, and were
silent.

The bodies of the two men lay together, side by side, in the
mortuary, the one white and slender, but laid rigidly at rest,
the other looking as if every moment it must rouse into life
again, so young and unused, from a slumber.

Aldous Huxley

THE TILLOTSON BANQUET

YOUNG Spode was not a snob; he was too intelligent for that, too fundamentally decent. Not a snob; but all the same he could not help feeling very well pleased at the thought that he was dining, alone and intimately, with Lord Badgery. It was a definite event in his life, a step forward, he felt, towards that final success, social, material, and literary, which he had come to London with the fixed intention of making. The conquest and capture of Badgery was an almost essential strategical move in the campaign.

Edmund, forty-seventh Baron Badgery, was a lineal descendant of that Edmund, surnamed Le Blayreau, who landed on English soil in the train of William the Conqueror. Ennobled by William Rufus, the Badgerys had been one of the very few baronial families to survive the Wars of the Roses and all the other changes and chances of English history. They were a sensible and philoprogenitive race. No Badgery had ever fought in any war, no Badgery had ever engaged in any kind of politics. They had been content to live and quietly to propagate their species in a huge machicolated Norman castle, surrounded by a triple moat, only sallying forth to cultivate their property and to collect their rents. In the eighteenth century, when life had become relatively secure, the Badgerys began to venture forth into civilised society. From boorish squires they blossomed into *grands seigneurs*, patrons of the arts, virtuosi. Their property was large, they were rich; and with the growth of industrialism their riches also grew. Villages on their estate turned into manufacturing towns, unsuspected coal was discovered beneath the surface of their barren moorlands. By the middle of the nineteenth century the Badgerys were among the richest of English noble families. The forty-seventh baron disposed of an income of at least two hundred thousand pounds a year. Following the great Badgery tradition, he had refused to have anything to do with politics or war. He occupied himself by collecting pictures; he took an interest in theatrical productions; he was the friend and patron of men of letters, of painters, and musicians. A personage, in a word, of considerable consequence in that particular world in which young Spode had elected to make his success.

Spode had only recently left the university. Simon Gollamy, the editor of the *World's Review* (the "Best of all possible Worlds"), had got to know him—he was always on the look out for youthful talent—had seen possibilities in the young man, and appointed him art critic of his paper. Gollamy liked to have young and teachable people about him. The possession of disciples flattered his vanity, and he found it easier, moreover, to run his paper with docile collaborators than with men grown obstinate and case-hardened with age. Spode had not done badly at his new job. At any rate, his articles had been intelligent enough to arouse the interest of Lord Badgery. It was, ultimately, to them that he owed the honour of sitting tonight in the dining-room of Badgery House.

Fortified by several varieties of wine and a glass of aged brandy, Spode felt more confident and at ease than he had done the whole evening. Badgery was rather a disquieting host. He had an alarming habit of changing the subject of any conversation that had lasted for more than two minutes. Spode had found it, for example, horribly mortifying when his host, cutting across what was, he prided himself, a particularly subtle and illuminating disquisition on baroque art, had turned a wandering eye about the room and asked him abruptly whether he liked parrots. He had flushed and glanced suspiciously towards him, fancying that the man was trying to be offensive. But no; Badgery's white, fleshy, Hanoverian face wore an expression of perfect good faith. There was no malice in his small greenish eyes. He evidently did genuinely want to know if Spode liked parrots. The young man swallowed his irritation and replied that he did. Badgery then told a good story about parrots. Spode was on the point of capping it with a better story, when his host began to talk about Beethoven. And so the game went on. Spode cut his conversation to suit his host's requirements. In the course of ten minutes he had made a more or less witty epigram on Benvenuto Cellini, Queen Victoria, sport, God, Stephen Phillips, and Moorish architecture. Lord Badgery thought him the most charming young man, and so intelligent.

"If you've quite finished your coffee," he said, rising to his feet as he spoke, "we'll go and look at the pictures."

Spode jumped up with alacrity, and only then realised that he had drunk just ever so little too much. He would have to be careful, talk deliberately, plant his feet consciously, one after the other.

"This house is quite cluttered up with pictures," Lord Badgery complained. "I had a whole wagon-load taken away to the country last week; but there are still far too many. My ancestors would have their portraits painted by Romney. Such a shocking artist, don't you think? Why couldn't they have chosen Gainsborough, or even Reynolds? I've had all the Romneys hung in the servants' hall now. It's such a comfort to know that one can never possibly see them again. I suppose you know all about the ancient Hittites?"

"Well . . ." the young man replied, with befitting modesty.

"Look at that, then." He indicated a large stone head which stood in a case near the dining-room door. "It's not Greek, or Egyptian, or Persian, or anything else; so if it isn't ancient Hittite, I don't know what it is. And that reminds me of that story about Lord George Sanger, the Circus King . . ." and, without giving Spode time to examine the Hittite relic, he led the way up the huge staircase, pausing every now and then in his anecdote to point out some new object of curiosity or beauty.

"I suppose you know Deburau's pantomimes?" Spode rapped out as soon as the story was over. He was in an itch to let out his information about Deburau. Badgery had given him a perfect opening with his ridiculous Sanger. "What a perfect man, isn't he? He used to . . ."

"This is my main gallery," said Lord Badgery, throwing open one leaf of a tall folding door. "I must apologise for it. It looks like a roller-skating rink." He fumbled with the electric switches and there was suddenly light—light that revealed an enormous gallery, duly receding into distance according to all the laws of perspective. "I dare say you've heard of my poor ather," Lord Badgery continued. "A little insane, you know; sort of mechanical genius with a screw loose. He used to have a toy railway in this room. No end of fun he had, crawling about the floor after his trains. And all the pictures were stacked in the cellars. I can't tell you what they were like when I found them: mushrooms growing out of the Botticellis. Now I'm rather proud of this Poussin; he painted it for Scarron."

"Exquisite!" Spode exclaimed, making with his hand a gesture as though he were modelling a pure form in the air. "How splendid the onrush of those trees and leaning figures is! And the way they're caught up, as it were, and stemmed by that single godlike form opposing them with his contrary movement! And the draperies . . ."

But Lord Badgery had moved on, and was standing in front of a little fifteenth-century Virgin of carved wood.

"School of Rheims," he explained.

They "did" the gallery at high speed. Badgery never permitted his guest to halt for more than forty seconds before any work of art. Spode would have liked to spend a few moments of recollection and tranquillity in front of some of these lovely things. But it was not permitted.

The gallery done, they passed into a little room leading out of it. At the sight of what the lights revealed, Spode gasped.

"It's like something out of Balzac," he exclaimed. "Un de ces salons dorés où se déploie un luxe insolent. You know."

"My nineteenth-century chamber," Badgery explained. "The best thing of its kind, I flatter myself, outside the State Apartments at Windsor."

Spode tiptoed round the room, peering with astonishment at all the objects in glass, in gilded bronze, in china, in feathers, in embroidered and painted silk, in beads, in wax, objects of the most fantastic shapes and colours, all the queer products of a decadent tradition, with which the room was crowded. There were paintings on the walls—a Martin, a Wilkie, an early Landseer, several Ettys, a big Haydon, a slight pretty water-colour of a girl by Wainewright, the pupil of Blake and arsenic poisoner, a score of others. But the picture which arrested Spode's attention was a medium sized canvas representing Troilus riding into Troy among the flowers and plaudits of an admiring crowd, and oblivious (you could see from his expression) of everything but the eyes of Cressida,

who looked down at him from a window, with Pandarus smil
ing over her shoulder.

"What an absurd and enchanting picture!" Spode ex
claimed.

"Ah, you've spotted my Troilus." Lord Badgery wa
pleased.

"What bright harmonious colours! Like Etty's, only
stronger, not so obviously pretty. And there's an energy abou
it that reminds one of Haydon. Only Haydon could never hav
done anything so impeccable in taste. Who is it by?" Spode
turned to his host inquiringly.

"You were right in detecting Haydon." Lord Badgery an
swered. "It's by his pupil, Tillotson. I wish I could get hold o
more of his work. But nobody seems to know anything abou
him. And he seems to have done so little."

This time it was the younger man who interrupted.

"Tillotson, Tillotson . . ." He put his hand to his fore
head. A frown incongruously distorted his round, floridly
curved face. "No . . . yes, I have it." He looked up tri
umphantly with serene and childish brows. "Tillotson, Walter
Tillotson—the man's still alive."

Badgery smiled. "This picture was painted in 1846, you
know."

"Well, that's all right. Say he was born in 1820, painted his
masterpiece when he was twenty-six, and it's 1913 now; that's
to say he's only ninety-three. Not as old as Titian yet."

"But he's not been heard of since 1860," Lord Badgery
protested.

"Precisely. Your mention of his name reminded me of the
discovery I made the other day when I was looking through
the obituary notices in the archives of the *World's Review*.
(One has to bring them up to date every year or so for fear of
being caught napping if one of these old birds chooses to shuffle
off suddenly.) Well, there, among them—I remember my as
tonishment at the time—there I found Walter Tillotson's
biography. Pretty full to 1860, and then a blank, except for
a pencil note in the early nineteen hundreds to the effect that
he had returned from the East. The obituary has never been
used or added to. I draw the obvious conclusion: the old chap
isn't dead yet. He's just been overlooked somehow."

"But this is extraordinary," Lord Badgery exclaimed. "You
must find him, Spode—you must find him. I'll commission

im to paint frescoes round this room. It's just what I've always vainly longed for—a real nineteenth-century artist to decorate this place for me. Oh, we must find him at once—at once."

Lord Badgery strode up and down in a state of great excitement.

"I can see how this room could be made quite perfect," he went on. "We'd clear away all these cases and have the whole of that wall filled by a heroic fresco of Hector and Andromache, or 'Distraining for Rent,' or Fanny Kemble as Belvidera in Venice Preserved'—anything like that, provided it's in the grand manner of the 'thirties and 'forties. And here I'd have a landscape with lovely receding perspectives, or else something architectural and grand in the style of Belshazzar's feast. Then we'll have this Adam fireplace taken down and replaced by something Mauro-Gothic. And on these walls I'll have mirrors, or no! let me see . . ."

He sank into meditative silence, from which he finally roused himself to shout:

"The old man, the old man! Spode, we must find this astonishing old creature. And don't breathe a word to anybody. Tillotson shall be our secret. Oh, it's too perfect, it's incredible! Think of the frescoes."

Lord Badgery's face had become positively animated. He had talked of a single subject for nearly a quarter of an hour.

ii

Three weeks later Lord Badgery was aroused from his usual after-luncheon somnolence by the arrival of a telegram. The message was a short one. "Found.—SPODE." A look of pleasure and intelligence made human Lord Badgery's clayey face of surfeit. "No answer," he said. The footman padded away on noiseless feet.

Lord Badgery closed his eyes and began to contemplate. Found! What a room he would have! There would be nothing like it in the world. The frescoes, the fireplace, the mirrors, the ceiling. . . . And a small, shrivelled old man clambering about the scaffolding, agile and quick like one of those whiskered little monkeys at the Zoo, painting away, painting away. . . . Fanny Kemble as Belvidera, Hector and Andromache, or why

not the Duke of Clarence in the Butt, the Duke of Malmsey
the Butt of Clarence. . . . Lord Badgery was asleep.

Spode did not lag long behind his telegram. He was at
Badgery House by six o'clock. His lordship was in the nineteenth-century chamber, engaged in clearing away with his
own hands the bric-à-brac. Spode found him looking hot and
out of breath.

"Ah, there you are," said Lord Badgery. "You see me
already preparing for the great man's coming. Now you must
tell me all about him."

"He's older even than I thought," said Spode. "He's ninety-
seven this year. Born in 1816. Incredible, isn't it! There, I'm
beginning at the wrong end."

"Begin where you like," said Badgery genially.

"I won't tell you all the incidents of the hunt. You've no
idea what a job I had to run him to earth. It was like a Sherlock Holmes story, immensely elaborate, too elaborate. I shall
write a book about it some day. At any rate, I found him at
last."

"Where?"

"In a sort of respectable slum in Holloway, older and poorer
and lonelier than you could have believed possible. I found
out how it was he came to be forgotten, how he came to drop
out of life in the way he did. He took it into his head, somewhere about the 'sixties, to go to Palestine to get local colour
for his religious pictures—scapegoats and things, you know.
Well, he went to Jerusalem and then on to Mount Lebanon
and on and on, and then, somewhere in the middle of Asia
Minor, he got stuck. He got stuck for about forty years."

"But what did he do all that time?"

"Oh, he painted, and started a mission, and converted three
Turks, and taught the local Pashas the rudiments of English,
Latin, and perspective, and God knows what else. Then, in
about 1904, it seems to have occurred to him that he was
getting rather old and had been away from home for rather
a long time. So he made his way back to England, only to
find that everyone he had known was dead, that the dealers
had never heard of him and wouldn't buy his pictures, that he
was simply a ridiculous old figure of fun. So he got a job as a
drawing-master in a girls' school in Holloway, and there he's
been ever since, growing older and older, and feebler and
feebler, and blinder and deafer, and generally more gaga, until

finally the school has given him the sack. He had about ten pounds in the world when I found him. He lives in a kind of black hole in a basement full of beetles. When his ten pounds are spent, I suppose he'll just quietly die there."

Badgery held up a white hand. "No more, no more. I find literature quite depressing enough. I insist that life at least shall be a little gayer. Did you tell him I wanted him to paint my room?"

"But he can't paint. He's too blind and palsied."

"Can't paint?" Badgery exclaimed in horror. "Then what's the good of the old creature?"

"Well, if you put it like that . . ." Spode began.

"I shall never have my frescoes. Ring the bell, will you?" Spode rang.

"What right has Tillotson to go on existing if he can't paint?" went on Lord Badgery petulantly. "After all, that was his only justification for occupying a place in the sun."

"He doesn't have much sun in his basement."

The footman appeared at the door.

"Get someone to put all these things back in their places," Lord Badgery commanded, indicating with a wave of the hand the ravaged cases, the confusion of glass and china with which he had littered the floor, the pictures unhooked. "We'll go to the library, Spode; it's more comfortable there."

He led the way through the long gallery and down the stairs.

"I'm sorry old Tillotson has been such a disappointment," said Spode sympathetically.

"Let us talk about something else; he ceases to interest me."

"But don't you think we ought to do something about him? He's only got ten pounds between him and the workhouse. And if you'd seen the blackbeetles in his basement!"

"Enough—enough. I'll do everything you think fitting."

"I thought we might get up a subscription amongst lovers of the arts."

"There aren't any," said Badgery.

"No; but there are plenty of people who will subscribe out of snobbism."

"Not unless you give them something for their money."

"That's true. I hadn't thought of that." Spode was silent for a moment. "We might have a dinner in his honour. The Great Tillotson Banquet. Doyen of the British Art. A Link

with the Past. Can't you see it in the papers? I'd make a stunt
of it in the *World's Review*. That ought to bring in the snobs."

"And we'll invite a lot of artists and critics—all the ones
who can't stand one another. It will be fun to see them squabbling." Badgery laughed. Then his face darkened once again.
"Still," he added, "it'll be a very poor second best to my
frescoes. You'll stay to dinner, of course."

"Well, since you suggest it. Thanks very much."

iii

The Tillotson Banquet was fixed to take place about three
weeks later. Spode, who had charge of the arrangements,
proved himself an excellent organiser. He secured the big
banqueting-room at the Café Bomba, and was successful in
bullying and cajoling the manager into giving fifty persons
dinner at twelve shillings a head, including wine. He sent out
invitations and collected subscriptions. He wrote an article on
Tillotson in the *World's Review*—one of those charming, witty
articles couched in the tone of amused patronage and contempt with which one speaks of the great men of 1840. Nor
did he neglect Tillotson himself. He used to go to Holloway
almost every day to listen to the old man's endless stories about
Asia Minor and the Great Exhibition of '51 and Benjamin
Robert Haydon. He was sincerely sorry for this relic of another age.

Mr. Tillotson's room was about ten feet below the level of
the soil of South Holloway. A little grey light percolated
through the area bars, forced a difficult passage through panes
opaque with dirt, and spent itself, like a drop of milk that
falls into an inkpot, among the inveterate shadows of the
dungeon. The place was haunted by the sour smell of damp
plaster and of woodwork that has begun to moulder secretly at
the heart. A little miscellaneous furniture, including a bed, a
washstand and chest of drawers, a table and one or two chairs,
lurked in the obscure corners of the den or ventured furtively
out into the open. Hither Spode now came almost every day,
bringing the old man news of the progress of the banquet
scheme. Every day he found Mr. Tillotson sitting in the same
place under the window, bathing, as it were, in his tiny puddle
of light. "The oldest man that ever wore grey hairs," Spode

reflected as he looked at him. Only there were very few hairs left on that bald, unpolished head. At the sound of the visitor's knock Mr. Tillotson would turn in his chair, stare in the direction of the door with blinking, uncertain eyes. He was always full of apologies for being so slow in recognising who was there.

"No discourtesy meant," he would say, after asking. "It's not as if I had forgotten who you were. Only it's so dark and my sight isn't what it was."

After that he never failed to give a little laugh, and, pointing out of the window at the area railings, would say:

"Ah, this is the place for somebody with good sight. It's the place for looking at ankles. It's the grand stand."

It was the day before the great event. Spode came as usual, and Mr. Tillotson punctually made his little joke about the ankles, and Spode, as punctually, laughed.

"Well, Mr. Tillotson," he said, after the reverberation of the joke had died away, "to-morrow you make your re-entry into the world of art and fashion. You'll find some changes."

"I've always had such extraordinary luck," said Mr. Tillotson, and Spode could see by his expression that he genuinely believed it, that he had forgotten the black hole and the black-beetles and the almost exhausted ten pounds that stood between him and the workhouse. "What an amazing piece of good fortune, for instance, that you should have found me just when you did. Now, this dinner will bring me back to my place in the world. I shall have money, and in a little while—who knows?—I shall be able to see well enough to paint again. I believe my eyes are getting better, you know. Ah, the future is very rosy."

Mr. Tillotson looked up, his face puckered into a smile, and nodded his head in affirmation of his words.

"You believe in the life to come?" said Spode, and immediately flushed for shame at the cruelty of the words.

But Mr. Tillotson was in far too cheerful a mood to have caught their significance.

"Life to come," he repeated. "No, I don't believe in any of that stuff—not since 1859. The 'Origin of Species' changed my views, you know. No life to come for me, thank you! You don't remember the excitement of course. You're very young, Mr. Spode."

"Well, I'm not so old as I was," Spode replied. "You know

how middle-aged one is as a schoolboy and undergraduat[e]
Now I'm old enough to know I'm young."

Spode was about to develop this little paradox further, bu[t]
he noticed that Mr. Tillotson had not been listening. He mad[e]
a note of the gambit for use in companies that were mo[re]
appreciative of the subtleties.

"You were talking about the 'Origin of Species,'" he sai[d.]

"Was I?" said Mr. Tillotson, waking from reverie.

"About its effect on your faith, Mr. Tillotson."

"To be sure, yes. It shattered my faith. But I remember [a]
fine thing by the Poet Laureate, something about there bein[g]
more faith in honest doubt, believe me, than in all the . . . a[nd]
the . . . I forget exactly what; but you see the train of thought[.]
Oh, it was a bad time for religion. I am glad my master Hay[-]
don never lived to see it. He was a man of fervour. I remembe[r]
him pacing up and down his studio in Lisson Grove, singin[g]
and shouting and praying all at once. It used almost t[o]
frighten me. Oh, but he was a wonderful man, a great man[.]
Take him for all in all, we shall not look upon his like again[.]
As usual, the Bard is right. But it was all very long ago, be[-]
fore your time, Mr. Spode."

"Well, I'm not as old as I was," said Spode, in the hope o[f]
having his paradox appreciated this time. But Mr. Tillotson
went on without noticing the interruption.

"It's a very, very long time. And yet, when I look back
on it, it all seems but a day or two ago. Strange that each
day should seem so long and that many days added together
should be less than an hour. How clearly I can see old Haydon
pacing up and down! Much more clearly, indeed, than I see
you, Mr. Spode. The eyes of memory don't grow dim. But my
sight is improving, I assure you; it's improving daily. I shall
soon be able to see those ankles." He laughed, like a cracked
bell—one of those little old bells, Spode fancied, that ring, with
much rattling of wires, in the far-off servants' quarters of
ancient houses. "And very soon," Mr. Tillotson went on, "I
shall be painting again. Ah, Mr. Spode, my luck is extraordinary. I believe in it, I trust in it. And after all, what is luck?
Simply another name for Providence, in spite of the 'Origin of
Species' and the rest of it. How right the Laureate was when
he said that there was more faith in honest doubt, believe me,
than in all the . . . er, the . . . er . . . well, you know. I
regard you, Mr. Spode, as the emissary of Providence. Your

coming marked a turning-point in my life, and the beginning, for me, of happier days. Do you know, one of the first
things I shall do when my fortunes are restored will be to buy
a hedgehog."

"A hedgehog, Mr. Tillotson?"

"For the blackbeetles. There's nothing like a hedgehog for
beetles. It will eat blackbeetles till it's sick, till it dies of surfeit. That reminds me of the time when I told my poor great
master Haydon—in joke, of course—that he ought to send
in a cartoon of King John dying of a surfeit of lampreys for
the frescoes in the new Houses of Parliament. As I told him,
it's a most notable event in the annals of British liberty—the
providential and exemplary removal of a tyrant."

Mr. Tillotson laughed again—the little bell in the deserted
house; a ghostly hand pulling the cord in the drawing-room,
and phantom footmen responding to the thin, flawed note.

"I remember he laughed, laughed like a bull in his old grand
manner. But oh, it was a terrible blow when they rejected his
design, a terrible blow! It was the first and fundamental cause
of his suicide."

Mr. Tillotson paused. There was a long silence. Spode felt
strangely moved, he hardly knew why, in the presence of this
man, so frail, so ancient, in body three parts dead, in the
spirit so full of life and hopeful patience. He felt ashamed.
What was the use of his own youth and cleverness? He saw
himself suddenly as a boy with a rattle scaring birds—rattling
his noisy cleverness, waving his arms in ceaseless and futile
activity, never resting in his efforts to scare away the birds
that were always trying to settle in his mind. And what birds!
wide-winged and beautiful, all those serene thoughts and
faiths and emotions that only visit minds that have humbled
themselves to quiet. Those gracious visitants he was for ever
using all his energies to drive away. But this old man, with
his hedgehogs and his honest doubts and all the rest of it—his
mind was like a field made beautiful by the free coming and
going, the unafraid alightings of a multitude of white, bright-
winged creatures. He felt ashamed. But then, was it possible
to alter one's life? Wasn't it a little absurd to risk a conversion? Spode shrugged his shoulders.

"I'll get you a hedgehog at once," he said. "They're sure
to have some at Whiteley's."

Before he left that evening Spode made an alarming discovery. Mr. Tillotson did not possess a dress-suit. It was hopeless to think of getting one made at this short notice, and, besides, what an unnecessary expense!

"We shall have to borrow a suit, Mr. Tillotson. I ought to have thought of that before."

"Dear me, dear me." Mr. Tillotson was a little chagrined by this unlucky discovery. "Borrow a suit?"

Spode hurried away for counsel to Badgery House. Lord Badgery surprisingly rose to the occasion. "Ask Boreham to come and see me," he told the footman who answered his ring.

Boreham was one of those immemorial butlers who linger on, generation after generation, in the houses of the great. He was over eighty now, bent, dried up, shrivelled with age.

"All old men are about the same size," said Lord Badgery. It was a comforting theory. "Ah, here he is. Have you got a spare suit of evening clothes, Boreham?"

"I have an old suit, my lord, that I stopped wearing in— let me see—was it nineteen seven or eight?"

"That's the very thing. I should be most grateful, Boreham, if you could lend it to me for Mr. Spode here for a day."

The old man went out, and soon reappeared carrying over his arm a very old black suit. He held up the coat and trousers for inspection. In the light of day they were deplorable.

"You've no idea, sir," said Boreham deprecatingly to Spode —"you've no idea how easy things get stained with grease and gravy and what not. However careful you are, sir—however careful."

"I should imagine so." Spode was sympathetic.

"However careful, sir."

"But in artificial light they'll look all right."

"Perfectly all right," Lord Badgery repeated. "Thank you, Boreham; you shall have them back on Thursday."

"You're welcome, my lord, I'm sure." And the old man bowed and disappeared.

On the afternoon of the great day Spode carried up to Holloway a parcel containing Boreham's retired evening-suit and all the necessary appurtenances in the way of shirts and collars. Owing to the darkness and his own feeble sight Mr. Tillotson was happily unaware of the defects in the suit. He was in a state of extreme nervous agitation. It was with some difficulty that Spode could prevent him, although it was only three o'clock, from starting his toilet on the spot.

"Take it easy, Mr. Tillotson, take it easy. We needn't start ill half-past seven, you know."

Spode left an hour later, and as soon as he was safely out f the room Mr. Tillotson began to prepare himself for the anquet. He lighted the gas and a couple of candles, and, linking myopically at the image that fronted him in the tiny boking-glass that stood on his chest of drawers, he set to work, ith all the ardour of a young girl preparing for her first all. At six o'clock, when the last touches had been given, he as not unsatisfied.

He marched up and down his cellar, humming to himself he gay song which had been so popular in his middle years:

"Oh, oh, Anna Maria Jones!
Queen of the tambourine, the cymbals, and the bones!"

Spode arrived an hour later in Lord Badgery's second Rolls-Royce. Opening the door of the old man's dungeon, he stood or a moment, wide-eyed with astonishment, on the threshold. Mr. Tillotson was standing by the empty grate, one elbow resting on the mantelpiece, one leg crossed over the other in a jaunty and gentlemanly attitude. The effect of the candlelight shining on his face was to deepen every line and wrinkle with ntense black shadow; he looked immeasurably old. It was a noble and pathetic head. On the other hand, Boreham's outworn evening-suit was simply buffoonish. The coat was too long in the sleeves and the tail; the trousers bagged in elephantine creases about his ankles. Some of the grease-spots were visible even in candlelight. The white tie, over which Mr. Tillotson had taken infinite pains and which he believed in his purblindness to be perfect, was fantastically lop-sided. He had buttoned up his waistcoat in such a fashion that one button was widowed of its hole and one hole of its button. Across his shirt front lay the broad green ribbon of some unknown Order.

"Queen of the tambourine, the cymbals, and the bones," Mr. Tillotson concluded in a gnat-like voice before welcoming his visitor.

"Well, Spode, here you are. I'm dressed already, you see. The suit, I flatter myself, fits very well, almost as though it had been made for me. I am all gratitude to the gentleman who was kind enough to lend it to me; I shall take the greatest

care of it. It's a dangerous thing to lend clothes. For loan of
loseth both itself and friend. The Bard is always right."

"Just one thing," said Spode. "A touch to your waistcoat.
He unbuttoned the dissipated garment and did it up agai
more symmetrically.

Mr. Tillotson was a little piqued at being found so absurdl;
in the wrong.

"Thanks, thanks," he said, protestingly, trying to edge awa⟩
from his valet. "It's all right, you know; I can do it myself
Foolish oversight. I flatter myself the suit fits very well."

"And perhaps the tie might . . ." Spode began tentatively
But the old man would not hear of it.

"No, no. The tie's all right. I can tie a tie, Mr. Spode. Th⟨
tie's all right. Leave it as it is, I beg."

"I like your Order."

Mr. Tillotson looked down complacently at his shirt front
"Ah, you've noticed my Order. It's a long time since I wor⟨
that. It was given me by the Grand Porte, you know, for services rendered in the Russo-Turkish War. It's the Order o⟨
Chastity, the second class. They only give the first class t⟨
crowned heads, you know—crowned heads and ambassadors
And only Pashas of the highest rank get the second. Mine'⟨
the second. They only give the first class to crowned
heads . . ."

"Of course, of course," said Spode.

"Do you think I look all right, Mr. Spode?" Mr. Tillotson
asked, a little anxiously.

"Splendid, Mr. Tillotson—splendid. The Order's magnificent."

The old man's face brightened once more. "I flatter myself,"
he said, "that this borrowed suit fits me very well. But I don't
like borrowing clothes. For loan oft loseth both itself and
friend, you know. And the Bard is always right."

"Ugh, there's one of those horrible beetles!" Spode exclaimed.

Mr. Tillotson bent down and stared at the floor. "I see it,"
he said, and stamped on a small piece of coal, which crunched
to powder under his foot. "I shall certainly buy a hedgehog."

It was time for them to start. A crowd of little boys and
girls had collected round Lord Badgery's enormous car. The
chauffeur, who felt that honour and dignity were at stake,
pretended not to notice the children, but sat gazing, like a

statue, into eternity. At the sight of Spode and Mr. Tillotson
emerging from the house a yell of mingled awe and derision
went up. It subsided to an astonished silence as they climbed
into the car. "Bomba's," Spode directed. The Rolls-Royce
gave a faintly stertorous sigh and began to move. The children
yelled again, and ran along beside the car, waving their arms
in a frenzy of excitement. It was then that Mr. Tillotson, with
an incomparably noble gesture, leaned forward and tossed
among the seething crowd of urchins his three last coppers.

iv

In Bomba's big room the company was assembling. The long
gilt-edged mirrors reflected a singular collection of people.
Middle-aged Academicians shot suspicious glances at youths
whom they suspected, only too correctly, of being iconoclasts,
organisers of Post-Impressionist Exhibitions. Rival art critics,
brought suddenly face to face, quivered with restrained hatred.
Mrs. Nobes, Mrs. Cayman, and Mrs. Mandragore, those indefatigable hunters of artistic big game, came on one another
all unawares in this well-stored menagerie, where each had
expected to hunt alone, and were filled with rage. Through this
crowd of mutually repellent vanities Lord Badgery moved with
a suavity that seemed unconscious of all the feuds and hatreds.
He was enjoying himself immensely. Behind the heavy waxen
mask of his face, ambushed behind the Hanoverian nose, the
little lustreless pig's eyes, the pale thick lips, there lurked a
small devil of happy malice that rocked with laughter.

"So nice of you to have come, Mrs. Mandragore, to do
honour to England's artistic past. And I'm so glad to see
you've brought dear Mrs. Cayman. And is that Mrs. Nobes,
too? So it is! I hadn't noticed her before. How delightful! I
knew we could depend on your love of art."

And he hurried away to seize the opportunity of introducing
that eminent sculptor, Sir Herbert Herne, to the bright young
critic who had called him, in the public prints, a monumental
mason.

A moment later the Maître d'Hôtel came to the door of the
gilded saloon and announced, loudly and impressively, "Mr.
Walter Tillotson." Guided from behind by young Spode, Mr.
Tillotson came into the room slowly and hesitatingly. In the

glare of the lights his eyelids beat heavily, painfully, like the wings of an imprisoned moth, over his filmy eyes. Once inside the door he halted and drew himself up with a conscious assumption of dignity. Lord Badgery hurried forward and seized his hand.

"Welcome, Mr. Tillotson—welcome in the name of English art!"

Mr. Tillotson inclined his head in silence. He was too full of emotion to be able to reply.

"I should like to introduce you to a few of your younger colleagues, who have assembled here to do you honour."

Lord Badgery presented everyone in the room to the old painter, who bowed, shook hands, made little noises in his throat, but still found himself unable to speak. Mrs. Nobes, Mrs. Cayman, and Mrs. Mandragore all said charming things.

Dinner was served; the party took their places. Lord Badgery sat at the head of the table, with Mr. Tillotson on his right hand and Sir Herbert Herne on his left. Confronted with Bomba's succulent cooking and Bomba's wines, Mr. Tillotson ate and drank a good deal. He had the appetite of one who has lived on greens and potatoes for ten years among the blackbeetles. After the second glass of wine he began to talk, suddenly and in a flood, as though a sluice had been pulled up.

"In Asia Minor," he began, "it is the custom when one goes to dinner, to hiccough as a sign of appreciative fullness. *Eructavit cor meum*, as the Psalmist has it; he was an Oriental himself."

Spode had arranged to sit next to Mrs. Cayman; he had designs upon her. She was an impossible woman, of course, but rich and useful; he wanted to bamboozle her into buying some of his young friends' pictures.

"In a cellar?" Mrs. Cayman was saying, "with blackbeetles? Oh, how dreadful! Poor old man! And he's ninety-seven, didn't you say? Isn't that shocking! I only hope the subscription will be a large one. Of course, one wishes one could have given more oneself. But then, you know, one has so many expenses, and things are so difficult now."

"I know, I know," said Spode, with feeling.

"It's all because of Labour," Mrs. Cayman explained. "Of course, I should simply love to have him in to dinner sometimes. But, then, I feel he's really too old, too *farouche* and

gâteux; it would not be doing a kindness to him, would it?
And so you are working with Mr. Gollamy now? What a
charming man, so talented, such conversation . . ."

"*Eructavit cor meum,*" said Mr. Tillotson for the third
time. Lord Badgery tried to head him off the subject of Turkish etiquette, but in vain.

By half-past nine a kinder vinolent atmosphere had put to
sleep the hatreds and suspicions of before dinner. Sir Herbert
Herne had discovered that the young Cubist sitting next him
was not insane and actually knew a surprising amount about
the Old Masters. For their part these young men had realised
that their elders were not at all malignant; they were just
very stupid and pathetic. It was only in the bosoms of Mrs.
Nobes, Mrs. Cayman, and Mrs. Mandragore that hatred still
reigned undiminished. Being ladies and old-fashioned, they had
drunk almost no wine.

The moment for speech-making arrived. Lord Badgery rose
to his feet, said what was expected of him, and called upon
Sir Herbert to propose the toast of the evening. Sir Herbert
coughed, smiled and began. In the course of a speech that
lasted twenty minutes he told anecdotes of Mr. Gladstone,
Lord Leighton, Sir Alma Tadema, and the late Bishop of
Bombay; he made three puns, he quoted Shakespeare and
Whittier, he was playful, he was eloquent, he was grave. . . .
At the end of his harangue Sir Herbert handed to Mr. Tillotson a silk purse containing fifty-eight pounds ten shillings,
the total amount of the subscription. The old man's health
was drunk with acclamation.

Mr. Tillotson rose with difficulty to his feet. The dry, snakelike skin of his face was flushed; his tie was more crooked
than ever; the green ribbon of the Order of Chastity of the
second class had somehow climbed up his crumpled and macu-
late shirt front.

"My lords, ladies, and gentlemen," he began in a choking
voice, and then broke down completely. It was a very painful
and pathetic spectacle. A feeling of intense discomfort
afflicted the minds of all who looked upon that trembling relic
of a man, as he stood there weeping and stammering. It was
as though a breath of the wind of death had blown suddenly
through the room, lifting the vapours of wine and tobacco-
smoke, quenching the laughter and the candle flames. Eyes
floated uneasily, not knowing where to look. Lord Badgery,

with great presence of mind, offered the old man a glass of wine. Mr. Tillotson began to recover. The guests heard him murmur a few disconnected words.

"This great honour . . . overwhelmed with kindness . . . this magnificent banquet . . . not used to it . . . in Asia Minor . . . *eructavit cor meum.*"

At this point Lord Badgery plucked sharply at one of his long coat tails. Mr. Tillotson paused, took another sip of wine, and then went on with a newly won coherence and energy.

"The life of the artist is a hard one. His work is unlike other men's work, which may be done mechanically, by rote and almost, as it were, in sleep. It demands from him a constant expense of spirit. He gives continually of his best life, and in return he receives much joy, it is true—much fame, it may be—but of material blessings, very few. It is eighty years since first I devoted my life to the service of art; eighty years, and almost every one of those years has brought me fresh and painful proof of what I have been saying: the artist's life is a hard one."

This unexpected deviation into sense increased the general feeling of discomfort. It became necessary to take the old man seriously, to regard him as a human being. Up till then he had been no more than an object of curiosity, a mummy in an absurd suit of evening-clothes with a green ribbon across the shirt front. People could not help wishing that they had subscribed a little more. Fifty-eight pounds ten—it wasn't enormous. But happily for the peace of mind of the company, Mr. Tillotson paused again, took another sip of wine, and began to live up to his proper character by talking absurdly.

"When I consider the life of that great man, Benjamin Robert Haydon, one of the greatest men England has ever produced . . ." The audience heaved a sigh of relief; this was all as it should be. There was a burst of loud bravoing and clapping. Mr. Tillotson turned his dim eyes round the room, and smiled gratefully at the misty figures he beheld. "That great man, Benjamin Robert Haydon," he continued, "whom I am proud to call my master and who, it rejoices my heart to see, still lives in your memory and esteem,—that great man, one of the greatest that England has ever produced, led a life so deplorable that I cannot think of it without a tear."

And with infinite repetitions and divagations, Mr. Tillotson related the history of B. R. Haydon, his imprisonments for debt, his battle with the Academy, his triumphs, his failures, his despair, his suicide. Half-past ten struck. Mr. Tillotson was declaiming against the stupid and prejudiced judges who had rejected Haydon's designs for the decoration of the new Houses of Parliament in favour of the paltriest German scribblings.

"That great man, one of the greatest England has ever produced, that great Benjamin Robert Haydon, whom I am proud to call my master and who, it rejoices me to see, still lives on in your memory and esteem—at that affront his great heart burst; it was the unkindest cut of all. He who had worked all his life for the recognition of the artist by the State, he who had petitioned every Prime Minister, including the Duke of Wellington, for thirty years, begging them to employ artists to decorate public buildings, he to whom the scheme for decorating the Houses of Parliament was undeniably due . . ." Mr. Tillotson lost a grip on his syntax and began a new sentence. "It was the unkindest cut of all, it was the last straw. The artist's life is a hard one."

At eleven Mr. Tillotson was talking about the pre-Raphaelites. At a quarter past he had begun to tell the story of B. R. Haydon all over again. At twenty-five minutes to twelve he collapsed quite speechless into his chair. Most of the guests had already gone away; the few who remained made haste to depart. Lord Badgery led the old man to the door and packed him into the second Rolls-Royce. The Tillotson Banquet was over; it had been a pleasant evening, but a little too long.

Spode walked back to his rooms in Bloomsbury, whistling as he went. The arc lamps of Oxford Street reflected in the polished surface of the road; canals of dark bronze. He would have to bring that into an article some time. The Cayman woman had been very successfully nobbled. "Voi che sapete," he whistled—somewhat out of tune, but he could not hear that.

When Mr. Tillotson's landlady came in to call him on the following morning, she found the old man lying fully dressed on his bed. He looked very ill and very, very old; Boreham's dress-suit was in a terrible state, and the green ribbon of the Order of Chastity was ruined. Mr. Tillotson lay very still, but he was not asleep. Hearing the sound of footsteps, he opened his eyes a little and faintly groaned. His landlady looked down at him menacingly.

"Disgusting!" she said; "disgusting, I call it. At your age."

Mr. Tillotson groaned again. Making a great effort, he drew out of his trouser pocket a large silk purse, opened it, and extracted a sovereign.

"The artist's life is a hard one, Mrs. Green," he said, handing her the coin. "Would you mind sending for the doctor? I don't feel very well. And oh, what shall I do about these clothes? What shall I say to the gentleman who was kind enough to lend them to me? Loan oft loseth both itself and friend. The Bard is always right."

ESSAYS

SECTION I

THE reader must not be surprised if the essays he is now invited to read deal chiefly with men of letters. I warned him in the introduction that I was putting in this book only the things that peculiarly interested me and, being a writer, it is not strange if I find everything connected with writers and writing of singular interest. They say that you should read books and that books about books are unprofitable. I dare say it is true. Notwithstanding I find them very amusing. I find criticism as entertaining as fiction. I admit that to read it is not a serious occupation, but it is surely a very innocent pastime. I like to read about technique in a general and about the technique of various great writers in particular; and even though an author's books mean nothing very much to me I like to know what sort of life he led, what he looked like and how he talked. I never knew anyone who discussed books and described their authors more engagingly than Edmund Gosse. Though his essay on Swinburne is long I do not think anyone will find it dull.

My choice in essays has been limited by my own inability to take any pleasure in the only sort of essay that is now written. No one any longer seems to write essays in the manner of Macaulay. I have not read them since I was a small boy, and I daresay that they would now seem old-fashioned, but I still have a lively recollection of their vigour. The essays on Clive and Warren Hastings introduced me to the glory and romance of India. I am sure they were wonderful things in their way, those essays; they told you in graphic language all you wanted to know about their subjects and left you with an ineffaceable impression of heroic character. There are many historical personages whom it is interesting to read about in an essay, but whose consequence is not such that you feel inclined to read a whole book about them. What a subject for instance is Sir Stamford Raffles who founded Singapore and ruled Java when it was under the British Crown! He was a man of charmingly diverse characteristics. Then there was James Brooke, the first Rajah of Sarawak, a private English gentleman who went out to the East to look for antimony and found a kingdom. These were eminent figures and it may be that the authors who write books about them are justified in thinking that their importance is so great that they merit description at a length that the essay does not permit. But there are smaller persons who for their singularity or their connection with circumstances of note deserve an essay but not a book. Of such was Laetitia Pilkington. I would read with delight a serious account of her. To my mind she is one of the great comic characters of the eighteenth century. Hers is the hard-luck story raised to the plane of farce. Everything went wrong with her. She went from misfortune to misfortune with a persistence that was astonishing. Her sorrows were such that she called herself Tristitia. She was driven out of her home by her husband the Reverend Matthew Pilkington because he could not endure her superior ability. She wrote letters to Mr Samuel Richardson, the novelist, and he succoured her and besought his friends to give her employment. But for one reason and another, envy, the lasciviousness of males, the hardness of fate, she lost every situation that was found her. Her daughter was seduced and gave birth to an illegitimate child. She sent her son to Mr Richardson in rags. Mr Richardson sent him to his tailor to have them patched and was much incensed when he was sent in a bill for an entirely new suit of clothes. Naturally enough he turned out badly too. But the charity of Mr Richardson and his friends was inexhaustible and Tristitia continued to give them every opportunity to exercise it. Finally they sent her back to Dublin and she wrote her memoirs. I have not read them, but I hope she took the opportunity to get back on her untiring benefactors.

But of course to write an essay of this sort you need as much work and as much research as to write a book; the author is but human and he craves for recognition: gone are the days when a writer can gain fame, as Macaulay did when the *Edinburgh Review* published his *Milton*, with a single essay. Gone too are the days when Jeffreys was able to offer his contribu-

tors sixteen guineas a sheet. There is little opportunity now
for the essayist of the old kind to place a substantial essay and
he can expect but small remuneration. It is comprehensible
that such essays are now seldom written.

There is an American gentleman who has passed very
many pleasant years in conducting a sort of evangelical mission in England in the cause of culture. He has sought, I am
afraid with indifferent success, to throw light in our darkness.
But he has done his best and we are all very much obliged to
him. He produces every now and then a small collection of his
thoughts and fancies which is much acclaimed by the intelligentsia, and rightly, for he has a sub-acid humour which is
engaging, and his reflections for the most part are sensible and
amusing. But in his last collection of this sort he informed the
world that "writers who write for money don't write for me."
The statement must interest all those who are interested in the
author, but if an aphorism should have a general application
then I venture to think that this one falls short of perfection.
The motive for which an author writes has nothing whatever to
do with the reader. His only concern is the result. Because
Shakespeare wanted a new play for his company and being
short of time took an old one and wrote it up it is no less a
masterpiece, and the fact that Samuel Johnson needed a few
pounds to bury his mother and so sat down and wrote *Rasselas*
does not prevent it from being a work of singular power and
impressiveness. Many writers find the burden of writing intolerable; others take so much enjoyment in the product of
their imagination that they dread the moment when its expression in black and white will rob them of it for ever, and the
need or the desire for money alone can force them to work. It
is only the very fortunate or the very virtuous who can afford
to write only when the spirit moves them. Economic conditions
then have in general brought the full-dress essay of the great
review to an end.

Now the essayist is for the most part confined to the two
columns which weekly papers of literary interests offer him.
Here he has no space to be instructive. Nor can he take a subject, study and develop it. He must deal with trivial topics.
He can do little more than touch upon things, brushing them
lightly with a butterfly wing, and hover off gaily till the following week. He is forced to be personal. And so we have
masses of these little essays in which the writer tells us what he

likes for tea and what it feels like to try on a new suit of clothes. We are told in fifteen hundred well-chosen words that the hawthorn blooms in May and that the lark carols like anything. It is often done with singular grace, but I confess that I can have enough of that sort of thing. These writers depend on their personality. That is all very well, but if that is all you have to offer you must be sure that your personality is interesting. Charm is not enough. A lady of quality once asked Jonathan Swift to write a discourse upon a broomstick. I am sure he did it very well, not because his subject was a broomstick, but because he was bitter and envious, passionate, sentimental and broken-hearted. The essayist of this kind must wear his heart on his sleeve, but he should take care that, like Hazlitt's, it is bleeding and lacerated.

W. S. M.

Edmund Gosse

SWINBURNE

Among the many names that claim more or less acknowledgment in the contemporary English Parnassus, three stand out far above the rest in brilliance and widespread reputation: Alfred Tennyson, Robert Browning, Algernon Swinburne. In Mr. Tennyson the "respectable" party have found their supreme singer, whose faultless delicacy and purity of form enshrine a somewhat tame and domestic theory of life, with its duties, sufferings and pleasures, for which they have rewarded him by a fame more immense than has ever before been granted to a poet in his lifetime. In Mr. Browning a more eclectic taste has been allied with a muscular strength of intellect unsurpassed, probably unequalled, in our poetic literature since Shakespeare, but a want of clearness in utterance and an inability to make music in verse have combined to frustrate in measure sublime gifts of brain and hand. These two great writers have ruled for a season, and approach their natural close; both are in the seventh decade. The rising star of our heavens is a fiery planet, palpitating and erratic, ominous of storm and a time of change, with little in common with either of his predecessors. Algernon Swinburne has shown little desire to be considered the laureate of the respectable party, and hardly more to be the tuneless exponent of remote philosophical theories or analytic anatomy of human emotion. The world corrects itself by a rising and a falling balance. After the domesticity of Mr. Tennyson and the subtlety of Mr. Browning, it is right that we should taste the perversity and the stormy melody of Swinburne.

Swinburne was born on the 5th of April 1837, at Henley-on-Thames. He is the only important English poet since Byron who has been of aristocratic extraction. The Swinburnes are

an old Border family, of Danish origin, the primal form of the
name having apparently been Svenbjörn, and in the wars between England and Scotland, in the reign of Edward III, they
took a prominent part. The present head of the family, Sir
John Swinburne, possesses Capheaton, the ancestral estate, in
the wildest and most picturesque part of Northumberland, on
the slopes of the Cheviot Hills, a half-uncivilised country,
thinly peopled and covered with vast woods. It was in the midst
of this scenery, and by the rocky sea-coast of Northumberland
that the poet's boyish days were passed. Among many brothers
and sisters, he, the eldest, was also the strongest from the first
and little given to join in their games and small enjoyments.
A true *enfant terrible* he appears to have been, turbulent, perverse and restless. Swinburne's physique is a very remarkable
one. A great head, balanced on a thick and sturdy neck, like
the neck of a Vespasian or a Caracalla, is adorned with full
curls of gold-red hair, falling over and half-concealing a forehead that else would overbalance all the rest of the face. This
massive head and neck, however, belong in truth to the frailest
little bird-like body conceivable, with fragile hands and arms,
rapidly sloping, narrow shoulders, like a woman's, broad hips
and short slight legs. Swinburne always walks bolt-upright, as
though he dared not stoop for fear his great head should overbalance him. His stature is only a little over five feet, and his
body is so light that one can lift him easily with one's hands.
In the early days at Capheaton he had two principal exercises.
Either he was riding all day long in the most furious way on
a little shaggy pony that just suited his size, or he was dashing into the river-pools or swimming in the sea.

About the year 1853 it was first perceived that this little
red-haired Algernon was to be something wonderful. As chance
would have it, William Bell Scott, the poet and painter, was
painting frescoes round the great hall of Sir Walter Trevelyan's house, the nearest neighbour of Sir John Swinburne. In
intervals of his work, sitting at the oriel window, Scott perceived this adorably handsome boy rush by on his rough pony.
Algernon Swinburne's head was the exact model for one Scott
needed in his fresco. Nothing was easier than to coax the boy
in, and soon he became a constant visitor at the Trevelyans'. In
a little while, as Scott was painting, the bird-like creature, who
could not be still a moment, would warble forth snatches of
strange verse, and when asked whose poetry that was, would

hesitate and laugh. Soon the shyness passed away, and Algernon's poetry became a matter of daily recitation. He was now about sixteen, and had become a scholar at Eton. Meanwhile Scott worked on at his great frescoes, which remain to this day the greatest trophies of his talent. As the holiday-months came round, Algernon Swinburne would re-appear, more lyrical, more brilliant, more restless than ever. Already he was fired with republican ideas; in the aristocratic household of Capheaton such ideas seemed monstrous and worthy of death; the irrepressible young poet was accordingly driven more and more to the enlightened and intellectual society of the Trevelyans. In Lady Trevelyan, a brilliant and amiable woman unhappily long since dead, Swinburne found a most useful and sympathetic friend, and it was to her that some of his earliest published verses were first read.

Those were days when all disinterested and noble-minded persons watched with deep and solemn anxiety the war of liberty in Italy. There were stars before the sunrise, stars that fell, quenched in blood. To young Swinburne, in the wild woods of Northumberland, came the story of the sorrows of Mazzini; then still sadder news of foiled tyrannicides, of Barbès, of Agesilas, of the noble Orsini, and the boy's heart burned within him to die, as they had died, for freedom. The instinct of martyrdom has always been strongly developed in Swinburne; sensitive as he is to pain, he feels nothing if he is suffering for an idea. The courage pent-up within that slight frame of his is irrepressible, and he is never really content without some opposition. All through his career he has put himself in defiance against the world; a born aristocrat, he has preached republicanism and atheism; to a respectable and hypocritical generation he has, for mere perversity, sung about Anactoria and Phedra. So in the boyish days, when the thought of the captivity of Italy thrilled him with a passionate agony of love, he would start out of the cool depths of the river where he was bathing, and while the water streamed off his sun-coloured hair and beautiful rosy limbs, he would strain his arms into the air in a rapture of longing that he too, like Felice Orsini, might die a martyr to Italian liberty, and that his stript body and open face might feel the Austrian bullets and not shrink.

Mingled with this extraordinary enthusiasm was an intense delight in all physical exercises. He was never very muscular, and could not wrestle or use his hands skilfully, but two things

he could do better than any boy he knew: swim and ride. About
1856 Scott went down to live at Newcastle, and often spent
weeks at a desolate part of the sea-coast near by; there, when
the sea was rough, Algernon used to love to come. He would
leap from rock to rock, half-smothered in the thundering foam
of the breakers, or trusting his light, lithe body to the curl of
an advancing wave, dash through the falling arch of cold
green water, and reappearing, revel like a mad thing in the
foam and fury of the roaring seas. No English poet has known
the different moods of the sea, and loved them so much, as
Swinburne; and it is no merely theoretical knowledge, he is a
fearless and rapid swimmer, needing nothing but a broader
chest to outstrip the most practised athletes.

To his riding and swimming may be added another kindred
accomplishment: he is the lightest and swiftest of runners. The
best portrait that exists of him was painted in 1860, by W. B.
Scott. He was then at the height of his beauty; the face is the
face of a Tuscan angel, of such a gracious and ethereal
creature as Botticelli or Filippino loved to paint holding the
lily of annunciation or the palm of martyrdom. The small, full
lips are the least pleasing part of the face, the upper lip being
prolonged and mobile, as now; the eyes are of a clear greenish
blue; the skin white and colourless; the hair, of a brilliant red,
threaded with gold, clusters over the brow, and falls in massive
curls behind the head. Such a miracle of strange beauty was
Swinburne in 1860; now, alas! illness and sorrow and hard
living have taken all the charm and freshness off the rapidly
ageing face. But the mind remains unchanged; he is still the
same warm and generous enthusiast.

In 1857 he went to the University of Oxford, and became an
undergraduate of Balliol College. This was an important epoch
in his life. There he met Dr. Jowett, the translator of Plato
and now Master of Balliol, a man whose lofty integrity and
warm-hearted fidelity have again and again interposed when
Swinburne has been on the point of committing one or another
act of fatal folly. There also he became acquainted with the
young men who were beginning to revolutionise English art,
and was enrolled in their so-called Pre-Raphaelite Brotherhood. William Morris was the first of these to attract Swinburne to him. Mr. Morris had hardly then given promise of his
extraordinary poetical genius. Though he was many years
older than Swinburne, he had scarcely written anything but

the little volume, *The Defence of Guenevere*, to be published, but without attracting much notice, in 1858. The extreme originality and beauty of these poems, exact revivals as they were of early mediaeval feeling, struck the young Swinburne with such force that he began to imitate them. Shortly afterwards Mr. Dante Gabriel Rossetti came down from London to Oxford to paint. This man, whose individual influence on young men of talent in England has been greater than that of any of his contemporaries, attracted Algernon Swinburne to him as the flame attracts the moth: Mr. Rossetti belonged to an earlier generation; he was a practised man of the world, used to rule other men, powerful in will and purpose. Swinburne clung to him as a rapid and affectionate nature, oppressed by its own delicacy, clings to a powerful and rough-hewn nature, whose physical massiveness overpowers it.

Swinburne failed completely at Oxford; he became a brilliant classical scholar, but could never master enough of the rudiments of mathematics to get through what is called the "Little-Go" examination. But while he was still a student, in 1862, he accompanied his mother to Switzerland and Italy. The former country made little impression upon him; the latter almost dazzled him to death. At Florence he visited the old exiled poet, Walter Savage Landor, the greatest English genius that Englishmen have never learned to love. He found the old man, nearly blind, growling and cursing his fate. The young poet threw himself at the old man's feet, kissed his hands and prayed for his poetic blessing. The grand old soul of Landor woke again within him; this visit was like sunshine and warm life; he became rejuvenescent, and stirring out of his lethargy, paced up and down the rooms, with his arm on Swinburne's shoulder. The younger poet, in a splendid elegy on Landor, written two years later, says:

> "I came as one whose thoughts half linger,
>   Half run before,
>   The youngest to the oldest singer
>   That England bore."

Algernon Swinburne has the most exquisite sympathy and tenderness for old and weak persons, and a wonderful power of helping and soothing them.

When he returned from Italy, a great sorrow came upon

him. Even in speaking to friends in a foreign nation I must
not say more than this. I would not say even this were it not
needful to point out that this event stimulated him to produce
his noblest poetry. After a long pause of bitterness and silence,
the anguished spirit found voice in what is, perhaps, the very
greatest of all his poems, *The Triumph of Time*. Next followed *Les Noyades*, then *Dolores*, and in quick succession the
drama of *Atalanta in Calydon*. From 1862 to 1864 was the
most prolific period in the poet's life hitherto. It must not be
forgotten that while he was in college he had written two
dramas, *The Queen Mother* and *Rosamond*, and begun *Chastelard*. I reserve all critical remark for a future section. From
this point it is not in my power to give a very detailed account
of the poet's life; it has had no very startling incidents; it has
been spent partly in London, partly at Henley, partly in
France.

The appearance of *Atalanta in Calydon* in 1864 placed
him at once on a level with the best living poets; *Chastelard*,
an earlier work, was published next, and increased his reputation. But *Poems and Ballads*, published in 1866, was received
with a howl from the Philistines such as had not been raised
since Byron brought out *Don Juan*. The reason of this indignation I hope to examine hereafter. In 1867 Swinburne met
Mazzini at the house of Karl Blind. They sat hand in hand
the whole evening, and when they parted Mazzini said: "You
must write no more erotic poems, but dedicate your powers to
the cause of Liberty." Swinburne rushed home and wrote the
Song of Italy, which came out the same year and was dedicated to Mazzini. Thereupon he began to write *Songs before
Sunrise*.

In 1869 he was living in Normandy. Bathing one day at
Etretat, the rush of the tide carried him out to sea; he swam
for nearly an hour. Just as breath and strength were failing
him, and he was consigning himself to death, a French fishing-
smack picked him up. The sailors gave him an old pair of
canvas trousers, and with no other clothes on, the poet sat in
the prow of the vessel, with the sunlight streaming on his hair,
and recited Victor Hugo's verses to his deliverers. They were
delighted with him, and took him back with them to their own
village, some distance off. The versatile poet, charmed with his
new phase of life, forgot his friends at Etretat, and came back
after some hours to find everyone in a frenzy of anxiety.

In 1870, in the midst of the great war, *Songs before Sunrise*
came out. In the thunders of that year their music was scarcely
heard, and the French version, which was to be published
simultaneously, disappeared during the siege of Paris. It was
not until the spring of 1871 that I had first the privilege of
speaking to the poet, whom I have now the happiness of num-
bering among my most intimate friends. He has published
since then, *Bothwell*—which appeared last summer, and finally
determined Swinburne's position as the greatest of all the poets
born since 1820—a volume of political poems, *Songs of Two
Nations*, 1875, and two prose works of a critical nature.

ii

In 1861 we have seen that the young poet brought out, in
one small volume, two dramas in verse, but they attracted no
attention even in his own immediate circle, and it was some
time before he again attempted to appear before the public.
But ever since 1857 he had been writing lyrical poetry with
great fluency, and by the year 1864 he had enough select
pieces to form a thick volume. It was in vain however that he
sought a publisher, no one would take the risk of bringing out
a book of verses by an unknown writer, and Swinburne never
had ready money enough to take the risk in his own hands.
But his desk was overflowing with MSS. Besides the lyrics, a
whole drama, *Chastelard*, had been finished as early as 1860,
and other books, now lost or thrown aside, were ready to be
printed. He was twenty-seven, and still unknown. It was necessary to do something. Accordingly, in the early part of 1864
he wrote his classical drama of *Atalanta in Calydon*, which was
taken by Messrs Moxon & Son, brought out by them in that
year, and received with an almost unanimous enthusiasm by
the whole English and American Press. It was now easy for
him to publish anything, and next year there appeared the
early play of *Chastelard*, and in 1866 a volume of lyrical
poems, also almost all written long before *Atalanta*. In reality
many portions of the book called *Poems and Ballads* belong to
Swinburne's earliest development, but this has never been
understood by the critics, who to this day point to the serenity
and fullness of *Atalanta* as a proof that Swinburne's style
had originally more finish than it now has. They judge by the

obvious immaturity of the next published but earlier volumes

The appearance of *Poems and Ballads* marked an epoch in our poetic literature. Seldom has a book been received with such a storm of abuse from all the organs of the Press. Perverse, eccentric and arrogant, the poet had dared in it to outrage almost every conventional axiom of poetic writing, and more especially of poetic thought. There has never been a period so desirous of sewing pillows to all arm-holes as the period which has just passed away from us; there has never been a generation so childishly timid, so delicately mealy-mouthed, so respectable and so refined, as that which viewed with rapturous homage the great deeds of its prime friend across the Channel, the Saviour of Society. In an atmosphere so moral in profession, so immoral in the highest reality, poetry was like a greenhouse plant, sickly, tame and pale. The one poet of that epoch was Tennyson, whose idyllic pictures of the amours of cottage-girls and curates were the strongest intellectual food the nation could digest. Robert Browning delivered his powerful and esoteric utterances unmarked by more than a few; Elizabeth Browning died in 1861, just as with her *Casa Guidi Windows*, and still more her stupendous epic-satire of *Aurora Leigh*, she was beginning to make the nation acknowledge a broader and robuster spirit possible in poetry. All was again sliding back into the most vapid condition possible; the only poets whom the Press accepted were those whose works could be put without hesitation into the hands of the youngest girl.

Suddenly Swinburne's *Poems and Ballads* appeared, challenging and defying every prejudice of the British Philistine, drowning the mild voices of the idyllists in thundering melodies of lust and cruelty and blasphemy. The contrast was excessive; the new poet went too far in his attack on existing things; above all he was found guilty of the greatest crime Society recognises, "bad taste," and he was hunted down like a mad dog. Or would have been, had it not presently been discovered that this new poet was not to be hunted down, or crushed, or annihilated; and had it not been discovered also that, in spite of the journalists who said that his poems were stupid as well as wicked, and that nobody would read them, in point of fact everybody did read them, and in process of time one voice and then another was heard above the howl of the crowd, asserting that the blasphemy and the wickedness had been much exaggerated, that the book was not so abominable as the newspapers said it was, and that in spite of much that was ill-advised, ugly, or even unnatural, there was enough of pure and perfect work to make the book worthily immoral.

Nine years have passed since that windy war over *Poems and Ballads*, and criticism has greatly modified its unfavourable verdict. The poet has written other soberer books; he has never written again in the same overfervid and irreverent way of the physiological phenomena of disease, mental or bodily, and by degrees Society is forgiving its *enfant terrible*. Besides, the poet is also a prophet, and by his unsparing audacity he has done not a little to redeem us from the horrible bondage of respectability. By all means let us be moral, pure and order-loving people, but do not let us, being men, pretend to be old maids, or slip into the chasms of social obscurantism to save our eyes from painful or agitating spectacles. The literature of the present moment, compared with that of twenty years ago, is robust, masculine and sincere. It is only just to attribute some of the emancipation to the courageous, if mistaken, vehemence of Swinburne.

Let us take this dangerous volume of 344 pages into our hands. At the first glance we see it to be no Christian book. A Pagan spirit interpenetrates it, and the sincerest utterances it contains are those which declaim most violently against the traditions and usurpations of Christianity. There is no abuse of doctrine, as in Shelley; there is no effort at reconciliation of antique philosophy and Christianity, as in Tennyson and others. This poet, left alone in the new age, wails after the old golden years, and rages blindly against the cords that bind him round. He has gone to sleep, ages ago, on the world's lap, free; but he wakes to find the woof and web of the Philistines tight about him, and the world itself has betrayed hi n. The poems are arranged in no proper order; with a kind of wil ul purpose they are so shuffled together that we can only with infinite labour arrange them in any sort of continuity. Chronological order, if that were possible, would help us little here. All are adolescent, that is certain:

"For the youngest were born of boy's pastime,
    The eldest are young";

in all this fervour and splendour, one thing is missing, a matured judgment. The lyrics are in most cases dramatic, and we may well divide them into two large classes: those belonging to a pre-Christian and those belonging to a Christian age. They are very distinct in manner. Judging them so, we head the list with the wonderful chant of *Itylus*. Out of the dim and prehistoric Greece there comes to us this melancholy and passionate music, the reproach that the nightingale makes to her light and forgetful sister the swallow, who bears not in mind the cruel ships and the foreign faces, her vigil at Itylus and all the pain and shame. This poem, written at Fiesole in the summer of 1862, is one of the most faultless passages of melody which our modern literature has to boast of; and no other, among Swinburne's lyrics, has an air so thoroughly antique. In *Anactoria* and *Phedra* we come down to historic times; there is force here, but without delicacy and without charm. These monodramas of fierce and pitiless lust, impotent and frantic, owe much of their character to the study of Baudelaire and his fungus-growth of morbid poetry. *Anactoria* has little of the true Sappho in it; the verses entitled *Sapphics*, on the contrary, burn and quiver with a fire and a passion that are almost worthy of the greatest of Greek lyrists herself. This adorable poem, at once the directest and most perfect that Swinburne has written, describes how the gods with terror and pity watched the Tenth Muse, Sappho, rise to the height of her great song, and fall, shattered and broken with sterile desire. It is hardly possible to quote it; stanza by stanza the great lyrical tragedy unfolds itself in language that could not be surpassed for majesty, harmony and passion, but woven together so subtly that it would break the direct chain of thought to divide it. The finest rhetorical characteristics of Swinburne's style are prominent in this great poem so modestly entitled *Sapphics*.

It is well known that these antique forms of verse do not easily suit our stubborn language. Another poem, conceived in quite another spirit, bears for title simply *Hendecasyllables;* where a mood of tender regret for the swift passage of sweet things is expressed in a manner rather mediaeval than classic, in language as cool and tender as a flower. The little piece called *Erotion* closes the category of pre-Christian classic poems, and is such a mysterious outburst of grief and desire as broke from the lips of Callimachus or Meleager in those sexless poems of strange love that the Greek Anthology is full of. The loved one has passed away to fresh conquests, new

xcitements, and the lover can but yearn towards the flying
ootsteps:

> "Yet leave me not; yet, if thou wilt, be free;
> Love me no more, but love my love of thee.
> Love where thou wilt, and live thy life, but I
> One thing I can, and one Love cannot—die."

Kindred with these Greek poems in some degree are the
poems of Hebrew theme. *A Litany* is a severe chant of denunciation in the spirit of Isaiah or Hosea; in *A Lamentation* we
find the grief and despair of a people who have left their god
and been deserted of him; in *Aholibah* the bride and handmaid
of God is described as Ezekiel describes her, when the painted
figures of Babylonian captains on the wall drew her heart and
lips away into strange sin, wherefore the curse and chastise-
ment of God fell bitterly upon her.

Another class among the *Poems and Ballads* may be desig-
nated Monodramas of the Later Empire. Among these we find
Hermaphroditus, four sonnets of exquisite tenderness and
grace, a reverie full of sadness in which it is asked which of
the gods, weary of the generations of men, has created as a
mere trophy of sterile beauty this faultless fruitless creature.
No answer is given, and Love himself, being blind, knows nothing of this. In *Fragoletta*, the same mysterious theme is dwelt
upon, but with less reticence, for reverie gives way to passion,
and the speaker confesses that, weary of the leopard's feet of
Love that flies, he is fain to find sweeter repose on this straight
breast and rounded sexless throat. In *Faustine* a gladiator in
whose arms the Empress has lain the night before stands up in
the arena about to die and denounces her cruel and pitiless
lust. In *Hesperia* a man who has loved overmuch, and suffered too much in the riotous pleasures of Rome, pallid and
worn, sails out into the golden west to reach, if he may, the
Fortunate Isles and find rest before death.

But besides these and more, three poems of this period stand
out with peculiar insistence. The *Hymn to Proserpine*, already
known to Danish readers by the forcible translation of Herr
Adolf Hansen, is the despairing outcry of a Pagan on the
proclamation of Christianity at Rome. He cries out against the
bondage of the Galilaean; he will have none of the new virgin
goddess: a new Cybele who rides out of Dindymus, heavily
laden, cold and forbidding. For him life has lost its sunlight,

love its passion, the world its hopes; and all his comfort i
that the Galilaean, also, is not immortal, and that he too i
process of time will fall, to make way for more genial deitie:
If in the *Hymn to Proserpine* there speaks a manly and a
heroic Pagan, in the marvellous poem of *Dolores* we have th
wild utterance of a man satiated with lascivious pleasure, anc
in his craving for physical excitement, full of desire for pai.
itself to stir his jaded nerves. Swinburne has never writte
anything more original, more superb, more powerful or mor
repulsive than this famous poem of *Dolores*. In verse that i
music itself, the speaker adores, upbraids, invokes and de
scribes the strange goddess whom he has created for his wor
ship, daughter of Cotytto and Priapus, extreme satiety mate
with untiring lust. In a crowning achievement of perversity h
pours out to this fanged and furious deity all the prayers, a.
the passion that a man gives to a lover, or a suppliant to ;
god. In vain! Men are no more what they were; the blood i
weak, the fire burns low, the splendid antique power of lovin;
and singing is gone by.

> "For the chaplets of old are above us,
>   And the oyster-beds teem out of reach;
> Old poets out-sing and out-love us,
>   And Catullus makes mouths at our speech.
> Who shall kiss, in thy father's old city,
>   With such lips as he sang with, again?
> Intercede for us all, of thy pity,
>   Our Lady of Pain."

It was in this poem, fierce chant worthy of Quartilla herself
that the passages were found which startled most of all th
English reviewers. To persons ignorant of Martial, o:
Apuleius, of Petronius, to write of "lips intertwisted and bitter
till the foam has a savour of blood," of "heavy white limbs anc
the cruel red mouth like a venomous flower," and of this hor
rible mixture of luxurious pleasure and pain, seemed a thing
inconceivably and unutterably startling. Even those more
learned in the obscure passions of the antique world could have
wished a less ardent and less enthusiastic exposition of its mysteries. However *Dolores* contains some of the most astounding
tours de force to be found in Swinburne's writings. Such a

:anza as this, describing how Nero fiddled when Rome was
urning;

> "When, with flame all around him aspirant,
> Stood flushed, as a harp-player stands,
> The implacable beautiful tyrant,
> Rose-crowned, having death in his hands,
> And a sound as the sound of loud water
> Smote far through the flight of the fires,
> And mixed with the lightning of slaughter,
> A thunder of lyres,"

as all the delicacy, hardness and sonorousness of a jewelled
up of Cellini's work, firm as iron, light as a flower. It is im-
)ossible to find lyrical work better done, from a mere technical
)oint of view, than these faultless verses. Last of all the
Roman poems comes *The Garden of Proserpine*. Tired of lust
ind laughter, weary of all things human and divine, the
peaker has this comfort only left him, that

> "From too much love of living,
> From hope and fear set free,
> We thank with brief thanksgiving
> Whatever gods may be.
> That no life lives for ever;
> That dead men rise up never;
> That even the weariest river
> Winds somewhere safe to see."

And so, like Adonis in Frederik Paludan-Muller's last and
loveliest poem, exhausted with the roses of Aphrodite, he
comes, with tottering footsteps, to the throne where the calm
Persephone sits silent, crowned with cold white blossoms. So
the cycle of passionate poems of the senses ends with sleep and
death.

It had been well if Swinburne had been content to publish
only the poems we have indicated, and in something of that
order. His other lyrics might have filled another volume; they
are, to our thinking, out of place among these utterances of
the ancient world. As well might the *Poèmes Barbares* of
Leconte de Lisle be mixed with Gautier's *Emaux et Camées*
and with a few of the *Odes et Ballades* of Victor Hugo. For

Swinburne has his mediaeval section also in the *Poems and Bal-lads*. They are extremely clever adaptations, or imitations rather than original works. In *The Ballad of Life*, *The Ballad of Death* and *The Ballad of Burdens* he imitates very closely the manner of the writer of canzonets who followed Dante and the earliest Italian lyrists. In *Laus Veneris* he tells the story of Tannhäuser and the Venus-demon in the manner of the French romancists of the sixteenth century; *St. Dorothy* is an exact reproduction of the peculiar narrative style of Chaucer. *In the Orchard* closely follows the early Provençal burden-ballads, while in *A Christmas Carol* and the *Masque of Queen Bersabe* a still earlier model is chosen, and we have poems that simulate the first dawnings of English lyrical writing in carols and mystery-plays so that it is hardly possible to believe that they are not genuine. Least successful of these resuscitations are the ballads written in imitation of the magnificent anony-mous poems of the fifteenth century which we call Border Bal-lads, having been principally composed by wandering minstrels on the Scottish Border.

We come at last to the modern erotic poems of this volume. The most important in every way is that entitled *The Triumph of Time*. The speaker, who has been betrayed and cast off by the girl that he truly and purely loved, in favour of a richer or newer rival, mournfully, but without resentment or rage, points out how her life as well as his own is ruined by her in-fidelity. A chance has been lost of two souls growing together into something ineffable and splendid. However, for him life has no more pleasures, and he turns to the sea for comfort. The sea alone, persistent, melancholy, chaste and the mother of men, can give him repose; and we leave him in the midst of the cold light and monotonous music of the sad green waves. Full of majesty and exalted thought, this poem is kept from being a masterpiece only by its excessive length and want of con-centration, two faults which mar most of Swinburne's writ-ings.

The rest of the modern love-poems are less elevated, less sin-cere than this, *The Triumph of Time*. There is too much repe-tition of the fierce phrases that suited a Faustine or a Dolores, but which are out of place addressed to a modern woman. *A Leave-Taking* repeats in some measure the feeling of *The Triumph of Time*, but in a minor key. *Rococo* and *Félise* ring the changes on the idea that the relative position of lovers oscillates, and that when one is passionate, the other is cold; so this one learns to love only when the first is satiated or weary of wooing. *Satia te sanguine* translates into modern life the savage and libidinous inclinations of a voluptuous Roman, and one shudders to read of a contemporary what one contemplates with philosophy in a civilisation seventeen centuries ago. It has been said that love has no place in this book of Swinburne's, and though the statement is not exactly true, since a few such poems as *The Triumph of Time* are full of pure and tender devotion, it is undeniable that the analysis of lust forms the great theme. It must be understood that the unpleasant subject is almost uniformly treated with gravity and delicacy. There is not an obscene phrase in the book, and, with a few unfortunate exceptions, nothing that can possibly shock a reader of tolerable mental robustness. This book, so famous, so fervid, so original, cannot be passed over in neglect. It holds a place in literature. The author has never attempted to repeat an experiment so audacious, and I have it from his own lips that he never will again.

There are still a few pieces in the volume unanalyzed. We find here a very beautiful elegy on the death of Walter Savage Landor. Swinburne is especially happy in his poems of this class. When Beaudelaire and Gautier died, he paid homage to their memories in elegies which have never yet passed from the pages of *The Fortnightly Review*, where they appeared, into any volume, but which were of the first excellence. When our Nestor, Bryan W. Proctor (Barry Cornwell) died last year, Swinburne dedicated some exquisite memorial verses to his name. I will refrain from noticing the few political poems contained in *Poems and Ballads*, because they belong more properly to the same class as the *Songs before Sunrise*, and will be examined with them. There remains to be mentioned only the beautiful *Dedication*, where, in the same magnificent verse-form created for *Dolores*, Swinburne dedicates the book to the great painter Edward Burne-Jones, whose genius in many respects is so closely allied to his own, and he fitly describes it as a handful of blown leaves:

"Leaves pallid and sombre and ruddy,
    Dead fruits of the fugitive years,
Some stained as with wine and made bloody,
    And some as with tears."

iii

The volume by which Swinburne first made his mark in literature was a drama in the manner of Sophocles, and dealing with an early Greek theme. We have already said that this poem, *Atalanta in Calydon*, was given to the public in 1864, and that its success was instantaneous. In many respects it remains the most perfect of his works; the rigidity of the Hellenic model did not leave much space for the poet's greatest faults: exaggerated use of imagery and profusion of mere melodious words. There had been no previous example in English of a drama composed so closely after the Sophoclean tragedies. Milton had, indeed, in his *Samson Agonistes*, had recourse to the lyrical drama, written in blank verse and interspersed with choric passages, but the whole spirit and theme of that somewhat austere poem were Hebrew, though the style was Greek. Shelley had employed the form of Greek tragedy in his *Prometheus Unbound*, but in the manner of Aeschylus, and with all his transcendental freedom of ideal and supernatural action. With Sophocles, with Swinburne, we find ourselves among human beings, acted upon by invisible but strenuous deities. There has been no attempt in the modern poet's work to interpret the legend as a myth, no discovery of modern passion in the kernel of the old hard story, such as William Morris and Paul Heyse have essayed; the tale is developed with all the realism possible, and the modern part of the treatment is simply the attitude of men towards the gods, and the gods toward men. How this is done will be manifest as we proceed to analyse the drama.

The story is the old familiar one of how Aeneus, King of Calydon, forgetting Artemis only of all the gods when he worshipped them, was by her cruelly tormented by a wild boar which wasted all his land and which could be slain of none; and how when the chief men of all Greece gathered together, it was no man, but Atalanta, a maiden of Arcadia, that slew the boar and delivered the land, Artemis loving her for her maidenhood; and how the brothers of Althea, wife of Aeneus, were jealous of her and would have taken the prize from her, but Meleager, Althea's son, slew them. Whereupon Althea, being mad with grief, took the brand of which the Fates had

aid that Meleager should live till it were burned, and cast it
upon a fire, so that he died in a brief space.

The drama opens with a soliloquy in which the Chief Huntsman prays to Artemis to give edge to the spears and speed to
the hounds and good luck to every man; and then the Chorus
takes up the word, and breaks into a melodious hymn to the
Virgin Goddess. This unrivalled passage, written in anapaestic
verse, passionate, elastic and exquisitely musical, charms the
attention at once, and is full of adoring worship. Then Althea
enters, complaining of the gods, and full of apprehension and
doubt. She upbraids the cruel purpose of Artemis, though the
Chorus reminds her that men get small honour who revile the
gods. She then recounts the old story of how when Meleager
was born the three Fates came into her bedchamber and prophesied of him three things—namely, great strength in his
hands, good fortune in his life, and that he should live until
the brand there on the hearth was consumed; and how, gathering her raiment, she leaped from the bed, and snatched the
brand away to extinguish it. Then she hastens out to prepare
her son for the hunt. The Chorus, left alone, and no longer so
jubilant, sing of the creation of man, and the gifts of grief
and tears and brief, sad days that the gods gave him. They
sing not angrily, but with the harsh voice of hopelessness, out
of which all the jubilant music of the first hymn to Artemis
has passed. Althea then returns with Meleager, who is full of
elation and hope, and who aids the faint eyes of his mother in
distinguishing the lords of Greece as they arrive. Then they
talk together of the past heroic years, she with melancholy
and rebellion against the gods, he with joy and worship.
Aeneus, coming in, tells them of the arrival of Atalanta, and
warns Meleager not to look at her with eyes of love. Althea,
hearing of the maiden, bursts out enraged against the gods:

"O King, thou art wise, but wisdom halts; and just,
    But the gods love not justice more than fate,
    And smite the righteous and the violent mouth,
    And mix with insolent blood the righteous man's,
    And bruise the holier as the lying lips."

But, turning to her son, in an exquisite invocation of maternal
passion, which recalls the speech of Clytemnestra when she
bares her breast before Orestes, Althea pours out a torrent of

memories and tender entreaties, the shadow of the coming calamity being heavy upon her; and sure that the love of this strange Arcadian virgin will bring ruin with it, she knows not how, she prays him by all his duty and loyalty as a son not to follow her with amorous words. Whereupon Meleager soothes her with assurances of his filial devotion, and they quit the stage again. The Chorus immediately sings of the birth of Aphrodite, an evil blossom born of sea-foam and froth of blood, a fleshly blossom, fair and perilous and deadly, whose flower is a curse to all men. Then with a clear note of fresh and stately blank verse, strongly contrasted with the short irregular measure of the angry Chorus, Atalanta herself enters, in calm faith resting on her own purity and the help of the dearly beloved Artemis. Meanwhile men gather for the hunt, and Meleager praises the chaste beauty of Atalanta, but the brothers of Althea, jealous of the maiden, chide him. Atalanta, overhearing what they say, defends her purity of purpose before them all, and silences their cavils, and they all start together for the hunt. The Chorus, becoming sadder and sadder as the certainty of ill-fortune comes nearer to it, upbraids the gods as having wilfully made the life of man a miserable thing, full of labour and sorrow; "a little fruit a little while is ours, and the worm finds it soon," but the high gods up in heaven thrust from their own lips the draught of mortal bitterness they make us drink, and watch human suffering for pastime. The Chorus ends with these rebellious words:

"Because thou art cruel and men are pietous,
　　And our hands labour, and thine hand scattereth;
　Lo, with hearts rent and knees made tremulous,
　　Lo, with ephemeral lips and casual breath,
　　　At least we witness of thee ere we die
　That these things are not otherwise, but thus:
　　That each man in his heart sigheth, and saith
　　　That all men even as I,
All we are against thee, against thee, O God most high."

In this utterance, so full of antitheistic rage, we lose all sense of antique feeling. There is none of this arrogant defiance of the high gods in the dramatic poems of antiquity. At most, as in the *Oresteia*, the Chorus bewails in bitter depression the

irresistible decrees of the divinities, or when, as in *Ajax*, one
man is insolent enough to choose to act in defiance to the gods,
swift and utter destruction closes the impious lips. It is noticeable, as I have attempted to show in an earlier section, that
Swinburne rarely succeeds in reproducing the sentiment of
the earliest civilisation; his own feelings are too modern, too
revolutionary and too sceptical. His attitude is that of Lucretius and the great poets of the Roman decline. In reading the
chorus just quoted, it is not Sophocles of whom one is reminded, but Statius and Seneca. The celebrated line of the
Thebaïd, "*Primus in orbe deos fecit timor,*" could well be introduced here as an annotation or a gloss. This passage, however, to return to the drama, is the central point of *Atalanta
in Calydon.* The herald arrives at its close, and tells in vigorous and picturesque language of the slaying of the boar, and
how Atalanta struck it first, but Meleager slew it. He then
describes how they sit together feasting after the combat
among lilies by a well-spring in a poplar valley. The Chorus
breaks out into singing and, like Falstaff, "babbles of green
fields," and of the maiden glory of Artemis. But while they
sing with glad voices, another messenger enters, with rent
raiment and dust upon his head, and tells them that sad news
is coming: the bodies of Althea's brethren are borne in upon a
bier. Meleager having crowned Atalanta with the garland of
conquest, the rude brothers have rushed upon her and snatched
it away; whereupon Meleager, being angry, has slain them
both. Althea, mad with shame and rage, determines to sacrifice her son to the manes of her brothers. With flying hair she
rushes hither and thither, pouring out her rage, her love and
her despair in language of inimitable fire and beauty, language that makes the verse shriek and quiver like an over-
strained violin, until she sees at the door the three fatal sisters,
with blood upon their raiment and their spindles, and then
she rushes out of sight into the house. The Chorus sings or
wails the fiery birth of Fate, before gods or men were made,
and deplores the beauty and strength of man that lasts but
a moment. They are interrupted by the return of Althea, who
leaves open the door, and far down the hall they see a fire and
a long brand that blackens and white dust. She pours out her
whole soul in weeping and bewailing the son whom she has
slain, and declares that she is kindled with the flames that fade

in him. She departs, vowing never to speak again. Another
messenger comes to declare the mysterious sickness of Meleager, who has suddenly wasted away and lies near death.
The whole party returns, and all speak in a choral measure of
extreme beauty. Atalanta deplores her coming to bring sorrow; Meleager moans for the shame of his dying; Aeneus
cries out upon Althea for her evil deed, and the Chorus sings
the praises of him who passes away. But Meleager, turning,
blesses Atalanta:

> "Though thou art as fire
> Fed with fuel in vain,
> My delight, my desire,
> Is more chaste than the rain,
> More pure than the dewfall, more holy than stars are that
> live without stain."

Aeneus asks him if he will not listen to the praise that is
sung to him in his home, but Meleager replies:

> "For the dead man no home is;
> Ah! better to be
> What the flower of the foam is
> In fields of the sea,
> That the sea-waves might be as my raiment, the gulf-
> stream a garment for me,"

and he repeats that the only good thing that the gods can give
him now is to change his life into the life of grass and the
leaves that spring out of the earth. Then, returning to blank
verse, he takes leave of his father, and then of his mother,
whom he upbraids, but not angrily, and to whom he most com-
mends his memory, and lastly, with tender passion, of Atalanta herself, and then dies. And so the poem ends.

It is no easy task in a mere dry résumé of this kind to give
any impression of the rare qualities which combined to ensure
for *Atalanta in Calydon* a warm reception at the time, and a
certain place in the literature of England. Mingled with much
exaltation of language and thought, with a marvellous variety
and melody of verse, and much vivid colouring, there was
found in the poem an originality of treatment highly fascinating and charming. To young readers, interpenetrated with

new and revolutionary thoughts, those very blemishes which
I have pointed out—the non-dramatic character of those out-
bursts against the gods—had an extraordinary charm. Others
again saw in these the germs of that destructive element which
in Swinburne's later works has so manifestly blossomed and
borne fruit, and under these diatribes against the gods discovered a lurking and dangerous atheism. Of modern writers,
the influence of Shelley was seen most strongly impressed upon
the style; in the blank verse there was a distinct flavour of
Tennyson, and in one or two of the lyrics a fainter, but dis-
tinguishable, tone borrowed from the still unpublished poems
of Rossetti. But over all and beyond all such, the strong individuality of a new poetic life was manifest to everyone competent to form an opinion on the subject, and after eleven
years this first successful book of Swinburne's still remains
the most successful.

iv

From his schooldays Swinburne has devoted himself with
peculiar enthusiasm to the early dramatic literature of our
country. It is well known that Shakespeare, so far from being
a lonely mountain arising out of a plain, was, if one may say
so, the loftiest and central peak of a whole group of great
dramatists. From 1590 to 1640 the poetry of our country took
an enormous start, and from having held a wholly insignificant
place in Europe came, at one bound, to place itself at the head
of the modern nations in that respect. That period, so glorious
in the person of the most able monarch England has possessed,
the great Elizabeth, distinguished itself as much in poetry as
in war, in commerce and in internal development. Out of the
rude elements of the ecclesiastical dramas, there suddenly
sprang Marlowe, adorable poet of the first order, and the
founder of English tragedy. Close on his steps came the august figures of Jonson, Fletcher and Webster, with Shakespeare supreme in their midst, while the genius dwindled again
in the persons of Massinger, Tourneur and Ford. Around
these great poets gathered an innumerable quantity of minor
dramatists, whose works still exist in hundreds, and of whom
there was hardly one that did not excel in some branch of
writing. These exquisite writers, neglected and scorned by
the seventeenth century, were restored to fame very mainly

by the efforts of the first really eminent English critic, Charles Lamb, whose essays, together with the labours of Hazlitt and Leigh Hunt, were the principal cause of the revival of the study of Elizabethan poetry among us. Of those who worship the dramatists of that age, few have a more ardent or a more learned devotion than Swinburne, who had written a whole comedy in close imitation of Fletcher before he left school, and whose essays on Ford and on Chapman rank among his finest and most important prose works. It was natural that he should himself essay to write in the form adopted by his beloved masters, Shakespeare, Marlowe and Webster; and his two earliest existing works, *The Queen Mother* and *Rosamund*, point distinctly enough to the strong bias in favour of the Elizabethan manner.

These plays, romantic tragedies full of lust and blood, resemble, too, in many respects the earlier productions of the French Romanticists. It cannot be pretended that they have much definite value; some ardent admirers of the poet have praised them, and their representations have induced him to reissue them. I cannot say, however, that they are readable. Clever, precocious as they are, they are scarcely promising, scarcely characteristic, and the turgid, heavy style in which they are composed gives little promise of the melody in store. Far other in character is another English drama hardly later than these in composition, though long postponed in publication. *Chastelard* was not brought out till 1865, when the success of *Atalanta in Calydon* had ensured its success, but it was really written as early as 1859, or when the author was scarcely twenty-two. From the death of John Ford in the middle of the seventeenth century until our own day, only two great tragedies had been written in England, the *Venice Preserved* of Otway and the *Cenci* of Shelley, these two poems witnessing through two barren centuries of the power of England in the tragic drama. For the rest, it seemed as though the brief clear fire of the Elizabethan age had burned too fiercely, and had left no fuel for serious dramatic writing in the nation. The once-famous piece of Thomas Otway survives still by dint of one or two admirable scenes; the subject and purpose of Shelley's drama remove it too far from ordinary sympathy to make it possible that it should be performed on the stage.

Swinburne's *Chastelard* has done much to encourage the hope that a fresh great dramatic school is conceivable for

English poetry. It is original, interesting and moving; if the plot be slight, the interest is intense and the action rapid. In all respects but one it is well calculated to make a great stage success, and that one is the want of nobility or exaltation of spirit in all the characters. The main figure, of course, is the fatal Mary Stuart, Queen of Scots. Of all the poets who have striven to place before us a dramatic likeness of this extraordinary woman—and the illustrious names of Schiller and Björnson are among them—not one has succeeded in fascinating the spectator so fully as Swinburne. In the magic mirror of his verse we see her splendid supple body, her long pale throat and pale bright breasts, her heavy scented hair, hot amorous eyes and lips, and all the wicked music of her words. There is no maudlin sentimentality in his rendering of her character. False, cruel, light of love, she is like that singing woman with fair lips, brought out of the sea in a fisher's net, that the old French *fabliau* tells of: she who was so fair that every man who saw her loved her, but died, having embraced her.

So Mary, with all her sweet tender ways, and the light of her beauty, leads men to death, inevitable death, one by one. And this is the central idea in *Chastelard;* he, the French minstrel, pupil of Ronsard, full of passion and amorous devotion, follows Mary to Scotland, and her love is like an evil fate, which he knows to be deadly, yet has no power to slip from. He is taken by Darnley and the rest in her chamber, clasping her knees, and is hurried away to prison. She wavers between love of him and shame of what men will say, reprieves him and withdraws her reprieve, but at last lets Mary Beaton, her maid, who loves Chastelard with an unrequited but pure and generous love, take his pardon to him in the prison. But he, knowing her so well, tears it up, assured of her change of mind; true enough, she comes to him in the prison to pray him to return it, and when he shows her the fragments, her love comes to her and she throws herself into his arms. But not for pardon, as he knows, and she is present at his beheading. There, at the execution, her heart veers again towards a new lover, Bothwell, whose iron face and thews recommend him to her appetite for force, physical or mental. Force is the one only power that quells this woman; nor can any man win her love who does not love her with a strong fury that is like a storm. This fickle, brilliant and perilous character Swinburne

has depicted with a master's precision. His portrait of Chastelard is less perfect; it is difficult to fail from feeling some contempt for this love-sick vassal of Aphrodite, in whose eyes
honour, fidelity, life itself are nothing in the balance with a
kiss. He is infatuated, and of the mingled agony and desire of
his heart has only such words as these to say before his death:

> "I do believe
> This fire shall never quite burn out to the ash,
> And leave no heat and flame upon my dust
> For witness that a man's heart was burnt up.
> For all Christ's work this Venus is not quelled,
> But reddens at the mouth with blood of men,
> Sucking between small teeth the sap of the veins,
> Dabbling with death her little tender lips,—
> A bitter beauty, poisonous-pearlèd mouth.
> I am not fit to live but for love's sake,
> So I were best die shortly."

Trained to amorous ways in a voluptuous school, the French
poet has no one thought in common with the hard-headed,
sober, God-fearing Scotch to whom he has come and who
understand him as little as he them. The third chief person in
the book, Mary Beaton, exhibits more true sweetness and lov-
ableness than any other, but she is thwarted by fortune, rendered impotent by Mary's falseness and Chastelard's wayward
obstinacy, and all she can do at last is to lie upon the ground
and wail out curses against her fate and the Queen's cruelty.

The drama is enlivened by a variety of very charming lyrics,
for the most part in French.

The first of these, in particular, is so delicate and so fresh
that Swinburne deserves a place among the French poets for
it. I can only quote one stanze:

> "Dans l'espace
> Du grand air
> Le vent passe
> Comme un fer;
> Stiffle et sonne,
> Tombe et tonne,
> Prend et donne
> A la mer."

Another, worthy of Joachim Du Bellay, begins:

"Après tant de jours, après tant de pleurs,
  Soyez secourable à mon âme en peine.
Voyez comme Avril fait l'amour aux fleurs ;
Dame d'amour, dame aux belles couleurs,
  Dieu vous a fait belle, Amour vous fait reine."

The last line in *Chastelard* was this:

"Room for my lord of Bothwell next the Queen,"

and it was reported long ago that Swinburne intended to return to this period of history in a new dramatic poem. In fact
the poet has always had in his thought the design of writing a
trilogy on the fate of his beloved Mary. Of this trilogy
Chastelard is to form the introduction, and in 1874, after
nine years' delay, *Bothwell*, the central piece, was published.
The finale, to be entitled *Mary in Prison*, still exists only in
a rough sketch. *Bothwell*, long promised and eagerly awaited,
was received with respect, but also with a certain disappointment. Those who were familiar with the modest size of *Chastelard* expected a drama of like dimensions ; what was their alarm
to receive in *Bothwell* a volume of nearly five hundred pages,
printed close, and containing nearly twice as much matter as
Ibsen's *Kejser og Galiloeer*. Such a huge chronicle was unsuited to the rapid habits of our time ; reduced to a third of
its size, it would have riveted the attention of all educated
persons, and must have enjoyed an immense success. As it was,
hardly anyone but the reviewers had sufficient energy to read
it, and it will always be a book to be dipped into or quoted
from rather than to study from end to end. Each of its five
acts is as long as an ordinary drama. The first, entitled
"Rizzio," repeats without freshness and with diminished fire
the amorous intrigues of *Chastelard*. The second, "Darnley,"
is of the highest order of dramatic writing, and would, published alone, have been recognised on all sides as a *chef
d'œuvre*. The miserable character of Darnley, the pretty
lady's man, with curled hair, fresh cheeks and amorous eyes,
tamer than a Frenchman, too effeminate to be a Scot, is represented to us gradually losing health, spirits, fortitude, and
even mind itself, under the perpetual scorn of harassing in-

juries of the Queen. He cannot get free from her; she follows
him to avenge upon him the ennuis and the indignities of her
life. Longing for Bothwell, she takes no pains to hide from
Darnley that she is weary of him. All the while we see the net
drawn closer and closer round him, and he, poor wretch, suspicious and half-conscious of what awaits him, grows frantic
and almost mad with dread and suspense. One by one she de-
taches from him every friend in whom he could confide; one by
one she places her own minions and Bothwell's troops round
him and near him. In a final scene, full of lurid light and the
passion of despair, we see him on the last fatal night, left alone
by the Queen and her attendants, alone with the sudden death
heaped up and ready in the vaults. His last soliloquy is a
masterpiece of agonised suspense, of mental torture and tension, fit prelude to a death so mysterious and appalling.

In the third act Mary has her way and Bothwell is her husband. But now, at the height of her success, with the scarred
body of Darnley at her feet, her ruin and her humiliation
begin. For she finds in the rough warrior she has chosen for
her husband a fierce and violent man, whose love for her is
mated with ambition, and who, having gained his ends, can be
brutal to the woman who placed him in power. For the first
time Mary, used to rule men at her will, finds herself overmas-
tered by a will stronger than her own, and, in spite of her
crimes, we are forced to lend her our pity as with masterly
insight the poet opens her heart before us, and we find her
cowed and stricken in the sight of the only man she has truly
loved and the only one that rejects her love. The last two acts
mainly occupied with State intrigues, the capture and imprisonment of Mary, her escape, Bothwell's last battle, and her
flight over the border to England, are long-spun and tedious,
a rough dark tissue, shot through indeed by gold threads of
splendid light and colour, but too shapeless and savage for
beauty or effect. Indeed, it is wonderful that a poet so learned,
so adroit, so critical as Swinburne should have permitted a
poem to come from his pen in so shapeless a state. The third
part of the trilogy, *Mary in Prison*, will, I understand, be as
short as *Chastelard*, and the poet himself believes that when
the work is complete the extreme length of the central drama
will be less apparent. It may be so, but I am distinctly of
opinion that the interest of the reader will always flag in the
later acts of *Bothwell*. The final drama will occupy itself with

Mary's flight into England, her rebuff and capture by Elizabeth, her imprisonment, and the intrigues of the Catholic
Party in her defence, closing with her execution, when, like
her great kinsman afterwards,

> "She nothing common did or mean
> Upon that memorable scene,
> But laid her comely head
> Down, as upon a bed."

It will need Swinburne's best skill to give interest and originality to this last phrase of the life of his heroine.

v

It is well known that Swinburne's political creed is of a
strongly pronounced character, and that it has found expression in poetry of great importance. There has been no political
lyrist since Shelley so fiery and so sincere as Swinburne, and
he more resembles in this respect the modern Italian writers,
Leopardi, Pellico, Aleardi and the rest, than a sober and law-
abiding Englishman His republicanism is of the most fervid
kind, uncompromising, unsparing and almost vindictive, and
he has not touched a very sympathetic chord in the nature of
his countrymen in producing these poems. In his *Poems and
Ballads* there were three lyrics of a decidedly political character which gave rise to almost as much unfavourable comment
among the Philistines as his erotic pieces. The first of these,
A Song in Time of Order, was a ballad of three patriots, who,
finding the lands divided among the tyrants, take to the sea,
which is not fettered, and are free there, waiting for liberty.

> "All the world has its burdens to bear
> From Cayenne to the Austrian whips;
> Forth, with the rain in our hair,
> And the salt sweet foam in our lips;

> "In the teeth of the hard glad weather,
> In the blown wet face of the sea;
> While three men hold together,
> The kingdoms are less by three."

Nothing could be more brilliant or more modern than this, but in the second, *A Song in Time of Revolution*, he fell into the worst error of his political poems: a tendency to substitute rhetoric for realism, and to lose the sharp forms of things in a torrent of Hebraic imagery. The third poem was a really noble ode, *To Victor Hugo*, in which Swinburne commended in quite unequivocal terms the French poet's hatred of kings and love of liberty and the Republic. After these utterances there was no doubt on which side the young poet was marshalled; in the ranks of the Extreme Left none were more eager than he to unfurl the red flag in its most startling redness. But English poets have been republicans in their youth and conservative in their old age; would not Swinburne also, like Dryden and Wordsworth, like Coleridge and Southey, desert the good cause for a laurel or a ribbon? On the contrary, with Milton, Shelley and Landor, he has grown firmer as years have passed.

His next book was purely political, and dedicated "with all devotion and reverence to Joseph Mazzini." *A Song of Italy*, published in 1867, is perhaps one of the least known, and certainly one of the most difficult, of the poet's works. There is nothing it resembles so much as one of the vast Sumatran or Javanese forests, that teem with luxurious and binding vegetation, a leafage that seems to groan under a plethora of vitality. It is full of a sense of warm, rapid growth; it abounds in hard knots, coils of parasitical or parenthetical entanglements, that the travelling foot is detained and annoyed by and that require for their unravelling a longer pause than so tropical an atmosphere suggests as convenient. Overhead are flying sprays of serpentine plants that coil from tree to tree, breathless thoughts that pass from page to page, tangled as they go into the general undergrowth of the text. The whole mass tingles and throbs with life; a lyrical pulse beats jubilantly in it all; it is irradiated with sunlight, but the blaze is broken by so much cross leafage, dimmed by so much shadow and vapour, that it is hardly possible to catch distinctly the forms of the ideas as they rush by. The metre, rhyming couplets of ten and six syllables respectively, runs on with a celerity that bewitches and betrays, while the poet has permitted himself for once to be as lax as it is possible to be without being slovenly. The result is that this "great song for our Italy free" is more like a piece of fine erratic music, a

symphony on flutes and timbrels, than an ordinary sober
poem. There is so much savage luxuriousness, such reckless
use of language, such a wild mingling of rhetoric, patriotism
and lyricism, that it hardly comes within the scope of criticism
at all.

The *Song of Italy* should be read aloud, in the open air and
in the sunlight, some May morning when everything rejoices,
and all the leafage is shooting and full of sap, and its verve
and melody could not fail to leave a brilliant, if vague, impression on the mind. In one point it contrasts unfavourably
with a still cruder book, Mrs. Browning's *Poems before Congress*, which, with all its irritating faults, had this one merit,
that, without being a minute student of modern Italian history, one could follow the drift of each poem. This is just what
is impossible in the *Song of Italy*. We are suddenly confronted
with "Agisilao whose name withers kings," and "the slayer
of splendid brown, the foiled tyrannicide," and we know not
who these are. Swinburne, of course, is familiar with the deeds
of Pisacane, Agisilao and the rest, but their names are quite
unknown to ninety-nine hundredths of the English reading
public, and must always remain so. Italians, reading the lyrics
of Aleardi, thrill at the sight of names like these; but an
English reader, with all the sympathy in the world for the
cause they fell for, is pained and puzzled by them as by ranks
of unfamiliar faces. There are a few names we all remember,
as Orsini's and Tazzoli's, because Garibaldi said of him
"*i buoni prete non sono tutte morte*," but they are few and far
between. In short, odious as annotations are, the *Song of Italy*
is one of the few poems that seem absolutely to demand one.
It is not easy to quote from; as I have hinted, the rapidity of
utterance carries the poet on from clause to clause till it is impossible to find an impressive passage within the limits I am
forced to set myself. One eloquent word of exhortation to
Mazzini not to fail because the end was not yet come I cannot
deny myself the pleasure of quoting:

> "But thou though all were not well done, O chief,
>   Must thou take shame or grief?
> Because one man is not as thou, or ten,
>   Must thou take shame for men?
> Because the supreme sunrise is not yet,
>   Is the young dew not wet?

"A little hour of doubt and of control
    Sustain thy sacred soul;
Withhold thy heart, our Father, but one hour;
    Is it not here, the flower?
Is it not blown and fragrant from the root
    And shall not be the fruit?"

In the same year, 1867, Swinburne turned his eyes towards Greece, and in a beautiful *Ode on the Insurrection in Canadia* expressed his sympathy with the victims of Turkish tyranny. All this time he was writing and storing up his *Songs before Sunrise,* which was preceded only a few months by the *Ode on the Proclamation of the French Republic,* in the September of 1870. It is a trumpet-blast of victory, a Pindaric strain of weighty and eloquent verse, full of dignity and force. It is the nature of poems of this kind to be almost oppressive when they are most successful. The *Ode* is too long to be an outburst of spontaneous ecstasy; it has not, as the war-songs of Tyrtaeus and Petöfi must have had, the terse brevity and electric force that stirs a nation to arms; on the other hand, it is without reflection or variety, and the sonorous strophes weary the attention at last. The joy of the poet must by this time, too, be tempered with regret and chagrin, as he sees the Republic still in rule, and yet France not free.

At last, at Christmas time, 1870, in the midst of the turmoil of the great Franco-Germanic war, the long-expected *Songs before Sunrise* came out. The occasion was unfortunate, and the impression made by the book was not immediate. It has, however, been lasting, and must on the whole be counted among Swinburne's signal successes. In a dedicatory poem he brought this sword of his songs to Mazzini, and called upon him to witness that this was the first English song to fight for the great universal Republic of the future. In an exquisite "Prelude" Swinburne gives a kind of biography of himself, and confesses that once the tendrils of the wild Loves and erotic verses were his delight, but that now all his thoughts and desires and aspirations are fixed on the dark edge of the sea of life, which must one day or other grow brilliant with the rising sun of Freedom. Until the good time comes, he will sing of Liberty and her martyrs; and he describes the mental attitude needful for such a vigil in words as sublime as they are philosophic, and as valuable as they are courageous. I can quote but one verse of this adorable apology for the liberty of thought and the dignity of man:

"His sould is even with the sun
    Whose spirit and whose eye are one,
        Who seeks no stars by day, nor light
        And heavy heat of day by night.
    Him can no God cast down, whom none
        Can lift in hope beyond the height
    Of fate and nature and things done
        By the calm rule of might and right
    That bids men be and bear and do,
    And die beneath blind skies and blue."

In the spirit of graver questions of human life, political and social, are considered in the rest of the volume. Everywhere the poet seeks for signs of the dawn, flying streaks of sunrise-colour before the supreme dawn. In the *Eve of Revolution* he hears the four trumpets of the four winds of the world blow to battle, and he goes forth to see which of the living nations will take the lead in the approaching contest against the powers of darkness and oppression. Eastward Greece lies slumbering, northward Russia. Westward the land of Milton and of Shelley, the seagirt island of the free, England, lies blind and inert, as one dead. Southward, past broken, bleeding France, it is Italy that wakens, and laughs in the flame of the sunrise. So in *The Litany of Nations* it is Italy that is most hopeful when the peoples speak in successive chorus. *A Watch in the Night* is finer still; less rhetorical, more real, personal and passionate, it yearns with perfume and colour like a rose. I know no modern poem in which a political theme is treated with so much tenderness and sweetness as this.

Another section of *Songs before Sunrise* deals with historical matters. Certain moments of modern history are made the subject of lyrical and romantic poetry. Of these the *Halt Before Rome*, in September 1867, takes a prominent place, ending as it does with the prayer for a glorious martyrdom for Italy, the beloved:

"Only her bosom to die on;
  Only her heart for a home,
And a name with her children to be
From Calabrian to Adrian sea
Famous in cities made free
That ring to the roar of the lion
  Proclaiming Republican Rome."

Another celebrates in brilliant anapaests the first anniversary of Mentana; another addresses, in language that imitates the homage paid to the Madonna, La Signora Cairoli, a heroine of Italian liberty. *Siena*, picturesque reverie over the delicious city of the doves, hardly deserves a place among these harsher military strains. Swinburne, it will be observed, has little sympathy with that very French Republic to which he had so lately addressed an ode of congratulation. The poison of the empire was not yet purged out of her, and her dealings with Rome not forgiven, and we find a protest against Mrs. Browning's famous poem on the French in Lombardy, praising them. As Swinburne says, the great poetess "had not seen Aspromonte." It must be allowed that the exact aims of the Republic here commended are not clearly stated; there is lack of form in the rhapsodies, of common sense in the rhetoric, and there is far too much of that impersonal, rapturous and somewhat invertebrate writing which Shelley is guilty of having recommended by the brilliance of his often overburdened style. However, nothing can be more earnest or more dignified than the manner in which the young English poet seeks to embrace all Europe in the arms of his love, and to awaken all the nations, if it may be, to a sense of the glorious future that may await them if they will be true to one another and to themselves. The method of his exhortation is certainly too scholastic, too literary. Not so Callicles, Runeberg, Campbell —the greatest patriot singers of all literature—not so did they waste words in sonorous periods. Swinburne is not of these; with all his purity of aspiration, his ardour, his seriousness of purpose, he has not the magic gift of leading or swaying men to action.

More important, to my thinking, than the political are the ethical poems contained in *Songs before Sunrise*. Most important of all is *Hertha*, in which he proclaims, with no doubtful voice, a pantheism which is at least as comprehensive and reasonable a creed as any other now presented to the human faculty of faith. In this poem it is the Earth who speaks, and she addresses man, her last and noblest offspring. She, existing before God, thrust forth from herself the forces that save and sway the soul, and nought is beside or above her, as nothing was before her. She alone is the god that blesses and the creature blessed; she is the grain and the furrow, the deed and the doer, the dust which is God. She cries out to man that the time of his childhood is past; he has served long enough in the bonds of kings, in the shadow of God; it is time now for Man to stand erect, independent, severe. For the one only thing which is light is truth, and it is unworthy of free eyes to shrink from this extreme radiance. Closely corresponding to this great lyric is the less perfect but equally audacious *Hymn of Man,* where the thought that God is but a shadow cast by the mind of man is urged to its final limit with unsparing logic, and the daring atheism of the new creed is summed up in the final lines:

"Thou art smitten, thou God, thou art smitten,
    Thy death is upon thee, O Lord;
And the love-song of earth as thou diest
    Resounds through the wind of her wing—
Glory to Man in the highest,
    For Man is the master of things!"

In a strange poem entitled *Before a Crucifix* the regnant creed of modern times is ridiculed and railed at in no measured terms. In *Genesis,* already known to Danish readers by the excellent version of Herr Adolf Hansen, the same idea is worked out, in terms at once more guarded and more philosophic. In *Tenebrae* Swinburne sings the emancipation of man in language more mystical and misty than usual, acknowledging that Christian and classic virtue have been robes for the infancy of man, but that now we are bound to cast from us the thrall of

"The names that exalt and transmute us,
The blood-bright splendour of Brutus,
The snow-bright splendour of Christ."

Ethical poems of more eloquence and metrical majesty than clear significance, but always worthy of careful study, are *Tiresias, On the Downs,* and *Christmas Antiphonies.*

There remains to mention how much that is peculiarly and exquisitely Swinburnesque this volume contains. The tenderest poems in the volume, *The Pilgrims* (also translated ably by Herr Hansen) and the faultless *Oblation,* are in their author's gravest, sweetest manner. For metrical skill and originality the book is unrivalled. Never since English was a language has it been possible to any poet to pour forth such a torrent of varied and majestic melody as this volume contains. The novelty, the force, the harmony of the versification is simply astounding. Such a stanza as this:

> "Green thing to green in the summer makes answer, and
>   rose-tree to rose;
> Lily by lily the year becomes perfect; and none of us
>   knows
> What thing is fairest of all things on earth as it brightens
>   and blows,"

is like one of the profoundest passages of the symphonies of Beethoven.

In the year 1873 a series of sonnets from Swinburne's hand appeared in the *Examiner* newspaper, and revealed quite a new phase of his individuality. Here all was personal and realistic enough. If these sonnets are not great, I do not know what it is that constitutes poetic greatness. If it be original and powerful thought, illuminated by a splendid imagination, and married to stately and august verse, then it is laid before us in these passages of masterly invective. Whether the object of the poet's indignation be a worm-eaten and a worm-worthy Bomba, a feeble and truckling monument of infallible impotence, or a self-styled Saviour of Society, alike, with a pen dipped in some Dantesque infusion of vitriolic scorn, and dragging the hair back from the miserable forehead, he inscribes there words that will not be erased while the English language survives. These are not poems lightly to be recommended for promiscuous circulation in boarding-schools or among the clergy; these are not flute-notes nicely modulated to charm the ears of idlers about town, or such well-conducted persons as sew pillows to all arm-holes. Those whose tongues are swift to condone wickedness in high places should pass them with averted eyes, for the words are strong as the wrong was, and the poet does not walk with mincing feet. But England needed someone to clear her from the dishonour done her at the death of that weak and ignoble tyrant, before whose feet, red with the blood of good men, so many of her sons went down in foolish worship; she needed some one voice to drown the babbling tongues that greeted him, gone down to shameful oblivion, as a great emperor dead. Here is the verdict of a nobler and a more final judge than these.

There is hardly anything that I know in literature, nothing in the Italian of Dante, more terrible than the four sonnets which Swinburne entitles *Intercession*. Written in September 1869, when a sudden accession of his fatal complaint gave some reason for anticipating the quick decease of Napoleon III, they intercede piteously with Death to wait a little longer before giving the wretched man the final grace of being blotted out of bodily pain and all human pity at once. It is hardly possible to quote the terrific lines in which the poet, inspired to curse, like an Ezekiel, prays that the bitter cup of life may be held to the blanched and quivering lips till the last intolerable dregs be drunk, and the vengeance of outraged manhood be complete. Addressed to any less completely evil, less wholly base, than this smooth-faced and sanguine-handed patron of civic order, such words and wishes would sound inhuman; in this one case they seem no more than just. And, written in 1869, they were already at the point of being fulfilled, the hour of retribution was just at hand, and the mortal misery was beginning that was to end at last at Chislehurst, in a burial honoured, not with the torches of a lamenting nation, but with the rancid and glimmering homage of a clique of alien shopkeepers. To those who think these denunciations too severe, and who shudder and wince before such invective, the poet himself has a word to say:

"If wrath embitter the sweet mouth of song,
    And make the sunlight fire before those eyes
    That would drink draughts of peace from the unstained skies,
The wrong-doing is not ours, but ours the wrong,

"Who hear too loud on earth and see too long,
    The grief that dies not with the groan that dies,
    Till the strong bitterness of pity cries
Within us that our anger should be strong."

Nothing is more characteristic of a generous nature than to lose resentment for an injury as soon as time has healed the wound, and it is just the generous natures that are wounded by the allocutions of a Pius or the tyrannies of a Louis Bonaparte. It is needful, then, now that the one is powerless and the other dead, to remember clearly and bring sternly back to the memory the crimes and cruelties of their time of rule; this being remembered, and liberty being strong to smite them down, the poet himself is the first to counsel the coming Republic to act mercifully to the fallen, and when their crowns and creeds are fully wasted beyond fear of revival, to spare to set upon the men themselves the heel that crushed their deeds. Greater punishment than to lie enshrined in Swinburne's immortal verse we need not wish to any fall tyrant; and to anyone who would emulate the deeds of Ferdinand II or Napoleon III we would say, moulding the words of Heine to suit our purpose:

"Kennst du die Hölle des Swinburne nicht,
Die schrecklichen Sonetten?
Wen da der Dichter hineingesperrt,
Den kann kein Gott mehr retten,—

"Kein Gott, kein Heiland, erlöst ihn je
Aus diesen singenden Flammen!
Nimm dich in Acht, dass wir dich nicht
Zu solcher Hölle verdammen!"

vi

It is impossible to deal at length with Swinburne as a prosaist. Few English poets have taken so prominent a place in the polemics of literature, and he has contributed largely to the journals and magazines of the day. His literary life in public has really extended over only eleven years, and yet in this short space of time, and in the intervals of poetic writing, he has contrived to impress a whole code of aesthetic laws upon the mind of his generation. He has done this more by the sheer strength and rapidity of his intellect than by the exercise of the imagination in his own technical sphere of art, and by the peculiar condition of the ground into which the

seeds of his opinion have fallen, for great as has been the reputation of his poetry there can be no doubt that his critical
papers have produced a wider and deeper change in the aspect
of intellectual thought. He arrived on the field of letters at a
moment when the spirit of the Renaissance had reached its
climax in the minds of a wide and earnest circle of workers in
branches of art quite distinct from his, and he translated that
spirit into poetic speech with a lyrical and passionate fervour
of expression which was potent in winning adherents to the
new school of art. But this was not all, not the main work which
he accomplished. The poems of Mr. Morris, and later those of
Mr. D. G. Rossetti, were destined to succeed his and to give a
far more uniform and exact reproduction in verse of the desires and aims that had actuated the reformers in the plastic
arts. But if Swinburne had not this, he had other and not less
powerful gifts. To those poets the future exists only as a
vaguely distrusted and mist-hidden land from which their
hearts and faces are resolutely averted, the present as a mere
sterile plain without feature or interest. Far different is Swinburne's attitude of mind; fiercely defiant of the delays and
obstacles of the present, he stands as if on tiptoe, yearning for
wings or winged feet to hurry him forward into that future
which to him is full of glorious visions and transcendent hopes.
Hence he takes something of the position of a prophet, and instead of the coldness of lips that say "I know nothing; meditate on the past," he presents to his followers the flaming ardour
of a face set full against the sunrise. It matters little whether
these hopes and aspirations are futile or not; sincerity of belief, generosity of purpose, are the great motive powers that
stir young hearts in their enthusiastic moods, and it is owing,
surely, to these qualities in his character, that Swinburne so
early in his career collected the attention of so many younger
men, for whom his essays, even more than his poems, stood in
the light of aesthetic revelations, eagerly awaited and ardently
discussed.

In an age that speaks scornfully of poetry as a thing for
boys and girls, a mere backwater of sluggish sentiment with
lyric lilies here and there, an idleness not to be tolerated at all
except when shackled and burdened with the results of analytic science, a writer like Swinburne, who uses the whole
majesty of his style, the whole rapidity of his intellect, in defending the nobility of the poetic art against all assailants,

confers a favour on the lovers of poetry hardly less than the
poet himself in the production of his best verses. We see in
daily conversation the good result of this championship; the
contempt of verse no longer stalks as unabashed in all high
places as it did fifteen years ago; no longer are folks so blatant in proclaiming that the art will die with Mr. Tennyson,
and will be buried with him for ever; some respect is shown,
we will not say for the living, but at least for the dead, as persons a little above the level of the nursery-governess and the
boarding-school miss, and for this restitution of honour to
the dishonoured we may in great part thank the essays Swinburne has put forth from time to time.

One of the earliest and most famous was that on Byron,
prefixed to a volume of selections from that poet brought out
in 1866. This has lately been presented to Danish readers *in
extenso* in the pages of *Naer og Fjern*. This study, with all
its vigour and splendour of style, unchastened and unrestrained, lacking the final elegancies of a finished manner, but
full of originality and fire, made a much wider impression
than the author in all probability suspected. It is not generally
known, however, even here in England, that this was not the
first of Swinburne's prose essays; a long review of Charles
Baudelaire's *Les Fleurs du Mal*, in the *Spectator* newspaper,
which preceded this essay on Byron by many months, was written by him, and indeed struck the first note of his peculiar
manner in criticism. It is curious that this bitter and sterile
book, full of the beauty of desolation, mirages of a life destroyed, should have been chosen as the theme on which to
flesh that maiden criticism which should soon find its highest
delight in glorifying all that is most exalted, masculine and
vital in the poetry of past and present times. It must have
been his perversity and rebellion that attracted to the sickly
genius of Baudelaire the fraternal affection of the young
Englishman, and his resistance to all tame and sentimental
conventionalities what condoned in Swinburne's eyes the utter
want of real healthiness of purpose or originality of intellect.
As time went by, the peculiar sympathetic insight did not increase—indeed nothing he has ever written has contained
more striking or more incisive thoughts than the early essay
on Byron—but a manlier and calmer tone has come to characterise the modes of expression, and the little tricks of rhetoric
and alliteration, which were so hateful to the cut-and-dried

critics, so delightful to the poet's younger admirers, have been restrained and pruned by a maturer judgment.

Yet it must be confessed that a certain freshness, a certain delightful buoyancy and joyousness of imagination seem to have left the writer. The essays dated since 1870 have lacked something of the incessant and flashing movement, the brilliant irregularity, the swift interchange of defiance and adoration which gave the earliest studies a character so completely their own. A huge volume on Blake, the mystical poet and painter of the eighteenth century, appeared from Swinburne's pen in 1868 and was full to overflowing of these delightful characteristics. Best of all are the prose writings dated 1867, the review of Morris's epic poem, *The Life and Death of Jason*, that of Matthew Arnold's *New Poems* and the sketch of the genius of Coleridge which was prefixed to a selection from that poet's works. The essay on Matthew Arnold in particular, rambling as it is, full of matter not strictly to the point, side-threads taken up so long as to perplex the central web of criticism, is nevertheless a masterpiece of delicate insight and high imaginative perception. However desultory this essay may be, there is no word in it hastily or thoughtlessly written, least of all anything bombastic or mouthy. In the analysis of Morris's poetry hardly less reticence and self-command are shown; in all this generous and unfettered appreciation there is nothing forced or feeble.

It must be confessed that it is not always so. The paper on *L'Homme qui rit* is too much the result of a theory that all works produced by a poet of the first rank must be themselves of foremost worth: that on the poems of Dante Gabriel Rossetti contains passages of what can only be called reckless and frantic extravagance. Swinburne makes no secret of his intimate personal friendship with Mr. Rossetti, and everyone knows how difficult it is in dealing with the work of a friend to avoid the opposite pitfalls of exaggeration and detraction, to speak out fully from the heart, and yet to miss the semblance of adulation. In other essays Swinburne has avoided this double danger with much tact; in this particular one he seems to me to have erred on the side of excessive laudation. Mr. Rossetti is a great and brilliant poet, worthy of all honour and dignity, but to use in speaking of him language which would sound extravagant if used to characterise a superhuman combination of Shakespeare, Dante and Goethe in one, is to

take off the edge of criticism altogether. I must only briefl
indicate the poet's remaining prose works. In 1872 he wrot
a weighty and earnest analysis of Victor Hugo's great book o
tears and blood, *L'Année Terrible;* another on the *Text o
Shelley,* full of brilliant suggestions, but far more critical an
more careful than the ardour of the writer would lead one t
expect; he also contributed to *The Fortnightly Review* i
1871 a famous paper on the old English dramatist John Forc
a masterpiece of searching criticism and noble language. Thes
several essays he has now collected into a thick volume, er
titled *Essays and Studies,* which has been received with almos
unanimous praise, and which has greatly widened the circl
of Swinburne's audience, so admirable and winning are it
qualities of just discrimination and catholic sympathy. Th
year, too, he has published a book on the early English gnomi
poet and dramatist, George Chapman (*b.* 1559, *d.* 1634), ε
an introductory volume to a large collected edition of th
neglected writer's works.

Swinburne's activity is untiring. At the present moment a
essay on Beaumont and Fletcher is in the press; a new dram
on the model of *Atalanta in Calydon* will be ready in a fe
weeks; a romantic epic, *Tristram and Yseult,* is being grac
ually finished, and the poet darkly hints of more works still o
the tapis. In writing of an author so living and so active i
development as this, one can do little more than chronicle wha
he has done. If he continues to thrive and to progress, one dai
set no limit to the extent of his success. It is possible that l
may develop into one of the greatest names of all moder
literature. In the meantime he has no rival to fear in Englan
among men of his own generation.
1875.

ROBERT LOUIS STEVENSON

PERSONAL MEMORIES

IN SETTING down my recollections of Louis Stevenson, I desii
to confine the record to what I have myself known and seei
His writings will be mentioned only in so far as I heard the

planned and discussed. Of his career and character I shall not attempt to give a complete outline; all I purpose to do is to present those sides of them which came under my personal notice. The larger portrait it will be his privilege to prepare who was the closest and the most responsible of all Stevenson's friends; and it is only while we wait for Mr. Sidney Colvin's biography that these imperfect sketches can retain their value. The most that can be hoped for them is that they may secure a niche in his gallery. And now, pen in hand, I pause to think how I can render in words a faint impression of the most inspiriting, the most fascinating human being that I have known.

i

It is nearly a quarter of a century since I first saw Stevenson. In the autumn of 1870, in company with a former schoolfellow, I was in the Hebrides. We had been wandering in the Long Island, as they name the outer archipelago, and our steamer, returning, called at Skye. At the pier of Portree, I think, a company came on board—"people of importance in their day," Edinburgh acquaintances, I suppose, who had accidentally met in Skye on various errands. At all events, they invaded our modest vessel with a loud sound of talk. Professor Blackie was among them, a famous figure that calls for no description; and a voluble, shaggy man, clad in homespun, with spectacles forward upon nose, who, it was whispered to us, was Mr. Sam Bough, the Scottish Academician, a watercolour painter of some repute, who was to die in 1878. There were also several engineers of prominence. At the tail of this chatty, jesting little crowd of invaders came a youth of about my own age, whose appearance, for some mysterious reason, instantly attracted me. He was tall, preternaturally lean, with longish hair, and as restless and questing as a spaniel. The party from Portree fairly took possession of us; at meals they crowded around the captain, and we common tourists sat silent, below the salt. The stories of Blackie and Sam Bough were resonant. Meanwhile, I knew not why, I watched the plain, pale lad who took the lowest place in this privileged company.

The summer of 1870 remains in the memory of western Scotland as one of incomparable splendour. Our voyage, especially as evening drew on, was like an emperor's progress. We stayed on deck till the latest moment possible, and I occasionally watched the lean youth, busy and serviceable, with some of the little tricks with which we were later on to grow familiar —the advance with hand on hip, the sidewise bending of the head to listen. Meanwhile darkness overtook us, a wonderful halo of moonlight swam up over Glenelg, the indigo of the peaks of the Cuchullins faded into the general blue night. I went below, but was presently aware of some change of course, and then of an unexpected stoppage. I tore on deck, and found that we had left our track among the islands, and had steamed up a narrow and unvisited fiord of the mainland—I think Loch Nevis. The sight was curious and bewildering. We lay in a gorge of blackness, with only a strip of the blue moonlit sky overhead; in the dark a few lanterns jumped about the shore, carried by agitated but unseen and soundless persons. As I leaned over the bulwarks, Stevenson was at my side, and he explained to me that we had come up this loch to take away to Glasgow a large party of emigrants driven from their homes in the interests of a deer-forest. As he spoke, a black mass became visible entering the vessel. Then, as we slipped off shore, the fact of their hopeless exile came home to these poor fugitives, and suddenly, through the absolute silence, there rose from them a wild kerning and wailing, reverberated by the cliffs of the loch, and at that strange place and hour infinitely poignant. When I came on deck next morning, my unnamed friend was gone. He had put off with the engineers to visit some remote lighthouse of the Hebrides.

This early glimpse of Stevenson is a delightful memory to me. When we met next, not only did I instantly recall him, but, what was stranger, he remembered me. This voyage in the *Clansman* was often mentioned between us, and it has received for me a sort of consecration from the fact that in the very last letter that Louis wrote, finished on the day of his death, he made a reference to it.

ii

In the very touching "Recollections" which our friend Mr. Andrew Lang has published, he says: "I shall not deny that my first impression [of Stevenson] was not wholly favourable." I remember, too, that John Addington Symonds was not pleased at first. It only shows how different are our moods. I must confess that in my case the invading army simply walked up and took the fort by storm. It was in 1877, or late in 1876, that I was presented to Stevenson, at the old Savile Club, by Mr. Sidney Colvin, who thereupon left us to our devices. We went downstairs and lunched together, and then we adjourned to the smoking-room. As twilight came on I tore myself away, but Stevenson walked with me across Hyde Park, and nearly to my house. He had an engagement, and so had I, but I walked a mile or two back with him. The fountains of talk had been unsealed, and they drowned the conventions. I came home dazzled with my new friend, saying, as Constance does of Arthur, "Was ever such a gracious creature born?" That impression of ineffable mental charm was formed at the first moment of acquaintance, and it never lessened or became modified. Stevenson's rapidity in the sympathetic interchange of ideas was, doubtless, the source of it. He has been described as an "egotist," but I challenge the description. If ever there was an altruist, it was Louis Stevenson; he seemed to feign an interest in himself merely to stimulate you to be liberal in your confidences.[1]

Those who have written about him from later impressions than those of which I speak seem to me to give insufficient prominence to the gaiety of Stevenson. It was his cardinal quality in those early days. A childlike mirth leaped and danced in him; he seemed to skip upon the hills of life. He was simply bubbling with quips and jests; his inherent earnestness or passion about abstract things was incessantly relieved by jocosity; and when he had built one of his intellectual castles in the sand, a wave of humour was certain to sweep in and destroy it. I cannot, for the life of me, recall any of his jokes; and written down in cold blood, they might not be funny if I did. They were not wit so much as humanity, the many-sided outlook upon life. I am anxious that his laughter-loving mood should not be forgotten, because later on it was partly, but I think never wholly, quenched by ill health, responsibility, and the advance of years. He was often, in the old days, excessively and delight-

[1] This continued to be his characteristic to the last. Thus he described an interview he had in Sydney with some man formerly connected with the "black-birding" trade, by saying: "He was very shy at first, and it was not till I told him of a good many of my escapades that I could get him to thaw, and then he poured it all out. I have always found that the best way of getting people to be confidential."

fully silly—silly with the silliness of an inspired schoolboy; and
I am afraid that our laughter sometimes sounded ill in the
ears of age.

A pathos was given to his gaiety by the fragility of his
health. He was never well, all the years I knew him; and we
looked upon his life as hanging by the frailest tenure. As he
never complained or maundered, this, no doubt—though we
were not aware of it—added to the charm of his presence. He
was so bright and keen and witty, and any week he might die.
No one, certainly, conceived it possible that he could reach his
forty-fifth year. In 1879 his health visibly began to run lower,
and he used to bury himself in lonely Scotch and French places,
"tinkering himself with solitude," as he used to say.

My experience of Stevenson during these first years was confined to London, upon which he would make sudden piratical
descents, staying a few days or weeks, and melting into air
again. He was much at my house; and it must be told that my
wife and I, as young married people, had possessed ourselves
of a house too large for our slender means immediately to
furnish. The one person who thoroughly approved of our
great, bare, absurd drawing-room was Louis, who very
earnestly dealt with us on the immorality of chairs and tables,
and desired us to sit always, as he delighted to sit, upon has-
socks on the floor. Nevertheless, as arm-chairs and settees
straggled into existence, he handsomely consented to use them,
although never in the usual way, but with his legs thrown
sidewise over the arms of them, or the head of a sofa treated as
a perch. In particular, a certain shelf, with cupboards below,
attached to a bookcase, is worn with the person of Stevenson,
who would spend half an evening while passionately discussing
some great question of morality or literature, leaping sidewise
in a seated posture to the length of this shelf, and then back
again. He was eminently peripatetic, too, and never better
company than walking in the street, this exercise seeming to
inflame his fancy. But his most habitual dwelling-place in the
London of those days was the Savile Club, then lodged in an
inconvenient but very friendly house in Savile Row. Louis
pervaded the club; he was its most affable and chatty member;
and he lifted it, by the ingenuity of his incessant dialectic, to
the level of a sort of humorous Academe or Mouseion.

At this time he must not be thought of as a successful author.
A very few of us were convinced of his genius; but with the

exception of Mr. Leslie Stephen, nobody of editorial status was sure of it. I remember the publication of *An Inland Voyage* in 1878, and the inability of the critics and the public to see anything unusual in it.

Stevenson was not without a good deal of innocent oddity in his dress. When I try to conjure up his figure, I can see only a slight, lean lad, in a suit of blue sea-cloth, a black shirt, and a wisp of yellow carpet that did duty for a necktie. This was long his attire, persevered in to the anguish of his more conventional acquaintances. I have a ludicrous memory of going, in 1878, to buy him a new hat, in company with Mr. Lang, the thing then upon his head having lost the semblance of a human article of dress. Aided by a very civil shopman, we suggested several hats and caps, and Louis at first seemed interested; but having presently hit upon one which appeared to us pleasing and decorous, we turned for a moment to inquire the price. We turned back, and found that Louis had fled, the idea of parting with the shapeless object having proved too painful to be entertained. By the way, Mr. Lang will pardon me if I tell, in exacter detail, a story of his. It was immediately after the adventure with the hat that, not having quite enough money to take him from London to Edinburgh, third class, he proposed to the railway clerk to throw in a copy of Mr. Swinburne's *Queen Mother and Rosamond.* The offer was refused with scorn, although the book was of the first edition, and even then worth more than the cost of a whole ticket.

Stevenson's pity was a very marked quality, and it extended to beggars, which is, I think, to go too far. His optimism, however, suffered a rude shock in South Audley Street one summer afternoon. We met a stalwart beggar, whom I refused to aid. Louis, however, wavered, and finally handed him sixpence. The man pocketed the coin, forbore to thank his benefactor, but, fixing his eye on me, said, in a loud voice, "And what is the other little gentleman going to give me?" "In future," said Louis, as we strode coldly on, "*I* shall be 'the other little gentleman.'"

In those early days he suffered many indignities on account of his extreme youthfulness of appearance and absence of self-assertion. He was at Inverness—being five or six and twenty at the time—and had taken a room in a hotel. Coming back about dinner-time, he asked the hour of table d'hôte,

whereupon the landlady said, in a motherly way: "Oh, I
knew you wouldn't like to sit in there among the grown-up
people, so I've had a place put for you in the bar." There wa
a frolic at the Royal Hotel, Bathgate, in the summer of 1879
Louis was lunching alone, and the maid, considering him a
negligible quantity, came and leaned out of the window. This
outrage on the proprieties was so stinging that Louis at length
made free to ask her, with irony, what she was doing there.
"I'm looking for my lad," she replied. "Is that he?" asked
Stevenson, with keener sarcasm. "Weel, I've been lookin' for
him a' my life, and I've never seen him yet," was the response.
Louis was disarmed at once, and wrote her on the spot some
beautiful verses in the vernacular. "They're no bad for a
beginner," she was kind enough to say when she had read
them.

The year 1879 was a dark one in the life of Louis. He had
formed a conviction that it was his duty to go out to the
extreme west of the United States, while his family and the
inner circle of his friends were equally certain that it was
neither needful nor expedient that he should make this journey. As it turned out, they were wrong, and he was right;
but in the circumstances their opinion seemed the only correct
one. His health was particularly bad, and he was ordered, not
West, but South. The expedition, which he has partly
described in *The Amateur Emigrant* and *Across the Plains*, was
taken, therefore, in violent opposition to all those whom he
left in England and Scotland; and this accounts for the mode
in which it was taken. He did not choose to ask for money to
be spent in going to California, and it was hoped that the withdrawal of supplies would make the voyage impossible. But
Louis, bringing to the front a streak of iron obstinacy which
lay hidden somewhere in his gentle nature, scraped together
enough to secure him a steerage passage across the Atlantic.

The day before he started he spent with my wife and me—
a day of stormy agitation, an April day of rain-clouds and
sunshine; for it was not in Louis to remain long in any mood. I
seem to see him now, pacing the room, a cigarette spinning in
his wasted fingers. To the last we were trying to dissuade him
from what seemed to us the maddest of enterprises. He was so
ill that I did not like to leave him, and at night—it was mid-
summer weather—we walked down into town together. We
were by this time, I suppose, in a pretty hysterical state of

nind, and as we went through Berkeley Square, in mournful
liscussion of the future, Louis suddenly proposed that we
should visit the so-called "Haunted House," which then occupied the newspapers. The square was quiet in the decency of
a Sunday evening. We found the house, and one of us boldly
knocked at the door. There was no answer and no sound, and
we jeered upon the door-step; but suddenly we were both
aware of a pale face—a phantasm in the dusk—gazing down
upon us from a surprising height. It was the caretaker, I
suppose, mounted upon a flight of steps: but terror gripped
us at the heart, and we fled with footsteps as precipitate as
those of schoolboys caught in an orchard. I think that ghostly
face in Berkeley Square must have been Louis's latest European impression for many months.

iii

All the world now knows, through the two books which I have
named, what immediately happened. Presently letters began
to arrive, and in one from Monterey, written early in October
1879, he told me of what was probably the nearest approach
of death that ever came until the end, fifteen years later. I
do not think it is generally known, even in the inner circle of
his friends, that in September of that year he was violently ill,
alone, at an Angora-goat ranch in the Santa Lucia Mountains.
"I scarcely slept or ate or thought for four days," he said.
"Two nights I lay out under a tree, in a sort of stupor, doing
nothing but fetch water for myself and horse, light a fire and
make coffee, and all night awake hearing the goat-bells ringing
and the tree-toads singing, when each new noise was enough to
set me mad." Then an old frontiersman, a mighty hunter of
bears, came round, and tenderly nursed him through his attack.
"By all rule this should have been my death; but after a while
my spirit got up again in a divine frenzy, and has since kicked
and spurred my vile body forward with great emphasis and
success."

Late in the winter of 1879, with renewed happiness and calm
of life, and also under the spur of a need of money, he wrote
with much assiduity. Among other things, he composed at
Monterey the earliest of his novels, a book called *A Vendetta
in the West*, the manuscript of which seems to have dis-

appeared. Perhaps we need not regret it; for, so he declared to
me, "It was about as bad as Ouida, but not quite, for it was not
so eloquent." He had made a great mystery of his whereabouts;
indeed, for several months no one was to know what had
become of him, and his letters were to be considered secret. At
length, in writing from Monterey, on November 15, 1879, he
removed the embargo: "That I am in California may now be
published to the brethren." In the summer of the next year,
after a winter of very serious ill health, during which more
than once he seemed on the brink of a galloping consumption,
he returned to England. He had married in California a charming lady whom we all soon learned to regard as the most appropriate and helpful companion that Louis could possibly have
secured. On October 8, 1880—a memorable day—he made his
first appearance in London since his American exile. A postcard from Edinburgh had summoned me to "appoint with an
appointment" certain particular friends; "and let us once
again," Louis wrote, "lunch together in the Savile Halls." Mr.
Lang and Mr. Walter Pollock, and, I think, Mr. Henley,
graced the occasion, and the club cellar produced a bottle of
Chambertin of quite uncommon merit. Louis, I may explain,
had a peculiar passion for Burgundy, which he esteemed the
wine of highest possibilities in the whole Bacchic order; and I
have often known him descant on a Pommard or a Montrachet
in terms so exquisite that the listeners could scarcely taste the
wine itself.

Davos-Platz was now prescribed for the rickety lungs; and
late in that year Louis and his wife took up their abode there,
at the Hôtel Buol, he carrying with him a note from me
recommending him to the care of John Addington Symonds.
Not at first, but presently and on the whole, these two men, so
singular in their generation, so unique and so unlike, "hit it
off," as people say, and were an intellectual solace to each
other; but their real friendship did not begin till a later year.
I remember Stevenson saying to me next spring that to be
much with Symonds was to "adventure in a thornwood." It was
at Davos, this winter of 1880, that Stevenson took up the study
of Hazlitt, having found a publisher who was willing to bring
out a critical and biographical memoir. This scheme occupied
a great part of Louis's attention, but was eventually dropped;
for the further he progressed in the investigation of Hazlitt's
character the less he liked it, and the squalid *Liber Amoris*

ave the *coup de grâce.* He did not know what he would be at.
His vocation was not yet apparent to him. He talked of writing on craniology and the botany of the Alps. The unwritten
books of Stevenson will one day attract the scholiast, who will
endeavour, perhaps, to reconstruct them from the references
to them in his correspondence. It may, therefore, be permissible to record here that he was long proposing to write a life
of the Duke of Wellington, for which he made some considerable collections. This was even advertised as "in preparation,"
on several occasions, from 1885 until 1887, but was ultimately
abandoned. I remember his telling me that he intended to give
emphasis to the "humour" of Wellington.

In June, 1881, we saw him again; but he passed very rapidly
through London to a cottage at Pitlochry in Perthshire. He
had lost his hold on town. "London," he wrote me, "now chiefly
means to me Colvin and Henley, Leslie Stephen and you." He
was now coursing a fresh literary hare, and set Mr. Austin
Dobson, Mr. Saintsbury, and me busily hunting out facts
about Jean Cavalier, the romantic eighteenth-century adven-
turer, whose life he fancied that he would write. His thoughts
had recurred, in fact, to Scottish history; and he suddenly
determined to do what seemed rather a mad thing—namely, to
stand for the Edinburgh professorship of history, then just
vacant. We were all whipped up for testimonials, and a little
pamphlet exists, in a pearl-grey cover—the despair of bib-
liophiles—in which he and a strange assortment of his friends
set forth his claims. These required nimble treatment, since, to
put it plainly, it was impossible to say that he had any. His
appeal was treated by the advocates, who were the electing
body, with scant consideration, and some worthy gentleman
was elected. The round Louis was well out of such a square
hole as a chair in a university.

But something better was at hand. It was now, and in the
peace of the Highlands, that Louis set out to become a popular
writer. The fine art of "booming" had not then been introduced, nor the race of those who week by week discover coveys
of fresh geniuses. Although Stevenson, in a sporadic way, had
written much that was delightful, and that will last, he was
yet—now at the close of his thirty-first year—by no means
successful. The income he made by his pen was still ridiculously
small; and Mr. John Morley, amazing as it sounds to-day, had
just refused to give him a book to write in the *English Men*

of Letters series, on the ground of his obscurity as an author
All this was to be changed, and the book that was to do it wa
even now upon the stocks. In August the Stevensons moved to
a house in Braemar—a place, as Louis said, "patronised by
the royalty of the Sister Kingdoms—Victoria and the Cairn
gorms, sir, honouring that country-side by their conjunct
presence." Hither I was invited, and here I paid an ever
memorable visit. The house, as Louis was careful to instruct
me, was entitled "The Cottage, late the late Miss McGregor's
Castleton of Braemar"; and thus I obediently addressed my
letters until Louis remarked that "the reference to a deceased
Highland lady, tending as it does to foster unavailing sorrow,
may be with advantage omitted from the address."

To the Cottage, therefore, heedless of the manes of the late
Miss McGregor, I proceeded in the most violent storm of hail
and rain that even Aberdeenshire can produce in August, and
found Louis as frail as a ghost, indeed, but better than I
expected. He had adopted a trick of stretching his thin limbs
over the back of a wicker sofa, which gave him an extraordinary resemblance to that quaint insect, the praying mantis;
but it was a mercy to find him out of bed at all. Among the
many attractions of the Cottage, the presence of Mr. Thomas
Stevenson—Louis's father—must not be omitted. He was then
a singularly charming and vigorous personality, indignantly
hovering at the borders of old age ("Sixty-three, sir, this
year; and, deuce take it! am I to be called 'an old gentleman'
by a cab-driver in the streets of Aberdeen?") and, to my gratitude and delight, my companion in long morning walks. The
detestable weather presently brought all the other members of
the household to their beds, and Louis in particular became
a wreck. However, it was a wreck that floated every day at
nightfall; for at the worst he was able to come down-stairs to
dinner and spend the evening with us.

We passed the days with regularity. After breakfast I went
to Louis's bedroom, where he sat up in bed, with dark, flashing
eyes and ruffled hair, and we played chess on the coverlet. Not
a word passed, for he was strictly forbidden to speak in the
early part of the day. As soon as he felt tired—often in the
middle of a game—he would rap with peremptory knuckles
on the board as a signal to stop, and then Mrs. Stevenson or
I would arrange his writing materials on the bed. Then I would
see no more of him till dinner-time, when he would appear,

smiling and voluble, the horrid bar of speechlessness having
been let down. Then every night, after dinner, he would read
us what he had written during the day. I find in a note to my
wife, dated September 3, 1881: "Louis has been writing, all
the time I have been here, a novel of pirates and hidden
treasure, in the highest degree exciting. He reads it to us
every night, chapter by chapter." This, of course, was
Treasure Island, about the composition of which, long afterward, in Samoa, he wrote an account in some parts of which
I think that his memory played him false. I look back to no
keener intellectual pleasure than those cold nights at Braemar,
with the sleet howling outside, and Louis reading his budding
romance by the lamplight, emphasising the purpler passages
with lifted voice and gesticulating finger.

iv

Hardly had I left the Cottage than the harsh and damp
climate of Aberdeenshire was felt to be rapidly destroying
Louis, and he and his wife fled for Davos. Before the end of
October they were ensconced there in a fairly comfortable
châlet. Here Louis and his step-son amused themselves by
setting up a hand-press, which Mr. Osbourne worked, and for
which Louis provided the literary material. Four or five
laborious little publications were put forth, some of them
illustrated by the daring hand of Stevenson himself. He complained to me that Mr. Osbourne was a very ungenerous publisher—"one penny a cut, and one halfpenny a set of verses!
What do you say to that for Grub Street?" These little
diversions were brought to a close by the printer-publisher
breaking, at one fell swoop, the press and his own finger. The
little "Davos Press" issues now fetch extravagant prices, which
would have filled author and printer with amazement. About
this time Louis and I had a good deal of correspondence about
a work which he had proposed that we should undertake in collaboration—a retelling, in choice literary form, of the most
picturesque murder cases of the last hundred years. We were
to visit the scenes of these crimes, and turn over the evidence.
The great thing, Louis said, was not to begin to write until
we were thoroughly alarmed. "These things must be done,
my boy, under the very shudder of the goose-flesh." We were

to begin with the "Story of the Red Barn," which indeed is a tale pre-eminently worthy to be retold by Stevenson. But the scheme never came off, and is another of the dead leaves in his Vallombrosa.

We saw him in London again, for a few days, in October 1882; but this was a melancholy period. For eight months at the close of that year and the beginning of 1883 he was capable of no mental exertion. He was in the depth of languor, and in nightly apprehension of a fresh attack. He slept excessively, and gave humorous accounts of the drowsiness that hung upon him, addressing his notes as "from the Arms of Porpus" (Morpheus) and "at the Sign of the Poppy." No climate seemed to relieve him, and so, in the autumn of 1882, a bold experiment was tried. As the snows of Davos were of no avail, the hot, damp airs of Hyères should be essayed. I am inclined to dwell in some fulness on the year he spent at Hyères, because, curiously enough, it was not so much as mentioned, to my knowledge, by any of the writers of obituary notices at Stevenson's death. It takes, nevertheless, a prominent place in his life's history, for his removal thither marked a sudden and brilliant, though only temporary, revival in his health and spirits. Some of his best work, too, was written at Hyères, and one might say that fame first found him in this warm corner of southern France.

The house at Hyères was called "La Solitude." It stood in a paradise of roses and aloes, fig-marigolds and olives. It had delectable and even, so Louis declared, "sub-celestial" views over a plain bounded by "certain mountains as graceful as Apollo, as severe as Zeus"; and at first the hot mistral, which blew and burned where it blew, seemed the only drawback. Not a few of the best poems in the *Underwoods* reflect the ecstasy of convalescence under the skies and perfumes of La Solitude. By the summer Louis could report "good health of a radiant order." It was while he was at Hyères that Stevenson first directly addressed an American audience, and I may record that, in September 1883, he told me to "beg Gilder your prettiest for a gentleman in pecuniary sloughs." Mr Gilder was quite alive to the importance of securing such a contributor, although when the Amateur Emigrant had entered the office of *The Century Magazine* in 1879 he had been very civilly but coldly shown the door. (I must be allowed to tease my good friends in Union Square by recording that fact!) Mr. Gilder asked for fiction, but received instead *The Silverado Squatters*, which duly appeared in the magazine.

It was also arranged that Stevenson should make an ascent of the Rhône for *The Century*, and Mr. Joseph Pennell was to accompany him to make sketches for the magazine. But Stevenson's health failed again: the sudden death of a very dear old friend was a painful shock to him, and the winter of that year was not propitious. Abruptly, however, in January 1884, another crisis came. He went to Nice, where he was thought to be dying. He saw no letters; all his business was kindly taken charge of by Mr. Henley; and again, for a long time, he passed beneath the penumbra of steady languor and infirmity. When it is known how constantly he suffered, how brief and flickering were the intervals of comparative health, it cannot but add to the impression of his radiant fortitude through all these trials, and of his persistent employment of all his lucid moments. It was pitiful, and yet at the same time very inspiriting, to see a creature so feeble and so ill equipped for the struggle bear himself so smilingly and so manfully through all his afflictions. There can be no doubt, however, that this latest breakdown vitally affected his spirits. He was never, after this, quite the gay child of genius that he had previously been. Something of a graver cast became natural to his thoughts; he had seen Death in the cave. And now for the first time we traced a new note in his writings—the note of "Pulvis et Umbra."

After 1883 my personal memories of Stevenson become very casual. In November 1884, he was settled at Bournemouth, in a villa called Bonaltie Towers, and there he stayed until, in March 1885, he took a house of his own, which, in pious memory of his grandfather, he named Skerryvore. In the preceding winter, when I was going to America to lecture, he was particularly anxious that I should lay at the feet of Mr. Frank R. Stockton his homage, couched in the following lines:

> *My Stockton if I failed to like,*
> *It were a sheer depravity;*
> *For I went down with the "Thomas Hyke,"*
> *And up with the "Negative Gravity."*

He adored these tales of Mr. Stockton's, a taste which must be shared by all good men. To my constant sorrow, I was never

able to go to Bournemouth during the years he lived there. I
has been described to me, by those who were more fortunate, as
a pleasure that was apt to tantalize and evade the visitor, so
constantly was the invalid unable, at the last, to see the friend
who had travelled a hundred miles to speak with him. It was
therefore during his visits to London, infrequent as these
were, that we saw him at his best, for these were made at
moments of unusual recovery. He generally lodged at what
he called the "Monument," this being his title for Mr. Colvin's
house, a wing of the vast structure of the British Museum. I
recall an occasion on which Louis dined with us (March 1886),
because of the startling interest in the art of strategy which
he had developed—an interest which delayed the meal with
arrangements of serried bottles counterscarped and lines of
cruets drawn up on horseback ready to charge. So infectious
was his enthusiasm that we forgot our hunger, and hung over
the embattled table-cloth, easily persuaded to agree with him
that neither poetry nor the plastic arts could compete for a
moment with "the finished conduct, sir, of a large body of men
in face of the enemy."

It was a little later that he took up the practice of modelling
clay figures as he sat up in bed. Some of these compositions
—which needed, perhaps, his eloquent commentary to convey
their full effect to the spectator—were not without a measure
of skill of design. I recollect his saying, with extreme gravity,
"I am in sculpture what Mr. Watts is in painting. We are both
of us pre-occupied with moral and abstract ideas." I wonder
whether any one has preserved specimens of these allegorical
groups of clay.

The last time I had the happiness of seeing Stevenson was
on Sunday, August 21, 1887. He had been brought up from
Bournemouth the day before in a wretched condition of health,
and was lodged in a private hotel in Finsbury Circus, in the
City, ready to be easily moved to a steamer in the Thames on
the morrow. I was warned, in a note, of his passage through
town, and of the uncertainty whether he could be seen. On the
chance, I went over early on the 21st, and, very happily for
me, he had had a fair night, and could see me for an hour or
two. No one else but Mrs. Stevenson was with him. His position
was one which might have daunted any man's spirit, doomed
to exile, in miserable health, starting vaguely across the Atlantic, with all his domestic interests rooted up, and with no notion

where, or if at all, they should be replanted. If ever a man of imagination could be excused for repining, it was now.

But Louis showed no white feather. He was radiantly humorous and romantic. It was church time, and there was some talk of my witnessing his will, which I could not do, because there could be found no other reputable witness, the whole crew of the hotel being at church. This set Louis off on a splendid dream of romance. "This," he said, "is the way in which our valuable city hotels—packed, doubtless, with rich objects of jewellery—are deserted on a Sunday morning. Some bold piratical fellow, defying the spirit of Sabbatarianism, might make a handsome revenue by sacking the derelict hotels between the hours of ten and twelve. One hotel a week would suffice to enable such a man to retire into private life within the space of a year. A mask might, perhaps, be worn for the mere fancy of the thing, and to terrify kitchen-maids, but no real disguise would be needful to an enterprise that would require nothing but a brave heart and a careful study of the City Postal Directory." He spoke of the matter with so much fire and gallantry that I blushed for the youth of England and its lack of manly enterprise. No one ever could describe preposterous conduct with such a convincing air as Louis could. Common sense was positively humbled in his presence.

The volume of his poems called *Underwoods* had just appeared, and he inscribed a copy of it to me in the words "at Todgers', as ever was, *chez Todgers*, Pecksniff street." The only new book he seemed to wish to carry away with him was Mr. Hardy's beautiful romance, *The Woodlanders*, which we had to scour London that Sunday afternoon to get hold of. In the evening Mr. Colvin and I each returned to "Todgers'" with the three volumes, borrowed or stolen somewhere, and wrapped up for the voyage next day. And so the following morning, in an extraordinary vessel called the *Ludgate Hill*—as though in compliment to Mr. Stockton's genius—and carrying, besides the Stevensons, a cargo of stallions and monkeys, Mr. and Mrs. Stevenson and Mr. Lloyd Osbourne steamed down the Thames in search of health across the Atlantic and the Pacific. The horses, Louis declared, protruded their noses in an unmannerly way between the passengers at dinner, and the poor little grey monkeys, giving up life for a bad job on board that strange, heaving cage, died by dozens, and were flung contemptuously out into the ocean. The strangest voyage,

however, some time comes to an end, and Louis landed in
America. He was never to cross the Atlantic again; and for
those who loved him in Europe he had already journeyed more
than half-way to another world.

v

It is impossible to deal, however lightly, with the personal
qualities of Robert Louis Stevenson without dwelling on the
extreme beauty of his character. In looking back over the
twenty years in which I knew him, I feel that, since he was
eminently human, I ought to recall his faults, but I protest
that I can remember none. Perhaps the nearest approach to a
fault was a certain want of discretion, always founded on a
wish to make people understand each other, but not exactly
according to wisdom. I recollect that he once embroiled me for
a moment with John Addington Symonds in a manner altogether bloodthirsty and ridiculous, so that we both fell upon
him and rended him. This little weakness is really the blackest
crime I can lay to his charge. And on the other side, what
courage, what love, what an indomitable spirit, what a melting
pity! He had none of the sordid errors of the little man who
writes—no sick ambition, no envy of others, no exaggeration
of the value of his ephemeral trick of scribbling. He was eager
to help his fellows, ready to take a second place, with great
difficulty offended, by the least show of repentance perfectly
appeased.

Quite early in his career he adjusted himself to the inevitable
sense of physical failure. He threw away from him all the
useless impediments: he sat loosely in the saddle of life. Many
men who get such a warning as he got take up something to
lean against; according to their education or temperament,
they support their maimed existence on religion, or on cynical
indifference, or on some mania of the collector or the *dilettante*.
Stevenson did none of these things. He determined to make
the sanest and most genial use of so much of life as was left
him. As any one who reads his books can see, he had a deep
strain of natural religion; but he kept it to himself; he made
no hysterical or ostentatious use of it.

Looking back at the past, one recalls a trait that had its
significance, though one missed its meaning then. He was care-

ful, as I have hardly known any other man to be, not to allow himself to be burdened by the weight of material things. It was quite a jest with us that he never acquired any possessions. In the midst of those who produced books, pictures, prints, bric-à-brac, none of these things ever stuck to Stevenson. There are some deep-sea creatures, the early part of whose life is spent dancing through the water; at length some sucker or tentacle touches a rock, adheres, pulls down more tentacles, until the creature is caught there, stationary for the remainder of its existence. So it happens to men, and Stevenson's friends, one after another, caught the ground with a house, a fixed employment, a "stake in life"; he alone kept dancing in the free element, unattached. I remember his saying to me that if ever he had a garden he should like it to be empty, just a space to walk and talk in, with no flowers to need a gardener nor fine lawns that had to be mown. Just a fragment of the bare world to move in, that was all Stevenson asked for. And we who gathered possessions around us—a little library of rare books, a little gallery of drawings or bronzes—he mocked us with his goblin laughter; it was only so much more luggage to carry on the march, he said, so much more to strain the arms and bend the back.

Stevenson thought, as we all must think, that literature is a delightful profession, a primrose path. I remember his once saying so to me, and then he turned, with the brimming look in his lustrous eyes and the tremulous smile on his lips, and added, "But it is not all primroses, some of it is brambly, and most of it uphill." He knew—no one better—how the hill catches the breath and how the brambles tear the face and hands; but he pushed strenuously, serenely on, searching for new paths, struggling to get up into the light and air.

One reason why it was difficult to be certain that Stevenson had reached his utmost in any direction was what I will call, for want of a better phrase, the *energetic modesty* of his nature. He was never satisfied with himself, yet never cast down. There are two dangers that beset the artist—the one is being pleased with what he has done, and the other being dejected with it. Stevenson, more than any other man whom I have known, steered the middle course. He never conceived that he had achieved a great success, but he never lost hope that by taking pains he might yet do so. Twelve years ago, when he was beginning to write that curious and fascinating book, *Prince Otto*, he wrote to me describing the mood in which one should go about one's work—golden words, which I have never forgotten. "One should strain," he said, "and then play, strain again, and play again. The strain is for us, it educates; the play is for the reader, and pleases. In moments of effort one learns to do the easy things that people like."

He learned that which he desired, and he gained more than he hoped for. He became the most exquisite English writer of his generation; yet those who lived close to him are apt to think less of this than of the fact that he was the most unselfish and the most lovable of human beings.

Max Beerbohm

NO. 2. THE PINES

[*Early in the year* 1914 *Mr. Edmund Gosse told me he was asking
certain of his friends to write for him a few words apiece in description of Swinburne as they had known or seen him at one time or
another; and he was so good as to wish to include in this gathering
a few words by myself. I found it hard to be brief without seeming
irreverent. I failed in the attempt to make of my subject a snapshot
that was not a grotesque. So I took refuge in an ampler scope. I
wrote a reminiscent essay. From that essay I made an extract,
which I gave to Mr. Gosse. From that extract he made a quotation
in his enchanting biography. The words quoted by him reappear here
in the midst of the whole essay as I wrote it. I dare not hope they are
unashamed of their humble surroundings.—M. B.*]

In my youth the suburbs were rather looked down on—I never
quite knew why. It was held anomalous, and a matter for merriment, that Swinburne lived in one of them. For my part, had
I known as a fact that Catullus was still alive, I should have
been as ready to imagine him living in Putney as elsewhere.
The marvel would have been merely that he lived. And Swinburne's survival struck as surely as could his have struck in
me the chord of wonder.

Not, of course, that he had achieved a feat of longevity. He
was far from the Psalmist's limit. Nor was he one of those
men whom one associates with the era in which they happened
to be young. Indeed, if there was one man belonging less than
any other to Mid-Victorian days, Swinburne was that man.
But by the calendar it was in those days that he had blazed—
blazed forth with so unexampled a suddenness of splendour;
and in the light of that conflagration all that he had since
done, much and magnificent though this was, paled. The essential Swinburne was still the earliest. He was and would always
be the flammiferous boy of the dim past—a legendary crea-

ture, sole kin to the phœnix. It had been impossible that he
should ever surpass himself in the artistry that was from the
outset his; impossible that he should bring forth rhythms
lovelier and greater than those early rhythms, or exercise over
them a mastery more than—absolute. Also, it had been impossible that the first wild ardour of spirit should abide unsink-
ingly in him. Youth goes. And there was not in Swinburne
that basis on which a man may in his maturity so build as to
make good, in some degree, the loss of what is gone. He was
not a thinker: his mind rose ever away from reason to rhap-
sody; neither was he human. He was a king crowned but not
throned. He was a singing bird that could build no nest. He
was a youth who could not afford to age. Had he died young,
literature would have lost many glories; but none so great as
the glories he had already given, nor any such as we should
fondly imagine ourselves bereft of by his early death. A great
part of Keats' fame rests on our assumption of what he *would*
have done. But—even granting that Keats may have had in
him more than had Swinburne of stuff for development—I
believe that had he lived on we should think of him as author
of the poems that in fact we know. Not philosophy, after all,
not humanity, just sheer joyous power of song, is the primal
thing in poetry. Ideas, and flesh and blood, are but reserves
to be brought up when the poet's youth is going. When the
bird can no longer sing in flight, let the nest be ready. After
the king has dazzled us with his crown, let him have something
to sit down on. But the session on throne or in nest is not the
divine period. Had Swinburne's genius been of the kind that
solidifies, he would yet at the close of the nineteenth century
have been for us young men virtually—though not so definitely
as in fact he was—the writer of "Atalanta in Calydon" and of
"Poems and Ballads."

Tennyson's death in '98 had not taken us at all by surprise.
We had been fully aware that he was alive. He had always
been careful to keep himself abreast of the times. Anything
that came along—the Nebular Hypothesis at one moment, the
Imperial Institute at another—won mention from his Muse.
He had husbanded for his old age that which he had long ago
inherited: middle age. If in our mourning for him there really
was any tincture of surprise, this was due to merely the vague
sense that he had in the fullness of time died rather prematurely: his middle age might have been expected to go on

flourishing for ever. But assuredly Tennyson dead laid no such strain on our fancy as Swinburne living.

It is true that Swinburne did, from time to time, take public notice of current affairs; but what notice he took did but seem to mark his remoteness from them, from us. The Boers, I remember, were the theme of a sonnet which embarrassed even their angriest enemies in our midst. He likened them, if I remember rightly, to "hell-hounds foaming at the jaws." This was by some people taken as a sign that he had fallen away from that high generosity of spirit which had once been his. To me it meant merely that he thought of poor little England writhing under the heel of an alien despotism, just as, in the days when he really was interested in such matters, poor little Italy had writhen. I suspect, too, that the first impulse to write about the Boers came not from the Muse within, but from Theodore Watts-Dunton without. . . . "Now, Algernon, we're at war, you know—at war with the Boers. I don't want to bother you at all, but I do think, my dear old friend, you oughtn't to let slip this opportunity of," etc., etc.

Some such hortation is easily imaginable by any one who saw the two old friends together. The first time I had this honour, this sight for lasting and affectionate memory, must have been in the Spring of '99. In those days Theodore Watts (he had but recently taken on the -Dunton) was still something of a gad-about. I had met him here and there, he had said in his stentorian tones pleasant things to me about my writing, I sent him a new little book of mine, and in acknowledging this he asked me to come down to Putney and "have luncheon and meet Swinburne." Meet Catullus!

On the day appointed "I came as one whose feet half linger." It is but a few steps from the railway-station in Putney High Street to No. 2. The Pines. I had expected a greater distance to the sanctuary—a walk in which to compose my mind and prepare myself for initiation. I laid my hand irresolutely against the gate of the bleak trim front-garden, I withdrew my hand, I went away. Out here were all the aspects of common modern life. In there was Swinburne. A butcher-boy went by, whistling. He was not going to see Swinburne. He could afford to whistle. I pursued my dilatory course up the slope of Putney, but at length it occurred to me that unpunctuality would after all be an imperfect expression of reverence, and I retraced my footsteps.

No. 2—prosaic inscription! But as that front-door closed behind me I had the instant sense of having slipped away from the harsh light of the ordinary and contemporary into the dimness of an odd august past. Here, in this dark hall, the past was the present. Here loomed vivid and vital on the walls those women of Rossetti whom I had known but as shades. Familiar to me in small reproductions by photogravure, here they *themselves* were, life-sized, "with curled-up lips and amorous hair" done in the original warm crayon, all of them intently looking down on me while I took off my overcoat—all wondering who was this intruder from posterity. That they hung in the hall, evidently no more than an overflow, was an earnest of packed plenitude within. The room I was ushered into was a back-room, a dining room, looking on to a good garden. It was, in form and "fixtures," an inalienably Mid-Victorian room, and held its stolid own in the riot of Rossettis. Its proportions, its window-sash bisecting the view of garden, its folding-doors (through which I heard the voice of Watts-Dunton booming mysteriously in the front room), its mantel-piece, its gas-brackets, all proclaimed that nothing ever would seduce them from their allegiance to Martin Tupper. "Nor me from mine," said the sturdy cruet-stand on the long expanse of table-cloth. The voice of Watts-Dunton ceased suddenly, and a few moments later its owner appeared. He had been dictating, he explained. "A great deal of work on hand just now—a great deal of work." . . . I remember that on my subsequent visits he was always, at the moment of my arrival, dictating, and always greeted me with that phrase, "A great deal of work on hand just now." I used to wonder what work it was, for he published little enough. But I never ventured to inquire, and indeed rather cherished the mystery: it was a part of the dear little old man; it went with the something gnome-like about his swarthiness and chubbiness—went with the shaggy hair that fell over the collar of his eternally crumpled frock-coat, the shaggy eyebrows that overhung his bright little brown eyes, the shaggy moustache that hid his small round chin. It was a mystery inherent in the richly-laden atmosphere of The Pines. . . .

While I stood talking to Watts-Dunton—talking as loudly as he, for he was very deaf—I enjoyed the thrill of suspense in watching the door through which would appear—Swinburne. I asked after Mr. Swinburne's health. Watts-Dunton said it was very good: "He always goes out for his long walk in the morning—wonderfully active. Active in mind, too. But I'm afraid you won't be able to get into touch with him. He's almost stone-deaf, poor fellow—almost stone-deaf now." He changed the subject, and I felt I must be careful not to seem interested in Swinburne exclusively. I spoke of "Aylwin." The parlour-maid brought in the hot dishes. The great moment was at hand.

Nor was I disappointed. Swinburne's entry was for me a great moment. Here, suddenly visible in the flesh, was the legendary being and divine singer. Here he was, shutting the door behind him as might anybody else, and advancing—a strange small figure in grey, having an air at once noble and roguish, proud and skittish. My name was roared to him. In shaking his hand, I bowed low, of course—a bow *de cœur;* and he, in the old aristocratic manner, bowed equally low, but with such swiftness that we narrowly escaped concussion. You do not usually associate a man of genius, when you see one, with any social class; and, Swinburne being of an aspect so unrelated as it was to any species of human kind, I wondered the more that almost the first impression he made on me, or would make on any one, was that of a very great gentleman indeed. Not of an *old* gentleman, either. Sparse and straggling though the grey hair was that fringed the immense pale dome of his head, and venerably haloed though he was for me by his greatness, there was yet about him something—boyish? girlish? childish, rather; something of a beautifully well-bred child. But he had the eyes of a god, and the smile of an elf. In figure, at first glance, he seemed almost fat; but this was merely because of the way he carried himself, with his long neck strained so tightly back that he all receded from the waist upwards. I noticed afterwards that this deportment made the back of his jacket hang quite far away from his legs; and so small and sloping were his shoulders that the jacket seemed ever so likely to slip right off. I became aware, too, that when he bowed he did not unbend his back, but only his neck—the length of the neck accounting for the depth of the bow. His hands were tiny, even for his size, and they fluttered helplessly, touchingly, unceasingly.

Directly after my introduction, we sat down to the meal. Of course I had never hoped to "get into touch with him" reciprocally. Quite apart from his deafness, I was too modest to suppose he could be interested in anything I might say. But

—for I knew he had once been as high and copious a singer in talk as in verse—I had hoped to hear utterances from him. And it did not seem that my hope was to be fulfilled. Watts-Dunton sat at the head of the table, with a huge and very Tupperesque joint of roast mutton in front of him, Swinburne and myself close up to him on either side. He talked only to me. This was the more tantalising because Swinburne seemed as though he were bubbling over with all sorts of notions. Not that he looked at either of us. He smiled only to himself, and to his plateful of meat, and to the small bottle of Bass's pale ale that stood before him—ultimate allowance of one who had erst clashed cymbals in Naxos. This small bottle he eyed often and with enthusiasm, seeming to waver between the rapture of broaching it now and the grandeur of having it to look forward to. It made me unhappy to see what trouble he had in managing his knife and fork. Watts-Dunton told me on another occasion that this infirmity of the hands had been lifelong—had begun before Eton days. The Swinburne family had been alarmed by it and had consulted a specialist, who said that it resulted from "an excess of electric vitality," and that any attempt to stop it would be harmful. So they had let it be. I have known no man of genius who had not to pay, in some affliction or defect either physical or spiritual, for what the gods had given him. Here, in this fluttering of his tiny hands, was a part of the price that Swinburne had to pay. No doubt he had grown accustomed to it many lustres before I met him, and I need not have felt at all unhappy at what I tried not to see. He, evidently, was quite gay, in his silence— and in the world that was for him silent. I had, however, the maddening suspicion that he would have liked to talk. Why wouldn't Watts-Dunton roar him an opportunity? I felt I had been right perhaps in feeling that the lesser man was—no, not jealous of the greater whom he had guarded so long and with such love, but anxious that he himself should be as fully impressive to visitors as his fine gifts warranted. Not, indeed, that he monopolised the talk. He seemed to regard me as a source of information about all the latest "movements," and I had to shout banalities while he munched his mutton—banalities whose one saving grace for me was that they were inaudible to Swinburne. Had I met Swinburne's gaze, I should have faltered. Now and again his shining light-grey eyes roved from the table, darting this way and that—across the room,

up at the ceiling, out of the window; only never at us. Somehow this aloofness gave no hint of indifference. It seemed to
be, rather, a point in good manners—the good manners of a
child "sitting up to table," not "staring," not "asking questions," and reflecting great credit on its invaluable old nurse.
The child sat happy in the wealth of its inner life; the child
was content not to speak until it were spoken to; but, but, I
felt it did want to be spoken to. And, at length, it *was*.

So soon as the mutton had been replaced by the apple-pie,
Watts-Dunton leaned forward and "Well, Algernon," he
roared, "how was it on the Heath to-day?" Swinburne, who
had meekly inclined his ear to the question, now threw back his
head, uttering a sound that was like the cooing of a dove, and
forthwith, rapidly, ever so musically, he spoke to us of his
walk; spoke not in the strain of a man who had been taking his
daily exercise on Putney Heath, but rather in that of a Peri
who had at long last been suffered to pass through Paradise.
And rather than that he spoke would I say that he cooingly
and flutingly *sang* of his experience. The wonders of this morning's wind and sun and clouds were expressed in a flow of words
so right and sentences so perfectly balanced that they would
have seemed pedantic had they not been clearly as spontaneous
as the wordless notes of a bird in song. The frail, sweet voice
rose and fell, lingered, quickened, in all manner of trills and
roulades. That he himself could not hear it, seemed to me the
greatest loss his deafness inflicted on him. One would have expected this disability to mar the music; but it didn't; save
that now and again a note would come out metallic and over-
shrill, the tones were under good control. The whole manner
and method had certainly a strong element of oddness; but no
one incapable of condemning as unmanly the song of a lark
would have called it affected. I had met young men of whose
enunciation Swinburne's now reminded me. In them the thing
had always irritated me very much; and I now became sure
that it had been derived from people who had derived it in old
Balliol days from Swinburne himself. One of the points familiar to me in such enunciation was the habit of stressing
extremely, and lackadaisically dwelling on, some particular
syllable. In Swinburne this trick was delightful—because it
wasn't a trick, but a need of his heart. Well do I remember his
ecstasy of emphasis and immensity of pause when he described
how he had seen in a perambulator on the Heath to-day "the

most BEAUT——iful babbie ever beheld by mortal eyes." For
babies, as some of his later volumes testify, he had a sort of
idolatry. After Mazzini had followed Landor to Elysium, and
Victor Hugo had followed Mazzini, babies were what among
live creatures most evoked Swinburne's genius for self-abasement. His rapture about this especial "babbie" was such as to
shake within me my hitherto firm conviction that, whereas the
young of the brute creation are already beautiful at the age
of five minutes, the human young never begin to be so before
the age of three years. I suspect Watts-Dunton of having
shared my lack of innate enthusiasm. But it was one of Swinburne's charms, as I was to find, that he took for granted
every one's delight in what he himself so fervidly delighted in.
He could as soon have imagined a man not loving the very sea
as not doting on the aspect of babies and not reading at least
one play by an Elizabethan or Jacobean dramatist every day.

I forget whether it was at this my first meal or at another
that he described a storm in which, one night years ago, with
Watts-Dunton, he had crossed the Channel. The rhythm of his
great phrases was as the rhythm of those waves, and his head
swayed in accordance to it like the wave-rocked boat itself.
He hymned in memory the surge and darkness, the thunder
and foam and phosphorescence—"You remember, Theodore?
You remember the PHOS——phosphorescence?"—all so beautifully and vividly that I almost felt storm-bound and in peril
of my life. To disentangle one from another of the several
occasions on which I heard him talk is difficult because the procedure was so invariable: Watts-Dunton always dictating
when I arrived, Swinburne always appearing at the moment
of the meal, always the same simple and substantial fare, Swinburne never allowed to talk before the meal was half over. As
to this last point, I soon realised that I had been quite unjust
in suspecting Watts-Dunton of selfishness. It was simply a
sign of the care with which he watched over his friend's welfare. Had Swinburne been admitted earlier to the talk, he
would not have taken his proper quantity of roast mutton. So
soon, always, as he had taken that, the embargo was removed,
the chance was given him. And, swiftly though he embraced
the chance, and much though he made of it in the courses of
apple-pie and of cheese, he seemed touchingly ashamed of
"holding forth." Often, before he had said his really full say
on the theme suggested by Watts-Dunton's loud interroga-

tion, he would curb his speech and try to eliminate himself, bowing his head over his plate; and then, when he had promptly been brought in again, he would always try to atone for his inhibiting deafness by much reference and deference to all that we might otherwise have to say. "I hope," he would coo to me, "my friend Watts-Dunton, who"—and here he would turn and make a little bow to Watts-Dunton—"is himself a scholar, will bear me out when I say"—or "I hardly know," he would flute to his old friend, "whether Mr. Beerbohm"—here a bow to me—"will agree with me in my opinion of" some delicate point in Greek prosody or some incident in an old French romance I had never heard of.

On one occasion, just before the removal of the mutton, Watts-Dunton had been asking me about an English translation that had been made of M. Rostand's "Cyrano de Bergerac." He then took my information as the match to ignite the Swinburnian tinder. "Well, Algernon, it seems that 'Cyrano de Bergerac' "—but this first spark was enough: instantly Swinburne was praising the works of Cyrano de Bergerac. Of M. Rostand he may have heard, but him he forgot. Indeed I never heard Swinburne mention a single contemporary writer. His mind ranged and revelled always in the illustrious or obscure past. To him the writings of Cyrano de Bergerac were as fresh as paint—as fresh as to me, alas, was the news of their survival. "Of course, of course, you have read 'L'Histoire Comique des Etats et des Empires de la Lune'?" I admitted, by gesture and facial expression, that I had not. Whereupon he reeled out curious extracts from that allegory—"almost as good as 'Gulliver' "—with a memorable instance of the way in which the traveller to the moon was shocked by the conversation of the natives, and the natives' sense of propriety was outraged by the conversation of the traveller.

In life, as in (that for him more truly actual thing) literature, it was always the preterit that enthralled him. Of any passing events, of anything the newspapers were full of, never a word from him; and I should have been sorry if there had been. But I did, through the medium of Watts-Dunton, sometimes start him on topics that might have led him to talk of Rossetti and other old comrades. For me the names of those men breathed the magic of the past, just as it was breathed for me by Swinburne's presence. For him, I suppose, they were

but a bit of the present, and the mere fact that they had
dropped out of it was not enough to hallow them. He never
mentioned them. But I was glad to see that he revelled as wistfully in the days just before his own as I in the days just before mine. He recounted to us things he had been told in his
boyhood by an aged aunt, or great-aunt—"one of the Ash-
burnhams"; how, for example, she had been taken by her
mother to a county ball, a distance of many miles, and on the
way home through the frosty and snowy night, the family-
coach had suddenly stopped: there was a crowd of dark figures
in the way . . . at which point Swinburne stopped too, before saying, with an ineffable smile and in a voice faint with
appreciation, "They were burying a suicide at the cross-
roads."

Vivid as this Hogarthian night-scene was to me, I saw beside
it another scene: a great panelled room, a grim old woman in
a high-backed chair, and, restless on a stool at her feet an
extraordinary little nephew with masses of auburn hair and
with tiny hands clasped in supplication—"Tell me more, Aunt
Ashburnham, tell me more!"

And now, clearlier still, as I write in these after-years, do I
see that dining-room of The Pines; the long white stretch of
table-cloth, with Swinburne and Watts-Dunton and another
at the extreme end of it; Watts-Dunton between us, very low
down over his plate, very cosy and hirsute, and rather like the
dormouse at that long tea-table which Alice found in Wonderland. I see myself sitting there wide-eyed, as Alice sat. And,
had the hare been a great poet, and the hatter a great gentleman, and neither of them mad but each only very odd and
vivacious, I might see Swinburne as a glorified blend of those
two.

When the meal ended—for, alas! it was not, like that meal
in Wonderland, unending—Swinburne would dart round the
table, proffer his hand to me, bow deeply, bow to Watts-Dunton also, and disappear. "He always walks in the morning,
writes in the afternoon, and reads in the evening," Watts-
Dunton would say with a touch of tutorial pride in this regi-
men.

That parting bow of Swinburne to his old friend was characteristic of his whole relation to him. Cronies though they
were, these two, knit together with bonds innumerable, the
greater man was always *aux petits soins* for the lesser, treating

him as a newly-arrived young guest might treat an elderly
host. Some twenty years had passed since that night when,
ailing and broken—thought to be nearly dying, Watts-Dunton
told me—Swinburne was brought in a four-wheeler to The
Pines. Regular private nursing-homes either did not exist in
those days or were less in vogue than they are now. The Pines
was to be a sort of private nursing-home for Swinburne. It was
a good one. He recovered. He was most grateful to his friend
and saviour. He made as though to depart, was persuaded to
stay a little longer, and then a little longer than that. But I
rather fancy that, to the last, he never did, in the fullness of
his modesty and good manners, consent to regard his presence
as a matter of course, or as anything but a terminable intrusion and obligation. His bow seemed always to convey that.

Swinburne having gone from the room, in would come the
parlourmaid. The table was cleared, the fire was stirred, two
leather arm-chairs were pushed up to the hearth. Watts-Dunton wanted gossip of the present. I wanted gossip of the great
past. We settled down for a long, comfortable afternoon together.

Only once was the ritual varied. Swinburne (I was told before luncheon) had expressed a wish to show me his library.
So after the meal he did not bid us his usual adieu, but with
much courtesy invited us and led the way. Up the staircase he
then literally bounded—three, literally three, stairs at a time.
I began to follow at the same rate, but immediately slackened
speed for fear that Watts-Dunton behind us might be embittered at sight of so much youth and legerity. Swinburne
waited on the threshold to receive us, as it were, and pass us
in. Watts-Dunton went and ensconced himself snugly in a
corner. The sun had appeared after a grey morning, and it
pleasantly flooded this big living-room whose walls were entirely lined with the mellow backs of books. Here, as host,
among his treasures, Swinburne was more than ever attractive.
He was as happy as was any mote in the sunshine about him;
and the fluttering of his little hands, and feet too, was but as
a token of so much felicity. He looked older, it is true, in the
strong light. But these added years made only more notable
his youngness of heart. An illustrious bibliophile among his
books? A birthday child, rather, among his toys.

Proudly he explained to me the general system under which
the volumes were ranged in this or that division of shelves.

Then he conducted me to a chair near the window, left me there, flew away, flew up the rungs of a mahogany ladder, plucked a small volume, and in a twinkling was at my side: "This, I *think*, will please you!" It did. It had a beautifully engraved title-page and a pleasing scent of old, old leather. It was *editio princeps* of a play by some lesser Elizabethan or Jacobean. "Of course you know it?" my host fluted.

How I wished I could say that I knew it and loved it well! I revealed to him (for by speaking very loudly towards his inclined head I was able to make him hear) that I had not read it. He envied any one who had such pleasure in store. He darted to the ladder, and came back thrusting gently into my hands another volume of like date: "Of course you know *this?*"

Again I had to confess that I did not, and to shout my appreciation of the fount of type, the margins, the binding. He beamed agreement, and fetched another volume. Archly he indicated the title, cooing, "You are a lover of *this*, I hope?" And again I was shamed by my inexperience.

I did not pretend to know this particular play, but my tone implied that I had always been *meaning* to read it and had always by some mischance been prevented. For his sake as well as my own I did want to acquit myself passably. I wanted for him the pleasure of seeing his joys shared by a representative, however humble, of the common world. I turned the leaves caressingly, looking from them to him, while he dilated on the beauty of this and that scene in the play. Anon he fetched another volume, and another, always with the same faith that *this* was a favourite of mine. I quibbled, I evaded, I was very enthusiastic and uncomfortable. It was with intense relief that I beheld the title-page of yet another volume which (silently, this time) he laid before me—THE COUNTRY WENCH. "*This* of *course* I have read," I heartily shouted.

Swinburne stepped back. "You have? You have read it? Where?" he cried, in evident dismay.

Something was wrong. Had I *not*, I quickly wondered, read this play? "Oh yes," I shouted, "I have read it."

"But when? Where?" entreated Swinburne, adding that he had supposed it to be the sole copy extant.

I floundered. I wildly said I thought I must have read it years ago in the Bodleian.

"Theodore! Do you hear this? It seems that they have now a copy of 'The Country Wench' in the Bodleian! Mr. Beer-

bohm found one there—oh when? in what year?" he appealed
to me.

I said it might have been six, seven, eight years ago. Swinburne knew for certain that no copy had been there *twelve*
years ago, and was surprised that he had not heard of the
acquisition. "They might have told me," he wailed.

I sacrificed myself on the altar of sympathy. I admitted
that I might have been mistaken—must have been—must have
confused this play with some other. I dipped into the pages
and "No," I shouted, "this I have *never* read."

His equanimity was restored. He was up the ladder and
down again, showing me further treasures with all pride and
ardour. At length, Watts-Dunton, afraid that his old friend
would tire himself, arose from his corner, and presently he
and I went downstairs to the dining-room. It was in the course
of our session together that there suddenly flashed across my
mind the existence of a play called "The Country Wife," by
—wasn't it Wycherley? I had once read it—or read something about it. . . . But this matter I kept to myself. I
thought I had appeared fool enough already.

I loved those sessions in that Tupperossettine dining-room,
lair of solid old comfort and fervid old romanticism. Its odd
duality befitted well its owner. The distinguished critic and
poet, Rossetti's closest friend and Swinburne's, had been, for a
while, in the dark ages, a solicitor; and one felt he had been
a good one. His frock-coat, though the Muses had crumpled
it, inspired confidence in his judgment of other things than
verse. But let there be no mistake. He was no mere *bourgeois
parnassien*, as his enemies insinuated. No doubt he had been
very useful to men of genius, in virtue of qualities they lacked,
but the secret of his hold on them was in his own rich nature.
He was not only a born man of letters, he was a deeply emotional human being whose appeal was as much to the heart as
to the head. The romantic Celtic mysticism of "Aylwin," with
its lack of fashionable Celtic nebulosity, lends itself, if you
will, to laughter, though personally I saw nothing funny in
it: it seemed to me, before I was in touch with the author, a
work of genuine expression from within; and that it truly
was so I presently knew. The mysticism of Watts-Dunton
(who, once comfortably settled at the fireside, knew no
reserve) was in contrast with the frock-coat and the practical
abilities; but it was essential, and they were of the surface.

For humorous Rossetti, I daresay, the very contrast made Theodore's company the more precious. He himself had assuredly been, and the memory of him still was, the master-fact in Watts-Dunton's life. "Algernon" was as an adopted child, "Gabriel" as a long-lost only brother. As he was to the outer world of his own day, so too to posterity Rossetti, the man, is conjectural and mysterious. We know that he was in his prime the most inspiring and splendid of companions. But we know this only by faith. The evidence is as vague as it is emphatic. Of the style and substance of not a few great talkers in the past we can piece together some more or less vivid and probably erroneous notion. But about Rossetti nothing has been recorded in such a way as to make him even faintly emerge. I suppose he had in him what reviewers seem to find so often in books: a quality that defies analysis. Listening to Watts-Dunton, I was always in hope that when next the long-lost turned up—for he was continually doing so—in the talk, I should *see* him, *hear* him, and share the rapture. But the revelation was not to be. You might think that to hear him called "Gabriel" would have given me a sense of propinquity. But I felt no nearer to him than you feel to the Archangel who bears that name and no surname.

It was always when Watts-Dunton spoke carelessly, casu-ally, of some to me illustrious figure in the past, that I had the sense of being wafted right into that past and plumped down in the very midst of it. When he spoke with reverence of this and that great man whom he had known, he did not thus waft and plump me; for I, too, revered those names. But I had the magical transition whenever one of the immortals was mentioned in the tone of those who knew him before he had put on immortality. Browning, for example, was a name deeply honoured by me. "Browning, yes," said Watts-Dunton, in the course of an afternoon, "Browning," and he took a sip of the steaming whisky-toddy that was a point in our day's ritual. "I was a great diner-out in the old times. I used to dine out every night in the week. Browning was a great diner-out, too. We were always meeting. What a pity he went on writing all those plays! He hadn't any gift for drama—none. I never could understand why he took to play-writing." He wagged his head, gazing regretfully into the fire, and added, "Such a *clever* fellow, too!"

Whistler, though alive and about, was already looked to

ɪs a hierarch by the young. Not so had he been looked to by
Rossetti. The thrill of the past was always strong in me when
Watts-Dunton mentioned—seldom without a guffaw did he
mention—"Jimmy Whistler." I think he put in the surname
because "that fellow" had not behaved well to Swinburne. But
he could not omit the nickname, because it was impossible for
him to feel the right measure of resentment against "such a
funny fellow." As heart-full of old hates as of old loves was
Watts-Dunton, and I take it as high testimony to the charm
of Whistler's quaintness that Watts-Dunton did not hate
him. You may be aware that Swinburne, in '88, wrote for one
of the monthly reviews a criticism of the "Ten O'Clock" lecture. He paid courtly compliments to Whistler as a painter,
but joined issue with his theories. Straightway there appeared
in the *World* a little letter from Whistler, deriding "one
Algernon Swinburne—outsider—Putney." It was not in itself
a very pretty or amusing letter; and still less so did it seem
in the light of the facts which Watts-Dunton told me in some
such words as these: "After he'd published that lecture of his,
Jimmy Whistler had me to dine with him at Kettner's or somewhere. He said 'Now, Theodore, I want you to do me a favour.' He wanted to get me to get Swinburne to write an
article about his lecture. I said 'No, Jimmy Whistler, I can't
ask Algernon to do that. He's got a great deal of work on
hand just now—a great deal of work. And besides, this sort
of thing wouldn't be at all in his line.' But Jimmy Whistler
went on appealing to me. He said it would do him no end of
good if Swinburne wrote about him. And—well, I half gave
in: I said perhaps I *would* mention the matter to Algernon.
And next day I did. I could see Algernon didn't want to do
it at all. But—well, there, he said he'd do it to please *me*. And
he did it. And then Jimmy Whistler published that letter. A
very shabby trick—very shabby indeed." Of course I do not
vouch for the exact words in which Watts-Dunton told me
this tale: but this was exactly the tale he told me. I expressed
my astonishment. He added that of course he "never wanted
to see the fellow again after that, and never did." But presently, after a long gaze into the coals, he emitted a chuckle, as
for earlier memories of "such a funny fellow." One quite recent
memory he had, too. "When I took on the name of Dunton,
I had a note from him. Just this, with his butterfly signature:
Theodore! What's Dunton? That was very good—very good.

. . . But, of course," he added gravely, "I took no notice.' And no doubt, quite apart from the difficulty of finding an answer in the same vein, he did well in not replying. Loyalty to Swinburne forbade. But I see a certain pathos in the unanswered message. It was a message from the hand of an old jester, but also, I think, from the heart of an old man—a signal waved jauntily, but in truth wistfully, across the gulf of years and estrangement; and one could wish it had not been ignored.

Some time after Whistler died I wrote for one of the magazines an appreciation of his curious skill in the art of writing. Watts-Dunton told me he had heard of this from Swinburne. "I myself," he said, "very seldom read the magazines. But Algernon always has a look at them." There was something to me very droll, and cheery too, in this picture of the illustrious recluse snatching at the current issues of our twaddle. And I was immensely pleased at hearing that my article had "interested him very much." I inwardly promised myself that as soon as I reached home I would read the article, to see just how it might have struck Swinburne. When in due course I did this, I regretted the tone of the opening sentences, in which I declared myself "no book-lover" and avowed a preference for "an uninterrupted view of my fellow-creatures." I felt that had I known my article would meet the eye of Swinburne I should have cut out that overture. I dimly remembered a fine passage in one of his books of criticism—something (I preferred not to verify it) about "the dotage of duncedom which cannot perceive, or the impudence of insignificance so presumptuous as to doubt, that the elements of life and literature are indivisibly mingled one in another, and that he to whom books are less real than life will assuredly find in men and women as little reality as in his accursed crassness he deserves to discover." I quailed, quailed. But mine is a resilient nature, and I promptly reminded myself that Swinburne's was a very impersonal one: he would not think the less highly of me, for he never had thought about me in any way whatsoever. All was well. I knew I could revisit The Pines, when next Watts-Dunton should invite me, without misgiving. And to this day I am rather proud of having been mentioned, though not by name, and not consciously, and unfavourably, by Swinburne.

I wonder that I cannot recall more than I do recall of those

.ours at The Pines. It is odd how little remains to a man of
.is own past—how few minutes of even his memorable hours
re not clean forgotten, and how few seconds in any one of
hose minutes can be recaptured. . . . I am middle-aged, and
.ave lived a vast number of seconds. Subtract one-third of
hese, for one mustn't count sleep as life. The residual num-
.er is still enormous. Not a single one of those seconds was
.nimportant to me in its passage. Many of them bored me, of
ourse; but even boredom is a positive state: one chafes at it
.nd hates it; strange that one should afterwards forget it!
.nd stranger still that of one's actual happinesses and unhap-
.inesses so tiny and tattered a remnant clings about one! Of
hose hours at The Pines, of that past within a past, there was
.ot a minute nor a second that I did not spend with pleasure.
.Iemory is a great artist, we are told; she selects and rejects
.nd shapes and so on. No doubt. Elderly persons would be
.tterly intolerable if they remembered *everything*. *Every-
hing*, nevertheless, is just what they themselves would like to
.emember, and just what they would like to tell to *everybody*.
.e sure that the Ancient Mariner, though he remembered
.uite as much as his audience wanted to hear, and rather more,
.bout the albatross and the ghastly crew, was inwardly raging
.t the sketchiness of his own mind; and believe me that his
.topping only one of three was the merest oversight. I should
ike to impose on the world many tomes about The Pines.

But, scant though my memories are of the moments there,
.ery full and warm in me is the whole fused memory of the
.wo dear old men that lived there. I wish I had Watts-
.unton's sure faith in meetings beyond the grave. I am glad I
.o not disbelieve that people may so meet. I like to think that
.ome day in Elysium I shall—not without diffidence—ap-
.roach those two and reintroduce myself. I can see just how
.ourteously Swinburne will bow over my hand, not at all re-
.membering who I am. Watts-Dunton will remember me after a
moment: "Oh, to be sure, yes indeed! I've a great deal of work
on hand just now—a great deal of work, but" we shall sit
down together on the asphodel, and I cannot but think we
shall have whisky-toddy even there. He will not have changed.
He will still be shaggy and old and chubby, and will wear the
same frock-coat, with the same creases in it. Swinburne, on
the other hand, will be quite, quite young, with a full mane of
flaming auburn locks, and no clothes to hinder him from

plunging back at any moment into the shining Elysian water
from which he will have just emerged. I see him skim lightly
away into that element. On the strand is sitting a man of noble
and furrowed brow. It is Mazzini, still thinking of Liberty
And anon the tiny young English amphibian comes ashore to
fling himself dripping at the feet of the patriot and to carol
the Republican ode he has composed in the course of his swim
"He's wonderfully active—active in mind and body," Watts-
Dunton says to me. "I come to the shore now and then, just
to see how he's getting on. But I spend most of my time inland. I find I've so much to talk over with Gabriel. Not that
he's quite the fellow he was. He always had rather a cult for
Dante, you know, and now he's more than ever under the Florentine influence. He lives in a sort of monastery that Dante
has here; and there he sits painting imaginary portraits of
Beatrice, and giving them all to Dante. But he still has his
great moments, and there's no one quite like him—no one.
Algernon won't ever come and see him, because that fellow
Mazzini's as Anti-Clerical as ever and makes a principle of
having nothing to do with Dante. Look!—there's Algernon
going into the water again! He'll tire himself out, he'll catch
cold, he'll———" and here the old man rises and hurries down
to the sea's edge. "Now, Algernon," he roars, "I don't want
to interfere with you, but I do think, my dear old friend,"—
and then, with a guffaw, he breaks off, remembering that his
friend is not deaf now nor old, and that here in Elysium,
where no ills are, good advice is not needed.

Aldous Huxley

WORDSWORTH IN THE TROPICS[1]

In the neighbourhood of latitude fifty north, and for the last hundred years or thereabouts, it has been an axiom that Nature is divine and morally uplifting. For good Wordsworthians— and most serious-minded people are now Wordsworthians, either by direct inspiration or at second hand—a walk in the country is the equivalent of going to church, a tour through Westmorland is as good as a pilgrimage to Jerusalem. To commune with the fields and waters, the woodlands and the hills, is to commune, according to our modern and northern ideas, with the visible manifestations of the "Wisdom and Spirit of the Universe."

The Wordsworthian who exports this pantheistic worship of Nature to the tropics is liable to have his religious convictions somewhat rudely disturbed. Nature, under a vertical sun, and nourished by the equatorial rains, is not at all like that chaste, mild deity who presides over the *gemüthlichkeit*, the prettiness, the cozy sublimities of the Lake District. The worst that Wordsworth's goddess ever did to him was to make him hear

> Low breathings coming after me and sounds
> Of undistinguishable motion, steps
> Almost as silent as the turf they trod;

was to make him realize, in the shape of a "huge peak, black and huge," the existence of "unknown modes of being." He seems to have imagined that this was the worst Nature *could* do. A few weeks in Malaya or Borneo would have undeceived him. Wandering in the hothouse darkness of the jungle, he would not have felt so serenely certain of those "Presences of

[1] This also appeared in *The Yale Review*.

Nature," those "Souls of Lonely Places," which he was in the habit of worshipping on the shores of Windermere and Rydal. The sparse inhabitants of the equatorial forest are all believers in devils. When one has visited, in even the most superficial manner, the places where they live, it is difficult not to share their faith. The jungle is marvellous, fantastic, beautiful; but it is also terrifying, it is also profoundly sinister. There is something in what, for lack of a better word, we must call the character of great forests—even in those of temperate lands—which is foreign, appalling, fundamentally and utterly inimical to intruding man. The life of those vast masses of swarming vegetation is alien to the human spirit and hostile to it. Meredith, in his "Woods of Westermain," has tried reassuringly to persuade us that our terrors are unnecessary, that the hostility of these vegetable forces is more apparent than real, and that if we will but trust Nature we shall find our fears transformed into serenity, joy, and rapture. This may be sound philosophy in the neighbourhood of Dorking; but it begins to be dubious, even in the forests of Germany—there is too much of them for a human being to feel himself at ease within their enormous glooms; and when the woods of Borneo are substituted for those of Westermain, Meredith's comforting doctrine becomes frankly ridiculous.

It is not the sense of solitude that distresses the wanderer in equatorial jungles. Loneliness is bearable enough—for a time, at any rate. There is something actually rather stimulating and exciting about being in an empty place where there is no life but one's own. Taken in reasonably small doses, the Sahara exhilarates, like alcohol. Too much of it, however (I speak, at any rate, for myself), has the depressing effect of the second bottle of Burgundy. But in any case it is not loneliness that oppresses the equatorial traveller: it is too much company; it is the uneasy feeling that he is an alien in the midst of an innumerable throng of hostile beings. To us who live beneath a temperate sky and in the age of Henry Ford, the worship of Nature comes almost naturally. It is easy to love a feeble and already conquered enemy. But an enemy with whom one is still at war, an unconquered, unconquerable, ceaselessly active enemy—no; one does not, one should not, love him. One respects him, perhaps; one has a salutary fear of him; and one goes on fighting. In our latitudes the hosts of Nature have mostly been vanquished and enslaved. Some few detachments, it s true, still hold the field against us. There are wild woods and mountains, marshes and heaths, even in England. But they are there only on sufferance, because we have chosen, out of our good pleasure, to leave them their freedom. It has not been worth our while to reduce them to slavery. We love them because we are the masters, because we know that at any moment we can overcome them as we overcame their fellows. The inhabitants of the tropics have no such comforting reasons for adoring the sinister forces which hem them in on every side. For us, the notion "river" implies (how obviously!) the notion "bridge." When we think of a plain, we think of agriculture, towns, and good roads. The corollary of mountain is tunnel; of swamp, an embankment; of distance, a railway. At latitude zero, however, the obvious is not the same as with us. Rivers imply wading, swimming, alligators. Plains mean swamps, forests, fevers. Mountains are either dangerous or impassable. To travel is to hack one's way laboriously through a tangled, prickly, and venomous darkness. "God made the country," said Cowper, in his rather too blank verse. In New Guinea he would have had his doubts; he would have longed for the man-made town.

The Wordsworthian adoration of Nature has two principal defects. The first, as we have seen, is that it is only possible in a country where Nature has been nearly or quite enslaved to man. The second is that it is only possible for those who are prepared to falsify their immediate intuitions of Nature. For Nature, even in the temperate zone, is always alien and inhuman, and occasionally diabolic. Meredith explicitly invites us to explain any unpleasant experiences away. We are to interpret them, Pangloss fashion, in terms of a preconceived philosophy; after which, all will surely be for the best in the the best of all possible Westermains. Less openly, Wordsworth asks us to make the same falsification of immediate experience. It is only very occasionally that he admits the existence in the world around him of those "unknown modes of being" of which our immediate intuitions of things make us so disquietingly aware. Normally what he does is to pump the dangerous Unknown out of Nature and refill the emptied forms of hills and woods, flowers and waters, with something more reassuringly familiar—with humanity, with Anglicanism. He will not admit that a yellow primrose is simply a yellow primrose—beautiful, but essentially strange, having its own alien life apart. He

wants it to possess some sort of soul, to exist humanly, no
simpy flowerily. He wants the earth to be more than earthy, to
be a divine person. But the life of vegetation is radically unlike
the life of man: the earth has a mode of being that is certainly
not the mode of being of a person. "Let Nature be your
teacher," says Wordsworth. The advice is excellent. But how
strangely he himself puts it into practice! Instead of listening
humbly to what the teacher says, he shuts his ears and himself
dictates the lesson he desires to hear. The pupil knows better
than his master; the worshipper substitutes his own oracles for
those of the god. Instead of accepting the lesson as it is given
to his immediate intuitions, he distorts it rationalistically into
the likeness of a parson's sermon or a professional lecture. Our
direct intuitions of Nature tell us that the world is bottom-
lessly strange: alien, even when it is kind and beautiful; having
innumerable modes of being that are not our modes; always
mysteriously not personal, not conscious, not moral; often hostile and sinister; sometimes even unimaginably, because
inhumanly, evil. In his youth, it would seem, Wordsworth left
his direct intuitions of the world unwarped.

> The sounding cataract
> Haunted me like a passion: the tall rock,
> The mountain, and the deep and gloomy wood,
> Their colours and their forms, were then to me
> An appetite; a feeling and a love,
> That had no need of a remoter charm,
> By thought supplied, nor any interest
> Unborrowed from the eye.

As the years passed, however, he began to interpret them in
terms of a preconceived philosophy. Procrustes-like, he tortured his feelings and perceptions until they fitted his system.
By the time he was thirty,

> The immeasurable height
> Of woods decaying, never to be decayed,
> The stationary blasts of waterfalls—
> The torrents shooting from the clear blue sky,
> The rocks that muttered close upon our ears,
> Black drizzling crags that spake by the wayside

As if a voice were in them, the sick sight
And giddy prospect of the raving stream,
The unfettered clouds and regions of the heavens,
Tumult and peace, the darkness and the light—
Were all like workings of one mind, the features
Of the same face, blossoms upon one tree,
Characters of the great Apocalypse,
The types and symbols of eternity,
Of first, and last, and midst, and without end.

"Something far more deeply interfused" had made its appearance on the Wordsworthian scene. The god of Anglicism had
crept under the skin of things, and all the stimulatingly inhuman strangeness of Nature had become as flatly familiar as a
page from a textbook of metaphysics or theology. As familiar
and as safely simple. Pantheistically interpreted, our intuitions
of Nature's endless varieties of impersonal mysteriousness lose
all their exciting and disturbing quality. It makes the world
seem delightfully cozy, if you can pretend that all the many
alien things about you are really only manifestations of one
person. It is fear of the labyrinthine flux and complexity of
phenomena that has driven men to philosophy, to science, to
theology—fear of the complex reality driving them to invent a
simpler, more manageable, and, therefore, consoling fiction.
For simple, in comparison with the external reality of which
we have direct intuitions, childishly simple is even the most
elaborate and subtle system devised by the human mind. Most
of the philosophical systems hitherto popular have not been
subtle and elaborate even by human standards. Even by human
standards they have been crude, bald, preposterously straightforward. Hence their popularity. Their simplicity has rendered them instantly comprehensible. Weary with much
wandering in the maze of phenomena, frightened by the inhospitable strangeness of the world, men have rushed into the
systems prepared for them by philosophers and founders of
religions, as they would rush from a dark jungle into the
haven of a well-lit, commodious house. With a sigh of relief and
a thankful feeling that here at last is their true home, they
settle down in their snug metaphysical villa and go to sleep.
And how furious they are when anyone comes rudely knocking
at the door to tell them that their villa is jerry-built, dilapidated, unfit for human habitation, even non-existent! Men
have been burned at the stake for even venturing to criticize

the colour of the front door or the shape of the third-floor windows.

That man must build himself some sort of metaphysical shelter in the midst of the jungle of immediately apprehended reality is obvious. No practical activity, no scientific research, no speculation is possible without some preliminary hypothesis about the nature and the purpose of things. The human mind cannot deal with the universe directly, nor even with its own immediate intuitions of the universe. Whenever it is a question of thinking about the world or of practically modifying it, men can only work on a symbolic plan of the universe, only on a simplified, two-dimensional map of things abstracted by the mind out of the complex and multifarious reality of immediate intuition. History shows that these hypotheses about the nature of things are valuable even when, as later experience reveals, they are false. Man approaches the unattainable truth through a succession of errors. Confronted by the strange complexity of things, he invents, quite arbitrarily, a simple hypothesis to explain and justify the world. Having invented, he proceeds to act and think in terms of this hypothesis, as though it were correct. Experience gradually shows him where his hypothesis is unsatisfactory and how it should be modified. Thus, great scientific discoveries have been made by men seeking to verify quite erroneous theories about the nature of things. The discoveries have necessitated a modification of the original hypotheses, and further discoveries have been made in the effort to verify the modifications—discoveries which, in their turn, have led to yet further modifications. And so on, indefinitely. Philosophical and religious hypotheses, being less susceptible of experimental verification than the hypotheses of science, have undergone far less modification. For example, the pantheistic hypothesis of Wordsworth is an ancient doctrine, which human experience has hardly modified throughout history. And rightly, no doubt. For it is obvious that there must be some sort of unity underlying the diversity of phenomena; for if there were not, the world would be quite unknowable. Indeed, it is precisely in the knowableness of things, in the very fact that they are known, that their fundamental unity consists. The world which we know, and which our minds have fabricated out of goodness knows what mysterious things in themselves, possesses the unity which our minds have imposed upon it. It is part of our thought, hence fundamentally homogeneous. Yes,

the world is obviously one. But at the same time it is no less
obviously diverse. For if the world were absolutely one, it
would no longer be knowable, it would cease to exist. Thought
must be divided against itself before it can come to any knowledge of itself. Absolute oneness is absolute nothingness: homogeneous perfection, as the Hindus perceived and courageously
recognized, is equivalent to non-existence, is Nirvana. The
Christian idea of a perfect heaven that is something other than
a non-existence is a contradiction in terms. The world in which
we live may be fundamentally one, but it is a unity divided up
into a great many diverse fragments. A tree, a table, a newspaper, a piece of artificial silk are all made of wood. But they
are, none the less, distinct and separate objects. It is the same
with the world at large. Our immediate intuitions are of diversity. We have only to open our eyes to recognize a multitude
of different phenomena. These intuitions of diversity are as
correct, as well justified, as our intellectual conviction of the
fundamental homogeneity of the various parts of the world
with one another and with ourselves. Circumstances have led
humanity to set an ever-increasing premium on the conscious
and intellectual comprehension of things. Modern man's besetting temptation is to sacrifice his direct perceptions and
spontaneous feelings to his reasoned reflections; to prefer in all
circumstances the verdict of his intellect to that of his immediate intuitions. *"L'homme est visiblement fait pour penser,"*
says Pascal; *"c'est toute sa dignité et toute son mérite; et tout
son devoir est de penser comme il faut."* Noble words; but do
they happen to be true? Pascal seems to forget that man has
something else to do besides think: he must live. Living may not
be so dignified or so meritorious as thinking (particularly when
you happen to be, like Pascal, a chronic invalid) ; but it is,
perhaps unfortunately, a necessary process. If one would live
well, one must live completely, with the whole being—with
the body and the instincts, as well as with the conscious mind.
A life lived, as far as may be, exclusively from the consciousness and in accordance with the considered judgments of the
intellect is a stunted life, a half-dead life. This is a fact that
can be confirmed by daily observation. But consciousness, the
intellect, the spirit, have acquired an inordinate prestige; and
such is men's snobbish respect for authority, such is their
pedantic desire to be consistent, that they go on doing their
best to lead the exclusively conscious, spiritual, and intellectual

life, in spite of its manifest disadvantages. To know is pleasant; it is exciting to be conscious; the intellect is a valuable instrument, and for certain purposes the hypotheses which it fabricates are of great practical value. Quite true. But, therefore, say the moralists and men of science, drawing conclusions only justified by their desire for consistency, therefore *all* life should be lived from the head, consciously, *all* phenomena should at *all* times be interpreted in terms of the intellect's hypotheses. The religious teachers are of a slightly different opinion. All life, according to them, should be lived spiritually, not intellectually. Why? On the grounds, as we discover when we push our analysis far enough, that certain occasional psychological states, currently called spiritual, are extremely agreeable and have valuable consequences in the realm of social behaviour. The unprejudiced observer finds it hard to understand why these people should set such store by consistency of thought and action. Because oysters are occasionally pleasant, it does not follow that one should make of oysters one's exclusive diet. Nor should one take castor oil every day because castor oil is occasionally good for one. Too much consistency is as bad for the mind as it is for the body. Consistency is contrary to nature, contrary to life. The only completely consistent people are the dead. Consistent intellectualism and spirituality may be socially valuable, up to a point; but they make, gradually, for individual death. And individual death, when the slow murder has been consummated, is finally social death. So that the social utility of pure intellectualism and pure spirituality is only apparent and temporary. What is needed is, as ever, a compromise. Life must be lived in different ways at different moments. The only satisfactory way of existing in the modern, highly specialized world is to live with two personalities. A Dr. Jekyll that does the metaphysical and scientific thinking, that transacts business in the city, adds up figures, designs machines, and so forth. And a natural, spontaneous Mr. Hyde to do the physical, instinctive living in the intervals of work. The two personalities should lead their unconnected lives apart, without poaching on one another's preserves or inquiring too closely into one another's activities. Only by living discreetly and inconsistently can we preserve both the man and the citizen, both the intellectual and the spontaneous animal being, alive within us. The solution may not be very satisfactory; but it is, I believe now (though once

(thought differently), the best that, in the modern circumstances, can be devised.

The poet's place, it seems to me, is with the Mr. Hydes of human nature. He should be, as Blake remarked of Milton, "of the devil's party without knowing it"—or preferably with the full consciousness of being of the devil's party. There are so many intellectual and moral angels battling for rationalism, good citizenship, and pure spirituality; so many and such eminent ones, so very vocal and authoritative! The poor devil in man needs all the support and advocacy he can get. The artist is his natural champion. When an artist deserts to the side of the angels, it is the most odious of treasons. How unforgivable, for example, is Tolstoy! Tolstoy, the perfect Mr. Hyde, the complete embodiment, if ever there was one, of non-intellectual, non-moral, instinctive life—Tolstoy, who betrayed his own nature, betrayed his art, betrayed life itself, in order to fight against the devil's party of his earlier allegiances, under the standard of Dr. Jesus-Jekyll. Wordsworth's betrayal was not so spectacular: he was never so wholly of the devil's party as Tolstoy. Still, it was bad enough. It is difficult to forgive him for so utterly repenting his youthful passions and enthusiasms, and becoming, personally as well as politically, the Anglican Tory. One remembers B. R. Haydon's account of the poet's reactions to that charming classical sculpture of Cupid and Psyche. "The devils!" he said malignantly, after a long-drawn contemplation of their marble embrace. "The devils!" And he was not using the word in the complimentary sense in which I have employed it here: he was expressing his hatred of passion and life, he was damning the young man he had himself been—the young man who had hailed the French Revolution with delight and begotten an illegitimate child. From being an ardent lover of the nymphs, he had become one of those all too numerous

> . . . woodmen who expel
> Love's gentle dryads from the haunts of life,
> And vex the nightingales in every dell.

Yes, even the nightingales he vexed. Even the nightingales, though the poor birds can never, like those all too human dryads, have led him into sexual temptation. Even the innocuous nightingales were moralized, spiritualized, turned into

citizens and Anglicans—and along with the nightingales, th
whole of animate and inanimate Nature.

The change in Wordsworth's attitude toward Nature i
symptomatic of his general apostasy. Beginning at what I ma
call a natural æsthete, he transformed himself, in the course o
years, into a moralist, a thinker. He used his intellect to dis
tort his exquisitely acute and subtle intuitions of the world, t
explain away their often disquieting strangeness, to simplif
them into a comfortable metaphysical unreality. Nature ha
endowed him with the poet's gift of seeing more than ordinaril
far into the brick walls of external reality, of intuitively com
prehending the character of the bricks, of feeling the qualit
of their being, and establishing the appropriate relationshi
with them. But he preferred to think his gifts away. He pre
ferred, in the interests of a preconceived religious theory, t
ignore the disquieting strangeness of things, to interpret th
impersonal diversity of Nature in terms of a divine, Anglica
unity. He chose, in a word, to be a philosopher, comfortably a
home with a man-made and, therefore, thoroughly compre
hensible system, rather than a poet adventuring for adventure'
sake through the mysterious world revealed by his direct an
undistorted intuitions.

It is a pity that he never travelled beyond the boundaries o
Europe. A voyage through the tropics would have cured hin
of his too easy and comfortable pantheism. A few months
in the jungle would have convinced him that the diversity an
utter strangeness of Nature are at least as real and significant
as its intellectually discovered unity. Nor would he have felt so
certain, in the damp and stifling darkness, among the leeches
and the malevolently tangled rattans, of the divinely Anglican
character of that fundamental unity. He would have learned
once more to treat Nature naturally, as he treated it in his
youth; to react to it spontaneously, loving where love was the
appropriate emotion, fearing hating, fighting whenever Nature
presented itself to his intuition as being, not merely strange,
but hostile, inhumanly evil. A voyage would have taught him
this. But Wordsworth never left his native continent. Europe
is so well gardened that it resembles a work of art, a scientific
theory, a neat metaphysical system. Man has re-created
Europe in his own image. Its tamed and temperate Nature
confirmed Wordsworth in his philosophizings. The poet, the
devil's partisan, were doomed; the angels triumphed. Alas!

John Galsworthy

REMINISCENCES OF CONRAD

MANY writers knew my dear friend, and will write of him better than I; but no other writer knew him quite so long, or knew him both as sailor and novelist.

It was in March, 1893, that I first met Conrad on board the English sailing ship *Torrens* in Adelaide Harbor. He was superintending the stowage of cargo. Very dark he looked in the burning sunlight—tanned, with a peaked brown beard, almost black hair, and dark brown eyes, over which the lids were deeply folded. He was thin, not tall, his arms very long, his shoulders broad, his head set rather forward. He spoke to me with a strong foreign accent. He seemed to me strange on an English ship. For fifty-six days I sailed in his company.

The chief mate bears the main burden of a sailing ship. All the first night he was fighting a fire in the hold. None of us seventeen passengers knew of it till long after. It was he who had most truck with the tail of that hurricane off the Leeuwin, and later with another storm. He was a good seaman, watchful of the weather; quick in handling the ship; considerate with the apprentices—we had a long, unhappy Belgian youth among them, who took unhandily to the sea and dreaded going aloft; Conrad compassionately spared him all he could. With the crew he was popular; they were individuals to him, not a mere gang; and long after he would talk of this or that among them, especially of old Andy the sail-maker: "I likéd that old fellow, you know." With the young second mate, a cheerful, capable young seaman, very English, he was friendly; and respectful, if faintly ironic, with his whiskered, stout old English captain. I was supposed to be studying navigation for the Admiralty Bar, and every day would work out the ship's position with the captain. On one side of the saloon table we would sit and check our observations on this important matter with those of Conrad, who would sit on the other side of the table and look at us a little quizzically. For Conrad had commanded ships, and his subordinate position on the *Torrens* was only due to the fact that he was then still convalescent from the Congo experience which had nearly killed him. Many evening watches in fine weather we spent on the poop. Ever the great teller of a tale, he had already nearly twenty years of tales to tell. Tales of ships and storms, of Polish revolution, of his youthful Carlist gun-running adventure, of the Malay seas, and the Congo; and of men and men; all to a listener who had the insatiability of a twenty-five year old.

When, seven or eight years later, Conrad, though then in his best period and long acclaimed a great writer by the few, was struggling, year in year out, to keep a roof over him amidst the apathy of the many who afterward fell over each other to read him in his worst period, I remember urging him to raise the wind by tale-telling in public. He wouldn't, and he was right. Still, so incomparable a *raconteur* must have made a success, even though his audience might have missed many words owing to his strange yet fascinating foreign accent.

On that ship he talked of life, not literature, and it is *not* true that I introduced him to the life of letters. At Cape Town, on my last evening, he asked me to his cabin, and I remember feeling that he out-weighed for me all the other experience of that voyage. Fascination was Conrad's great characteristic—the fascination of vivid expressiveness and zest, of his deeply affectionate heart, and his far-ranging subtle mind. He was extraordinarily perceptive and receptive. If we remember his portraits of the simple Englishmen of action— the inexpressive Creightons, McWhirrs, Lingards, Bakers, Allistouns, and the half-savage figures of some of his books, we get some conception of his sympathetic scope by reading the following passages in a letter to me of February 1899 on the work of Henry James:

"Technical perfection, unless there is some real glow to illumine and warm it from within, must necessarily be cold. I argue that in Henry James there is such a glow, and not a dim one either; but to us, used, absolutely accustomed, to unartistic expression of fine headlong honest (or dishonest) sentiments, the art of Henry James does appear heartless. The outlines are

so clear, the figures so finished, chiselled, carved, and brought
out, that we exclaim—we, used to the shades of the contemporary fiction, to the more or less malformed shades—we
exclaim: 'Stone!' Not at all. I say flesh and blood—very perfectly presented—perhaps with too much perfection of *method*.
. . . His heart shows itself in the delicacy of his handling. . . .
He is never in deep gloom or in violent sunshine. But he feels
deeply and vividly every delicate shade. We cannot ask for
more. Not every one is a Turgenev. Moreover, Turgenev is
not civilized (therein much of his charm for us) in the sense
Henry James is civilized. *Satis*."

From these sensitive words it is clear that he appreciated
the super-subtle, the ultra-civilized, as completely as he
grasped the life and thoughts of simple folk. And yet there
is not, so far as I can remember, a single portrait in his gallery
of a really subtle English type, for Marlowe, though English
in name, is not so in nature.

Between his voyages in those last days of his sailor's life
Conrad used to stay at rooms in Gillingham Street, near
Victoria Station. It was there that he read so prodigiously,
and there that he suffered from bouts of that lingering Congo
fever which dogged his health and fastened a deep, fitful gloom
over his spirit. In a letter to me he once said: "I don't say
anything of actual bodily pain, for, God is my witness, I care
for that less than nothing." He was, indeed, truly stoical, and
his naturally buoyant spirit reacted with extreme suddenness.
But all the years I knew him—thirty-one—he had to fight
for decent health. Such words as: "I have been abominably
ill—abominably is the right word," occur again and again in
his letters, and his creative achievement in a language not
native to him, in face of these constant bouts of illness, approaches the marvellous.

It was the sea that gave Conrad to the English language.
A fortunate accident—he could so easily have written in the
French language. He started his manhood, as it were, at Marseilles. In a letter to me, 1905, he says: "In Marseilles I did
begin life thirty-one years ago. It's the place where the puppy
opened his eyes." He was ever more at home with French
literature than with English, spoke that language with less
accent, liked Frenchmen, and better understood their clearer
thoughts. And yet, perhaps, not quite an accident; for, after
all, he had the roving quality which has made the English

the great sea nation of the world; and, I suppose, his instinct
led him to seek in English ships the fullest field of expression
for his roving nature. England, too, was to him the romantic
country; it had been enshrined for him, as a boy in Poland, by
Charles Dickens. He always spoke of Dickens with the affection we have for the writers who captivate our youth.

No one, I take it, ever read the earliest Conrad without the
bewildered fascination of one opening eyes on a new world:
without, in fact, the feeling he himself describes in that passage
of "Youth," where he wakes up in the open boat in his first
Eastern port, and sees "the East looking at him." I doubt if
he will ever be surpassed as a creator of what we Westerners
term "exotic atmosphere." The Malay coasts and rivers of
"Almayer's Folly," "An Outcast of the Islands" and the first
pages of "The Rescue"; the Congo of "Heart of Darkness";
the Central Southern America of "Nostromo," with many
other land and sea scapes, are bits of atmospheric painting
"in excelsis." Only one expression adequately describes the
sensations of us who read "Almayer's Folly" in 1894. We
rubbed our eyes. Conrad was critically accepted from the very
start; he never published a book that did not rouse a chorus
of praise; but it was twenty years before he was welcomed by
the public with sufficient warmth to give him a decent income.

"Chance," in 1914—an indifferent Conrad—at last brought
him fortune. From that year on to the end his books sold
well; yet, with the exception of "The Secret Sharer" and some
parts of "Victory," none of his work in that late period was
quite up to his own exalted mark. Was it natural that popular
success should have coincided with the lesser excellence; or was
it simply an example of how long the strange takes to pierce
the pickled hide of the reader of fiction?

It does disservice to Conrad's memory to be indiscriminate
in praise of his work. Already, in reaction from this wholesale laudation, one notices a tendency in the younger generation to tilt the nose skyward and talk of his "parade." The
shining work of his great period was before their time; it
places him among the finest writers of all ages. Conrad's work,
from "An Outcast of the Islands" to "The Secret Agent," his
work in "The Secret Sharer," in the first chapters of "The
Rescue" (written in 1898), and in some portions of "Victory,"
are to his work in "The Arrow of Gold" and the last part of
"The Rescue," as the value of pearl to that of mother-of-

pearl. He was very tired toward the end; he wore himself clean out. To judge him by tired work is absurd; to lump all his work together, as if he were always the same Conrad, imperils a just estimate of his greatness.

I first re-encountered Conrad some months after that voyage when we paid a visit together to "Carmen" at Covent Garden Opera. "Carmen" was a vice with us both. It was already his fourteenth time of seeing that really dramatic opera. The blare of Wagner left him as cold as it leaves me; but he had a curious fancy for Meyerbeer. In June 1910 he wrote: "I suppose I am now the only human being in these islands who thinks Meyerbeer a great composer; and I am an alien at that, and not to be wholly trusted." But music, fond though he was of it, could play no great part in a life spent at sea, and, after his marriage in 1895, in the country. He went up to town but seldom. He wrote always with blood and tears and needed seclusion for it. A letter to me, from Pent Farm in July 1900, thus describes the finish of "Lord Jim." "The end of 'Lord Jim' has been pulled off with a steady drag of twenty-one hours. I sent wife and child out of the house (to London) and sat down at 9 A. M. with a desperate resolve to be done with it. Now and then I took a walk round the house, out at one door, in at the other. Ten-minute meals—a great hush. Cigarette ends growing into a mound similar to a cairn over a dead hero. Moon rose over the barn, looked in at the window and climbed out of sight. Dawn broke, brightened. I put the lamp out, and went on with the morning breeze blowing the sheets of MS. all over the room. Sun rose. I wrote the last word and went into the dining-room. Six o'clock. I shared a piece of cold chicken with Escamillo" (his dog), "who was very miserable and in want of sympathy, having missed the child dreadfully all day. Felt very well, only sleepy; had a bath at seven, and at 8:30 was on my way to London."

I find another letter, on the finish of "Nostromo."

PENT FARM,
1st September, 1904.

"Finished! Finished on the 30th, in Hope's house in Stanford in Essex, to which I had to take my brain that seemed to turn to water. For a solid fortnight I've been sitting up. And all the time horrible toothache. On the 27th had to wire for dentist (couldn't leave the work), who came at 2 and dragged at the infernal thing, which seemed rooted in my very soul. The horror came away at last, leaving, however, one root in the gum. Then he grabbed for *that* till I leapt out of the chair. Thereupon he said: 'Don't think your nerves will stand any more of this.' I went back to my MS. at 6 P. M. At 11:30 something happened—what, I don't know. I was writing, and raised my eyes to look at the clock. The next thing I knew, I was sitting (not lying), sitting on the concrete outside the door. When I crawled in I found it was nearly one. I managed to get up-stairs and said to Jessie" (his wife) : " 'We must be off to-morrow.' I took thirty drops of chlorodyne and slept till 7. At 10 the motor-car from Ashford was in the yard, a 12 h. p. Darracq. I sat by the man's side like a corpse. Between Canterbury and Faversham he said to me, 'You look ill, Sir. Shall I stop?' Sittingbourne I remember as a brandy and soda. Good road, twenty-four miles an hour. In Chatham street crowded, packed. Going dead slow. Knocked down a man—old chap, apparently a bricklayer. Crowd around, cursing and howling. Helped him to my front seat, and I, standing on the step, got him to the hospital. No harm, only shaken. Got to Hope's at 5. That night I slept. Worked all day. In the evening Mrs. Hope gave me four candles, and on I went. Finished at 3."

I put this letter on record to show the painful and hectic conditions under which the end of "Nostromo" was written, because the melodramatic finish of that great book is the weakness thereof.

This spurt was characteristic of Conrad's endings; he finished most of his books in that way—his vivid nature instinctively staged itself with dramatic rushes. Moreover, all those long early years he worked under the whip-lash of sheer necessity. In 1909, writing to my wife, he says: "Excuse this discordant strain, but the fact is that I've just received the accounts of all my publishers, from which I perceive that all my immortal works (13 in all) have brought me last year something under five pounds in royalties. That sort of thing quenches that *joie de vivre* which should burn like a flame in an author's breast and, in the manner of an explosive engine, drive his pen onwards at thirty pages an hour."

A sailor and an artist, he had little sense of money. He was not of those who can budget exactly and keep within it; and anyway he had too little, however neatly budgeted. It is true that his dramatic instinct and his subtlety would take a sort of pleasure in plotting against the lack of money, but it was at best a lugubrious amusement for one who had to whip his brain along when he was tired, when he was ill, when he was almost desperate. Letter after letter, talk after talk, unfolded to me the travail of those years. He needed to be the Stoic he really was.

I used to stay with him a good deal from 1895–1905, first at Stanford in Essex, and then at Stanford in Kent. He was indefatigably good to me while my own puppy's eyes were opening to literature. In 1901, when I was still in the early stages of that struggle with his craft which a writer worth his salt never quite abandons, he could write thus: "That the man who has written once the 'Four Winds,' has written now the 'Man of Devon' volume, is a source of infinite gratification to me. It vindicates my insight, my opinion, my judgment, and it satisfies my affection for you—in whom I believed and am believing. Because that *is* the point: I *am* believing. You've gone now beyond the point when I could be of use to you otherwise than just by my belief."

His affectionate interest was always wholly generous like that. In his letters to me, two to three hundred, there is not a sentence which breaks, or even jars, the feeling that he cared that one should do good work. There is some valuable criticism, but never any impatience, and no stinting of appreciation or encouragement. He never went back on friendship. He never went back on anything, I think. The word "loyalty" has been much used by those who write or speak of him. It has been well used. He was always loyal to what he had at heart—to his philosophy, to his work, and to his friends; he was loyal even to his dislikes (not few) and to his scorn. People talk of Conrad as an aristocrat; I think it rather a silly word to apply to him. His mother's family, the Bebrowskis, were Polish land-owners; the Korzeniowskis, too, his father's family, came, I think, of landowning stock; but the word aristocrat is much too dry to fit Conrad; he had no touch with "ruling," no feeling for it, except, maybe, such as is necessary to sail a ship; he was first and last the rover and the artist, with such a first-hand knowledge of men and things that he was habitually impatient with labels and pigeon-holes, with cheap theorizing and word debauchery. He stared life very much in the face, and distrusted those who don't. Above all, he had the keen humor which spifflicates all class and catalogues, and all ideals and aspirations that are not grounded in the simplest springs of human nature. He laughed at the clichés of so-called civilization. His sense of humor, indeed, was far greater than one might think from his work. He had an almost ferocious enjoyment of the absurd. Writing seemed to dry or sardonize his sense of fun. "Borys" (his eldest son, then very small) "wants to know whether you are related to Jack the Giant-Killer— otherwise he is well." In a letter to my wife he thus describes the advent of his second son, who happened to be born in our house. "He arrived here to-day at 9:30 A. M. in a modest and unassuming manner which struck me very favorably. His manner is quiet—somnolent, his eyes contemplative, his forehead noble, his stature short, his nose pug, his countenance ruddy and weather-beaten." Referring to a little harmless carriage accident we had at Charing Cross, he writes: "I always feel that the bit of Strand in front of Charing Cross Station is about as near Eternity as any spot on earth." But in conversation his sense of fun was much more vivid; it would leap up in the midst of gloom or worry, and take charge with a shout.

Conrad had six country homes after his marriage, besides two temporary abodes. He wrote jestingly to my wife: "Houses are naturally rebellious and inimical to man." And, perhaps, having lived so much on ships, he really had a feeling of that sort. He certainly grew tired of them after a time.

I best remember Pent Farm—that little, very old, charming, if inconvenient, farmhouse, with its great barn beyond the yard, under the lee of the almost overhanging Pent. It was a friendly dwelling where you had to mind your head in connection with beams; and from whose windows you watched ducks and cats and lambs in the meadows beyond. He liked those quiet fields and that sheltering hill. Though he was not what we should call a "lover of nature" in the sense of one who spends long hours lost in the life of birds and flowers, of animals and trees, he could be vividly impressed by the charm and the variety of such things. He was fond, too, of Hudson's books; and no lover of Hudson's work is insensible to nature.

In Conrad's study at the Pent, we burned together many midnight candles, much tobacco. In that house was written some of the "Youth" volume, "Lord Jim," most of the

"Typhoon" volume, "Nostromo," "The Mirror of the Sea," "The Secret Agent," and other of Conrad's best work. Save that "The Nigger of the *Narcissus*" and the story "Youth" were written just before, at Stanford in Essex, the Pent may be said to synchronize with Conrad's best period. Kent was undoubtedly the county of his adoption, and this was the first of his four Kentish homes. Many might suppose that Conrad would naturally settle by the sea. He never did. He had seen too much of it; like the sailor, who when he turns into his bunk takes care that no sea air shall come in, he lived always well inland. The sea was no friend of one too familiar with its moods. He disliked being labelled a novelist of the sea. He wrote of the sea, as perhaps no one, not even Herman Melville, has written; but dominant in all his writing of the sea is the note of struggle and escape. His hero is not the sea, but man in conflict with that cruel and treacherous element. Ships he loved, but the sea—no. Not that he ever abused it, or talked of it with aversion; he accepted it as he accepted all the inscrutable remorselessness of Nature. It was man's job to confront Nature with a loyal and steady heart—that was Conrad's creed, his contribution to the dignity of life. Is there a better? First and last he was interested in men, fascinated by the terrific spectacle of their struggles in a cosmos about which he had no illusions. He was sardonic, but he had none of the cynicism characteristic of small, cold-hearted beings.

He customarily labored in the morning, and often would sit long hours over a single page. In 1906, when he was staying in our London house, he wrote to my wife: "I don't know that I am writing much in the little wooden house" (out in the garden), "but I smoke there religiously for $3\frac{1}{2}$ hours every morning, with a sheet of paper before me and an American fountain pen in my hand. What more could be expected from a conscientious author, I can't imagine."

In later years, when his enemy, gout, often attacked his writing hand, he was obliged to resort a good deal to dictation of first drafts. I cannot but believe that his work suffered from that necessity. But there were other and increasing handicaps —the war, which he felt keenly, and those constant bouts of ill-health which dragged at his marvellous natural vitality. I think I never saw Conrad quite in repose. His hands, his feet, his knees, his lips—sensitive, expressive, and ironical—something was always in motion, the dynamo never quite at rest within

him. His mind was extraordinarily active and his memory mo:
retentive, so that he stored with wonderful accuracy all th
observations of his dark-brown eyes, that were so piercing an
yet could be so soft. He had the precious faculty of interest i
detail. To that we owe his pictures of scenes and life long pa:
—their compelling verisimilitude, the intensely vivid variet
of their composition. The storehouse of his subconscious sel
was probably as interesting and comprehensive a museum a
any in the world. It is from the material in our subconsciou
minds that we create. Conrad's eyes never ceased snapshotting
and the millions of photographs they took were laid away b
him to draw on. Besides, he was not hampered in his natura
watchfulness by the preoccupation of an egoistic personality
He was not an egoist; he had far too much curiosity anc
genuine interest in things and people to be that. I don't mean
to say that he had not an interest in himself and a belief in his
own powers. His allusions to his work are generally disparaging; but at heart he knew the value of his gifts; and he liked
appreciation, especially from those (not many) in whose judgment he had faith. He received more praise, probably, than
any other writer of our time; but he never suffered from that
parvenu disease, swelled head; and "I," "I," "I," played no
part in his talk.

People have speculated on the literary influences that for
him were formative. Flaubert and Henry James have been
cited as his spiritual fathers. It won't do. Conrad was a most
voracious reader, and he was trilingual. A Slav temperament,
a life of duty and adventure, vast varied reading, and the
English language—those were the elements from which his
highly individual work emerged. Not I, who have so often
heard him speak of them, will deny his admiration for Flaubert, de Maupassant, Turgenev, and Henry James: but one
has only to read Conrad's first book, "Almayer's Folly," to
perceive that he started out on a path of his own, with a method
quite peculiar to himself, involuted to a dangerous degree,
perhaps; and I can trace no definite influence on him by any
writer. He was as different from Henry James as East from
West. Both had a certain natural intricacy and a super-
psychological bent, but there the likeness stops. As for
Flaubert—whom he read with constancy—that conscientious
Frenchman and determined stylist could do nothing for Conrad except give him pleasure. No one could help Conrad. He

had to subdue to the purposes of his imagination a language that was not native to him; to work in a medium that was not the natural clothing of his Polish temperament. There were no guides to the desert that he crossed. I think perhaps he most delighted in the writings of Turgenev, but there is not the slightest evidence that he was influenced by him. He loved Turgenev's personality, and disliked Tolstoi's. The name Dostoievski was in the nature of a red rag to him. I am told that he once admitted that Dostoievski was "deep as the sea." Perhaps that was why he could not bear him, or possibly it was that Dostoievski was too imbued with Russian essence for Polish appetite. In any case, his riderless extremisms offended something deep in Conrad.

I have spoken of his affection for Dickens. Trollope he liked. Thackeray I think not over much, though he had a due regard for such creations as Major Pendennis. Meredith's characters to him were "seven feet high," and his style too inflated. He admired Hardy's poetry. He always spoke with appreciation of Howells, especially of the admirable "Rise of Silas Lapham." His affectionate admiration for Stephen Crane we know from his introduction to Thomas Beers's biography of that gifted writer. Henry James in his middle period —the Henry James of "Daisy Miller," "The Madonna of the Future," "Greville Fane," "The Real Thing," "The Pension Beaurepas"—was precious to him. But of his feeling for that delicate master, for Anatole France, De Maupassant, Daudet, and Turgenev, he has written in his "Notes on Life and Letters." I remember he had a great liking for those two very different writers Balzac and Merimée.

Of philosophy he had read a good deal, but on the whole spoke little. Schopenhauer used to give him satisfaction twenty years and more ago, and he liked both the personality and the writings of William James.

I saw little of Conrad during the war. Of whom did one see much? He was caught in Poland at the opening of that business, and it was some months before he succeeded in getting home. Tall words such as "War to end War" left him, a Continental and a realist, appropriately cold. When it was over he wrote: "So I send these few lines to convey to you both all possible good wishes for unbroken felicity in your new home and many years of peace. At the same time I'll confess that neither felicity nor peace inspire me with much confidence.

There is an air of 'the packed valise' about these two divine
but unfashionable figures. I suppose the North Pole would be
the only place for them, where there is neither thought nor
heat, where the very water is stable, and the democratic
bawlings of the virtuous leaders of mankind die out into a
frozen, unsympathetic silence." Conrad had always a great
regard for men of action, for workmen who stuck to their last
and did their own jobs well; he had a corresponding distrust
of amateur omniscience and handy wiseacres; he curled his
lip at political and journalistic protestation; cheap-jackery
and clap-trap of all sorts drew from him a somewhat violently
expressed detestation. I suppose what he most despised in life
was ill-educated theory, and what he most hated, blatancy and
pretence. He smelled it coming round the corner and at once
his bristles would rise. He was an extremely quick judge of a
man. I remember a dinner convoked by me, that he might meet
a compatriot of his own married to one who was not a compatriot. The instant dislike he took to that individual was so
full of electricity that we did not dine in comfort. The dislike
was entirely merited. This quick instinct for character and
types inimical to him was balanced by equally sure predilections, so that his friendships were always, or nearly always,
lasting—I can think of only one exception. He illustrated
vividly the profound truth that friendship is very much an
affair of nerves, grounded in instinct rather than in reason or
in circumstance, the outcome of a sort of deep affinity which
prevents jarring. His Preface to the "Life of Stephen Crane"
supplies all the evidence we need of Conrad's instantaneous
yet lasting sympathy with certain people, and of his instant
antipathy to others. It contains also the assurance that he
"never kept a diary and never owned a notebook"—a statement
which surprised no one who knew the resources of his memory
and the brooding nature of his creative spirit. "Genius" has
somewhere been defined as the power to make much out of
little. In "Nostromo" Conrad made a continent out of a few
casual sailors' landings on the Central American coast twenty
years before. In "The Secret Agent" he created an underworld out of probably as little actual experience. On the
other hand, we have in "The Nigger," in "Youth" and "Heart
of Darkness" the raw material of his own life transmuted into
the gold of fine art. People, and there are such, who think
that writers like Conrad, if there be any, can shake things

from their sleeve, would be staggered if they could have watched the pain and stress of his writing life. In his last letter to me but one, February 1924, speaking of "The Rover," he says: "I have wanted for a long time to do a seaman's 'return' (before my own departure), and this seemed a possible peg to hang it on. The reception was good—and so were the sales—but when the book came out I was too seedy to care. I had about ten weeks of pretty bad time. My recovery was swift, but my confidence has been badly shaken. However, I have begun to work a little—on my runaway novel. I call it 'runaway' because I've been after it for two years ('The Rover' is a mere interlude) without being able to overtake it. The end seems as far as ever! It's like a chase in a nightmare— weird and exhausting. Your news that you have finished a novel brings me a bit of comfort. So there are novels that *can* be finished—then why not mine? Of course I see 'fiction' advertised in the papers—heaps of it. But published announcements seem to me mere phantasms. . . . I don't believe in their reality." There are dozens of such allusions to almost despairing effort in his letters. He must, like all good workmen, have had his hours of compensation; but if ever a man worked in the sweat of spirit and body, it was Conrad. That is what makes his great achievement so inspiring. He hung on to his job through every kind of weather, mostly foul. He never shirked. In an age more and more mechanical, more and more given to short cuts and the line of least resistance, the example of his life's work shines out; its instinctive fidelity, his artist's desire to make the best thing he could. Fidelity! Yes, that is the word which best sums up his life and work.

The last time I saw Conrad—about a year ago—I wasn't very well, and he came and sat in my bedroom, full of affectionate solicitude. It seems, still, hardly believable that I shall not see him again. His wife tells me that a sort of homing instinct was on him in the last months of his life, that he seemed sometimes to wish to drop everything and go back to Poland. Birth calling to Death—no more than that, perhaps, for he loved England, the home of his wandering, of his work, of his last long landfall.

If to a man's deserts is measured out the quality of his rest, Conrad shall sleep well.

Desmond MacCarthy

A HERMIT'S DAY

BLUE damask curtains were drawn across the windows, but one long slit of daylight made every shadowy object in the room discernible: a cold white pyramidal stove opposite the marble fireplace, the portraits and the magnificent mirror on the walls, five writing-tables piled with neat papers, and under its canopy of blue silk the low, plain bed, with a deep cleft in the swelling pillow. Absolute stillness reigned.

Outside a dazzling sun had long ago drunk up the freshness of morning. The balustrade of the Château steps was warm to the touch, and a surprising number of men were moving about watering newly planted trees. In the near distance a busy little village hummed and clanked and smoked, while far off, across fields of corn and vines, higher in the sky than the eye expected, above a scarf of cloud, shone mildly the snow mountains of Geneva.

Presently a quietly dressed man entered, followed by a lackey in a gorgeous livery carrying before him a satin suit with long lace cuffs, white stockings, and a pair of red-heeled shoes. At the rattle of drawn curtains a hollow groan came from the bed, and the being in it rolled round to the light. Part of a turban with wisps of grey hair hanging from it, part of a high yellow forehead, and one large uncommonly bright eye became visible between the peaks of the pillow. The eye watched the movements of the two men with the suspicious intensity of a jackdaw fixing some shiny object. Suddenly a voice of startling resonance—could it proceed from the old creature in the bed? —broke the silence.

"I am dying," it said.

The valet continued methodically to lay out the clothes.

More groans followed.

The voice spoke again, this time with a more plangent, peremptory ring:

"I am dying, my poor Wagnière, I am dying! Fetch Madame Denis."

"Certainly, monsieur."

The turbaned figure in the bed sat up suddenly.

"What!! Ten thousand panniers full of devils! I tell the man I'm dying, and he says, 'Certainly, monsieur'! Fly, idiot!"

The valet and the footman vanished the emaciated old head sank back upon the pillows with a gasp.

In a large room, beyond the antechamber, a man and two women were standing in the recess of a sunny window, waiting. The first was a priest of singularly simple, self-indulgent aspect, with a brown smear of snuff under his nose and the stains of many meals upon his cassock; and of the two women, one was middle-aged, plump, and self-important, and dressed in a manner which exhibited at once an absence of youthful charms and a desire to possess them, while the younger, who held an ape in her arms, though not very pretty, had a fresh, sweet, round, good-tempered face. The sound of voices, exaggerated by the well of the hall, penetrated through the open door. A tall man, whose fine physique and flawless health were accentuated by the severe neatness of his dress, was seen mounting the stairs, laughing as he listened to the vivacious chatter of a Swiss servant-girl.

"I assure Monsieur," she was saying, "it was because he couldn't wait for his coffee to cool. He burnt his mouth, and so he poured the rose-water into his cup. I told him he was more stupid than any one of his own turkeys, in spite of all his cleverness. Oh, he *was* sick! He kept on making himself sick all day, and he swallowed all the medicines in the house—though he said he didn't believe in them."

"Hold your tongue, Barbara!" exclaimed the round-about lady, moving majestically towards them. "How dare you speak like that of my Lord! Doctor Tronchin." She made a low courtesy. "Madame, your servant," he replied, with his hand on his chest. "The servant also of Mademoiselle Belle et Bonne," he added, with another bow and a smile to the younger. "And how is the illustrious old baby this morning, Mademoiselle?"

At that moment the other door opened and the secretary appeared.

"Mesdames, M. de Voltaire bids me tell you he is dying. Will you go at once?"

"Order breakfast and the clyster to be brought up immediately," said Madame Denis, leading the way.

The sage lay still with his withered arms outside the coverlet; at the sound of steps he began to moan softly. "Belle et Bonne" went up to the bed and kissed him. His eyes opened, and he looked at her intently for a moment. "It is life kissing death," he said presently, raising his hand and letting it drop gently on the counterpane. The next moment he was twisting in a spasm of colic and uttering imprecations.

"Oh, my poor Calas, what must you have suffered! Scoundrels, fiends, devils! Ou-ooo! Ou-ooo! Ecrasez l'infâme! Quick, Tronchin; my friend! how I suffer!"

After the physician's deft injection he was propped up with pillows, and, exhausted but smiling, he began to enjoy the sunshine and to feel hungry. A table with coffee was pushed near the bed. The day had begun. The phoenix had risen once more from its ashes.

"Ah! my Tronchin, a grain of opium and a little water can do more for me than all the systems of philosophy."

Madame Denis began to pour coffee, the hermit of Ferney to mumble his crust, Luc, the ape, to play with the curtains of the bed, and "Belle et Bonne" and Doctor Tronchin to take their breakfast.

"Adam, where art thou!" called the sage in his sombre and majestic tones, and the fat priest sidled awkwardly into view.

"Sit down, Adam. You have eaten of the Tree of Knowledge; so perhaps while I breakfast you will explain to me some of the contradictions which are so necessary to the salvation of the soul. . . ."

"Monsieur, if Monsieur will forgive . . ."

"Adam, the Tree of Knowledge is a little worm-eaten now; its roots are the works of rabbis, of Pope Gregory the Great, of Saint Thomas and Saint Bonaventura, of Saint Bernard, Luther, Calvin, the reverend Father Garasse, of Bellarmine, Suarez, and of the doctors Tournelli and Tamponet. Its bark is wrinkled; its leaves sting like nettles; its fruit is bitter as gall, and the juice of it flies to the head like opium; it produces sleep; indeed, it makes everyone go to sleep; but as soon as they wake up they carry their heads very high and look down on humanity; they proceed to speak unintelligible words which often bring them considerable wealth. How was it, Adam, to begin at the beginning, since it was said that the day that you eat of this fruit you would 'surely die,' that you managed nevertheless to live another nine hundred and thirty years?"

"Monsieur. . . ."

"Don't tease the poor Father, uncle," said "Belle et Bonne."

"The poor Father, indeed! the poor Calas! Ah, my child, as long as people continue to believe absurdities they will continue to commit atrocities! No, Adam, you must travel. We will play chess when you come back. You must penetrate into the land of Nod, where Cain built the City of Enoch, and there investigated carefully the number of masons, carpenters, ironworkers, locksmiths, weavers, shepherds, farmers, labourers, and overseers he employed, when there were still only four or five people on the face of the earth. Remember to tell me about the giants the angels begot upon the daughters of men. Only be careful, above all things, to address them civilly, for they are deficient in humour. I rely upon you to climb Mount Ararat, to examine the remains of the ark which was built of gopher wood, and to verify the calculations which the illustrious M. le Pelletier made on the spot. Measure the height of the mountain itself, and afterwards the altitude of Chimborazo in Peru, and of our Mont Saint-Gothard; then calculate how many inches of rainfall were required to cover them. Greet Father Noah, too, who first planted the vine for us all. We all deplore his having got drunk. Do not imitate him in this respect. And don't fail to visit the Tower of Babel, or to find out if Saint Gregory of Tours has estimated its dimensions correctly. From Babel you must go to Ur, in Chaldea. Try to discover from Abraham's descendants why he left that beautiful country to buy a tomb in Hebron and corn in Memphis; why he told everybody his wife was his sister; and, above all, what face-wash she used which made her still beautiful at ninety."

At this moment Wagnière entered with letters, and announced that the courier had arrived from Geneva and also several gentlemen.

"Save me," exclaimed the sage, holding up his hands devoutly, "save me from my friends, O God, and I will deal with my enemies myself. Who have come to see the rhinoceros this morning? What, that fellow! I wrote to him last week saying that, since I was dead, I should no more have the honour of

corresponding with him. He prints every word I say. Show him
up. I'll finish him, and then I'll see the Englishman."

A solemn man in a cherry-coloured coat was ushered in.

"Monsieur, I know absolutely nothing about any single question you are going to ask me."

The visitor, as though fascinated by the eyes of this extraordinary old mummy, advanced bowing:

"M. de Voltaire, you are the candle which lights the
world. . . ."

A piercing voice cut him short: "Quick, Babette, the ex-
tinguisher!"

"Has he gone?" inquired the old gentleman from under the
blankets. "Then I am ready to receive my Englishman. They
are a wonderful people," he said, rearranging his turban.
"When I was in London they buried a mathematician with the
pomp of a king."

A young man was graciously received.

"Sir," said the sage, in answer to some compliments on
French literature, "an Englishman who knows France well and
a Frenchman who knows England well are both the better for
it. The English know how to think; the French know how to
please. We are the whipped cream of Europe. There are not
twenty Frenchmen who understand Newton." Going on to talk
of science, he indulged in rather a pompous eulogy of the
Swiss savant, Haller.

"I am surprised, monsieur, that you should praise him so
much," said the young man, "for he does nothing but abuse
you."

"Perhaps," replied the sage sweetly, "we are both mistaken.
You have been amiable enough to say I have done a great work
for posterity. It is true—I have planted four thousand feet of
timber. I will rejoin you in the garden. Now for my letters."

The first one to be opened was the weekly budget of gossip
from Paris. To the enormous delight of Voltaire, it reported
that M. de Pompignan could not now appear in his carriage
without the boys in the street singing one of the songs the
hermit of Ferney had written in his honour; and sitting up in
bed, he began to sing in a nasal and spectral voice:

> *"Oui, ce Le Franc de Pompignan*
> *Est un terrible personnage,*
> *Oui, ses psaumes sont un ouvrage*
> *Qui nous fait bâiller longuement.*

"Oui, de province un président
Plein d'orgueil et de verbiage,
Nous paraît un pauvre pédant
Malgré son riche mariage.

"Ah, Tronchin, you never gave me a better prescription than when you ordered me to hunt Pompignan for two hours every morning!" And, turning to Father Adam, his eyes glowing like carbuncles, he went on, with great show of solemnity, stretching out a bony finger, and ending in a whisper of horror:

"Savez-vous pourquoi Jérémie
A tant pleuré pendant sa vie?
C'est qu'en prophéte il prévoyait
Qu'un jour Le Franc le traduirait."

"Go on, go on, read me more. So they sing it in the street!"
But when the letter went on to report that someone had written to say that Voltaire, gentleman-in-waiting to the King, was the nephew of a pastry-cook, he became extremely excited. "I'll have him Bastilled! Slander must be suppressed. I shall write to the Pompadour. He is not fit to live with human beings"; and the concluding passage produced still more violent effect. It reported that a young man, M. Arnaud, being in Berlin, had addressed a letter in verse to Frederick II, who had himself replied in verse, saying that the sun of young Arnaud was rising, while the sun of Voltaire was going to bed.
"The dawn of Arnaud!" he screamed, throwing off the cloths. "Voltaire setting! It's Frederick's business to govern, not to judge. I'll teach this king with his *œuvres de poésie* that Voltaire is not in bed"; and, tearing on his stockings, he dismissed the company.
All the morning more and more visitors kept arriving. Indeed, they sat down more than thirty to a dinner, at which the host made only a brief appearance—still in his dressing-gown. He laughed till the tears came into his eyes at a young man's answer to the effect that he had been turning Catholic: "You see he does not say he is one *now*. What a splendid answer! My friend," he added, when he had recovered, "he only half lives who half thinks. The consolation of life is to say what one thinks." He received compliments on his adopted daughter, Mademoiselle Corneille, now happily married, saying that nothing had given more satisfaction at the time; but that now,

alas! he could not be happy till he had married Mademoiselle
Calas to two counsellors of the Parliament Toulouse. A
dramatic performance of *Zaïre* was decided on as the evening's
entertainment. The bustle of preparations, the cries, the laughter, the embraces, seemed to put the old man in a fever. He
sang, he talked, he shouted down the others; he seemed to be
everywhere at once, hauling out costumes, reciting verses,
acting, gesticulating: and then he vanished like a ghost for
two hours. At the performance he sat in the wings, but in view
of the audience, leading the applause; when the actors went
wrong lifting eyes and hands to heaven, when they spoke or
acted well breaking out into exclamations: "Clarion could not
have done it better!" "It's Lekain, pure Lekain! Incomparable!" When Madame Denis appeared herself on the scene,
acting, indeed, with great spirit, despite her solid proportions,
he was moved to tears. His forty-two diseases were forgotten.
Then his face suddenly contracted with rage: the President
de Brosses had fallen into a gentle sleep; it was unmistakable—
he was actually snoring. "Do you imagine you're on the bench?"
he screamed, flinging his hat in the face of the sleeping man.
There was a shout of laughter, and the tragedy went on again.
In the dining-room a gorgeous supper had been prepared.
Outside in the darkness the noise of chatter and laughter could
be heard, and the lighted windows shone far down the long new
avenue. M. Voltaire sat at the head of his table, telling stories
and mimicking actors, till a breath of cool air from the gardens
suddenly reminded him of his seventy years. He got up and
addressed the company: "Love like fools when you are young;
work like devils when you are old. It is the only way to live.
Good night, my children." The question where they were all
to sleep—for it was too late for them to get back to Geneva—
was left for Madame Denis to decide; and with a parting and
perhaps too lively joke the hermit of Ferney disappeared.

Hours after the candles of the supper table began to gutter
down, the old man, once more in his turban and Persian robe,
his wig and satin suit upon a chair, was writing, now at this
table and now at that, now dictating to Wagnière from his bed,
now drawing up a pamphlet purporting to be written by someone else, now making notes from that cold moving document
The History of the Calas, now bombarding Villars and
Richelieu with amusing letters, now tickling the vanity of
Madame de Pompadour ("always one of us") and Madame

a duchesse de Choiseul—letters in which every line, however airy and discursive, had an end in view. Last, having twice dismissed Wagnière and twice recalled him by thumping on the wall, he took a four-sided sheet of quarto paper and, inscribing neatly in one cornor *"écras: l'inf;"* he began a letter to Comte d'Argental and his wife.

"My angels," it ran, "it is now fifty years since you were good enough to love me a little. I regard myself already as a dead man, although I enliven my last agonies as best I can. I know that wherever you are you are making others happy, and that is the best way of being happy oneself. As for me, poor shivery old mortal, I am waging war till the last moment with priests, persecutors, Jesuits, Jansenists, Molinists, Frérons, Pompignans, right and left, preachers of all sorts and J. J. Rousseau. I receive a hundred thrusts. I return two hundred. I can still laugh; and thank God! I still see this life as a farce which sometimes turns to tragedy. . . ." And so on, and so on, till the paper was covered, and the sky had begun to turn hard and clear above the mountains behind Geneva, when the turbaned head rested again in the cleft of the pillow.

Virginia Woolf

DR. BURNEY'S EVENING PARTY

THE party was given either in 1777 or in 1778; on which day or month of the year is not known, but the night was cold. Fanny Burney, from whom we get much of our information, was accordingly either twenty-five or twenty-six, as we choose. But in order to enjoy the party to the full it is necessary to go back some years and to scrape acquaintance with the guests.

Fanny, from the earliest days, had always been fond of writing. There was a cabin at the end of her stepmother's garden at King's Lynn, where she used to sit and write of an afternoon till the oaths of the seamen sailing up and down the river drove her in. But it was only in the afternoon and in remote places that her half-suppressed, uneasy passion for writing had its way. Writing was held to be slightly ridiculous in a girl; rather unseemly in a woman. Besides, one never knew, if a girl kept a diary, whether she might not say something indiscreet—so Miss Dolly Young warned her; and Miss Dolly Young, though exceedingly plain, was esteemed a woman of the highest character in King's Lynn. Fanny's step-mother also disapproved of writing. Yet so keen was the joy— "I cannot express the pleasure I have in writing down my thoughts at the very moment, and my opinion of people when I first see them," she wrote—that scribble she must. Loose sheets of paper fell from her pocket and were picked up and read by her father to her agony and shame; once she was forced to make a bonfire of all her papers in the back garden. At last some kind of compromise seems to have been arrived at. The morning was sacred to serious tasks like sewing; it was only in the afternoon that she allowed herself to scribble —letters, diaries, stories, verses in the look-out place which overhung the river, till the oaths of the sailors drove her in.

There was something strange in that, perhaps, for the eighteenth century was the age of oaths. Fanny's early diary is larded with them. "God help me." "Split me." "Stap my vitals," together with damned and devilishes dropped daily and hourly from the lips of her adored father and her venerated Daddy Crisp. Perhaps Fanny's attitude to language was altogether a little abnormal. She was immensely susceptible to the power of words, but not nervously or acutely as Jane Austen was. She adored fluency and the sound of language pouring warmly and copiously over the printed page. Directly she read *Rasselas*, enlarged and swollen sentences formed on the tip of her childish pen, in the manner of Dr. Johnson. Quite early in life she would go out of her way to avoid the plain name of Tomkins. Thus, whatever she heard from her Cabin at the end of the garden was sure to affect her more than most girls, and it is also clear that while her ears were sensitive to sound, her soul was sensitive to meaning. There was something a little prudish in her nature. Just as she avoided the name of Tomkins, so she avoided the roughnesses, the asperities, the plainnesses of daily life. The chief fault that mars the extreme vivacity and vividness of the early diary is that the profusion of words tends to soften the edges, and the sweetness of the sentiment to smooth out the outlines. Thus, when she heard the sailors swearing, though Maria Allen, her half-sister would, one believes, have liked to stay, and perhaps toss a kiss over the water—her future history allows us to take the liberty of thinking so—Fanny went indoors.

Fanny went indoors, but not to solitary meditation. The house, whether it was in Lynn or in London—and by far the greater part of the year was spent in Poland Street—hummed with activity. There was the sound of the harpsichord; the sound of singing; there was the sound—for such concentration seems to pervade a whole house with its murmur—of Dr. Burney writing furiously, surrounded by notebooks in his study; and there were great bursts of chatter and laughter when, returning from their various occupations, the Burney children met together. Nobody enjoyed family life more than Fanny did. For there her shyness only served to fasten the nickname of Old Lady upon her; there she had a familiar audience for her humour; there she need not bother about her clothes; there—perhaps the fact that their mother had died when they were all young was partly the cause of it—was that intimacy which expresses itself in jokes and legends and a private language ("The wig is wet," they would say, winking at each other) ; there were endless confabulations, and confidences between sisters and brothers and brothers and sisters. Nor could there be any doubt that the Burneys—Susan and James and Charles and Fanny and Hetty and Charlotte—were a gifted race. Charles was a scholar; James was a humorist; Fanny was a writer; Susan was musical—each had some special gift or characteristic to add to the common stock. And besides their natural gifts they were happy in the fact that their father was a very popular man; a man, too, so admirably situated by his talents, which were social, and his birth, which was gentle, that they could mix without difficulty either with lords or with book-binders, and had, in fact, as free a run of life as could be wished.

As for Dr. Burney himself, there are some points about which, at this distance of time, one may feel dubious. It is difficult to be sure what, had one met him now, one would have felt for him. One thing is certain—one would have met him everywhere. Hostesses would be competing to catch him. Notes would wait for him. Telephone bells would interrupt him. For he was the most sought-after, the most occupied of men. He was always dashing in and dashing off. Sometimes he dined off a box of sandwiches in his carriage. Sometimes he went out at seven in the morning, and was not back from his round of music lessons till eleven at night. And when he was not teaching he was writing. The "habitual softness of his manners," his great social charm, his haphazard untidy ways; everything, notes, money, manuscripts, was tossed into a drawer, and he was robbed of all his savings once, but his friends were delighted to make it up for him; his odd adventures—did he not fall asleep after a bad crossing at Dover, and so return to France and so have to cross the Channel again?—endeared him to everybody. It is, perhaps, his diffuseness that makes him a trifle nebulous. He seems to be for ever writing and then re-writing, and requiring his daughters to write for him, endless books and articles, while over him unchecked, unfiled, unread, perhaps, pour down notes, letters, invitations to dinner which he cannot destroy and means some day to annotate and collect, until he seems to melt away at last in a cloud of words. When he died at the age of eighty-eight, there was nothing to be done by the most devoted of daughters but to burn the whole accumulation entire. Even Fanny's love of language was suffocated. But if we fumble a little as to our feeling for Dr. Burney, Fanny certainly did not. She adored her father. She never minded how many times she had to lay aside her own writing in order to copy out his. And he returned her affection. Though his ambition for her success at Court was foolish, perhaps, and almost cost her her life, she had only to cry when a distasteful suitor was pressed on her, "Oh Sir, I wish for nothing! Only let me live with you!" for the emotional doctor to reply "My Life! Thou shalt live with me for ever if thou wilt. Thou canst not think I meant to get rid of thee?" And not only were his eyes full of tears, but, what was more remarkable, he never mentioned Mr. Barlow again. Indeed, the Burneys were a happy family; a mixed composite, oddly assorted family; for there were the Allens, too, and little half-brothers and half-sisters were being born and growing up.

So time passed, and the passage of the years made it impossible for the family to continue in Poland Street any longer. First they moved to Queen Square, and then, in 1774, to the house where Newton had lived, in St. Martin's Street, Leicester Fields; where his Observatory still stood, and his room with the painted panels was still to be seen. Here in a mean street, but in the centre of the town, the Burneys set up their establishment. Here Fanny went on scribbling, stealing to the Observatory as she had stolen to the Cabin at Lynn, for she exclaimed, "I cannot any longer resist what I find to be irresistible, the pleasure of popping down my thoughts from time to time upon paper." Here came so many famous people either to be closeted with the doctor, or, like Garrick, to sit with him while his fine head of natural hair was brushed, or to join the lively family dinner, or, more formally to gather together in a musical party, where all the Burney children played and their father "dashed away" on the harpsichord, and perhaps some foreign musician of distinction performed a solo—so many people came for one reason or another to the house in St. Martin's Street that it is only the eccentrics, the grotesques that catch the eye. One remembers, for instance, the Ajujari, the astonishing soprano, because she had been "mauled as an infant by a pig, in consequence of which she is reported to have a silver side." One remembers Bruce, the traveller, because he had a "most extraordinary complaint. When he attempted to speak, his whole stomach suddenly seemed to heave like an organ bellows. He did not wish to make any secret about it, but spoke of it as having originated in Abyssinia. However, one evening, when he appeared rather agitated, it lasted much longer than usual, and was so violent that it alarmed the company." One seems to remember, for she paints herself while she paints the others, Fanny herself slipping eagerly and lightly in and out of all this company, with her rather prominent gnat-like eyes, her shy, awkward manners that concealed the quickest observation, the most retentive memory, so that as soon as the company had gone, she stole to the Observatory and wrote down every word, every scene, in letters twelve pages long for her beloved Daddy Crisp at Chessington. For that old hermit—he had retired to a house in a field in dudgeon with society—though professing to be better pleased with a bottle of wine in his cellar and a horse in his stable, and a game of backgammon at night, than with all the fine company in the world, was always agog for news. He scolded his Fannikin if she did not tell him all about her fine goings-on. And he scolded her again if she did not write at full tilt exactly as the words came into her head.

Mr. Crisp wanted to know in particular "about Mr. Greville and his notions." For, indeed, Mr. Greville was a perpetual source of curiosity. It is a thousand pities that time with her poppy dust has covered Mr. Greville, who was once so eminent so that only his most prominent features, his birth, his person, and his nose emerge. Fulke Greville was the descendant—he must, one fancies, have emphasized the fact from the way in which it is repeated—of the friend of Sir Philip Sidney. A coronet, indeed, "hung almost suspended over his head." In person he was tall and well proportioned. "His face, features, and complexion were striking for masculine beauty." "His air and carriage were noble with conscious dignity"; his bearing was "lofty, yet graceful." But all these gifts and qualities, to which one must add that he rode and fenced and danced and played tennis to admiration, were marred by prodigious faults. He was supercilious in the extreme; he was selfish; he was fickle. He was a man of violent temper. His introduction to Dr. Burney in the first place was due to his doubt whether a musician could be fit company for a gentleman. When he found that young Burney not only played the harpsichord to perfection, but curved his finger and rounded his

hand as he played; that he answered plain "Yes, Sir," or "No,
Sir," being more interested in the music than in his patron;
that it was only indeed when Greville himself thrummed per-
tinaciously from memory that he could stand it no longer, and
broke into vivacious conversation—it was only when he found
that young Burney was not only gifted but well bred into the
bargain that, being himself a very clever man, he no longer
stood upon his dignity. Burney became his friend and equal.
Burney, indeed, almost became his victim. For if there was one
thing that the descendant of the friend of Sir Philip Sidney
detested it was what he called "fogrum." By that expressive
word he seems to have meant the middle-class virtues of discretion and respectability, as opposed to the aristocratic virtues of what he called "*ton.*" Life must be lived dashingly,
daringly, with perpetual display, even if the display was extremely expensive, and, as seemed possible to those who trailed
dismally round his grounds praising the improvements, as
boring to the man who had made them as to the unfortunate
guests whose admiration he insisted upon extorting. But Greville could not endure fogrum in himself or in his friends. He
threw the obscure young musician into the fast life of White's
and Newmarket, and watched with amusement to see if he sank
or swam. Burney, most adroit of men, swam as if born to the
water, and the descendant of the friend of Sir Philip Sidney
was pleased. From being his protégé, Burney became his confidant. Indeed, the splendid gentleman, for all his high carriage, was in need of one. For Greville, could one wipe away
the poppy dust that covers him, was one of those tortured and
unhappy souls who find themselves torn asunder by opposite
desires. On the one hand he was consumed with the wish to be
in the first flight of fashion and to do "the thing," however
costly or dreary "the thing" might be. On the other, he was
secretly persuaded that "the proper bent of his mind and
understanding was for metaphysics." Burney, perhaps, was
a link between the world of *ton* and the world of fogrum. He
was a man of breeding who could dice and bet with the bloods;
he was also a musician who could talk of intellectual things
and ask clever people to his house.

Thus Greville treated the Burneys as his equals, and came
to their house, though his visits were often interrupted by the
violent quarrels which he managed to pick even with the amiable Dr. Burney himself. Indeed, as time went on there was no-

body with whom Greville did not quarrel. He had lost heavily
at the gambling-tables. His prestige in society was sunk. His
habits were driving his family from him. Even his wife, by
nature gentle and conciliatory, though excessive thinness
made her seem fitted to sit for a portrait "of a penetrating,
puissant and sarcastic fairy queen," was wearied by his infi-
delities. Inspired by them she had suddenly produced that famous Ode to Indifference, "which had passed into every collection of fugitive pieces in the English language" and (it is
Madam D'Arblay who speaks) "twined around her brow a
garland of wide-spreading and unfading fragrance." Her
fame, it may be, was another thorn in her husband's side, for
he, too, was an author. He himself had produced a volume of
Maxims and Characters; and having "waited for fame with
dignity rather than anxiety, because with expectation un-
clogged with doubt," was beginning perhaps to become a little
impatient. Fame held aloof. Meanwhile he was fond of the
society of clever people, and it was largely at his desire that
the famous party in St. Martin's Street met together that
very cold night.

ii

In those days, when London was so small, it was easier than
now for people to stand out on an eminence which they
scarcely struggled to keep, but enjoyed by unanimous consent. Everybody knew and remembered when they saw her
that Mrs. Greville had written an Ode to Indifference; everybody knew that Mr. Bruce had travelled in Abyssinia; so, too,
everybody knew that there was a house at Streatham presided
over by a lady called Mrs. Thrale. Without troubling to write
an ode, without hazarding her life among savages, without
possessing either high rank or vast wealth, Mrs. Thrale was
a celebrity. By the exercise of powers difficult to define—for
to feel them one must have sat at table and noticed a thousand audacities and deftnesses and skilful combinations which
die with the moment—Mrs. Thrale had the reputation of a
great hostess. Her fame spread far beyond her house. People
who had never seen her discussed her. People wanted to know
what she was like; whether she was really so witty and so well
read; whether it was a pose; whether she had a heart; whether
she loved her husband the brewer, who seemed a dull dog; why

she had married him; whether Dr. Johnson was in love with her—what, in short, was the secret of her power. For power she had—that was indisputable.

Even then, perhaps, it would have been difficult to say in what it consisted. For she possessed the one quality which can never be named; she enjoyed the one gift which never ceases to excite discussion. Somehow or other she was a personality. The young Burneys, for instance, had never seen Mrs. Thrale or been to Streatham, but the stir which she set going round her had reached them in St. Martin's Street. When their father came back from giving his first music lesson to Miss Thrale at Streatham they flocked about him to hear his account of her mother. Was she as brilliant as people made out? Was she kind? Was she cruel? Had he liked her? Dr. Burney was in high good temper—in itself a proof of his hostess's power—and he replied, not, we may be sure, as Fanny rendered it, that she was a "star of the first constellation of female wits: surpassing, rather than equalizing the reputation which her extraordinary endowments, and the splendid fortune which made them conspicuous, had blazoned abroad" —that was written when Fanny's style was odd and tarnished, and its leaves were fluttering and falling profusely to the ground; the doctor, we may suppose, answered briskly that he had enjoyed himself hugely; that the lady was a very clever lady; that she had interrupted the lesson all the time; that she had a very sharp tongue—there was no doubt of that; but he would go to the stake for it that she was a good-hearted woman at bottom. Then they must have pressed to know what she looked like. She looked younger than her age—which was about forty. She was rather plump, very small, fair with very blue eyes, and had a scar or cut on her lip. She painted her cheeks, which was unnecessary, because her complexion was rosy by nature. The whole impression she made on one was of bustle and gaiety and good temper. She was, he said, a woman "full of sport," whom nobody could have taken for a creature that the doctor could not bear, a learned lady. Less obviously, she was very observant, as her anecdotes were to prove; capable of passion, though that was not yet visible at Streatham; and, while curiously careless and good-tempered about her dues as a wit or a blue stocking, had an amusing pride in being descended from a long line of Welsh gentry (whereas the Thrales were obscure), and drew satisfaction now and then from the reflection that in her veins ran the blood, as the College of Heralds acknowledged, of Adam of Salzburg.

Many women might have possessed these qualities without being remembered for them. Mrs. Thrale possessed besides one that has given her immortality: the power of being the friend of Dr. Johnson. Without that addition, her life might have fizzled and flamed to extinction, leaving nothing behind it. But the combination of Dr. Johnson and Mrs. Thrale created something as solid, as lasting, as remarkable in its way as a work of art. And this was an achievement that called for much rarer powers on the part of Mrs. Thrale than the qualities of a good hostess. When the Thrales first met Johnson he was in a state of profound gloom, crying out such lost and terrible words that Mr. Thrale put his hand before his mouth to silence him. Physically, too, he was afflicted with asthma and dropsy; his manners were rough; his habits were gross; his clothes were dirty; his wig was singed; his linen was soiled; and he was the rudest of men. Yet Mrs. Thrale carried this monster off with her to Brighton and then domesticated him in her house at Streatham, where he was given a room to himself, and where he spent habitually some days in the middle of every week. This might have been on her part but the enthusiasm of a curiosity hunter, ready to put up with a host of disagreeables for the sake of having at her house the original Dr. Johnson, whom anybody in England would gladly pay to see. But it is clear that her connoisseurship was of a finer type. She understood—her anecdotes prove it—that Dr. Johnson was somehow a rare, an important, an impressive human being whose friendship might be a burden but was certainly an honour. And it was not by any means so easy to know this then as it is now. What one knew then was that Dr. Johnson was coming to dinner. Who would be there, one wondered with anxiety? For if it was a Cambridge man there might be an outburst. If it was a Whig there would certainly be a scene. If it was a Scotsman anything might happen. Such were his whims and prejudices. Next one would have to bethink one, what had one ordered for dinner? For the food never went uncriticized; and even when one had provided him with young peas from the garden, one must not praise them. Were not the young peas charming, Mrs. Thrale asked once? and he turned upon her, after gobbling down masses of pork and veal pie with lumps of sugar in it, and snapped "Perhaps they

ould be so—to a pig." And then what would the talk be
bout, one must have speculated? If it got upon painting or
music he was apt to dismiss it with scorn, for both arts were
indifferent to him. Then if a traveller told a tale he was sure
o pooh-pooh it, because he believed nothing that he had not
seen. Then if any one were to express sorrow in his presence
t might well draw down upon one a rebuke for insincerity.
'When, one day, I lamented the loss of a cousin killed in
America: 'Prithee, my dear,' said he, 'have done with cant-
ng: how would the world be the worse for it, I may ask, if all
your relations were at once spitted like larks, and roasted for
Presto's supper?' In short, the meal would be strewn with
difficulties; the whole affair might run upon the rocks at any
moment."

Had Mrs. Thrale been a shallow curiosity hunter she would
have shown him for a season or so and then let him drop. But
Mrs. Thrale realized even at the moment that one must submit to be snubbed and bullied and irritated and offended by
Dr. Johnson because—well, what was the force that sent an
impudent and arrogant young man like Boswell slinking back
to his chair like a beaten boy when Johnson bade him? Why
did she herself sit up till four in the morning pouring out tea
for him? There was a force in him that awed even a competent woman of the world, that subdued even a thick-skinned,
conceited boy. He had a right to scold Mrs. Thrale for inhumanity, when she knew that he spent only seventy pounds a
year on himself and with the rest of his income supported a
houseful of decrepit and ungrateful lodgers. If he gobbled at
table and tore the peaches from the wall he went back punctually to London to see that his wretched inmates had their
three good meals over the week-end. Moreover, he was a ware-
house of knowledge. If the dancing-master talked about dancing, Johnson could out-talk him. He could keep one amused
by the hour with his tales of the underworld, of the topers and
scallywags who haunted his lodgings and claimed his bounty.
He said things casually that one never forgot. But what was
perhaps more engaging than all his learning and virtue, was
his love of pleasure, his detestation of the hermit, of the mere
book-worm, his passion for life and society. And then, as a
woman would, Mrs. Thrale loved him for his courage—that
he had separated two fierce dogs that were tearing each other
to pieces in Mr. Beauclerc's sitting-room; that he had thrown

a man, chair and all, into the pit of a theatre; that, blind and
twitching as he was, he rode to hounds on Brightelmston
Downs, and followed the hunt as if he had been a gay dog in
stead of a huge and melancholy old man. Moreover, there was
a natural affinity between them. She drew him out: she made
him say what without her he would never have said; indeed
he had confessed to her some painful secret of his youth which
she never revealed to anybody. Above all, they shared the
same passion. Of talk they could neither of them ever have
enough.

Thus Mrs. Thrale could always be counted on to produce
Dr. Johnson; and it was, of course, Dr. Johnson whom Mr
Greville most particularly wished to meet. As it happened
Dr. Burney had renewed his acquaintance with Dr. Johnson
after many years, when he went to Streatham to give his first
music lesson. Dr. Johnson had been there, "wearing his mildest aspect." For he remembered Dr. Burney with kindness.
He remembered a letter that Dr. Burney had written to him
in praise of the dictionary. He remembered, too, that Dr.
Burney having called upon him, years ago, and found him
out, had dared to cut some bristles from the hearth broom to
send to an admirer. When he met Dr. Burney again at Streatham, he had instantly taken a liking to him; soon he was
brought by Mrs. Thrale to see Dr. Burney's books; it was
quite easy, therefore, for Dr. Burney to arrange that on a
certain night in the early spring of 1777 or 1778, Mr. Greville's great wish to meet Dr. Johnson and Mrs. Thrale should
be gratified. A day was fixed and the engagement was made.

Nobody could fail to be aware that the meeting of so many
marked and distinguished characters might be difficult. Dr.
Johnson was, of course, notoriously formidable. But the danger was not confined to Dr. Johnson; Mr. Greville himself
was domineering and exacting; his temper had grown still
more uncertain since his gambling losses had made him of less
account in the world of *ton*. Then Mrs. Greville was a poetess;
it was likely enough that she would prove her right to the
laurel by some contest with a lady whose fame was at the moment brighter than her own. Mrs. Thrale was good humour
itself; still, it was likely that she would try for a tilt with
Mrs. Greville; nor was she wholly dependable, for she had
"sudden flashes of wit which she left to their own consequences." Besides, it was an occasion; everybody felt it to be

so; wits would be on the strain; expectation on tiptoe. Dr.
Burney, with the tact of a man of the world, foresaw these
difficulties, and took steps to avert them. But there was, one
vaguely feels, something a little obtuse about Dr. Burney.
The eager, kind, busy man, with his head full of music and his
desk stuffed with notes, lacked discrimination. He had not
noticed that Dr. Johnson, when he visited them the other day,
and found them at the harpsichord, had withdrawn to the
bookcase and browsed upon a volume of the *British Encyclopædia*, till the music was over. He was not aware, in spite of
the way in which Mrs. Thrale interrupted his lessons, that she
did not know "a flat from a sharp." To his innocent mind,
music was the universal specific. If there was going to be any
difficulty music would solve it. He therefore asked Signor
Piozzi to be of the party.

The night arrived. The fire was lit. The chairs were placed.
The company arrived. As Dr. Burney had foreseen, the awkwardness was great. Things indeed seemed to go wrong from
the start. Dr. Johnson had come in his worsted wig, very clean
and prepared evidently for enjoyment. But after one look at
him, Mr. Greville seemed to decide that there was something
formidable about the old man; it would be better not to compete; it would be better to play the fine gentleman, and leave
it to literature to make the first advances. Murmuring, apparently, something about having the toothache, Mr. Greville "assumed his most supercilious air of distant superiority
and planted himself, immovable as a noble statue, upon the
hearth." He said nothing. Mrs. Greville was longing to distinguish herself, but judging it proper for Dr. Johnson to begin, she said nothing. Mrs. Thrale, who might have been expected to break up the solemnity, felt, it seemed, that the
party was not her party and, waiting for the principals to
engage, resolved to say nothing. Mrs. Crewe, the Grevilles'
daughter, lovely and vivacious as she was, had come to be
entertained and instructed and therefore very naturally she,
too, said nothing. Nobody said anything. Everybody waited.
Here was the very moment for which Dr. Burney in his wisdom had prepared. He nodded to Signor Piozzi; and Signor
Piozzi stepped to the instrument and began to sing. Accompanying himself on the pianoforte, he sang an *aria parlante*.
He sang beautifully, he sang his best. But far from breaking
the awkwardness and loosing the tongues, the music increased

the constraint. Nobody spoke. Everybody waited for Dr.
Johnson to begin. There, indeed, they showed their fatal
ignorance, for if there was one thing that Dr. Johnson never
did, it was to begin. Somebody had always to start a topic
before he consented to pursue it or demolish it. Now he waited
in silence to be challenged. But he waited in vain. Nobody
dared. The roulades of Signor Piozzi continued uninterrupted. As he saw his chance of a pleasant evening of conversation diminish, Dr. Johnson sank into silent abstraction and
sat with his back to the piano gazing at the fire. The *aria
parlante* continued uninterrupted. At last the strain became
unendurable. At last Mrs. Thrale could stand it no longer. It
was the attitude of Mr. Greville, apparently, that roused her
resentment. There he stood on the hearth in front of the fire
"staring around him at the whole company in curious silence
sardonically." What right had he, even if he were the descendant of the friend of Sir Philip Sidney, to despise the company
and absorb the fire? Her own pride of ancestry suddenly
asserted itself. Did not the blood of Adam of Salzburg run in
her veins? Was it not as blue as that of the Grevilles and far
more sparkling? Giving rein to the spirit of recklessness which
sometimes bubbled in her, she rose, and stole on tiptoe to the
pianoforte. Signor Piozzi was still singing and accompanying
himself dramatically as he sang. She began a ludicrous mimicry of his gestures: she shrugged her shoulders, she cast up
her eyes, she reclined her head on one side just as he did. At
this singular display the company began to titter—indeed, it
was a scene that was to be described "from coterie to coterie
throughout London, with comments and sarcasms of endless
variety." People who saw Mrs. Thrale at her mockery that
night never forgot that this was the beginning of that criminal affair, the first scene of that "most extraordinary drama"
which lost Mrs. Thrale the respect of friends and children,
which drove her in ignominy from England, and scarcely allowed her to show herself in London again—this was the beginning of her most reprehensible, her most unnatural passion
for one who was not only a musician but a foreigner. All this
still lay on the laps of the gods. Nobody yet knew of what
iniquity the vivacious lady was capable. She was still the respected wife of a wealthy brewer. Happily, Dr. Johnson was
staring at the fire, and knew nothing of the scene at the piano.
But Dr. Burney put a stop to the laughter instantly. He was

shocked that his guest, even if he were a foreigner and a musi-
c an, should be ridiculed behind his back, and stealing to Mrs.
Thrale he whispered kindly but with authority in her ear that
if she had no taste for music herself she should consider the
feelings of those who had. Mrs. Thrale took the rebuke with
admirable sweetness, nodded her acquiescence and returned to
her chair. But she had done her part. After that nothing more
could be expected from her. Let them now do what they chose
—she washed her hands of it, and seated herself "like a pretty
little Miss," as she said afterwards, to endure what yet remained to be endured "of one of the most humdrum evenings
that she had ever passed."

If no one had dared to tackle Dr. Johnson in the beginning
it was scarcely likely that they would dare now. He had apparently decided that the evening was a failure so far as talk
was concerned. If he had not come dressed in his best clothes
he might have had a book in his pocket which he could have
pulled out and read. As it was, nothing but the resources of
his own mind were left him; but these were huge; and these he
explored as he sat with his back to the piano, looking the very
image of gravity, dignity and composure.

At last the *aria parlante* came to an end. Signor Piozzi indeed, finding nobody to talk to, fell asleep in his solitude. Even
Dr. Burney by this time must have been aware that music is
not an infallible specific; but there was nothing for it now.
Since people would not talk, the music must continue. He
called upon his daughters to sing a duet. And then, when that
was over, there was nothing for it but that they must sing
another. Signor Piozzi still slept, or still feigned sleep. Dr.
Johnson explored still further the magnificent resources of
his own mind. Mr. Greville still stood superciliously upon the
hearth-rug. And the night was cold.

But it was a grave mistake to suppose that because Dr.
Johnson was apparently lost in thought, and certainly almost
blind, he was not aware of anything, particularly of anything
reprehensible, that was taking place in the room. His "starts
of vision" were always astonishing and almost always painful. So it was on the present occasion. He suddenly woke up.
He suddenly roused himself. He suddenly uttered the words
for which the company had been waiting all the evening.

"If it were not for depriving the ladies of the fire," he said,
looking fixedly at Mr. Greville, "I should like to stand upon

the hearth myself!" The effect of the outburst was prodigious.
The Burney children said afterwards that it was as good as a
comedy. The descendant of the friend of Sir Philip Sidney
quailed before the Doctor's glance. All the blood of all the
Brookes rallied itself to overcome the insult. The son of a
bookseller should be taught his place. Greville did his best to
smile—a faint, scoffing smile. He did his best to stand where
he had stood the whole evening. He stood smiling, or trying
to smile, for two or perhaps for three minutes more. But when
he looked round the room and saw all eyes cast down, all faces
twitching with amusement, all sympathies plainly on the side
of the bookseller's son, he could stand there no longer. Fulke
Greville slunk away, sloping even his proud shoulders, to a
chair. But as he went, he rang the bell "with force." He demanded his carriage.

"The party then broke up; and no one from amongst it ever
asked, or wished for its repetition."

H. W. Garrod

HOW TO KNOW A GOOD
BOOK FROM A BAD

How do we know a good book from a bad? A contemporary of
Shakespeare wrote a play, very popular in its time, bearing the
title *How a Man may chuse a Good Wife from a Bad;* and, if it
really answered the question, the play may be accounted one of
the great books of the world. The right choice of books is, no
doubt, in comparison with the right choice of wives, a subject
of secondary importance. Only in the East is man polygamous;
nearly everywhere he is polybiblous—a creature of many books.
Always it is open to him to burn or sell, or, at the least, to
criticize his books; an unsatisfactory wife can be neither
burnt nor sold—and it is not often that she will allow herself to
be criticized. On the other hand, a man, once married, is able
immediately and certainly to formulate a reasoned account of
those qualities in his wife which create in him dissatisfaction or
uneasiness; but I have known many men who have lived all their
lives with books of whom never a one could discover to me what,
in a book, are those qualities by which it is confidently pronounced good or bad.

But let me say first what I mean by a book. A book of
logarithm tables is not a book; nor a book of dates; not a
spelling book; nor a Latin grammar; nor Newton's *Principia;*
nor Darwin's *Origin of Species;* nor any other book, of however great importance to mankind, which aims at instruction
and information rather than at delight and edification. In a
word, I call nothing a book which does not address a large part
of its appeal to imagination and emotion. Among books so
defined, how do we distinguish the good from the bad? For
of both kinds there are plenty—though let me say at once
that I think we grumble a great deal too much at the mounting tale of bad books. For myself, I can never enough admire

that there should be that infinity of good books that there
is in the world. Indeed, in a sense, all books are good. Have
you ever reflected what a world of talents goes to the making even of what is admitted to be a bad book? It is sometimes
said that it requires more talent and training to paint even a
poor picture than to make a tolerable book. But this is to forget
the infinite pains with which we learn speech itself, grammar,
accidence, writing, spelling—there are long years of training
here before we can even approach those higher exercises which
consist in the rhythmizing of speech and that selection and
ordering of fact and fancy called narrative. It requires some
training and technique to ask for the butter; a great deal to
write home for five shillings; an infinite deal to write a really
good letter (an art almost dead) ; and that a man should write
a book, just a tolerable book, even what is called a bad book,
this may well be thought the top of miracle.

All books, then, may be called good, in virtue of the talent
and technique necessary to the production of any book. And
though I am here to commend to you, among books, the best,
and to make suggestions as to how these may be known, I feel
disposed to say a word on behalf of bad books. I am sure, at any
rate, that the best critic of books, in the long run, is the man
who brings to the study of them a large charity, and that the
worst criticism is the "highbrow," as it is called. There are a
great many books in the world which are poor literature, but
which afford none the less the means of agreeable and harmless
recreation; and to brush them aside, to pretend that one does
not like them, that they count for nothing in the sum of life's
conveniences, is to be first pedantic and then dishonest. Robert
Louis Stevenson loved what are called "penny dreadfuls," and
said so like a man. Study the sources of Shakespeare's plays,
and you will find an infinite deal of poor literature which
Shakespeare read with very obvious pleasure and edification.
He was unscholarly enough to like blood and thunder; and
honest enough to let us find it out. Our world has too many
drab parts for it to be worth our while to disparage even an
ill-written book if it gives us something of the colour of life.
Perhaps, indeed, any book is worth having that quickens the
pulse or softens feeling.

Let us hate pedantry, then, and, as we grow more and more
educated, fight against literary pride; remembering that a bad
book, at its worst, is not like a bad man. The chances are ten

to one that it is the best part of the man who wrote it, and that he was a good enough fellow. Indeed, that is why he wrote it; it sprang—all literature springs—from the ineradicable instinct in man to communicate good; and thus almost all books assure us that the soul is divine.

None the less, it is well that we should be able, in a world too narrow for the books it holds, to distinguish, if we can, good literature from bad, and the best from the mediocre. For not to do so is, firstly, to waste time; and though life is longer than we commonly allow, the books really worth reading are, as I have said, so many. And secondly, though I have wished to say a good word for bad books, they are at least less good than good ones; and read by the wrong persons, or at the wrong season, they may easily prejudice our faculty of appreciating what is really best in literature. Reading a book is not like buying a piece of goods in the market; or, if it is, it is so with this difference—you take this particular kind of goods home, not in a parcel or cart, but in the soul. A moment ago I suggested that almost any book was worth having that softened feeling. I think that is true; but it needs qualifying. I have noted among persons who read novels, and see plays, that, in respect of a particular kind of play or novel, they tend to measure excellence by a tear-bottle: to suppose that, of literature which is tragic or pathetic, a necessary character is its power to make them cry. I am not sure that the truth is not just the other way. Of the most moving passages of Homer a great French critic said, I think properly, that what was marvellous in them was the fact that nowhere does Homer's voice tremble, nor his hand shake. I have cried, I can remember, to read Mrs. Henry Wood's *East Lynne*, and Canon Farrar's *Eric*. But God forbid that I should cry over *Lear* or *Othello*—I should know that there was something the matter with Shakespeare or with myself. I remember reading *East Lynne* in a crowded third-class railway carriage; and the manner in which the tears ran down my cheeks made me an object of general attention. So much so, that an elderly and benevolent clergyman seated opposite expressed the hope that I was not in any trouble; and I perplexed him, I know, not a little by telling him with perfect truth that I was only crying because this was so bad a book. Thereafter he left me alone, not because he saw that I had made him an inspired answer, but because he supposed me to be beyond his art, to be past praying for. Of tragedy, of that whole department of literature which we call the pathetic, the proper function is to steady us. It is life that shakes us and rocks us, literature which stabilizes and confirms.

Even as I say this, I am sensible of the many objections which can be raised against it; some of them very powerful; so powerful, indeed, that I am content here not to meet them, but to allow some parts of my case to go by default. Temperament is, from man to man, infinitely diversified; and the effects of literature depend often upon accidents of past experience, of situation, of physical health. And in general the critic who bids tragedy not make him cry courts the mortification of the king who bade the waves come no nigher. I will not say more, therefore, than that it is, as I think, true upon the whole that the great poet, the great artist in literature, rarely tempts us beyond what we are able to bear. We speak of him as "swaying" our emotions; and sway is governance. In proportion as he knows his trade, he never drives the car of passion so as to let it get out of control.

I mentioned just now Shakespeare's *King Lear*. If you want to know how a poet truly "sways" the emotions, look at the last scene of the fourth act of that play. There is no greater example in literature of artistic control; passion is driven there urgently, but not cruelly; the restraining hand is throughout present and felt.

Lear.

                    Pray, do not mock me:
I am a very foolish fond old man,
Fourscore and upward, not an hour more or less;
And, to deal plainly,
I fear I am not in my perfect mind.
Methinks I should know you and know this man;
Yet I am doubtful: for I am mainly ignorant
What place this is, and all the skill I have
Remembers not these garments; nor I know not
Where I did lodge last night. Do not laugh at me;
For, as I am a man, I think this lady
To be my child Cordelia.

Cor.

                    And so I am, I am.

Lear.

Be your tears wet? Yes, faith. I pray, weep not:
If you have poison for me, I will drink it.
I know you do not love me; for your sisters
Have, as I do remember, done me wrong:
You have some cause, they have not.

Cor.

No cause, no cause.

Lear.

Am I in France?

Kent.
In your own kingdom, sir.

Lear.

Do not abuse me.

Doc.

Be comforted, good madam; the great rage,
You see, is kill'd in him; and yet it is danger
To make him even o'er the time he has lost.
Desire him to go in; trouble him no more
Till further settling.

That matter-of-fact Doctor has saved a break-down. A lesser artist than Shakespeare would have been tempted to take the dialogue between father and daughter too far, to try over again something in the same pitch as Cordelia's wonderful "And so I am, I am." But Shakespeare never loses control.

I have sought an illustration from tragedy because, from the time when literary criticism first begins, tragedy has commonly been accounted the supreme literary form; and in any case it is from those parts of literature where tragic or pathetic incident is handled that the difference is most clearly discerned between the master and the amateur, between supreme work and second-rate work. It should be said, however, that, while the supreme effects are easily known, it is precisely in this department that, without a standard of comparison, we are apt to be taken in by inferior effects. The sentimental and the false-pathetic too often "overcome us like a summer cloud"; and if they are good in the sense that everything is good that softens feeling, yet they encourage a prodigality of nature by which we may easily waste what is best and rarest in us on incidents and reflections not worthy of it, and by which, in the end, we may come to lose the distinction between true and pure feeling and feeling that is factitious and unreal. I suggest to you, therefore, that in this matter of tragic and pathetic effects—which are, as I say, the highest effects of literature—nothing is so likely to help us to distinguish the good from the bad as that we should satisfy ourselves that we are really "swayed" by what we read, that we are conscious that the poet, or writer, not only drives, but controls, our affections and emotions. And this control which the great poet exercises is, if not easily defined, easily perceived, as I think. It is atmospheric, if you like. We are conscious of a presence—much as, in social intercourse, we are conscious, very often, in a chance-assorted crowd, of the domination of some individual temperament, drawing all eyes, compelling attention.

Where this sense of control manifests itself, it is, I suggest, the most distinctive note of great literature, the trademark of an inalienable excellence. What other marks are there by which we may know the good from the bad?

First, I would hazard the suggestion that there is no better test of excellence than to ask oneself of any book a very simple question: Does it speak to the point? The question seems, indeed, so simple that you may doubt whether the answer to it will carry you very far; you may even doubt whether one has any business to interrogate literature, especially romantic literature (with all of us the first of our literary loves), in a fashion so elementary, so matter-of-fact. But after all, good and bad are elementary distinctions, and are, if life has any meaning, very matter-of-fact indeed. Just now I mentioned in passing those classes of literature which we call "exciting," and I said something in excuse of our untutored fondness for them. But what is it in them which alienates criticism? What is the matter with them? In part what is the matter with them is what I have already indicated—they spur what they cannot rein. But they have commonly a technical defect at once more obvious and less venial. The "exciting" book nearly always accumulates episodes; it tends to pile incident upon incident without regard to necessary or probable connexions; it tends to be a series of sensational happenings which are not organically connected, which are a sequence and not a chain; any one of them might be removed without affecting any other or the disposition of the whole. The book, in other words, is, over large tracts of it, not *to the point*.

A large part of life, you will say, is faulty in the same particular—throwing together unrelated happenings. And you will be saying what is true enough; and, perhaps without knowing it, you will be saying why it is that literature exists at all. The end of literature is, truly enough, to present life; but to present it in such a fashion as to eliminate what is unessential, unrelated, inorganic; to present it as a whole of which all the parts are seen to be co-operative. Much of life is off the point; literature, where it is off the point, is not good, but bad. It is in this sense, and perhaps in this sense only, that literature is, in the phrase of a great writer, a criticism of life. Literature is always to the point. It does what life does not, what because we cannot do it for our lives makes them so hard, it eliminates the unessential.

You will see that, beginning from something very simple, we are now reaching towards a theme of some complexity. We have thrown a pebble; and on the waters of criticism it shapes a circle as wide as the world. A good test of a good book is to ask, Is it to the point? Are its parts a whole? Ask that of nine-tenths of the novels you read, of the plays you see, and you will know that, judged by the highest standards (though I do not say that a cheerful disposition will always insist on these), they are bad novels, bad plays. That is, I think, helpful in itself, it is a practical aid. But it opens, as you see, wide vistas of literary theory. A good book possesses organic unity; but in so far as it does so, it is a criticism of life.

Let us linger for a moment in what I may call the practicalities; and presently I will say something of the manner in which we may conceive a good book to criticize life. A good book speaks to the point. It studies what the French call "l'art de ne pas tout dire," the art of not saying everything. It does not heap incident on incident, but combines only those actions which stand to one another in a relation of cause and effect. But that is not all. A book may so combine its actions or episodes that they constitute a unity, and yet not be a good book; it may, indeed, be less a good book than one in which unity is less perfect, but in which another demand is satisfied, a demand of which the nature is, I think, easily explained. When you have read your novel, or seen your play, and have satisfied yourself that its actions present an organic unity, you must then proceed to a further question: Are these actions the actions of somebody? That has a cryptic ring. But the fact is that of most plays, and most novels, the actions are the actions of nobody at all. By that, I mean, as you guess, that the actions have no ground in character. If you met in real life the persons who performed them, you would not know them again—they have no gesture, no air, no sweetness, no human outline. They are just labels attached to their own behaviour. The question is sometimes asked whether in poetry, the drama, novels, and romance, character is more important than plot or action. Here —I would suggest—the good may be known from the bad, or at least the very best from the second best, by the fact that the question will not occur to you. At the top of fiction, the distinction of plot and character falls away. A man does what he is; and what he does is the man.

I have said nothing thus far of what is called style in writing, and of the ornament of words; yet by their style, it is commonly thought, books are most easily distinguished as good and bad. Of this I have said nothing, but I have, I think, implied something. The good book, I said, talks to the point. I used the expression in a different connexion—with reference to unity in the theme of a book. But it has a wider application; and, indeed, I am not sure that style can better be defined than by saying that a book that talks to the point has style. At once, you answer the question whether there is a language of literature which is different from that of real life; at once you solve the puzzle of the romantics, whether there is such a thing as poetic diction. When from the speech of common men you eliminate the unessential, the accidental, what is inexpressive, or less expressive than something else, Style arises. Poetry, after all, is called poetry because it is not prose; and equally truly, though Molière's Bourgeois Gentilhomme took a naïve pleasure in discovering that he had been talking prose all his life without knowing it, he was wrong; nobody talks prose; and that is why, when anybody does, we call him prosy. The fact is that very few of us talk to the point; very few of us, that is, truly relate what we say to what happens, or is, or to what we or others are, to character. I can recall, in the casual intercourse of life, but one occasion upon which I was witness to a supreme effect of style; and it is, I think, worth putting on record. In the first year of the war, I talked with a Belgian refugee, a man of education, whose acquaintance with the English language, however, was notably limited. He had come from Antwerp in the first days of its siege. He complained, no doubt with truth, that we, in England, did not know what war meant. "But I," he said, "I know. For I have seen the flight of old men, and it is terrible." That has always stayed with me: an effect of style which you will hardly equal, as I think, outside Homer. And you can see for yourselves the conditions of it. Here was a man whose resources in our language were so confined in their scope as to throw him back upon bare essentials. Accident worked like art; everything unessential was eliminated; and, on a living theme, he spoke to the point.

Just now I acquiesced in the dictum, to which a good deal of objection has been taken, that literature, and particularly poetry, was a criticism of life. I acquiesced in it in the sense that that unity which is properly demanded of a work of art has for its corollary such a presentation of life as frees it from the tie of accidental circumstance, from the irrelevance, confusion, incoherence, which make up so much of what we call real life. But this is not to say that literature is, or should be, didactic, that it preaches, that it endeavours consciously to make men better. I should prefer to say, with a great man who in my time was Master of this college,[1] that literature is a criticism of life exactly in the sense that a good man is a criticism of a bad one. And good men, or at any rate wise ones, never preach. If you ask me whether art, or literature, must be moral, I can only answer you by a method not much liked by such persons as mostly ask the question, the method, that is, of common sense. It is hateful—I know—to carry common sense into the rarefied atmosphere of artistic discussion; and yet a man might as well ask, Should mankind be moral? A book of an unpleasant theme, or of an immoral tendency, may, as well as a man of like constitution, both exhibit talent and afford entertainment; and a prude in literature is as tiresome as a prude in life. But the fact is that, in the long run, in books and in life alike, morality can be trusted to look after itself. There are periods of immoral literature, just as there are periods of social convulsion. But the average citizen never dies; and the good sense of the ordinary decent man, like charity, never fails in the long run. Literature does not please by moralizing us; it moralizes us because it pleases: and the world is pleased by what is unpleasant only for a limited time. I see no reason why literature should be moral, except that people prefer it; nor any ground, out of faith, why you and I should be moral, save that society insists on making us so.

[1] Edward Caird (the lecture was delivered in Balliol College).

I have tried to put my finger upon some marks whereby you may know the good book from the bad. I have not travelled outside poetry, the drama, and the novel; but with a little goodwill, and some not difficult adjustments what I have said is capable of being applied, I think, to other departments; to history, for example, and to oratory. One species of poetry, I am conscious, I have neglected—the species called, rather inappropriately, lyric. Here action and character, for the most part, stand down; not the relations between these, but a certain relation of the writer to the reader, usurps the place of primacy. To-day, it might almost be said, this species alone lives; and it must be acknowledged to have an amazingly developing life. Never perhaps was there an equally bewildering exuberance of talent; and it is idle to pretend that the poetry of to-day does not matter; it is cowardly not to try and judge it. I can think of no greater service that I could perform than to be able to turn you loose into the wide and diversified field of what is called absurdly "Georgian" poetry, with a few plain rules for distinguishing the good lyric from the bad. For myself I know what I like, and why I like it. I like most in the Georgian poetry what is least like the rest of it and most like the poetry I know better; and that is why I like it. I will hazard, indeed, one monition. Let everything be done in order. It is no use to begin here: it is not safe to begin here. We must begin farther back. We must endeavor to be wise as Time is, which always works forwards, never backwards. Albeit "great spirits now on earth are sojourning," yet a sensible man will work from Milton to Masefield, and not the easier, the more delightful, way. And by this time you divine, no doubt, a lame and impotent conclusion to an inquiry which promised better things. I fear, indeed, that you came to this lecture with better hopes than I did—or you had not come at all. For to be wholly honest (since it has come to that), the only test—after all that I have said—the only test that I know of a good book is the best books. The highest scholarship is, in fact, the humblest pupilage. The masters of criticism are those who are still at school to Shakespeare, Milton, Wordsworth. Taste is still conditioned by the palate; and a safe diet makes a clean palate. Shakespeare and Milton and Wordsworth are a safe diet. The good book is not necessarily the book that is like the books of any of these three; but it is the book that savours well to a palate which these three have kept pure and sensitive.

More than once in this lecture I have said good things of bad books; and I seem to end now in what I most dislike, a dictum of the highbrows. It is too late (and it would be too uninteresting) to make myself consistent. The fact is that what is the matter with the highbrows is, not that they are wrong, but that they are irritating. To the good fortune of being right, they add the impudence of knowing it. They make also the mistake of supposing that our strength comes always from the hills; whereas the truth is that we are human creatures, and that we wilt sometimes in this fine mountain atmosphere, and pine for the coarse air of cities, the smoke of the plains. After all, literature is a part of life—else it were so dull that it died. There is nothing so good for us as the best books; but from the ambition to be the saints of literary study heaven shield us! I hope that you may all go away from this lecture with enough adventure left in you to want to rub shoulders with bad books.

POEMS

SECTION I

It is with diffidence that I write a few words to present to the reader the poets I have gathered together in the following section. I cannot speak of poetry with any authority. I do not know anything about prosody. Because at school I was forced to write a certain number of very bad hexameters in Latin I still vaguely remember what they are, and I know blank verse and the alexandrine when I see it; but though from time to time I have known what iambics and trochaics are, I have always forgotten again. I treasure the useful information that in the poetry of Provence there were nine hundred forms of stanza construction, but I am afraid I could not tell you one of them. Mr J. C. Squire, in the article he wrote on the death of Arnold Bennett, tells how the novelist, for the edification of a young lady who wished to write poetry, asked him the name of the best book there was on English prosody. I wish he had given his answer. I would have read it and then might have been able to make this brief note instructive.

Edmund Gosse used to say that it gave him as much pleasure to read verse as to read fiction, and indeed he preferred it as a means of passing an idle day because it was shorter; he said it gave him just the same sort of mild entertainment as he found in reading the debates in the House of Commons. My appetite for verse is by no means so keen and I find that after I have read a certain amount of it, however accomplished, I am sated. Nor can I read it at all times and under all conditions. The other day in a crowded tube, in a smoking carriage, I saw a young woman, with a white face and pale lips, hanging on to a strap with one hand and in the other holding a small volume which she read intently. She paid no attention to the stopping of the train at one station after another and did not notice the

people who jostled her as they got in and out. I was curious
to know what it was that she could read with such absorption
and looking over her shoulder saw that it was *The Sensitive
Plant*. It is, I am sure, a great poem, but its rhythm has always
fallen on my ear disagreeably. All the same in spirit I took off
my hat to her. That is the real thing. For my part I need
exactly the right surroundings to take delight in poetry. I like
to be slightly tired physically, for then I find that my spirit is
most at ease, and I like a comfortable chair in a garden and
the waning of an English day in June. There is a cliff in Capri
where many years ago Norman Douglas planted cypress trees.
These are now grown up and you can lie in their shade, with
the Mediterranean at your feet, and in front of you the Sor-
rentine peninsula, and feel yourself alone in the world. That is
the place I should choose to read Shelley.

I have no doubt that poetry is the highest achievement of the
human mind and the writer of prose is not to be considered in
the same breath as the poet. It is the poet alone who can achieve
beauty. But I am so constituted that I cannot contemplate
beauty very long at a time. The rapture with which I am uplifted holds me but for a little while and my attention wanders.
I remember, the first time I opened *Paradise Lost* I read the
first five books at a sitting, entranced, but then I lost interest
and though I have since tried several times I can never recover
my first excitement. I shall never finish it now. I am sorry, for
I should have liked to know what happened and how the story
ended. I like my poems short. I have a notion that poets write
verses and it is their readers who transmute them into poems.
It is with verse as, according to Stendhal, with love. Everyone
knows the image he made such pleasant use of, of the branch
of a tree which, placed in the waters of Strasburg, gradually
collects upon itself crystallisations till it becomes a scintillating, delicate, exquisite thing that has only the basis of the
dead wood which it originally was. So the readers add to verse
the charm of place and time, their own youth, and love and
pain, and thus in the course of time make it something infinitely more poignant and lovely than the poet ever wrote. I
do not know how else one can explain the fact that good and
sensitive judges did not at once see what a miracle was the
Ode on a Grecian Urn. One would have thought it impossible
without ravishment to read those lines of Shelley's:

And, like a dying lady, lean and pale,
Who totters forth, wrapt in a gauzy veil,
Out of her chamber, led by the insane
And feeble wanderings of her fading brain,
The moon arose up in the murky east,
A white and shapeless mass.

Yet we know that the admirers of these poets were few, and that when attention was paid to them it was more often to condemn than to praise. Keats spoke of Shelley with nonchalance, and Shelley's interest in the surgeon's apprentice was cool till his death gave him the opportunity for a composition of his own. Neither Keats, Shelley, nor Wordsworth set the Thames on fire as Byron did. Why? The only reasonable explanation seems to be that these lovely poems were not then lovely poems, but good verse; and if their readers kept their heads about them it was because there was nothing in them to lose their heads about. In short the *Ode on a Grecian Urn*, the lines to the moon, were not the poems they are now. It is their innumerable readers that have made them that. But what it is in a set of verses that makes it possible for it to become a great poem needs a more acute and learned critic than I am to say. At all events I may hazard the suggestion that it requires a poet to write it.

What I here offer the readers is a brief selection of verse that seems to me moving, significant and sometimes beautiful. But all these things are modern and there has been no chance for this crystallisation to take place, which according to my notion may turn them into poetry. But in my judgement they have the potentiality. I do not know why in a hundred years a good many at least of these pieces should not be treasured in every memory like some fragments of Shelley or the great odes of Keats.

W. S. M.

Roy Campbell

THE MAKING OF A POET

In every herd there is some restive steer
Who leaps the cows and heads each hot stampede,
Till the old bulls unite in jealous fear
To hunt him from the pastures where they feed.

Lost in the night he hears the jungles crash
And desperately, lest his courage fail,
Across his hollow flanks with sounding lash
Scourges the heavy whipcord of his tail.

Far from the phalanxes of horns that ward
The sleeping herds he keeps the wolf at bay,
At nightfall by the slinking leopard spoored,
And goaded by the fly-swarm through the day.

THE SERF

His naked skin clothed in the torrid mist
That puffs in smoke around the patient hooves,
The ploughman drives, a slow somnambulist,
And through the green his crimson furrow grooves.
His heart, more deeply than he wounds the plain,
Long by the rasping share of insult torn,
Red cloth, to which the war-cry once was rain
And tribal spears the fatal sheaves of corn,
Lies fallow now. But as the turf divides
I see in the slow progress of his strides

551

Over the toppled clods and falling flowers,
The timeless, surly patience of the serf
That moves the nearest to the naked earth
And ploughs down palaces, and thrones, and towers.

HORSES ON THE CAMARGUE

In the grey wastes of dread,
The haunt of shattered gulls where nothing moves
But in a shroud of silence like the dead,
I heard a sudden harmony of hooves,
And, turning, saw afar
A hundred snowy horses unconfined,
The silver runaways of Neptune's car
Racing, spray-curled, like waves before the wind.
Sons of the Mistral, fleet
As him with whose strong gusts they love to flee,
Who shod the flying thunders on their feet
And plumed them with the snortings of the sea;
Theirs is no earthly breed
Who only haunt the verges of the earth
And only on the sea's salt herbage feed—
Surely the great white breakers gave them birth.
For when for years a slave,
A horse of the Camargue, in alien lands,
Should catch some far-off fragrance of the wave
Carried far inland from his native sands,
Many have told the tale
Of how in fury, foaming at the rein,
He hurls his rider; and with lifted tail,
With coal-red eyes and cataracting mane,
Heading his course for home,
Though sixty foreign leagues before him sweep,
Will never rest until he breathes the foam
And hears the native thunder of the deep.
But when the great gusts rise
And lash their anger on these arid coasts,
When the scared gulls career with mournful cries
And whirl across the waste like driven ghosts:

When hail and fire converge,
The only souls to which they strike no pain
Are the white-crested fillies of the surge
And the white horses of the windy plain.
Then in their strength and pride
The stallions of the wilderness rejoice;
They feel their Master's trident in their side,
And high and shrill they answer to his voice.
With white tails smoking free,
Long streaming manes, and arching necks, they show
Their kinship to their sisters of the sea—
And forward hurl their thunderbolts of snow.
Still out of hardship bred,
Spirits of power and beauty and delight
Have ever on such frugal pastures fed
And loved to course with tempests through the night.

ON SOME SOUTH AFRICAN NOVELISTS

You praise the firm restraint with which they write—
I'm with you there, of course:
They use the snaffle and the curb all right,
But where's the bloody horse?

Siegfried Sassoon

"BLIGHTERS"

The House is crammed: tier beyond tier they grin
And cackle at the Show, while prancing ranks
Of harlots shrill the chorus, drunk with din;
"We're sure the Kaiser loves the dear old Tanks!"

I'd like to see a Tank comé down the stalls,
Lurching to rag-time tunes, or "Home, Sweet Home,"—
And there'd be no more jokes in music-halls
To mock the riddled corpses round Bapaume.
1916

BASE DETAILS

If I were fierce and bald and short of breath,
   I'd live with scarlet Majors at the Base,
And speed glum heroes up the line to death.
   You'd see me with my puffy petulant face,
Guzzling and gulping in the best hotel,
   Reading the Roll of Honour. "Poor young chap,"
I'd say—"I used to know his father well;
   Yes, we've lost heavily in this last scrap."
And when the war is done and youth stone dead,
I'd toddle safely home and die—in bed.
1917

IDYLL

In the grey summer garden I shall find you
With day-break and the morning hills behind you.
There will be rain-wet roses; stir of wings;
And down the wood a thrush that wakes and sings.
Not from the past you'll come, but from that deep
Where beauty murmurs to the soul asleep:
And I shall know the sense of life re-born
From dreams into the mystery of morn
Where gloom and brightness meet. And standing there
Till that calm song is done, at last we'll share
The league-spread quiring symphonies that are
Joy in the world, and peace, and dawn's one star.
1918

VISION

I love all things that pass: their briefness is
Music that fades on transient silences.
Winds, birds, and glittering leaves that flare and fall—
They fling delight across the world; they call
To rhythmic-flashing limbs that rove and race
      A moment in the dawn for Youth's lit face;
      A moment's passion, closing on the cry—
      "O Beauty, born of lovely things that die!"
1918

EVERYONE SANG

Everyone suddenly burst out singing;
And I was filled with such delight
As prisoned birds must find in freedom
Winging wildly across the white
Orchards and dark green fields; on; on; and out of sight.

Everyone's voice was suddenly lifted,
And beauty came like the setting sun.
My heart was shaken with tears, and horror
Drifted away. . . . O but every one
Was a bird; and the song was wordless; the singing will
     never be done.

1919

Hilaire Belloc

TARANTELLA

Do you remember an Inn,
Miranda?
Do you remember an Inn?
And the tedding and the spreading
Of the straw for a bedding,
And the fleas that tease in the High Pyrenees,
And the wine that tasted of the tar?
And the cheers and the jeers of the young muleteers
(Under the vine of the dark verandah)?
Do you remember an Inn, Miranda,
Do you remember an Inn?
And the cheers and the jeers of the young muleteers
Who hadn't got a penny,
And who weren't paying any,
And the hammer at the doors and the Din?
And the Hip! Hop! Hap!
Of the clap
Of the hands to the twirl and the swirl
Of the girl gone chancing,
Glancing,
Dancing,
Backing and advancing,
Snapping of the clapper to the spin
Out and in—
And the Ting, Tong, Tang of the Guitar!
Do you remember an Inn,
Miranda?
Do you remember an Inn?

Never more;
Miranda,
Never more.
Only the high peaks hoar:
And Aragon a torrent at the door.
No sound
In the walls of the Halls where falls
The tread
Of the feet of the dead to the ground
No sound: .
But the boom
Of the far Waterfall like Doom.

LINES TO A DON

Remote and ineffectual Don
That dared attack my Chesterton,
With that poor weapon, half-impelled,
Unlearnt, unsteady, hardly held,
Unworthy for a tilt with men—
Your quavering and corroded pen;
Don poor at Bed and worse at Table,
Don pinched, Don starved, Don miserable;
Don stuttering, Don with roving eyes,
Don nervous, Don of crudities;
Don clerical, Don ordinary,
Don self-absorbed and solitary;
Don here-and-there, Don epileptic;
Don puffed and empty, Don dyspeptic;
Don middle-class, Don sycophantic,
Don dull, Don brutish, Don pedantic;
Don hypocritical, Don bad,
Don furtive, Don three-quarters mad;
Don (since a man must make an end),
Don that shall never be my friend.

    ·   ·   ·   ·   ·

Don different from those regal Dons!
With hearts of gold and lungs of bronze,

Who shout and bang and roar and bawl
The Absolute across the hall,
Or sail in amply bellowing gown
Enormous through the Sacred Town
Bearing from College to their homes
Deep cargoes of gigantic tomes;
Dons admirable! Dons of Might!
Uprising on my inward sight
Compact of ancient tales, and port
And sleep—and learning of a sort.
Dons English, worthy of the land;
Dons rooted; Dons that understand.
Good Dons perpetual that remain
A landmark, walling in the plain—
The horizon of my memories—
Like large and comfortable trees.

   .   .   .   .

Don very much apart from these,
Thou scapegoat Don, thou Don devoted,
Don to thine own damnation quoted,
Perplexed to find thy trivial name
Reared in my verse to lasting shame.
Don dreadful, rasping Don and wearing,
Repulsive Don—Don past all bearing.
Don of the cold and doubtful breath,
Don despicable, Don of death;
Don nasty, skimpy, silent, level;
Don evil; Don that serves the devil.
Don ugly—that makes fifty lines.
There is a Canon which confines
A Rhymed Octosyllabic Curse
If written in Iambic Verse
To fifty lines. I never cut;
I far prefer to end it—but
Believe me I shall soon return.
My fires are banked, but still they burn
To write some more about the Don
That dared attack my Chesterton.

THE STATUE

When we are dead, some Hunting-boy will pass
And find a stone half-hidden in tall grass
And grey with age: but having seen that stone
(Which was your image), ride more slowly on.

ON A DEAD HOSTESS

Of this bad world the loveliest and the best
Has smiled and said "Good Night," and gone to rest.

ON A GREAT ELECTION

The accursèd power which stands on Privilege
(And goes with Women, and Champagne and Bridge)
Broke—and Democracy resumed her reign:
(Which goes with Bridge, and Women and Champagne).

PARTLY FROM THE GREEK

She would be as the stars in your sight
That turn in the endless hollow;
That tremble, and always follow
The quiet wheels of the Night.

Frances Cornford

AUTUMN EVENING

The shadows flickering, the daylight dying,
And I upon the old red sofa lying,
The great brown shadows leaping up the wall,
The sparrows twittering; and that is all.

I thought to send my soul to far-off lands,
Where fairies scamper on the windy sands,
Or where the autumn rain comes drumming down
On huddled roofs in an enchanted town.

But O my sleepy soul, it will not roam,
It is too happy and too warm at home:
With just the shadows leaping up the wall,
The sparrows twittering; and that is all.

TO A LADY SEEN FROM THE TRAIN

O why do you walk through the fields in gloves,
    Missing so much and so much?
O fat white woman whom nobody loves,
Why do you walk through the field in gloves,
When the grass is soft as the breast of doves
    And shivering-sweet to the touch?
O why do you walk through the fields in gloves,
    Missing so much and so much?

IN THE CAVES OF AUVERGNE

He carved the red deer and the bull
    Upon the smooth cave rock
Returned from war, with belly full,
    And scarred with many a knock,
He carved the red deer and the bull
    Upon the smooth cave rock.

The stars flew by the cave's wide door,
    The clouds wild trumpets blew,
Trees rose in wild dreams from the floor,
    Flowers with dream faces grew
Up to the sky, and softly hung
    Golden and white and blue.

The woman ground her heap of corn,
    Her heart a guarded fire;
The wind played in his trembling soul
    Like a hand upon a lyre,
The wind drew faintly on the stone
    Symbols of his desire:

The red deer of the forests dark,
    Whose antlers cut the sky,
That vanishes into the mirk
    And like a dream flits by,
And by an arrow slain at last
    Is but the wind's dark body.

The bull that stands in marshy lakes
  As motionless and still
As a dark rock jutting from a plain
  Without a tree or hill,
The bull that is the sign of life,
  Its sombre, phallic will.

And from the dead, white eyes of them
  The wind springs up anew,
It blows upon the trembling heart,
  And bull and deer renew
Their flitting life in the dim past
  When that dead Hunter drew.

I sit beside him in the night,
  And, fingering his red stone,
I chase through endless forests dark
  Seeking that thing unknown,
That which is not red deer or bull,
  But which by them was shown.

By those stiff shapes in which he drew
  His soul's exalted cry,
When flying down the forest dark
  He slew and knew not why,
When he was filled with song, and strength
  Flowed to him from the sky.

The wind blows from red deer and bull,
  The clouds wild trumpets blare,
Trees rise in wild dreams from the earth,
  Flowers with dream faces stare—
O Hunter, your own shadow stands
  Within your forest lair.

Ralph Hodgson

THE BULL

See an old unhappy bull,
Sick in soul and body both,
Slouching in the undergrowth
Of the forest beautiful,
Banished from the herd he led,
Bulls and cows a thousand head.

Cranes and gaudy parrots go
Up and down the burning sky;
Tree-top cats purr drowsily
In the dim-day green below;
And troops of monkeys, nutting, some,
All disputing, go and come;

And things abominable sit
Picking offal buck or swine,
On the mess and over it
Burnished flies and beetles shine,
And spiders big as bladders lie
Under hemlocks ten foot high;

And a dotted serpent curled
Round and round and round a tree,
Yellowing its greenery,
Keeps a watch on all the world,
All the world and this old bull
In the forest beautiful.

564

Bravely by his fall he came:
One he led, a bull of blood
Newly come to lustihood,
Fought and put his prince to shame,
Snuffed and pawed the prostrate head
Tameless even while it bled.

There they left him, every one,
Left him there without a lick,
Left him for the birds to pick,
Left him there for carrion,
Vilely from their bosom cast
Wisdom, worth and love at last.

When the lion left his lair
And roared his beauty through the hills,
And the vultures pecked their quills
And flew into the middle air,
Then this prince no more to reign
Came to life and lived again.

He snuffed the herd in far retreat,
He saw the blood upon the ground,
And snuffed the burning airs around
Still with beevish odours sweet,
While the blood ran down his head
And his mouth ran slaver red.

Pity him, this fallen chief,
All his splendour, all his strength,
All his body's breadth and length
Dwindled down with shame and grief,
Half the bull he was before,
Bones and leather, nothing more.

See him standing dewlap-deep
In the rushes at the lake,
Surly, stupid, half asleep,
Waiting for his heart to break
And the birds to join the flies
Feasting at his bloodshot eyes;

Standing with his head hung down
In a stupor, dreaming things:
Green savannas, jungles brown,
Battlefields and bellowings,
Bulls undone and lions dead
And vultures flapping overhead.

Dreaming things: of days he spent
With his mother gaunt and lean
In the valley warm and green,
Full of baby wonderment,
Blinking out of silly eyes
At a hundred mysteries;

Dreaming over once again
How he wondered with a throng
Of bulls and cows a thousand strong,
Wandered on from plain to plain,
Up the hill and down the dale,
Always at his mother's tail;

How he lagged behind the herd,
Lagged and tottered, weak of limb,
And she turned and ran to him
Blaring at the loathly bird
Stationed always in the skies,
Waiting for the flesh that dies.

Dreaming maybe of a day
When her drained and drying paps
Turned him to the sweets and saps,
Richer fountains by the way,
And she left the bull she bore
And he looked to her no more;

And his little frame grew stout,
And his little legs grew strong,
And the way was not so long;
And his little horns came out,
And he played at butting trees
And boulder-stones and tortoises,

Joined a game of knobby skulls
With the youngsters of his year,
All the other little bulls,
Learning both to bruise and bear,
Learning how to stand a shock
Like a little bull of rock.

Dreaming of a day less dim,
Dreaming of a time less far,
When the faint but certain star
Of destiny burned clear for him,
And a fierce and wild unrest
Broke the quiet of his breast,

And the gristles of his youth
Hardened in his comely pow,
And he came to fighting growth,
Beat his bull and won his cow,
And flew his tail and trampled off
Past the tallest, vain enough.

And curved about in splendour full
And curved again and snuffed the airs
As who should say Come out who dares!
And all beheld a bull, a Bull,
And knew that here was surely one
That backed for no bull, fearing none.

And the leader of the herd
Looked and saw, and beat the ground,
And shook the forest with his sound,
Bellowed at the loathly bird
Stationed always in the skies,
Waiting for the flesh that dies.

Dreaming, this old bull forlorn,
Surely dreaming of the hour
When he came to sultan power,
And they owned him master-horn,
Chiefest bull of all among
Bulls and cows a thousand strong;

And in all the tramping herd
Not a bull that barred his way,
Not a cow that said him nay,
Not a bull or cow that erred
In the furnace of his look
Dared a second, worse rebuke;

Not in all the forest wide,
Jungle, thicket, pasture, fen,
Not another dared him then,
Dared him and again defied;
Not a sovereign buck or boar
Came a second time for more;

Not a serpent that survived
Once the terrors of his hoof
Risked a second time reproof,
Came a second time and lived,
Not a serpent in its skin
Came again for discipline;

Not a leopard bright as flame,
Flashing fingerhooks of steel,
That a wooden tree might feel,
Met his fury once and came
For a second reprimand,
Not a leopard in the land;

Not a lion of them all,
Not a lion of the hills,
Hero of a thousand kills,
Dared a second fight and fall,
Dared that ram terrific twice,
Paid a second time the price.

Pity him, this dupe of dream,
Leader of the herd again
Only in his daft old brain,
Once again the bull supreme
And bull enough to bear the part
Only in his tameless heart.

Pity him that he must wake;
Even now the swarm of flies
Blackening his bloodshot eyes
Bursts and blusters round the lake,
Scattered from the feast half-fed,
By great shadows overhead;

And the dreamer turns away
From his visionary herds
And his splendid yesterday,
Turns to meet the loathly birds
Flocking round him from the skies,
Waiting for the flesh that dies.

THE MYSTERY

He came and took me by the hand
    Up to a red rose tree,
He kept His meaning to Himself
    But gave a rose to me.

I did not pray Him to lay bare
    The mystery to me,
Enough the rose was Heaven to smell,
    And His own face to see.

William H. Davies

LEISURE

What is this life if, full of care,
We have no time to stand and stare.

No time to stand beneath the boughs
And stare as long as sheep or cows.

No time to see, when woods we pass,
Where squirrels hide their nuts in grass.

No time to see, in broad daylight,
Streams full of stars, like skies at night.

No time to turn at Beauty's glance,
And watch her feet, how they can dance.

No time to wait till her mouth can
Enrich that smile her eyes began.

A poor life this if, full of care,
We have no time to stand and stare.

John Masefield

SEA–FEVER

I must go down to the seas again, to the lonely sea and the sky,
And all I ask is a tall ship and a star to steer her by,
And the wheel's kick and the wind's song and the white sail's
    shaking,
And a grey mist on the sea's face and a grey dawn breaking.

I must go down to the seas again, for the call of the running
    tide
Is a wild call and a clear call that may not be denied;
And all I ask is a windy day with the white clouds flying,
And the flung spray and the blown spume, and the sea-gulls
    crying.

I must go down to the seas again to the vagrant gypsy life,
To the gull's way and the whale's way where the wind's like a
    whetted knife;
And all I ask is a merry yarn from a laughing fellow-rover,
And quiet sleep and a sweet dream when the long trick's over.

Joseph Plunkett

I SEE HIS BLOOD UPON THE ROSE

I see his blood upon the rose
And in the stars the glory of his eyes,
His body gleams amid eternal snows,
His tears fall from the skies.

I see his face in every flower;
The thunder and the singing of the birds
Are but his voice—and carven by his power
Rocks are his written words.

All pathways by his feet are worn,
His strong heart stirs the ever-beating sea,
His crown of thorns is twined with every thorn,
His cross is every tree.

Sacheverell Sitwell

THE RIO GRANDE

By the Rio Grande
They dance no sarabande
On level banks like lawns above the glassy, lolling tide;
Nor sing they forlorn madrigals
Whose sad note stirs the sleeping gales
Till they wake among the trees, and shake the boughs,
And fright the nightingales;
But they dance in the city, down the public squares,
On the marble pavers with each colour laid in shares,
At the open church doors loud with light within,
At the bell's huge tolling,
By the river music, gurgling, thin,
Through the soft Brazilian air,
The Comendador and Alguacil are there
On horseback, hid with feathers, loud and shrill
Blowing orders on their trumpets like a bird's sharp bill
Through boughs, like a bitter wind, calling
They shine like steady starlight while those other sparks are
    falling
In burnished armour, with their plumes of fire,
Tireless, while all others tire.
The noisy streets are empty and hushed is the town
To where, in the square, they dance and the band is playing;
Such a space of silence through the town to the river
That the water murmurs loud
Above the band and crowd together;
And the strains of the sarabande,
More lively than a madrigal,
Go hand in hand

Like the river and its waterfall
As the great Rio Grande rolls down to the sea.
Loud is the marimba's note
Above these half-salt waves,
And louder still the tympanum,
The plectrum, and the kettle-drum,
Sullen and menacing
Do these brazen voices ring.
They ride outside,
Above the salt-sea's tide,
Till the ships at anchor there
Hear this enchantment
Of the soft Brazilian air,
By those Southern winds wafted,
Slow and gentle,
Their fierceness tempered
By the air that flows between.

ON ARNOLD BENNETT

I FIRST knew Arnold Bennett in 1904 when we were both living
in Paris. I had taken a very small flat near the Lion de Belfort,
on the fifth floor, from which I had a spacious view of the
cemetery of Montparnasse; I used to dine at the *Chat Blanc*
in the rue d'Odessa. A number of painters, sculptors and
writers were in the habit of dining there and we had a little
room to ourselves. We got a very good dinner, *vin compris*, for
two francs fifty, and it was usual to give four sous to Marie,
the good-humoured and sharp-tongued maid who waited on us.
We were of all nationalities and the conversation was carried
on indifferently in English and French. Sometimes a painter
would bring his mistress and her mother, whom he introduced
politely to the company as *ma belle mère*, but for the most
part we were men only. We discussed every subject under the
sun, generally with heat, and by the time we came to coffee
(with which I seem to remember a *fine* was thrown in) and
lit our cigars, *demi londrès* at three sou apiece, the air was
heady. We differed with extreme acrimony. Arnold used to
come there once a week. He reminded me years later that the
first time we met, which was at this restaurant, I was white with
passion. The conversation was upon the merits of Heredia. I
asserted that there was no sense in him and a painter who was
there scornfully replied that you didn't want sense in poetry.
From this an argument arose upon the objects and limitations
of poetry which soon embroiled the whole company. I exercised such powers as I had of sarcasm, invective and vituperation; and my antagonist, a taciturn Irishman, than whom there
is no man more difficult to cope with, was coldly and bitingly
virulent. The entire table took up the dispute and I have still
a dim recollection of Arnold, smiling a little, calm and a trifle

Olympian, putting in now and then a brief, dogmatic, but, I am certain, judicious remark. He was older than most of us. He was then a thin man, with dark hair very smoothly done in a fashion that suggested the private soldier of the day. He was much more neatly dressed than the rest of us and more conventionally. He looked like a managing clerk in a city office. At that time the only book he had written that we knew of was *The Grand Babylon Hotel* and our attitude towards him was somewhat patronising. We were very highbrow. Some of us had read the book and enjoyed it, which was enough for us to decide that there was nothing in it, but the rest shrugged their shoulders, though with good nature, and declined to waste their time over such trash. Had you read *Bubu de Montparnasse?* That was the stuff to give the troops.

Arnold lived in Montmartre, I think in the rue des Dames, and he had a small dark apartment filled with Empire furniture. He was exceedingly proud of it. It was very tidy. Everything was in its place. It was not very comfortable and you could not imagine anyone making himself at home in it. It gave you the impression of a man who saw himself in a certain role, which he was playing carefully, but into the skin of which he had not quite got. As everyone knows Arnold had then given up the editing of a magazine called *Woman* and had settled in Paris to train himself for the profession of literature. He was reading Stendhal and Flaubert, but chiefly Balzac, and I think he told me that in a year he had read through the whole of the *Comédie Humaine.* He was just beginning on the Russians and talked with enthusiasm of *Anna Karenina.* He thought it at that time the greatest novel ever written. I am under the impression that he did not discover Chekov till much later. When he did he began to admire Tolstoi less. Like everyone who lives in Paris he had come across a particular little restaurant where you could get a better meal for less money than anywhere else. This one was on the first floor, somewhere in Montmartre, and now and then I used to go over to dine, Dutch Treat, with him. After dinner we went back to his apartment and he would play Beethoven on a cottage piano. Through Marcel Schwob he had got to know a good many of the French writers of the day and I seem to remember his telling me that Schwob had taken him to Anatole France who was then the high priest of French letters. Arnold's plan of campaign was cut and dried. He proposed to make his annual income by writing novels and by writing plays to make provision for his old age. Because I had lately had my first play produced he gave me one of his to read. I thought it dull. He had made up his mind to write two or three books to get his hand in and then to write a masterpiece. I listened to him, but attached no importance to what he said. I did not think him capable of writing anything of consequence. When I asked him what sort of book his masterpiece was going to be he said, something on the lines of *A Great Man;* but this, he added, had brought him in nothing at all and he couldn't afford to go on in that style till he was properly established.

Arnold was good company and I always enjoyed spending an evening with him, but I did not much like him. He was very cocksure and bumptious, and he was rather common. I do not say this of him depreciatingly, but as I might say of someone else that he was short or fat. I left Paris and it was many years before I saw much of him again.

The Stage Society produced a play of his which I liked. I wrote and told him so, and he wrote a letter to me, thanking me, in which he laid out the critics who had not thought so well of the play as I did. He wrote one or two books which I did not read. At last I came across *The Old Wives' Tale.* I was astounded to discover that it was a great book. I was thrilled. I was enchanted. I was deeply impressed. It would be impertinent of me to say anything in praise of it. I have read many appreciations of it, and I think everything has been said but one thing, and that is that it is eminently readable. I should not mention a merit that is so obvious except that many great books do not possess it. It is the greatest gift of the story-teller and one that Arnold Bennett had even in his slightest and most trivial pieces. I thought at first that he owed it to his journalistic training, but since the other writer of our day in whom I find this characteristic most marked is Marcel Proust, it is clear that this is not the reason; and now I am under the impression that it is due to the intense interest the author has in what he is writing at the moment. Even when Proust is at his dullest he is so absorbed in his subject that you cannot help but read on, eager to know what is coming next; and with Arnold (to my mind) in the same way, though you felt sometimes that what you were reading was rather childish, you were constrained to turn over one page after the other till you reached the end. The success of *The Old Wives' Tale* came slowly. I think I am right in saying that it was reviewed favourably, but not with frantic eulogies, and that its circulation was moderate. For a time it looked as though it would have no more than a *succès d'éstime* and be forgotten as all but one novel out of a thousand are forgotten. By a happy chance which would take too long to narrate *The Old Wives' Tale* was brought to the attention of Mr George Doran who had bought sheets of it; he forthwith acquired the American rights, set it up and launched it on its triumphal course. It was not till after its great success in America that it was taken over by another publisher in England and attracted the attention of the British public. For many years, what with one thing and another, I do not think I met Arnold, or if I did it was only at a party, literary or otherwise, at which I had the opportunity to say no more than a few words to him; but after the war and until his death I saw much of him. Much has been written of him during these later years and I have little to add. He was become a great figure. He was very different from the thin, rather insignificant man, looking like a city clerk, with his black hair plastered down on his head, that I had known in Paris. He had grown stout. His hair, very gray, was worn much longer and he had cultivated the amusing cock's comb that the caricaturists made famous. He had always been neat in his dress, disconcertingly even, but now he was grand. He wore frilled shirts in the evening and took an immense pride in his white waistcoats. He has related the story of a picnic I took him on while he was staying with me in the South of France when, a storm preventing us from leaving the island on which we were, he took stock with his humorous detachment of the reactions of the various persons present to the slight danger we found ourselves faced with. He did not say that the women were all in pyjamas and the men in tennis shirts, duck trousers and *espadrilles;* but that he, refusing to permit himself such *sans gêne,* was arrayed in a check suit of a sort of mustard colour, wore fancy socks and fancy shoes, a starched collar, a striped shirt and a foulard tie; and that when at six next morning we all got home, bedraggled, unshaven and looking like nothing on earth, he, in his smart shirt and neat suit, looked, as he had looked eighteen hours before, as though he had just come out of a band-box. To the end of the experience he remained dignified, self-possessed, good-tempered and interested.

But it was not only in appearance that he was a very dif-

ferent man from the one that I had known in Paris. I dare say
it was all there then and perhaps it was only my stupidity and
youth that prevented me from seeing it. Perhaps also it was
that life had changed him. I think it possible that at first he
was hampered by his extreme diffidence, and his bumptiousness
was a protection he assumed to his own timidity, and that success had given him confidence. It had certainly mellowed him.
He had acquired a very sensible assurance of his own merit. He
told me once that there were only two novels written during
the last thirty years that he was confident would survive and
one of these was *The Old Wives' Tale.* It was impossible to
know him without liking him. He was a character. His very
oddities were endearing. Indeed it was to them that the great
affection in which he was universally held was partly due, for
people laughed at foibles in him which they were conscious of
not possessing themselves and thus mitigated the oppression
which admiration for his talent must otherwise have made them
feel. He was never what in England is technically known as a
gentleman, but he was not vulgar any more than the traffic
surging up Ludgate Hill is vulgar. His common sense was
matchless. He was entirely devoid of envy. He was generous.
He was courageous. He always said with perfect frankness
what he thought and because it never struck him that he
could offend he never did; but if, with his quick sensitiveness,
he imagined that he had hurt somebody's feelings he did everything in reason to salve the wound. His kindness glowed like a
halo about a saint.

I was surprised to see how patronising on the whole were
the obituary notices written at his death. A certain amount of
fun was made of his obsession with grandeur and luxury, and
the pleasure he took in *trains de luxe* and first-class hotels. He
never quite grew accustomed to the appurtenances of wealth.
Once he said to me, "If you've ever really been poor you remain
poor at heart all your life. I've often walked," he added, "when
I could very well afford to take a taxi because I simply couldn't
bring myself to waste the shilling it would cost." He admired
and disapproved of extravagance.

The criticism to which he devoted much time during his later
years came in for a good deal of adverse comment. He loved
his position on *The Evening Standard.* He liked the power it
gave him and enjoyed the interest his articles aroused. The
immediate response, like the applause an actor receives after

an effective scene, gratified his appetite for actuality. It
gave him the illusion, peculiarly pleasant to the author whose
avocation necessarily entails a sense of apartness, that he was
in the midst of things. He read as a man of letters and whatever he thought he said without fear or favour. He had no
patience with the precious, the affected or the pompous. If he
thought little of certain writers who are now more praised than
read it is not certain that he thought wrong. He was more
interested in life than in art. In criticism he was an amateur.
The professional critic is probably somewhat shy of life, for
otherwise it is unlikely that he would devote himself to the reading and judging of books rather than to the stress and turmoil of living. He is more at ease with it when the sweat has
dried and the acrid odour of humanity has ceased to offend the
nostrils. He can be sympathetic enough to the realism of Defoe
and the tumultuous vitality of Balzac, but when it comes to
the productions of his own day he feels more comfortable with
works in which a deliberately literary attitude has softened the
asperities of reality. That is why, I suppose, the praise that
was accorded to Arnold Bennet for *The Old Wives' Tale* after
his death was cooler than one would have expected. Some of
the critics said that notwithstanding everything he had a sense
of beauty and they quoted passages to show his poetic power
and his feeling for the mystery of existence. I do not see the
point of making out that he had something of what you would
like him to have had a great deal more of and ignoring that
in which his power and value was. He was neither mystic nor
poet. He was interested in material things and in the passions
common to all men. He described life, as every writer does, in
the terms of his own temperament. He was more concerned
with the man in the street than with the exceptional person.
Everyone knows that Arnold was afflicted with a very bad
stammer; it was painful to watch the struggle he had sometimes to get the words out. It was torture to him. Few realised
the exhaustion it caused him to speak. What to most men was
as easy as breathing to him was a constant strain. It tore his
nerves to pieces. Few knew the humiliations it exposed him to,
the ridicule it excited in many, the impatience it aroused, the
awkwardness of feeling that it made people find him tiresome;
and the minor exasperation of thinking of a good, amusing or
apt remark and not venturing to say it in case the stammer
ruined it. Few knew the distressing sense it gave rise to of a

bar to complete contact with other men. It may be that except for the stammer which forced him to introspection Arnold would never have become a writer. But I think it is not the least proof of his strong and sane character that notwithstanding this impediment he was able to retain his splendid balance and regard the normal life of man from a normal point of view.

The Old Wives' Tale is certainly the best book he wrote. He never lost the desire to write another as good and because it was written by an effort of will he thought he could repeat it. He tried in *Clayhanger*, and for a time it looked as though he might succeed. I think he failed only because his material fizzled out. After *The Old Wives' Tale* he had not enough left to complete the vast structure he had designed. No writer can get more than a certain amount of ore out of one seam; when he has got that, though it remains, miraculously, as rich as before, it is only others who can profitably work it. He tried again in *Lord Raingo* and he tried for the last time in *Imperial Palace*. Here I think the subject was at fault. Because it profoundly interested him he thought it was of universal interest. He gathered his data systematically, but they were jotted down in note-books and not garnered (as were those of *The Old Wives' Tale*) unconsciously and preserved, not in black and white, but as old memories in his bones, in his nerves, in his heart. But that Arnold should have spent the last of his energy and determination in the description of a hotel seems to me to have a symbolical significance. For I feel that he was never quite at home in the world. It was to him perhaps a sumptuous hotel, with marble bathrooms and a marvellous cuisine, in which he was a transient guest. For all his assurance and his knowing air I felt that he was, here among men, impressed, delighted, but a little afraid of doing the wrong thing and never entirely at his ease. Just as his little apartment in the rue des Dames years before had suggested to me a rôle played carefully, but from the outside, I feel that to him life was a rôle that he played conscientiously, and with ability, but into the skin of which he never quite got.

W. S. M.

Arnold Bennett

THE OLD WIVES' TALE

BOOK I
MRS. BAINES

CHAPTER I
THE SQUARE

THOSE two girls, Constance and Sophia Baines, paid no heed to the manifold interest of their situation, of which, indeed, they had never been conscious. They were, for example, established almost precisely on the fifty-third parallel of latitude. A little way to the north of them, in the creases of a hill famous for its religious orgies, rose the river Trent, the calm and characteristic stream of middle England. Somewhat further northwards, in the near neighbourhood of the highest public-house in the realm, rose two lesser rivers, the Dane and the Dove, which, quarrelling in early infancy, turned their backs on each other, and, the one by favour of the Weaver and the other by favour of the Trent, watered between them the whole width of England, and poured themselves respectively into the Irish Sea and the German Ocean. What a county of modest, unnoticed rivers! What a natural, simple county, content to fix its boundaries by these tortuous island brooks, with their comfortable names—Trent, Mease, Dove, Tern, Dane, Mees, Stour, Tame, and even hasty Severn! Not that the Severn is suitable to the county! In the county excess is deprecated. The county is happy in not exciting remark. It is content that Shropshire should possess that swollen bump, the Wrekin, and that the exaggerated wildness of the Peak should lie over its border. It does not desire to be a pancake like Cheshire. It has everything that England has, including thirty miles of Watling Street; and England can show nothing more beautiful and nothing uglier than the works of nature and the works of man to be seen within the limits of the county. It is England in little, lost in

the midst of England, unsung by searchers after the extreme
perhaps occasionally somewhat sore at this neglect, but how
proud in the instinctive cognizance of its representative fea
tures and traits!

Constance and Sophia, busy with the intense preoccupation
of youth, recked not of such matters. They were surrounded by
the county. On every side the fields and moors of Staffordshire
intersected by roads and lanes, railways, watercourses and tele
graph-lines, patterned by hedges, ornamented and made re
spectable by halls and genteel parks, enlivened by villages at
the intersections, and warmly surveyed by the sun, spread out
undulating. And trains were rushing round curves in deep cuttings, and carts and waggons trotting and jingling on the yellow roads, and long, narrow boats passing in a leisure majestic
and infinite over the surface of the stolid canals; the rivers had
only themselves to support, for Staffordshire rivers have remained virgin of keels to this day. One could imagine the messages concerning prices, sudden death, and horses, in their flight
through the wires under the feet of birds. In the inns Utopians
were shouting the universe into order over beer, and in the halls
and parks the dignity of England was being preserved in a
fitting manner. The villages were full of women who did nothing but fight against dirt and hunger, and repair the effects
of friction on clothes. Thousands of labourers were in the fields,
but the fields were so broad and numerous that this scattered
multitude was totally lost therein. The cuckoo was much more
perceptible than man, dominating whole square miles with his
resounding call. And on the airy moors heath-larks played in
the ineffaceable mule-tracks that had served centuries before
even the Romans thought of Watling Street. In short, the usual
daily life of the county was proceeding with all its immense
variety and importance; but though Constance and Sophia
were in it they were not of it.

The fact is, that while in the county they were also in the
district; and no person who lives in the district, even if he
should be old and have nothing to do but reflect upon things
in general, ever thinks about the county. So far as the county
goes, the district might almost as well be in the middle of the
Sahara. It ignores the county, save that it uses it nonchalantly
sometimes as leg-stretcher on holiday afternoons, as a man may
use his back garden. It has nothing in common with the county;
it is richly sufficient to itself. Nevertheless, its self-sufficiency

nd the true salt savour of its life can only be appreciated by
picturing it hemmed in by county. It lies on the face of the
county like an insignificant stain, like a dark Pleiades in a
green and empty sky. And Hanbridge has the shape of a horse
and its rider, Bursley of half a donkey, Knype of a pair of trousers, Longshaw of an octopus, and little Turnhill of a beetle.
The Five Towns seem to cling together for safety. Yet the idea
of clinging together for safety would make them laugh. They
are unique and indispensable. From the north of the county
right down to the south they alone stand for civilization, applied science, organized manufacture, and the century—until
you come to Wolverhampton. They are unique and indispensable because you cannot drink tea out of a teacup without the aid
of the Five Towns; because you cannot eat a meal in decency
without the aid of the Five Towns. For this the architecture
of the Five Towns is an architecture of ovens and chimneys;
for this its atmosphere is as black as its mud; for this it burns
and smokes all night, so that Longshaw has been compared to
hell; for this it is unlearned in the ways of agriculture, never
having seen corn except as packing straw and in quartern
loaves; for this, on the other hand, it comprehends the mysterious habits of fire and pure, sterile earth; for this it lives
crammed together in slippery streets where the housewife must
change white window-curtains at least once a fortnight if she
wishes to remain respectable; for this it gets up in the mass at
six a.m., winter and summer, and goes to bed when the public-
houses close; for this it exists—that you may drink tea out of a
teacup and toy with a chop on a plate. All the everyday crockery used in the kingdom is made in the Five Towns—all, and
much besides. A district capable of such gigantic manufacture,
of such a perfect monopoly—and which finds energy also to
produce coal and iron and great men—may be an insignificant
stain on a county, considered geographically, but it is surely
well justified in treating the county as its back garden once a
week, and in blindly ignoring it the rest of the time.

Even the majestic thought that whenever and wherever in
all England a woman washes up, she washes up the product
of the district; that whenever and wherever in all England a
plate is broken the fracture means new business for the district
—even this majestic thought had probably never occurred to
either of the girls. The fact is, that while in the Five Towns
they were also in the Square, Bursley and the Square ignored

the staple manufacture as perfectly as the district ignored th
county. Bursley has the honours of antiquity in the Five Town.
No industrial development can ever rob it of its superiority i
age, which makes it absolutely sure in its conceit. And th
time will never come when the other towns—let them swe
and bluster as they may—will not pronounce the name o
Bursley as one pronounces the name of one's mother. Ad
to this that the Square was the centre of Bursley's retail trad
(which scorned the staple as something wholesale, vulgar, an
assuredly filthy), and you will comprehend the importance an
the self-isolation of the Square in the scheme of the create
universe. There you have it, embedded in the district, and th
district embedded in the county, and the county lost and dream
ing in the heart of England!

The Square was named after St. Luke. The Evangelis
might have been startled by certain phenomena in his square
but, except in Wakes Week, when the shocking always hap
pened, St. Luke's Square lived in a manner passably saintly—
though it contained five public-houses. It contained five public
houses, a bank, a barber's, a confectioner's, three grocers', tw
chemists', an ironmonger's, a clothier's, and five drapers'. These
were all the catalogue. St. Luke's Square had no room for mino
establishments. The aristocracy of the Square undoubtedly
consisted of the drapers (for the bank was impersonal) ; and
among the five the shop of Baines stood supreme. No busi
ness establishment could possibly be more respected than that
of Mr. Baines was respected. And though John Baines had
been bedridden for a dozen years, he still lived on the lips of
admiring ceremonious burgesses as "our honoured fellow-
townsman." He deserved his reputation.

The Baines's shop, to make which three dwellings had at in
tervals been thrown into one, lay at the bottom of the Square.
It formed about one-third of the south side of the Square, the
remainder being made up of Critchlow's (chemist), the
clothier's, and the Hanover Spirit Vaults. ("Vaults" was a
favourite synonym of the public-house in the Square. Only
two of the public-houses were crude public-houses: the rest
were "vaults.") It was a composite building of three storeys,
in blackish-crimson brick, with a projecting shop-front and,
above and behind that, two rows of little windows. On the
sash of each window was a red cloth roll stuffed with sawdust, to
prevent draughts; plain white blinds descended about six inches

'rom the top of each window. There were no curtains to any
of the windows save one; this was the window of the drawing-room, on the first floor at the corner of the Square and
King Street. Another window, on the second storey, was peculiar, in that it had neither blind nor pad, and was very
dirty; this was the window of an unused room that had a
separate staircase to itself, the staircase being barred by a door
always locked. Constance and Sophia had lived in continual
expectation of the abnormal issuing from that mysterious room,
which was next to their own. But they were disappointed.
The room had no shameful secret except the incompetence of
the architect who had made one house out of three; it was
just an empty, unemployable room. The building had also
a considerable frontage on King Street, where, behind the shop,
was sheltered the parlour, with a large window and a door
that led directly by two steps into the street. A strange pe-
culiarity of the shop was that it bore no signboard. Once it
had had a large signboard which a memorable gale had blown
into the Square. Mr. Baines had decided not to replace it.
He had always objected to what he called "puffing," and for
this reason would never hear of such a thing as a clearance
sale. The hatred of "puffing" grew on him until he came to
regard even a sign as "puffing." Uninformed persons who
wished to find Baines's must ask and learn. For Mr. Baines,
to have replaced the sign would have been to condone, yea,
to participate in, the modern craze for unscruplous self-adver-
tisement. This abstention of Mr. Baines's from indulgence
in signboards was somehow accepted by the more thoughtful
members of the community as evidence that the height of Mr.
Baines's principles was greater even than they had imagined.

Constance and Sophia were the daughters of this credit to
human nature. He had no other children.

ii

They pressed their noses against the window of the showroom, and gazed down into the Square as perpendicularly as
the projecting front of the shop would allow. The show-room
was over the millinery and silken half of the shop. Over the
woollen and shirting half were the drawing-room and the chief
bedroom. When in quest of articles of coquetry, you mounted

from the shop by a curving stair, and your head gradually
rose level with a large apartment having a mahogany counter
in front of the window and along one side, yellow linoleum on
the floor, many cardboard boxes, a magnificent hinged cheval
glass, and two chairs. The window-sill being lower than the
counter, there was a gulf between the panes and the back of
the counter, into which important articles such as scissors, pencils, chalk, and artificial flowers were continually disappearing: another proof of the architect's incompetence.

The girls could only press their noses against the window by
kneeling on the counter, and this they were doing. Constance's
nose was snub, but agreeably so. Sophia had a fine Roman
nose; she was a beautiful creature, beautiful and handsome at
the same time. They were both of them rather like racehorses,
quivering with delicate, sensitive, and luxuriant life; exquisite,
enchanting proof of the circulation of the blood; innocent, art-
ful, roguish, prim, gushing, ignorant, and miraculously wise.
Their ages were sixteen and fifteen; it is an epoch when, if one
is frank, one must admit that one has nothing to learn: one has
learnt simply everything in the previous six months.

"There she goes!" exclaimed Sophia.

Up the Square, from the corner of King Street, passed a
woman in a new bonnet with pink strings, and a new blue
dress that sloped at the shoulders and grew to a vast circumference at the hem. Through the silent sunlit solitude of the
Square (for it was Thursday afternoon, and all the shops shut
except the confectioner's and one chemist's) this bonnet and
this dress floated northwards in search of romance, under the
relentless eyes of Constance and Sophia. Within them, somewhere, was the soul of Maggie, domestic servant at Baines's.
Maggie had been at the shop since before the creation of Constance and Sophia. She lived seventeen hours of each day in
an underground kitchen and larder, and the other seven in an
attic, never going out except to chapel on Sunday evenings,
and once a month on Thursday afternoons. "Followers" were
most strictly forbidden to her; but on rare occasions an aunt
from Longshaw was permitted as a tremendous favour to
see her in the subterranean den. Everybody, including herself, considered that she had a good "place," and was well
treated. It was undeniable, for instance, that she was allowed
to fall in love exactly as she chose, provided she did not "carry
on" in the kitchen or the yard. And as a fact, Maggie had

fallen in love. In seventeen years she had been engaged eleven times. No one could conceive how that ugly and powerful organism could softly languish to the undoing of even a butty-collier, nor why, having caught a man in her sweet toils, she could ever be imbecile enough to set him free. There are, however, mysteries in the souls of Maggies. The drudge had probably been affianced oftener than any woman in Bursley. Her employers were so accustomed to an interesting announcement that for years they had taken to saying naught in reply but "Really, Maggie." Engagements and tragic partings were Maggie's pastime. Fixed otherwise, she might have studied the piano instead.

"No gloves, of course!" Sophia criticized.

"Well, you can't expect her to have gloves," said Constance.

Then a pause, as the bonnet and dress neared the top of the Square.

"Supposing she turns round and sees us?" Constance suggested.

"I don't care if she does," said Sophia, with a haughtiness almost impassioned; and her head trembled slightly.

There were, as usual, several loafers at the top of the Square, in the corner between the bank and the "Marquis of Granby." And one of these loafers stepped forward and shook hands with an obviously willing Maggie. Clearly it was a rendezvous, open, unashamed. The twelfth victim had been selected by the virgin of forty, whose kiss would not have melted lard! The couple disappeared together down Oldcastle Street.

"*Well!*" cried Constance. "Did you ever see such a thing?"

While Sophia, short of adequate words, flushed and bit her lip.

With the profound, instinctive cruelty of youth, Constance and Sophia had assembled in their favourite haunt, the showroom, expressly to deride Maggie in her new clothes. They obscurely thought that a woman so ugly and soiled as Maggie was had no right to possess new clothes. Even her desire to take the air of a Thursday afternoon seemed to them unnatural and somewhat reprehensible. Why should she want to stir out of her kitchen? As for her tender yearnings, they positively grudged these to Maggie. That Maggie should give rein to chaste passion was more than grotesque; it was offensive and wicked. But let it not for an instant be doubted that they were nice, kind-hearted, well-behaved, and delightful girls! Because they were. They were not angels.

"It's too ridiculous!" said Sophia, severely. She had youth, beauty, and rank in her favour. And to her it really was ridiculous.

"Poor old Maggie!" Constance murmured. Constance was foolishly good-natured, a perfect manufactory of excuses for other people; and her benevolence was eternally rising up and overpowering her reason.

"What time did mother say she should be back?" Sophia asked.

"Not until supper."

"Oh! Hallelujah!" Sophia burst out, clasping her hands in joy. And they both slid down from the counter just as if they had been little boys, and not, as their mother called them, "great girls."

"Let's go and play the Osborne quadrilles," Sophia suggested (the Osborne quadrilles being a series of dances arranged to be performed on drawing-room pianos by four jewelled hands).

"I couldn't think of it," said Constance, with a precocious gesture of seriousness. In that gesture, and in her tone, was something which conveyed to Sophia: "Sophia, how can you be so utterly blind to the gravity of our fleeting existence as to ask me to go and strum the piano with you?" Yet a moment before she had been a little boy.

"Why not?" Sophia demanded.

"I shall never have another chance like to-day for getting on with this," said Constance, picking up a bag from the counter.

She sat down and took from the bag a piece of loosely woven canvas, on which she was embroidering a bunch of roses in coloured wools. The canvas had once been stretched on a frame, but now, as the delicate labour of the petals and leaves was done, and nothing remained to do but the monotonous background, Constance was content to pin the stuff to her knee. With the long needle and several skeins of mustard-tinted wool, she bent over the canvas and resumed the filling-in of the tiny squares. The whole design was in squares—the gradations of red and greens, the curves of the smallest buds—all was contrived in squares, with a result that mimicked a fragment of uncompromising Axminster carpet. Still, the fine texture of the wool, the regular and rapid grace of those fingers moving incessantly at back and front of the canvas, the gentle sound of the wool as it passed through the holes, and the intent, youthful earnestness of that lowered gaze, excused and invested with charm an activity which, on artistic grounds, could not possibly be justified. The canvas was destined to adorn a gilt firescreen in the drawing-room, and also to form a birthday gift to Mrs. Baines from her elder daughter. But whether the enterprise was as secret from Mrs. Baines as Constance hoped, none save Mrs. Baines knew.

"Con," murmured Sophia, "you're too sickening sometimes."

"Well," said Constance, blandly, "it's no use pretending that this hasn't got to be finished before we go back to school, because it has."

Sophia wandered about, a prey ripe for the Evil One. "Oh," she exclaimed joyously—even ecstatically—looking behind the cheval glass, "here's mother's new skirt! Miss Dunn's been putting the gimp on it! Oh, mother, what a proud thing you will be!"

Constance heard swishings behind the glass. "What are you doing, Sophia?"

"Nothing."

"You surely aren't putting that skirt on?"

"Why not?"

"You'll catch it finely, I can tell you!"

Without further defence, Sophia sprang out from behind the immense glass. She had already shed a notable part of her own costume, and the flush of mischief was in her face. She ran across to the other side of the room and examined carefully a large coloured print that was affixed to the wall.

This print represented fifteen sisters, all of the same height and slimness of figure, all of the same age—about twenty-five or so, and all with exactly the same haughty and bored beauty. That they were in truth sisters was clear from the facial resemblance between them; their demeanour indicated that they were princesses, offspring of some impossibly prolific king and queen. Those hands had never toiled, nor had those features ever relaxed from the smile of courts. The princesses moved in a landscape of marble steps and verandahs, with a bandstand and strange trees in the distance. One was in a riding-habit, another in evening attire, another dressed for tea, another for the theatre; another seemed to be ready to go to bed. One held a little girl by the hand; it could not have been her own little girl, for these princesses were far beyond human passions. Where had she obtained the little girl? Why was one sister going to the theatre, another to tea, another to the stable, and another to bed? Why was one in a heavy mantle, and another sheltering from the sun's rays under a parasol? The picture was drenched in mystery, and the strangest thing about it was that all these highnesses were apparently content with the most ridiculous and out-moded fashions. Absurd hats, with veils flying behind; absurd bonnets, fitting close to the head, and spotted; absurd coiffures that nearly lay on the nape; absurd, clumsy sleeves; absurd waists, almost above the elbow's level; absurd scolloped jackets! And the skirts! What a sight were those skirts! They were nothing but vast decorated pyramids; on the summit of each was stuck the upper half of a princess. It was astounding that princesses should consent to be so preposterous and so uncomfortable. But Sophia perceived nothing uncanny in the picture, which bore the legend: "Newest summer fashions from Paris. Gratis supplement to *Myra's Journal.*" Sophia had never imagined anything more stylish, lovely, and dashing than the raiment of the fifteen princesses.

For Constance and Sophia had the disadvantage of living in the middle ages. The crinoline had not quite reached its full circumference, and the dress-improver had not even been thought of. In all the Five Towns there was not a public bath, nor a free library, nor a municipal park, nor a telephone, nor yet a board-school. People had not understood the vital necessity of going away to the seaside every year. Bishop Colenso had just staggered Christianity by his shameless notions on the Pentateuch. Half Lancashire was starving on account of the American war. Garroting was the chief amusement of the homicidal classes. Incredible as it may appear, there was nothing but a horse-tram running between Bursley and Hanbridge—and that only twice an hour; and between the other towns no stage of any kind! One went to Longshaw as one now goes to Pekin. It was an era so dark and backward that one might wonder how people could sleep in their beds at night for thinking about their sad state.

Happily the inhabitants of the Five Towns in that era were passably pleased with themselves, and they never even suspected that they were not quite modern and quite awake. They thought that the intellectual, the industrial, and the social movements had gone about as far as these movements could go, and they were amazed at their own progress. Instead of being humble and ashamed, they actually showed pride in their pitiful achievements. They ought to have looked forward meekly to the prodigious feats of posterity; but, having too little faith and too much conceit, they were content to look behind and make comparisons with the past. They did not foresee the miraculous generation which is us. A poor, blind, complacent people! The ludicrous horse-car was typical of them. The driver rang a huge bell, five minutes before starting, that could be heard from the Wesleyan Chapel to the Cock Yard, and then after deliberations and hesitations the vehicle rolled off on its rails into unknown dangers while passengers shouted good-bye. At Bleakridge it had to stop for the turnpike, and it was assisted up the mountains of Leveson Place and Sutherland Street (towards Hanbridge) by a third horse, on whose back was perched a tiny, whip-cracking boy; that boy lived like a shuttle on the road between Leveson Place and Sutherland Street, and even in wet weather he was the envy of all other boys. After half an hour's perilous transit the car drew up solemnly in a narrow street by the *Signal* office in Hanbridge, and the ruddy driver, having revolved many times the polished iron handle of his sole brake, turned his attention to his passengers in calm triumph, dismissing them with a sort of unsung doxology.

And this was regarded as the last word of traction! A whip-cracking boy on a tip horse! Oh, blind, blind! You could not foresee the hundred and twenty electric cars that now rush madly bumping and thundering at twenty miles an hour through all the main streets of the district!

So that naturally Sophia, infected with the pride of her period, had no misgivings whatever concerning the final elegance of the princesses. She studied them as the fifteen apostles of the *ne plus ultra;* then, having taken some flowers and plumes out of a box, amid warnings from Constance, she retreated behind the glass, and presently emerged as a great lady in the style of the princesses. Her mother's tremendous new gown ballooned about her in all its fantastic richness and expensiveness. And with the gown she had put on her mother's importance—that mien of assured authority, of capacity tested in many a crisis, which characterized Mrs. Baines, and which Mrs. Baines seemed to impart to her dresses even before she had regularly worn them. For it was a fact that Mrs. Baines's empty garments inspired respect, as though some essence had escaped from her and remained in them.

"Sophia!"

Constance stayed her needle, and, without lifting her head, gazed, with eyes raised from the wool-work, motionless at the posturing figure of her sister. It was sacrilege that she was witnessing, a prodigious irreverence. She was conscious of an expectation that punishment would instantly fall on this daring, impious child. But she, who never felt these mad, amazing impulses, could nevertheless only smile fearfully.

"Sophia!" she breathed, with an intensity of alarm that merged into condoning admiration. "Whatever will you do next?"

Sophia's lovely flushed face crowned the extraordinary structure like a blossom, scarcely controlling its laughter. She was as tall as her mother, and as imperious, as crested, and proud; and in spite of the pigtail, the girlish semi-circular comb, and the loose foal-like limbs, she could support as well as her mother the majesty of the gimp-embroidered dress. Her eyes sparkled with all the challenges of the untried virgin as she minced about the showroom. Abounding life inspired her movements. The confident and fierce joy of youth shone on her brow. "What thing on earth equals me?" she seemed to demand with enchanting and yet ruthless arrogance. She was the daughter of a respected, bedridden draper in an insignificant town, lost in the central labyrinth of England, if you like; yet what manner of man, confronted with her, would or could have denied her naïve claim to dominion? She stood, in her mother's hoops, for the desire of the world. And in the innocence of her soul she knew it! The heart of a young girl mysteriously speaks and tells her of her power long ere she can use her power. If she can find nothing else to subdue, you may catch her in the early years subduing a gate-post or drawing homage from an empty chair. Sophia's experimental victim was Constance, with suspended needle and soft glance that shot out from the lowered face.

Then Sophia fell, in stepping backwards; the pyramid was overbalanced; great distended rings of silk trembled and swayed gigantically on the floor, and Sophia's small feet lay like the feet of a doll on the rim of the largest circle, which curved and arched above them like a cavern's mouth. The abrupt transition of her features from assured pride to ludicrous astonishment and alarm was comical enough to have sent into wild uncharitable laughter any creature less humane than Constance. But Constance sprang to her, a single embodied instinct of benevolence, with her snub nose, and tried to raise her.

"Oh, Sophia!" she cried compassionately—that voice seemed not to know the tones of reproof—"I do hope you've not messed it, because mother would be so——"

The words were interrupted by the sound of groans beyond the door leading to the bedrooms. The groans, indicating direst physical torment, grew louder. The two girls stared, wonder-struck and afraid, at the door, Sophia with her dark head raised, and Constance with her arms round Sophia's waist. The door opened, letting in a much-magnified sound of groans, and there entered a youngish, undersized man, who was frantically clutching his head in his hands and contorting all the muscles of his face. On perceiving the sculptural group of two prone, interlocked girls, one enveloped in a crinoline, and the other with a wool-work bunch of flowers pinned to her knee, he jumped back, ceased groaning, arranged his face, and seriously tried to pretend that it was not he who had been vocal in anguish, that, indeed, he was just passing as a casual, ordinary wayfarer through the showroom to the shop below. He blushed darkly; and the girls also blushed.

"Oh, I beg pardon, I'm sure!" said this youngish man suddenly; and with a swift turn he disappeared whence he had come.

He was Mr. Povey, a person universally esteemed, both within and without the shop, the surrogate of bedridden Mr. Baines, the unfailing comfort and stand-by of Mrs. Baines, the fount and radiating centre of order and discipline in the shop; a quiet, diffident, secretive, tedious, and obstinate youngish man, absolutely faithful, absolutely efficient in his sphere; without brilliance, without distinction; perhaps rather little-minded, certainly narrow-minded; but what a force in the shop! The shop was inconceivable without Mr. Povey. He was under twenty and not out of his apprenticeship when Mr. Baines had been struck down, and he had at once proved his worth. Of the assistants, he alone slept in the house. His bedroom was next to that of his employer; there was a door between the two chambers, and the two steps led down from the larger to the less.

The girls regained their feet, Sophia with Constance's help. It was not easy to right a capsized crinoline. They both began to laugh nervously, with a trace of hysteria.

"I thought he'd gone to the dentist's," whispered Constance.

Mr. Povey's toothache had been causing anxiety in the microcosm for two days, and it had been clearly understood at dinner that Thursday morning that Mr. Povey was to set forth to Oulsnam Bros., the dentists at Hillport, without any delay. Only on Thursdays and Sundays did Mr. Povey dine with the family. On other days he dined later, by himself, but at the family table, when Mrs. Baines or one of the assistants could "relieve" him in the shop. Before starting out to visit her elder sister at Axe, Mrs. Baines had insisted to Mr. Povey that he had eaten practically nothing but "slops" for twenty-four hours, and that if he was not careful she would have him on her hands. He had replied in his quietest, most sagacious, matter-of-fact tone—the tone that carried weight with all who heard it—that he had only been waiting for Thursday afternoon, and should of course go instantly to Oulsnams' and have the thing attended to in a proper manner. He had even added that persons who put off going to the dentist's were simply sowing trouble for themselves.

None could possibly have guessed that Mr. Povey was afraid of going to the dentist's. But such was the case. He had not dared to set forth. The paragon of commonsense, pictured by most people as being somehow unliable to human frailties, could not yet screw himself up to the point of ringing a dentist's door-bell.

"He did look funny," said Sophia. "I wonder what he thought. I couldn't help laughing!"

Constance made no answer; but when Sophia had resumed her own clothes, and it was ascertained beyond doubt that the new dress had not suffered, and Constance herself was calmly stitching again, she said, poising her needle as she had poised it to watch Sophia:

"I was just wondering whether something oughtn't to be done for Mr. Povey."

"What?" Sophia demanded.

"Has he gone back to his bedroom?"

"Let's go and listen," said Sophia the adventuress.

They went, through the showroom door, past the foot of the stairs leading to the second storey, down the long corridor broken in the middle by two steps and carpeted with a narrow bordered carpet whose parallel lines increased its apparent length. They went on tiptoe, sticking close to one another. Mr. Povey's door was slightly ajar. They listened; not a sound.

"Mr. Povey!" Constance coughed discreetly.

No reply. It was Sophia who pushed the door open. Constance made an elderly prim plucking gesture at Sophia's bare arm, but she followed Sophia gingerly into the forbidden room, which was, however, empty. The bed had been ruffled, and on it lay a book, "The Harvest of a Quiet Eye."

"Harvest of a quiet tooth!" Sophia whispered, giggling very low.

"Hsh!" Constance put her lips forward.

From the next room came a regular, muffled, oratorical sound, as though some one had begun many years ago to address a meeting and had forgotten to leave off and never would leave off. They were familiar with the sound, and they quitted Mr. Povey's chamber in fear of disturbing it. At the same moment Mr. Povey reappeared, this time in the drawing-room doorway at the other extremity of the long corridor. He seemed to be trying ineffectually to flee from his tooth as a murderer tries to flee from his conscience.

"Oh, Mr. Povey!" said Constance quickly—for he had surprised them coming out of his bedroom; "we were just looking for you."

"To see if we could do anything for you," Sophia added.

"Oh no, thanks!" said Mr. Povey.

Then he began to come down the corridor, slowly.

"You haven't been to the dentist's," said Constance sympathetically.

"No, I haven't," said Mr. Povey, as if Constance was indicating a fact which had escaped his attention. "The truth is, I thought it looked like rain, and if I'd got wet—you see——"

Miserable Mr. Povey!

"Yes," said Constance, "you certainly ought to keep out of draughts. Don't you think it would be a good thing if you went and sat in the parlour? There's a fire there."

"I shall be all right, thank you," said Mr. Povey. And after a pause: "Well, thanks, I will."

iii

The girls made way for him to pass them at the head of the twisting stairs which led down to the parlour. Constance followed, and Sophia followed Constance.

"Have father's chair," said Constance.

There were two rocking-chairs with fluted backs covered by antimacassars, one on either side of the hearth. That to the left was still entitled "father's chair," though its owner had not sat in it since long before the Crimean war, and would never sit in it again.

"I think I'd sooner have the other one," said Mr. Povey, "because it's on the right side, you see." And he touched his right cheek.

Having taken Mrs. Baines's chair, he bent his face down to the fire, seeking comfort from its warmth. Sophia poked the fire, whereupon Mr. Povey abruptly withdrew his face. He then felt something light on his shoulders. Constance had taken the antimacassar from the back of the chair, and protected him with it from the draughts. He did not instantly rebel, and therefore was permanently barred from rebellion. He was entrapped by the antimacassar. It formally constituted him an invalid, and Constance and Sophia his nurses. Constance drew the curtain across the street door. No draught could come from the window, for the window was not "made to open." The age of ventilation had not arrived. Sophia shut the other two doors. And, each near a door, the girls gazed at Mr. Povey behind his back, irresolute, but filled with a delicious sense of responsibility.

The situation was on a different plane now. The seriousness of Mr. Povey's toothache, which became more and more manifest, had already wiped out the ludicrous memory of the encounter in the showroom. Looking at these two big girls, with their short-sleeved black frocks and black aprons, and their smooth hair, and their composed serious faces, one would have judged them incapable of the least lapse from an archangelic primness; Sophia especially presented a marvellous imitation of saintly innocence. As for the toothache, its action on Mr.

Povey was apparently periodic; it gathered to a crisis like a
wave, gradually, the torture increasing till the wave broke and
left Mr. Povey exhausted, but free for a moment from pain.
These crises recurred about once a minute. And now, accustomed to the presence of the young virgins, and having tacitly
acknowledged by his acceptance of the antimacassar that his
state was abnormal, he gave himself up frankly to affliction.
He concealed nothing of his agony, which was fully displayed
by sudden contortions of his frame, and frantic oscillations of
the rocking-chair. Presently, as he lay back enfeebled in the
wash of a spent wave, he murmured with a sick man's voice:

"I suppose you haven't got any laudanum?"

The girls started into life. "Laudanum, Mr. Povey?"

"Yes, to hold in my mouth."

He sat up, tense; another wave was forming. The excellent
fellow was lost to all self-respect, all decency.

"There's sure to be some in mother's cupboard," said Sophia.

Constance, who bore Mrs. Baines's bunch of keys at her
girdle, a solemn trust, moved a little fearfully to a corner cupboard which was hung in the angle to the right of the projecting fireplace, over a shelf on which stood a large copper
tea-urn. That corner cupboard, of oak inlaid with maple and
ebony in a simple border pattern, was typical of the room. It
was of a piece with the deep green "flock" wall paper, and the
tea-urn, and the rocking-chairs with their antimacassars, and
the harmonium in rosewood with a Chinese papier-mâché tea-
caddy on the top of it; even with the carpet, certainly the
most curious parlour carpet that ever was, being made of
lengths of the stair-carpet sewn together side by side. That
corner cupboard was already old in service; it had held the
medicines of generations. It gleamed darkly with the grave and
genuine polish which comes from ancient use alone. The key
which Constance chose from her bunch was like the cupboard,
smooth and shining with years; it fitted and turned very easily,
yet with a firm snap. The single wide door opened sedately as
a portal.

The girls examined the sacred interior, which had the air of
being inhabited by an army of diminutive prisoners, each crying aloud with the full strength of its label to be set free on a
mission.

"There it is!" said Sophia eagerly.

And there it was: a blue bottle, with a saffron label, "Caution. POISON. Laudanum. Charles Critchlow, M.P.S. Dispensing Chemist. St. Luke's Square, Bursley."

Those large capitals frightened the girls. Constance took the bottle as she might have taken a loaded revolver, and she glanced at Sophia. Their omnipotent, all-wise mother was not present to tell them what to do. They, who had never decided, had to decide now. And Constance was the elder. Must this fearsome stuff, whose very name was a name of fear, be introduced in spite of printed warnings into Mr. Povey's mouth? The responsibility was terrifying.

"Perhaps I'd just better ask Mr. Critchlow," Constance faltered.

The expectation of beneficent laudanum had enlivened Mr. Povey, had already, indeed, by a sort of suggestion, half cured his toothache.

"Oh no!" he said. "No need to ask Mr. Critchlow . . . Two or three drops in a little water." He showed impatience to be at the laudanum.

The girls knew that an antipathy existed between the chemist and Mr. Povey.

"It's sure to be all right," said Sophia. "I'll get the water."

With youthful cries and alarms they succeeded in pouring four mortal dark drops (one more than Constance intended) into a cup containing a little water. And as they handed the cup to Mr. Povey their faces were the faces of affrighted comical conspirators. They felt so old and they looked so young.

Mr. Povey imbibed eagerly of the potion, put the cup on the mantelpiece, and then tilted his head to the right so as to submerge the affected tooth. In this posture he remained, awaiting the sweet influence of the remedy. The girls, out of a nice modesty, turned away, for Mr. Povey must not swallow the medicine, and they preferred to leave him unhampered in the solution of a delicate problem. When next they examined him, he was leaning back in the rocking-chair with his mouth open and his eyes shut.

"Has it done you any good, Mr. Povey?"

"I think I'll lie down on the sofa for a minute," was Mr. Povey's strange reply; and forthwith he sprang up and flung himself on to the horse-hair sofa between the fireplace and the window, where he lay stripped of all his dignity, a mere beaten animal in a grey suit with peculiar coat-tails, and a very

creased waistcoat, and a lapel that was planted with pins, and
a paper collar and close-fitting paper cuffs.

Constance ran after him with the antimacassar, which she
spread softly on his shoulders; and Sophia put another one
over his thin little legs, all drawn up.

They then gazed at their handiwork, with secret self-accusa-
tions and the most dreadful misgivings.

"He surely never swallowed it!" Constance whispered.

"He's asleep, anyhow," said Sophia, more loudly.

Mr. Povey was certainly asleep, and his mouth was very
wide open—like a shop-door. The only question was whether
his sleep was not an eternal sleep; the only question was
whether he was not out of his pain for ever.

Then he snored—horribly; his snore seemed a portent of
disaster.

Sophia approached him as though he were a bomb, and
stared, growing bolder, into his mouth.

"Oh, Con," she summoned her sister, "do come and look!
It's too droll!"

In an instant all their four eyes were exploring the singular
landscape of Mr. Povey's mouth. In a corner, to the right of
that interior, was one sizeable fragment of a tooth, that was
attached to Mr. Povey by the slenderest tie, so that at each
respiration of Mr. Povey, when his body slightly heaved and
the gale moaned in the cavern, this tooth moved separately,
showing that its long connection with Mr. Povey was drawing
to a close.

"That's the one," said Sophia, pointing. "And it's as loose
as anything. Did you ever see such a funny thing?"

The extreme funniness of the thing had lulled in Sophia the
fear of Mr. Povey's sudden death.

"I'll see how much he's taken," said Constance, preoccupied, going to the mantelpiece.

"Why, I do believe——" Sophia began, and then stopped,
glancing at the sewing-machine, which stood next to the sofa.

It was a Howe sewing-machine. It had a little tool-drawer,
and in the tool-drawer was a small pair of pliers. Constance,
engaged in sniffing at the lees of the potion in order to estimate its probable deadliness, heard the well-known click of the
little tool-drawer, and then she saw Sophia nearing Mr.
Povey's mouth with the pliers.

"Sophia!" she exclaimed, aghast. "What in the name of goodness are you doing?"

"Nothing," said Sophia.

The next instant Mr. Povey sprang up out of his laudanum dream.

"It jumps!" he muttered; and, after a reflective pause, "but it's much better." He had at any rate escaped death.

Sophia's right hand was behind her back.

Just then a hawker passed down King Street, crying mussels and cockles.

"Oh!" Sophia almost shrieked. "Do let's have mussels and cockles for tea!" And she rushed to the door, and unlocked and opened it, regardless of the risk of draughts to Mr. Povey.

In those days people often depended upon the caprices of hawkers for the tastiness of their teas; but it was an adventurous age, when errant knights of commerce were numerous and enterprising. You went on to your doorstep, caught your meal as it passed, withdrew, cooked it and ate it, quite in the manner of the early Briton.

Constance was obliged to join her sister on the top step. Sophia descended to the second step.

"Fresh mussels and cockles all alive oh!" bawled the hawker, looking across the road in the April breeze. He was the celebrated Hollins, a professional Irish drunkard, aged in iniquity, who cheerfully saluted magistrates in the street, and referred to the workhouse, which he occasionally visited, as the Bastile.

Sophia was trembling from head to foot.

"What *are* you laughing at, you silly thing?" Constance demanded.

Sophia surreptitiously showed the pliers, which she had partly thrust into her pocket. Between their points was a most perceptible, and even recognizable, fragment of Mr. Povey.

This was the crown of Sophia's career as a perpetrator of the unutterable.

"What!" Constance's face showed the final contortions of that horrified incredulity which is forced to believe.

Sophia nudged her violently to remind her that they were in the street, and also quite close to Mr. Povey.

"Now, my little missies," said the vile Hollins. "Three pence a pint, and how's your honoured mother to-day? Yes, fresh, so help me God!"

CHAPTER II

The Tooth

The two girls came up the unlighted stone staircase which led from Maggie's cave to the door of the parlour. Sophia, foremost, was carrying a large tray, and Constance a small one. Constance, who had nothing on her tray but a teapot, a bowl of steaming and balmy-scented mussels and cockles, and a plate of hot buttered toast, went directly into the parlour on the left. Sophia had in her arms the entire material and apparatus of a high tea for two, including eggs, jam, and toast (covered with the slop-basin turned upside down), but not including mussels and cockles. She turned to the right, passed along the corridor by the cutting-out room, up two steps into the sheeted and shuttered gloom of the closed shop, up the showroom stairs, through the showroom, and so into the bedroom corridor. Experience had proved it easier to make this long detour than to round the difficult corner of the parlour stairs with a large loaded tray. Sophia knocked with the edge of the tray at the door of the principal bedroom. The muffled oratorical sound from within suddenly ceased, and the door was opened by a very tall, very thin, black-bearded man, who looked down at Sophia as if to demand what she meant by such an interruption.

"I've brought the tea, Mr. Critchlow," said Sophia.

And Mr. Critchlow carefully accepted the tray.

"Is that my little Sophia?" asked a faint voice from the depths of the bedroom.

"Yes, father," said Sophia.

But she did not attempt to enter the room. Mr. Critchlow put the tray on a white-clad chest of drawers near the door, and then he shut the door, with no ceremony. Mr. Critchlow was John Baines's oldest and closest friend, though decidedly younger than the draper. He frequently "popped in" to have a word with the invalid; but Thursday afternoon was his special afternoon, consecrated by him to the service of the sick. From two o'clock precisely till eight o'clock precisely he took charge of John Baines, reigning autocratically over the bedroom. It was known that he would not tolerate invasions, nor even ambassadorial visits. No! He gave up his weekly holiday to this business of friendship, and he must be allowed to conduct the business in his own way. Mrs. Baines herself avoided disturbing Mr. Critchlow's ministrations on her husband. She was glad to do so; for Mr. Baines was never to be left alone under any circumstances, and the convenience of being able to rely upon the presence of a staid member of the Pharmaceutical Society for six hours of a given day every week outweighed the slight affront to her prerogatives as wife and house-mistress. Mr. Critchlow was an extremely peculiar man, but when he was in the bedroom she could leave the house with an easy mind. Moreover, John Baines enjoyed these Thursday afternoons. For him, there was "none like Charles Critchlow." The two old friends experienced a sort of grim, desiccated happiness, cooped up together in the bedroom, secure from women and fools generally. How they spent the time did not seem to be certainly known, but the impression was that politics occupied them. Undoubtedly Mr. Critchlow was an extremely peculiar man. He was a man of habits. He must always have the same things for his tea. Black-currant jam, for instance. (He called it "preserve.") The idea of offering Mr. Critchlow a tea which did not comprise black-currant jam was inconceivable by the intelligence of St. Luke's Square. Thus for years past, in the fruit-preserving season, when all the house and all the shop smelt richly of fruit boiling in sugar, Mrs. Baines had filled an extra number of jars with black-currant jam, "because Mr. Critchlow wouldn't *touch* any other sort."

So Sophia, faced with the shut door of the bedroom, went down to the parlour by the shorter route. She knew that on going up again, after tea, she would find the devastated tray on the doormat.

Constance was helping Mr. Povey to mussels and cockles. And Mr. Povey still wore one of the antimacassars. It must have stuck to his shoulders when he sprang up from the sofa, woollen antimacassars being notoriously parasitic things. Sophia sat down, somewhat self-consciously. The serious Constance was also perturbed. Mr. Povey did not usually take tea in the house on Thursday afternoons; his practice was to go out into the great, mysterious world. Never before had he shared a meal with the girls alone. The situation was indubitably unexpected, unforeseen; it was, too, piquant, and

what added to its piquancy was the fact that Constance and
Sophia were, somehow, responsible for Mr. Povey. They felt
that they were responsible for him. They had offered the practical sympathy of two intelligent and well-trained young
women, born nurses by reason of their sex, and Mr. Povey had
accepted; he was now on their hands. Sophia's monstrous, sly
operation in Mr. Povey's mouth did not cause either of them
much alarm, Constance having apparently recovered from the
first shock of it. They had discussed it in the kitchen while
preparing the teas; Constance's extraordinarily severe and dic-
tatorial tone in condemning it had led to a certain heat. But
the success of the impudent wrench justified it despite any
irrefutable argument to the contrary. Mr. Povey was better
already, and he evidently remained in ignorance of his loss.

"Have some?" Constance asked of Sophia, with a large
spoon hovering over the bowl of shells.

"Yes, *please*," said Sophia, positively.

Constance well knew that she would have some, and had only
asked from sheer nervousness.

"Pass your plate, then."

Now when everybody was served with mussels, cockles, tea,
and toast, and Mr. Povey had been persuaded to cut the crust
off his toast, and Constance had, quite unnecessarily, warned
Sophia against the deadly green stuff in the mussels, and Constance had further pointed out that the evenings were getting
longer, and Mr. Povey had agreed that they were, there remained nothing to say. An irksome silence fell on them all,
and no one could lift it off. Tiny clashes of shell and crockery
sounded with the terrible clearness of noises heard in the
night. Each person avoided the eyes of the others. And both
Constance and Sophia kept straightening their bodies at intervals, and expanding their chests, and then looking at their
plates; occasionally a prim cough was discharged. It was a sad
example of the difference between young women's dreams of
social brilliance and the reality of life. These girls got more
and more girlish, until, from being women at the administering of laudanum, they sank back to about eight years of age
—perfect children—at the tea-table.

The tension was snapped by Mr. Povy. "My God!" he muttered, moved by a startling discovery to this impious and disgraceful oath (he, the pattern and exemplar—and in the
presence of innocent girlhood too!). "I've swallowed it!"

"Swallowed what, Mr. Povey?" Constance inquired.

The tip of Mr. Povey's tongue made a careful voyage of inspection all round the right side of his mouth.

"Oh yes!" he said, as if solemnly accepting the inevitable. "I've swallowed it!"

Sophia's face was now scarlet; she seemed to be looking for some place to hide it. Constance could not think of anything to say.

"That tooth has been loose for two years," said Mr. Povey, "and now I've swallowed it with a mussel."

"Oh, Mr. Povey!" Constance cried in confusion, and added, "There's one good thing, it can't hurt you any more now."

"Oh!" said Mr. Povey. "It wasn't *that* tooth that was hurting me. It's an old stump at the back that's upset me so this last day or two. I wish it had been."

Sophia had her teacup close to her red face. At these words of Mr. Povey her cheeks seemed to fill out like plump apples. She dashed the cup into its saucer, spilling tea recklessly, and then ran from the room with stifled snorts.

"Sophia!" Constance protested.

"I must just——" Sophia incoherently spluttered in the doorway. "I shall be all right. Don't——"

Constance, who had risen, sat down again.

ii

Sophia fled along the passage leading to the shop and took refuge in the cutting-out room, a room which the astonishing architect had devised upon what must have been a backyard of one of the three constituent houses. It was lighted from its roof, and only a wooden partition, eight feet high, separated it from the passage. Here Sophia gave rein to her feelings; she laughed and cried together, weeping generously into her handkerchief and wildly giggling, in a hysteria which she could not control. The spectacle of Mr. Povey mourning for a tooth which he thought he had swallowed, but which in fact lay all the time in her pocket, seemed to her to be by far the most ridiculous, side-splitting thing that had ever happened or could happen on earth. It utterly overcame her. And when she fancied that she had exhausted and conquered its surpassing ridiculousness, this ridiculousness seized her again and rolled her anew in depths of mad, trembling laughter.

Gradually she grew calmer. She heard the parlour door open, and Constance descend the kitchen steps with a rattling tray of tea-things. Tea, then, was finished, without her! Constance did not remain in the kitchen, because the cups and saucers were left for Maggie to wash up as a fitting *coda* to Maggie's monthly holiday. The parlour door closed. And the vision of Mr. Povey in his antimacassar swept Sophia off into another convulsion of laughter and tears. Upon this the parlour door opened again, and Sophia choked herself into silence while Constance hastened along the passage. In a minute Constance returned with her woolwork, which she had got from the showroom, and the parlour received her. Not the least curiosity on the part of Constance as to what had become of Sophia!

At length Sophia, a faint meditative smile being all that was left of the storm in her, ascended slowly to the showroom, through the shop. Nothing there of interest! Thence she wandered towards the drawing-room, and encountered Mr. Critchlow's tray on the mat. She picked it up and carried it by way of the showroom and shop down to the kitchen, where she dreamily munched two pieces of toast that had cooled to the consistency of leather. She mounted the stone steps and listened at the door of the parlour. No sound! This seclusion of Mr. Povey and Constance was really very strange. She roved right round the house, and descended creepingly by the twisted house-stairs, and listened intently at the other door of the parlour. She now detected a faint regular snore. Mr. Povey, a prey to laudanum and mussels, was sleeping while Constance worked at her firescreen! It was now in the highest degree odd, this seclusion of Mr. Povey and Constance; unlike anything in Sophia's experience! She wanted to go into the parlour, but she could not bring herself to do so. She crept away again, forlorn and puzzled, and next discovered herself in the bedroom which she shared with Constance at the top of the house; she lay down in the dusk on the bed and began to read "The Days of Bruce;" but she read only with her eyes.

Later, she heard movements on the house-stairs, and the familiar whining creak of the door at the foot thereof. She skipped lightly to the door of the bedroom.

"Good-night, Mr. Povey. I hope you'll be able to sleep."
Constance's voice!

"It will probably come on again."

Mr. Povey's voice, pessimistic!

Then the shutting of doors. It was almost dark. She went back to the bed, expecting a visit from Constance. But a clock struck eight, and all the various phenomena connected with the departure of Mr. Critchlow occurred one after another. At the same time Maggie came home from the land of romance. Then long silences! Constance was now immured with her father, it being her "turn" to nurse; Maggie was washing up in her cave, and Mr. Povey was lost to sight in his bedroom. Then Sophia heard her mother's lively, commanding knock on the King Street door. Dusk had definitely yielded to black night in the bedroom. Sophia dozed and dreamed. When she awoke, her ear caught the sound of knocking. She jumped up, tip-toed to the landing, and looked over the balustrade, whence she had a view of all the first-floor corridor. The gas had been lighted; through the round aperture at the top of the porcelain globe she could see the wavering flame. It was her mother, still bonneted, who was knocking at the door of Mr. Povey's room. Constance stood in the doorway of her parents' room. Mrs. Baines knocked twice with an interval, and then said to Constance, in a resonant whisper that vibrated up the corridor—

"He seems to be fast asleep. I'd better not disturb him."

"But suppose he wants something in the night?"

"Well, child, I should hear him moving. Sleep's the best thing for him."

Mrs. Baines left Mr. Povey to the effects of laudanum, and came along the corridor. She was a stout woman, all black stuff and gold chain, and her skirt more than filled the width of the corridor. Sophia watched her habitual heavy mounting gesture as she climbed the two steps that gave variety to the corridor. At the gas-jet she paused, and, putting her hand to the tap, gazed up into the globe.

"Where's Sophia?" she demanded, her eyes fixed on the gas as she lowered the flame.

"I think she must be in bed, mother," said Constance, non-chalantly.

The returned mistress was point by point resuming knowledge and control of that complicated machine—her household.

Then Constance and her mother disappeared into the bed-room, and the door was shut with a gentle, decisive bang that to the silent watcher on the floor above seemed to create a special excluding intimacy round about the figures of Con-stance and her father and mother. The watcher wondered, with a little prick of jealousy, what they would be discussing in the large bedroom, her father's beard wagging feebly and his long arms on the counterpane, Constance perched at the foot of the bed, and her mother walking to and fro, putting her cameo brooch on the dressing-table or stretching creases out of her gloves. Certainly, in some subtle way, Constance had a stand-ing with her parents which was more confidential than Sophia's.

iii

When Constance came to bed, half an hour later, Sophia was already in bed. The room was fairly spacious. It had been the girls' retreat and fortress since their earliest years. Its features seemed to them as natural and unalterable as the features of a cave to a cave-dweller. It had been repapered twice in their lives, and each papering stood out in their memories like an epoch; a third epoch was due to the replacing of a drugget by a resplendent old carpet degraded from the drawing-room. There was only one bed, the bedstead being of painted iron; they never interfered with each other in that bed, sleeping with a detachment as perfect as if they had slept on opposite sides of St. Luke's Square; yet if Constance had one night lain down on the half near the window instead of on the half near the door, the secret nature of the universe would have seemed to be altered. The small fire-grate was filled with a mass of shav-ings of silver paper; now the rare illnesses which they had suffered were recalled chiefly as periods when that silver paper was crammed into a large slipper-case which hung by the mantelpiece, and a fire of coals unnaturally reigned in its place —the silver paper was part of the order of the world. The sash of the window would not work quite properly, owing to a slight subsidence in the wall, and even when the window was fastened there was always a narrow slit to the left hand between the window and its frame; through this slit came draughts, and thus very keen frosts were remembered by the nights when Mrs. Baines caused the sash to be forced and kept at its full height by means of wedges—the slit of exposure was part of the order of the world.

They possessed only one bed, one washstand, and one dressing-table; but in some other respects they were rather fortunate girls, for they had two mahogany wardrobes; this mutual independence as regards wardrobes was due partly to Mrs. Baines's strong commonsense, and partly to their father's tendency to spoil them a little. They had, moreover, a chest of drawers with a curved front, of which structure Constance occupied two short drawers and one long one, and Sophia two long drawers. On it stood two fancy work-boxes, in which each sister kept jewellery, a savings-bank book, and other treasures, and these boxes were absolutely sacred to their respective owners. They were different, but one was not more magnificent than the other. Indeed, a rigid equality was the rule in the chamber, the single exception being that behind the door were three hooks, of which Constance commanded two.

"Well," Sophia began, when Constance appeared. "How's darling Mr. Povey?" She was lying on her back, and smiling at her two hands, which she held up in front of her.

"Asleep," said Constance. "At least mother thinks so. She says sleep is the best thing for him."

" 'It will probably come on again,' " said Sophia.

"What's that you say?" Constance asked, undressing.

" 'It will probably come on again.' "

These words were a quotation from the utterances of darling Mr. Povey on the stairs, and Sophia delivered them with an exact imitation of Mr. Povey's vocal mannerism.

"Sophia," said Constance, firmly, approaching the bed, "I wish you wouldn't be so silly!" She had benevolently ignored the satirical note in Sophia's first remark, but a strong instinct in her rose up and objected to further derision. "Surely you've done enough for one day!" she added.

For answer Sophia exploded into violent laughter, which she made no attempt to control. She laughed too long and too freely while Constance stared at her.

"*I* don't know what's come over you!" said Constance.

"It's only because I can't look at it without simply going off into fits!" Sophia gasped out. And she held up a tiny object in her left hand.

Constance started, flushing. "You don't mean to say you've

Arnold Bennett

ept it!" she protested earnestly. "How horrid you are,
ophia! Give it me at once and let me throw it away. I never
eard of such doings. Now give it me!"

"No," Sophia objected, still laughing. "I wouldn't part with
for worlds. It's too lovely."

She had laughed away all her secret resentment against Con-
tance for having ignored her during the whole evening and
or being on such intimate terms with their parents. And she
vas ready to be candidly jolly with Constance.

"Give it me," said Constance, doggedly.

Sophia hid her hand under the clothes. "You can have his
ld stump, when it comes out, if you like. But not this. What
. pity it's the wrong one!"

"Sophia, I'm ashamed of you! Give it me."

Then it was that Sophia first perceived Constance's extreme
eriousness. She was surprised and a little intimidated by it.
'or the expression of Constance's face, usually so benign and
alm, was harsh, almost fierce. However, Sophia had a great
leal of what is called "spirit," and not even ferocity on the face
)f mild Constance could intimidate her for more than a few
econds. Her gaiety expired and her teeth were hidden.

"I've said nothing to mother——" Constance proceeded.

"I should hope you haven't," Sophia put in tersely.

"But I certainly shall if you don't throw that away," Con-
tance finished.

"You can say what you like," Sophia retorted, adding contemptuously a term of opprobrium which has long since passed
)ut of use: "Cant!"

"Will you give it me or won't you?"

"No!"

It was a battle suddenly engaged in the bedroom. The
atmosphere had altered completely with the swiftness of magic.
The beauty of Sophia, the angelic tenderness of Constance,
and the youthful, naïve, innocent charm of both of them, were
transformed into something sinister and cruel. Sophia lay back
on the pillow amid her dark-brown hair, and gazed with
relentless defiance into the angry eyes of Constance, who stood
threatening by the bed. They could hear the gas singing over
the dressing-table, and their hearts beating the blood wildly
in their veins. They ceased to be young without growing old;
the eternal had leapt up in them from its sleep.

Constance walked away from the bed to the dressing-tab
and began to loose her hair and brush it, holding back h
head, shaking it, and bending forward, in the changeless ge
ture of that rite. She was so disturbed that she had uncor
sciously reversed the customary order of the toilette. After
moment Sophia slipped out of bed and, stepping with her bar
feet to the chest of drawers, opened her work-box and de
posited the fragment of Mr. Povey therein; she dropped th
lid with an uncompromising bang, as if to say, "We shall se
if I am to be trod upon, miss!" Their eyes met again in th
looking-glass. Then Sophia got back into bed.

Five minutes later, when her hair was quite finished, Con
stance knelt down and said her prayers. Having said he
prayers, she went straight to Sophia's work-box, opened i
seized the fragment of Mr. Povey, ran to the window, and fran
tically pushed the fragment through the slit into the Square.

"There!" she exclaimed nervously.

She had accomplished this inconceivable transgression o
the code of honour, beyond all undoing, before Sophia coul
recover from the stupefaction of seeing her sacred work-bo
impudently violated. In a single moment one of Sophia's chie
ideals had been smashed utterly, and that by the sweetest
gentlest creature she had ever known. It was a revealing ex
perience for Sophia—and also for Constance. And it fright
ened them equally. Sophia, staring at the text, "Thou Goo
seest me," framed in straw over the chest of drawers, did no
stir. She was defeated, and so profoundly moved in her defea
that she did not even reflect upon the obvious inefficacy o
illuminated texts as a deterrent from evil-doing. Not that sh
cared a fig for the fragment of Mr. Povey! It was the mora
aspect of the affair, and the astounding, inexplicable develop
ment in Constance's character, that staggered her into silen
acceptance of the inevitable.

Constance, trembling, took pains to finish undressing with
dignified deliberation. Sophia's behaviour under the blow
seemed too good to be true; but it gave her courage. At lengt
she turned out the gas and lay down by Sophia. And there
was a little shuffling, and then stillness for a while.

"And if you want to know," said Constance in a tone tha
mingled amicableness with righteousness, "mother's decided
with Aunt Harriet that we are *both* to leave school next term."

CHAPTER III

A BATTLE

THE day sanctioned by custom in the Five Towns for the making of pastry is Saturday. But Mrs. Baines made her pastry on Friday, because Saturday afternoon was, of course, a busy time in the shop. It is true that Mrs. Baines made her pastry in the morning, and that Saturday morning in the shop was scarcely different from any other morning. Nevertheless, Mrs. Baines made her pastry on Friday morning instead of Saturday morning because Saturday afternoon was a busy time in the shop. She was thus free to do her marketing without breath-taking flurry on Saturday morning.

On the morning after Sophia's first essay in dentistry, therefore, Mrs. Baines was making her pastry in the underground kitchen. This kitchen, Maggie's cavern-home, had the mystery of a church, and on dark days it had the mystery of a crypt. The stone steps leading down to it from the level of earth were quite unlighted. You felt for them with the feet of faith, and when you arrived in the kitchen, the kitchen, by contrast, seemed luminous and gay; the architect may have considered and intended this effect of the staircase. The kitchen saw day through a wide, shallow window whose top touched the ceiling and whose bottom had been out of the girls' reach until long after they had begun to go to school. Its panes were small, and about half of them were of the "knot" kind, through which no object could be distinguished; the other half were of a later date, and stood for the march of civilization. The view from the window consisted of the vast plate-glass windows of the newly built Sun vaults, and of passing legs and skirts. A strong wire grating prevented any excess of illumination, and also protected the glass from the caprices of wayfarers in King Street. Boys had a habit of stopping to kick with their full strength at the grating.

Forget-me-nots on a brown field ornamented the walls of the kitchen. Its ceiling was irregular and grimy, and a beam ran across it; in this beam were two hooks; from these hooks had once depended the ropes of a swing, much used by Constance and Sophia in the old days before they were grown up. A large range stood out from the wall between the stairs and the window. The rest of the furniture comprised a table—against the wall opposite the range—a cupboard, and two Windsor chairs. Opposite the foot of the steps was a doorway, without a door, leading to two larders, dimmer even than the kitchen, vague retreats made visible by whitewash, where bowls of milk, dishes of cold bones, and remainders of fruit-pies, reposed on stillages; in the corner nearest the kitchen was a great steen in which the bread was kept. Another doorway on the other side of the kitchen led to the first coal-cellar, where was also the slopstone and tap, and thence a tunnel took you to the second coal-cellar, where coke and ashes were stored; the tunnel proceeded to a distant, infinitesimal yard, and from the yard, by ways behind Mr. Critchlow's shop, you could finally emerge, astonished, upon Brougham Street. The sense of the vast-obscure of those regions which began at the top of the kitchen steps and ended in black corners of larders or abruptly in the common dailiness of Brougham Street, a sense which Constance and Sophia had acquired in infancy, remained with them almost unimpaired as they grew old.

Mrs. Baines wore black alpaca, shielded by a white apron whose string drew attention to the amplitude of her waist. Her sleeves were turned up, and her hands, as far as the knuckles, covered with damp flour. Her ageless smooth pasteboard occupied a corner of the table, and near it were her paste-roller, butter, some pie-dishes, shredded apples, sugar, and other things. Those rosy hands were at work among a sticky substance in a large white bowl.

"Mother, are you there?" she heard a voice from above.

"Yes, my chuck."

Footsteps apparently reluctant and hesitating clinked on the stairs, and Sophia entered the kitchen.

"Put this curl straight," said Mrs. Baines, lowering her head slightly and holding up her floured hands, which might not touch anything but flour. "Thank you. It bothered me. And now stand out of my light. I'm in a hurry. I must get into the shop so that I can send Mr. Povey off to the dentist's. What is Constance doing?"

"Helping Maggie to make Mr. Povey's bed."

"Oh!"

Though fat, Mrs. Baines was a comely woman, with fine

brown hair, and confidently calm eyes that indicated her belief
in her own capacity to accomplish whatever she could be called
on to accomplish. She looked neither more nor less than her
age, which was forty-five. She was not a native of the district,
having been culled by her husband from the moorland town of
Axe, twelve miles off. Like nearly all women who settle in a
strange land upon marriage, at the bottom of her heart she
had considered herself just a trifle superior to the strange land
and its ways. This feeling, confirmed by long experience, had
never left her. It was this feeling which induced her to continue making her own pastry—with two thoroughly trained
"great girls" in the house! Constance could make good pastry,
but it was not her mother's pastry. In pastry-making everything can be taught except the "hand," light and firm, which
wields the roller. One is born with this hand, or without it.
And if one is born without it, the highest flights of pastry
are impossible. Constance was born without it. There were
days when Sophia seemed to possess it; but there were other
days when Sophia's pastry was uneatable by any one except
Maggie. Thus Mrs. Baines, though intensely proud and fond
of her daughters, had justifiably preserved a certain condescension towards them. She honestly doubted whether either
of them would develop into the equal of their mother.

"Now you little vixen!" she exclaimed. Sophia was stealing
and eating slices of half-cooked apple. "This comes of having
no breakfast! And why didn't you come down to supper last
night?"

"I don't know. I forgot."

Mrs. Baines scrutinized the child's eyes, which met hers with
a sort of diffident boldness. She knew everything that a mother
can know of a daughter, and she was sure that Sophia had no
cause to be indisposed. Therefore she scrutinized those eyes
with a faint apprehension.

"If you can't find anything better to do," said she, "butter
me the inside of this dish. Are your hands clean? No, better
not touch it."

Mrs. Baines was now at the stage of depositing little pats of
butter in rows on a large plain of paste. The best fresh butter!
Cooking butter, to say naught of lard, was unknown in that
kitchen on Friday mornings. She doubled the expanse of paste
on itself and rolled the butter in—supreme operation!

"Constance has told you about leaving school?" said Mrs.

Baines, in the vein of small-talk, as she trimmed the paste to the shape of a pie-dish.

"Yes," Sophia replied shortly. Then she moved away from the table to the range. There was a toasting-fork on the rack, and she began to play with it.

"Well, are you glad? Your aunt Harriet thinks you are quite old enough to leave. And as we'd decided in any case that Constance was to leave, it's really much simpler that you should both leave together."

"Mother," said Sophia, rattling the toasting-fork, "what am I going to do after I've left school?"

"I hope," Mrs. Baines answered with that sententiousness which even the cleverest of parents are not always clever enough to deny themselves, "I hope that both of you will do what you can to help your mother—and father," she added.

"Yes," said Sophia, irritated. "But what am I going to *do*?"

"That must be considered. As Constance is to learn the millinery, I've been thinking that you might begin to make yourself useful in the underwear, gloves, silks, and so on. Then between you, you would one day be able to manage quite nicely all that side of the shop, and I should be——"

"I don't want to go into the shop, mother."

This interruption was made in a voice apparently cold and inimical. But Sophia trembled with nervous excitement as she uttered the words. Mrs. Baines gave a brief glance at her, unobserved by the child, whose face was towards the fire. She deemed herself a finished expert in the reading of Sophia's moods; nevertheless, as she looked at that straight back and proud head, she had no suspicion that the whole essence and being of Sophia was silently but intensely imploring sympathy.

"I wish you would be quiet with that fork," said Mrs. Baines with the curious, grim politeness which often characterized her relations with her daughters.

The toasting-fork fell on the brick floor, after having rebounded from the ash-tin. Sophia hurriedly replaced it on the rack.

"Then what *shall* you do?" Mrs. Baines proceeded, conquering the annoyance caused by the toasting-fork. "I think it's me that should ask you instead of you asking me. What shall you do? Your father and I were both hoping you would take kindly to the shop and try to repay us for all the——"

Mrs. Baines was unfortunate in her phrasing that morning.

She happened to be, in truth, rather an exceptional parent, but that morning she seemed unable to avoid the absurd pretensions which parents of those days assumed quite sincerely and which every good child with meekness accepted.

Sophia was not a good child, and she obstinately denied in her heart the cardinal principle of family life, namely, that the parent has conferred on the offspring a supreme favour by bringing it into the world. She interrupted her mother again, rudely.

"I don't want to leave school at all," she said passionately.

"But you will have to leave school sooner or later," argued Mrs. Baines, with an air of quiet reasoning, of putting herself on a level with Sophia. "You can't stay at school for ever, my pet, can you? Out of my way!"

She hurried across the kitchen with a pie, which she whipped into the oven, shutting the iron door with a careful gesture.

"Yes," said Sophia. "I should like to be a teacher. That's what I want to be."

The tap in the coal-cellar, out of repair, could be heard distinctly and systematically dropping water into a jar on the slopstone.

"A school-teacher?" inquired Mrs. Baines.

"Of course. What other kind is there?" said Sophia sharply. "With Miss Chetwynd."

"I don't think your father would like that," Mrs. Baines replied. "I'm sure he wouldn't like it."

"Why not?"

"It wouldn't be quite suitable."

"Why not, mother?" the girl demanded with a sort of ferocity. She had now quitted the range. A man's feet twinkled past the window.

Mrs. Baines was startled and surprised. Sophia's attitude was really very trying; her manners deserved correction. But it was not these phenomena which seriously affected Mrs. Baines; she was used to them and had come to regard them as somehow the inevitable accompaniment of Sophia's beauty, as the penalty of that surpassing charm which occasionally emanated from the girl like a radiance. What startled and surprised Mrs. Baines was the perfect and unthinkable madness of Sophia's infantile scheme. It was a revelation to Mrs. Baines. Why in the name of heaven had the girl taken such a notion into her head? Orphans, widows, and spinsters of a

certain age suddenly thrown on the world—these were the
women who, naturally, became teachers, because they had to
become something. But that the daughter of comfortable
parents, surrounded by love and the pleasures of an excellent
home, should wish to teach in a school was beyond the horizons
of Mrs. Baines's common sense. Comfortable parents of to-day
who have a difficulty in sympathizing with Mrs. Baines, should
picture what their feelings would be if their Sophias showed
a rude desire to adopt the vocation of chauffeur.

"It would take you too much away from home," said Mrs.
Baines, achieving a second pie.

She spoke softly. The experience of being Sophia's mother
for nearly sixteen years had not been lost on Mrs. Baines, and
though she was now discovering undreamt-of dangers in
Sophia's erratic temperament, she kept her presence of mind
sufficiently well to behave with diplomatic smoothness. It was
undoubtedly humiliating to a mother to be forced to use
diplomacy in dealing with a girl in short sleeves. In *her* day
mothers had been autocrats. But Sophia was Sophia.

"What if it did?" Sophia curtly demanded.

"And there's no opening in Bursley," said Mrs. Baines.

"Miss Chetwynd would have me, and then after a time I
could go to her sister."

"Her sister? What sister?"

"Her sister that has a big school in London somewhere."

Mrs. Baines covered her unprecedented emotions by gazing
into the oven at the first pie. The pie was doing well, under
all the circumstances. In those few seconds she reflected rapidly
and decided that to a desperate disease a desperate remedy
must be applied.

London! She herself had never been further than Manchester. London, "after a time"! No, diplomacy would be misplaced in this crisis of Sophia's development!

"Sophia," she said, in a changed and solemn voice, fronting
her daughter, and holding away from her apron those floured,
ringed hands, "I don't know what has come over you. Truly
I don't! Your father and I are prepared to put up with a certain amount, but the line must be drawn. The fact is, we've
spoilt you, and instead of getting better as you grow up, you're
getting worse. Now let me hear no more of this, please. I wish
you would imitate your sister a little more. Of course if you
won't do your share in the shop, no one can make you. If you

choose to be an idler about the house, we shall have to endure it. We can only advise you for your own good. But as for this . . ." She stopped, and let silence speak, and then finished: "Let me hear no more of it."

It was a powerful and impressive speech, enunciated clearly in such a tone as Mrs. Baines had not employed since dismissing a young lady assistant five years ago for light conduct.

"But, mother——"

A commotion of pails resounded at the top of the stone steps. It was Maggie in descent from the bedrooms. Now, the Baines family passed its life in doing its best to keep its affairs to itelf, the assumption being that Maggie and all the shop-staff (Mr. Povey possibly excepted) were obsessed by a ravening appetite for that which did not concern them. Therefore the voices of the Baineses always died away, or fell to a hushed, mysterious whisper, whenever the foot of the eavesdropper was heard.

Mrs. Baines put a floured finger to her double chin. "That will do," said she, with finality.

Maggie appeared, and Sophia, with a brusque precipitation of herself, vanished upstairs.

ii

"Now, really, Mr. Povey, this is not like you," said Mrs. Baines, who, on her way into the shop, had discovered the Indispensable in the cutting-out room.

It is true that the cutting-out room was almost Mr. Povey's sanctum, whither he retired from time to time to cut out suits of clothes and odd garments for the tailoring department. It is true that the tailoring department flourished with orders, employing several tailors who crossed legs in their own homes, and that appointments were continually being made with customers for trying-on in that room. But these considerations did not affect Mrs. Baines's attitude of disapproval.

"I'm just cutting out that suit for the minister," said Mr. Povey.

The Reverend Mr. Murley, superintendent of the Wesleyan Methodist circuit, called on Mr. Baines every week. On a recent visit Mr. Baines had remarked that the parson's coat was ageing into green, and had commanded that a new suit should be built and presented to Mr. Murley. Mr. Murley, who had a genuine mediæval passion for souls, and who spent his money and health freely in gratifying the passion, had accepted the offer strictly on behalf of Christ, and had carefully explained to Mr. Povey Christ's use for multifarious pockets.

"I see you are," said Mrs. Baines tartly. "But that's no reason why you should be without a coat—and in this cold room too. You with toothache!"

The fact was that Mr. Povey always doffed his coat when cutting out. Instead of a coat he wore a tape-measure.

"My tooth doesn't hurt me," said he, sheepishly, dropping the great scissors and picking up a cake of chalk.

"Fiddlesticks!" said Mrs. Baines.

This exclamation shocked Mr. Povey. It was not unknown on the lips of Mrs. Baines, but she usually reserved it for members of her own sex. Mr. Povey could not recall that she had ever applied it to any statement of his. "What's the matter with the woman?" he thought. The redness of her face did not help him to answer the question, for her face was always red after the operations of Friday in the kitchen.

"You men are all alike," Mrs. Baines continued. "The very thought of the dentist's cures you. Why don't you go in at once to Mr. Critchlow and have it out—like a man?"

Mr. Critchlow extracted teeth, and his shop sign said "Bone-setter and chemist." But Mr. Povey had his views.

"I make no account of Mr. Critchlow as a dentist," said he.

"Then for goodness' sake go up to Oulsnam's."

"When? I can't very well go now, and to-morrow is Saturday."

"Why can't you go now?"

"Well, of course, I *could* go now," he admitted.

"Let me advise you to go, then, and don't come back with that tooth in your head. I shall be having you laid up next. Show some pluck, do!"

"Oh! pluck—!" he protested, hurt.

At that moment Constance came down the passage singing.

"Constance, my pet!" Mrs. Baines called.

"Yes, mother." She put her head into the room. "Oh!" Mr. Povey was assuming his coat.

"Mr. Povey is going to the dentist's."

"Yes, I'm going at once," Mr. Povey confirmed.

"Oh! I'm so *glad!*" Constance exclaimed. Her face ex-

ressed a pure sympathy, uncomplicated by critical sentiments. Mr. Povey rapidly bathed in that sympathy, and then
decided that he must show himself a man of oak and iron.

"It's always best to get these things done with," said he,
with stern detachment. "I'll just slip my overcoat on."

"Here it is," said Constance, quickly. Mr. Povey's overcoat and hat were hung on a hook immediately outside the
room, in the passage. She gave him the overcoat, anxious to
be of service.

"I didn't call you in here to be Mr. Povey's valet," said
Mrs. Baines to herself with mild grimness; and aloud: "I can't
stay in the shop long, Constance, but you can be there, can't
you, till Mr. Povey comes back? And if anything happens run
upstairs and tell me."

"Yes, mother," Constance eagerly consented. She hesitated
and then turned to obey at once.

"I want to speak to you first, my pet," Mrs. Baines stopped
her. And her tone was peculiar, charged with import, confidential, and therefore very flattering to Constance.

"I think I'll go out by the side-door," said Mr. Povey. "It'll
be nearer."

This was truth. He would save about ten yards, in two
miles, by going out through the side-door instead of through
the shop. Who could have guessed that he was ashamed to be
seen going to the dentist's, afraid lest, if he went through the
shop, Mrs. Baines might follow him and utter some remark
prejudicial to his dignity before the assistants? (Mrs. Baines
could have guessed, and did.)

"You won't want that tape-measure," said Mrs. Baines,
dryly, as Mr. Povey dragged open the side-door. The ends of
the forgotten tape-measure were dangling beneath coat and
overcoat.

"Oh!" Mr. Povey scowled at his forgetfulness.

"I'll put it in its place," said Constance, offering to receive
the tape-measure.

"Thank you," said Mr. Povey, gravely. "I don't suppose
they'll be long over my bit of a job," he added, with a difficult,
miserable smile.

Then he went off down King Street, with an exterior of gay
briskness and dignified joy in the fine May morning. But there
was no May morning in his cowardly human heart.

"Hi! Povey!" cried a voice from the Square.

But Mr. Povey disregarded all appeals. He had put hi‌
hand to the plough, and he would not look back.

"Hi, Povey!"

Useless!

Mrs. Baines and Constance were both at the door. A middl‌
aged man was crossing the road from Boulton Terrace, th‌
lofty erection of new shops which the envious rest of th‌
Square had decided to call "showy." He waved a hand to Mrs
Baines, who kept the door open.

"It's Dr. Harrop," she said to Constance. "I shouldn't b‌
surprised if that baby's come at last, and he wanted to tel‌
Mr. Povey."

Constance blushed, full of pride. Mrs. Povey, wife of "ou‌
Mr. Povey's" renowned cousin, the high-class confectioner an‌
baker in Boulton Terrace, was a frequent subject of discussio‌
in the Baines family, but this was absolutely the first time tha‌
Mrs. Baines had acknowledged, in presence of Constance, th‌
marked and growing change which had characterized Mrs‌
Povey's condition during recent months. Such frankness o‌
the part of her mother, coming after the decision about leav‌
ing school, proved indeed that Constance had ceased to be ‌
mere girl.

"Good morning, doctor."

The doctor, who carried a little bag and wore riding-breeche‌
(he was the last doctor in Bursley to abandon the saddle fo‌
the dog-cart), saluted and straightened his high, black stock.

"Morning! Morning, missy! Well, it's a boy."

"What? Yonder?" asked Mrs. Baines, indicating the con‌
fectioner's.

Dr. Harrop nodded. "I wanted to inform him," said he,
jerking his shoulder in the direction of the swaggering coward.

"What did I tell you, Constance?" said Mrs. Baines, turn‌
ing to her daughter.

Constance's confusion was equal to her pleasure. The alert
doctor had halted at the foot of the two steps, and with one
hand in the pocket of his "full-fall" breeches, he gazed up,
smiling out of little eyes, at the ample matron and the slender
virgin.

"Yes," he said. "Been up most of th' night. Difficult!
Difficult!"

"It's all *right*, I hope?"

"Oh yes. Fine child! Fine child! But he put his mother to

ome trouble, for all that. Nothing fresh?" This time he lifted his eyes to indicate Mr. Baines's bedroom.

"No," said Mrs. Baines, with a different expression.

"Keeps cheerful?"

"Yes."

"Good! A very good morning to you."

He strode off towards his house, which was lower down the street.

"I hope she'll turn over a new leaf now," observed Mrs. Baines to Constance as she closed the door. Constance knew that her mother was referring to the confectioner's wife; she gathered that the hope was slight in the extreme.

"What did you want to speak to me about, mother?" she asked, as a way out of her delicious confusion.

"Shut that door," Mrs. Baines replied, pointing to the door which led to the passage; and while Constance obeyed, Mrs. Baines herself shut the staircase-door. She then said, in a low, guarded voice —

"What's all this about Sophia wanting to be a school-teacher?"

"Wanting to be a school-teacher?" Constance repeated, in tones of amazement.

"Yes. Hasn't she said anything to you?"

"Not a word!"

"Well, I never! She wants to keep on with Miss Chetwynd and be a teacher." Mrs. Baines had half a mind to add that Sophia had mentioned London. But she restrained herself. There are some things which one cannot bring one's self to say. She added, "Instead of going into the shop!"

"I never heard of such a thing!" Constance murmured brokenly, in the excess of her astonishment. She was rolling up Mr. Povey's tape-measure.

"Neither did I!" said Mrs. Baines.

"And shall you let her, mother?"

"Neither your father nor I would ever dream of it!" Mrs. Baines replied, with calm and yet terrible decision. "I only mentioned it to you because I thought Sophia would have told you something."

"No, mother!"

As Constance put Mr. Povey's tape-measure neatly away in its drawer under the cutting-out counter, she thought how serious life was—what with babies and Sophias. She was very

proud of her mother's confidence in her; this simple pride fille
her ardent breast with a most agreeable commotion. And sh
wanted to help everybody, to show in some way how much sh
sympathized with and loved everybody. Even the madness o
Sophia did not weaken her longing to comfort Sophia.

iii

That afternoon there was a search for Sophia, whom no on
had seen since dinner. She was discovered by her mother, sit
ting alone and unoccupied in the drawing-room. The circum
stance was in itself sufficiently peculiar, for on weekdays th
drawing-room was never used, even by the girls during thei
holidays, except for the purpose of playing the piano. How
ever, Mrs. Baines offered no comment on Sophia's geograph
ical situation, nor on her idleness.

"My dear," she said, standing at the door, with a self-con
scious effort to behave as though nothing had happened, "wil
you come and sit with your father a bit?"

"Yes, mother," answered Sophia, with a sort of cold alac
rity.

"Sophia is coming, father," said Mrs. Baines at the oper
door of the bedroom, which was at right-angles with, and clos
to, the drawing-room door. Then she surged swishing along th
corridor and went into the showroom, whither she had beer
called.

Sophia passed to the bedroom, the eternal prison of Johr
Baines. Although, on account of his nervous restlessness, Mr
Baines was never left alone, it was not a part of the usua
duty of the girls to sit with him. The person who undertook
the main portion of the vigils was a certain Aunt Maria—
whom the girls knew to be not a real aunt, not a powerful,
effective aunt like Aunt Harriet of Axe—but a poor second
cousin of John Baines; one of those necessitous, pitiful relatives who so often make life difficult for a great family in a
small town. The existence of Aunt Maria, after being rathei
a "trial" to the Baineses, had for twelve years past developed
into something absolutely "providential" for them. (It is to
be remembered that in those days Providence was still busying
himself with everybody's affairs, and foreseeing the future in

the most extraordinary manner. Thus, having foreseen that John Baines would have a "stroke" and need a faithful, tireless nurse, he had begun fifty years in advance by creating Aunt Maria, and had kept her carefully in misfortune's way, so that at the proper moment she would be ready to cope with the stroke. Such at least is the only theory which will explain the use by the Baineses, and indeed by all thinking Bursley, of the word "providential" in connection with Aunt Maria.) She was a shrivelled little woman, capable of sitting twelve hours a day in a bedroom and thriving on the *régime*. At nights she went home to her little cottage in Brougham Street; she had her Thursday afternoons and generally her Sundays, and during the school vacations she was supposed to come only when she felt inclined, or when the cleaning of her cottage permitted her to come. Hence, in holiday seasons, Mr. Baines weighed more heavily on his household than at other times, and his nurses relieved each other according to the contingencies of the moment rather than by a set programme of hours.

The tragedy in ten thousand acts of which that bedroom was the scene, almost entirely escaped Sophia's perception, as it did Constance's. Sophia went into the bedroom as though it were a mere bedroom, with its majestic mahogany furniture, its crimson rep curtains (edged with gold), and its white, heavily tasselled counterpane. She was aged four when John Baines had suddenly been seized with giddiness on the steps of his shop, and had fallen, and, without losing consciousness, had been transformed from John Baines into a curious and pathetic survival of John Baines. She had no notion of the thrill which ran through the town on that night when it was known that John Baines had had a stroke, and that his left arm and left leg and his right eyelid were paralyzed, and that the active member of the Local Board, the orator, the religious worker, the very life of the town's life, was permanently done for. She had never heard of the crisis through which her mother, assisted by Aunt Harriet, had passed, and out of which she had triumphantly emerged. She was not yet old enough even to suspect it. She possessed only the vaguest memory of her father before he had finished with the world. She knew him simply as an organism on a bed, whose left side was wasted, whose eyes were often inflamed, whose mouth was crooked, who had no creases from the nose to the corners of the mouth like other people, who experienced difficulty in eating because the food would somehow get between his gums and his cheek, who slept a great deal but was excessively fidgety while awake, who seemed to hear what was said to him a long time after it was uttered, as if the sense had to travel miles by labyrinthine passages to his brain, and who talked very, very slowly in a weak, trembling voice.

And she had an image of that remote brain as something with a red spot on it, for once Constance had said: "Mother, why did father have a stroke?" and Mrs. Baines had replied: "It was a hæmorrhage of the brain, my dear, here"—putting a thimbled finger on a particular part of Sophia's head.

Not merely had Constance and Sophia never really felt their father's tragedy; Mrs. Baines herself had largely lost the sense of it—such is the effect of use. Even the ruined organism only remembered fitfully and partially that it had once been John Baines. And if Mrs. Baines had not, by the habit of years, gradually built up a gigantic fiction that the organism remained ever the supreme consultative head of the family; if Mr. Critchlow had not obstinately continued to treat it as a crony, the mass of living and dead nerves on the rich Victorian bedstead would have been of no more account than some Aunt Maria in similar case. These two persons, his wife and his friend, just managed to keep him morally alive by indefatigably feeding his importance and his dignity. The feat was a miracle of stubborn self-deceiving, splendidly blind devotion, and incorrigible pride.

When Sophia entered the room, the paralytic followed her with his nervous gaze until she had sat down on the end of the sofa at the foot of the bed. He seemed to study her for a long time, and then he murmured in his slow, enfeebled, irregular voice:

"Is that Sophia?"

"Yes, father," she answered cheerfully.

And after another pause, the old man said: "Ay! It's Sophia."

And later: "Your mother said she should send ye."

Sophia saw that this was one of his bad, dull days. He had, occasionally, days of comparative nimbleness, when his wits seized almost easily the meanings of external phenomena.

Presently his sallow face and long white beard began to slip down the steep slant of the pillows, and a troubled look came

into his left eye. Sophia rose and, putting her hands under
his armpits, lifted him higher in the bed. He was not heavy,
but only a strong girl of her years could have done it.

"Ay!" he muttered. "That's it. That's it."

And, with his controllable right hand, he took her hand as
she stood by the bed. She was so young and fresh, such an
incarnation of the spirit of health, and he was so far gone in
decay and corruption, that there seemed in this contact of
body with body something unnatural and repulsive. But
Sophia did not so feel it.

"Sophia," he addressed her, and made preparatory noises
in his throat while she waited.

He continued after an interval, now clutching her arm,
"Your mother's been telling me you don't want to go in the
shop."

She turned her eyes on him, and his anxious, dim gaze met
hers. She nodded.

"Nay, Sophia," he mumbled, with the extreme of slowness.
"I'm surprised at ye . . . Trade's bad, bad! Ye know trade's
bad?" He was still clutching her arm.

She nodded. She was, in fact, aware of the badness of trade,
caused by a vague war in the United States. The words
"North" and "South" had a habit of recurring in the conversation of adult persons. That was all she knew, though people
were starving in the Five Towns as they were starving in Manchester.

"There's your mother," his thought struggled on, like an
aged horse over a hilly road. "There's your mother!" he repeated, as if wishful to direct Sophia's attention to the spectacle of her mother. "Working hard! Con—Constance and you
must help her. . . . Trade's bad! What can I do . . . lying
here?"

The heat from his dry fingers was warming her arm. She
wanted to move, but she could not have withdrawn her arm
without appearing impatient. For a similar reason she would
not avert her glance. A deepening flush increased the lustre
of her immature loveliness as she bent over him. But though it
was so close he did not feel that radiance. He had long outlived
a susceptibility to the strange influences of youth and beauty.

"Teaching!" he muttered. "Nay, nay! I canna' allow that."

Then his white beard rose at the tip as he looked up at the
ceiling above his head, reflectively.

"You understand me?" he questioned finally.

She nodded again; he loosed her arm, and she turned away. She could not have spoken. Glittering tears enriched her eyes. She was saddened into a profound and sudden grief by the ridiculousness of the scene. She had youth, physical perfection; she brimmed with energy, with the sense of vital power; all existence lay before her; when she put her lips together she felt capable of outvying no matter whom in fortitude of resolution. She had always hated the shop. She did not understand how her mother and Constance could bring themselves to be deferential and flattering to every customer that entered. No, she did not understand it; but her mother (though a proud woman) and Constance seemed to practise such behaviour so naturally, so unquestioningly, that she had never imparted to either of them her feelings; she guessed that she would not be comprehended. But long ago she had decided that she would never "go into the shop." She knew that she would be expected to do something, and she had fixed on teaching as the one possibility. These decisions had formed part of her inner life for years past. She had not mentioned them, being secretive and scarcely anxious for unpleasantness. But she had been slowly preparing herself to mention them. The extraordinary announcement that she was to leave school at the same time as Constance had taken her unawares, before the preparations ripening in her mind were complete—before, as it were, she had girded up her loins for the fray. She had been caught unready, and the opposing forces had obtained the advantage of her. But did they suppose she was beaten?

No argument from her mother! No hearing, even! Just a curt and haughty "Let me hear no more of this"! And so the great desire of her life, nourished year after year in her inmost bosom, was to be flouted and sacrificed with a word! Her mother did not appear ridiculous in the affair, for her mother was a genuine power, commanding by turns genuine love and genuine hate, and always, till then, obedience and the respect of reason. It was her father who appeared tragically ridiculous; and, in turn, the whole movement against her grew grotesque in its absurdity. Here was this antique wreck, helpless, useless, powerless—merely pathetic—actually thinking that he had only to mumble in order to make her "understand"! He knew nothing; he perceived nothing; he was a ferocious egoist, like most bedridden invalids, out of touch with life—

nd he thought himself justified in making destinies, and
apable of making them! Sophia could not, perhaps, define the
eelings which overwhelmed her; but she was conscious of their
endency. They aged her, by years. They aged her so that, in
kind of momentary ecstasy of insight, she felt older than her
ather himself.

"You will be a good girl," he said. "I'm sure o' that."

It was too painful. The grotesqueness of her father's complacency humiliated her past bearing. She was humiliated, not
or herself, but for him. Singular creature! She ran out of
he room.

Fortunately Constance was passing in the corridor, other-
vise Sophia had been found guilty of a great breach of duty.
"Go to father," she whispered hysterically to Constance,
nd fled upwards to the second floor.

iv

At supper, with her red, downcast eyes, she had returned to
heer girlishness again, overawed by her mother. The meal had
n unusual aspect. Mr. Povey, safe from the dentist's, but
aving lost two teeth in two days, was being fed on "slops"—
read and milk, to wit; he sat near the fire. The others had
old pork, half a cold apple-pie, and cheese; but Sophia only
retended to eat; each time she tried to swallow, the tears came
nto her eyes, and her throat shut itself up. Mrs. Baines and
Constance had a too careful air of eating just as usual. Mrs.
Baines's handsome ringlets dominated the table under the gas.

"I'm not so set up with my pastry to-day," observed Mrs.
Baines, critically munching a fragment of pie-crust.

She rang a little hand-bell. Maggie appeared from the cave.
She wore a plain white bib-less apron, but no cap.

"Maggie, will you have some pie?"

"Yes, if you can spare it, ma'am."

This was Maggie's customary answer to offers of food.

"We can always spare it, Maggie," said her mistress, as
usual. "Sophia, if you aren't going to use that plate, give it
o me."

Maggie disappeared with liberal pie.

Mrs. Baines then talked to Mr. Povey about his condition,
nd in particular as to the need for precautions against taking

cold in the bereaved gum. She was a brave and determine
woman; from start to finish she behaved as though nothin;
whatever in the household except her pastry and Mr. Pove
had deviated that day from the normal. She kissed Constanc
and Sophia with the most exact equality, and called them "m
chucks" when they went up to bed.

Constance, excellent kind heart, tried to imitate her mother'
tactics as the girls undressed in their room. She thought sh
could not do better than ignore Sophia's deplorable state.

"Mother's new dress is quite finished, and she's going t
wear it on Sunday," said she, blandly.

"If you say another word I'll scratch your eyes out!" Sophi
turned on her viciously, with a catch in her voice, and the
began to sob at intervals. She did not mean this threat, but it
utterance gave her relief. Constance, faced with the fact tha
her mother's shoes were too big for her, decided to preserv
her eyesight.

Long after the gas was out, rare sobs from Sophia shoo
the bed, and they both lay awake in silence.

"I suppose you and mother have been talking me over finel
to-day?" Sophia burst forth, to Constance's surprise, in a we
voice.

"No," said Constance soothingly. "Mother only told me.
"Told you what?"

"That you wanted to be a teacher."

"And I will be, too!" said Sophia, bitterly.

"You don't know mother," thought Constance; but she mad
no audible comment.

There was another detached, hard sob. And then, such is th
astonishing talent of youth, they both fell asleep.

The next morning, early, Sophia stood gazing out of th
window at the Square. It was Saturday, and all over the Squar
little stalls, with yellow linen roofs, were being erected for th
principal market of the week. In those barbaric days Bursle
had a majestic edifice, black as basalt, for the sale of dead ani
mals by the limb and rib—it was entitled "the Shambles"—
but vegetables, fruit, cheese, eggs, and pikelets were still sol
under canvas. Eggs are now offered at five farthings apiec
in a palace that cost twenty-five thousand pounds. Yet you wil
find people in Bursley ready to assert that things generall
are not what they were, and that in particular the romance o
life has gone. But until it has gone it is never romance. T

Sophia, though she was in a mood which usually stimulates the sense of the romantic, there was nothing of romance in this picturesque tented field. It was just the market. Holl's, the leading grocer's, was already open, at the extremity of the Square, and a boy apprentice was sweeping the pavement in front of it. The public-houses were open, several of them specializing in hot rum at 5.30 a.m. The town-crier, in his blue coat with red facings, crossed the Square, carrying his big bell by the tongue. There was the same shocking hole in one of Mrs. Povey's (confectioner's) window-curtains—a hole which even her recent travail could scarcely excuse. Such matters it was that Sophia noticed with dull, smarting eyes.

"Sophia, you'll take your death of cold standing there like that!"

She jumped. The voice was her mother's. That vigorous woman, after a calm night by the side of the paralytic, was already up and neatly dressed. She carried a bottle and an egg-cup, and a small quantity of jam in a table-spoon.

"Get into bed again, do! There's a dear! You're shivering."

White Sophia obeyed. It was true; she was shivering. Constance awoke. Mrs. Baines went to the dressing-table and filled the egg-cup out of the bottle.

"Who's that for, mother?" Constance asked sleepily.

"It's for Sophia," said Mrs. Baines, with good cheer. "Now, Sophia!" and she advanced with the egg-cup in one hand and the table-spoon in the other.

"What is it, mother?" asked Sophia, who well knew what it was.

"Castor-oil, my dear," said Mrs. Baines, winningly.

The ludicrousness of attempting to cure obstinacy and yearnings for a freer life by means of castor-oil is perhaps less real than apparent. The strange interdependence of spirit and body, though only understood intelligently in these intelligent days, was guessed at by sensible mediæval mothers. And certainly, at the period when Mrs. Baines represented modernity, castor-oil was still the remedy of remedies. It had supplanted cupping. And, if part of its vogue was due to its extreme unpleasantness, it had at least proved its qualities in many a contest with disease. Less than two years previously old Dr. Harrop (father of him who told Mrs. Baines about Mrs. Povey), being then aged eighty-six, had fallen from top to

bottom of his staircase. He had scrambled up, taken a dose o
castor-oil at once, and on the morrow was as well as if he ha
never seen a staircase. This episode was town property and ha
sunk deep into all hearts.

"I don't want any, mother," said Sophia, in dejection. "I'n
quite well."

"You simply ate nothing all day yesterday," said Mrs
Baines. And she added, "Come!" As if to say, "There's alway
this silly fuss with castor-oil. Don't keep me waiting."

"I don't *want* any," said Sophia, irritated and captious.

The two girls lay side by side, on their backs. They seeme
very thin and fragile in comparison with the solidity of thei
mother. Constance wisely held her peace.

Mrs. Baines put her lips together, meaning: "This is becom
ing tedious. I shall have to be angry in another moment!"

"Come!" said she again.

The girls could hear her foot tapping on the floor.

"I really don't want it, mamma," Sophia fought. "I sup
pose I ought to know whether I need it or not!" This wa
insolence.

"Sophia, will you take this medicine, or won't you?"

In conflicts with her children, the mother's ultimatum alway
took the formula in which this phrase was cast. The girls knew
when things had arrived at the pitch of "or won't you," spoke
in Mrs. Baines's firmest tone, that the end was upon them
Never had the ultimatum failed.

There was a silence.

"And I'll thank you to mind your manners," Mrs. Baine
added.

"I won't take it," said Sophia, sullenly and flatly; and sh
hid her face in the pillow.

It was a historic moment in the family life. Mrs. Baine
thought the last day had come. But still she held herself i
dignity while the apocalypse roared in her ears.

"*Of course I can't force you to take it*," she said with su
perb evenness, masking anger by compassionate grief. "You'r
a big girl and a naughty girl. And if you will be ill yo
must."

Upon this immense admission, Mrs. Baines departed.

Constance trembled.

Nor was that all. In the middle of the morning, wher
Mrs. Baines was pricing new potatoes at a stall at the top en

of the Square, and Constance choosing threepennyworth of flowers at the same stall, whom should they both see, walking all alone across the empty corner by the Bank, but Sophia Baines! The Square was busy and populous, and Sophia was only visible behind a foreground of restless, chattering figures. But she was unmistakably seen. She had been beyond the Square and was returning. Constance could scarcely believe her eyes. Mrs. Baines's heart jumped. For let it be said that the girls never under any circumstances went forth without permission, and scarcely ever alone. That Sophia should be at large in the town, without leave, without notice, exactly as if she were her own mistress, was a proposition which a day earlier had been inconceivable. Yet there she was, and moving with a leisureliness that must be described as effrontery!

Red with apprehension, Constance wondered what would happen. Mrs. Baines said nought of her feelings, did not even indicate that she had seen the scandalous, the breath-taking sight. And they descended the Square laden with the lighter portions of what they had bought during an hour of buying. They went into the house by the King Street door; and the first thing they heard was the sound of the piano upstairs. Nothing happened. Mr. Povey had his dinner alone; then the table was laid for them, and the bell rang, and Sophia came insolently downstairs to join her mother and sister. And nothing happened. The dinner was silently eaten, and Constance having rendered thanks to God, Sophia rose abruptly to go.

"Sophia."

"Yes, mother."

"Constance, stay where you are," said Mrs. Baines suddenly to Constance, who had meant to flee. Constance was therefore destined to be present at the happening, doubtless in order to emphasize its importance and seriousness.

"Sophia," Mrs. Baines resumed to her younger daughter in an ominous voice. "No, please shut the door. There is no reason why everybody in the house should hear. Come right into the room—right in! That's it. Now, what were you doing out in the town this morning?"

Sophia was fidgeting nervously with the edge of her little black apron, and worrying a seam of the carpet with her toes. She bent her head towards her left shoulder, at first smiling vaguely. She said nothing, but every limb, every glance, every curve, was speaking. Mrs. Baines sat firmly in her own rocking-chair, full of the sensation that she had Sophia, as it were, writhing on the end of a skewer. Constance was braced into a moveless anguish.

"I will have an answer," pursued Mrs. Baines. "What were you doing out in the town this morning?"

"I just went out," answered Sophia at length, still with eyes downcast, and in a rather simpering tone.

"Why did you go out? You said nothing to me about going out. I heard Constance ask you if you were coming with us to the market, and you said, very rudely, that you weren't."

"I didn't say it rudely," Sophia objected.

"Yes you did. And I'll thank you not to answer back."

"I didn't mean to say it rudely, did I, Constance?" Sophia's head turned sharply to her sister. Constance knew not where to look.

"Don't answer back," Mrs. Baines repeated sternly. "And don't try to drag Constance into this, for I won't have it."

"Oh, of course Constance is always right!" observed Sophia, with an irony whose unparalleled impudence shook Mrs. Baines to her massive foundations.

"Do you want me to have to smack you, child?"

Her temper flashed out and you could see ringlets vibrating under the provocation of Sophia's sauciness. Then Sophia's lower lip began to fall and to bulge outwards, and all the muscles of her face seemed to slacken.

"You are a very naughty girl," said Mrs. Baines, with restraint. ("I've got her," said Mrs. Baines to herself. "I may just as well keep my temper.")

And a sob broke out of Sophia. She was behaving like a little child. She bore no trace of the young maiden sedately crossing the Square without leave and without an escort.

("I knew she was going to cry," said Mrs. Baines, breathing relief.)

"I'm waiting," said Mrs. Baines aloud.

A second sob. Mrs. Baines manufactured patience to meet the demand.

"You tell me not to answer back, and then you say you're waiting," Sophia blubbered thickly.

"What's that you say? How can I tell what you say if you talk like that?" (But Mrs. Baines failed to hear out of discretion, which is better than valour.)

"It's of no consequence," Sophia blurted forth in a sob. She was weeping now, and tears were ricocheting off her lovely crimson cheeks on to the carpet; her whole body was trembling.

"Don't be a great baby," Mrs. Baines enjoined, with a touch of rough persuasiveness in her voice.

"It's you who make me cry," said Sophia, bitterly. "You make me cry and then you call me a great baby!" And sobs ran through her frame like waves one after another. She spoke so indistinctly that her mother now really had some difficulty in catching her words.

"Sophia," said Mrs. Baines, with god-like calm, "it is not I who make you cry. It is your guilty conscience makes you cry. I have merely asked you a question, and I intend to have an answer."

"I've told you." Here Sophia checked the sobs with an immense effort.

"What have you told me?"

"I just went out."

"I will have no trifling," said Mrs. Baines. "What did you go out for, and without telling me? If you had told me afterwards, when I came in, of your own accord, it might have been different. But no, not a word! It is I who have to ask! Now, quick! I can't wait any longer."

("I gave way over the castor-oil, my girl," Mrs. Baines said in her own breast. "But not again! Not again!")

"I don't know," Sophia murmured.

"What do you mean—you don't know?"

The sobbing recommenced tempestuously. "I mean I don't know. I just went out." Her voice rose; it was noisy, but scarcely articulate. "What if I did go out?"

"Sophia, I am not going to be talked to like this. If you think because you're leaving school you can do exactly as you like——"

"Do I want to leave school?" yelled Sophia, stamping. In a moment a hurricane of emotion overwhelmed her, as though that stamping of the foot had released the demons of the storm. Her face was transfigured by uncontrollable passion. "You all want to make me miserable!" she shrieked with terrible violence. "And now I can't even go out! You are a horrid, cruel woman, and I hate you! And you can do what you like! Put me in prison if you like! I know you'd be glad if I was dead!"

She dashed from the room, banging the door with a shock

that made the house rattle. And she had shouted so loud th.
she might have been heard in the shop, and even in the kitche
It was a startling experience for Mrs. Baines. Mrs. Baine
why did you saddle yourself with a witness? Why did you :
positively say that you intended to have an answer?

"Really," she stammered, pulling her dignity about h*
shoulders like a garment that the wind has snatched off. "
never dreamed that poor girl had such a dreadful tempe*
What a pity it is, for her *own* sake!" It was the best she coul
do.

Constance, who could not bear to witness her mother
humiliation, vanished very quietly from the room. She g*
halfway upstairs to the second floor, and then, hearing th
loud, rapid, painful, regular intake of sobbing breaths, sh
hesitated and crept down again.

This was Mrs. Baines's first costly experience of the chil*
thankless for having been brought into the world. It robbe*
her of her profound, absolute belief in herself. She had though
she knew everything in her house and could do everythin*
there. And lo! she had suddenly stumbled against an unsus
pected personality at large in her house, a sort of hard marbl*
affair that informed her by means of bumps that if she did no*
want to be hurt she must keep out of the way.

v

On the Sunday afternoon Mrs. Baines was trying to repos*
a little in the drawing-room, where she had caused a fire to b*
lighted. Constance was in the adjacent bedroom with her
father. Sophia lay between blankets in the room overhead with
a feverish cold. This cold and her new dress were Mrs. Baines's
sole consolation at the moment. She had prophesied a cold for
Sophia, refuser of castor-oil, and it had come. Sophia had
received, for standing in her nightdress at a draughty window
of a May morning, what Mrs. Baines called "nature's slap in
the face." As for the dress, she had worshipped God in it, and
prayed for Sophia in it, before dinner; and its four double
rows of gimp on the skirt had been accounted a great success.
With her lace-bordered mantle and her low, stringed bonnet
she had assuredly given a unique lustre to the congregation
at chapel. She was stout; but the fashions, prescribing vague

outlines, broad downward slopes, and vast amplitudes, were favourable to her shape. It must not be supposed that stout women of a certain age never seek to seduce the eye and trouble the meditations of man by other than moral charms. Mrs. Baines knew that she was comely, natty, imposing, and elegant; and the knowledge gave her real pleasure. She would look over her shoulder in the glass as anxious as a girl: make no mistake.

She did not repose; she could not. She sat thinking, in exactly the same posture as Sophia's two afternoons previously. She would have been surprised to hear that her attitude, bearing, and expression powerfully recalled those of her reprehensible daughter. But it was so. A good angel made her restless, and she went idly to the window and glanced upon the empty, shuttered Square. She too, majestic matron, had strange, brief yearnings for an existence more romantic than this; shootings across her spirit's firmament of tailed comets; soft, inexplicable melancholies. The good angel, withdrawing her from such a mood, directed her gaze to a particular spot at the top of the square.

She passed at once out of the room—not precisely in a hurry, yet without wasting time. In a recess under the stairs, immediately outside the door, was a box about a foot square and eighteen inches deep covered with black American cloth. She bent down and unlocked this box, which was padded within and contained the Baines silver tea-service. She drew from the box teapot, sugar-bowl, milk-jug, sugar-tongs, hot-water jug, and cake-stand (a flattish dish with an arching semicircular handle)—chased vessels, silver without and silver-gilt within; glittering heirlooms that shone in the dark corner like the secret pride of respectable families. These she put on a tray that always stood on end in the recess. Then she looked upwards through the banisters to the second floor.

"Maggie!" she piercingly whispered.

"Yes, mum," came a voice.

"Are you dressed?"

"Yes, mum. I'm just coming."

"Well, put on your muslin." "Apron," Mrs. Baines implied. Maggie understood.

"Take these for tea," said Mrs. Baines when Maggie descended. "Better rub them over. You know where the cake is—that new one. The best cups. And the silver spoons."

They both heard a knock at the side-door, far off, below.

"There!" exclaimed Mrs. Baines. "Now take these right down into the kitchen before you open."

"Yes, mum," said Maggie, departing.

Mrs. Baines was wearing a black alpaca apron. She removed it and put on another one of black satin embroidered with yellow flowers, which, by merely inserting her arm into the chamber, she had taken from off the chest of drawers in her bedroom. Then she fixed herself in the drawing-room.

Maggie returned, rather short of breath, convoying the visitor.

"Ah! Miss Chetwynd," said Mrs. Baines, rising to welcome. "I'm sure I'm delighted to see you. I saw you coming down the Square, and I said to myself, 'Now I do hope Miss Chetwynd isn't going to forget us.'"

Miss Chetwynd, simpering momentarily, came forward with that self-conscious, slightly histrionic air, which is one of the penalties of pedagogy. She lived under the eyes of her pupils. Her life was one ceaseless effort to avoid doing anything which might influence her charges for evil or shock the natural sensitiveness of their parents. She had to wind her earthly way through a forest of the most delicate susceptibilities—fern-fronds that stretched across the path, and that she must not even accidentally disturb with her skirt as she passed. No wonder she walked mincingly! No wonder she had a habit of keeping her elbows close to her sides, and drawing her mantle tight in the streets! Her prospectus talked about "a sound and religious course of training," "study embracing the usual branches of English, with music by a talented master, drawing, dancing, and calisthenics." Also "needlework plain and ornamental;" also "moral influence," and finally about terms, "which are very moderate, and every particular, with references to parents and others, furnished on application." (Sometimes, too, without application.) As an illustration of the delicacy of fern-fronds, that single word "dancing" had nearly lost her Constance and Sophia seven years before!

She was a pinched virgin, aged forty, and not "well off;" in her family the gift of success had been monopolized by her elder sister. For these characteristics Mrs. Baines, as a matron in easy circumstances, pitied Miss Chetwynd. On the other hand, Miss Chetwynd could choose ground from which to look down upon Mrs. Baines, who after all was in trade. Miss

Chetwynd had no trace of the local accent; she spoke with a southern refinement which the Five Towns, while making fun of it, envied. All her O's had a genteel leaning towards "ow," as ritualism leans towards Romanism. And she was the fount of etiquette, a wonder of correctness; in the eyes of her pupils' parents not so much "a perfect *lady*" as "a *perfect* lady." So that it was an extremely nice question whether, upon the whole, Mrs. Baines secretly condescended to Miss Chetwynd or Miss Chetwynd to Mrs. Baines. Perhaps Mrs. Baines, by virtue of her wifehood, carried the day.

Miss Chetwynd, carefully and precisely seated, opened the conversation by explaining that even if Mrs. Baines had not written she should have called in any case, as she made a practice of calling at the home of her pupils in vacation time: which was true. Mrs. Baines, it should be stated, had on Friday afternoon sent to Miss Chetwynd one of her most luxurious notes—lavender-coloured paper with scalloped edges, the selectest mode of the day—to announce, in her Italian hand, that Constance and Sophia would both leave school at the end of the next term, and giving reasons in regard to Sophia.

Before the visitor had got very far, Maggie came in with a lacquered tea-caddy and the silver teapot and a silver spoon on a lacquered tray. Mrs. Baines, while continuing to talk, chose a key from her bunch, unlocked the tea-caddy, and transferred four teaspoonfuls of tea from it to the teapot and relocked the caddy.

"Strawberry," she mysteriously whispered to Maggie; and Maggie disappeared, bearing the tray and its contents.

"And how is your sister? It is quite a long time since she was down here," Mrs. Baines went on to Miss Chetwynd, after whispering "strawberry."

The remark was merely in the way of small-talk—for the hostess felt a certain unwilling hesitation to approach the topic of daughters—but it happened to suit the social purpose of Miss Chetwynd to a nicety. Miss Chetwynd was a vessel brimming with great tidings.

"She is very well, thank you," said Miss Chetwynd, and her expression grew exceedingly vivacious. Her face glowed with pride as she added, "Of course everything is changed now."

"Indeed?" murmured Mrs. Baines, with polite curiosity.

"Yes," said Miss Chetwynd. "You've not heard?"

"No," said Mrs. Baines. Miss Chetwynd knew that she had not heard.

"About Elizabeth's engagement? To the Reverend Archibald Jones?"

It is the fact that Mrs. Baines was taken aback. She did nothing indiscreet; she did not give vent to her excusable amazement that the elder Miss Chetwynd should be engaged to any one at all, as some women would have done in the stress of the moment. She kept her presence of mind.

"This is really *most* interesting!" said she.

It was. For Archibald Jones was one of the idols of the Wesleyan Methodist Connexion, a special preacher famous throughout England. At "Anniversaries" and "Trust sermons," Archibald Jones had probably no rival. His Christian name helped him; it was a luscious, resounding mouthful for admirers. He was not an itinerant minister, migrating every three years. His function was to direct the affairs of the "Book Room," the publishing department of the Connexion. He lived in London, and shot out into the provinces at week-ends, preaching on Sundays and giving a lecture, tinctured with bookishness, "in the chapel" on Monday evenings. In every town he visited there was competition for the privilege of entertaining him. He had zeal, indefatigable energy, and a breezy wit. He was a widower of fifty, and his wife had been dead for twenty years. It had seemed as if women were not for this bright star. And here Elizabeth Chetwynd, who had left the Five Towns a quarter of a century before at the age of twenty, had caught him! Austere, moustached, formidable, desiccated, she must have done it with her powerful intellect! It must be a union of intellects! He had been impressed by hers, and she by his, and then their intellects had kissed. Within a week fifty thousand women in forty counties had pictured to themselves this osculation of intellects, and shrugged their shoulders, and decided once more that men were incomprehensible. These great ones in London, falling in love like the rest! But no! Love was a ribald and voluptuous word to use in such a matter as this. It was generally felt that the Reverend Archibald Jones and Miss Chetwynd the elder would lift marriage to what would now be termed an astral plane.

After tea had been served, Mrs. Baines gradually recovered her position, both in her own private esteem and in the deference of Miss Aline Chetwynd.

"Yes," said she. "You can talk about your sister, and you can call *him* Archibald, and you can mince up your words. But have you got a tea-service like this? Can you conceive more perfect strawberry jam than this? Did not my dress cost more than you spend on your clothes in a year? Has a man ever looked at you? After all, is there not something about my situation . . . in short, something . . .?"

She did not say this aloud. She in no way deviated from the scrupulous politeness of a hostess. There was nothing in even her tone to indicate that Mrs. John Baines was a personage. Yet it suddenly occurred to Miss Chetwynd that her pride in being the prospective sister-in-law of the Rev. Archibald Jones would be better for a while in her pocket. And she inquired after Mr. Baines. After this the conversation limped somewhat.

"I suppose you weren't surprised by my letter?" said Mrs. Baines.

"I was and I wasn't," answered Miss Chetwynd, in her professional manner and not her manner of a prospective sister-in-law. "Of course I am naturally sorry to lose two such good pupils, but we can't keep our pupils for ever." She smiled; she was not without fortitude—it is easier to lose pupils than to replace them. "Still"—a pause—"what you say of Sophia is perfectly true, perfectly. She is quite as advanced as Constance. Still"—another pause and a more rapid enunciation —"Sophia is by no means an ordinary girl."

"I hope she hasn't been a very great trouble to you?"

"Oh *no!*" exclaimed Miss Chetwynd. "Sophia and I have got on very well together. I have always tried to appeal to her reason. I have never *forced* her. . . . Now, with some girls. . . . In some ways I look on Sophia as the most remarkable girl—not pupil—but the most remarkable—what shall I say?—individuality, that I have ever met with." And her demeanour added, "And, mind you, this is something—from me!"

"Indeed!" said Mrs. Baines. She told herself, "I am not your common foolish parent. I see my children impartially. I am incapable of being flattered concerning them."

Nevertheless she was flattered, and the thought shaped itself that really Sophia was no ordinary girl.

"I suppose she has talked to you about becoming a teacher?" asked Miss Chetwynd, taking a morsel of the unparalleled jam.

She held the spoon with her thumb and three fingers. Her fourth finger, in matters of honest labour, would never associate with the other three; delicately curved, it always drew proudly away from them.

"Has she mentioned that to you?" Mrs. Baines demanded, startled.

"Oh yes!" said Miss Chetwynd. "Several times. Sophia is a very secretive girl, very—but I think I may say I have always had her confidence. There have been times when Sophia and I have been very near each other. Elizabeth was much struck with her. Indeed, I may tell you that in one of her last letters to me she spoke of Sophia and said she had mentioned her to Mr. Jones, and Mr. Jones remembered her quite well."

Impossible for even a wise, uncommon parent not to be affected by such an announcement!

"I dare say your sister will give up her school now," observed Mrs. Baines, to divert attention from her self-consciousness.

"Oh *no!*" And this time Mrs. Baines had genuinely shocked Miss Chetwynd. "Nothing would induce Elizabeth to give up the cause of education. Archibald takes the keenest interest in the school. Oh no! Not for worlds!"

"*Then you think Sophia would make a good teacher?*" asked Mrs. Baines with apparent inconsequence, and with a smile. But the words marked an epoch in her mind. All was over.

"I think she is very much set on it and——"

"That wouldn't affect her father—or me," said Mrs. Baines quickly.

"Certainly not! I merely say that she is very much set on it. Yes, she would, at any rate, make a teacher far superior to the average." ("That girl has got the better of her mother without me!" she reflected.) "Ah! Here is dear Constance!"

Constance, tempted beyond her strength by the sounds of the visit and the colloquy, had slipped into the room.

"I've left both doors open; mother," she excused herself for quitting her father, and kissed Miss Chetwynd.

She blushed, but she blushed happily, and really made a most creditable *début* as a young lady. Her mother rewarded her by taking her into the conversation. And history was soon made.

So Sophia was apprenticed to Miss Aline Chetwynd. Mrs. Baines bore herself greatly. It was Miss Chetwynd who had

urged, and her respect for Miss Chetwynd. . . . Also somehow the Reverend Archibald Jones came into the cause. . . .
Of course the idea of Sophia ever going to London was ridicu-
ous, ridiculous! (Mrs. Baines secretly feared that the ridiculous might happen; but, with the Reverend Archibald Jones
on the spot, the worst could be faced.) Sophia must understand
that even the apprenticeship in Bursley was merely a trial.
They would see how things went on. She had to thank Miss
Chetwynd. . . .

"I made Miss Chetwynd come and talk to mother," said
Sophia magnificently one night to simple Constance, as if to
imply, "Your Miss Chetwynd is my washpot."

To Constance, Sophia's mere enterprise was just as staggering as her success. Fancy her deliberately going out that Saturday morning, after her mother's definite decision, to enlist
Miss Chetwynd in her aid!

There is no need to insist on the tragic grandeur of Mrs.
Baines's renunciation—a renunciation which implied her acceptance of a change in the balance of power in her realm.
Part of its tragedy was that none, not even Constance, could
divine the intensity of Mrs. Baines's suffering. She had no
confidant; she was incapable of showing a wound. But when
she lay awake at night by the organism which had once been
her husband, she dwelt long and deeply on the martyrdom of
her life. What had she done to deserve it? Always had she
conscientiously endeavoured to be kind, just, patient. And she
knew herself to be sagacious and prudent. In the frightful and
unguessed trials of her existence as a wife, surely she might
have been granted consolations as a mother! Yet no; it had
not been! And she felt all the bitterness of age against youth
—youth egotistic, harsh, cruel, uncompromising; youth that is
so crude, so ignorant of life, so slow to understand! She had
Constance. Yes, but it would be twenty years before Constance
could appreciate the sacrifice of judgment and of pride which
her mother had made, in a sudden decision, during that rambling, starched, simpering interview with Miss Aline Chetwynd.
Probably Constance thought that she had yielded to Sophia's
passionate temper! Impossible to explain to Constance that
she had yielded to nothing but a perception of Sophia's complete inability to hear reason and wisdom. Ah! Sometimes as
she lay in the dark, she would, in fancy, snatch her heart
from her bosom and fling it down before Sophia, bleeding, and

cry: "See what I carry about with me, on your account!" Then she would take it back and hide it again, and sweeten her bitterness with wise admonitions to herself.

All this because Sophia, aware that if she stayed in the house she would be compelled to help in the shop, chose an honourable activity which freed her from the danger. Heart, how absurd of you to bleed!

CHAPTER IV
ELEPHANT

"SOPHIA, will you come and see the elephant? Do come!" Constance entered the drawing-room with this request on her eager lips.

"No," said Sophia, with a touch of condescension. "I'm far too busy for elephants."

Only two years had passed; but both girls were grown up now; long sleeves, long skirts, hair that had settled down in life; and a demeanour immensely serious, as though existence were terrific in its responsibilities; yet sometimes childhood surprisingly broke through the crust of gravity, as now in Constance, aroused by such things as elephants, and proclaimed with vivacious gestures that it was not dead after all. The sisters were sharply differentiated. Constance wore the black alpaca apron and the scissors at the end of a long black elastic, which indicated her vocation in the shop. She was proving a considerable success in the millinery department. She had learnt how to talk to people, and was, in her modest way, very self-possessed. She was getting a little stouter. Everybody liked her. Sophia had developed into the student. Time had accentuated her reserve. Her sole friend was Miss Chetwynd, with whom she was, having regard to the disparity of their ages, very intimate. At home she spoke little. She lacked amiability; as her mother said, she was "touchy." She required diplomacy from others, but did not render it again. Her attitude, indeed, was one of half-hidden disdain, now gentle, now coldly bitter. She would not wear an apron, in an age when aprons were almost essential to decency. No! She would *not* wear an apron, and there was an end of it. She was not so tidy

as Constance, and if Constance's hands had taken on the coarse
texture which comes from commerce with needles, pins, artificial flowers, and stuffs, Sophia's fine hands were seldom innocent of ink. But Sophia was splendidly beautiful. And even
her mother and Constance had an instinctive idea that that
face was, at any rate, a partial excuse for her asperity.

"Well," said Constance, "if you won't, I do believe I shall
ask mother if she will."

Sophia, bending over her books, made no answer. But the
top of her head said: "This has no interest for me whatever."

Constance left the room, and in a moment returned with her
mother.

"Sophia," said her mother, with gay excitement, "you might
go and sit with your father for a bit while Constance and I
just run up to the playground to see the elephant. You can
work just as well in there as here. Your father's asleep."

"Oh, very well!" Sophia agreed haughtily. "Whatever is
all this fuss about an elephant? Anyhow, it'll be quieter in your
room. The noise here is splitting." She gave a supercilious
glance into the Square as she languidly rose.

It was the morning of the third day of Bursley Wakes; not
the modern finicking and respectable, but an orgiastic carnival,
gross in all its manifestations of joy. The whole centre of the
town was given over to the furious pleasures of the people.
Most of the Square was occupied by Wombwell's Menagerie, in
a vast oblong tent, whose raging beasts roared and growled day
and night. And spreading away from this supreme attraction,
right up through the market-place past the Town Hall to Duck
Bank, Duck Square and the waste land called the "playground," were hundreds of booths with banners displaying all
the delights of the horrible. You could see the atrocities of the
French Revolution, and of the Fiji Islands, and the ravages of
unspeakable diseases, and the living flesh of a nearly nude
human female guaranteed to turn the scale at twenty-two
stone, and the skeletons of the mysterious phantoscope, and the
bloody contests of champions naked to the waist (with the
chance of picking up a red tooth as a relic). You could try
your strength by hitting an image of a fellow-creature in the
stomach, and test your aim by knocking off the heads of other
images with a wooden ball. You could also shoot with rifles at
various targets. All the streets were lined with stalls loaded
with food in heaps, chiefly dried fish, the entrails of animals,

and gingerbread. All the public-houses were crammed, and frenzied jolly drunkards, men and women, lunged along the pavements everywhere, their shouts vying with the trumpets, horns, and drums of the booths, and the shrieking, rattling toys that the children carried.

It was a glorious spectacle, but not a spectacle for the leading families. Miss Chetwynd's school was closed, so that the daughters of leading families might remain in seclusion till the worst was over. The Baineses ignored the Wakes in every possible way, choosing that week to have a show of mourning goods in the left-hand window, and refusing to let Maggie outside on any pretext. Therefore the dazzling social success of the elephant, which was quite easily drawing Mrs. Baines into the vortex, cannot imaginably be over-estimated.

On the previous night one of the three Wombwell elephants had suddenly knelt on a man in the tent; he had then walked out of the tent and picked up another man at haphazard from the crowd which was staring at the great pictures in front, and tried to put this second man into his mouth. Being stopped by his Indian attendant with a pitchfork, he placed the man on the ground and stuck his tusk through an artery of the victim's arm. He then, amid unexampled excitement, suffered himself to be led away. He was conducted to the rear of the tent, just in front of Baines's shuttered windows, and by means of stakes, pulleys, and ropes forced to his knees. His head was whitewashed, and six men of the Rifle Corps were engaged to shoot at him at a distance of five yards, while constables kept the crowd off with truncheons. He died instantly, rolling over with a soft thud. The crowd cheered, and, intoxicated by their importance, the Volunteers fired three more volleys into the carcase, and were then borne off as heroes to different inns. The elephant, by the help of his two companions, was got on to a railway lorry and disappeared into the night. Such was the greatest sensation that has ever occurred, or perhaps will ever occur, in Bursley. The excitement about the repeal of the Corn Laws, or about Inkerman, was feeble compared to that excitement. Mr. Critchlow, who had been called on to put a hasty tourniquet round the arm of the second victim, had popped in afterwards to tell John Baines all about it. Mr. Baines's interest, however, had been slight. Mr. Critchlow succeeded better with the ladies, who, though they had witnessed the shooting from the drawing-room, were thirsty for the most trifling details.

The next day it was known that the elephant lay near the playground, pending the decision of the Chief Bailiff and the Medical Officer as to his burial. And everybody had to visit the corpse. No social exclusiveness could withstand the seduction of that dead elephant. Pilgrims travelled from all the Five Towns to see him.

"We're going now," said Mrs. Baines, after she had assumed her bonnet and shawl.

"All right," said Sophia, pretending to be absorbed in study, as she sat on the sofa at the foot of her father's bed.

And Constance, having put her head in at the door, drew her mother after her like a magnet.

Then Sophia heard a remarkable conversation in the passage.

"Are you going up to see the elephant, Mrs. Baines?" asked the voice of Mr. Povey.

"Yes. Why?"

"I think I had better come with you. The crowd is sure to be very rough." Mr. Povey's tone was firm; he had a position.

"But the shop?"

"We shall not be long," said Mr. Povey.

"Oh yes, mother," Constance added appealingly.

Sophia felt the house thrill as the side-door banged. She sprang up and watched the three cross King Street diagonally, and so plunge into the Wakes. This triple departure was surely the crowning tribute to the dead elephant! It was simply astonishing. It caused Sophia to perceive that she had miscalculated the importance of the elephant. It made her regret her scorn of the elephant as an attraction. She was left behind; and the joy of life was calling her. She could see down into the Vaults on the opposite side of the street, where working men—potters and colliers—in their best clothes, some with high hats, were drinking, gesticulating, and laughing in a row at a long counter.

She noticed, while she was thus at the bedroom window, a young man ascending King Street, followed by a porter trundling a flat barrow of luggage. He passed slowly under the very window. She flushed. She had evidently been startled by the sight of this young man into no ordinary state of commotion. She glanced at the books on the sofa, and then at her father. Mr. Baines, thin and gaunt, and acutely pitiable, still slept. His brain had almost ceased to be active now; he had to be fed and tended like a bearded baby, and he would sleep for hours at a stretch even in the daytime. Sophia left the room. A moment later she ran into the shop, an apparition that amazed the three young lady assistants. At the corner near the window on the fancy side a little nook had been formed by screening off a portion of the counter with large flower-boxes placed end-up. This corner had come to be known as "Miss Baines's corner." Sophia hastened to it, squeezing past a young lady assistant in the narrow space between the back of the counter and the shelf-lined wall. She sat down in Constance's chair and pretended to look for something. She had examined herself in the cheval-glass in the showroom, on her way from the sick-chamber. When she heard a voice near the door of the shop asking first for Mr. Povey and then for Mrs. Baines, she rose, and seizing the object nearest to her, which happened to be a pair of scissors, she hurried towards the showroom stairs as though the scissors had been a grail, passionately sought and to be jealously hidden away. She wanted to stop and turn round, but something prevented her. She was at the end of the counter, under the curving stairs, when one of the assistants said:

"I suppose you don't know when Mr. Povey or your mother are likely to be back, Miss Sophia? Here's—"

It was a divine release for Sophia.

"They're—I—" she stammered, turning round abruptly. Luckily she was still sheltered behind the counter.

The young man whom she had seen in the street came boldly forward.

"Good morning, Miss Sophia," said he, hat in hand. "It is a long time since I had the pleasure of seeing you."

Never had she blushed as she blushed then. She scarcely knew what she was doing as she moved slowly towards her sister's corner again, the young man following her on the customer's side of the counter.

ii

She knew that he was a traveller for the most renowned and gigantic of all Manchester wholesale firms—Birkinshaws. But she did not know his name, which was Gerald Scales. He was a rather short but extremely well-proportioned man of thirty, with fair hair, and a distinguished appearance, as became a representative of Birkinshaws. His broad, tight necktie, with an edge of white collar showing above it, was particularly elegant. He had been on the road for Birkinshaws for several years; but Sophia had only seen him once before in her life, when she was a little girl, three years ago. The relations between the travellers of the great firms and their solid, sure clients in small towns were in those days often cordially intimate. The traveller came with the lustre of a historic reputation around him; there was no need to fawn for orders; and the client's immense and immaculate respectability made him the equal of no matter what ambassador. It was a case of mutual esteem, and of that confidence-generating phenomenon, "an old account." The tone in which a commercial traveller of middle age would utter the phrase "an old account" revealed in a flash all that was romantic, prim, and stately in mid-Victorian commerce. In the days of Baines, after one of the elaborately engraved advice-circulars had arrived ("Our Mr. —— will have the pleasure of waiting upon you on — day next, the — inst.") John might in certain cases be expected to say, on the morning of — day, "Missis, what have ye gotten for supper to-night?"

Mr. Gerald Scales had never been asked to supper; he had never even seen John Baines; but, as the youthful successor of an aged traveller who had had the pleasure of St. Luke's Square, on behalf of Birkinshaws, since before railways, Mrs. Baines had treated him with a faint agreeable touch of maternal familiarity; and, both her daughters being once in the shop during his visit, she had on that occasion commanded the gawky girls to shake hands with him.

Sophia had never forgotten that glimpse. The young man without a name had lived in her mind, brightly glowing, as the very symbol and incarnation of the masculine and the elegant.

The renewed sight of him seemed to have wakened her out of a sleep. Assuredly she was not the same Sophia. As she sat in her sister's chair in the corner, entrenched behind the perpendicular boxes, playing nervously with the scissors, her beautiful face was transfigured into the ravishingly angelic. It would have been impossible for Mr. Gerald Scales, or anybody else, to credit, as he gazed at those lovely, sensitive, vivacious, responsive features, that Sophia was not a character of heavenly sweetness and perfection. She did not know what she was doing; she was nothing but the exquisite expression of a deep instinct to attract and charm. Her soul itself emanated from her in an atmosphere of allurement and acquiescence. Could those laughing lips hang in a heavy pout? Could that delicate and mild voice be harsh? Could those burning eyes be coldly inimical? Never! The idea was inconceivable! And Mr. Gerald Scales, with his head over the top of the boxes, yielded to the spell. Remarkable that Mr. Gerald Scales, with all his experience, should have had to come to Bursley to find the pearl, the paragon, the ideal! But so it was. They met in an equal abandonment; the only difference between them was that Mr. Scales, by force of habit, kept his head.

"I see it's your wakes here," said he.

He was polite to the wakes; but now, with the least inflection in the world, he put the wakes at its proper level in the scheme of things as a local unimportance! She adored him for this; she was athirst for sympathy in the task of scorning everything local.

"I expect you didn't know," she said, implying that there was every reason why a man of his mundane interests should not know.

"I should have remembered if I had thought," said he. "But I didn't think. What's this about an elephant?"

"Oh!" she exclaimed. "Have you heard of that?"

"My porter was full of it."

"Well," she said, "of course it's a very big thing in Bursley."

As she smiled in gentle pity of poor Bursley, he naturally did the same. And he thought how much more advanced and broad the younger generation was than the old! He would never have dared to express his real feelings about Bursley to Mrs. Baines, or even to Mr. Povey (who was, however, of no generation); yet here was a young woman actually sharing them.

She told him all the history of the elephant.

"Must have been very exciting," he commented, despite himself.

"Do you know," she replied, "it *was*."

After all, Bursley was climbing in their opinion.

"And mother and my sister and Mr. Povey have all gone to see it. That's why they're not here."

That the elephant should have caused both Mr. Povey and Mrs. Baines to forget that the representative of Birkinshaws was due to call was indeed a final victory for the elephant.

"But not you!" he exclaimed.

"No," she said. "Not me."

"Why didn't you go too?" He continued his flattering investigations with a generous smile.

"I simply didn't care to," said she, proudly nonchalant.

"And I suppose you are in charge here?"

"No," she answered. "I just happened to have run down here for these scissors. That's all."

"I often see your sister," said he. " 'Often' do I say?—that is, generally, when I come; but never you."

"I'm never in the shop," she said. "It's just an accident today."

"Oh! So you leave the shop to your sister?"

"Yes." She said nothing of her teaching.

Then there was a silence. Sophia was very thankful to be hidden from the curiosity of the shop. The shop could see nothing of her, and only the back of the young man; and the conversation had been conducted in low voices. She tapped her foot, stared at the worn, polished surface of the counter, with the brass yard-measure nailed along its edge, and then she uneasily turned her gaze to the left and seemed to be examining the backs of the black bonnets which were perched on high stands in the great window. Then her eyes caught his for an important moment.

"Yes," she breathed. Somebody had to say something. If the shop missed the murmur of their voices the shop would wonder what had happened to them.

Mr. Scales looked at his watch. "I dare say if I come in again about two—" he began.

"Oh yes, they're *sure* to be in then," she burst out before he could finish his sentence.

He left abruptly, queerly, without shaking hands (but then it would have been difficult—she argued—for him to have put his arm over the boxes), and without expressing the hope of seeing her again. She peeped through the black bonnets, and saw the porter put the leather strap over his shoulders, raise the rear of the barrow, and trundle off; but she did not see Mr. Scales. She was drunk; thoughts were tumbling about in her brain like cargo loose in a rolling ship. Her entire conception of herself was being altered; her attitude towards life was being altered. The thought which knocked hardest against its fellows was, "Only in these moments have I begun to live!"

And as she flitted upstairs to resume watch over her father she sought to devise an innocent-looking method by which she might see Mr. Scales when he next called. And she speculated as to what his name was.

iii

When Sophia arrived in the bedroom, she was startled because her father's head and beard were not in their accustomed place on the pillow. She could only make out something vaguely unusual sloping off the side of the bed. A few seconds passed— not to be measured in time—and she saw that the upper part of his body had slipped down, and his head was hanging, inverted, near the floor between the bed and the ottoman. His face, neck, and hands were dark and congested; his mouth was open, and the tongue protruded between the black, swollen, mucous lips; his eyes were prominent and coldly staring. The fact was that Mr. Baines had wakened up, and, being restless, had slid out partially from his bed and died of asphyxia. After having been unceasingly watched for fourteen years, he had, with an invalid's natural perverseness, taken advantage of Sophia's brief dereliction to expire. Say what you will, amid Sophia's horror, and her terrible grief and shame, she had visitings of the idea: he did it on purpose!

She ran out of the room, knowing by intuition that he was dead, and shrieked out, "Maggie," at the top of her voice; the house echoed.

"Yes, miss," said Maggie, quite close, coming out of Mr. Povey's chamber with a slop-pail.

"Fetch Mr. Critchlow at once. Be quick. Just as you are. It's father—"

Maggie, perceiving darkly that disaster was in the air, and instantly filled with importance and a sort of black joy, dropped her pail in the exact middle of the passage, and almost fell down the crooked stairs. One of Maggie's deepest instincts, always held in check by the stern dominance of Mrs. Baines, was to leave pails prominent on the main routes of the house; and now, divining what was at hand, it flamed into insurrection.

No sleepless night had ever been so long to Sophia as the three minutes which elapsed before Mr. Critchlow came. As she stood on the mat outside the bedroom door she tried to draw her mother and Constance and Mr. Povey by magnetic force out of the wakes into the house, and her muscles were contracted in this strange effort. She felt that it was impossible to continue living if the secret of the bedroom remained unknown one instant longer, so intense was her torture, and yet that the torture which could not be borne must be borne. Not a sound in the house! Not a sound from the shop! Only the distant murmur of the wakes!

"Why did I forget father?" she asked herself with awe. "I only meant to tell *him* that they were all out, and run back. Why did I forget father?" She would never be able to persuade anybody that she had literally forgotten her father's existence for quite ten minutes; but it was true, though shocking.

Then there were noises downstairs.

"Bless us! Bless us!" came the unpleasant voice of Mr. Critchlow as he bounded up the stairs on his long legs; he strode over the pail. "What's amiss?" He was wearing his white apron, and he carried his spectacles in his bony hand.

"It's father—he's—" Sophia faltered.

She stood away so that he should enter the room first. He glanced at her keenly, and as it were resentfully, and went in. She followed, timidly, remaining near the door while Mr. Critchlow inspected her handiwork. He put on his spectacles with strange deliberation, and then, bending his knees outwards, thus lowered his body so that he could examine John Baines point-blank. He remained staring like this, his hands on his sharp apron-covered knees, for a little space; and then he seized the inert mass and restored it to the bed, and wiped those clotted lips with his apron.

Sophia heard loud breathing behind her. It was Maggie. She heard a huge, snorting sob; Maggie was showing her emotion.

"Go fetch doctor!" Mr. Critchlow rasped. "And don't stand gaping there!"

"Run for the doctor, Maggie," said Sophia.

"How came ye to let him fall?" Mr. Critchlow demanded.

"I was out of the room. I just ran down into the shop—"

"Gallivanting with that young Scales!" said Mr. Critchlow,

with devilish ferocity. "Well, you've killed yer father; that's all!"

He must have been at his shop door and seen the entry of the traveller! And it was precisely characteristic of Mr. Critch low to jump in the dark at a horrible conclusion, and to be right after all. For Sophia Mr. Critchlow had always been the personification of malignity and malevolence, and now these qualities in him made him, to her, almost obscene. Her pride brought up tremendous reinforcements, and she approached the bed.

"Is he dead?" she asked in a quiet tone. (Somewhere within a voice was whispering, "So his name is Scales.")

"Don't I tell you he's dead?"

"Pail on the stairs!"

This mild exclamation came from the passage. Mrs. Baines, misliking the crowds abroad, had returned alone; she had left Constance in charge of Mr. Povey. Coming into her house by the shop and showroom, she had first noted the phenomenon of the pail—proof of her theory of Maggie's incurable untidiness.

"Been to see the elephant, I reckon!" said Mr. Critchlow, in fierce sarcasm, as he recognized Mrs. Baines's voice.

Sophia leaped towards the door, as though to bar her mother's entrance. But Mrs. Baines was already opening the door.

"Well, my pet—" she was beginning cheerfully.

Mr. Critchlow confronted her. And he had no more pity for the wife than for the daughter. He was furiously angry because his precious property had been irretrievably damaged by the momentary carelessness of a silly girl. Yes, John Baines was his property, his dearest toy! He was convinced that he alone had kept John Baines alive for fourteen years, that he alone had fully understood the case and sympathized with the sufferer, that none but he had been capable of displaying ordinary common sense in the sick-room. He had learned to regard John Baines as, in some sort, his creation. And now, with their stupidity, their neglect, their elephants, between them they had done for John Baines. He had always known it would come to that, and it had come to that.

"She let him fall out o' bed, and ye're a widow now, missis!" he announced with a virulence hardly conceivable. His angular features and dark eyes expressed a murderous hate for every woman named Baines.

"Mother!" cried Sophia, "I only ran down into the shop to —to—"

She seized her mother's arm in frenzied agony.

"My child!" said Mrs. Baines, rising miraculously to the situation with a calm benevolence of tone and gesture that remained for ever sublime in the stormy heart of Sophia, "do not hold me." With infinite gentleness she loosed herself from those clasping hands. "Have you sent for the doctor?" she questioned Mr. Critchlow.

The fate of her husband presented no mysteries to Mrs. Baines. Everybody had been warned a thousand times of the danger of leaving the paralytic, whose life depended on his position, and whose fidgetiness was thereby a constant menace of death to him. For five thousand nights she had wakened infallibly every time he stirred, and rearranged him by the flicker of a little oil lamp. But Sophia, unhappy creature, had merely left him. That was all.

Mr. Critchlow and the widow gazed, helplessly waiting, at the pitiable corpse, of which the salient part was the white beard. They knew not that they were gazing at a vanished era. John Baines had belonged to the past, to the age when men really did think of their souls, when orators by phrases could move crowds to fury or to pity, when no one had learnt to hurry, when Demos was only turning in his sleep, when the sole beauty of life resided in its inflexible and slow dignity, when hell really had no bottom, and a gilt-clasped Bible really was the secret of England's greatness. Mid-Victorian England lay on that mahogany bed. Ideals had passed away with John Baines. It is thus that ideals die; not in the conventional pageantry of honoured death, but sorrily, ignobly, while one's head is turned—

And Mr. Povey and Constance, very self-conscious, went and saw the dead elephant, and came back; and at the corner of King Street, Constance exclaimed brightly—

"Why! who's gone out and left the side-door open?"

For the doctor had at length arrived, and Maggie, in showing him upstairs with pious haste, had forgotten to shut the door.

And they took advantage of the side-door, rather guiltily, to avoid the eyes of the shop. They feared that in the parlour they would be the centre of a curiosity half ironical and half reproving; for had they not accomplished an escapade? So they walked slowly.

The real murderer was having his dinner in the commercial room up at the Tiger, opposite the Town Hall.

iv

Several shutters were put up in the windows of the shop, to indicate a death, and the news instantly became known in trading circles throughout the town. Many people simultaneously remarked upon the coincidence that Mr. Baines should have died while there was a show of mourning goods in his establishment. This coincidence was regarded as extremely sinister, and it was apparently felt that, for the sake of the mind's peace, one ought not to inquire into such things too closely. From the moment of, putting up the prescribed shutters, John Baines and his funeral began to acquire importance in Bursley, and their importance grew rapidly almost from hour to hour. The wakes continued as usual, except that the Chief Constable, upon representations being made to him by Mr. Critchlow and other citizens, descended upon St. Luke's Square and forbade the activities of Wombwell's orchestra. Wombwell and the Chief Constable differed as to the justice of the decree, but every well-minded person praised the Chief Constable, and he himself considered that he had enhanced the town's reputation for a decent propriety. It was noticed, too, not without a shiver of the uncanny, that that night the lions and tigers behaved like lambs, whereas on the previous night they had roared the whole Square out of its sleep.

The Chief Constable was not the only individual enlisted by Mr. Critchlow in the service of his friend's fame. Mr. Critchlow spent hours in recalling the principal citizens to a due sense of John Baines's past greatness. He was determined that his treasured toy should vanish underground with due pomp, and he left nothing undone to that end. He went over to Hanbridge on the still wonderful horse-car, and saw the editor-proprietor of the *Staffordshire Signal* (then a two-penny weekly with no thought of Football editions), and on the very day of the funeral the *Signal* came out with a long and eloquent biography of John Baines. This biography, giving details of his public life, definitely restored him to his legitimate position in the civic memory as an ex-chief bailiff, an ex-chairman of the Burial Board, and of the Five Towns Association for the Advancement of Useful Knowledge, and also as a "prime mover" in the local Turnpike Act, in the negotiations for the new Town Hall, and in the Corinthian façade of the Wesleyan Chapel; it narrated the anecdote of his courageous speech from the portico of the Shambles during the riots of 1848, and it did not omit a eulogy of his steady adherence to the wise old English maxims of commerce and his avoidance of dangerous modern methods. Even in the sixties the modern had reared its shameless head. The panegyric closed with an appreciation of the dead man's fortitude in the terrible affliction with which a divine providence had seen fit to try him; and finally the *Signal* uttered its absolute conviction that his native town would raise a cenotaph to his honour. Mr. Critchlow, being unfamiliar with the word "cenotaph," consulted Worcester's Dictionary, and when he found that it meant "a sepulchral monument to one who is buried elsewhere," he was as pleased with the *Signal's* language as with the idea, and decided that a cenotaph should come to pass.

The house and shop were transformed into a hive of preparation for the funeral. All was changed. Mr. Povey kindly slept for three nights on the parlour sofa, in order that Mrs. Baines might have his room. The funeral grew into an obsession, for multitudinous things had to be performed and done sumptuously and in strict accordance with precedent. There were the family mourning, the funeral repast, the choice of the text on the memorial card, the composition of the legend on the coffin, the legal arrangements, the letters to relations, the selection of guests, and the questions of bell-ringing, hearse, plumes, number of horses, and grave-digging. Nobody had leisure for the indulgence of grief except Aunt Maria, who, after she had helped in the laying-out, simply sat down and bemoaned unceasingly for hours her absence on the fatal morning. "If I hadn't been so fixed on polishing my candle-sticks," she weepingly repeated, "he mit ha' been alive and well now." Not that Aunt Maria had been informed of the precise circumstances of the death; she was not clearly aware that Mr. Baines had died through a piece of neglect. But, like Mr. Critchlow, she was convinced that there had been only one person in the world truly capable of nursing Mr. Baines. Beyond the family, no one save Mr. Critchlow and Dr. Harrop knew just how

the martyr had finished his career. Dr. Harrop, having been
asked bluntly if an inquest would be necessary, had reflected
a moment and had then replied: "No." And he added, "Least
said soonest mended—mark me!" They had marked him. He
was commonsense in breeches.

As for Aunt Maria, she was sent about her snivelling business by Aunt Harriet. The arrival in the house of this genuine
aunt from Axe, of this majestic and enormous widow whom
even the imperial Mrs. Baines regarded with a certain awe, set
a seal of ultimate solemnity on the whole event. In Mr. Povey's
bedroom Mrs. Baines fell like a child into Aunt Harriet's arms
and sobbed:

"If it had been anything else but that elephant!"

Such was Mrs. Baines's sole weakness from first to last.

Aunt Harriet was an exhaustless fountain of authority upon
every detail concerning interments. And, to a series of questions ending with the word "sister," and answers ending with
the word "sister," the prodigious travail incident to the funeral
was gradually and successfully accomplished. Dress and the
repast exceeded all other matters in complexity and difficulty.
But on the morning of the funeral Aunt Harriet had the satisfaction of beholding her younger sister the centre of a
tremendous cocoon of crape, whose slightest pleat was perfect.
Aunt Harriet seemed to welcome her then, like a veteran,
formally into the august army of relicts. As they stood side
by side surveying the special table which was being laid in
the showroom for the repast, it appeared inconceivable that
they had reposed together in Mr. Povey's limited bed. They
descended from the showroom to the kitchen, where the last
delicate dishes were inspected. The shop was, of course, closed
for the day, but Mr. Povey was busy there, and in Aunt
Harriet's all-seeing glance he came next after the dishes. She
rose from the kitchen to speak with him.

"You've got your boxes of gloves all ready?" she questioned
him.

"Yes, Mrs. Maddack."

"You'll not forget to have a measure handy?"

"No, Mrs. Maddack."

"You'll find you'll want more of seven-and-three-quarters
and eights than anything."

"Yes. I have allowed for that."

"If you place yourself behind the side-door and put your

boxes on the harmonium, you'll be able to catch every one as they come in."

"That is what I had thought of, Mrs. Maddack."

She went upstairs. Mrs. Baines had reached the showroom again, and was smoothing out creases in the white damask cloth and arranging glass dishes of jam at equal distances from each other.

"Come, sister," said Mrs. Maddack. "A last look."

And they passed into the mortuary bedroom to gaze at Mr. Baines before he should be everlastingly nailed down. In death he had recovered some of his earlier dignity; but even so he was a startling sight. The two widows bent over him, one on either side, and gravely stared at that twisted, worn white face all neatly tucked up in linen.

"I shall fetch Constance and Sophia," said Mrs. Maddack, with tears in her voice. "Do you go into the drawing-room, sister."

But Mrs. Maddack only succeeded in fetching Constance.

Then there was the sound of wheels in King Street. The long rite of the funeral was about to begin. Every guest, after having been measured and presented with a pair of the finest black kid gloves by Mr. Povey, had to mount the crooked stairs and gaze upon the carcase of John Baines, going afterwards to the drawing-room to condole briefly with the widow. And every guest, while conscious of the enormity of so thinking, thought what an excellent thing it was that John Baines should be at last dead and gone. The tramping on the stairs was continual, and finally Mr. Baines himself went downstairs, bumping against corners, and led a *cortège* of twenty vehicles.

The funeral tea was not over at seven o'clock, five hours after the commencement of the rite. It was a gigantic and faultless meal, worthy of John Baines's distant past. Only two persons were absent from it—John Baines and Sophia. The emptiness of Sophia's chair was much noticed; Mrs. Maddack explained that Sophia was very high-strung and could not trust herself. Great efforts were put forth by the company to be lugubrious and inconsolable, but the secret relief resulting from the death would not be entirely hidden. The vast pretence of acute sorrow could not stand intact against that secret relief and the lavish richness of the food.

To the offending of sundry important relatives from a distance, Mr. Critchlow informally presided over that assemblage

of grave men in high stocks and crinolined women. He had
closed his shop, which had never before been closed on a week-
day, and he had a great deal to say about this extraordinary
closure. It was due as much to the elephant as to the funeral.
The elephant had become a victim to the craze for souvenirs.
Already in the night his tusks had been stolen; then his feet
disappeared for umbrella-stands, and most of his flesh had departed in little hunks. Everybody in Bursley had resolved to
participate in the elephant. One consequence was that all the
chemists' shops in the town were assaulted by strings of boys.
"Please a pennorth o' alum to tak' smell out o' a bit o' elephant." Mr. Critchlow hated boys.

"'I'll alum ye!' says I, and I did. I alummed him out o'
my shop with a pestle. If there'd been one there'd been twenty
between opening and nine o'clock. 'George,' I says to my apprentice, 'shut shop up. My old friend John Baines is going
to his long home to-day, and I'll close. I've had enough o' alum
for one day.'"

The elephant fed the conversation until after the second
relay of hot muffins. When Mr. Critchlow had eaten to his
capacity, he took the *Signal* importantly from his pocket,
posed his spectacles, and read the obituary all through in slow,
impressive accents. Before he reached the end Mrs. Baines
began to perceive that familiarity had blinded her to the heroic
qualities of her late husband. The fourteen years of ceaseless
care were quite genuinely forgotten, and she saw him in his
strength and in his glory. When Mr. Critchlow arrived at the
eulogy of the husband and father, Mrs. Baines rose and left
the showroom. The guests looked at each other in sympathy
for her. Mr. Critchlow shot a glance at her over his spectacles
and continued steadily reading. After he had finished he approached the question of the cenotaph.

Mrs. Baines, driven from the banquet by her feelings, went
into the drawing-room. Sophia was there, and Sophia, seeing
tears in her mother's eyes, gave a sob, and flung herself bodily
against her mother, clutching her, and hiding her face in that
broad crape, which abraded her soft skin.

"Mother," she wept passionately, "I want to leave the school
now. I want to please you. I'll do anything in the world to
please you. I'll go into the shop if you'd like me to!" Her
voice lost itself in tears.

"Calm yourself, my pet," said Mrs. Baines, tenderly,

aressing her. It was a triumph for the mother in the very
hour when she needed a triumph.

CHAPTER V

THE TRAVELLER

"EXQUISITE, 1s. 11d."

These singular signs were being painted in shiny black on
an unrectangular parallelogram of white cardboard by Constance one evening in the parlour. She was seated, with her
left side to the fire and to the fizzing gas, at the dining-table,
which was covered with a checked cloth in red and white. Her
dress was of dark crimson; she wore a cameo brooch and a gold
chain round her neck; over her shoulders was thrown a white
knitted shawl, for the weather was extremely cold, the English
climate being much more serious and downright at that day
than it is now. She bent low to the task, holding her head
slightly askew, putting the tip of her tongue between her lips,
and expending all the energy of her soul and body in an
intense effort to do what she was doing as well as it could be
done.

"Splendid!" said Mr. Povey.

Mr. Povey was fronting her at the table; he had his elbows
on the table, and watched her carefully, with the breathless
and divine anxiety of a dreamer who is witnessing the realization of his dream. And Constance, without moving any part
of her frame except her head, looked up at him and smiled
for a moment, and he could see her delicious little nostrils at
the end of her snub nose.

Those two, without knowing or guessing it, were making
history—the history of commerce. They had no suspicion that
they were the forces of the future insidiously at work to destroy
what the forces of the past had created, but such was the case.
They were conscious merely of a desire to do their duty in the
shop and to the shop; probably it had not even occurred to
them that this desire, which each stimulated in the breast of
the other, had assumed the dimensions of a passion. It was
ageing Mr. Povey, and it had made of Constance a young
lady tremendously industrious and preoccupied.

Mr. Povey had recently been giving attention to the question of tickets. It is not too much to say that Mr. Povey, to whom heaven had granted a minimum share of imagination, had nevertheless discovered his little parcel of imagination in the recesses of being, and brought it effectively to bear on tickets. Tickets ran in conventional grooves. There were heavy oblong tickets for flannels, shirting, and other stuffs in the piece; there were smaller and lighter tickets for intermediate goods; and there were diamond-shaped tickets (containing nothing but the price) for bonnets, gloves, and flimflams generally. The legends on the tickets gave no sort of original invention. The words "lasting," "durable," "unshrinkable," "latest," "cheap," "stylish," "novelty," "choice" (as an adjective), "new," and "tasteful," exhausted the entire vocabulary of tickets. Now Mr. Povey attached importance to tickets, and since he was acknowledged to be the best window-dresser in Bursley, his views were entitled to respect. He dreamed of other tickets, in original shapes, with original legends. In brief, he achieved, in regard to tickets, the rare feat of ridding himself of preconceived notions, and of approaching a subject with fresh, virginal eyes. When he indicated the nature of his wishes to Mr. Chawner, the wholesale stationer who supplied all the Five Towns with shop-tickets, Mr. Chawner grew uneasy and worried; Mr. Chawner was indeed shocked. For Mr. Chawner there had always been certain well-defined genera of tickets, and he could not conceive the existence of other genera. When Mr. Povey suggested circular tickets—tickets with a blue and a red line round them, tickets with legends such as "unsurpassable," "very dainty," or "please note," Mr. Chawner hummed and hawed, and finally stated that it would be impossible to manufacture these preposterous tickets, these tickets which would outrage the decency of trade.

If Mr. Povey had not happened to be an exceedingly obstinate man, he might have been defeated by the crass Toryism of Mr. Chawner. But Mr. Povey was obstinate, and he had resources of ingenuity which Mr. Chawner little suspected. The great, tramping march of progress was not to be impeded by Mr. Chawner. Mr. Povey began to make his own tickets. At first he suffered as all reformers and inventors suffer. He used the internal surface of collar-boxes and ordinary ink and pens, and the result was such as to give customers the idea that Baineses were too poor or too mean to buy tickets like other hops. For bought tickets had an ivory-tinted gloss, and the ink was black and glossy, and the edges were very straight and did not show yellow between two layers of white. Whereas Mr. Povey's tickets were of a bluish-white, without gloss; the ink was neither black nor shiny, and the edges were amateur-shly rough: the tickets had an unmistakable air of having been "made out of something else"; moreover, the lettering had not the free, dashing style of Mr. Chawner's tickets.

And did Mrs. Baines encourage him in his single-minded enterprise on behalf of *her* business? Not a bit! Mrs. Baines's attitude, when not disdainful, was inimical! So curious is human nature, so blind is man to his own advantage! Life was very complex for Mr. Povey. It might have been less complex had Bristol board and Chinese ink been less expensive; with these materials he could have achieved marvels to silence all prejudice and stupidity; but they were too costly. Still, he persevered, and Constance morally supported him; he drew his inspiration and his courage from Constance. Instead of the internal surface of collar-boxes, he tried the external surface, which was at any rate shiny. But the ink would not "take" on it. He made as many experiments as Edison was to make, and as many failures. Then Constance was visited by a notion for mixing sugar with ink. Simple, innocent creature—why should providence have chosen her to be the vessel of such a sublime notion? Puzzling enigma, which, however, did not exercise Mr. Povey! He found it quite natural that she should save him. Save him she did. Sugar and ink would "take" on anything, and it shone like a "patent leather" boot. Further, Constance developed a "hand" for lettering which outdid Mr. Povey's. Between them they manufactured tickets by the dozen and by the score—tickets which, while possessing nearly all the smart-ness and finish of Mr. Chawner's tickets, were much superior to these in originality and strikingness. Constance and Mr. Povey were delighted and fascinated by them. As for Mrs. Baines, she said little, but the modern spirit was too elated by its success to care whether she said little or much. And every few days Mr. Povey thought of some new and wonderful word to put on a ticket.

His last miracle was the word "exquisite." "Exquisite," pinned on a piece of broad tartan ribbon, appeared to Con-stance and Mr. Povey as the finality of appropriateness. A climax worthy to close the year! Mr. Povey had cut the card and sketched the word and figures in pencil, and Constanc was doing her executive portion of the undertaking. The were very happy, very absorbed, in this strictly busine matter. The clock showed five minutes past ten. Stern duty, pure desire for the prosperity of the shop, had kept them a hard labour since before eight o'clock that morning!

The stairs-door opened, and Mrs. Baines appeared, in bonne and furs and gloves, all clad for going out. She had abandone the cocoon of crape, but still wore weeds. She was stouter tha ever.

"What!" she cried. "Not ready! Now really!"

"Oh, mother! How you made me jump!" Constance pro tested. "What time is it? It surely isn't time to go yet!"

"Look at the clock!" said Mrs. Baines, drily.

"Well, I never!" Constance murmured, confused.

"Come, put your things together, and don't keep me wait ing," said Mrs. Baines, going past the table to the window and lifting the blind to peep out. "Still snowing," she ob served. "Oh, the band's going away at last! I wonder how the can play at all in this weather. By the way, what was tha tune they gave us just now? I couldn't make out whether i was 'Redhead,' or—"

"Band?" questioned Constance—the simpleton!

Neither she nor Mr. Povey had heard the strains of th Bursley Town Silver Prize Band which had been enlivening th season according to its usual custom. These two practica duteous, commonsense young and youngish persons had bee so absorbed in their efforts for the welfare of the shop tha they had positively not only forgotten the time, but had als failed to notice the band! But if Constance had had her wit about her she would at least have pretended that she ha heard it.

"What's this?" asked Mrs. Baines, bringing her vast forn to the table and picking up a ticket.

Mr. Povey said nothing. Constance said: "Mr. Pove thought of it to-day. Don't you think it's very good, mother?"

"I'm afraid I don't," Mrs. Baines coldly replied.

She had mildly objected already to certain words; but "ex quisite" seemed to her silly; it seemed out of place; she con sidered that it would merely bring ridicule on her shop "Exquisite" written upon a window-ticket! No! What woul John Baines have thought of "exquisite"?

" 'Exquisite!' " She repeated the word with a sarcastic inflection, putting the accent, as every one put it, on the second syllable. "I don't think that will quite do."

"But why not, mother?"

"It's not suitable, my dear."

She dropped the ticket from her gloved hand. Mr. Povey had darkly flashed. Though he spoke little, he was as sensitive as he was obstinate. On this occasion he said nothing. He expressed his feelings by seizing the ticket and throwing it into the fire.

The situation was extremely delicate. Priceless employés like Mr. Povey cannot be treated as machines, and Mrs. Baines of course instantly saw that tact was needed.

"Go along to my bedroom and get ready, my pet," said she to Constance. "Sophia is there. There's a good fire. I must just speak to Maggie." She tactfully left the room.

Mr. Povey glanced at the fire and the curling red remains of the ticket. Trade was bad; owing to weather and war, restitution was abroad; and he had been doing his utmost for the welfare of the shop; and here was the reward!

Constance's eyes were full of tears. "Never mind!" she murmured, and went upstairs.

It was all over in a moment.

ii

In the Wesleyan Methodist Chapel on Duck Bank there was a full and influential congregation. For in those days influential people were not merely content to live in the town where their fathers had lived, without dreaming of country residences and smokeless air—they were content also to believe what their fathers had believed about the beginning and the end of all. There was no such thing as the unknowable in those days. The eternal mysteries were as simple as an addition sum; a child could tell you with absolute certainty where you would be and what you would be doing a million years hence, and exactly what God thought of you. Accordingly, every one being of the same mind, every one met on certain occasions in certain places in order to express the universal mind. And in the Wesleyan Methodist Chapel, for example, instead of a sparse handful of persons disturbingly conscious of being in a minority, as

now, a magnificent and proud majority had collected, deeply
aware of its rightness and its correctness.

And the minister, backed by minor ministers, knelt and
covered his face in the superb mahogany rostrum; and behind
him, in what was then still called the "orchestra" (though no
musical instruments except the grand organ had sounded in
it for decades), the choir knelt and covered their faces; and
all around, in the richly painted gallery and on the ground
floor, multitudinous rows of people, in easy circumstances of
body and soul, knelt in high pews and covered their faces.
And there floated before them, in the intense and prolonged
silence, the clear vision of Jehovah on a throne, a God of
sixty or so with a moustache and a beard, and a non-committal
expression which declined to say whether or not he would
require more bloodshed; and this God, destitute of pinions, was
surrounded by white-winged creatures that wafted themselves
to and fro while chanting; and afar off was an obscene
monstrosity, with cloven hoofs and a tail, very dangerous and
rude and interfering, who could exist comfortably in the
middle of a coal-fire, and who took a malignant and exhaustless
pleasure in coaxing you by false pretences into the same fire,
but of course you had too much sense to swallow his wicked
absurdities. Once a year, for ten minutes by the clock, you
knelt thus, in mass, and by meditation convinced yourself that
you had too much sense to swallow his wicked absurdities. And
the hour was very solemn, the most solemn of all the hours.

Strange that immortal souls should be found with the
temerity to reflect upon mundane affairs in that hour! Yet
there were undoubtedly such in the congregation; there were
perhaps many to whom the vision, if clear, was spasmodic and
fleeting. And among them the inhabitants of the Baines family
pew! Who would have supposed that Mr. Povey, a recent
convert from Primitive Methodism in King Street to Wesleyan
Methodism on Duck Bank, was dwelling upon window-tickets
and the injustice of women, instead of upon his relations with
Jehovah and the tailed one? Who would have supposed that
the gentle-eyed Constance, pattern of daughters, was risking
her eternal welfare by smiling at the tailed one, who, concealing
his tail, had assumed the image of Mr. Povey? Who would have
supposed that Mrs. Baines, instead of resolving that Jehovah
and not the tailed one should have ultimate rule over her, was
resolving that she and not Mr. Povey should have ultimate

rule over her house and shop? It was a pew-ful that belied
its highly satisfactory appearance. (And possibly there were
other pew-fuls equally deceptive.)

Sophia alone, in the corner next to the wall, with her beautiful stern face pressed convulsively against her hands, was truly
busy with immortal things. Turbulent heart, the violence of
her spiritual life had made her older! Never was a passionate,
proud girl in a harder case than Sophia! In the splendour
of her remorse for a fatal forgetfulness, she had renounced
that which she loved and thrown herself into that which she
loathed. It was her nature so to do. She had done it haughtily,
and not with kindness, but she had done it with the whole force
of her will. Constance had been compelled to yield up to her
the millinery department, for Sophia's fingers had a gift of
manipulating ribbons and feathers that was beyond Constance.
Sophia had accomplished miracles in the millinery. Yes, and
she would be utterly polite to customers; but afterwards, when
the customers were gone, let mothers, sisters, and Mr. Poveys
beware of her fiery darts!

But why, when nearly three months had elapsed after her
father's death, had she spent more and more time in the shop,
secretly aflame with expectancy? Why, when one day a strange
traveller entered the shop and announced himself the new
representative of Birkinshaws—why had her very soul died
away within her and an awful sickness seized her? She knew
then that she had been her own deceiver. She recognized and
admitted, abasing herself lower than the lowest, that her motive
in leaving Miss Chetwynd's and joining the shop had been, at
the best, very mixed, very impure. Engaged at Miss Chetwynd's, she might easily have never set eyes on Gerald Scales
again. Employed in the shop, she could not fail to meet him.
In this light was to be seen the true complexion of the
splendour of her remorse. A terrible thought for her! And she
could not dismiss it. It contaminated her existence, this
thought! And she could confide in no one. She was incapable
of showing a wound. Quarter had succeeded quarter, and
Gerald Scales was no more heard of. She had sacrificed her
life for worse than nothing. She had made her own tragedy.
She had killed her father, cheated and shamed herself with a
remorse horribly spurious, exchanged content for misery and
pride for humiliation—and with it all, Gerald Scales had
vanished! She was ruined.

She took to religion, and her conscientious Christian virtues
practised with stern inclemency, were the canker of the family.
Thus a year and a half had passed.

And then, on this last day of the year, the second year of
her shame and of her heart's widowhood, Mr. Scales had reappeared. She had gone casually into the shop and found him
talking to her mother and Mr. Povey. He had come back to
the provincial round and to her. She shook his hand and fled
because she could not have stayed. None had noticed her agitation, for she had held her body as in a vice. She knew the
reason neither of his absence nor of his return. She knew
nothing. And not a word had been said at meals. And the
day had gone and the night come; and now she was in chapel
with Constance by her side and Gerald Scales in her soul.
Happy beyond previous conception of happiness! Wretched
beyond an unutterable woe! And none knew! What was she to
pray for? To what purpose and end ought she to steel herself?
Ought she to hope, or ought she to despair? "O God, help
me!" she kept whispering to Jehovah whenever the heavenly
vision shone through the wrack of her meditation. "O God
help me!" She had a conscience that, when it was in the mood
for severity, could be unspeakably cruel to her.

And whenever she looked, with dry, hot eyes, through her
gloved fingers, she saw in front of her on the wall a marble
tablet inscribed in gilt letters, the cenotaph! She knew all the
lines by heart, in their spacious grandiloquence; lines such
as:

EVER READY WITH HIS TONGUE HIS PEN AND HIS PURSE
TO HELP THE CHURCH OF HIS FATHERS
IN HER HE LIVED AND IN HER HE DIED
CHERISHING A DEEP AND ARDENT AFFECTION
FOR HIS BELOVED FAITH AND CREED.

And again:

HIS SYMPATHIES EXTENDED BEYOND HIS OWN COMMUNITY
HE WAS ALWAYS TO THE FORE IN GOOD WORKS
AND HE SERVED THE CIRCUIT THE TOWN AND THE DISTRICT
WITH GREAT ACCEPTANCE AND USEFULNESS.

Thus had Mr. Critchlow's vanity been duly appeased.
As the minutes sped in the breathing silence of the chapel

the emotional tension grew tighter; worshippers sighed heavily, or called upon Jehovah for a sign, or merely coughed an invocation. And then at last the clock in the middle of the balcony gave forth the single stroke to which it was limited; the ministers rose, and the congregation after them; and everybody smiled as though it was the millennium, and not simply the new year, that had set in. Then, faintly, through walls and shut windows, came the sound of bells and of steam syrens and whistles. The superintendent minister opened his hymn-book, and the hymn was sung which had been sung in Wesleyan Chapels on New Year's morn since the era of John Wesley himself. The organ finished with a clangour of all its pipes; the minister had a few last words with Jehovah, and nothing was left to do except to persevere in well-doing. The people leaned towards each other across the high backs of the pews.

"A happy New Year!"

"Eh, thank ye! The same to you!"

"Another Watch Night service over!"

"Eh, yes!" And a sigh.

Then the aisles were suddenly crowded, and there was a good-humoured, optimistic pushing towards the door. In the Corinthian porch occurred a great putting-on of cloaks, ulsters, goloshes, and even pattens, and a great putting-up of umbrellas. And the congregation went out into the whirling snow, dividing into several black, silent-footed processions, down Trafalgar Road, up towards the playground, along the market-place, and across Duck Square in the direction of St. Luke's Square.

Mr. Povey was between Mrs. Baines and Constance.

"You must take my arm, my pet," said Mrs. Baines to Sophia.

Then Mr. Povey and Constance waded on in front through the drifts. Sophia balanced that enormous swaying mass, her mother. Owing to their hoops, she had much difficulty in keeping close to her. Mrs. Baines laughed with the complacent ease of obesity, yet a fall would have been almost irremediable for her; and so Sophia had to laugh too. But, though she laughed, God had not helped her. She did not know where she was going, nor what might happen to her next.

"Why, bless us!" exclaimed Mrs. Baines, as they turned the corner into King Street. "There's some one sitting on our doorstep!"

There was: a figure swathed in an ulster, a maud over the ulster, and a high hat on the top of all. It could not have been there very long, because it was only speckled with snow. Mr. Povey plunged forward.

"It's Mr. Scales, of all people!" said Mr. Povey.

"Mr. Scales!" cried Mrs. Baines.

And, "Mr. Scales!" murmured Sophia, terribly afraid.

Perhaps she was afraid of miracles. Mr. Scales sitting on her mother's doorstep in the middle of the snowy night had assuredly the air of a miracle, of something dreamed in a dream, of something pathetically and impossibly appropriate —"pat," as they say in the Five Towns. But he was a tangible fact there. And years afterwards, in the light of further knowledge of Mr. Scales, Sophia came to regard his being on the doorstep as the most natural and characteristic thing in the world. Real miracles never seem to be miracles, and that which at the first blush resembles one usually proves to be an instance of the extremely prosaic.

iii

"Is that you, Mrs. Baines?" asked Gerald Scales, in a half-witted voice, looking up, and then getting to his feet. "Is this your house? So it is! Well, I'd no idea I was sitting on your doorstep."

He smiled timidly, nay, sheepishly, while the women and Mr. Povey surrounded him with their astonished faces under the light of the gas-lamp. Certainly he was very pale.

"But whatever is the matter, Mr. Scales?" Mrs. Baines demanded in an anxious tone. "Are you ill? Have you been suddenly—"

"Oh, no," said the young man lightly. "It's nothing. Only I was set on just now, down there,"—he pointed to the depths of King Street.

"Set on!" Mrs. Baines repeated, alarmed.

"That makes the fourth case in a week, that we *know* of!" said Mr. Povey. "It really is becoming a scandal."

The fact was that, owing to depression of trade, lack of employment, and rigorous weather, public security in the Five Towns was at that period not as perfect as it ought to have been. In the stress of hunger the lower classes were forgetting their manners—and this in spite of the altruistic and noble efforts of their social superiors to relieve the destitution due, of course, to short-sighted improvidence. When (the social superiors were asking in despair) will the lower classes learn to put by for a rainy day? (They might have said a snowy and a frosty day.) It was "really too bad" of the lower classes, when everything that could be done was being done for them, to kill, or even attempt to kill, the goose that lays the golden eggs! And especially in a respectable town! What, indeed, were things coming to? Well, here was Mr. Gerald Scales, gentleman from Manchester, a witness and victim to the deplorable moral condition of the Five Towns. What would he think of the Five Towns? The evil and the danger had been a topic of discussion in the shop for a week past, and now it was brought home to them.

"I hope you weren't—" said Mrs. Baines, apologetically and sympathetically.

"Oh no!" Mr. Scales interrupted her quite gaily. "I managed to beat them off. Only my elbow——"

Meanwhile it was continuing to snow.

"Do come in!" said Mrs. Baines.

"I couldn't think of troubling you," said Mr. Scales. "I'm all right now, and I can find my way to the Tiger."

"You must come in, if it's only for a minute," said Mrs. Baines, with decision. She had to think of the honour of the town.

"You're very kind," said Mr. Scales.

The door was suddenly opened from within, and Maggie surveyed them from the height of the two steps.

"A happy New Year, mum, to all of you."

"Thank you, Maggie," said Mrs. Baines, and primly added: "The same to you!" And in her own mind she said that Maggie could best prove her desire for a happy new year by contriving in future not to "scamp her corners," and not to break so much crockery.

Sophia, scarce knowing what she did, mounted the steps.

"Mr. Scales ought to let our New Year in, my pet," Mrs. Baines stopped her.

"Oh, of course, mother!" Sophia concurred with a gasp, springing back nervously.

Mr. Scales raised his hat, and duly let the new year, and much snow, into the Baines parlour. And there was a vast deal of stamping of feet, agitating of umbrellas, and shaking of cloaks and ulsters on the doormat in the corner by the harmonium. And Maggie took away an armful of everything snowy, including goloshes, and received instructions to boil milk and to bring "mince." Mr. Povey said "B-r-r-r!" and shut the door (which was bordered with felt to stop ventilation) ; Mrs. Baines turned up the gas till it sang, and told Sophia to poke the fire, and actually told Constance to light the second gas.

Excitement prevailed.

The placidity of existence had been agreeably disturbed (yes, agreeably, in spite of horror at the attack on Mr. Scales's elbow) by an adventure. Moreover, Mr. Scales proved to be in evening-dress. And nobody had ever worn evening-dress in that house before.

Sophia's blood was in her face, and it remained there, enhancing the vivid richness of her beauty. She was dizzy with a strange and disconcerting intoxication. She seemed to be in a world of unrealities and incredibilities. Her ears heard with indistinctness, and the edges of things and people had a prismatic colouring. She was in a state of ecstatic, unreasonable, inexplicable happiness. All her misery, doubts, despair, rancour, churlishness, had disappeared. She was as softly gentle as Constance. Her eyes were the eyes of a fawn, and her gestures delicious in their modest and sensitive grace. Constance was sitting on the sofa, and, after glancing about as if for shelter, she sat down on the sofa by Constance's side. She tried not to stare at Mr. Scales, but her gaze would not leave him. She was sure that he was the most perfect man in the world. A shortish man, perhaps, but a perfect. That such perfection could be was almost past her belief. He excelled all her dreams of the ideal man. His smile, his voice, his hand, his hair—never were such! Why, when he spoke—it was positively music! When he smiled—it was heaven! His smile, to Sophia, was one of those natural phenomena which are so lovely that they make you want to shed tears. There is no hyperbole in this description of Sophia's sensations, but rather an understatement of them. She was utterly obsessed by the unique qualities of Mr. Scales. Nothing would have persuaded her that the peer of Mr. Scales existed among men, or could possibly exist. And it was her intense and profound conviction of his complete pre-eminence that gave him, as he sat there ı the rocking-chair in her mother's parlour, that air of the nreal and the incredible.

"I stayed in the town on purpose to go to a New Year's arty at Mr. Lawton's," Mr. Scales was saying.

"Ah! So you know Lawyer Lawton!" observed Mrs. Baines, npressed, for Lawyer Lawton did not consort with trades-eople. He was jolly with them, and he did their legal business or them, but he was not of them. His friends came from afar.

"My people are old acquaintances of his," said Mr. Scales, ipping the milk which Maggie had brought.

"Now, Mr. Scales, you must taste my mince. A happy month or every tart you eat, you know," Mrs. Baines reminded him.

He bowed. "And it was as I was coming away from there hat I got into difficulties." He laughed.

Then he recounted the struggle, which had, however, been rief, as the assailants lacked pluck. He had slipped and fallen n his elbow on the kerb, and his elbow might have been roken, had not the snow been so thick. No, it did not hurt im now; doubtless a mere bruise. It was fortunate that the niscreants had not got the better of him, for he had in his ocket-book a considerable sum of money in notes—accounts aid! He had often thought what an excellent thing it would e if commercials could travel with dogs, particularly in winter. There was nothing like a dog.

"You are fond of dogs?" asked Mr. Povey, who had always ad a secret but impracticable ambition to keep a dog.

"Yes," said Mr. Scales, turning now to Mr. Povey.

"Keep one?" asked Mr. Povey, in a sporting tone.

"I have a fox-terrier bitch," said Mr. Scales, "that took ι first at Knutsford; but she's getting old now."

The sexual epithet fell queerly on the room. Mr. Povey, eing a man of the world, behaved as if nothing had happened; ut Mrs. Baines's curls protested against this unnecessary oarseness. Constance pretended not to hear. Sophia did not inderstandingly hear. Mr. Scales had no suspicion that he vas transgressing a convention by virtue of which dogs have 10 sex. Further, he had no suspicion of the local fame of Mrs. Baines's mince-tarts. He had already eaten more mince-tarts than he could enjoy, before beginning upon hers, and Mrs. Baines missed the enthusiasm to which she was habituated from consumers of her pastry.

Mr. Povey, fascinated, proceeded in the direction of dogs,

and it grew more and more evident that Mr. Scales, who went out to parties in evening dress, instead of going in respectable broad-cloth to watch-night services, who knew the great ones of the land, and who kept dogs of an inconvenient sex, was neither an ordinary commercial traveller nor the kind of man to which the Square was accustomed. He came from a different world. He was jolly with them, and he did their level best

"Lawyer Lawton's party broke up early—at least I mean considering—" Mrs. Baines hesitated.

After a pause Mr. Scales replied, "Yes, I left immediately the clock struck twelve. I've a heavy day to-morrow—I mean to-day."

It was not an hour for a prolonged visit, and in a few minutes Mr. Scales was ready again to depart. He admitted a certain feebleness ("wankiness," he playfully called it, being proud of his skill in the dialect), and a burning in his elbow; but otherwise he was quite well—thanks to Mrs. Baines's most kind hospitality . . . He really didn't know how he came to be sitting on her doorstep. Mrs. Baines urged him, if he met a policeman on his road to the Tiger, to furnish all particulars about the attempted highway robbery, and he said he decidedly would.

He took his leave with distinguished courtliness.

"If I have a moment I shall run in to-morrow morning just to let you know I'm all right," said he, in the white street.

"Oh, do!" said Constance. Constance's perfect innocence made her strangely forward at times.

"A happy New Year and many of them!"

"Thanks! Same to you! Don't get lost."

"Straight up the Square and first on the right," called the commonsense of Mr. Povey.

Nothing else remained to say, and the visitor disappeared silently in the whirling snow. "Brrr!" murmured Mr. Povey, shutting the door. Everybody felt: "What a funny ending of the old year!"

"Sophia, my pet," Mrs. Baines began.

But Sophia had vanished to bed.

"Tell her about her new night-dress," said Mrs. Baines to Constance.

"Yes, mother."

"I don't know that I'm so set up with that young man, after all," Mrs. Baines reflected aloud.

"Oh, mother!" Constance protested. "I think he's just lovely."

"He never looks you straight in the face," said Mrs. Baines.

"Don't tell *me!*" laughed Constance, kissing her mother good night. "You're only on your high horse because he didn't praise your mince. *I* noticed it."

iv

"If anybody thinks I'm going to stand the cold in this show-room any longer, they're mistaken," said Sophia the next morning loudly, and in her mother's hearing. And she went down into the shop carrying bonnets.

She pretended to be angry, but she was not. She felt, on the contrary, extremely joyous, and charitable to all the world. Usually she would take pains to keep out of the shop; usually she was preoccupied and stern. Hence her presence on the ground-floor, and her demeanour, excited interest among the three young lady assistants who sat sewing round the stove in the middle of the shop, sheltered by the great pile of shirtings and linseys that fronted the entrance.

Sophia shared Constance's corner. They had hot bricks under their feet, and fine-knitted wraps on their shoulders. They would have been more comfortable near the stove, but greatness has its penalties. The weather was exceptionally severe. The windows were thickly frosted over, so that Mr. Povey's art in dressing them was quite wasted. And—rare phenomenon!—the doors of the shop were shut. In the ordinary way they were not merely open, but hidden by a display of "cheap lines." Mr. Povey, after consulting Mrs. Baines, had decided to close them, foregoing the customary display. Mr. Povey had also, in order to get a little warmth into his limbs, personally assisted two casual labourers to scrape the thick frozen snow off the pavement; and he wore his kid mittens. All these things together proved better than the evidence of barometers how the weather nipped.

Mr. Scales came about ten o'clock. Instead of going to Mr. Povey's counter, he walked boldly to Constance's corner, and looked over the boxes, smiling and saluting. Both the girls candidly delighted in his visit. Both blushed; both laughed—without knowing why they laughed. Mr. Scales said he was just departing and had slipped in for a moment to thank a of them for their kindness of last night—"or rather this morn ing." The girls laughed again at this witticism. Nothing coul have been more simple than his speech. Yet it appeared t them magically attractive. A customer entered, a lady; one o the assistants rose from the neighbourhood of the stove, bu the daughters of the house ignored the customer; it was par of the etiquette of the shop that customers, at any rate chanc customers, should not exist for the daughters of the house until an assistant had formally drawn attention to them. Other wise every one who wanted a pennyworth of tape would b expecting to be served by Miss Baines, or Miss Sophia, if Mis Sophia were there. Which would have been ridiculous.

Sophia, glancing sidelong, saw the assistant parleying witl the customer; and then the assistant came softly behind th counter and approached the corner.

"Miss Constance, can you spare a minute?" the assistan whispered discreetly.

Constance extinguished her smile for Mr. Scales, and, turn ing away, lighted an entirely different and inferior smile fo the customer.

"Good morning, Miss Baines. Very cold, isn't it?"

"Good morning, Mrs. Chatterley. Yes, it is. I suppose you're getting anxious about those—" Constance stopped.

Sophia was now alone with Mr. Scales, for in order to discuss the unnameable freely with Mrs. Chatterley her sister was edging up the counter. Sophia had dreamed of a private con versation as something delicious and impossible. But chance had favoured her. She was alone with him. And his neat fair hair and his blue eyes and his delicate mouth were as wonder ful to her as ever. He was gentlemanly to a degree that im pressed her more than anything had impressed her in her life. And all the proud and aristocratic instinct that was at the base of her character sprang up and seized on his gentleman liness like a famished animal seizing on food.

"The last time I saw you," said Mr. Scales, in a new tone, "you said you were never in the shop."

"What? Yesterday? Did I?"

"No, I mean the last time I saw you alone," said he.

"Oh!" she exclaimed. "It's just an accident."

"That's exactly what you said last time."

"Is it?"

Was it his manner, or what he said, that flattered her, that intensified her beautiful vivacity?

"I suppose you don't often go out?" he went on.

"What? In this weather?"

"Any time."

"I go to chapel," said she, "and marketing with mother." There was a little pause. "And to the Free Library."

"Oh yes. You've got a Free Library here now, haven't you?"

"Yes. We've had it over a year."

"And you belong to it? What do you read?"

"Oh, stories, you know. I get a fresh book out once a week."

"Saturdays, I suppose?"

"No," she said. "Wednesdays." And she smiled. "Usually."

"It's Wednesday to-day," said he. "Not been already?"

She shook her head. "I don't think I shall go to-day. It's too cold. I don't *think* I shall venture out to-day."

"You must be very fond of reading," said he.

Then Mr. Povey appeared, rubbing his mittened hands. And Mrs. Chatterley went.

"I'll run and fetch mother," said Constance.

Mrs. Baines was very polite to the young man. He related his interview with the police, whose opinion was that he had been attacked by stray members of a gang from Hanbridge. The young lady assistants, with ears cocked, gathered the nature of Mr. Scales's adventure, and were thrilled to the point of questioning Mr. Povey about it after Mr. Scales had gone. His farewell was marked by much handshaking, and finally Mr. Povey ran after him into the Square to mention something about dogs.

At half-past one, while Mrs. Baines was dozing after dinner, Sophia wrapped herself up, and with a book under her arm went forth into the world, through the shop. She returned in less than twenty minutes. But her mother had already awakened, and was hovering about the back of the shop. Mothers have supernatural gifts.

Sophia nonchalantly passed her and hurried into the parlour where she threw down her muff and a book and knelt before the fire to warm herself.

Mrs. Baines followed her. "Been to the Library?" questioned Mrs. Baines.

"Yes, mother. And it's simply perishing."

"I wonder at your going on a day like to-day. I thought you always went on Thursdays?"

"So I do. But I'd finished my book."

"What is this?" Mrs. Baines picked up the volume, which was covered with black oil-cloth.

She picked it up with a hostile air. For her attitude towards the Free Library was obscurely inimical. She never read anything herself except *The Sunday at Home*, and Constance never read anything except *The Sunday at Home*. There were scriptural commentaries, Dugdale's Gazetteer, Culpepper's Herbal, and works by Bunyan and Flavius Josephus in the drawing-room bookcase; also Uncle Tom's Cabin. And Mrs. Baines, in considering the welfare of her daughters, looked askance at the whole remainder of printed literature. If the Free Library had not formed part of the Famous Wedgwood Institution, which had been opened with immense *éclat* by the semi-divine Gladstone; if the first book had not been ceremoniously "taken out" of the Free Library by the Chief Bailiff in person—a grandfather of stainless renown—Mrs. Baines would probably have risked her authority in forbidding the Free Library.

"You needn't be afraid," said Sophia, laughing. "It's Miss Sewell's Experience of Life."

"A novel, I see," observed Mrs. Baines, dropping the book.

Gold and jewels would probably not tempt a Sophia of these days to read Experience of Life; but to Sophia Baines the bland story had the piquancy of the disapproved.

The next day Mrs. Baines summoned Sophia into her bed-room.

"Sophia," said she, trembling, "I shall be glad if you will not walk about the streets with young men until you have my permission."

The girl blushed violently. "I—I—"

"You were seen in Wedgwood Street," said Mrs. Baines.

"Who's been gossiping—Mr. Critchlow, I suppose?" Sophia exclaimed scornfully.

"No one has been 'gossiping,'" said Mrs. Baines.

"Well, if I meet some one by accident in the street I can't help it, can I?" Sophia's voice shook.

"You know what I mean, my child," said Mrs. Baines, with careful calm.

Sophia dashed angrily from the room.

"I like the idea of him having 'a heavy day'!" Mrs. Baines reflected ironically, recalling a phrase which had lodged in her mind. And very vaguely, with an uneasiness scarcely perceptible, she remembered that "he," and no other, had been in the shop on the day her husband died.

CHAPTER VI

Escapade

The uneasiness of Mrs. Baines flowed and ebbed, during the next three months, influenced by Sophia's moods. There were days when Sophia was the old Sophia—the forbidding, difficult, waspish, and even hedgehog Sophia. But there were other days on which Sophia seemed to be drawing joy and gaiety and goodwill from some secret source, from some fount whose nature and origin none could divine. It was on these days that the uneasiness of Mrs. Baines waxed. She had the wildest suspicions; she was almost capable of accusing Sophia of carrying on a clandestine correspondence; she saw Sophia and Gerald Scales deeply and wickedly in love; she saw them with their arms round each other's necks. . . . And then she called herself a middle-aged fool, to base such a structure of suspicion on a brief encounter in the street and on an idea, a fancy, a curious and irrational notion! Sophia had a certain streak of pure nobility in that exceedingly heterogeneous thing, her character. Moreover, Mrs. Baines watched the posts, and she also watched Sophia—she was not the woman to trust to a streak of pure nobility—and she came to be sure that Sophia's sinfulness, if any, was not such as could be weighed in a balance, or collected together by stealth and then suddenly placed before the girl on a charger.

Still, she would have given much to see inside Sophia's lovely head. Ah! Could she have done so, what sleep-destroying wonders she would have witnessed! By what bright lamps burning in what mysterious grottos and caverns of the brain would her mature eyes have been dazzled! Sophia was living for months on the exhaustless ardent vitality absorbed during a magical two minutes in Wedgwood Street. She was living chiefly on the flaming fire struck in her soul by the shock of seeing Gerald Scales in the porch of the Wedgwood Institution as she came out of the Free Library with Experience of Life tucked into her large astrakhan muff. He had stayed to meet her, then: she knew it! "After all," her heart said, "I must be very beautiful, for I have attracted the pearl of men!" And she remembered her face in the glass. The value and the power of beauty were tremendously proved to her. He, the great man of the world, the handsome and elegant man with a thousand strange friends and a thousand interests far remote from her, had remained in Bursley on the mere chance of meeting her! She was proud, but her pride was drowned in bliss. "I was just looking at this inscription about Mr. Gladstone." "So you decided to come out as usual!" "And may I ask what book you have chosen?" These were the phrases she heard, and to which she responded with similar phrases. And meanwhile a miracle of ecstasy had opened—opened like a flower. She was walking along Wedgwood Street by his side, slowly, on the scraped pavements, where marble bulbs of snow had defied the spade and remained. She and he were exactly of the same height, and she kept looking into his face and he into hers. This was all the miracle. Except that she was not walking on the pavement—she was walking on the intangible sward of paradise! Except that the houses had receded and faded, and the passers-by were subtilized into unnoticeable ghosts! Except that her mother and Constance had become phantasmal beings existing at an immense distance!

What had happened? Nothing! The most commonplace occurrence! The eternal cause had picked up a commercial traveller (it might have been a clerk or curate, but it in fact was a commercial traveller), and endowed him with all the glorious, unique, incredible attributes of a god, and planted him down before Sophia in order to produce the eternal effect. A miracle performed specially for Sophia's benefit! No one else in Wedgwood Street saw the god walking along by her side. No one else saw anything but a simple commercial traveller. Yes, the most commonplace occurrence!

Of course at the corner of the street he had to go. "Till next time!" he murmured. And fire came out of his eyes and lighted in Sophia's lovely head those lamps which Mrs. Baines was mercifully spared from seeing. And he had shaken hands

and raised his hat. Imagine a god raising his hat! And he
went off on two legs, precisely like a dashing little commercial
traveller.

And, escorted by the equivocal Angel of Eclipses, she had
turned into King Street, and arranged her face, and courageously met her mother. Her mother had not at first perceived
the unusual; for mothers, despite their reputation to the contrary, really are the blindest creatures. Sophia, the naïve
ninny, had actually supposed that her walking along a hundred yards of pavement with a god by her side was not going
to excite remark! What a delusion! It is true, certainly, that
no one saw the god by direct vision. But Sophia's cheeks,
Sophia's eyes, the curve of Sophia's neck as her soul yearned
towards the soul of the god—these phenomena were immeasurably more notable than Sophia guessed. An account of them,
in a modified form to respect Mrs. Baines's notorious dignity,
had healed the mother of her blindness and led to that characteristic protest from her, "I shall be glad if you will not
walk about the streets with young men," etc.

When the period came for the reappearance of Mr. Scales,
Mrs. Baines outlined a plan, and when the circular announcing
the exact time of his arrival was dropped into the letter-box,
she formulated the plan in detail. In the first place, she was
determined to be indisposed and invisible herself, so that Mr.
Scales might be foiled in any possible design to renew social
relations in the parlour. In the second place, she flattered Constance with a single hint—oh, the vaguest and briefest!—and
Constance understood that she was not to quit the shop on the
appointed morning. In the third place, she invented a way
of explaining to Mr. Povey that the approaching advent of
Gerald Scales must not be mentioned. And in the fourth place,
she deliberately made appointments for Sophia with two millinery customers in the showroom, so that Sophia might be
imprisoned in the showroom.

Having thus left nothing to chance, she told herself that
she was a foolish woman full of nonsense. But this did not
prevent her from putting her lips together firmly and resolving
that Mr. Scales should have no finger in the pie of *her* family.
She had acquired information concerning Mr. Scales, at
second-hand, from Lawyer Pratt. More than this, she posed the
question in a broader form—why should a young girl be permitted any interest in any young man whatsoever? The ever-

lasting purpose had made use of Mrs. Baines and cast her off, and, like most persons in a similar situation, she was, unconsciously and quite honestly, at odds with the everlasting purpose.

ii

On the day of Mr. Scales's visit to the shop to obtain orders and money on behalf of Birkinshaws, a singular success seemed to attend the machinations of Mrs. Baines. With Mr. Scales punctuality was not an inveterate habit, and he had rarely been known, in the past, to fulfil exactly the prophecy of the letter of advice concerning his arrival. But that morning his promptitude was unexampled. He entered the shop, and by chance Mr. Povey was arranging unshrinkable flannels in the doorway. The two youngish little men talked amiably about flannels, dogs, and quarter-day (which was just past), and then Mr. Povey led Mr. Scales to his desk in the dark corner behind the high pile of twills, and paid the quarterly bill, in notes and gold—as always; and then Mr. Scales offered for the august inspection of Mr. Povey all that Manchester had recently invented for the temptation of drapers, and Mr. Povey gave him an order which, if not reckless, was nearer "handsome" than "good." During the process Mr. Scales had to go out of the shop twice or three times in order to bring in from his barrow at the kerbstone certain small black boxes edged with brass. On none of these excursions did Mr. Scales glance wantonly about him in satisfaction of the lust of the eye. Even if he had permitted himself this freedom he would have seen nothing more interesting than three young lady assistants seated round the stove and sewing with pricked fingers from which the chilblains were at last deciding to depart. When Mr. Scales had finished writing down the details of the order with his ivory-handled stylo, and repacked his boxes, he drew the interview to a conclusion after the manner of a capable commercial traveller; that is to say, he implanted in Mr. Povey his opinion that Mr. Povey was a wise, a shrewd and an upright man, and that the world would be all the better for a few more like him. He inquired for Mrs. Baines, and was deeply pained to hear of her indisposition while finding consolation in the assurance that the Misses Baines were well. Mr. Povey was on the point of accompanying the pattern of commercial

travellers to the door, when two customers simultaneously came
in—ladies. One made straight for Mr. Povey, whereupon
Mr. Scales parted from him at once, it being a universal
maxim in shops that even the most distinguished commercial
shall not hinder the business of even the least distinguished
customer. The other customer had the effect of causing Constance to pop up from her cloistral corner. Constance had been
there all the time, but of course, though she heard the remembered voice, her maidenliness had not permitted that she should
show herself to Mr. Scales.

Now, as he was leaving, Mr. Scales saw her, with her agreeable snub nose and her kind, simple eyes. She was requesting
the second customer to mount to the showroom, where was Miss
Sophia. Mr. Scales hesitated a moment, and in that moment
Constance, catching his eye, smiled upon him, and nodded.
What else could she do? Vaguely aware though she was that
her mother was not "set up" with Mr. Scales, and even feared
the possible influence of the young man on Sophia, she could
not exclude him from her general benevolence towards the universe. Moreover, she liked him; she liked him very much and
thought him a very fine specimen of a man.

He left the door and went across to her. They shook hands
and opened a conversation instantly; for Constance, while retaining all her modesty, had lost all her shyness in the shop,
and could chatter with anybody. She sidled towards her corner, precisely as Sophia had done on another occasion, and Mr.
Scales put his chin over the screening boxes, and eagerly prose-
cuted the conversation.

There was absolutely nothing in the fact of the interview
itself to cause alarm to a mother, nothing to render futile the
precautions of Mrs. Baines on behalf of the flower of Sophia's
innocence. And yet it held danger for Mrs. Baines, all unconscious in her parlour. Mrs. Baines could rely utterly on
Constance not to be led away by the dandiacal charms of Mr.
Scales (she knew in what quarter sat the wind for Constance);
in her plan she had forgotten nothing, except Mr. Povey; and
it must be said that she could not possibly have foreseen the
effect on the situation of Mr. Povey's character.

Mr. Povey, attending to his customer, had noticed the
bright smile of Constance on the traveller, and his heart did
not like it. And when he saw the lively gestures of a Mr. Scales
in apparently intimate talk with a Constance hidden behind

boxes, his uneasiness grew into fury. He was a man capable of black and terrible furies. Outwardly insignificant, possessing a mind as little as his body, easily abashed, he was none the less a very susceptible young man, soon offended, proud, vain, and obscurely passionate. You might offend Mr. Povey without guessing it, and only discover your sin when Mr. Povey had done something too decisive as a result of it.

The reason of his fury was jealousy. Mr. Povey had made great advances since the death of John Baines. He had consolidated his position, and he was in every way a personage of the first importance. His misfortune was that he could never translate his importance, or his sense of his importance, into terms of outward demeanour. Most people, had they been told that Mr. Povey was seriously aspiring to enter the Baines family, would have laughed. But they would have been wrong. To laugh at Mr. Povey was invariably wrong. Only Constance knew what inroads he had effected upon her.

The customer went, but Mr. Scales did not go. Mr. Povey, free to reconnoitre, did so. From the shadow of the till he could catch glimpses of Constance's blushing, vivacious face. She was obviously absorbed in Mr. Scales. She and he had a tremendous air of intimacy. And the murmur of their chatter continued. Their chatter was nothing, and about nothing, but Mr. Povey imagined that they were exchanging eternal vows. He endured Mr. Scales's odious freedom until it became insufferable, until it deprived him of all his self-control; and then he retired into his cutting-out room. He meditated there in a condition of insanity for perhaps a minute, and excogitated a device. Dashing back into the shop, he spoke up, half across the shop, in a loud, curt tone:

"Miss Baines, your mother wants you at once."

He was launched on the phrase before he noticed that, during his absence, Sophia had descended from the showroom and joined her sister and Mr. Scales. The danger and scandal were now less, he perceived, but he was glad he had summoned Constance away, and he was in a state to despise consequences.

The three chatterers, startled, looked at Mr. Povey, who left the shop abruptly. Constance could do nothing but obey the call.

She met him at the door of the cutting-out room in the passage leading to the parlour.

"Where is mother? In the parlour?" Constance inquired in-
.ocently.

There was a dark flush on Mr. Povey's face. "If you wish
o know," said he in a hard voice, "she hasn't asked for you
nd she doesn't want you."

He turned his back on her, and retreated into his lair.

"Then what——?" she began, puzzled.

He fronted her. "Haven't you been gabbling long enough
vith that jackanapes?" he spit at her. There were tears in his
yes.

Constance, though without experience in these matters, com-
)rehended. She comprehended perfectly and immediately. She
ught to have put Mr. Povey into his place. She ought to have
)rotested with firm, dignified finality against such a ridiculous
und monstrous outrage as that which Mr. Povey had com-
nitted. Mr. Povey ought to have been ruined for ever in her
steem and in her heart. But she hesitated.

"And only last Sunday——afternoon," Mr. Povey blubbered.

(Not that anything overt had occurred, or been articulately
,aid, between them last Sunday afternoon. But they had been
_lone together, and had each witnessed strange and disturbing
natters in the eyes of the other.)

Tears now fell suddenly from Constance's eyes. "You ought
:o be ashamed——" she stammered.

Still, the tears were in her eyes, and in his too. What he or
she merely said, therefore, was of secondary importance.

Mrs. Baines, coming from the kitchen, and hearing Con-
tance's voice, burst upon the scene, which silenced her.
Parents are sometimes silenced. She found Sophia and Mr.
Scales in the shop.

iii

That afternoon Sophia, too busy with her own affairs to
notice anything abnormal in the relations between her mother
and Constance, and quite ignorant that there had been an unsuccessful plot against her, went forth to call upon Miss
Chetwynd, with whom she had remained very friendly: she considered that she and Miss Chetwynd formed an aristocracy of
intellect, and the family indeed tacitly admitted this. She prac-

tised no secrecy in her departure from the shop; she merely
dressed, in her second-best hoop, and went, having been ready
at any moment to tell her mother, if her mother caught her
and inquired, that she was going to see Miss Chetwynd. And
she did go to see Miss Chetwynd, arriving at the house-school
which lay amid trees on the road to Turnhill, just beyond the
turnpike, at precisely a quarter-past four. As Miss Chetwynd's
pupils left at four o'clock, and as Miss Chetwynd invariably
took a walk immediately afterwards, Sophia was able to contain her surprise upon being informed that Miss Chetwynd
was not in. She had not intended that Miss Chetwynd should
be in.

She turned off to the right, up the side road which, starting
from the turnpike, led in the direction of Moorthorne and Red
Cow, two mining villages. Her heart beat with fear as she
began to follow that road, for she was upon a terrific adventure. What most frightened her, perhaps, was her own astounding audacity. She was alarmed by something within herself which seemed to be no part of herself and which produced
in her curious, disconcerting, fleeting impressions of unreality.

In the morning she had heard the voice of Mr. Scales from
the showroom—that voice whose even distant murmur caused
creepings of the skin in her back. And she had actually stood
on the counter in front of the window in order to see down
perpendicularly into the Square; by so doing she had had a
glimpse of the top of his luggage on a barrow, and of the
crown of his hat occasionally when he went outside to tempt
Mr. Povey. She might have gone down into the shop—there
was no slightest reason why she should not; three months
had elapsed since the name of Mr. Scales had been mentioned,
and her mother had evidently forgotten the trifling incident of
New Year's Day—but she was incapable of descending the
stairs! She went to the head of the stairs and peeped through
the balustrade—and she could not get further. For nearly a
hundred days those extraordinary lamps had been brightly
burning in her head; and now the light-giver had come again,
and her feet would not move to the meeting; now the moment
had arrived for which alone she had lived, and she could not
seize it as it passed! "Why don't I go downstairs?" she asked
herself. "Am I afraid to meet him?"

The customer sent up by Constance had occupied the surface of her life for ten minutes, trying on hats; and during this

ime she was praying wildly that Mr. Scales might not go, ind asserting that it was impossible he should go without at east asking for her. Had she not counted the days to this lay? When the customer left Sophia followed her downstairs, ind saw Mr. Scales chatting with Constance. All her self-possession instantly returned to her, and she joined them with i rather mocking smile. After Mr. Povey's strange summons iad withdrawn Constance from the corner, Mr. Scales's tone iad changed; it had thrilled her. "You are *you*," it had said, "there is you—and there is the rest of the universe!" Then he iad not forgotten; she had lived in his heart; she had not for hree months been the victim of her own fancies! . . . She saw iim put a piece of folded white paper on the top edge of the creening box and flick it down to her. She blushed scarlet, taring at it as it lay on the counter. He said nothing, and she ould not speak. . . . . He had prepared that paper, then,)eforehand, on the chance of being able to give it to her! This thought was exquisite but full of terror. "I must really go," ie had said, lamely, with emotion in his voice, and he had gone —like that! And she put the piece of paper into the pocket of ier apron, and hastened away. She had not even seen, as she turned up the stairs, her mother standing by the till—that pot which was the conning-tower of the whole shop. She ran, an, breathless to the bedroom. . . .

"I am a wicked girl!" she said quite frankly, on the road to the rendezvous. "It is a dream that I am going to meet him. It cannot be true. There is time to go back. If I go back I am safe. I have simply called at Miss Chetwynd's and she wasn't in, and no one can say a word. But if I go on—if I'm seen! What a fool I am to go on!"

And she went on, impelled by, amongst other things, an immense, naïve curiosity, and the vanity which the bare fact of his note had excited. The Loop railway was being constructed at that period, and hundreds of navvies were at work on it between Bursley and Turnhill. When she came to the new bridge over the cutting, he was there, as he had written that he would be.

They were very nervous, they greeted each other stiffly and as though they had met then for the first time that day. Nothing was said about his note, nor about her response to it. Her presence was treated by both of them as a basic fact of the situation which it would be well not to disturb by comment.

Sophia could not hide her shame, but her shame only aggra
vated the stinging charm of her beauty. She was wearing
hard Amazonian hat, with a lifted veil, the final word o
fashion that spring in the Five Towns; her face, beaten b
the fresh breeze, shone rosily; her eyes glittered under th
dark hat, and the violent colours of her Victorian frock—
green and crimson—could not spoil those cheeks. If she looke
earthwards, frowning, she was the more adorable so. He ha
come down the clayey incline from the unfinished red bridg
to welcome her, and when the salutations were over they stoo
still, he gazing apparently at the horizon and she at the yellow
marl round the edges of his boots. The encounter was as fa
away from Sophia's ideal conception as Manchester from
Venice.

"So this is the new railway!" said she.

"Yes," said he. "This is your new railway. You can see i
better from the bridge."

"But it's very sludgy up there," she objected with a pout

"Further on it's quite dry," he reassured her.

From the bridge they had a sudden view of a raw gash i
the earth; and hundreds of men were crawling about in it
busy with minute operations, like flies in a great wound. Ther
was a continuous rattle of picks, resembling a muffled showe
of hail, and in the distance a tiny locomotive was leading a
procession of tiny waggons.

"And those are the navvies!" she murmured.

The unspeakable doings of the navvies in the Five Town
had reached even her: how they drank and swore all day or
Sundays, how their huts and houses were dens of the most
appalling infamy, how they were the curse of a God-fearing
and respectable district! She and Gerald Scales glanced down
at these dangerous beasts of prey in their yellow corduroy
and their open shirts revealing hairy chests. No doubt the
both thought how inconvenient it was that railways could no
be brought into existence without the aid of such revolting and
swinish animals. They glanced down from the height of their
nice decorum and felt the powerful attraction of similar
superior manners. The manners of the navvies were such tha
Sophia could not even regard them, nor Gerald Scales permi
her to regard them, without blushing.

In a united blush they turned away, up the gradual slope.
Sophia knew no longer what she was doing. For some minutes

she was as helpless as though she had been in a balloon with him.

"I got my work done early," he said; and added complacently, "As a matter of fact I've had a pretty good day."

She was reassured to learn that he was not neglecting his duties. To be philandering with a commercial traveller who has finished a good day's work seemed less shocking than dalliance with a neglecter of business; it seemed indeed, by comparison, respectable.

"It must be very interesting," she said primly.

"What, my trade?"

"Yes. Always seeing new places and so on."

"In a way it is," he admitted judicially. "But I can tell you it was much more agreeable being in Paris."

"Oh! Have you been to Paris?"

"Lived there for nearly two years," he said carelessly. Then, looking at her, "Didn't you notice I never came for a long time?"

"I didn't know you were in Paris," she evaded him.

"I went to start a sort of agency for Birkinshaws," he said.

"I suppose you talk French like anything."

"Of course one has to talk French," said he. "I learnt French when I was a child from a governess—my uncle made me—but I forgot most of it at school, and at the Varsity you never learn anything—precious little, anyhow! Certainly not French!"

She was deeply impressed. He was a much greater personage than she had guessed. It had never occurred to her that commercial travellers had to go to a university to finish their complex education. And then, Paris! Paris meant absolutely nothing to her but pure, impossible, unattainable romance. And he had been there! The clouds of glory were around him. He was a hero, dazzling. He had come to her out of another world. He was her miracle. He was almost too miraculous to be true.

She, living her humdrum life at the shop! And he, elegant, brilliant, coming from far cities! They together, side by side, strolling up the road towards the Moorthorne ridge! There was nothing quite like this in the stories of Miss Sewell.

"Your uncle . . . . ?" she questioned vaguely.

"Yes, Mr. Boldero. He's a partner in Birkinshaws."

"Oh!"

"You've heard of him? He's a great Wesleyan."

"Oh yes," she said. "When we had the Wesleyan Conference here, he——"

"He's always very great at Conferences," said Gerald Scales.

"I didn't know he had anything to do with Birkinshaws."

"He isn't a working partner of course," Mr. Scales explained. "But he means me to be one. I have to learn the business from the bottom. So now you understand why I'm a traveller."

"I see," she said, still more deeply impressed.

"I'm an orphan," said Gerald. "And Uncle Boldero took me in hand when I was three."

"I *see!*" she repeated.

It seemed strange to her that Mr. Scales should be a Wesleyan—just like herself. She would have been sure that he was "Church." Her notions of Wesleyanism, with her notions of various other things, were sharply modified.

"Now tell me about you," Mr. Scales suggested.

"Oh! I'm nothing!" she burst out.

The exclamation was perfectly sincere. Mr. Scales's disclosures concerning himself, while they excited her, discouraged her.

"You're the finest girl I've ever met, anyhow," said Mr. Scales with gallant emphasis, and he dug his stick into the soft ground.

She blushed and made no answer.

They walked on in silence, each wondering apprehensively what might happen next.

Suddenly Mr. Scales stopped at a dilapidated low brick wall, built in a circle, close to the side of the road.

"I expect that's an old pit-shaft," said he.

"Yes, I expect it is."

He picked up a rather large stone and approached the wall.

"Be careful!" she enjoined him.

"Oh! It's all right," he said lightly. "Let's listen. Come near and listen."

She reluctantly obeyed, and he threw the stone over the dirty ruined wall, the top of which was about level with his hat. For two or three seconds there was no sound. Then a faint reverberation echoed from the depths of the shaft. And on Sophia's brain arose dreadful images of the ghosts of miners wandering for ever in subterranean passages, far, far beneath. The noise of the falling stone had awakened for her the secret terrors of the earth. She could scarcely even look at the wall without a spasm of fear.

"How strange," said Mr. Scales, a little awe in his voice, too, "that that should be left there like that! I suppose it's very deep."

"Some of them are," she trembled.

"I must just have a look," he said, and put his hands on the top of the wall.

"Come away!" she cried.

"Oh! It's all right!" he said again, soothingly. "The wall's as firm as a rock." And he took a slight spring and looked over.

She shrieked loudly. She saw him at the distant bottom of the shaft, mangled, drowning. The ground seemed to quake under her feet. A horrible sickness seized her. And she shrieked again. Never had she guessed that existence could be such pain.

He slid down from the wall, and turned to her. "No bottom to be seen!" he said. Then, observing her transformed face, he came close to her, with a superior masculine smile. "Silly little thing!" he said coaxingly, endearingly, putting forth all his power to charm.

He perceived at once that he had miscalculated the effects of his action. Her alarm changed swiftly to angry offence. She drew back with a haughty gesture, as if he had intended actually to touch her. Did he suppose, because she chanced to be walking with him, that he had the right to address her familiarly, to tease her, to call her "silly little thing" and to put his face against hers? She resented his freedom with quick and passionate indignation.

She showed him her proud back and nodding head and wrathful skirts; and hurried off without a word, almost running. As for him, he was so startled by unexpected phenomena that he did nothing for a moment—merely stood looking and feeling foolish.

Then she heard him in pursuit. She was too proud to stop or even to reduce her speed.

"I didn't mean to—" he muttered behind her.

No recognition from her.

"I suppose I ought to apologize," he said.

"I should just think you ought," she answered, furious.

"Well, I do!" said he. "Do stop a minute."

"I'll thank you not to follow me, Mr. Scales." She paused, and scorched him with her displeasure. Then she went forward. And her heart was in torture because it could not persuade her to remain with him, and smile and forgive, and win his smile.

"I shall write to you," he shouted down the slope.

She kept on, the ridiculous child. But the agony she had suffered as he clung to the frail wall was not ridiculous, nor her dark vision of the mine, nor her tremendous indignation when, after disobeying her, he forgot that she was a queen. To her the scene was sublimely tragic. Soon she had recrossed the bridge, but not the same she! So this was the end of the incredible adventure!

When she reached the turnpike she thought of her mother and of Constance. She had completely forgotten them; for a space they had utterly ceased to exist for her.

iv

"You've been out, Sophia?" said Mrs. Baines in the parlour, questioningly. Sophia had taken off her hat and mantle hurriedly in the cutting-out room, for she was in danger of being late for tea; but her hair and face showed traces of the March breeze. Mrs. Baines, whose stoutness seemed to increase, sat in the rocking-chair with a number of *The Sunday at Home* in her hand. Tea was set.

"Yes, mother. I called to see Miss Chetwynd."

"I wish you'd tell me when you are going out."

"I looked all over for you before I started."

"No, you didn't, for I haven't stirred from this room since four o'clock. . . . You should not say things like that," Mrs. Baines added in a gentler tone.

Mrs. Baines had suffered much that day. She knew that she was in an irritable, nervous state, and therefore she said to herself, in her quality of wise woman, "I must watch myself. I mustn't let myself go." And she thought how reasonable she was. She did not guess that all her gestures betrayed her; nor did it occur to her that few things are more galling than the spectacle of a person, actuated by lofty motives, obviously rying to be kind and patient under what he considers to be extreme provocation.

Maggie blundered up the kitchen stairs with the teapot and ot toast; and so Sophia had an excuse for silence. Sophia oo had suffered much, suffered excruciatingly; she carried at hat moment a whole tragedy in her young soul, unaccustomed o such burdens. Her attitude towards her mother was half earful and half defiant; it might be summed up in the phrase hich she had repeated again and again under her breath on he way home, "Well, mother can't kill me!"

Mrs. Baines put down the blue-covered magazine and twisted er rocking-chair towards the table.

"You can pour out the tea," said Mrs. Baines.

"Where's Constance?"

"She's not very well. She's lying down."

"Anything the matter with her?"

"No."

This was inaccurate. Nearly everything was the matter with onstance, who had never been less Constance than during that fternoon. But Mrs. Baines had no intention of discussing onstance's love-affairs with Sophia. The less said to Sophia bout love, the better! Sophia was excitable enough already!

They sat opposite to each other, on either side of the fire —the monumental matron whose black bodice heavily overung the table, whose large rounded face was creased and rinkled by what seemed countless years of joy and disillusion; nd the young slim girl, so fresh, so virginal, so ignorant, ith all the pathos of an unsuspecting victim about to be sacificed to the minotaur of Time! They both ate hot toast, ith careless haste, in silence, preoccupied, worried, and outardly nonchalant.

"And what has Miss Chetwynd got to say?" Mrs. Baines iquired.

Here was a blow for Mrs. Baines, whose suspicions about ophia, driven off by her certainties regarding Constance, iddenly sprang forward in her mind, and prowled to and fro ke a band of tigers.

Still, Mrs. Baines was determined to be calm and careful. Oh! What time did you call?"

"I don't know. About half-past four." Sophia finished her ea quickly, and rose. "Shall I tell Mr. Povey he can come?"

(Mr. Povey had his tea after the ladies of the house.)

"Yes, if you will stay in the shop till I come. Light m
the gas before you go."

Sophia took a wax taper from a vase on the mantelpiec
stuck it in the fire and lit the gas, which exploded in its crysta
cloister with a mild report.

"What's all that clay on your boots, child?" asked Mrs
Baines.

"Clay?" repeated Sophia, staring foolishly at her boots.

"Yes," said Mrs. Baines. "It looks like marl. Where o
earth have you been?"

She interrogated her daughter with an upward gaze, frigi
and unconsciously hostile, through her gild-rimmed glasses.

"I must have picked it up on the roads," said Sophia, an
hastened to the door.

"Sophia!"

"Yes, mother."

"Shut the door."

Sophia unwillingly shut the door which she had half opened

"Come here."

Sophia obeyed, with falling lip.

"You are deceiving me, Sophia," said Mrs. Baines, wit
fierce solemnity. "Where have you been this afternoon?"

Sophia's foot was restless on the carpet behind the table

"I haven't been anywhere," she murmured glumly.

"Have you seen young Scales?"

"Yes," said Sophia with grimness, glancing audaciously fo
an instant at her mother. ("She can't kill me: She can't kil
me," her heart muttered. And she had youth and beauty in he
favour, while her mother was only a fat middle-aged woman
"She can't kill me," said her heart, with the trembling, crue
insolence of the mirror-flattered child.)

"How came you to meet him?"

No answer.

"Sophia, you heard what I said!"

Still no answer. Sophia looked down at the table. ("Sh
can't kill me.")

"If you are going to be sullen, I shall have to suppose th
worst," said Mrs. Baines.

Sophia kept her silence.

"Of course," Mrs. Baines resumed, "if you choose to b
wicked, neither your mother nor any one else can stop you
There are certain things I *can* do, and these I *shall* do . .

,et me warn you that young Scales is a thoroughly bad lot.
 know all about him. He has been living a wild life abroad,
nd if it hadn't been that his uncle is a partner in Birkinshaws,
ley would never have taken him on again." A pause. "I hope
lat one day you will be a happy wife, but you are much too
oung yet to be meeting young men, and nothing would ever
iduce me to let you have anything to do with this Scales.
 won't have it. In future you are not to go out alone. You
nderstand me?"

Sophia kept silence.

"I hope you will be in a better frame of mind to-morrow.
 can only hope so. But if you aren't, I shall take very severe
leasures. You think you can defy me. But you never were
lore mistaken in your life. I don't want to see any more of
ou now. Go and tell Mr. Povey; and call Maggie for the
resh tea. You make me almost glad that your father died
ven as he did. He has, at any rate, been spared this."

Those words "died even as he did" achieved the intimida-
ion of Sophia. They seemed to indicate that Mrs. Baines,
lough she had magnanimously never mentioned the subject to
ophia, knew exactly how the old man had died. Sophia
scaped from the room in fear, cowed. Nevertheless, her
hought was, "She hasn't killed me. I made up my mind I
ouldn't talk, and I didn't."

In the evening, as she sat in the shop primly and sternly
ewing at hats —while her mother wept in secret on the first
oor, and Constance remained hidden on the second—Sophia
ved over again the scene at the old shaft; but she lived it
ifferently, admitting that she had been wrong, guessing by
istinct that she had shown a foolish mistrust of love. As she
at in the shop, she adopted just the right attitude and said
ust the right things. Instead of being a silly baby she was an
ccomplished and dazzling woman, then. When customers came
l, and the young lady assistants unobtrusively turned higher
he central gas, according to the *régime* of the shop, it was
eally extraordinary that they could not read in the heart of
he beautiful Miss Baines the words which blazed there:
You' the finest girl I ever met," and *"I shall write to you."*
'he young lady assistants had their notions as to both Con-
tance and Sophia, but the truth, at least as regarded Sophia,
'as beyond the flight of their imaginations. When eight o'clock
truck and she gave the formal order for dust-sheets, the shop

being empty, they never supposed that she was dreaming abou
posts and plotting how to get hold of the morning's letters be
fore Mr. Povey.

CHAPTER VII

A Defeat

It was during the month of June that Aunt Harriet came ove
from Axe to spend a few days with her little sister, Mrs. Baine
The railway between Axe and the Five Towns had not ye
been opened; but even if it had been opened Aunt Harrie
would probably not have used it. She had always travelle
from Axe to Bursley in the same vehicle, a small waggonett
which she hired from Bratt's livery stables at Axe, driven by
coachman who thoroughly understood the importance, and th
peculiarities, of Aunt Harriet.

Mrs. Baines had increased in stoutness, so that now Aun
Harriet had very little advantage over her, physically. Bu
the moral ascendency of the elder still persisted. The tw
vast widows shared Mrs. Baines's bedroom, spending much o
their time there in long, hushed conversations—interviews fro
which Mrs. Baines emerged with the air of one who has re
ceived enlightenment and Aunt Harriet with the air of on
who has rendered it. The pair went about together, in th
shop, the showroom, the parlour, the kitchen, and also int
the town, addressing each other as "Sister," "Sister." Every
where it was "sister," "sister," "my sister," "your dea
mother," "your Aunt Harriet." They referred to each other a
oracular sources of wisdom and good taste. Respectabilit
stalked abroad when they were afoot. The whole Squar
wriggled uneasily as though God's eye were peculiarly upo
it. The meals in the parlour became solemn collations, at whic
shone the best silver and the finest diaper, but from whic
gaiety and naturalness seemed to be banished. (I say "seemed
because it cannot be doubted that Aunt Harriet was natura
and there were moments when she possibly considered hersel
to be practising gaiety—a gaiety more desolating than he
severity.) The younger generation was extinguished, presse
flat and lifeless under the ponderosity of the widows.

Mr. Povey was not the man to be easily flattened by pon-erosity of any kind, and his suppression was a striking roof of the prowess of the widows; who, indeed, went over Mr. Povey like traction-engines, with the sublime unconscious-ess of traction-engines, leaving an inanimate object in the road behind them, and scarce aware even of the jolt. Mr. Povey hated Aunt Harriet, but, lying crushed there in the road, how could he rebel? He felt all the time that Aunt Harriet was adding him up, and reporting the result at frequent intervals to Mrs. Baines in the bedroom. He felt that she knew every-thing about him—even to those tears which had been in his eyes. He felt that he could hope to do nothing right for Aunt Harriet, that absolute perfection in the performance of duty would make no more impression on her than a caress on the fly-wheel of a traction-engine. Constance, the dear Constance, was also looked at askance. There was nothing in Aunt Harriet's demeanour to her that you could take hold of, but there was emphatically something that you could not take hold of—a hint, an inkling, that insinuated to Constance, "Have a care, lest peradventure you become the second cousin of the scarlet woman."

Sophia was petted. Sophia was liable to be playfully tapped by Aunt Harriet's thimble when Aunt Harriet was hemming dusters (for the elderly lady could lift a duster to her own dignity). Sophia was called on two separate occasions, "My little butterfly." And Sophia was entrusted with the trimming of Aunt Harriet's new summer bonnet. Aunt Harriet deemed that Sophia was looking pale. As the days passed, Sophia's pallor was emphasized by Aunt Harriet until it developed into an article of faith, to which you were compelled to subscribe on pain of excommunication. Then dawned the day when Aunt Harriet said, staring at Sophia as an affectionate aunt may: "That child would do with a change." And then there dawned another day when Aunt Harriet, staring at Sophia compas-sionately, as a devoted aunt may, said: "It's a pity that child can't have a change." And Mrs. Baines also stared and said: "It is."

And on another day Aunt Harriet said: "I've been wonder-ing whether my little Sophia would care to come and keep her old aunt company a while."

There were few things for which Sophia would have cared less. The girl swore to herself angrily that she would not go, that no allurement would induce her to go. But she was in a net; she was in the meshes of family correctness. Do wha she would, she could not invent a reason for not going. Cer tainly she could not tell her aunt that she merely did not wan to go. She was capable of enormities, but not of that. An then began Aunt Harriet's intricate preparations for going Aunt Harriet never did anything simply. And she could no be hurried. Seventy-two hours before leaving she had to com mence upon her trunk; but first the trunk had to be wiped by Maggie with a damp cloth under the eye and direction of Aun Harriet. And the liveryman at Axe had to be written to, and the servants at Axe written to, and the weather prospect weighed and considered. And somehow, by the time these mat ters were accomplished, it was tacitly understood that Sophi should accompany her kind aunt into the bracing moorland air of Axe. No smoke at Axe! No stuffiness at Axe! The spacious existence of a wealthy widow in a residential town with a low death-rate and famous scenery! "Have you packed your box, Sophia?" No, she had not. "Well, I will come and help you."

Impossible to bear up against the momentum of a massive body like Aunt Harriet's! It was irresistible.

The day of departure came, throwing the entire household into a commotion. Dinner was put a quarter of an hour earlier than usual so that Aunt Harriet might achieve Axe at her accustomed hour of tea. After dinner Maggie was the recipient of three amazing muslin aprons, given with a regal gesture. And the trunk and the box were brought down, and there was a slight odour of black kid gloves in the parlour. The waggon- ette was due and the waggonette appeared ("I can always rely upon Bladen!" said Aunt Harriet), and the door was opened, and Bladen, stiff on his legs, descended from the box and touched his hat to Aunt Harriet as she filled up the door- way.

"Have you baited, Bladen?" asked she.

"Yes'm," said he, assuringly.

Bladen and Mr. Povey carried out the trunk and the box, and Constance charged herself with parcels which she bestowed in the corners of the vehicle according to her aunt's prescrip- tion; it was like stowing the cargo of a vessel.

"Now, Sophia, my chuck!" Mrs. Baines called up the stairs.

And Sophia came slowly downstairs. Mrs. Baines offered her mouth. Sophia glanced at her.

"You needn't think I don't see why you're sending me away!" exclaimed Sophia in a hard, furious voice, with glistening eyes. "I'm not so blind as all that!" She kissed her mother —nothing but a contemptuous peck. Then, as she turned away she added: "But you let Constance do just as she likes!"

This was her sole bitter comment on the episode, but into it she put all the profound bitterness accumulated during many mutinous nights.

Mrs. Baines concealed a sigh. The explosion certainly disturbed her. She had hoped that the smooth surface of things would not be ruffled.

Sophia bounced out. And the assembly, including several urchins, watched with held breath while Aunt Harriet, after having bid majestic good-byes, got on to the step and introduced herself through the doorway of the waggonette into the interior of the vehicle; it was an operation like threading a needle with cotton too thick. Once within, her hoops distended in sudden release, filling the waggonette. Sophia followed, agilely.

As, with due formalities, the equipage drove off, Mrs. Baines gave another sigh, one of relief. The sisters had won. She could now await the imminent next advent of Mr. Gerald Scales with tranquillity.

ii

Those singular words of Sophia's, "But you let Constance do just as she likes," had disturbed Mrs. Baines more than was at first apparent. They worried her like a late fly in autumn. For she had said nothing to any one about Constance's case, Mrs. Maddack of course excepted. She had instinctively felt that she could not show the slightest leniency towards the romantic impulses of her elder daughter without seeming unjust to the younger, and she had acted accordingly. On the memorable morn of Mr. Povey's acute jealousy, she had, temporarily at any rate, slaked the fire, banked it down, and hidden it; and since then no word had passed as to the state of Constance's heart. In the great peril to be feared from Mr. Scales, Constance's heart had been put aside as a thing that

could wait; so one puts aside the mending of linen when earth
quake shocks are about. Mrs. Baines was sure that Constanc
had not chattered to Sophia concerning Mr. Povey. Constance
who understood her mother, had too much commonsense an
too nice a sense of propriety to do that—and yet here wa
Sophia exclaiming, "But you let Constance do just as sh
likes." Were the relations between Constance and Mr. Pove
then, common property? Did the young lady assistants discus
them?

As a fact, the young lady assistants did discuss them; no
in the shop—for either one of the principal parties, or Mrs
Baines herself, was always in the shop, but elsewhere. The
discussed little else, when they were free; how she had looke
at him to-day, and how he had blushed, and so forth inter
minably. Yet Mrs. Baines really thought that she alone knew
Such is the power of the ineradicable delusion that one's ow
affairs, and especially one's own children, are mysteriously dif
ferent from those of others.

After Sophia's departure Mrs. Baines surveyed her daugh
ter and her manager at supper-time with a curious and
diffident eye. They worked, talked, and ate just as thoug
Mrs. Baines had never caught them weeping together in th
cutting-out room. They had the most matter-of-fact air. The
might never have heard whispered the name of love. And ther
could be no deceit beneath that decorum; for Constance woul
not deceive. Still, Mrs. Baines's conscience was unruly. Orde
reigned, but nevertheless she knew that she ought to do some
thing, find out something, decide something; she ought, if sh
did her duty, to take Constance aside and say: "Now, Con
stance, my mind is freer now. Tell me frankly what has bee
going on between you and Mr. Povey. I have never under
stood the meaning of that scene in the cutting-out room. Tel
me." She ought to have talked in this strain. But she coul
not. That energetic woman had not sufficient energy left. Sh
wanted rest, rest—even though it were a coward's rest, a
ostrich's tranquillity—after the turmoil of apprehension
caused by Sophia. Her soul cried out for peace. She was not
however, to have peace.

On the very first Sunday after Sophia's departure, Mr
Povey did not go to chapel in the morning, and he offered n
reason for his unusual conduct. He ate his breakfast with
appetite, but there was something peculiar in his glance that

made Mrs. Baines a little uneasy; this something she could not seize upon and define. When she and Constance returned from chapel Mr. Povey was playing "Rock of Ages" on the harmonium—again unusual! The serious part of the dinner comprised roast beef and Yorkshire pudding—the pudding being served as a sweet course before the meat. Mrs. Baines ate freely of these things, for she loved them, and she was always hungry after a sermon. She also did well with the Cheshire cheese. Her intention was to sleep in the drawing-room after the repast. On Sunday afternoons she invariably tried to sleep in the drawing-room, and she did not often fail. As a rule the girls accompanied her thither from the table, and either "settled down" likewise or crept out of the room when they perceived the gradual sinking of the majestic form into the deep hollows of the easy-chair. Mrs. Baines was anticipating with pleasure her somnolent Sunday afternoon.

Constance said grace after meat, and the formula on this particular occasion ran thus—

"Thank God for our good dinner, Amen.—Mother, I must just run upstairs to my room." ("*My* room"—Sophia being far away.)

And off she ran, strangely girlish.

"Well, child, you needn't be in such a hurry," said Mrs. Baines, ringing the bell and rising.

She hoped that Constance would remember the conditions precedent to sleep.

"I should like to have a word with you, if it's all the same to you, Mrs. Baines," said Mr. Povey suddenly, with obvious nervousness. And his tone struck a rude unexpected blow at Mrs. Baines's peace of mind. It was a portentous tone.

"What about?" asked she, with an inflection subtly to remind Mr. Povey what day it was.

"About Constance," said the astonishing man.

"Constance!" exclaimed Mrs. Baines with a histrionic air of bewilderment.

Maggie entered the room, solely in response to the bell, yet a thought jumped up in Mrs. Baines's brain, "How prying servants are, to be sure!" For quite five seconds she had a grievance against Maggie. She was compelled to sit down again and wait while Maggie cleared the table. Mr. Povey put both his hands in his pockets, got up, went to the window, whistled, and generally behaved in a manner which foretold the worst.

At last Maggie vanished, shutting the door.

"What is it, Mr. Povey?"

"Oh!" said Mr. Povey, facing her with absurd nervous brusqueness, as though pretending: "Ah, yes! We have something to say—I was forgetting!" Then he began: "It's about Constance and me."

Yes, they had evidently plotted this interview. Constance had evidently taken herself off on purpose to leave Mr. Povey unhampered. They were in league. The inevitable had come. No sleep! No repose! Nothing but worry once more!

"I'm not at all satisfied with the present situation," said Mr. Povey, in a tone that corresponded to his words.

"I don't know what you mean, Mr. Povey," said Mrs. Baines stiffly. This was a simple lie.

"Well, really, Mrs. Baines!" Mr. Povey protested, "I suppose you won't deny that you know there is something between me and Constance? I suppose you won't deny that?"

"What is there between you and Constance? I can assure you I——"

"That depends on you," Mr. Povey interrupted her. When he was nervous his manners deteriorated into a behaviour that resembled rudeness. "That depends on you!" he repeated grimly.

"But——"

"Are we to be engaged or are we not?" pursued Mr. Povey, as though Mrs. Baines had been guilty of some grave lapse and he was determined not to spare her. "That's what I think ought to be settled, one way or the other. I wish to be perfectly open and aboveboard—in the future, as I have been in the past."

"But you have said nothing to me at all!" Mrs. Baines remonstrated, lifting her eyebrows. The way in which the man had sprung this matter upon her was truly too audacious.

Mr. Povey approached her as she sat at the table, shaking her ringlets and looking at her hands.

"You know there's something between us!" he insisted.

"How should I know there is something between you? Constance has never said a word to me. And have you?"

"Well," said he. "We've hidden nothing."

"What is there between you and Constance? If I may ask!"

"That depends on you," said he again.

"Have you asked her to be your wife?"

"No. I haven't exactly asked her to be my wife." He hesitated. "You see——"

Mrs. Baines collected her forces. "Have you kissed her?" This in cold voice.

Mr. Povey now blushed. "I haven't exactly kissed her," he stammered, apparently shocked by the inquisition. "No, I should not say that I had kissed her."

It might have been that before committing himself he felt a desire for Mrs. Baines's definition of a kiss.

"You are very extraordinary," she said loftily. It was no less than the truth.

"All I want to know is—have you got anything against me?" he demanded roughly. "Because if so——"

"Anything against you, Mr. Povey? Why should I have anything against you?"

"Then why can't we be engaged?"

She considered that he was bullying her. "That's another question," said she.

"Why can't we be engaged? Ain't I good enough?"

The fact was that he was not regarded as good enough. Mrs. Maddack had certainly deemed that he was not good enough. He was a solid mass of excellent qualities; but he lacked brilliance, importance, dignity. He could not impose himself. Such had been the verdict.

And now, while Mrs. Baines was secretly reproaching Mr. Povey for his inability to impose himself, he was most patently imposing himself on her—and the phenomenon escaped her! She felt that he was bullying her, but somehow she could not perceive his power. Yet the man who could bully Mrs. Baines was surely no common soul!

"You know my very high opinion of you," she said.

Mr. Povey pursued in a mollified tone. "Assuming that Constance is willing to be engaged, do I understand you consent?"

"But Constance is too young."

"Constance is twenty. She is more than twenty."

"In any case you won't expect me to give you an answer now."

"Why not? You know my position."

She did. From a practical point of view the match would be ideal: no fault could be found with it on that side. But Mrs. Baines could not extinguish the idea that it would be a "come-down" for her daughter. Who, after all, was Mr. Povey? Mr. Povey was nobody.

"I must think things over," she said firmly, putting her lips together. "I can't reply like this. It is a serious matter."

"When can I have your answer? To-morrow?"

"No—really—"

"In a week, then?"

"I cannot bind myself to a date," said Mrs. Baines, haughtily. She felt that she was gaining ground.

"Because I can't stay on here indefinitely as things are," Mr. Povey burst out, and there was a touch of hysteria in his tone.

"Now, Mr. Povey, please do be reasonable."

"That's all very well," he went on. "That's all very well. But what I say is that employers have no right to have male assistants in their houses unless they are prepared to let their daughters marry! That's what I say! No *right!*"

Mrs. Baines did not know what to answer.

The aspirant wound up: "I must leave if that's the case."

"If what's the case?" she asked herself. "What has come over him? And aloud: "You know you would place me in a very awkward position by leaving, and I hope you don't want to mix up two quite different things. I hope you aren't trying to threaten me."

"Threaten you!" he cried. "Do you suppose I should leave here for fun? If I leave it will be because I can't *stand* it. That's all. I can't stand it. I want Constance, and if I can't have her, then I can't *stand* it. What do you think I'm made of?"

"I'm sure—" she began.

"That's all very well!" he almost shouted.

"But please let me speak," she said quietly.

"All I say is I can't *stand* it. That's all. . . . . Employers have no *right*. . . . We have our feelings like other men."

He was deeply moved. He might have appeared somewhat grotesque to the strictly impartial observer of human nature. Nevertheless he was deeply and genuinely moved, and possibly human nature could have shown nothing more human than Mr. Povey at the moment when, unable any longer to restrain the paroxysm which had so surprisingly overtaken him, he fled from the parlour, passionately, to the retreat of his bedroom.

"That's the worst of those quiet calm ones," said Mrs. Baines to herself. "You never know if they won't give way. And when they do, it's awful—awful. . . . . What did I do, what did I say, to bring it on? Nothing! Nothing!"

And where was her afternoon sleep? What was going to happen to her daughter? What could she say to Constance? How next could she meet Mr. Povey? Ah! It needed a brave, indomitable woman not to cry out brokenly: "I've suffered too much. Do anything you like; only let me die in peace!" And so saying, to let everything indifferently slide!

iii

Neither Mr. Povey nor Constance introduced the delicate subject to her again, and she was determined not to be the first to speak of it. She considered that Mr. Povey had taken advantage of his position, and that he had also been infantile and impolite. And somehow she privately blamed Constance for his behaviour. So the matter hung, as it were, suspended in the ether between the opposing forces of pride and passion.

Shortly afterwards events occurred compared to which the vicissitudes of Mr. Povey's heart were of no more account than a shower of rain in April. And fate gave no warning of them; it rather indicated a complete absence of events. When the customary advice circular arrived from Birkinshaws, the name of "our Mr. Gerald Scales" was replaced on it by another and an unfamiliar name. Mrs. Baines, seeing the circular by accident, experienced a sense of relief, mingled with the professional disappointment of a diplomatist who has elaborately provided for contingencies which have failed to happen. She had sent Sophia away for nothing; and no doubt her maternal affection had exaggerated a molehill into a mountain. Really, when she reflected on the past, she could not recall a single fact that would justify her theory of an attachment secretly budding between Sophia and the young man Scales! Not a single little fact! All she could bring forward was that Sophia had twice encountered Scales in the street.

She felt a curious interest in the fate of Scales, for whom in her own mind she had long prophesied evil, and when Birkinshaws' representative came she took care to be in the shop: her intention was to converse with him, and ascertain as much as was ascertainable, after Mr. Povey had transacted business.

For this purpose, at a suitable moment, she traversed the shop to Mr. Povey's side, and in so doing she had a fleeting view of King Street, and in King Street of a familiar vehicle. She stopped, and seemed to catch the distant sound of knocking. Abandoning the traveller, she hurried towards the parlour, in the passage she assuredly did hear knocking, angry and impatient knocking, the knocking of someone who thinks he has knocked too long.

"Of course Maggie is at the top of the house!" she muttered sarcastically.

She unchained, unbolted, and unlocked the side-door.

"At last!" It was Aunt Harriet's voice, exacerbated. "What! You, sister? You're soon up. What a blessing!"

The two majestic and imposing creatures met on the mat, craning forward so that their lips might meet above their terrific bosoms.

"What's the matter?" Mrs. Baines asked, fearfully.

"Well, I do declare!" said Mrs. Maddack. "And I've driven specially over to ask *you!*"

"Where's Sophia?" demanded Mrs. Baines.

"You don't mean to say she's not come, sister?" Mrs. Maddack sank down on to the sofa.

"Come?" Mrs. Baines repeated. "Of course she's not come. What do you mean, sister?"

"The very moment she got Constance's letter yesterday, saying you were ill in bed and she'd better come over to help in the shop, she started. I got Bratt's dog-cart for her."

Mrs. Baines in her turn also sank down on to the sofa.

"I've not been ill," she said. "And Constance hasn't written for a week! Only yesterday I was telling her——"

"Sister—it can't be! Sophia had letters from Constance every morning. At least she said they were from Constance. I told her to be sure and write me how you were last night, and she promised faithfully she would. And it was because I got nothing by this morning's post that I decided to come over myself, to see if it was anything serious."

"Serious it is!" murmured Mrs. Baines.

"What——"

"Sophia's run off. That's the plain English of it!" said Mrs. Baines with frigid calm.

"Nay! That I'll never believe. I've looked after Sophia night and day as if she was my own, and——"

"If she hasn't run off, where is she?"

Mrs. Maddack opened the door with a tragic gesture.

"Bladen," she called in a loud voice to the driver of the aggonette, who was standing on the pavement.

"Yes'm."

"It was Pember drove Miss Sophia yesterday, wasn't it?"

"Yes'm."

She hesitated. A clumsy question might enlighten a member of the class which ought never to be enlightened about one's rivate affairs.

"He didn't come all the way here?"

"No'm. He happened to say last night when he got back s Miss Sophia had told him to set her down at Knype Staon."

"I thought so!" said Mrs. Maddack, courageously.

"Yes'm."

"Sister!" she moaned, after carefully shutting the door.

They clung to each other.

The horror of what had occurred did not instantly take ull possession of them, because the power of credence, of naginatively realizing a supreme event, whether of great grief r of great happiness, is ridiculously finite. But every minute he horror grew more clear, more intense, more tragically dominant over them. There were many things that they could not ay to each other,—from pride, from shame, from the inadequacy of words. Neither could utter the name of Gerald Scales. And Aunt Harriet could not stoop to defend herself rom a possible charge of neglect; nor could Mrs. Baines stoop o assure her sister that she was incapable of preferring such , charge. And the sheer, immense criminal folly of Sophia ould not even be referred to: it was unspeakable. So the interiew proceeded, lamely, clumsily, inconsequently, leading to aught.

Sophia was gone. She was gone with Gerald Scales. That eautiful child, that incalculable, untamable, impossible creaure, had committed the final folly; without pretext or excuse, nd with what elaborate deceit! Yes, without excuse! She had lot been treated harshly; she had had a degree of liberty vhich would have astounded and shocked her grandmothers; he had been petted, humoured, spoilt. And her answer was to lisgrace the family by an act as irrevocable as it was utterly vicious. If among her desires was the desire to humiliate those

majesties, her mother and Aunt Harriet, she would have bee~
content could she have seen them on the sofa there, humbled
shamed, mortally wounded! Ah, the monstrous Chinese cruelt~
of youth!

What was to be done? Tell dear Constance? No, this wa~
not, at the moment, an affair for the younger generation. I~
was too new and raw for the younger generation. Moreove~
capable, proud, and experienced as they were, they felt th~
need of a man's voice, and a man's hard, callous ideas. It wa~
a case for Mr. Critchlow. Maggie was sent to fetch him, wit~
a particular request that he should come to the side-door. H~
came expectant, with the pleasurable anticipation of disaste~
and he was not disappointed. He passed with the sisters the hap~
piest hour that had fallen to him for years. Quickly he arrange~
the alternatives for them. Would they tell the police, or woul~
they take the risks of waiting? They shied away, but wit~
fierce brutality he brought them again and again to the im~
mediate point of decision. . . . Well, they could not tell th~
police! They simply could not. . . . Then they must fac~
another danger. . . . He had no mercy for them. And whil~
he was torturing them there arrived a telegram, despatche~
from Charing Cross, "I am all right, Sophia." That proved
at any rate, that the child was not heartless, not merely care~
less.

Only yesterday, it seemed to Mrs. Baines, she had born~
Sophia; only yesterday she was a baby, a schoolgirl to b~
smacked. The years rolled up in a few hours. And now sh~
was sending telegrams from a place called Charing Cross! Ho~
unlike was the hand of the telegram to Sophia's hand! Ho~
mysteriously curt and inhuman was that official hand, a~
Mrs. Baines stared at it through red, wet eyes!

Mr. Critchlow said some one should go to Manchester, t~
ascertain about Scales. He went himself, that afternoon, an~
returned with the news that an aunt of Scales had recentl~
died, leaving him twelve thousand pounds, and that he had
after quarrelling with his uncle Boldero, abandoned Birkin~
shaws at an hour's notice and vanished with his inheritance.

"It's as plain as a pikestaff," said Mr. Critchlow. "I coul~
ha' warned ye o' all this years ago, ever since she killed he~
father!"

Mr. Critchlow left nothing unsaid.

During the night Mrs. Baines lived through all Sophia'~

life, lived through it more intensely than ever Sophia had done.

The next day people began to know. A whisper almost inaudible went across the Square, and into the town: and in the stillness every one heard it. "Sophia Baines run off with a commercial!"

In another fortnight a note came, also dated from London.

"Dear Mother, I am married to Gerald Scales. Please don't worry about me. We are going abroad. Your affectionate Sophia. Love to Constance." No tear-stains on that pale blue sheet! No sign of agitation!

And Mrs. Baines said: "My life is over." It was, though she was scarcely fifty. She felt old, old and beaten. She had fought and been vanquished. The everlasting purpose had been too much for her. Virtue had gone out of her—the virtue to hold up her head and look the Square in the face. She, the wife of John Baines! She, a Syme of Axe!

Old houses, in the course of their history, see sad sights, and never forget them! And ever since, in the solemn physiognomy of the triple house of John Baines at the corner of St. Luke's Square and King Street, have remained the traces of the sight it saw on the morning of the afternoon when Mr. and Mrs. Povey returned from their honeymoon— the sight of Mrs. Baines getting into the waggonette for Axe; Mrs. Baines, encumbered with trunks and parcels, leaving the scene of her struggles and her defeat, whither she had once come as slim as a wand, to return stout and heavy, and heavy-hearted, to her childhood; content to live with her grandiose sister until such time as she should be ready for burial! The grimy and impassive old house perhaps heard her heart saying: "Only yesterday they were little girls, ever so tiny, and now—" The driving-off of a waggonette can be a dreadful thing.

BOOK II

CONSTANCE

CHAPTER I

REVOLUTION

"WELL," said Mr. Povey, rising from the rocking-chair that in a previous age had been John Baines's, "I've got to make a start some time, so I may as well begin now!"

And he went from the parlour into the shop. Constance's eye followed him as far as the door, where their glances met for an instant in the transient gaze which expresses the tenderness of people who feel more than they kiss.

It was on the morning of this day that Mrs. Baines, relinquishing the sovereignty of St. Luke's Square, had gone to live as a younger sister in the house of Harriet Maddack at Axe. Constance guessed little of the secret anguish of that departure. She only knew that it was just like her mother, having perfectly arranged the entire house for the arrival of the honeymoon couple from Buxton, to flit early away so as to spare the natural blushing diffidence of the said couple. It was like her mother's commonsense and her mother's sympathetic comprehension. Further, Constance did not pursue her mother's feelings, being far too busy with her own. She sat there full of new knowledge and new importance, brimming with experience and strange, unexpected aspirations, purposes, yes—and cunnings! And yet, though the very curves of her cheeks seemed to be mysteriously altering, the old Constance still lingered in that frame, an innocent soul hesitating to spread its wings and quit for ever the body which had been its home; you could see the timid thing peeping wistfully out of the eyes of the married woman.

Constance rang the bell for Maggie to clear the table; and as she did so she had the illusion that she was not really a married woman and a house-mistress, but only a kind of counterfeit. She did most fervently hope that all would go right in the house—at any rate until she had grown more accustomed to her situation.

The hope was to be disappointed. Maggie's rather silly,

obsequious smile concealed but for a moment the ineffable tragedy that had lain in wait for unarmed Constance.

"If you please, Mrs. Povey," said Maggie, as she crushed
cups together on the tin tray with her great, red hands, which
always looked like something out of a butcher's shop; then a
pause, "Will you please accept of this?"

Now, before the wedding Maggie had already, with tears of
affection, given Constance a pair of blue glass vases (in order
to purchase which she had been obliged to ask for special permission to go out), and Constance wondered what was coming
now from Maggie's pocket. A small piece of folded paper
came from Maggie's pocket. Constance accepted of it, and
read: "I begs to give one month's notice to leave. Signed Maggie. June 10, 1867."

"Maggie!" exclaimed the old Constance, terrified by this incredible occurrence, ere the married woman could strangle her.

"I never give notice before, Mrs. Povey," said Maggie, "so
I don't know as I know how it ought for be done—not rightly.
But I hope as you'll accept of it, Mrs. Povey."

"Oh! of course," said Mrs. Povey, primly, just as if Maggie
was not the central supporting pillar of the house, just as if
Maggie had not assisted at her birth, just as if the end of the
world had not abruptly been announced, just as if St. Luke's
Square were not inconceivable without Maggie. "But why—"

"Well, Mrs. Povey, I've been a-thinking it over in my kitchen, and I said to myself: 'If there's going to be one change
there'd better be two,' I says. Not but what I wouldn't work my
fingers to the bone for ye, Miss Constance."

Here Maggie began to cry into the tray.

Constance looked at her. Despite the special muslin of that
day she had traces of the slatternliness of which Mrs. Baines
had never been able to cure her. She was over forty, big,
gawky. She had no figure, no charms of any kind. She was
what was left of a woman after twenty-two years in the cave
of a philanthropic family. And in her cave she had actually
been thinking things over! Constance detected for the first
time, beneath the dehumanized drudge, the stirrings of a separate and perhaps capricious individuality. Maggie's engagements had never been real to her employers. Within the house
she had never been, in practice, anything but "Maggie"—an
organism. And now she was permitting herself ideas about
changes!

"You'll soon be suited with another, Mrs. Povey," said Maggie. "There's many a—many a—" She burst into sobs.

"But if you really want to leave, what are you crying for, Maggie?" asked Mrs. Povey, at her wisest. "Have you told mother?"

"No, miss," Maggie whimpered, absently wiping her wrinkled cheeks with ineffectual muslin. "I couldn't seem to fancy telling your mother. And as you're the mistress now, I thought as I'd save it for you when you come home. I hope you'll excuse me, Mrs. Povey."

"Of course I'm very sorry. You've been a very good servant. And in these days——"

The child had acquired this turn of speech from her mother. It did not appear to occur to either of them that they were living in the sixties.

"Thank ye, miss."

"And what are you thinking of doing, Maggie? You know you won't get many places like this."

"To tell ye the truth, Mrs. Povey, I'm going to get married mysen."

"Indeed!" murmured Constance, with the perfunctoriness of habit in replying to these tidings.

"Oh! but I am, mum," Maggie insisted. "It's all settled. Mr. Hollins, mum."

"Not Hollins, the fish-hawker!"

"Yes, mum. I seem to fancy him. You don't remember as him and me was engaged in '48. He was my first, like. I broke it off because he was in that Chartist lot, and I knew as Mr. Baines would never stand that. Now he's asked me again. He's been a widower this long time."

"I'm sure I hope you'll be happy, Maggie. But what about his habits?"

"He won't have no habits with me, Mrs. Povey."

A woman was definitely emerging from the drudge.

When Maggie, having entirely ceased sobbing, had put the folded cloth in the table-drawer and departed with the tray, her mistress became frankly the girl again. No primness about her as she stood alone there in the parlour; no pretence that Maggie's notice to leave was an everyday document, to be casually glanced at as one glances at an unpaid bill! She would be compelled to find a new servant, making solemn inquiries into character, and to train the new servant, and to talk to her from heights from which she had never addressed Maggie. At that moment she had an illusion that there were no other available, suitable servants in the whole world. And the arranged marriage? She felt that this time—the thirteenth or fourteenth time—the engagement was serious and would only end at the altar. The vision of Maggie and Hollins at the altar shocked her. Marriage was a series of phenomena, and a general state, very holy and wonderful—too sacred, somehow, for such creatures as Maggie and Hollins. Her vague, instinctive revolt against such a usage of matrimony centred round the idea of a strong, eternal smell of fish. However, the projected outrage on a hallowed institution troubled her much less than the imminent problem of domestic service.

She ran into the shop—or she would have run if she had not checked her girlishness betimes—and on her lips, ready to be whispered importantly into a husband's astounded ear, were the words, "Maggie has given notice! Yes! Truly!" But Samuel Povey was engaged. He was leaning over the counter and staring at an outspread paper upon which a certain Mr. Yardley was making strokes with a thick pencil. Mr. Yardley, who had a long red beard, painted houses and rooms. She knew him only by sight. In her mind she always associated him with the sign over his premises in Trafalgar Road, "Yardley Bros., Authorised plumbers. Painters. Decorators. Paper-hangers. Facia writers." For years, in childhood, she had passed that sign without knowing what sort of things "Bros." and "Facia" were, and what was the mysterious similarity between a plumber and a version of the Bible. She could not interrupt her husband, he was wholly absorbed; nor could she stay in the shop (which appeared just a little smaller than usual), for that would have meant an unsuccessful endeavour to front the young lady-assistants as though nothing in particular had happened to her. So she went sedately up the showroom stairs and thus to the bedroom floors of the house —her house! Mrs. Povey's house! She even climbed to Constance's old bedroom; her mother had stripped the bed—that was all, except a slight diminution of this room, corresponding to that of the shop! Then to the drawing-room. In the recess outside the drawing-room door the black box of silver plate still lay. She had expected her mother to take it; but no! Assuredly her mother was one to do things handsomely—when she did them. In the drawing-room, not a tassel of an antimacassar touched! Yes, the fire-screen, the luscious bunch of roses on an expanse of mustard, which Constance had worked for her mother years ago, was gone! That her mother should have clung to just that one souvenir, out of all the heavy opulence of the drawing-room, touched Constance intimately. She perceived that if she could not talk to her husband she must write to her mother. And she sat down at the oval table and wrote, "Darling mother, I am sure you will be very surprised to hear. . . . She means it. . . . I think she is making a serious mistake. Ought I to put an advertisement in the *Signal*, or will it do if. . . . Please write by return. We are back and have enjoyed ourselves very much. Sam says he enjoys getting up late. . . ." And so on to the last inch of the fourth scolloped page.

She was obliged to revisit the shop for a stamp, stamps being kept in Mr. Povey's desk in the corner—a high desk, at which you stood. Mr. Povey was now in earnest converse with Mr. Yardley at the door, and twilight, which began a full hour earlier in the shop than in the Square, had cast faint shadows in corners behind counters.

"Will you just run out with this to the pillar, Miss Dadd?"

"With pleasure, Mrs. Povey."

"Where are you going to?" Mr. Povey interrupted his conversation to stop the flying girl.

"She's just going to the post for me," Constance called out from the region of the till.

"Oh! All right!"

A trifle! A nothing! Yet somehow, in the quiet customerless shop, the episode, with the scarce perceptible difference in Samuel's tone at his second remark, was delicious to Constance. Somehow it was the *real* beginning of her wifehood. (There had been about nine other real beginnings in the past fortnight.)

Mr. Povey came in to supper, laden with ledgers and similar works which Constance had never even pretended to understand. It was a sign from him that the honeymoon was over. He was proprietor now, and his ardour for ledgers most justifiable. Still, there was the question of her servant.

"Never!" he exclaimed, when she told him all about the end of the world. A "never" which expressed extreme astonishment and the liveliest concern!

But Constance had anticipated that he would have been just

a little more knocked down, bowled over, staggered, stunned, flabbergasted. In a swift gleam of insight she saw that she had been in danger of forgetting her *rôle* of experienced, capable married woman.

"I shall have to set about getting a fresh one," she said hastily, with an admirable assumption of light and easy casualness.

Mr. Povey seemed to think that Hollins would suit Maggie pretty well. He made no remark to the betrothed when she answered the final bell of the night.

He opened his ledgers, whistling.

"I think I shall go up, dear," said Constance. "I've a lot of things to put away."

"Do," said he. "Call out when you've done."

ii

"Sam!" she cried from the top of the crooked stairs.

No answer. The door at the foot was closed.

"Sam!"

"Hello?" Distantly, faintly.

"I've done all I'm going to do to-night."

And she ran back along the corridor, a white figure in the deep gloom, and hurried into bed, and drew the clothes up to her chin.

In the life of a bride there are some dramatic moments. If she has married the industrious apprentice, one of those moments occurs when she first occupies the sacred bed-chamber of her ancestors, and the bed on which she was born. Her parents' room had always been to Constance, if not sacred, at least invested with a certain moral solemnity. She could not enter it as she would enter another room. The course of nature, with its succession of deaths, conceptions, and births, slowly makes such a room august with a mysterious quality which interprets the grandeur of mere existence and imposes itself on all. Constance had the strangest sensations in that bed, whose heavy dignity of ornament symbolized a past age; sensations of sacrilege and trespass, of being a naughty girl to whom punishment would accrue for this shocking freak. Not since she was quite tiny had she slept in that bed—one night with her mother, before her father's seizure, when he had been

away. What a limitless, unfathomable bed it was then! Now
it was just a bed—so she had to tell herself—like any other
bed. The tiny child that, safely touching its mother, had slept
in the vast expanse, seemed to her now a pathetic little thing;
its image made her feel melancholy. And her mind dewlt
on sad events: the death of her father, the flight of darling
Sophia; the immense grief, and the exile, of her mother. She
esteemed that she knew what life was, and that it was grim. And
she sighed. But the sigh was an affectation, meant partly to
convince herself that she was grown-up, and partly to keep her
in countenance in the intimidating bed. This melancholy was
factitious, was less than transient foam on the deep sea of her
joy. Death and sorrow and sin were dim shapes to her; the
ruthless egoism of happiness blew them away with a puff, and
their wistful faces vanished. To see her there in the bed, framed
in mahogany and tassels, lying on her side, with her young
glowing cheeks, and honest but not artless gaze, and the rich
curve of her hip lifting the counterpane, one would have said
that she had never heard of aught but love.

Mr. Povey entered, the bridegroom, quickly, firmly, carrying
it off rather well, but still self-conscious. "After all," his shoulders were trying to say, "what's the difference between this
bedroom and the bedroom of a boarding-house? Indeed, ought
we not to feel more at home here? Besides, confound it, we've
been married a fortnight!"

"Doesn't it give you a funny feeling, sleeping in this room?
It does me," said Constance. Women, even experienced women,
are so foolishly frank. They have no decency, no self-respect.

"Really?" replied Mr. Povey, with loftiness, as who should
say: "What an extraordinary thing that a reasonable creature
can have such fancies! Now to me this room is exactly like any
other room." And he added aloud, glancing away from the
glass, where he was unfastening his necktie: "It's not a bad
room at all." This, with the judicial air of an auctioneer.

Not for an instant did he deceive Constance, who read his
real sensations with accuracy. But his futile poses did not in
the slightest degree lessen her respect for him. On the contrary, she admired him the more for them; they were a sort of
embroidery on the solid stuff of his character. At that period
he could not do wrong for her. The basis of her regard for
him was, she often thought, his honesty, his industry, his genu-

ne kindliness of act, his grasp of the business, his perseverance, his passion for doing at once that which had to be done.
She had the greatest admiration for his qualities, and he was in
her eyes an indivisible whole; she could not admire one part of
him and frown upon another. Whatever he did was good because he did it. She knew that some people were apt to smile at
certain phases of his individuality; she knew that far down in
her mother's heart was a suspicion that she had married ever
so little beneath her. But this knowledge did not disturb her.
She had no doubt as to the correctness of her own estimate.

Mr. Povey was an exceedingly methodical person, and he
was also one of those persons who must always be "beforehand" with time. Thus at night he would arrange his raiment
so that in the morning it might be reassumed in the minimum
of minutes. He was not a man, for example, to leave the changing of studs from one shirt to another till the morrow. Had
it been practicable, he would have brushed his hair the night
before. Constance already loved to watch his meticulous preparations. She saw him now go into his old bedroom and return
with a paper collar, which he put on the dressing-table next
to a black necktie. His shop-suit was laid out on a chair.

"Oh, Sam!" she exclaimed impulsively, "you surely aren't
going to begin wearing those horrid paper collars again!" During the honeymoon he had worn linen collars.

Her tone was perfectly gentle, but the remark, nevertheless,
showed a lack of tact. It implied that all his life Mr. Povey
had been enveloping his neck in something which was horrid.
Like all persons with a tendency to fall into the ridiculous, Mr.
Povey was exceedingly sensitive to personal criticisms. He
flushed darkly.

"I didn't know they were 'horrid,'" he snapped. He was
hurt and angry. Anger had surprised him unawares.

Both of them suddenly saw that they were standing on the
edge of a chasm, and drew back. They had imagined themselves
to be wandering safely in a flowered meadow, and here was this
bottomless chasm! It was most disconcerting.

Mr. Povey's hand hovered undecided over the collar. "However——" he muttered.

She could feel that he was trying with all his might to be
gentle and pacific. And she was aghast at her own stupid clumsiness, she so experienced!

"Just as you like, dear," she said quickly. "Please!"

"Oh no!" And he did his best to smile, and went off gawkily with the collar and came back with a linen one.

Her passion for him burned stronger than ever. She knew then that she did not love him for his good qualities, but for something boyish and naïve that there was about him, an indescribable something that occasionally, when his face was close to hers, made her dizzy.

The chasm had disappeared. In such moments, when each must pretend not to have seen or even suspected the chasm, small-talk is essential.

"Wasn't that Mr. Yardley in the shop to-night?" began Constance.

"Yes."

"What did he want?"

"I'd sent for him. He's going to paint us a signboard."

Useless for Samuel to make-believe that nothing in this world is more ordinary than a signboard.

"Oh!" murmured Constance. She said no more, the episode of the paper collar having weakened her self-confidence.

But a signboard!

What with servants, chasms, and signboards, Constance considered that her life as a married woman would not be deficient in excitement. Long afterwards, she fell asleep, thinking of Sophia.

iii

A few days later Constance was arranging the more precious of her wedding presents in the parlour; some had to be wrapped in tissue and in brown paper and then tied with string and labelled; others had special cases of their own, leather without and velvet within. Among the latter was the resplendent egg-stand holding twelve silver-gilt egg-cups and twelve chased spoons to match, presented by Aunt Harriet. In the Five Towns' phrase, "it must have cost money." Even if Mr. and Mrs. Povey had ten guests or ten children, and all the twelve of them were simultaneously gripped by a desire to eat eggs at breakfast or tea—even in this remote contingency Aunt Harriet would have been pained to see the egg-stand in use; such treasures are not designed for use. The presents, few in number, were mainly of this character, because, owing to her mother's heroic cession of the entire interior, Constance already possessed every necessary. The fewness of the presents was accounted for by the fact that the wedding had been strictly private and had taken place at Axe. There is nothing like secrecy in marriage for discouraging the generous impulses of one's friends. It was Mrs. Baines, abetted by both the chief parties, who had decided that the wedding should be private and secluded. Sophia's wedding had been altogether too private and secluded; but the casting of a veil over Constance's (whose union was irreproachable) somehow justified, after the event, the circumstances of Sophia's, indicating as it did that Mrs. Baines believed in secret weddings on principle. In such matters Mrs. Baines was capable of extraordinary subtlety.

And while Constance was thus taking her wedding presents with due seriousness, Maggie was cleaning the steps that led from the pavement of King Street to the side-door, and the door was ajar. It was a fine June morning.

Suddenly, over the sound of scouring, Constance heard a dog's low growl and then the hoarse voice of a man:

"Mester in, wench?"

"Happen he is, happen he isn't," came Maggie's answer. She had no fancy for being called wench.

Constance went to the door, not merely from curiosity, but from a feeling that her authority and her responsibilities as house-mistress extended to the pavement surrounding the house.

The famous James Boon, of Buck Row, the greatest dog-fancier in the Five Towns, stood at the bottom of the steps: a tall, fat man, clad in stiff, stained brown and smoking a black clay pipe less than three inches long. Behind him attended two bull-dogs.

"Morning, missis!" cried Boon, cheerfully. "I've heerd tell as th' mister is looking out for a dog, as you might say."

"I don't stay here with them animals a-sniffing at me—no, that I don't!" observed Maggie, picking herself up.

"Is he?" Constance hesitated. She knew that Samuel had vaguely referred to dogs; she had not, however, imagined that he regarded a dog as aught but a beautiful dream. No dog had ever put paw into that house, and it seemed impossible that one should ever do so. As for those beasts of prey on the pavement . . . !

"Ay!" said James Boon, calmly.

"I'll tell him you're here," said Constance. "But I don'
know if he's at liberty. He seldom is at this time of day. Mag
gie, you'd better come in."

She went slowly to the shop, full of fear for the future.

"Sam," she whispered to her husband, who was writing a
his desk, "here's a man come to see you about a dog."

Assuredly he was taken aback. Still, he behaved with much
presence of mind.

"Oh, about a dog! Who is it?"

"It's that Jim Boon. He says he's heard you want one."

The renowned name of Jim Boon gave him pause; but he
had to go through with the affair, and he went through with it
though nervously. Constance followed his agitated footsteps to
the side-door.

"Morning, Boon."

"Morning, mester."

They began to talk dogs, Mr. Povey, for his part, with due
caution.

"Now, there's a dog!" said Boon, pointing to one of the
bull-dogs, a miracle of splendid ugliness.

"Yes," responded Mr. Povey, insincerely. "He is a beauty
What's it worth now, at a venture?"

"I'll tak' a hundred and twenty sovereigns for her," said
Boon. "Th' other's a bit cheaper—a hundred."

"Oh, Sam!" gasped Constance.

And even Mr. Povey nearly lost his nerve. "That's more
than I want to give," said he timidly.

"But look at her!" Boon persisted, roughly snatching up the
more expensive animal, and displaying her cannibal teeth.

Mr. Povey shook his head. Constance glanced away.

"That's not quite the sort of dog I want," said Mr. Povey.

"Fox-terrier?"

"Yes, that's more like," Mr. Povey agreed eagerly.

"What'll ye run to?"

"Oh," said Mr. Povey, largely, "I don't know."

"Will ye run to a tenner?"

"I thought of something cheaper."

"Well, hoo much? Out wi' it, mester."

"Not more than two pounds," said Mr. Povey. He would
have said one pound had he dared. The prices of dogs amazed
him.

"I thowt it was a *dog* as ye wanted!" said Boon. "Look 'ere, mester. Come up to my yard and see what I've got."

"I will," said Mr. Povey.

"And bring missis along too. Now, what about a cat for th' missis? Or a gold-fish?"

The end of the episode was that a young lady aged some twelve months entered the Povey household on trial. Her exiguous legs twinkled all over the parlour, and she had the oddest appearance in the parlour. But she was so confiding, so affectionate, so timorous, and her black nose was so icy in that hot weather, that Constance loved her violently within an hour. Mr. Povey made rules for her. He explained to her that she must never, never go into the shop. But she went, and he whipped her to the squealing point, and Constance cried an instant, while admiring her husband's firmness.

The dog was not all.

On another day Constance, prying into the least details of the parlour, discovered a box of cigars inside the lid of the harmonium, on the keyboard. She was so unaccustomed to cigars that at first she did not realize what the object was. Her father had never smoked, nor drunk intoxicants; nor had Mr. Critchlow. Nobody had ever smoked in that house, where tobacco had always been regarded as equally licentious with cards, "the devil's playthings." Certainly Samuel had never smoked in the house, though the sight of the cigar-box reminded Constance of an occasion when her mother had announced an incredulous suspicion that Mr. Povey, fresh from an excursion into the world on a Thursday evening, "smelt of smoke."

She closed the harmonium and kept silence.

That very night, coming suddenly into the parlour, she caught Samuel at the harmonium. The lid went down with a resonant bang that awoke sympathetic vibrations in every corner of the room.

"What is it?" Constance inquired, jumping.

"Oh, nothing!" replied Mr. Povey, carelessly.

Each was deceiving the other: Mr. Povey hid his crime, and Constance hid her knowledge of his crime. False, false! But this is what marriage is.

And the next day Constance had a visit in the shop from a possible new servant, recommended to her by Mr. Holl, the grocer.

"Will you please step this way?" said Constance, with affable primness, steeped in the novel sense of what it is to be the sole responsible mistress of a vast household. She preceded the girl to the parlour, and as they passed the open door of Mr. Povey's cutting-out room, Constance had the clear vision and titillating odour of her husband smoking a cigar. He was in his shirt-sleeves, calmly cutting out, and Fan (the lady companion), at watch on the bench, yapped at the possible new servant.

"I think I shall try that girl," said she to Samuel at tea. She said nothing as to the cigar; nor did he.

On the following evening, after supper, Mr. Povey burst out:

"I think I'll have a weed! You didn't know I smoked, did you?"

Thus Mr. Povey came out in his true colours as a blood, a blade, and a gay spark.

But dogs and cigars, disconcerting enough in their degree, were to the signboard, when the signboard at last came, as skim milk is to hot brandy. It was the signboard that, more startlingly than anything else, marked the dawn of a new era in St. Luke's Square. Four men spent a day and a half in fixing it; they had ladders, ropes, and pulleys, and two of them dined on the flat lead roof of the projecting shop-windows. The signboard was thirty-five feet long and two feet in depth; over its centre was a semicircle about three feet in radius; this semicircle bore the legend, judiciously disposed, "S. Povey. Late." All the signboard proper was devoted to the words, "John Baines," in gold letters a foot and a half high, on a green ground.

The Square watched and wondered; and murmured: "Well, bless us! What next?"

It was agreed that in giving paramount importance to the name of his late father-in-law, Mr. Povey had displayed a very nice feeling.

Some asked with glee: "What'll the old lady have to say?"

Constance asked herself this, but not with glee. When Constance walked down the Square homewards, she could scarcely bear to look at the sign; the thought of what her mother might say frightened her. Her mother's first visit of state was imminent, and Aunt Harriet was to accompany her. Constance felt almost sick as the day approached. When she faintly hinted

her apprehensions to Samuel, he demanded, as if surprised—
"Haven't you mentioned it in one of your letters?"

"Oh *no!*"

"If that's all," said he, with bravado, "I'll write and tell her myself."

iv

So that Mrs. Baines was duly apprised of the signboard before her arrival. The letter written by her to Constance after receiving Samuel's letter, which was merely the amiable epistle of a son-in-law anxious to be a little more than correct, contained no reference to the signboard. This silence, however, did not in the least allay Constance's apprehensions as to what might occur when her mother and Samuel met beneath the signboard itself. It was therefore with a fearful as well as an eager, loving heart that Constance opened her side-door and ran down the steps when the waggonette stopped in King Street on the Thursday morning of the great visit of the sisters. But a surprise awaited her. Aunt Harriet had not come. Mrs. Baines explained, as she soundly kissed her daughter, that at the last moment Aunt Harriet had not felt well enough to undertake the journey. She sent her fondest love, and cake. Her pains had recurred. It was these mysterious pains which had prevented the sisters from coming to Bursley earlier. The word "cancer"—the continual terror of stout women—had been on their lips, without having been actually uttered; then there was a surcease, and each was glad that she had refrained from the dread syllables. In view of the recurrence, it was not unnatural that Mrs. Baines's vigorous cheerfulness should be somewhat forced.

"What is it, do you think?" Constance inquired.

Mrs. Baines pushed her lips out and raised her eyebrows—a gesture which meant that the pains might mean God knew what.

"I hope she'll be all right alone," observed Constance.

"Of course," said Mrs. Baines, quickly. "But you don't suppose I was going to disappoint you, do you?" she added, looking round as if to defy the fates in general.

This speech, and its tone, gave intense pleasure to Constance; and, laden with parcels, they mounted the stairs together, very content with each other, very happy in the discovery that they were still mother and daughter, very intimate in an inarticulate way.

Constance had imagined long, detailed, absorbing, and highly novel conversations between herself and her mother upon this their first meeting after her marriage. But alone in the bedroom, and with a clear half-hour to dinner, they neither of them seemed to have a great deal to impart.

Mrs. Baines slowly removed her light mantle and laid it with precautions on the white damask counterpane. Then, fingering her weeds, she glanced about the chamber. Nothing was changed. Though Constance had, previous to her marriage, envisaged certain alterations, she had determined to postpone them, feeling that one revolutionist in a house was enough.

"Well, my chick, you all right?" said Mrs. Baines, with hearty and direct energy, gazing straight into her daughter's eyes.

Constance perceived that the question was universal in its comprehensiveness, the one unique expression that the mother would give to her maternal concern and curiosity, and that it condensed into six words as much interest as would have overflowed into a whole day of the chatter of some mothers. She met the candid glance, flushing.

"Oh *yes!*" she answered with ecstatic fervour. "Perfectly!"

And Mrs. Baines nodded, as if dismissing *that*. "You're stouter," said she, curtly. "If you aren't careful you'll be as big as any of us."

"Oh, mother!"

The interview fell to a lower plane of emotion. It even fell as far as Maggie. What chiefly preoccupied Constance was a subtle change in her mother. She found her mother fussy in trifles. Her manner of laying down her mantle, of smoothing out her gloves, and her anxiety that her bonnet should not come to harm, were rather trying, were perhaps, in the very slightest degree, pitiable. It was nothing; it was barely perceptible, and yet it was enough to alter Constance's mental attitude to her mother. "Poor dear!" thought Constance. "I'm afraid she's not what she was." Incredible that her mother could have aged in less than six weeks! Constance did not allow for the chemistry that had been going on in herself.

The encounter between Mrs. Baines and her son-in-law was of the most satisfactory nature. He was waiting in the parlour for her to descend. He made himself exceedingly agreeable, kissing her, and flattering her by his evidently sincere desire to please. He explained that he had kept an eye open for the waggonette, but had been called away. His "Dear me!" on learning about Aunt Harriet lacked nothing in conviction, though both women knew that his affection for Aunt Harriet would never get the better of his reason. To Constance, her husband's behaviour was marvellously perfect. She had not suspected him to be such a man of the world. And her eyes said to her mother, quite unconsciously: "You see, after all, you didn't rate Sam as high as you ought to have done. Now you see your mistake."

As they sat waiting for dinner, Constance and Mrs. Baines on the sofa, and Samuel on the edge of the nearest rocking-chair, a small scuffling noise was heard outside the door which gave on the kitchen steps, the door yielded to pressure, and Fan rushed importantly in, deranging mats. Fan's nose had been hinting to her that she was behind the times, not up-to-date in the affairs of the household, and she had hurried from the kitchen to make inquiries. It occurred to her *en route* that she had been washed that morning. The spectacle of Mrs. Baines stopped her. She stood, with her legs slightly outstretched, her nose lifted, her ears raking forward, her bright eyes blinking, and her tail undecided. "I was sure I'd never smelt anything like that before," she was saying to herself, as she stared at Mrs. Baines.

And Mrs. Baines, staring at Fan, had a similar though not the same sentiment. The silence was terrible. Constance took on the mien of a culprit, and Sam had obviously lost his easy bearing of a man of the world. Mrs. Baines was merely thunderstruck.

A dog!

Suddenly Fan's tail began to wag more quickly; and then, having looked in vain for encouragement to her master and mistress, she gave one mighty spring and alighted in Mrs. Baines's lap. It was an aim she could not have missed. Constance emitted an "Oh, *Fan!*" of shocked terror, and Samuel betrayed his nervous tension by an involuntary movement. But Fan had settled down into that titanic lap as into heaven. It was a greater flattery than Mr. Povey's.

"So your name's Fan!" murmured Mrs. Baines, stroking the animal. "You are a dear!"

"Yes, isn't she?" said Constance, with inconceivable rapidity.

The danger was past. Thus, without any explanation, Fan became an accepted fact.

The next moment Maggie served the Yorkshire pudding.

"Well, Maggie," said Mrs. Baines. "So you are going to get married this time? When is it?"

"Sunday, ma'am."

"And you leave here on Saturday?"

"Yes, ma'am."

"Well, I must have a talk with you before I go."

During the dinner, not a word as to the signboard! Several times the conversation curved towards that signboard in the most alarming fashion, but invariably it curved away again, like a train from another train when two trains are simultaneously leaving a station. Constance had frights, so serious as to destroy her anxiety about the cookery. In the end she comprehended that her mother had adopted a silently disapproving attitude. Fan was socially very useful throughout the repast.

After dinner Constance was on pins lest Samuel should light a cigar. She had not requested him not to do so, for though she was entirely sure of his affection, she had already learned that a husband is possessed by a demon of contrariety which often forces him to violate his higher feelings. However, Samuel did not light a cigar. He went off to superintend the shutting-up of the shop, while Mrs. Baines chatted with Maggie and gave her £5 for a wedding present. Then Mr. Critchlow called to offer his salutations.

A little before tea Mrs. Baines announced that she would go out for a short walk by herself.

"Where has she gone to?" smiled Samuel, superiorly, as with Constance at the window he watched her turn down King Street towards the church.

"I expect she has gone to look at father's grave," said Constance.

"Oh!" muttered Samuel, apologetically.

Constance was mistaken. Before reaching the church, Mrs. Baines deviated to the right, got into Brougham Street and thence, by Acre Lane, into Oldcastle Street, whose steep she climbed. Now, Oldcastle Street ends at the top of St. Luke's Square, and from the corner Mrs. Baines had an excellent view of the signboard. It being Thursday afternoon, scarce a soul was about. She returned to her daughter's by the same extraordinary route, and said not a word on entering. But she was markedly cheerful.

The waggonette came after tea, and Mrs. Baines made her final preparations to depart. The visit had proved a wonderful success; it would have been utterly perfect if Samuel had not marred it at the very door of the waggonette. Somehow, he contrived to be talking of Christmas. Only a person of Samuel's native clumsiness would have mentioned Christmas in July.

"You know you'll spend Christmas with us!" said he into the waggonette.

"Indeed I shan't!" replied Mrs. Baines. "Aunt Harriet and I will expect you at Axe. We've already settled that."

Mr. Povey bridled. "Oh no!" he protested, hurt by this summariness.

Having had no relatives, except his cousin the confectioner, for many years, he had dreamt of at last establishing a family Christmas under his own roof, and the dream was dear to him.

Mrs. Baines said nothing. "We couldn't possibly leave the shop," said Mr. Povey.

"Nonsense!" Mrs. Baines retorted, putting her lips together. "Christmas Day is on a Monday."

The waggonette in starting jerked her head towards the door and set all her curls shaking. No white in those curls yet, scarcely a touch of grey!

"I shall take good care we don't go there anyway," Mr. Povey mumbled, in his heat, half to himself and half to Constance.

He had stained the brightness of the day.

CHAPTER II

Christmas and the Future

MR. POVEY was playing a hymn tune on the harmonium, it having been decided that no one should go to chapel. Constance, in mourning, with a white apron over her dress, sat on a hassock in front of the fire; and near her, in a rocking-chair, Mrs. Baines swayed very gently to and fro. The weather was ex-

tremely cold. Mr. Povey's mittened hands were blue and red;
but, like many shopkeepers, he had apparently grown almost
insensible to vagaries of temperature. Although the fire was
immense and furious, its influence, owing to the fact that the
mediæval grate was designed to heat the flue rather than the
room, seemed to die away at the borders of the fender. Constance could not have been much closer to it without being a
salamander. The era of good old-fashioned Christmases, so
agreeably picturesque for the poor, was not yet at an end.

Yes, Samuel Povey had won the battle concerning the *locus*
of the family Christmas. But he had received the help of a
formidable ally, death. Mrs. Harriet Maddack had passed
away, after an operation, leaving her house and her money to
her sister. The solemn rite of her interment had deeply affected
all the respectability of the town of Axe, where the late Mr.
Maddack had been a figure of consequence; it had even shut up
the shop in St. Luke's Square for a whole day. It was such a
funeral as Aunt Harriet herself would have approved, a tremendous ceremonial which left on the crushed mind an ineffaceable, intricate impression of shiny cloth, crape, horses with
arching necks and long manes, the drawl of parsons, cake,
port, sighs, and Christian submission to the inscrutable decrees
of Providence. Mrs. Baines had borne herself with unnatural
calmness until the funeral was over: and then Constance perceived that the remembered mother of her girlhood existed no
longer. For the majority of human souls it would have been
easier to love a virtuous principle, or a mountain, than to love
Aunt Harriet, who was assuredly less a woman than an institution. But Mrs. Baines had loved her, and she had been the
one person to whom Mrs. Baines looked for support and guidance. When she died, Mrs. Baines paid the tribute of respect
with the last hoarded remains of her proud fortitude, and weepingly confessed that the unconquerable had been conquered,
the inexhaustible exhausted; and became old with whitening
hair.

She had persisted in her refusal to spend Christmas in Bursley, but both Constance and Samuel knew that the resistance
was only formal. She soon yielded. When Constance's second
new servant took it into her head to leave a week before Christmas, Mrs. Baines might have pointed out the finger of Providence at work again, and this time in her favour. But no! With
amazing pliancy she suggested that she should bring one of her

own servants to "tide Constance over" Christmas. She was met with all the forms of loving solicitude, and she found that her daughter and son-in-law had "turned out of" the state bedroom in her favour. Intensely flattered by this attention (which was Mr. Povey's magnanimous idea), she nevertheless protested strongly. Indeed she "would not hear of it."

"Now, mother, don't be silly," Constance had said firmly. "You don't expect us to be at all the trouble of moving back again, do you?" And Mrs. Baines had surrendered in tears.

Thus had come Christmas. Perhaps it was fortunate that, the Axe servant being not quite the ordinary servant, but a benefactor where a benefactor was needed, both Constance and her mother thought it well to occupy themselves in household work, "sparing" the benefactor as much as possible. Hence Constance's white apron.

"There he is!" said Mr. Povey, still playing, but with his eye on the street.

Constance sprang up eagerly. Then there was a knock on the door. Constance opened, and an icy blast swept into the room. The postman stood on the steps, his instrument for knocking (like a drumstick) in one hand, a large bundle of letters in the other, and a yawning bag across the pit of his stomach.

"Merry Christmas, ma'am!" cried the postman, trying to keep warm by cheerfulness.

Constance, taking the letters, responded, while Mr. Povey, playing the harmonium with his right hand, drew half a crown from his pocket with the left.

"Here you are!" he said, giving it to Constance, who gave it to the postman.

Fan, who had been keeping her muzzle warm with the extremity of her tail on the sofa, jumped down to superintend the transaction.

"Brrr!" vibrated Mr. Povey as Constance shut the door.

"What lots!" Constance exclaimed, rushing to the fire. "Here, mother! Here, Sam!"

The girl had resumed possession of the woman's body.

Though the Baines family had few friends (sustained hospitality being little practised in those days) they had, of course, many acquaintances, and, like other families, they counted their Christmas cards as an Indian counts scalps. The tale was satisfactory. There were between thirty and forty envelopes. Constance extracted Christmas cards rapidly, reading their contents aloud, and then propping them up on the mantelpiece. Mrs. Baines assisted. Fan dealt with the envelopes on the floor. Mr. Povey, to prove that his soul was above toys and gewgaws, continued to play the harmonium.

"Oh, mother!" Constance murmured in a startled, hesitant voice, holding an envelope.

"What is it, my chuck?"

"It's——"

The envelope was addressed to "Mrs. and Miss Baines" in large, perpendicular, dashing characters which Constance instantly recognised as Sophia's. The stamps were strange, the postmark "Paris." Mrs. Baines leaned forward and looked.

"Open it, child," she said.

The envelope contained an English Christmas card of a common type, a spray of holly with greetings, and on it was written, "I do hope this will reach you on Christmas morning. Fondest love." No signature, nor address.

Mrs. Baines took it with a trembling hand, and adjusted her spectacles. She gazed at it a long time.

"And it has done!" she said, and wept.

She tried to speak again, but not being able to command herself, held forth the card to Constance and jerked her head in the direction of Mr. Povey. Constance rose and put the card on the keyboard of the harmonium.

"Sophia!" she whispered.

Mr. Povey stopped playing. "Dear, dear!" he muttered.

Fan, perceiving that nobody was interested in her feats, suddenly stood still.

Mrs. Baines tried once more to speak, but could not. Then, her ringlets shaking beneath the band of her weeds, she found her feet, stepped to the harmonium, and, with a movement almost convulsive, snatched the card from Mr. Povey, and returned to her chair.

Mr. Povey abruptly left the room, followed by Fan. Both the women were in tears, and he was tremendously surprised to discover a dangerous lump in his own throat. The beautiful and imperious vision of Sophia, Sophia as she had left them, innocent, wayward, had swiftly risen up before him and made even him a woman too! Yet he had never liked Sophia. The awful secret wound in the family pride revealed itself to him as never before, and he felt intensely the mother's tragedy, which she carried in her breast as Aunt Harriet had carried a cancer.

At dinner he said suddenly to Mrs. Baines, who still wept: "Now, mother, you must cheer up, you know."

"Yes, I must," she said quickly. And she did do.

Neither Samuel nor Constance saw the card again. Little was said. There was nothing to say. As Sophia had given no address she must be still ashamed of her situation. But she had thought of her mother and sister. She . . . she did not even know that Constance was married . . . What sort of a place was Paris? To Bursley, Paris was nothing but the site of a great exhibition which had recently closed.

Through the influence of Mrs. Baines a new servant was found for Constance in a village near Axe, a raw, comely girl who had never been in a "place." And through the post it was arranged that this innocent should come to the cave on the thirty-first of December. In obedience to the safe rule that servants should never be allowed to meet for the interchange of opinions, Mrs. Baines decided to leave with her own servant on the thirtieth. She would not be persuaded to spend the New Year in the Square. On the twenty-ninth poor Aunt Maria died all of a sudden in her cottage in Brougham Street. Everybody was duly distressed, and in particular Mrs. Baines's demeanour under this affliction showed the perfection of correctness. But she caused it to be understood that she should not remain for the funeral. Her nerves would be unequal to the ordeal; and, moreover, her servant must not stay to corrupt the new girl, nor could Mrs. Baines think of sending her servant to Axe in advance, to spend several days in idle gossip with her colleague.

This decision took the backbone out of Aunt Maria's funeral, which touched the extreme of modesty: a hearse and a one-horse coach. Mr. Povey was glad, because he happened to be very busy. An hour before his mother-in-law's departure he came into the parlour with the proof of a poster.

"What is that, Samuel?" asked Mrs. Baines, not dreaming of the blow that awaited her.

"It's for my first Annual Sale," replied Mr. Povey with false tranquillity.

Mrs. Baines merely tossed her head. Constance, happily for Constance, was not present at this final defeat of the old order. Had she been there, she would certainly not have known where to look.

ii

"Forty next birthday!" Mr. Povey exclaimed one day, with an expression and in a tone that were at once mock-serious and serious. This was on his thirty-ninth birthday.

Constance was startled. She had, of course, been aware that they were getting older, but she had never realized the phenomenon. Though customers occasionally remarked that Mr. Povey was stouter, and though when she helped him to measure himself for a new suit of clothes the tape proved the fact, he had not changed for her. She knew that she too had become somewhat stouter; but for herself, she remained exactly the same Constance. Only by recalling dates and by calculations could she really grasp that she had been married a little over six years and not a little over six months. She had to admit that, if Samuel would be forty next birthday, she would be twenty-seven next birthday. But it would not be a real twenty-seven; nor would Sam's forty be a real forty, like other people's twenty-sevens and forties. Not long since she had been in the habit of regarding a man of forty as senile, as practically in his grave.

She reflected, and the more she reflected the more clearly she saw that after all the almanacs had not lied. Look at Fan! Yes, it must be five years since the memorable morning when doubt first crossed the minds of Samuel and Constance as to Fan's moral principles. Samuel's enthusiasm for dogs was equalled by his ignorance of the dangers to which a young female of temperament may be exposed, and he was much disturbed as doubt developed into certainty. Fan, indeed, was the one being who did not suffer from shock and who had no fears as to the results. The animal, having a pure mind, was bereft of modesty. Sundry enormities had she committed, but none to rank with this one! The result was four quadrupeds recognizable as fox-terriers. Mr. Povey breathed again. Fan had had more luck than she deserved, for the result might have been simply anything. Her owners forgave her and disposed of these fruits of iniquity, and then married her lawfully to a husband who was so high up in the world that he could demand a dowry. And now Fan was a grandmother, with fixed ideas and habits, and a son in the house, and various grandchildren scattered over the town. Fan was a sedate and disillusioned dog.

She knew the world as it was, and in learning it she had taught her owners above a bit.

Then there was Maggie Hollins. Constance could still vividly recall the self-consciousness with which she had one day received Maggie and the heir of the Hollinses; but it was a long time ago. After staggering half the town by the production of this infant (of which she nearly died) Maggie allowed the angels to waft it away to heaven, and everybody said that she ought to be very thankful—at her age. Old women dug up out of their minds forgotten histories of the eccentricities of the goddess Lucina. Mrs. Baines was most curiously interested; she talked freely to Constance, and Constance began to see what an incredible town Bursley had always been—and she never suspected it! Maggie was now mother of other children, and the draggled, lame mistress of a drunken home, and looked sixty. Despite her prophecy, her husband had conserved his "habits." The Poveys ate all the fish they could, and sometimes more than they enjoyed, because on his sober days Hollins invariably started his round at the shop, and Constance had to buy for Maggie's sake. The worst of the worthless husband was that he seldom failed to be cheery and polite. He never missed asking after the health of Mrs. Baines. And when Constance replied that her mother was "pretty well considering," but that she would not come over to Bursley again until the Axe railway was opened, as she could not stand the drive, he would shake his grey head and be sympathetically gloomy for an instant.

All these changes in six years! The almanacs were in the right of it.

But nothing had happened to her. Gradually she had obtained a sure ascendency over her mother, yet without seeking it, merely as the outcome of time's influences on her and on her mother respectively. Gradually she had gained skill and use in the management of her household and of her share of the shop, so that these machines ran smoothly and effectively and a sudden contretemps no longer frightened her. Gradually she had constructed a chart of Samuel's individuality, with the submerged rocks and perilous currents all carefully marked, so that she could now voyage unalarmed in those seas. But nothing happened. Unless their visits to Buxton could be called happenings! Decidedly the visit to Buxton was the one little hill that rose out of the level plain of the year. They formed the annual habit of going to Buxton for ten days. They had a way of saying: "Yes, we always go to Buxton. We went there for our honeymoon, you know." They had become confirmed Buxtonites, with views concerning St. Anne's Terrace, the Broad Walk and Peel's Cavern. They could not dream of deserting their Buxton. It was the sole possible resort. Was it not the highest town in England? Well, then! They always stayed at the same lodgings, and grew to be special favourites of the landlady, who whispered of them to all her other guests as having come to her house for their honeymoon, and as never missing a year, and as being most respectable, superior people in quite a large way of business. Each year they walked out of Buxton station behind their luggage on a truck, full of joy and pride because they knew all the landmarks, and the lie of all the streets, and which were the best shops.

At the beginning, the notion of leaving the shop to hired custody had seemed almost fantastic, and the preparations for absence had been very complicated. Then it was that Miss Insull had detached herself from the other young lady assistants as a creature who could be absolutely trusted. Miss Insull was older than Constance; she had a bad complexion, and she was not clever, but she was one of your reliable ones. The six years had witnessed the slow, steady rise of Miss Insull. Her employers said "Miss Insull" in a tone quite different from that in which they said "Miss Hawkins," or "Miss Dadd." "Miss Insull" meant the end of a discussion. "Better tell Miss Insull." "Miss Insull will see to that." "I shall ask Miss Insull." Miss Insull slept in the house ten nights every year. Miss Insull had been called into consultation when it was decided to engage a fourth hand in the shape of an apprentice.

Trade had improved in the point of excellence. It was now admitted to be good—a rare honour for trade! The coal-mining boom was at its height, and colliers, in addition to getting drunk, were buying American organs and expensive bull-terriers. Often they would come to the shop to purchase cloth for coats for their dogs. And they would have good cloth. Mr. Povey did not like this. One day a butty chose for his dog the best cloth of Mr. Povey's shop—at 12s. a yard. "Will ye make it up? I've gotten th' measurements," asked the collier. "No, I won't!" said Mr. Povey, hotly. "And what's more, I won't sell you the cloth either! Cloth at 12s. a yard on a dog's back indeed! I'll thank you to get out of my shop!" The incident be-

came historic, in the Square. It finally established that Mr.
Povey was a worthy son-in-law and a solid and successful man.
It vindicated the old pre-eminence of "Baines's." Some surprise
was expressed that Mr. Povey showed no desire nor tendency
towards entering the public life of the town. But he never
would, though a keen satirical critic of the Local Board in private. And at the chapel he remained a simple private worshipper, refusing stewardships and trusteeships.

iii

Was Constance happy? Of course there was always something on her mind, something that had to be dealt with, either
in the shop or in the house, something to employ all the skill
and experience which she had acquired. Her life had much in
it of laborious tedium—tedium never-ending and monotonous.
And both she and Samuel worked consistently hard, rising
early, "pushing forward," as the phrase ran, and going to bed
early from sheer fatigue; week after week and month after
month as season changed imperceptibly into season. In June
and July it would happen to them occasionally to retire before
the last silver of dusk was out of the sky. They would lie in
bed and talk placidly of their daily affairs. There would be a
noise in the street below. "Vaults closing!" Samuel would say,
and yawn. "Yes, it's quite late," Constance would say. And the
Swiss clock would rapidly strike eleven on its coil of resonant
wire. And then, just before she went to sleep, Constance might
reflect upon her destiny, as even the busiest and smoothest
women do, and she would decide that it was kind. Her mother's
gradual decline and lonely life at Axe saddened her. The cards
which came now and then at extremely long intervals from
Sophia had been the cause of more sorrow than joy. The naïve
ecstasies of her girlhood had long since departed—the price
paid for experience and self-possession and a true vision of
things. The vast inherent melancholy of the universe did not
exempt her. But as she went to sleep she would be conscious of
a vague contentment. The basis of this contentment was the
fact that she and Samuel comprehended and esteemed each
other, and made allowances for each other. Their characters
had been tested and had stood the test. Affection, love, was not
to them a salient phenomenon in their relations. Habit had in-

evitably dulled its glitter. It was like a flavouring, scarce remarked; but had it been absent, how they would have turned
from that dish!

Samuel never, or hardly ever, set himself to meditate upon
the problem whether or not life had come up to his expecta-
tions. But he had, at times, strange sensations which he did not
analyze, and which approached nearer to ecstasy than any feeling of Constance's. Thus, when he was in one of his dark furies,
molten within and black without, the sudden thought of his
wife's unalterable benignant calm, which nothing could over-
throw, might strike him into a wondering cold. For him she was
astoundingly feminine. She would put flowers on the mantelpiece, and then, hours afterwards, in the middle of a meal, ask
him unexpectedly what he thought of her "garden;" and he
gradually divined that a perfunctory reply left her unsatisfied;
she wanted a genuine opinion; a genuine opinion mattered to
her. Fancy calling flowers on a mantelpiece a "garden"! How
charming, how childlike! Then she had a way, on Sunday
mornings, when she descended to the parlour all ready for
chapel, of shutting the door at the foot of the stairs with a
little bang, shaking herself, and turning round swiftly as if
for his inspection, as if saying: "Well, what about this? Will
this do?" A phenomenon always associated in his mind with
the smell of kid gloves! Invariably she asked him about the
colours and cut of her dresses. Would he prefer this, or that?
He could not take such questions seriously until one day he
happened to hint, merely hint, that he was not a thorough-
going admirer of a certain new dress—it was her first new
dress after the definite abandonment of crinolines. She never
wore it again. He thought she was not serious at first, and remonstrated against a joke being carried too far. She said:
"It's not a bit of use you talking, I shan't wear it again."
And then he so far appreciated her seriousness as to refrain,
by discretion, from any comment. The incident affected him
for days. It flattered him; it thrilled him; but it baffled him.
Strange that a woman subject to such caprices should be so
sagacious, capable, and utterly reliable as Constance was! For
the practical and commonsense side of her eternally compelled
his admiration. The very first example of it—her insistence that
the simultaneous absence of both of them from the shop for
half an hour or an hour twice a day would not mean the immediate downfall of the business—had remained in his mind

ever since. Had she not been obstinate—in her benevolent way —against the old superstition which he had acquired from his employers, they might have been eating separately to that day. Then her handling of her mother during the months of the siege of Paris, when Mrs. Baines was convinced that her sinful daughter was in hourly danger of death, had been extraordinarily fine, he considered. And the sequel, a card for Constance's birthday, had completely justified her attitude.

Sometimes some blundering fool would jovially exclaim to them:

"What about that baby?"

Or a woman would remark quietly: "I often feel sorry you've no children."

And they would answer that really they did not know what they would do if there was a baby. What with the shop and one thing or another . . . . ! And they were quite sincere.

iv

It is remarkable what a little thing will draw even the most regular and serious people from the deep groove of their habits. One morning in March, a boneshaker, an affair on two equal wooden wheels joined by a bar of iron, in the middle of which was a wooden saddle, disturbed the gravity of St. Luke's Square. True, it was probably the first boneshaker that had ever attacked the gravity of St. Luke's Square. It came out of the shop of Daniel Povey, the confectioner and baker, and Samuel Povey's celebrated cousin, in Boulton Terrace. Boulton Terrace formed nearly a right angle with the Baines premises, and at the corner of the angle Wedgwood Street and King Street left the Square. The boneshaker was brought forth by Dick Povey, the only son of Daniel, now aged eleven years, under the superintendence of his father, and the Square soon perceived that Dick had a natural talent for breaking-in an untrained boneshaker. After a few attempts he could remain on the back of the machine for at least ten yards, and his feats had the effect of endowing St. Luke's Square with the attractiveness of a circus. Samuel Povey watched with candid interest from the ambush of his door, while the unfortunate young lady assistants, though aware of the performance that was going on, dared not stir from the stove. Samuel was tre-

mendously tempted to sally out boldly, and chat with his cousin
about the toy; he had surely a better right to do so than any
other tradesman in the Square, since he was of the family; but
his diffidence prevented him from moving. Presently Daniel
Povey and Dick went to the top of the Square with the machine, opposite Holl's, and Dick, being carefully installed in
the saddle, essayed to descend the gentle paven slopes of the
Square. He failed time after time; the machine had an astonishing way of turning round, running uphill, and then lying
calmly on its side. At this point of Dick's life-history every
shop-door in the Square was occupied by an audience. At last
the boneshaker displayed less unwillingness to obey, and lo!
in a moment Dick was riding down the Square, and the spectators held their breath as if he had been Blondin crossing
Niagara. Every second he ought to have fallen off, but he contrived to keep upright. Already he had accomplished twenty
yards—thirty yards! It was a miracle that he was performing! The transit continued, and seemed to occupy hours. And
then a faint hope rose in the breast of the watchers that the
prodigy might arrive at the bottom of the Square. His speed
was increasing with his "nack." But the Square was enormous,
boundless. Samuel Povey gazed at the approaching phenomenon, as a bird at a serpent, with bulging, beady eyes. The
child's speed went on increasing and his path grew straighter.
Yes, he would arrive; he would do it! Samuel Povey involuntarily lifted one leg in his nervous tension. And now the hope
that Dick would arrive became a fear, as his pace grew still
more rapid. Everybody lifted one leg, and gaped. And the in-
trepid child surged on, and, finally victorious, crashed into the
pavement in front of Samuel at the rate of quite six miles an
hour.

Samuel picked him up, unscathed. And somehow this picking
up of Dick invested Samuel with importance, gave him a share
in the glory of the feat itself.

Daniel Povey came running and joyous. "Not so bad for a
start, eh?" exclaimed the great Daniel. Though by no means
a simple man, his pride in his offspring sometimes made him a
little naïve.

Father and son explained the machine to Samuel, Dick incessantly repeating the exceedingly strange truth that if you felt
you were falling to your right you must turn to your right and
vice versa. Samuel found himself suddenly admitted, as it were,

to the inner fellowship of the boneshaker, exalted above the rest
of the Square. In another adventure more thrilling events occurred. The fair-haired Dick was one of those dangerous, frenzied madcaps who are born without fear. The secret of the
machine had been revealed to him in his recent transit, and he
was silently determining to surpass himself. Precariously balanced, he descended the Square again, frowning hard, his teeth
set, and actually managed to swerve into King Street. Constance, in the parlour, saw an incomprehensible winged thing
fly past the window. The cousins Povey sounded an alarm and
protest and ran in pursuit; for the gradient of King Street is,
in the strict sense, steep. Half-way down King Street Dick was
travelling at twenty miles an hour, and heading straight for
the church, as though he meant to disestablish it and perish.
The main gate of the churchyard was open, and that affright-
ing child, with a lunatic's luck, whizzed safely through the portals into God's acre. The cousins Povey discovered him lying on
a green grave, clothed in pride. His first words were: "Dad,
did you pick my cap up?" The symbolism of the amazing ride
did not escape the Square; indeed, it was much discussed.

This incident led to a friendship between the cousins. They
formed a habit of meeting in the Square for a chat. The meetings were the subject of comment, for Samuel's relations with
the greater Daniel had always been of the most distant. It was
understood that Samuel disapproved of Mrs. Daniel Povey
even more than the majority of people disapproved of her.
Mrs. Daniel Povey, however, was away from home; probably,
had she not been, Samuel would not even have gone to the
length of joining Daniel on the neutral ground of the open
Square. But having once broken the ice, Samuel was glad to be
on terms of growing intimacy with his cousin. The friendship
flattered him, for Daniel, despite his wife, was a figure in a
world larger than Samuel's; moreover, it consecrated his position as the equal of no matter what tradesman (apprentice
though he had been), and also he genuinely liked and admired
Daniel, rather to his own astonishment.

Every one liked Daniel Povey; he was a favourite among all
ranks. The leading confectioner, a member of the Local Board,
and a sidesman at St. Luke's, he was, and had been for twenty-
five years, very prominent in the town. He was a tall, handsome
man, with a trimmed, greying beard, a jolly smile, and a flashing, dark eye. His good humour seemed to be permanent. He

had dignity without the slightest stiffness; he was welcomed by his equals and frankly adored by his inferiors. He ought to have been Chief Bailiff, for he was rich enough; but there intervened a mysterious obstacle between Daniel Povey and the supreme honour, a scarcely tangible impediment which could not be definitely stated. He was capable, honest, industrious, successful, and an excellent speaker; and if he did not belong to the austerer section of society, if, for example, he thought nothing of dropping into the Tiger for a glass of beer, or of using an oath occasionally, or of telling a facetious story—well, in a busy, broad-minded town of thirty thousand inhabitants, such proclivities are no bar whatever to perfect esteem. But—how is one to phrase it without wronging Daniel Povey? He was entirely moral; his views were unexceptionable. The truth is that, for the ruling classes of Bursley, Daniel Povey was just a little too fanatical a worshipper of the god Pan. He was one of the remnant who had kept alive the great Pan tradition from the days of the Regency through the vast, arid Victorian expanse of years. The flighty character of his wife was regarded by many as a judgment upon him for the robust Rabelaisianism of his more private conversation, for his frank interest in, his eternal preoccupation with, aspects of life and human activity which, though essential to the divine purpose, are not openly recognized as such—even by Daniel Poveys. It was not a question of his conduct; it was a question of the cast of his mind. If it did not explain his friendship with the rector of St. Luke's, it explained his departure from the Primitive Methodist connexion, to which the Poveys as a family had belonged since Primitive Methodism was created in Turnhill in 1807.

Daniel Povey had a way of assuming that every male was boiling over with interest in the sacred cult of Pan. The assumption, though sometimes causing inconvenience at first, usually conquered by virtue of its inherent truthfulness. Thus it fell out with Samuel. Samuel had not suspected that Pan had silken cords to draw him. He had always averted his eyes from the god—that is to say, within reason. Yet now Daniel, on perhaps a couple of fine mornings a week, in full Square, with Fan sitting behind on the cold stones, and Mr. Critchlow ironic at his door in a long white apron, would entertain Samuel Povey for half an hour with Pan's most intimate lore, and Samuel Povey would not blench. He would, on the contrary, stand up to Daniel like a little man, and pretend with all his might to be, potentially, a perfect arch-priest of the god. Daniel taught him a lot; turned over the page of life for him, as it were, and, showing the reverse side, seemed to say: "You were missing all that." Samuel gazed upwards at the handsome long nose and rich lips of his elder cousin, so experienced, so agreeable, so renowned, so esteemed, so philosophic, and admitted to himself that he had lived to the age of forty in a state of comparative boobyism. And then he would gaze downwards at the faint patch of flour on Daniel's right leg, and conceive that life was, and must be, life.

Not many weeks after his initiation into the cult he was startled by Constance's preoccupied face one evening. Now, a husband of six years' standing, to whom it has not happened to become a father, is not easily startled by such a face as Constance wore. Years ago he had frequently been startled, had frequently lived in suspense for a few days. But he had long since grown impervious to these alarms. And now he was startled again—but as a man may be startled who is not altogether surprised at being startled. And seven endless days passed, and Samuel and Constance glanced at each other like guilty things, whose secret refuses to be kept. Then three more days passed, and another three. Then Samuel Povey remarked, in a firm, masculine, fact-fronting tone:

"Oh, there's no doubt about it!"

And they glanced at each other like conspirators who have lighted a fuse and cannot take refuge in flight. Their eyes said continually, with a delicious, an enchanting mixture of ingenuous modesty and fearful joy:

"Well, we've gone and done it!"

There it was, the incredible, incomprehensible future—coming!

Samuel had never correctly imagined the manner of its heralding. He had imagined in his early simplicity that one day Constance, blushing, might put her mouth to his ear and whisper—something positive. It had not occurred in the least like that. But things are so obstinately, so incurably unsentimental.

"I think we ought to drive over and tell mother, on Sunday," said Constance.

His impulse was to reply, in his grand, offhand style: "Oh, a letter will do!"

But he checked himself and said, with careful deference: "You think that will be better than writing?"

All was changed. He braced every fibre to meet destiny, and to help Constance to meet it.

The weather threatened on Sunday. He went to Axe without Constance. His cousin drove him there in a dog-cart, and he announced that he should walk home, as the exercise would do him good. During the drive Daniel, in whom he had not confided, chattered as usual, and Samuel pretended to listen with the same attitude as usual; but secretly he despised Daniel for a man who has got something not of the first importance on the brain. His perspective was truer than Daniel's.

He walked home, as he had decided, over the wavy moorland of the county dreaming in the heart of England. Night fell on him in mid-career, and he was tired. But the earth, as it whirled through naked space, whirled up the moon for him, and he pressed on at a good speed. A wind from Arabia wandering cooled his face. And at last, over the brow of Toft End, he saw suddenly the Five Towns a-twinkle on their little hills down in the vast amphitheatre. And one of those lamps was Constance's lamp—one, somewhere. He lived, then. He entered into the shadow of nature. The mysteries made him solemn. What! A boneshaker, his cousin, and then this!

"Well, I'm damned! Well, I'm damned!" he kept repeating, he who never swore.

CHAPTER III

CYRIL

CONSTANCE stood at the large, many-paned window in the parlour. She was stouter. Although always plump, her figure had been comely, with a neat, well-marked waist. But now the shapeliness had gone; the waist-line no longer existed, and there were no more crinolines to create it artificially. An observer not under the charm of her face might have been excused for calling her fat and lumpy. The face, grave, kind, and expectant, with its radiant, fresh cheeks, and the rounded softness of its curves, atoned for the figure. She was nearly twenty-nine years of age.

It was late in October. In Wedgwood Street, next to Boulton Terrace, all the little brown houses had been pulled down to make room for a palatial covered market, whose foundations were then being dug. This destruction exposed a vast area of sky to the north-east. A great dark cloud with an untidy edge rose massively out of the depths and curtained off the tender blue of approaching dusk; while in the west, behind Constance, the sun was setting in calm and gorgeous melancholy on the Thursday hush of the town. It was one of those afternoons which gather up all the sadness of the moving earth and transform it into beauty.

Samuel Povey turned the corner from Wedgwood Street, and crossed King Street obliquely to the front-door, which Constance opened. He seemed tired and anxious.

"Well?" demanded Constance, as he entered.

"She's no better. There's no getting away from it, she's worse. I should have stayed, only I knew you'd be worrying. So I caught the three-fifty."

"How is that Mrs. Gilchrist shaping as a nurse?"

"She's very good," said Samuel, with conviction. "Very good!"

"What a blessing! I suppose you didn't happen to see the doctor?"

"Yes, I did."

"What did he say to you?"

Samuel gave a deprecating gesture. "Didn't say anything particular. With dropsy, at that stage, you know . . ."

Constance had returned to the window, her expectancy apparently unappeased.

"I don't like the look of that cloud," she murmured.

"What! Are they out still?" Samuel inquired, taking off his overcoat.

"Here they are!" cried Constance. Her features suddenly transfigured, she sprang to the door, pulled it open, and descended the steps.

A perambulator was being rapidly pushed up the slope by a breathless girl.

"Amy," Constance gently protested, "I told you not to venture far."

"I hurried all I could, mum, soon as I seed that cloud," the girl puffed, with the air of one who is seriously thankful to have escaped a great disaster.

Constance dived into the recesses of the perambulator and extricated from its cocoon the centre of the universe, and scrutinized him with quiet passion, and then rushed with him into the house, though not a drop of rain had yet fallen.

"Precious!" exclaimed Amy, in ecstasy, her young virginal eyes following him till he disappeared. Then she wheeled away the perambulator, which now had no more value nor interest than an egg-shell. It was necessary to take it right round to the Brougham Street yard entrance, past the front of the closed shop.

Constance sat down on the horsehair sofa and hugged and kissed her prize before removing his bonnet.

"Here's Daddy!" she said to him, as if imparting strange and rapturous tidings. "Here's Daddy come back from hanging up his coat in the passage! Daddy rubbing his hands!" And then, with a swift transition of voice and features: "Do look at him, Sam!"

Samuel, preoccupied, stooped forward. "Oh, you little scoundrel! Oh, you little scoundrel!" he greeted the baby, advancing his finger towards the baby's nose.

The baby, who had hitherto maintained a passive indifference to external phenomena, lifted elbows and toes, blew bubbles from his tiny mouth, and stared at the finger with the most ravishing, roguish smile, as though saying: "I know that great sticking-out limb, and there's a joke about it which no one but me can see, and which is my secret joy that you shall never share."

"Tea ready?" Samuel asked, resuming his gravity and his ordinary pose.

"You must give the girl time to take her things off," said Constance. "We'll have the table drawn away from the fire, and baby can lie on his shawl on the hearthrug while we're having tea." Then to the baby, in rapture: "And play with his toys; all his nice, nice toys!"

"You know Miss Insull is staying for tea?"

Constance, her head bent over the baby, who formed a white patch on her comfortable brown frock, nodded without speaking.

Samuel Povey, walking to and fro, began to enter into details of his hasty journey to Axe. Old Mrs. Baines, having beheld her grandson, was preparing to quit this world. Never again would she exclaim, in her brusque tone of genial ruthlessness: "Fiddlesticks!" The situation was very difficult and distressing, for Constance could not leave her baby, and she would not, until the last urgency, run the risks of a journey with him to Axe. He was being weaned. In any case Constance could not have undertaken the nursing of her mother. A nurse had to be found. Mr. Povey had discovered one in the person of Mrs. Gilchrist, the second wife of a farmer at Malpas in Cheshire, whose first wife had been a sister of the late John Baines. All the credit of Mrs. Gilchrist was due to Samuel Povey. Mrs. Baines fretted seriously about Sophia, who had given no sign of life for a very long time. Mr. Povey went to Manchester and ascertained definitely from the relatives of Scales that nothing was known of the pair. He did not go to Manchester especially on this errand. About once in three weeks, on Tuesdays, he had to visit the Manchester warehouses; but the tracking of Scales's relative cost him so much trouble and time that, curiously, he came to believe that he had gone to Manchester one Tuesday for no other end. Although he was very busy indeed in the shop, he flew over to Axe and back whenever he possibly could, to the neglect of his affairs. He was glad to do all that was in his power; even if he had not done it graciously his sensitive, tyrannic conscience would have forced him to do it. But nevertheless he felt rather virtuous, and worry and fatigue and loss of sleep intensified this sense of virtue.

"So that if there is any sudden change they will telegraph," he finished, to Constance.

She raised her head. The words, clinching what had led up to them, drew her from her dream and she saw, for a moment, her mother in an agony.

"But you don't surely mean——?" she began, trying to disperse the painful vision as unjustified by the facts.

"My dear girl," said Samuel, with head singing, and hot eyes, and a consciousness of high tension in every nerve of his body, "I simply mean that if there's any sudden change they will telegraph."

While they had tea, Samuel sitting opposite to his wife, and Miss Insull nearly against the wall (owing to the moving of the table), the baby rolled about on the hearthrug, which had been covered with a large soft woollen shawl, originally the property of his great-grandmother. He had no cares, no responsibilities. The shawl was so vast that he could not clearly distinguish objects beyond its confines. On it lay an indiarubber ball, an indiarubber doll, a rattle, and fan. He vaguely recollected all four items, with their respective properties. The fire also was an old friend. He had occasionally tried to touch it, but a high bright fence always came in between. For ten months he had never spent a day without making experiments on this shifting universe in which he alone remained firm and stationary. The experiments were chiefly conducted out of idle amusement, but he was serious on the subject of food. Lately the behaviour of the universe in regard to his food had somewhat perplexed him, had indeed annoyed him. However, he was of a forgetful, happy disposition, and so long as the universe continued to fulfil its sole end as a machinery for the satisfaction, somehow, of his imperious desires, he was not inclined to remonstrate. He gazed at the flames and laughed, and laughed because he had laughed. He pushed the ball away and wriggled after it, and captured it with the assurance of practice. He tried to swallow the doll, and it was not until he had tried several times to swallow it that he remembered the failure of previous efforts and philosophically desisted. He rolled with a fearful shock, arms and legs in air, against the mountainous flank of that mammoth Fan, and clutched at Fan's ear. The whole mass of Fan upheaved and vanished from his view, and was instantly forgotten by him. He seized the doll and tried to swallow it, and repeated the exhibition of his skill with the ball. Then he saw the fire again and laughed. And so he existed for centuries: no responsibilities, no appetites; and the shawl was vast. Terrific operations went on over his head. Giants moved to and fro. Great vessels were carried off and great books were brought and deep voices rumbled regularly in the spaces beyond the shawl. But he remained oblivious. At last he became aware that a face was looking down at his. He recognized it, and immediately an uncomfortable sensation in his stomach disturbed him; he tolerated it for fifty years or so, and then he gave a little cry. Life had resumed its seriousness.

"Black alpaca. B quality. Width 20, t.a. 22 yards," Miss Insull read out of a great book. She and Mr. Povey were checking stock.

And Mr. Povey responded, "Black alpaca B quality. Width 20, t.a. 22 yards. It wants ten minutes yet." He had glanced at the clock.

"Does it?" said Constance, well knowing that it wanted ten minutes.

The baby did not guess that a high invisible god named Samuel Povey, whom nothing escaped, and who could do everything at once, was controlling his universe from an inconceivable distance. On the contrary, the baby was crying to himself, There is no God.

His weaning had reached the stage at which a baby really does not know what will happen next. The annoyance had begun exactly three months after his first tooth, such being the rule of the gods, and it had grown more and more disconcerting. No sooner did he accustom himself to a new phenomenon than it mysteriously ceased, and an old one took its place which he had utterly forgotten. This afternoon his mother nursed him, but not until she had foolishly attempted to divert him from the seriousness of life by means of gewgaws of which he was sick. Still, once at her rich breast, he forgave and forgot all. He preferred her simple natural breast to more modern inventions. And he had no shame, no modesty. Nor had his mother. It was an indecent carouse at which his father and Miss Insull had to assist. But his father had shame. His father would have preferred that, as Miss Insull had kindly offered to stop and work on Thursday afternoon, and as the shop was chilly, the due rotation should have brought the bottle round at half-past five o'clock, and not the mother's breast. He was a self-conscious parent, rather apologetic to the world, rather apt to stand off and pretend that he had nothing to do with the affair; and he genuinely disliked that anybody should witness the intimate scene of *his* wife feeding *his* baby. Especially Miss Insull, that prim, dark, moustached spinster! He would not have called it an outrage on Miss Insull, to force her to witness the scene, but his idea approached within sight of the word.

Constance blandly offered herself to the child, with the unconscious primitive savagery of a young mother, and as the baby fed, thoughts of her own mother flitted to and fro ceaselessly like vague shapes over the deep sea of content which filled her mind. This illness of her mother's was abnormal, and the baby was now, for the first time perhaps, entirely normal in her consciousness. The baby was something which could be disturbed, not something which did disturb. What a change! What a change that had seemed impossible until its full accomplishment!

For months before the birth, she had glimpsed at nights and in other silent hours the tremendous upset. She had not allowed herself to be silly in advance; by temperament she was too sagacious, too well balanced for that; but she had

had fitful instants of terror, when solid ground seemed to sink away from her, and imagination shook at what faced her. Instants only! Usually she could play the comedy of sensible calmness to almost perfection. Then the appointed time drew nigh. And still she smiled, and Samuel smiled. But the preparations, meticulous, intricate, revolutionary, belied their smiles. The intense resolve to keep Mrs. Baines, by methods scrupulous or unscrupulous, away from Bursley until all was over, belied their smiles. And then the first pains, sharp, shocking, cruel, heralds of torture! But when they had withdrawn, she smiled, again, palely. Then she was in bed, full of the sensation that the whole house was inverted and disorganized, hopelessly. And the doctor came into the room. She smiled at the doctor apologetically, foolishly, as if saying: "We all come to it. Here I am." She was calm without. Oh, but what a prey of abject fear within! "I am at the edge of the precipice," her thought ran; "in a moment I shall be over." And then the pains—not the heralds but the shattering army, endless, increasing in terror as they thundered across her. Yet she could think, quite clearly: "Now I'm in the middle of it. This is *it*, the horror that I have not dared to look at. My life's in the balance. I may never get up again. All has at last come to pass. It seemed as if it would never come, as if this thing could not happen to *me*. But at last it has come to pass!"

Ah! Some one put the twisted end of a towel into her hand again—she had loosed it; and she pulled, pulled, enough to break cables. And then she shrieked. It was for pity. It was for some one to help her, at any rate to take notice of her. She was dying. Her soul was leaving her. And she was alone, panic-stricken, in the midst of a cataclysm a thousand times surpassing all that she had imagined of sickening horror. "I cannot endure this," she thought passionately. "It is impossible that I should be asked to endure this!" And then she wept; beaten, terrorized, smashed and riven. No commonsense now! No wise calmness now! No self-respect now! Why, not even a woman now! Nothing but a kind of animalized victim! And then the supreme endless spasm, during which she gave up the ghost and bade good-bye to her very self. . . .

She was lying quite comfortable in the soft bed; idle, silly; happiness forming like a thin crust over the lava of her anguish and her fright. And by her side was the soul that had fought its way out of her, ruthlessly; the secret disturber revealed to the light of morning. Curious to look at! Not like any baby that she had ever seen; red, creased, brutish! But—for some reason that she did not examine—she folded it in an immense tenderness.

Sam was by the bed, away from her eyes. She was so comfortable and silly that she could not move her head nor even ask him to come round to her eyes. She had to wait till he came.

In the afternoon the doctor returned, and astounded her by saying that hers had been an ideal confinement. She was too weary to rebuke him for a senseless, blind, callous old man. But she knew what she knew. "No one will ever guess," she thought, "no one ever can guess, what I've been through! Talk as you like. I *know*, now."

Gradually she had resumed cognizance of her household, perceiving that it was demoralized from top to bottom, and that when the time came to begin upon it she would not be able to settle where to begin, even supposing that the baby were not there to monopolize her attention. The task appalled her. Then she wanted to get up. Then she got up. What a blow to self-confidence! She went back to bed like a little scared rabbit to its hole, glad, glad to be on the soft pillows again. She said: "Yet the time must come when I shall be downstairs, and walking about and meeting people, and cooking and superintending the millinery." Well, it did come—except that she had to renounce the millinery to Miss Insull—but it was not the same. No, different! The baby pushed everything else on to another plane. He was a terrific intruder; not one minute of her old daily life was left; he made no compromise whatever. If she turned away her gaze from him he might pop off into eternity and leave her.

And now she was calmly and sensibly giving him suck in presence of Miss Insull. She was used to his importance, to the fragility of his organism, to waking twice every night, to being fat. She was strong again. The convulsive twitching that for six months had worried her repose, had quite disappeared. The state of being a mother was normal, and the baby was so normal that she could not conceive the house without him.

All in ten months!

When the baby was installed in his cot for the night, she came downstairs and found Miss Insull and Samuel still working, and harder than ever, but at addition sums now. She sat down, leaving the door open at the foot of the stairs. She had embroidery in hand: a cap. And while Miss Insull and Samuel combined pounds, shillings, and pence, whispering at great speed, she bent over the delicate, intimate, wasteful handiwork, drawing the needle with slow exactitude. Then she would raise her head and listen.

"Excuse me," said Miss Insull, "I think I hear baby crying."

"And two are eight and three are eleven. He must cry," said Mr. Povey, rapidly, without looking up.

The baby's parents did not make a practice of discussing their domestic existence even with Miss Insull; but Constance had to justify herself as a mother.

"I've made perfectly sure he's comfortable," said Constance. "He's only crying because he fancies he's neglected. And we think he can't begin too early to learn."

"How right you are!" said Miss Insull. "Two and carry three."

That distant, feeble, querulous, pitiful cry continued obstinately. It continued for thirty minutes. Constance could not proceed with her work. The cry disintegrated her will, dissolved her hard sagacity.

Without a word she crept upstairs, having carefully deposed the cap on her rocking-chair.

Mr. Povey hesitated a moment and then bounded up after her, startling Fan. He shut the door on Miss Insull, but Fan was too quick for him. He saw Constance with her hand on the bedroom door.

"My dear girl," he protested, holding himself in. "Now what *are* you going to do?"

"I'm just listening," said Constance.

"Do be reasonable and come downstairs."

He spoke in a low voice, scarcely masking his nervous irritation, and tiptoed along the corridor towards her and up the two steps past the gas-burner. Fan followed, wagging her tail expectant.

"Suppose he's not well?" Constance suggested.

"Pshaw!" Mr. Povey exclaimed contemptuously. "You remember what happened last night and what you said!"

They argued, subduing their tones to the false semblance of good-will, there in the closeness of the corridor. Fan, deceived, ceased to wag her tail and then trotted away. The baby's cry, behind the door, rose to a mysterious despairing howl, which had such an effect on Constance's heart that she could have walked through fire to reach the baby. But Mr. Povey's will held her. And she rebelled, angry, hurt, resentful. Common-sense, the ideal of mutual forbearance, had winged away from that excited pair. It would have assuredly ended in a quarrel, with Samuel glaring at her in black fury from the other side of a bottomless chasm, had not Miss Insull most surprisingly burst up the stairs.

Mr. Povey turned to face her, swallowing his emotion.

"A telegram!" said Miss Insull. "The postmaster brought it down himself—"

"What? Mr. Derry?" asked Samuel, opening the telegram with an affectation of majesty.

"Yes. He said it was too late for delivery by rights. But as it seemed very important . . ."

Samuel scanned it and nodded gravely; then gave it to his wife. Tears came into her eyes.

"I'll get Cousin Daniel to drive me over at once," said Samuel, master of himself and of the situation.

"Wouldn't it be better to hire?" Constance suggested. She had a prejudice against Daniel.

Mr. Povey shook his head. "He offered," he replied. "I can't refuse his offer."

"Put your thick overcoat on, dear," said Constance, in a dream, descending with him.

"I hope it isn't—" Miss Insull stopped.

"Yes it is, Miss Insull," said Samuel, deliberately.

In less than a minute he was gone.

Constance ran upstairs. But the cry had ceased. She turned the door-knob softly, slowly, and crept into the chamber. A night-light made large shadows among the heavy mahogany and the crimson, tasselled rep in the close-curtained room. And between the bed and the ottoman (on which lay Samuel's newly-bought family Bible) the cot loomed in the shadows. She picked up the night-light and stole round the bed. Yes, he had decided to fall asleep. The hazard of death afar off had just defeated his devilish obstinacy. Fate had bested him. How marvellously soft and delicate that tear-stained cheek! How frail that tiny, tiny clenched hand! In Constance grief and joy were mystically united.

ii

The drawing-room was full of visitors, in frocks of ceremony. The old drawing-room, but newly and massively arranged with the finest Victorian furniture from dead Aunt Harriet's house at Axe; two "Canterburys," a large bookcase, a splendid scintillant table solid beyond lifting, intricately tortured chairs and armchairs! The original furniture of the drawing-room was now down in the parlour, making it grand. All the house breathed opulence; it was gorged with quiet, restrained expensiveness; the least considerable objects, in the most modest corners, were what Mrs. Baines would have termed "good." Constance and Samuel had half of all Aunt Harriet's money and half of Mrs. Baines's; the other half was accumulating for a hypothetical Sophia, Mr. Critchlow being the trustee. The business continued to flourish. People knew that Samuel Povey was buying houses. Yet Samuel and Constance had not made friends; they had not, in the Five Towns phrase, "branched out socially," though they had very meetly branched out on subscription lists. They kept themselves to themselves (emphasizing the preposition). These guests were not their guests; they were the guests of Cyril.

He had been named Samuel because Constance would have him named after his father, and Cyril because his father secretly despised the name of Samuel; and he was called Cyril; "Master Cyril," by Amy, definite successor to Maggie. His mother's thoughts were on Cyril as long as she was awake. His father, when not planning Cyril's welfare, was earning money whose unique object could be nothing but Cyril's welfare. Cyril was the pivot of the house; every desire ended somewhere in Cyril. The shop existed now solely for him. And those houses that Samuel bought by private treaty, or with a shamefaced air at auctions—somehow they were aimed at Cyril. Samuel and Constance had ceased to be self-justifying beings; they never thought of themselves save as the parents of Cyril.

They realized this by no means fully. Had they been accused of monomania they would have smiled the smile of people confident in their commonsense and their mental balance. Nevertheless, they were monomaniacs. Instinctively they concealed the fact as much as possible. They never admitted it even to themselves. Samuel, indeed, would often say: "That child is not everybody. That child must be kept in his place." Constance was always teaching him consideration for his father as the most important person in the household. Samuel was always teaching him consideration for his mother as the most important person in the household. Nothing was left undone to convince him that he was a cipher, a nonentity, who ought to be very glad to be alive. But he knew all about his importance. He knew that the entire town was his. He knew that his parents were deceiving themselves. Even when he was punished he well knew that it was because he was so important. He never imparted any portion of this knowledge to his parents; a primeval wisdom prompted him to retain it strictly in his own bosom.

He was four and a half years old, dark, like his father; handsome like his aunt, and tall for his age; not one of his features resembled a feature of his mother's, but sometimes he "had her look." From the capricious production of inarticulate sounds, and then a few monosyllables that described concrete things and obvious desires, he had gradually acquired an astonishing idiomatic command over the most difficult of Teutonic languages; there was nothing that he could not say. He could walk and run, was full of exact knowledge about God, and entertained no doubt concerning the special partiality of a minor deity called Jesus towards himself.

Now, this party was his mother's invention and scheme. His father, after flouting it, had said that if it was to be done at all, it should be done well, and had brought to the doing all his organizing skill. Cyril had accepted it at first—merely accepted it; but, as the day approached and the preparations increased in magnitude, he had come to look on it with favour, then with enthusiasm. His father having taken him to Daniel Povey's opposite, to choose cakes, he had shown, by his solemn and fastidious waverings, how seriously he regarded the affair.

Of course it had to occur on a Thursday afternoon. The season was summer, suitable for pale and fragile toilettes. And the eight children who sat round Aunt Harriet's great table glittered like the sun. Not Constance's specially provided napkins could hide that wealth and profusion of white lace and stitchery. Never in after-life are the genteel children of the Five Towns so richly clad as at the age of four or five years. Weeks of labour, thousands of cubic feet of gas, whole nights stolen from repose, eyesight, and general health, will disappear into the manufacture of a single frock that accidental jam may ruin in ten seconds. Thus it was in those old days; and thus it is to-day. Cyril's guests ranged in years from four to six; they were chiefly older than their host; this was a pity, it impaired his importance; but up to four years a child's sense of propriety, even of common decency, is altogether too unreliable for a respectable party.

Round about the outskirts of the table were the elders, ladies the majority; they also in their best, for they had to meet each other. Constance displayed a new dress, of crimson silk; after having mourned for her mother she had definitely abandoned the black which, by reason of her duties in the shop, she had constantly worn from the age of sixteen to within a few months of Cyril's birth; she never went into the shop now, except casually, on brief visits of inspection. She was still fat; the destroyer of her figure sat at the head of the table. Samuel kept close to her; he was the only male, until Mr. Critchlow astonishingly arrived; among the company Mr. Critchlow had a grand-niece. Samuel, if not in his best, was certainly not in his everyday suit. With his large frilled shirt-front, and small black tie, and his little black beard and dark face over that, he looked very nervous and self-conscious. He had not the habit of entertaining. Nor had Constance; but her benevolence ever bubbling up to the calm surface of her personality made self-consciousness impossible for her. Miss Insull was also present, in shop-black, "to help." Lastly there was Amy, now as the years passed slowly assuming the character of a faithful retainer, though she was only twenty-three. An ugly, abrupt, downright girl, with convenient notions of pleasure! For she would rise early and retire late in order to contrive an hour to go out with Master Cyril; and to be allowed to put Master Cyril to bed was, really, her highest bliss.

All these elders were continually inserting arms into the fringe of fluffy children that surrounded the heaped table; removing dangerous spoons out of cups into saucers, replacing plates, passing cakes, spreading jam, whispering consolations, explanations, and sage counsel. Mr. Critchlow, snow-white now but unbent, remarked that there was "a pretty cackle," and he sniffed. Although the window was slightly open, the air was heavy with the natural human odour which young children transpire. More than one mother, pressing her nose into a lacy mass, to whisper, inhaled that pleasant perfume with a voluptuous thrill.

Cyril, while attending steadily to the demands of his body, was in a mood which approached the ideal. Proud and radiant, he combined urbanity with a certain fine condescension. His bright eyes, and his manner of scraping up jam with a spoon, said: "I am the king of this party. This party is solely in my honour. I know that. We all know it. Still, I will pretend that we are equals, you and I." He talked about his picture-books to a young woman on his right named Jennie, aged four, pale, pretty, the belle in fact, and Mr. Critchlow's grand-niece. The boy's attractiveness was indisputable; he could put on quite an aristocratic air. It was the most delicious sight to see them, Cyril and Jennie, so soft and delicate, so infantile on their piles of cushions and books, with their white socks and black shoes dangling far distant from the carpet; and yet so old, so self-contained! And they were merely an epitome of the whole table. The whole table was bathed in the charm and mystery of young years, of helpless fragility, gentle forms, timid elegance, unshamed instincts, and waking souls. Constance and Samuel were very satisfied; full of praise for other people's children, but with the reserve that of course Cyril was *hors concours*. They both really did believe, at that moment, that Cyril was, in some subtle way which they felt but could not define, superior to all other infants.

Some one, some officious relative of a visitor, began to pass a certain cake which had brown walls, a roof of cocoa-nut icing, and a yellow body studded with crimson globules. Not a conspicuously gorgeous cake, not a cake to which a catholic child would be likely to attach particular importance; a good, average cake! Who could have guessed that it stood, in Cyril's esteem, as the cake of cakes? He had insisted on his father buying it at Cousin Daniel's, and perhaps Samuel ought to have divined that for Cyril that cake was the gleam that an ardent spirit would follow through the wilderness. Samuel, however, was not a careful observer, and seriously lacked imagination. Constance knew only that Cyril had mentioned the cake once or twice. Now by the hazard of destiny that cake found much favour, helped into popularity as it was by the blundering officious relative who, not dreaming what volcano she was treading on, urged its merits with simpering enthusiasm. One boy took two slices, a slice in each hand; he happened to be the visitor of whom the cake-distributor was a relative and she protested; she expressed the shock she suffered. Whereupon both Constance and Samuel sprang forward and swore with angelic smiles that nothing could be more perfect than the propriety of that dear little fellow taking two slices of that cake. It was this hullabaloo that drew Cyril's attention to the evanescence of the cake of cakes. His face at once changed from calm pride to a dreadful anxiety. His eyes bulged out. His tiny mouth grew and grew, like a mouth in a nightmare. He was no longer human; he was a cake-eating tiger being balked of his prey. Nobody noticed him. The officious fool of a woman persuaded Jennie to take the last slice of the cake, which was quite a thin slice.

Then every one simultaneously noticed Cyril, for he gave a yell. It was not the cry of a despairing soul who sees his beautiful iridescent dream shattered at his feet; it was the cry of the strong, masterful spirit, furious. He turned upon Jennie sobbing, and snatched at her cake. Unaccustomed to such behaviour from hosts, and being besides a haughty put-you-in-your-place beauty of the future, Jennie defended her cake. After all, it was not she who had taken two slices at once. Cyril hit her in the eye, and then crammed most of the slice of cake into his enormous mouth. He could not swallow it, nor even masticate it, for his throat was rigid and tight. So the cake projected from his red lips, and big tears watered it. The most awful mess you can conceive! Jennie wept loudly, and one or two others joined her in sympathy, but the rest went on eating tranquilly, unmoved by the horror which transfixed their elders.

A host to snatch food from a guest! A host to strike a guest! A gentleman to strike a lady!

Constance whipped up Cyril from his chair and flew with him to his own room (once Samuel's), where she smacked him on the arm and told him he was a very, very naughty boy and that she didn't know what his father would say. She took the food out of his disgusting mouth—or as much of it as she could get at—and then she left him, on the bed. Miss Jennie was still in tears when, blushing scarlet and trying to smile, Constance returned to the drawing-room. Jennie would not be appeased. Happily Jennie's mother (being about to present Jennie with a little brother—she hoped) was not present. Miss

Insull had promised to see Jennie home, and it was decided that she should go. Mr. Critchlow, in high sardonic spirits, said that he would go too; the three departed together, heavily charged with Constance's love and apologies. Then all pretended, and said loudly, that what had happened was naught, that such things were always happening at children's parties. And visitors' relatives asseverated that Cyril was a perfect darling and that really Mrs. Povey must not . . .

But the attempt to keep up appearance was a failure.

The Methuselah of visitors, a gaping girl of nearly eight years, walked across the room to where Constance was standing, and said in a loud, confidential, fatuous voice:

"Cyril *has* been a rude boy, hasn't he, Mrs. Povey?"

The clumsiness of children is sometimes tragic.

Later, there was a trickling stream of fluffy bundles down the crooked stairs and through the parlour and so out into King Street. And Constance received many compliments and sundry appeals that darling Cyril should be forgiven.

"I thought you said that boy was in his bedroom," said Samuel to Constance, coming into the parlour when the last guest had gone. Each avoided the other's eyes.

"Yes, isn't he?"

"No."

"The little jockey!" ("Jockey," an essay in the playful, towards making light of the jockey's sin!) "I expect he's been in search of Amy."

She went to the top of the kitchen stairs and called out: "Amy, is Master Cyril down there?"

"Master Cyril? No, mum. But he was in the parlour a bit ago, after the first and second lot had gone. I told him to go upstairs and be a good boy."

Not for a few moments did the suspicion enter the minds of Samuel and Constance that Cyril might be missing, that the house might not contain Cyril. But having once entered, the suspicion became a certainty. Amy, cross-examined, burst into sudden tears, admitting that the side-door might have been open when, having sped "the second lot," she criminally left Cyril alone in the parlour in order to descend for an instant to her kitchen. Dusk was gathering. Amy saw the defenceless innocent wandering about all night in the deserted streets of a great city. A similar vision with precise details of canals, tramcar-wheels, and cellar-flaps, disturbed Constance. Samuel said that anyhow he could not have got far, that some one was bound to remark and recognize him, and restore him. "Yes, of course," thought sensible Constance. "But supposing——"

They all three searched the entire house again. Then, in the drawing-room (which was in a sad condition of anticlimax) Amy exclaimed:

"Eh, master! There's town-crier crossing the Square. Hadn't ye better have him cried?"

"Run out and stop him," Constance commanded.

And Amy flew.

Samuel and the aged town-crier parleyed at the side-door, the women in the background.

"I canna' cry him without my bell," drawled the crier, stroking his shabby uniform. "My bell's at wum (home). I mun go and fetch my bell. Yo' write it down on a bit o' paper for me so as I can read it, and I'll foot off for my bell. Folk wouldna' listen to me if I hadna' gotten my bell."

Thus was Cyril cried.

"Amy," said Constance, when she and the girl were alone, "there's no use in you standing blubbering there. Get to work and clear up that drawing-room, do! The child is sure to be found soon. Your master's gone out, too."

Brave words! Constance aided in the drawing-room and kitchen. Theirs was the woman's lot in a great crisis. Plates have always to be washed.

Very shortly afterwards, Samuel Povey came into the kitchen by the underground passage which led past the two cellars to the yard and to Brougham Street. He was carrying in his arms an obscene black mass. This mass was Cyril, once white.

Constance screamed. She was at liberty to give way to her feelings, because Amy happened to be upstairs.

"Stand away!" cried Mr. Povey. "He isn't fit to touch."

And Mr. Povey made as if to pass directly onward, ignoring the mother.

"Wherever did you find him?"

"I found him in the far cellar," said Mr. Povey, compelled to stop, after all. "He was down there with me yesterday, and it just occurred to me that he might have gone there again."

"What! All in the dark?"

"He'd lighted a candle, if you please! I'd left a candlestick and a box of matches handy because I hadn't finished that shelving."

"Well!" Constance murmured. "I can't think how ever he dared go there all alone!"

"Can't you?" said Mr. Povey, cynically. "I can. He simply did it to frighten us."

"Oh, Cyril!" Constance admonished the child. "Cyril!"

The child showed no emotion. His face was an enigma. It might have hidden sullenness or mere callous indifference, or a perfect unconsciousness of sin.

"Give him to me," said Constance.

"I'll look after him this evening," said Samuel, grimly.

"But you can't wash him," said Constance, her relief yielding to apprehension.

"Why not?" demanded Mr. Povey. And he moved off.

"But Sam—"

"I'll look after him, I tell you!" Mr. Povey repeated, threateningly.

"But what are you going to do?" Constance asked with fear.

"Well," said Mr. Povey, "has this sort of thing got to be dealt with, or hasn't it?" He departed upstairs.

Constance overtook him at the door of Cyril's bedroom. Mr. Povey did not wait for her to speak. His eyes were blazing.

"See here!" he admonished her cruelly. "You get away downstairs, mother!"

And he disappeared into the bedroom with his vile and helpless victim.

A moment later he popped his head out of the door. Constance was disobeying him. He stepped into the passage and shut the door so that Cyril should not hear.

"Now please do as I tell you," he hissed at his wife. "Don't let's have a scene, please."

She descended, slowly, weeping. And Mr. Povey retired again to the place of execution.

Amy nearly fell on the top of Constance with a final tray of things from the drawing-room. And Constance had to tell the girl that Cyril was found. Somehow she could not resist the instinct to tell her also that the master had the affair in hand. Amy then wept.

After about an hour Mr. Povey at last reappeared. Constance was trying to count silver teaspoons in the parlour.

"He's in bed now," said Mr. Povey, with a magnificent attempt to be nonchalant. "You mustn't go near him."

"But have you washed him?" Constance whimpered.

"I've washed him," replied the astonishing Mr. Povey.

"What have you done to him?"

"I've punished him, of course," said Mr. Povey, like a god who is above human weaknesses. "What did you expect me to do? *Someone* had to do it."

Constance wiped her eyes with the edge of the white apron which she was wearing over her new silk dress. She surrendered; she accepted the situation; she made the best of it. And all the evening was spent in dismally and horribly pretending that their hearts were beating as one. Mr. Povey's elaborate, cheery kindliness was extremely painful.

They went to bed, and in their bedroom Constance, as she stood close-to Samuel, suddenly dropped the pretence, and with eyes and voice of anguish said:

"You must let me look at him."

They faced each other. For a brief instant Cyril did not exist for Constance. Samuel alone obsessed her, and yet Samuel seemed a strange, unknown man. It was in Constance's life one of those crises when the human soul seems to be on the very brink of mysterious and disconcerting cognitions, and then the wave recedes as inexplicably as it surged up.

"Why, of course!" said Mr. Povey, turning away lightly, as though to imply that she was making tragedies out of nothing.

She gave an involuntary gesture of almost childish relief.

Cyril slept calmly. It was a triumph for Mr. Povey.

Constance could not sleep. As she lay darkly awake by her husband, her secret being seemed to be a-quiver with emotion. Not exactly sorrow; not exactly joy; an emotion more elemental than these! A sensation of the intensity of her life in that hour; troubling, anxious, yet not sad! She said that Samuel was quite right, quite right. And then she said that the poor little thing wasn't yet five years old, and that it was monstrous. The two had to be reconciled. And they never could be reconciled. Always she would be between them, to reconcile them, and to be crushed by their impact. Always she would have to bear the burden of both of them. There could be no ease for her, no surcease from a tremendous preoccupation and responsibility. She could not change Samuel; besides, he was right! And though Cyril was not yet five, she felt that she could not change Cyril either. He was just as unchangeable as a growing plant.

The thought of her mother and Sophia did not present itself to her; she felt, however, somewhat as Mrs. Baines had felt on historic occasions; but, being more softly kind, younger, and less chafed by destiny, she was conscious of no bitterness, conscious rather of a solemn blessedness.

CHAPTER IV

CRIME

"Now, Master Cyril," Amy protested, "will you leave that fire alone? It's not you that can mend my fires."

A boy of nine, great and heavy for his years, with a full face and very short hair, bent over the smoking grate. It was about five minutes to eight on a chilly morning after Easter. Amy, hastily clad in blue, with a rough brown apron, was setting the breakfast table. The boy turned his head, still bending.

"Shut up, Ame," he replied, smiling. Life being short, he usually called her Ame when they were alone together. "Or I'll catch you one in the eye with the poker."

"You ought to be ashamed of yourself," said Amy. "And you know your mother told you to wash your feet this morning, and you haven't done. Fine clothes is all very well, but——"

"Who says I haven't washed my feet?" asked Cyril, guiltily.

Amy's mention of fine clothes referred to the fact that he was that morning wearing his Sunday suit for the first time on a week-day.

"I say you haven't," said Amy.

She was more than three times his age, still, but they had been treating each other as intellectual equals for years.

"And how do you know?" asked Cyril, tired of the fire.

"I know," said Amy.

"Well, you just don't, then!" said Cyril. "And what about *your* feet? I should be sorry to see your feet, Ame."

Amy was excusably annoyed. She tossed her head. "My feet are as clean as yours any day," she said. "And I shall tell your mother."

But he would not leave her feet alone, and there ensued one of those endless monotonous altercations on a single theme which occur so often between intellectual equals when one is a young son of the house and the other an established servant who adores him. Refined minds would have found the talk disgusting, but the sentiment of disgust seemed to be unknown to either of the wranglers. At last, when Amy by superior tactics had cornered him, Cyril said suddenly:

"Oh, go to hell!"

Amy banged down the spoon for the bacon gravy. "Now I shall tell your mother. Mark my words, this time I *shall* tell your mother."

Cyril felt that in truth he had gone rather far. He was perfectly sure that Amy would not tell his mother. And yet, supposing that by some freak of her nature she did! The consequences would be unutterable; the consequences would more than extinguish his private glory in the use of such a dashing word. So he laughed, a rather silly, giggling laugh, to reassure himself.

"You daren't," he said.

"Daren't I?" she said grimly. "You'll see. *I* don't know where you learn! It fair beats me. But it isn't Amy Bates as is going to be sworn at. As soon as ever your mother comes into this room!"

The door at the foot of the stairs creaked and Constance came into the room. She was wearing a dress of magenta merino, and a gold chain descended from her neck over her rich bosom. She had scarcely aged in five years. It would have been surprising if she had altered much, for the years had passed over her head at an incredible rate. To her it appeared only a few months since Cyril's first and last party.

"Are you all ready, my pet? Let me look at you." Constance greeted the boy with her usual bright, soft energy.

Cyril glanced at Amy, who averted her head, putting spoons into three saucers.

"Yes, mother," he replied in a new voice.

"Did you do what I told you?"

"Yes, mother," he said simply.

"That's right."

Amy made a faint noise with her lips, and departed.

He was saved once more. He said to himself that never again would he permit his soul to be disturbed by any threat of old Ame's.

Constance's hand descended into her pocket and drew out a hard paper packet, which she clapped on to her son's head.

"Oh, mother!" He pretended that she had hurt him, and then he opened the packet. It contained Congleton butterscotch, reputed a harmless sweetmeat.

"Good!" he cried, "good! Oh! Thanks, mother."

"Now don't begin eating them at once."

"Just one, mother."

"No! And how often have I told you to keep your feet off that fender. See how it's bent. And it's nobody but you."

"Sorry."

"It's no use being sorry if you persist in doing it."

"Oh, mother, I had such a funny dream!"

They chatted until Amy came up the stairs with tea and bacon. The fire had developed from black to clear red.

"Run and tell father that breakfast is ready."

After a little delay a spectacled man of fifty, short and stoutish, with grey hair and a small beard half grey and half black, entered from the shop. Samuel had certainly very much aged, especially in his gestures, which, however, were still quick. He sat down at once—his wife and son were already seated—and served the bacon with the rapid assurance of one who needs not to inquire about tastes and appetites. Not a word was said, except a brief grace by Samuel. But there was no restraint. Samuel had a mild, benignant air. Constance's eyes were a fountain of cheerfulness. The boy sat between them and ate steadily.

Mysterious creature, this child, mysteriously growing and growing in the house! To his mother he was a delicious joy at all times save when he disobeyed his father. But now for quite a considerable period there had been no serious collision. The boy seemed to be acquiring virtue as well as sense. And really he was charming. So big, truly enormous (every one remarked on it), and yet graceful, lithe, with a smile that could ravish. And he was distinguished in his bearing. Without depreciating Samuel in her faithful heart, Constance saw plainly the singular differences between Samuel and the boy. Save that he was dark, and that his father's "dangerous look" came into those childish eyes occasionally, Cyril had now scarcely any obvious resemblance to his father. He was a Baines. This naturally deepened Constance's family pride. Yes, he was mysterious to Constance, though probably not more so than any other boy to any other parent. He was equally mysterious to Samuel, but otherwise Mr. Povey had learned to regard him in the light of a parcel which he was always attempting to wrap up in a piece of paper imperceptibly too small. When he successfully covered the parcel at one corner it burst out at another, and this went on for ever, and he could never get the string on. Nevertheless, Mr. Povey had unabated confidence in his skill as a parcel-wrapper. The boy was strangely subtle at times, but then at times he was astoundingly ingenuous, and then his dodges would not deceive the dullest. Mr. Povey knew himself more than a match for his son. He was proud of him because he regarded him as not an ordinary boy; he took it as a matter of course that his boy should not be an ordinary boy. He never, or very rarely, praised Cyril. Cyril thought of his father as a man who, in response to any request, always began by answering with a thoughtful, serious "No, I'm afraid not."

"So you haven't lost your appetite!" his mother commented.

Cyril grinned. "Did you expect me to, mother?"

"Let me see," said Samuel, as if vaguely recalling an unimportant fact. "It's to-day you begin to go to school, isn't it?"

"I wish father wouldn't be such a chump!" Cyril reflected. And, considering that this commencement of school (real school, not a girls' school, as once) had been the chief topic in the house for days, weeks; considering that it now occupied and filled all hearts, Cyril's reflection was excusable.

"Now, there's one thing you must always remember, my boy," said Mr. Povey. "Promptness. Never be late either in going to school or in coming home. And in order that you may have no excuse"—Mr. Povey pressed on the word "excuse," as though condemning Cyril in advance—"here's something for you!" He said the last words quickly, with a sort of modest shame.

It was a silver watch and chain.

Cyril was staggered. So also was Constance, for Mr. Povey could keep his own counsel. At long intervals he would prove, thus, that he was a mighty soul, capable of sublime deeds. The watch was the unique flowering of Mr. Povey's profound but harsh affection. It lay on the table like a miracle. This day was a great day, a supremely exciting day in Cyril's history, and not less so in the history of his parents.

The watch killed its owner's appetite dead.

Routine was ignored that morning. Father did not go back into the shop. At length the moment came when father put on

his hat and overcoat to take Cyril, and Cyril's watch and
satchel, to the Endowed School, which had quarters in the
Wedgwood Institution close by. A solemn departure, and Cyril
could not pretend by his demeanour that it was not! Constance
desired to kiss him, but refrained. He would not have liked it.
She watched them from the window. Cyril was nearly as tall as
his father; that is to say, not nearly as tall, but creeping up
his father's shoulder. She felt that the eyes of the town must
be on the pair. She was very happy, and nervous.

At dinner-time a triumph seemed probable, and at tea-time,
when Cyril came home under a mortar-board hat and with a
satchel full of new books and a head full of new ideas, the
triumph was actually and definitely achieved. He had been
put into the third form, and he announced that he should
soon be at the top of it. He was enchanted with the life of
school; he liked the other boys, and it appeared that the other
boys liked him. The fact was that, with a new silver watch and
a packet of sweets, he had begun his new career in the most
advantageous circumstances. Moreover, he possessed qualities
which ensure success at school. He was big, and easy, with a
captivating smile and a marked aptitude to learn those things
which boys insist on teaching to their new comrades. He had
muscle, a brave demeanour, and no conceit.

During tea the parlour began to accustom itself to a new
vocabulary, containing such words as "fellows," "kept in,"
"lines," "rot," "recess," "jolly." To some of these words the
parents, especially Mr. Povey, had an instinct to object, but
they could not object, somehow they did not seem to get an
opportunity to object; they were carried away on the torrent,
and after all, their excitement and pleasure in the exceeding
romantic novelty of existence were just as intense and nearly as
ingenuous as their son's.

He demonstrated that unless he was allowed to stay up
later than aforetime he would not be able to do his home-work,
and hence would not keep that place in the school to which
his talents entitled him. Mr. Povey suggested, but only with
half a heart, that he should get up earlier in the morning. The
proposal fell flat. Everybody knew and admitted that nothing
save the scorpions of absolute necessity, or a tremendous occasion such as that particular morning's, would drive Cyril from
his bed until the smell of bacon rose to him from the kitchen.
The parlour table was consecrated to his lessons. It became

generally known that "Cyril was doing his lessons." His father scanned the new text-books while Cyril condescendingly explained to him that all others were superseded and worthless. His father contrived to maintain an air of preserving his mental equilibrium, but not his mother; she gave it up, she who till that day had under his father's direction taught him nearly all that he knew, and Cyril passed above her into regions of knowledge where she made no pretence of being able to follow him.

When the lessons were done, and Cyril had wiped his fingers on bits of blotting-paper, and his father had expressed qualified approval and had gone into the shop, Cyril said to his mother, with that delicious hesitation which overtook him sometimes:

"Mother."

"Well, my pet."

"I want you to do something for me."

"Well, what is it?"

"No, you must promise."

"I'll do it if I can."

"But you *can*. It isn't doing. It's *not* doing."

"Come, Cyril, out with it."

"I don't want you to come in and look at me after I'm asleep any more."

"But, you silly boy, what difference can it make to you if you're asleep?"

"I don't want you to. It's like as if I was a baby. You'll *have* to stop doing it some day, and so you may as well stop now."

It was thus that he meant to turn his back on his youth.

She smiled. She was incomprehensibly happy. She continued to smile.

"Now you'll promise, won't you, mother?"

She rapped him on the head with her thimble, lovingly. He took the gesture for consent.

"You are a baby," she murmured.

"Now I shall *trust* you," he said, ignoring this. "Say 'honour bright.'"

"Honour bright."

With what a long caress her eyes followed him, as he went up to bed on his great sturdy legs! She was thankful that school had not contaminated her adorable innocent. If she could have been Ame for twenty-four hours, she perhaps would not have hesitated to put butter into his mouth lest it should melt.

Mr. Povey and Constance talked late and low that night. They could neither of them sleep; they had little desire to sleep. Constance's face said to her husband: "I've always stuck up for that boy, in spite of your severities, and you see how right I was!" And Mr. Povey's face said: "You see now the brilliant success of my system. You see how my educational theories have justified themselves. Never been to a school before, except that wretched little dame's school, and he goes practically straight to the top of the third form—at nine years of age!" They discussed his future. There could be no sign of lunacy in discussing his future up to a certain point, but each felt that to discuss the ultimate career of a child nine years old would not be the act of a sensible parent; only foolish parents would be so fond. Yet each was dying to discuss his ultimate career. Constance yielded first to the temptation, as became her. Mr. Povey scoffed, and then, to humour Constance, yielded also. The matter was soon fairly on the carpet. Constance was relieved to find that Mr. Povey had no thought whatever of putting Cyril in the shop. No; Mr. Povey did not desire to chop wood with a razor. Their son must and would ascend. Doctor! Solicitor! Barrister! Not barrister—barrister was fantastic. When they had argued for about half an hour Mr. Povey intimated suddenly that the conversation was unworthy of their practical commonsense, and went to sleep.

ii

Nobody really thought that this almost ideal condition of things would persist: an enterprise commenced in such glory must surely traverse periods of difficulty and even of temporary disaster. But no! Cyril seemed to be made specially for school. Before Mr. Povey and Constance had quite accustomed themselves to being the parents of "a great lad," before Cyril had broken the glass of his miraculous watch more than once, the summer term had come to an end and there arrived the excitations of the prize-giving, as it was called; for at that epoch the smaller schools had not found the effrontery to dub the breaking-up ceremony a "speech-day." This prize-giving furnished a particular joy to Mr. and Mrs. Povey. Although

the prizes were notoriously few in number—partly to add to
their significance, and partly to diminish their cost (the foundation was poor)—Cyril won a prize, a box of geometrical
instruments of precision; also he reached the top of his form,
and was marked for promotion to the formidable Fourth.
Samuel and Constance were bidden to the large hall of the
Wedgwood Institution of a summer afternoon, and they saw
the whole Board of Governors raised on a rostrum, and in the
middle, in front of what he referred to, in his aristocratic
London accent, as "a beggarly array of rewards," the aged and
celebrated Sir Thomas Wilbraham Wilbraham, ex-M.P., last
respectable member of his ancient line. And Sir Thomas gave
the box of instruments to Cyril, and shook hands with him.
And everybody was very well dressed. Samuel, who had never
attended anything but a National School, recalled the simple
rigours of his own boyhood, and swelled. For certainly, of all
the parents present, he was among the richest. When, in the
informal promiscuities which followed the prize distribution,
Cyril joined his father and mother, sheepishly, they duly did
their best to make light of his achievements, and failed. The
walls of the hall were covered with specimens of the pupils'
skill, and the headmaster was observed to direct the attention
of the mighty to a map done by Cyril. Of course it was a map
of Ireland, Ireland being the map chosen by every map-draw-
ing schoolboy who is free to choose. For a third-form boy it was
considered a masterpiece. In the shading of mountains Cyril was
already a prodigy. Never, it was said, had the Macgillycuddy
Reeks been indicated by a member of that school with a more
amazing subtle refinement than by the young Povey. From a
proper pride in themselves, from a proper fear lest they should
be secretly accused of ostentation by other parents, Samuel
and Constance did not go near that map. For the rest, they
had lived with it for weeks, and Samuel (who, after all, was
determined not to be dirt under his son's feet) had scratched
a blot from it with a completeness that defied inquisitive examination.

The fame of this map, added to the box of compasses and
Cyril's own desire, pointed to an artistic career. Cyril had
always drawn and daubed, and the drawing-master of the Endowed School, who was also headmaster of the Art School, had
suggested that the youth should attend the Art School one
night a week. Samuel, however, would not listen to the idea;

Cyril was too young. It is true that Cyril was too young, but Samuel's real objection was to Cyril's going out alone in the evening. On that he was adamant.

The Governors had recently made the discovery that a sports department was necessary to a good school, and had rented a field for cricket, football, and rounders up at Bleakridge, an innovation which demonstrated that the town was moving with the rapid times. In June this field was open after school hours till eight p.m. as well as on Saturdays. The Squire learnt that Cyril had a talent for cricket, and Cyril wished to practise in the evenings, and was quite ready to bind himself with Bible oaths to rise at no matter what hour in the morning for the purpose of home lessons. He scarcely expected his father to say "Yes," as his father never did say "Yes," but he was obliged to ask. Samuel nonplussed him by replying that on fine evenings, when he could spare time from the shop, he would go up to Bleakridge with his son. Cyril did not like this in the least. Still, it might be tried. One evening they went, actually, in the new steam-car which had superseded the old horse-cars, and which travelled all the way to Longshaw, a place that Cyril had only heard of. Samuel talked of the games played in the Five Towns in his day, of the Titanic sport of prison-bars, when the team of one "bank" went forth to the challenge of another "bank," preceded by a drum-and-fife band, and when, in the heat of the chase, a man might jump into the canal to escape his pursuer; Samuel had never played at cricket.

Samuel, with a very young grandson of Fan (deceased), sat in dignity on the grass and watched his cricketer for an hour and a half (while Constance kept an eye on the shop and superintended its closing). Samuel then conducted Cyril home again. Two days later the father of his own accord offered to repeat the experience. Cyril refused. Disagreeable insinuations that he was a baby in arms had been made at school in the meantime.

Nevertheless, in other directions Cyril sometimes surprisingly conquered. For instance, he came home one day with the information that a dog that was not a bull-terrier was not worth calling a dog. Fan's grandson had been carried off in earliest prime by a chicken-bone that had pierced his vitals, and Cyril did indeed persuade his father to buy a bull-terrier. The animal was a superlative of forbidding ugliness, but father

and son vied with each other in stern critical praise of his surpassing beauty, and Constance, from good nature, joined in
the pretence. He was called Lion, and the shop, after one or
two untoward episodes, was absolutely closed to him.

But the most striking of Cyril's successes had to do with the
question of the annual holiday. He spoke of the sea soon after
becoming a schoolboy. It appeared that his complete ignorance
of the sea prejudicially affected him at school. Further, he had
always loved the sea; he had drawn hundreds of three-masted
ships with studding-sails set, and knew the difference between a
brig and a brigantine. When he first said: "I say, mother, why
can't we go to Llandudno instead of Buxton this year?" his
mother thought he was out of his senses. For the idea of going
to any place other than Buxton was inconceivable! Had they
not always been to Buxton? What would their landlady say?
How could they ever look her in the face again? Besides . . .
well . . . . . ! They went to Llandudno, rather scared, and
hardly knowing how the change had come about. But they
went. And it was the force of Cyril's will, Cyril the theoretic
cypher, that took them.

iii

The removal of the Endowed School to more commodious
premises in the shape of Shawport Hall, an ancient mansion
with fifty rooms and five acres of land round about it, was not
a change that quite pleased Samuel or Constance. They admitted the hygienic advantages, but Shawport Hall was three-
quarters of a mile distant from St. Luke's Square—in the hollow that separates Bursley from its suburb of Hillport;
whereas the Wedgwood Institution was scarcely a minute away.
It was as if Cyril, when he set off to Shawport Hall of a morning, passed out of their sphere of influence. He was leagues off,
doing they knew not what. Further, his dinner-hour was cut
short by the extra time needed for the journey to and fro, and
he arrived late for tea; it may be said that he often arrived
very late for tea; the whole machinery of the meal was disturbed. These matters seemed to Samuel and Constance to be
of tremendous import, seemed to threaten the very foundations
of existence. Then they grew accustomed to the new order, and
wondered sometimes, when they passed the Wedgwood Institu-

tion and the insalubrious Cock Yard—once sole playground of the boys—that the school could ever have "managed" in the narrow quarters once allotted to it.

Cyril, though constantly successful at school, a rising man, an infallible bringer-home of excellent reports, and a regular taker of prizes, became gradually less satisfactory in the house. He was "kept in" occasionally, and although his father pretended to hold that to be kept in was to slur the honour of a spotless family, Cyril continued to be kept in; a hardened sinner, lost to shame. But this was not the worst. The worst undoubtedly was that Cyril was "getting rough." No definite accusation could be laid against him; the offence was general, vague, everlasting; it was in all he did and said, in every gesture and movement. He shouted, whistled, sang, stamped, stumbled, lunged. He omitted such empty rites as saying "Yes" or "Please," and wiping his nose. He replied gruffly and nonchalantly to polite questions, or he didn't reply until the questions were repeated, and even then with a "lost" air that was not genuine. His shoelaces were a sad sight, and his finger-nails no sight at all for a decent woman; his hair was as rough as his conduct; hardly at the pistol's point could he be forced to put oil on it. In brief, he was no longer the nice boy that he used to be. He had unmistakably deteriorated. Grievous! But what can you expect when *your* boy is obliged, month after month and year after year, to associate with other boys? After all, he was a *good* boy, said Constance, often to herself and now and then to Samuel. For Constance, his charm was eternally renewed. His smile, his frequent ingenuousness, his funny self-conscious gesture when he wanted to "get round" her—these characteristics remained; and his pure heart remained; she could read that in his eyes. Samuel was inimical to his tastes for sports and his triumphs therein. But Constance had pride in all that. She liked to feel him and to gaze at him, and to smell that faint, uncleanly odour of sweat that hung in his clothes.

In this condition he reached the advanced age of thirteen. And his parents, who despite their notion of themselves as wideawake parents were a simple pair, never suspected that his heart, conceived to be still pure, had become a crawling, horrible mass of corruption.

One day the head-master called at the shop. Now, to see a head-master walking about the town during school-hours is a

startling spectacle, and is apt to give you the same uncanny
sensation as when, alone in a room, you think you see something move which ought not to move. Mr. Povey was startled.
Mr. Povey had a thumping within his breast as he rubbed his
hands and drew the head-master to the private corner where
his desk was. "What can I do for you to-day?" he almost
said to the head-master. But he did not say it. The boot was
emphatically not on that leg. The head-master talked to Mr.
Povey, in tones carefully low, for about a quarter of an hour,
and then he closed the interview. Mr. Povey escorted him across
the shop, and the head-master said with ordinary loudness: "Of
course it's nothing. But my experience is that it's just as well
to be on the safe side, and I thought I'd tell you. Forewarned
is forearmed. I have other parents to see." They shook hands
at the door. Then Mr. Povey stepped out on to the pavement
and, in front of the whole Square, detained an unwilling head-
master for quite another minute.

His face was deeply flushed as he returned into the shop. The
assistants bent closer over their work. He did not instantly rush
into the parlour and communicate with Constance. He had
dropped into a way of conducting many operations by his own
unaided brain. His confidence in his skill had increased with
years. Further, at the back of his mind, there had established
itself a vision of Mr. Povey as the seat of government and of
Constance and Cyril as a sort of permanent opposition. He
would not have admitted that he saw such a vision, for he was
utterly loyal to his wife; but it was there. This unconfessed
vision was one of several causes which had contributed to intensify his inherent tendency towards Machiavellianism and
secretiveness. He said nothing to Constance, nothing to Cyril;
but, happening to encounter Amy in the showroom, he was inspired to interrogate her sharply. The result was that they
descended to the cellar together, Amy weeping. Amy was commanded to hold her tongue. And as she went in mortal fear of
Mr. Povey she did hold her tongue.

Nothing occurred for several days. And then one morning
—it was Constance's birthday: children are nearly always horribly unlucky in their choice of days for sin—Mr. Povey, having executed mysterious movements in the shop after Cyril's
departure to school, jammed his hat on his head and ran forth
in pursuit of Cyril, whom he intercepted with two other boys,
at the corner of Oldcastle Street and Acre Passage.

Cyril stood as if turned into salt. "Come back home!" said Mr. Povey, grimly; and for the sake of the other boys: "Please."

"But I shall be late for school, father," Cyril weakly urged.

"Never mind."

They passed through the shop together, causing a terrific concealed emotion, and then they did violence to Constance by appearing in the parlour. Constance was engaged in cutting straws and ribbons to make a straw-frame for a water-colour drawing of a moss-rose which her pure-hearted son had given her as a birthday present.

"Why—what—?" she exclaimed. She said no more at the moment because she was sure, from the faces of her men, that the time was big with fearful events.

"Take your satchel off," Mr. Povey ordered coldly. "And your mortar-board," he added with a peculiar intonation, as if glad thus to prove that Cyril was one of those rude boys who have to be told to take their hats off in a room.

"Whatever's amiss?" Constance murmured under her breath, as Cyril obeyed the command. "Whatever's amiss?"

Mr. Povey made no immediate answer. He was in charge of these proceedings, and was very anxious to conduct them with dignity and with complete effectiveness. Little fat man over fifty, with a wizened face, grey-haired and grey-bearded, he was as nervous as a youth. His heart beat furiously. And Constance, the portly matron who would never see forty again, was just as nervous as a girl. Cyril had gone very white. All three felt physically sick.

"What money have you got in your pockets?" Mr. Povey demanded, as a commencement.

Cyril, who had had no opportunity to prepare his case, offered no reply.

"You heard what I said," Mr. Povey thundered.

"I've got three-halfpence," Cyril murmured glumly, looking down at the floor. His lower lip seemed to hang precariously away from his gums.

"Where did you get that from?"

"It's part of what mother gave me," said the boy.

"I did give him a threepenny bit last week," Constance put in guiltily. "It was a long time since he had had any money."

"If you gave it him, that's enough," said Mr. Povey, quickly, and to the boy: "That's all you've got?"

"Yes, father," said the boy.

"You're sure?"

"Yes, father."

Cyril was playing a hazardous game for the highest stakes, and under grave disadvantages; and he acted for the best. He guarded his own interests as well as he could.

Mr. Povey found himself obliged to take a serious risk. "Empty your pockets, then."

Cyril, perceiving that he had lost that particular game, emptied his pockets.

"Cyril," said Constance, "how often have I told you to change your handkerchiefs oftener! Just look at this!"

Astonishing creature! She was in the seventh hell of sick apprehension, and yet she said that!

After the handkerchief emerged the common schoolboy stock of articles useful and magic, and then, last, a silver florin!

Mr. Povey felt relief.

"Oh, Cyril!" whimpered Constance.

"Give it your mother," said Mr. Povey.

The boy stepped forward awkwardly, and Constance, weeping, took the coin.

"Please look at it, mother," said Mr. Povey. "And tell me if there's a cross marked on it."

Constance's tears blurred the coin. She had to wipe her eyes.

"Yes," she whispered faintly. "There's something on it."

"I thought so," said Mr. Povey. "Where did you steal it from?" he demanded.

"Out of the till," answered Cyril.

"Have you ever stolen anything out of the till before?"

"Yes."

"Yes, what."

"Yes, father."

"Take your hands out of your pockets and stand up straight, if you can. How often?"

"I—I don't know, father."

"I blame myself," said Mr. Povey, frankly. "I blame myself. The till ought always to be locked. All tills ought always to be locked. But we felt we could trust the assistants. If anybody had told me that I ought not to trust you, if anybody had told me that my own son would be the thief, I should have —well, I don't know what I should have said!"

Mr. Povey was quite justified in blaming himself. The fact was that the functioning of that till was a patriarchal survival, which he ought to have revolutionized, but which it had never occurred to him to revolutionize, so accustomed to it was he. In the time of John Baines, the till, with its three bowls, two for silver and one for copper (gold had never been put into it), was invariably unlocked. The person in charge of the shop took change from it for the assistants, or temporarily authorized an assistant to do so. Gold was kept in a small linen bag in a locked drawer of the desk. The contents of the till were never checked by any system of book-keeping, as there was no system of book-keeping; when all transactions, whether in payment or receipt, are in cash—the Baineses never owed a penny save the quarterly wholesale accounts, which were discharged instantly to the travellers—a system of book-keeping is not indispensable. The till was situate immediately at the entrance to the shop from the house; it was in the darkest part of the shop, and the unfortunate Cyril had to pass it every day on his way to school. The thing was a perfect device for the manufacture of young criminals.

"And how have you been spending this money?" Mr. Povey inquired.

Cyril's hands slipped into his pockets again. Then, noticing the lapse, he dragged them out.

"Sweets," said he.

"Anything else?"

"Sweets and things."

"Oh!" said Mr. Povey. "Well, now you can go down into the cinder-cellar and bring up here all the things there are in that little box in the corner. Off you go!"

And off went Cyril. He had to swagger through the kitchen.

"What did I tell you, Master Cyril?" Amy unwisely asked of him. "You copped it finely this time."

"Copped" was a word which she had learned from Cyril.

"Go on, you old bitch!" Cyril growled.

As he returned from the cellar, Amy said angrily:

"I told you I should tell your father the next time you called me that, and I shall. You mark my words."

"Cant! cant!" he retorted. "Do you think I don't know who's been canting? Cant! cant!"

Upstairs in the parlour Samuel was explaining the matter to

his wife. There had been a perfect epidemic of smoking in the school. The head-master had discovered it and, he hoped, stamped it out. What had disturbed the head-master far more than the smoking was the fact that a few boys had been found to possess somewhat costly pipes, cigar-holders, or cigarette-holders. The head-master, wily, had not confiscated these articles; he had merely informed the parents concerned. In his opinion the articles came from one single source, a generous thief; he left the parents to ascertain which of them had brought a thief into the world.

Further information Mr. Povey had culled from Amy, and there could remain no doubt that Cyril had been providing his chums with the utensils of smoking, the till supplying the means. He had told Amy that the things which he secreted in the cellar had been presented to him by blood-brothers. But Mr. Povey did not believe that. Anyhow, he had marked every silver coin in the till for three nights, and had watched the till in the mornings from behind the merino-pile; and the florin on the parlour-table spoke of his success as a detective.

Constance felt guilty on behalf of Cyril. As Mr. Povey outlined his case she could not free herself from an entirely irrational sensation of sin; at any rate of special responsibility. Cyril seemed to be her boy and not Samuel's boy at all. She avoided her husband's glance. This was very odd.

Then Cyril returned, and his parents composed their faces and he deposited, next to the florin, a sham meerschaum pipe in a case, a tobacco-pouch, a cigar of which one end had been charred but the other not cut, and a half-empty packet of cigarettes without a label.

Nothing could be hid from Mr. Povey. The details were distressing.

"So Cyril is a liar and a thief, to say nothing of this smoking!" Mr. Povey concluded.

He spoke as if Cyril had invented strange and monstrous sins. But deep down in his heart a little voice was telling him, as regards the smoking, that *he* had set the example. Mr. Baines had never smoked. Mr. Critchlow never smoked. Only men like Daniel smoked.

Thus far Mr. Povey had conducted the proceedings to his own satisfaction. He had proved the crime. He had made Cyril confess. The whole affair lay revealed. Well—what next? Cyril ought to have dissolved in repentance; something dramatic ought to have occurred. But Cyril simply stood with hanging, sulky head, and gave no sign of proper feeling.

Mr. Povey considered that, until something did happen, he must improve the occasion.

"Here we have trade getting worse every day," said he (it was true), "and you are robbing your parents to make a beast of yourself, and corrupting your companions! I wonder your mother never smelt you!"

"I never dreamt of such a thing!" said Constance, grievously.

Besides, a young man clever enough to rob a till is usually clever enough to find out that the secret of safety in smoking is to use cachous and not to keep the stuff in your pockets a minute longer than you can help.

"There's no knowing how much money you have stolen," said Mr. Povey. "A thief!"

If Cyril had stolen cakes, jam, string, cigars, Mr. Povey would never have said "thief" as he did say it. But money! Money was different. And a till was not a cupboard or a larder. A till was a till. Cyril had struck at the very basis of society.

"And on your mother's birthday!" Mr. Povey said further.

"There's one thing I can do!" he said. "I can burn all this. Built on lies! How dared you?"

And he pitched into the fire—not the apparatus of crime, but the water-colour drawing of a moss-rose and the straws and the blue ribbon for bows at the corners.

"How dared you?" he repeated.

"You never gave me any money," Cyril muttered.

He thought the marking of coins a mean trick, and the dragging-in of bad trade and his mother's birthday roused a familiar devil that usually slept quietly in his breast.

"What's that you say?" Mr. Povey almost shouted.

"You never gave me any money," the devil repeated in a louder tone than Cyril had employed.

(It was true. But Cyril "had only to ask," and he would have received all that was good for him.)

Mr. Povey sprang up. Mr. Povey also had a devil. The two devils gazed at each other for an instant; and then, noticing that Cyril's head was above Mr. Povey's, the elder devil controlled itself. Mr. Povey had suddenly had as much drama as he wanted.

"Get away to bed!" said he with dignity.

Cyril went, defiantly.

"He's to have nothing but bread and water, mother," Mr. Povey finished. He was, on the whole, pleased with himself.

Later in the day Constance reported, tearfully, that she had been up to Cyril and that Cyril had wept. Which was to Cyril's credit. But all felt that life could never be the same again. During the remainder of existence this unspeakable horror would lift its obscene form between them. Constance had never been so unhappy. Occasionally, when by herself, she would rebel for a brief moment, as one rebels in secret against a mummery which one is obliged to treat seriously. "After all," she would whisper, "suppose he *has* taken a few shillings out of the till! What then? What does it matter?" But these moods of moral insurrection against society and Mr. Povey were very transitory. They were come and gone in a flash.

CHAPTER V

ANOTHER CRIME

ONE night—it was late in the afternoon of the same year, about six months after the tragedy of the florin—Samuel Povey was wakened up by a hand on his shoulder and a voice that whispered: "Father!"

The thief and the liar was standing in his night-shirt by the bed. Samuel's sleepy eyes could just descry him in the thick gloom.

"What—what?" questioned the father, gradually coming to consciousness. "What are you doing there?"

"I didn't want to wake mother up," the boy whispered. "There's someone been throwing dirt or something at our windows, and has been for a long time."

"Eh, what?"

Samuel stared at the dim form of the thief and liar. The boy was tall, not in the least like a little boy; and yet, then, he seemed to his father as quite a little boy, a little "thing" in a night-shirt, with childish gestures and childish inflections, and a childish, delicious, quaint anxiety not to disturb his mother, who had lately been deprived of sleep owing to an illness of Amy's which had demanded nursing. His father had not so perceived him for years. In that instant the conviction that Cyril was permanently unfit for human society finally expired in the father's mind. Time had already weakened it very considerably. The decision that, be Cyril what he might, the summer holiday must be taken as usual, had dealt it a fearful blow. And yet, though Samuel and Constance had grown so accustomed to the companionship of a criminal that they frequently lost memory of his guilt for long periods, nevertheless the convention of his leprosy had more or less persisted with Samuel until that moment: when it vanished with strange suddenness, to Samuel's conscious relief.

There was a rain of pellets on the window.

"Hear that?" demanded Cyril, whispering dramatically. "And it's been like that on my window too."

Samuel arose. "Go back to your room!" he ordered in the same dramatic whisper; but not as father to son—rather as conspirator to conspirator.

Constance slept. They could hear her regular breathing.

Barefooted, the elderly gowned figure followed the younger, and one after the other they creaked down the two steps which separated Cyril's room from his parents'.

"Shut the door quietly!" said Samuel.

Cyril obeyed.

And then, having lighted Cyril's gas, Samuel drew the blind, unfastened the catch of the window, and began to open it with many precautions of silence. All the sashes in that house were difficult to manage. Cyril stood close to his father, shivering without knowing that he shivered, astonished only that his father had not told him to get back into bed at once. It was, beyond doubt, the proudest hour of Cyril's career. In addition to the mysterious circumstances of the night, there was in the situation that thrill which always communicates itself to a father and son when they are afoot together upon an enterprise unsuspected by the woman from whom their lives have no secrets.

Samuel put his head out of the window.

A man was standing there.

"That you, Samuel?" The voice came low.

"Yes," replied Samuel, cautiously. "It's not Cousin Daniel, is it?"

"I want ye," said Daniel Povey, curtly.

Samuel paused. "I'll be down in a minute," he said.

Cyril at length received the command to get back into bed at once.

"Whatever's up, father?" he asked joyously.

"I don't know. I must put some things on and go and see."

He shut down the window on all the breezes that were pouring into the room.

"Now quick, before I turn the gas out!" he admonished, his hand on the gas-tap.

"You'll tell me in the morning, won't you, father?"

"Yes," said Mr. Povey, conquering his habitual impulse to say "No."

He crept back to the large bedroom to grope for clothes.

When, having descended to the parlour and lighted the gas there, he opened the side-door, expecting to let Cousin Daniel in, there was no sign of Cousin Daniel. Presently he saw a figure standing at the corner of the Square. He whistled—Samuel had a singular faculty of whistling, the envy of his son—and Daniel beckoned to him. He nearly extinguished the gas and then ran out, hatless. He was wearing most of his clothes, except his linen collar and necktie, and the collar of his coat was turned up.

Daniel advanced before him, without waiting, into the confectioner's shop opposite. Being part of the most modern building in the Square, Daniel's shop was provided with the new roll-down iron shutter, by means of which you closed your establishment with a motion similar to the winding of a large clock, instead of putting up twenty separate shutters one by one as in the sixteenth century. The little portal in the vast sheet of armour was ajar, and Daniel had passed into the gloom beyond. At the same moment a policeman came along on his beat, cutting off Mr. Povey from Daniel.

"Good-night, officer! Brrr!" said Mr. Povey, gathering his dignity about him and holding himself as though it was part of his normal habit to take exercise bareheaded and collarless in St. Luke's Square on cold November nights. He behaved so because, if Daniel had desired the services of a policeman, Daniel would of course have spoken to this one.

"Goo' night, sir," said the policeman, after recognizing him.

"What time is it?" asked Samuel, bold.

"A quarter-past one, sir."

The policeman, leaving Samuel at the little open door, went

forward across the lamplit Square, and Samuel entered his cousin's shop.

Daniel Povey was standing behind the door, and as Samuel came in he shut the door with a startling sudden movement. Save for the twinkle of gas, the shop was in darkness. It had the empty appearance which a well-managed confectioner's and baker's always has at night. The large brass scales near the flour-bins glinted; and the glass cake-stands, with scarce a tart among them, also caught the faint flare of the gas.

"What's the matter, Daniel? Anything wrong?" Samuel asked, feeling boyish as he usually did in the presence of Daniel.

The well-favoured white-haired man seized him with one hand by the shoulder in a grip that convicted Samuel of frailty.

"Look here, Sam'l," said he in his low, pleasant voice, somewhat altered by excitement. "You know as my wife drinks?"

He stared defiantly at Samuel.

"N—no," said Samuel. "That is—no one's ever *said*—"

This was true. He did not know that Mrs. Daniel Povey, at the age of fifty, had definitely taken to drink. There had been rumours that she enjoyed a glass with too much gusto; but "drinks" meant more than that.

"She drinks," Daniel Povey continued. "And has done this last two year!"

"I'm very sorry to hear it," said Samuel, tremendously shocked by this brutal rending of the cloak of decency.

Always, everybody had feigned to Daniel, and Daniel had feigned to everybody, that his wife was as other wives. And now the man himself had torn to pieces in a moment the veil of thirty years' weaving.

"And if that was the worst!" Daniel murmured reflectively, loosening his grip.

Samuel was excessively disturbed. His cousin was hinting at matters which he himself, at any rate, had never hinted at even to Constance, so abhorrent were they; matters unutterable, which hung like clouds in the social atmosphere of the town, and of which at rare intervals one conveyed one's cognizance, not by words, but by something scarce perceptible in a glance, an accent. Not often is a town such as Bursley starred with such a woman as Mrs. Daniel Povey.

"But what's wrong?" Samuel asked, trying to be firm.

And, "What *is* wrong?" he asked himself. "What does all this mean, at after one o'clock in the morning?"

"Look here, Sam'l," Daniel recommenced, seizing his shoulder again. "I went to Liverpool corn market to-day, and missed the last train, so I came by mail from Crewe. And what do I find? I find Dick sitting on the stairs in the dark pretty nigh naked."

"Sitting on the stairs? Dick?"

"Ay! This is what I come home to!"

"But——"

"Hold on! He's been in bed a couple of days with a feverish cold, caught through lying in damp sheets as his mother had forgot to air. She brings him no supper to-night. He calls out. No answer. Then he gets up to go down-stairs and see what's happened, and he slips on th' stairs and breaks his knee, or puts it out or summat. Sat there hours, seemingly! Couldn't walk neither up nor down."

"And was your——wife——was Mrs.——?"

"Dead drunk in the parlour, Sam'l."

"But the servant?"

"Servant!" Daniel Povey laughed. "We can't keep our servants. They won't stay. *You* know that."

He did. Mrs. Daniel Povey's domestic methods and idiosyncrasies could at any rate be freely discussed, and they were.

"And what have you done?"

"Done? Why, I picked him up in my arms and carried him upstairs again. And a fine job I had too! Here! Come here!"

Daniel strode impulsively across the shop——the counterflap was up——and opened a door at the back. Samuel followed. Never before had he penetrated so far into his cousin's secrets. On the left, within the doorway, were the stairs, dark; on the right a shut door; and in front an open door giving on to a yard. At the extremity of the yard he discerned a building, vaguely lit, and naked figures strangely moving in it.

"What's that? Who's there?" he asked sharply.

"That's the bakehouse," Daniel replied, as if surprised at such a question. "It's one of their long nights."

Never, during the brief remainder of his life, did Samuel eat a mouthful of common bread without recalling that midnight apparition. He had lived for half a century, and thoughtlessly eaten bread as though loaves grew ready-made on trees.

"Listen!" Daniel commanded him.

He cocked his ear, and caught a feeble, complaining wail from an upper floor.

"That's Dick! That is!" said Daniel Povey.

It sounded more like the distress of a child than of an adventurous young man of twenty-four or so.

"But is he in pain? Haven't you fetched the doctor?"

"Not yet," answered Daniel, with a vacant stare.

Samuel gazed at him closely for a second. And Daniel seemed to him very old and helpless and pathetic, a man unequal to the situation in which he found himself; and yet, despite the dignified snow of his age, wistfully boyish. Samuel thought swiftly: "This has been too much for him. He's almost out of his mind. That's the explanation. Some one's got to take charge, and I must." And all the courageous resolution of his character braced itself to the crisis. Being without a collar, being in slippers, and his suspenders imperfectly fastened anyhow,—these things seemed to be a part of the crisis.

"I'll just run upstairs and have a look at him," said Samuel, in a matter-of-fact tone.

Daniel did not reply.

There was a glimmer at the top of the stairs. Samuel mounted, found the gas-jet, and turned it on full. A dingy, dirty, untidy passage was revealed, the very antechamber of discomfort. Guided by the moans, Samuel entered a bedroom, which was in a shameful condition of neglect, and lighted only by a nearly expired candle. Was it possible that a housemistress could so lose her self-respect? Samuel thought of his own abode, meticulously and impeccably "kept," and a hard bitterness against Mrs. Daniel surged up in his soul.

"Is that you, doctor?" said a voice from the bed; the moans ceased.

Samuel raised the candle.

Dick lay there, his face, on which was a beard of several days' growth, distorted by anguish, sweating; his tousled brown hair was limp with sweat.

"Where the hell's the doctor?" the young man demanded brusquely. Evidently he had no curiosity about Samuel's presence; the one thing that struck him was that Samuel was not the doctor.

"He's coming, he's coming," said Samuel, soothingly.

"Well, if he isn't here soon I shall be damn well dead," said Dick, in feeble resentful anger. "I can tell you that."

Samuel deposited the candle and ran downstairs. "I say, Daniel," he said, roused and hot, "this is really ridiculous. Why on earth didn't you fetch the doctor while you were waiting for me? Where's the missis?"

Daniel Povey was slowly emptying grains of Indian corn out of his jacket-pocket into one of the big receptacles behind the counter on the baker's side of the shop. He had provisioned himself with Indian corn as ammunition for Samuel's bedroom window; he was now returning the surplus.

"Are ye going for Harrop?" he questioned hesitatingly.

"Why, of course!" Samuel exclaimed. "Where's the missis?"

"Happen you'd better go and have a look at her," said Daniel Povey. "She's in th' parlour."

He preceded Samuel to the shut door on the right. When he opened it the parlour appeared in full illumination.

"Here! Go in!" said Daniel.

Samuel went in, afraid. In a room as dishevelled and filthy as the bedroom, Mrs. Daniel Povey lay stretched awkwardly on a worn horse-hair sofa, her head thrown back, her face discoloured, her eyes bulging, her mouth wet and yawning: a sight horribly offensive. Samuel was frightened; he was struck with fear and with disgust. The singing gas beat down ruthlessly on that dreadful figure. A wife and mother! The lady of a house! The centre of order! The fount of healing! The balm for worry, and the refuge of distress! She was vile. Her scanty yellow-grey hair was dirty, her hollowed neck all grime, her hands abominable, her black dress in decay. She was the dishonour of her sex, her situation, and her years. She was a fouler obscenity than the inexperienced Samuel had ever conceived. And by the door stood her husband, neat, spotless, almost stately, the man who for thirty years had marshalled all his immense pride to suffer this woman, the jolly man who had laughed through thick and thin! Samuel remembered when they were married. And he remembered when, years after their marriage, she was still as pretty, artificial, coquettish, and adamantine in her caprices as a young harlot with a fool at her feet. Time and the slow wrath of God had changed her.

He remained master of himself and approached her; then stopped.

"But——" he stammered.

"Ay, Sam'l, lad!" said the old man from the door. "I doubt I've killed her! I doubt I've killed her! I took and shook her.

I got her by the neck. And before I knew where I was, I'd done it. She'll never drink brandy again. This is what it's come to!"

He moved away.

All Samuel's flesh tingled as a heavy wave of emotion rolled through his being. It was just as if some one had dealt him a blow unimaginably tremendous. His heart shivered, as a ship shivers at the mountainous crash of the waters. He was numbed. He wanted to weep, to vomit, to die, to sink away. But a voice was whispering to him: "You will have to go through with this. You are in charge of this." He thought of *his* wife and child, innocently asleep in the cleanly pureness of *his* home. And he felt the roughness of his coat-collar round his neck and the insecurity of his trousers. He passed out of the room, shutting the door. And across the yard he had a momentary glimpse of those nude nocturnal forms, unconsciously attitudinizing in the bakehouse. And down the stairs came the protests of Dick, driven by pain into a monotonous silly blasphemy.

"I'll fetch Harrop," he said, melancholily, to his cousin.

The doctor's house was less than fifty yards off, and the doctor had a night-bell, which, though he was a much older man than his father had been at his age, he still answered promptly. No need to bombard the doctor's premises with Indian corn! While Samuel was parleying with the doctor through a window, the question ran incessantly through his mind: "What about telling the police?"

But when, in advance of old Harrop, he returned to Daniel's shop, lo! the policeman previously encountered had returned upon his beat, and Daniel was talking to him in the little doorway. No other soul was about. Down King Street, along Wedgwood Street, up the Square, towards Brougham Street, nothing but gas-lamps burning with their everlasting patience, and the blind façades of shops. Only in the second storey of the Bank Building at the top of the Square a light showed mysteriously through a blind. Somebody ill there!

The policeman was in a high state of nervous excitement. That had happened to him which had never happened to him before. Of the sixty policemen in Bursley, just he had been chosen by fate to fit the socket of destiny. He was startled.

"What's this, what's this, Mr. Povey?" he turned hastily to Samuel. "What's this as Mr. Councillor Povey is a-telling me?"

"You come in, sergeant," said Daniel.

"If I come in," said the policeman to Samuel, "you mun' go along Wedgwood Street, Mr. Povey, and bring my mate. He should be on Duck Bank, by rights."

It was astonishing, when once the stone had begun to roll, how quickly it ran. In half an hour Samuel had actually parted from Daniel at the police-office behind the Shambles, and was hurrying to rouse his wife so that she could look after Dick Povey until he might be taken off to Pirehill Infirmary, as old Harrop had instantly, on seeing him, decreed.

"Ah!" he reflected in the turmoil of his soul: "God is not mocked!" That was his basic idea: God is not mocked! Daniel was a good fellow, honourable, brilliant; a figure in the world. But what of his licentious tongue? What of his frequenting of bars? (How had he come to miss that train from Liverpool? How?) For many years he, Samuel, had seen in Daniel a living refutation of the authenticity of the old Hebrew menaces. But he had been wrong, after all! God is not mocked! And Samuel was aware of a revulsion in himself towards that strict codified godliness from which, in thought, he had perhaps been slipping away.

And with it all he felt, too, a certain officious self-importance, as he woke his wife and essayed to break the news to her in a manner tactfully calm. He had assisted at the most overwhelming event ever known in the history of the town.

ii

"Your muffler—I'll get it," said Constance. "Cyril, run up-stairs and get father's muffler. You know the drawer."

Cyril ran. It behoved everybody, that morning, to be prompt and efficient.

"I don't need any muffler, thank you," said Samuel, coughing and smothering the cough.

"Oh! But, Sam—" Constance protested.

"Now please don't worry me!" said Samuel with frigid finality. "I've got quite enough—!" He did not finish.

Constance sighed as her husband stepped, nervous and self-important, out of the side-door into the street. It was early, not yet eight o'clock, and the shop still unopened.

"Your father couldn't wait," Constance said to Cyril when

he had thundered down the stairs in his heavy schoolboy boots. "Give it to me." She went to restore the muffler to its place.

The whole house was upset, and Amy still an invalid! Existence was disturbed; there vaguely seemed to be a thousand novel things to be done, and yet she could think of nothing whatever that she needed to do at that moment; so she occupied herself with the muffler. Before she reappeared Cyril had gone to school, he who was usually a laggard. The truth was that he could no longer contain within himself a recital of the night, and in particular of the fact that he had been the first to hear the summons of the murderer on the window-pane. This imperious news had to be imparted to somebody, as a preliminary to the thrilling of the whole school; and Cyril had issued forth in search of an appreciative and worthy confidant. He was scarcely five minutes after his father.

In St. Luke's Square was a crowd of quite two hundred persons, standing moveless in the November mud. The body of Mrs. Daniel Povey had already been taken to the Tiger Hotel, and young Dick Povey was on his way in a covered waggonette to Pirehill Infirmary on the other side of Knype. The shop of the crime was closed, and the blinds drawn at the upper windows of the house. There was absolutely nothing to be seen, not even a policeman. Nevertheless the crowd stared with an extraordinary obstinate attentiveness at the fatal building in Boulton Terrace. Hypnotized by this face of bricks and mortar, it had apparently forgotten all earthly ties, and, regardless of breakfast and a livelihood, was determined to stare at it till the house fell down or otherwise rendered up its secret. Most of its component individuals wore neither overcoats nor collars, but were kept warm by a scarf round the neck and by dint of forcing their fingers into the furthest inch of their pockets. Then they would slowly lift one leg after the other. Starers of infirm purpose would occasionally detach themselves from the throng and sidle away, ashamed of their fickleness. But reinforcements were continually arriving. And to these new-comers all that had been said in gossip had to be repeated and repeated: the same questions, the same answers, the same exclamations, the same proverbial philosophy, the same prophecies recurred in all parts of the Square with an uncanny iterance. Well-dressed men spoke to mere professional loiterers; for this unparalleled and glorious sensation, whose uniqueness grew every instant more impressive, brought out the essential

brotherhood of mankind. All had a peculiar feeling that the
day was neither Sunday nor week-day, but some eighth day of
the week. Yet in the St. Luke's Covered Market close by, the
stall-keepers were preparing their stalls just as though it were
Saturday, just as though a Town Councillor had not murdered
his wife—at last! It was stated, and restated infinitely, that the
Povey baking had been taken over by Brindley, the second-best
baker and confectioner, who had a stall in the market. And it
was asserted, as a philosophical truth, and reasserted infinitely,
that there would have been no sense in wasting good food.

Samuel's emergence stirred the multitude. But Samuel
passed up the Square with a rapt expression; he might have
been under an illusion, caused by the extreme gravity of his
preoccupations, that he was crossing a deserted Square. He
hurried past the Bank and down the Turnhill Road, to the
private residence of "Young Lawton," son of the deceased
"Lawyer Lawton." Young Lawton followed his father's profession; he was, as his father had been, the most successful
solicitor in the town (though reputed by his learned rivals to
be a fool), but the custom of calling men by their occupations
had died out with horse-cars. Samuel caught young Lawton at
his breakfast, and presently drove with him, in the Lawton
buggy, to the police-station, where their arrival electrified a
crowd as large as that in St. Luke's Square. Later, they drove
together to Hanbridge, informally to brief a barrister; and
Samuel, not permitted to be present at the first part of the
interview between the solicitor and the barrister, was humbled
before the pomposity of legal etiquette.

It seemed to Samuel a game. The whole rigmarole of police
and police-cells and formalities seemed insincere. His cousin's
case was not like any other case, and, though formalities might
be necessary, it was rather absurd to pretend that it was like
any other case. In what manner it differed from other cases
Samuel did not analytically inquire. He thought young Lawton
was self-important, and Daniel too humble, in the colloquy of
these two, and he endeavoured to indicate, by the dignity of his
own demeanour, that in his opinion the proper relative tones
had not been set. He could not understand Daniel's attitude,
for he lacked imagination to realize what Daniel had been
through. After all, Daniel was not a murderer; his wife's death
was due to accident, was simply a mishap.

But in the crowded and stinking court-room of the Town

Hall, Samuel began to feel qualms. It occurred that the Stipendiary Magistrate was sitting that morning at Bursley. He sat alone, as not one of the Borough Justices cared to occupy the Bench while a Town Councillor was in the dock. The Stipendiary, recently appointed, was a young man, from the southern part of the county; and a Town Councillor of Bursley was no more to him than a petty tradesman to a man of fashion. He was youthfully enthusiastic for the majesty and the impartiality of English justice, and behaved as though the entire responsibility for the safety of that vast fabric rested on his shoulders. He and the barrister from Hanbridge had had a historic quarrel at Cambridge, and their behaviour to each other was a lesson to the vulgar in the art of chill and consummate politeness. Young Lawton, having been to Oxford, secretly scorned the pair of them, but, as he had engaged counsel, he of course was precluded from adding to the eloquence, which chagrined him. These three were the aristocracy of the court-room; they knew it; Samuel Povey knew it; everybody knew it, and felt it. The barrister brought an unexceptionable zeal to the performance of his duties; he referred in suitable terms to Daniel's character and high position in the town, but nothing could hide the fact that for him too his client was a petty tradesman accused of simple murder. Naturally the Stipendiary was bound to show that before the law all men are equal—the Town Councillor and the common tippler; he succeeded. The policeman gave his evidence, and the Inspector swore to what Daniel Povey had said when charged. The hearing proceeded so smoothly and quickly that it seemed naught but an empty rite, with Daniel as a lay figure in it. The Stipendiary achieved marvellously the illusion that to him a murder by a Town Councillor in St. Luke's Square was quite an everyday matter. Bail was inconceivable, and the barrister, being unable to suggest any reason why the Stipendiary should grant a remand—indeed, there was no reason—Daniel Povey was committed to the Stafford Assizes for trial. The Stipendiary instantly turned to the consideration of an alleged offence against the Factory Acts by a large local firm of potters. The young magistrate had mistaken his vocation. With his steely calm, with his imperturbable detachment from weak humanity, he ought to have been a General of the Order of Jesuits.

Daniel was removed—he did not go: he was removed, by two bare-headed constables. Samuel wanted to have speech with

him, and could not. And later, Samuel stood in the porch of
the Town Hall, and Daniel appeared out of a corridor, still
in the keeping of two policemen, helmeted now. And down below
at the bottom of the broad flight of steps, up which passed
dancers on the nights of subscription balls, was a dense crowd,
held at bay by other policemen; and beyond the crowd a black
van. And Daniel—to his cousin a sort of Christ between thieves
—was hurried past the privileged loafers in the corridor, and
down the broad steps. A murmuring wave agitated the crowd.
Unkempt idlers and ne'er-do-wells in corduroy leaped up like
tigers in the air, and the policemen fought them back furiously.
And Daniel and his guardians shot through the little living
lane. Quick! Quick! For the captive is more sacred even than
a messiah. The law has him in charge! And like a feat of
prestidigitation Daniel disappeared into the blackness of the
van. A door slammed loudly, triumphantly, and a whip cracked.
The crowd had been balked. It was as though the crowd had
yelled for Daniel's blood and bones, and the faithful constables
had saved him from their lust.

Yes, Samuel had qualms. He had a sickness in the stomach.

The aged Superintendent of Police walked by, with the aged
Rector. The Rector was Daniel's friend. Never before had the
Rector spoken to the Nonconformist Samuel, but now he spoke
to him; he squeezed his hand.

"Ah, Mr. Povey!" he ejaculated grievously.

"I—I'm afraid it's serious!" Samuel stammered. He hated
to admit that it was serious, but the words came out of his
mouth.

He looked at the Superintendent of Police, expecting the
Superintendent to assure him that it was not serious; but the
Superintendent only raised his small white-bearded chin, saying nothing. The Rector shook his head, and shook a senile tear
out of his eye.

After another chat with young Lawton, Samuel, on behalf
of Daniel, dropped his pose of the righteous man to whom a
mere mishap has occurred, and who is determined, with the lofty
pride of innocence, to indulge all the whims of the law, to be
more royalist than the king. He perceived that the law must
be fought with its own weapons, that no advantage must be
surrendered, and every possible advantage seized. He was truly
astonished at himself that such a pose had ever been adopted.
His eyes were opened; he saw things as they were.

He returned home through a Square that was more interested than ever in the façade of his cousin's house. People were beginning to come from Hanbridge, Knype, Longshaw, Turnhill, and villages such as Moorthorne, to gaze at that façade. And the fourth edition of the *Signal*, containing a full report of what the Stipendiary and the barrister had said to each other, was being cried.

In his shop he found customers, as absorbed in the trivialities of purchase as though nothing whatever had happened. He was shocked; he resented their callousness.

"I'm too busy now," he said curtly to one who accosted him.

"Sam!" his wife called him in a low voice. She was standing behind the till.

"What is it?" He was ready to crush, and especially to crush indiscreet babble in the shop. He thought she was going to vent her womanly curiosity at once.

"Mr. Huntbach is waiting for you in the parlour," said Constance.

"Mr. Huntbach?"

"Yes, from Longshaw." She whispered, "It's Mrs. Povey's cousin. He's come to see about the funeral and so on, the— the inquest, I suppose."

Samuel paused. "Oh, has he!" said he defiantly. "Well, I'll see him. If he *wants* to see me, I'll see him."

That evening Constance learned all that was in his mind of bitterness against the memory of the dead woman whose failings had brought Daniel Povey to Stafford gaol and Dick to the Pirehill Infirmary. Again and again, in the ensuing days, he referred to the state of foul discomfort which he had discovered in Daniel's house. He nursed a feud against all her relatives, and when, after the inquest, at which he gave evidence full of resentment, she was buried, he vented an angry sigh of relief, and said: "Well, *she's* out of the way!" Thenceforward he had a mission, religious in its solemn intensity, to defend and save Daniel. He took the enterprise upon himself, spending the whole of himself upon it, to the neglect of his business and the scorn of his health. He lived solely for Daniel's trial, pouring out money in preparation for it. He thought and spoke of nothing else. The affair was his one preoccupation. And as the weeks passed, he became more and more sure of success, more and more sure that he would return with Daniel to Bursley in triumph after the assize. He was convinced of the impossibility that "anything should happen" to Daniel; the circumstances were too clear, too overwhelmingly in Daniel's favour.

When Brindley, the second-best baker and confectioner, made an offer for Daniel's business as a going concern, he was indignant at first. Then Constance, and the lawyer, and Daniel (whom he saw on every permitted occasion) between them persuaded him that if some arrangement was not made, and made quickly, the business would lose all its value, and he consented, on Daniel's behalf, to a temporary agreement under which Brindley should reopen the shop and manage it on certain terms until Daniel regained his freedom towards the end of January. He would not listen to Daniel's plaintive insistence that he would never care to be seen in Bursley again. He poohpoohed it. He protested furiously that the whole town was seething with sympathy for Daniel; and this was true. He became Daniel's defending angel, rescuing Daniel from Daniel's own weakness and apathy. He became, indeed, Daniel.

One morning the shop-shutter was wound up, and Brindley, inflated with the importance of controlling two establishments, strutted in and out under the sign of Daniel Povey. And traffic in bread and cakes and flour was resumed. Apparently the sea of time had risen and covered Daniel and all that was his; for his wife was under earth, and Dick lingered at Pirehill, unable to stand, and Daniel was locked away. Apparently, in the regular flow of the life of the Square, Daniel was forgotten. But not in Samuel Povey's heart was he forgotten! There, before an altar erected to the martyr, the sacred flame of a new faith burned with fierce consistency. Samuel, in his greying middle-age, had inherited the eternal youth of the apostle.

iii

On the dark winter morning when Samuel set off to the grand assize, Constance did not ask his views as to what protection he would adopt against the weather. She silently ranged special underclothing, and by the warmth of the fire, which for days she had kept ablaze in the bedroom, Samuel silently donned the special underclothing. Over that, with particular fastidious care, he put his best suit. Not a word was spoken. Constance and he were not estranged, but the relations between

them were in a state of feverish excitation. Samuel had had a
cold on his flat chest for weeks, and nothing that Constance
could invent would move it. A few days in bed or even in one
room at a uniform temperature would have surely worked the
cure. Samuel, however, would not stay in one room; he would
not stay in the house, nor yet in Bursley. He would take his
lacerating cough on chilly trains to Stafford. He had no ears
for reason; he simply could not listen; he was in a dream. After
Christmas a crisis came. Constance grew desperate. It was a
battle between her will and his that occurred one night when
Constance, marshalling all her forces, suddenly insisted that he
must go out no more until he was cured. In the fight Constance
was scarcely recognizable. She deliberately gave way to
hysteria; she was no longer soft and gentle; she flung bitterness
at him like vitriol; she shrieked like a common shrew. It seems
almost incredible that Constance should have gone so far; but
she did. She accused him, amid sobs, of putting his cousin before his wife and son, of not caring whether or not she was left
a widow as the result of this obstinacy. And she ended by crying passionately that she might as well talk to a post. She
might just as well have talked to a post. Samuel answered
quietly and coldly. He told her that it was useless for her to put
herself about, as he should act as he thought fit. It was a most
extraordinary scene, and quite unique in their annals. Constance was beaten. She accepted the defeat, gradually controlling her sobs and changing her tone to the tone of the
vanquished. She kissed him in bed, kissing the rod. And he
gravely kissed her.

Henceforward she knew, in practice, what the inevitable,
when you have to live with it, may contain of anguish wretched
and humiliating. Her husband was risking his life, so she was
absolutely convinced, and she could do nothing; she had come
to the bed-rock of Samuel's character. She felt that, for the
time being, she had a madman in the house, who could not be
treated according to ordinary principles. The continual strain
aged her. Her one source of relief was to talk with Cyril.
She talked to him without reserve, and the words "your father,"
"your father," were everlastingly on her complaining tongue.
Yes, she was utterly changed. Often she would weep when alone.

Nevertheless she frequently forgot that she had been beaten.
She had no notion of honourable warfare. She was always beginning again, always firing under a flag of truce; and thus

she constituted a very inconvenient opponent. Samuel was
obliged, while hardening on the main point, to compromise on
lesser questions. She too could be formidable, and when her
lips took a certain pose, and her eyes glowed, he would have put
on forty mufflers had she commanded. Thus it was she who
arranged all the details of the supreme journey to Stafford.
Samuel was to drive to Knype, so as to avoid the rigours of the
Loop Line train from Bursley and the waiting on cold plat-
forms. At Knype he was to take the express, and to travel first-
class.

After he was dressed on that gas-lit morning, he learnt bit
by bit the extent of her elaborate preparations. The breakfast
was a special breakfast, and he had to eat it all. Then the
cab came, and he saw Amy put hot bricks into it. Constance
herself put goloshes over his boots, not because it was damp,
but because indiarubber keeps the feet warm. Constance herself bandaged his neck, and unbuttoned his waistcoat and stuck
an extra flannel under his dickey. Constance herself warmed
his woollen gloves, and enveloped him in his largest overcoat.

Samuel then saw Cyril getting ready to go out. "Where are
you off?" he demanded.

"He's going with you as far as Knype," said Constance
grimly. "He'll see you into the train and then come back here
in the cab."

She had sprung this indignity upon him. She glared. Cyril
glanced with timid bravado from one to the other. Samuel had
to yield.

Thus in the winter darkness—for it was not yet dawn—
Samuel set forth to the trial, escorted by his son. The reverbera-
tion of his appalling cough from the cab was the last thing that
Constance heard.

During most of the day Constance sat in "Miss Insull's
corner" in the shop. Twenty years ago this very corner had
been hers. But now, instead of large millinery-boxes enwrapped
in brown paper, it was shut off from the rest of the counter by
a rich screen of mahogany and ground-glass, and within the
enclosed space all the apparatus necessary to the activity of
Miss Insull had been provided for. However, it remained the
coldest part of the whole shop, as Miss Insull's fingers testified.
Constance established herself there more from a desire to do
something, to interfere in something, than from a necessity of
supervising the shop, though she had said to Samuel that she

would keep an eye on the shop. Miss Insull, whose throne was usurped, had to sit by the stove with less important creatures; she did not like it, and her underlings suffered accordingly.

It was a long day. Towards tea-time, just before Cyril was due from school, Mr. Critchlow came surprisingly in. That is to say, his arrival was less of a surprise to Miss Insull and the rest of the staff than to Constance. For he had lately formed an irregular habit of popping in at tea-time, to chat with Miss Insull. Mr. Critchlow was still defying time. He kept his long, thin figure perfectly erect. His features had not altered. His hair and beard could not have been whiter than they had been for years past. He wore his long white apron, and over that a thick reefer jacket. In his long, knotty fingers he carried a copy of the *Signal*.

Evidently he had not expected to find the corner occupied by Constance. She was sewing.

"So it's you!" he said, in his unpleasant, grating voice, not even glancing at Miss Insull. He had gained the reputation of being the rudest old man in Bursley. But his general demeanour expressed indifference rather than rudeness. It was a manner that said: "You've got to take me as I am. I may be an egotist, hard, mean, and convinced; but those who don't like it can lump it. I'm indifferent."

He put one elbow on the top of the screen, showing the *Signal*.

"Mr. Critchlow!" said Constance, primly; she had acquired Samuel's dislike of him.

"It's begun!" he observed with mysterious glee.

"Has it?" Constance said eagerly. "Is it in the paper already?"

She had been far more disturbed about her husband's health than about the trial of Daniel Povey for murder, but her interest in the trial was of course tremendous. And this news, that it had actually begun, thrilled her.

"Ay!" said Mr. Critchlow. "Didn't ye hear the *Signal* boy hollering just now all over the Square?"

"No," said Constance. For her, newspapers did not exist. She never had the idea of opening one, never felt any curiosity which she could not satisfy, if she could satisfy it at all, without the powerful aid of the press. And even on this day it had not occurred to her that the *Signal* might be worth opening.

"Ay!" repeated Mr. Critchlow. "Seemingly it began at two

o'clock—or thereabouts." He gave a moment of his attention to a noisy gas-jet, which he carefully lowered.

"What does it say?"

"Nothing yet!" said Mr. Critchlow; and they read the few brief sentences, under their big heading, which described the formal commencement of the trial of Daniel Povey for the murder of his wife. "There was some as said," he remarked, pushing up his spectacles, "that grand jury would alter the charge, or summat!" He laughed, grimly tolerant of the extreme absurdity. "Ah!" he added contemplatively, turning his head to see if the assistants were listening. They were. It would have been too much, on such a day, to expect a strict adherence to the etiquette of the shop.

Constance had been hearing a good deal lately of grand juries, but she had understood nothing, nor had she sought to understand.

"I'm very glad it's come on so soon," she said. "In a sense, that is! I was afraid Sam might be kept at Stafford for days. Do you think it will last long?"

"Not it!" said Mr. Critchlow, positively. "There's naught in it to spin out."

Then a silence, punctuated by the sound of stitching.

Constance would really have preferred not to converse with the old man; but the desire for reassurance, for the calming of her own fears, forced her to speak, though she knew well that Mr. Critchlow was precisely the last man in the town to give moral assistance if he thought it was wanted.

"I do hope everything will be all right!" she murmured.

"Everything'll be all right!" he said gaily. "Everything'll be all right. Only it'll be all wrong for Dan."

"Whatever do you mean, Mr. Critchlow?" she protested. Nothing, she reflected, could rouse pity in that heart, not even a tragedy like Daniel's. She bit her lip for having spoken.

"Well," he said in loud tones, frankly addressing the girls round the stove as much as Constance. "I've met with some rare good arguments this new year, no mistake! There's been some as say that Dan never meant to do it. That's as may be. But if it's a good reason for not hanging, there's an end to capital punishment in this country. 'Never meant'! There's a lot of 'em as 'never meant'! Then I'm told as she was a gallivanting woman and no housekeeper, and as often drunk as

sober. I'd no call to be told that. If strangling is a right punishment for a wife as spends her time in drinking brandy instead of sweeping floors and airing sheets, then Dan's safe.
But I don't seem to see Judge Lindley telling the jury as it is.
I've been a juryman under Judge Lindley myself—and more
than once—and I don't seem to see him, like!" He paused with
his mouth open. "As for all them nobs," he continued, "including th' rector, as have gone to Stafford to kiss the book and
swear that Dan's reputation is second to none—if they could
ha' sworn as Dan wasn't in th' house at all that night, if they
could ha' sworn he was in Jericho, there'd ha' been some sense
in their going. But as it is, they'd ha' done better to stop at
home and mind their business. Bless us! Sam wanted *me* to go!"

He laughed again, in the faces of the horrified and angry
women.

"I'm surprised at you, Mr. Critchlow! I really am!" Constance exclaimed.

And the assistants inarticulately supported her with vague
sounds. Miss Insull got up and poked the stove. Every soul
in the establishment was loyally convinced that Daniel Povey
would be acquitted, and to breathe a doubt on the brightness
of this certainty was a hideous crime. The conviction was not
within the domain of reason; it was an act of faith; and arguments merely fretted, without in the slightest degree disturbing it.

"Ye may be!" Mr. Critchlow gaily concurred. He was very
content.

Just as he shuffled round to leave the shop, Cyril entered.

"Good afternoon, Mr. Critchlow," said Cyril, sheepishly
polite.

Mr. Critchlow gazed hard at the boy, then nodded his head
several times rapidly, as though to say: "Here's another fool
in the making! So the generations follow one another!" He
made no answer to the salutation, and departed.

Cyril ran round to his mother's corner, pitching his bag on
to the showroom stairs as he passed them. Taking off his hat,
he kissed her, and she unbuttoned his overcoat with her cold
hands.

"What's old Methuselah after?" he demanded.

"Hush!" Constance softly corrected him. "He came in to
tell me the trial had started."

"Oh, I knew that! A boy bought a paper and I saw it. I say, mother, will father be in the paper?" And then in a different tone: "I say, mother, what is there for tea?"

When his stomach had learnt exactly what there was for tea, the boy began to show an immense and talkative curiosity in the trial. He would not set himself to his home-lessons. "It's no use, mother," he said, "I can't." They returned to the shop together, and Cyril would go every moment to the door to listen for the cry of a newsboy. Presently he hit upon the idea that perhaps newsboys might be crying the special edition of the *Signal* in the market-place, in front of the Town Hall, to the neglect of St. Luke's Square. And nothing would satisfy him but he must go forth and see. He went, without his overcoat, promising to run. The shop waited with a strange anxiety. Cyril had created, by his restless movements to and fro, an atmosphere of strained expectancy. It seemed now as if the whole town stood with beating heart, fearful of tidings and yet burning to get them. Constance pictured Stafford, which she had never seen, and a court of justice, which she had never seen, and her husband and Daniel in it. And she waited.

Cyril ran in. "No!" he announced breathlessly. "Nothing yet."

"Don't take cold, now you're hot," Constance advised.

But he would keep near the door. Soon he ran off again.

And perhaps fifteen seconds after he had gone, the strident cry of a *Signal* boy was heard in the distance, faint and indistinct at first, then clearer and louder.

"There's a paper!" said the apprentice.

"Sh!" said Constance, listening.

"Sh!" echoed Miss Insull.

"Yes, it is!" said Constance. "Miss Insull, just step out and get a paper. Here's a halfpenny."

The halfpenny passed quickly from one thimbled hand to another. Miss Insull scurried.

She came in triumphantly with the sheet, which Constance tremblingly took. Constance could not find the report at first. Miss Insull pointed to it, and read—

" 'Summing up!' Lower down, lower down! 'After an absence of thirty-five minutes the jury found the prisoner guilty of murder, with a recommendation to mercy. The judge assumed the black cap and pronounced sentence of death, saying that he would forward the recommendation to the proper quarter.' "

Cyril returned. "Not yet!" he was saying—when he saw the paper lying on the counter. His crest fell.

Long after the shop was shut, Constance and Cyril waited in the parlour for the arrival of the master of the house. Constance was in the blackest despair. She saw nothing but death around her. She thought: misfortunes never come singly. Why did not Samuel come? All was ready for him, everything that her imagination could suggest, in the way of food, remedies, and the means of warmth. Amy was not allowed to go to bed, lest she might be needed. Constance did not even hint that Cyril should go to bed. The dark, dreadful minutes ticked themselves off on the mantelpiece until only five minutes separated Constance from the moment when she would not know what to do next. It was twenty-five minutes past eleven. If at half-past Samuel did not appear, then he could not come that night, unless the last train from Stafford was inconceivably late.

The sound of a carriage! It ceased at the door. Mother and son sprang up.

Yes, it was Samuel! She beheld him once more. And the sight of his condition, moral and physical, terrified her. His great strapping son and Amy helped him upstairs. "Will he ever come down those stairs again?" This thought lanced Constance's heart. The pain was come and gone in a moment, but it had surprised her tranquil commonsense, which was naturally opposed to, and gently scornful of, hysterical fears. As she puffed, with her stoutness, up the stairs, that bland cheerfulness of hers cost her an immense effort of will. She was profoundly troubled; great disasters seemed to be slowly approaching her from all quarters.

Should she send for the doctor? No. To do so would only be a concession to the panic instinct. She knew exactly what was the matter with Samuel: a severe cough persistently neglected, no more. As she had expressed herself many times to inquirers, "He's never been what you may call ill." Nevertheless, as she laid him in bed and posseted him, how frail and fragile he looked! And he was so exhausted that he would not even talk about the trial.

"If he's not better to-morrow I *shall* send for the doctor!" she said to herself. As for his getting up, she swore she would keep him in bed by force if necessary.

iv

The next morning she was glad and proud that she had not
yielded to a scare. For he was most strangely and obviously
better. He had slept heavily, and she had slept a little. True
that Daniel was condemned to death! Leaving Daniel to his
fate, she was conscious of joy springing in her heart. How
absurd to have asked herself: "Will he ever come down those
stairs again?"!

A message reached her from the forgotten shop during the
morning, that Mr. Lawton had called to see Mr. Povey.
Already Samuel had wanted to arise, but she had forbidden it
in the tone of a woman who is dangerous, and Samuel had
been very reasonable. He now said that Mr. Lawton must be
asked up. She glanced round the bedroom. It was "done";
it was faultlessly correct as a sick chamber. She agreed to the
introduction into it of the man from another sphere, and after
a preliminary minute she left the two to talk together. This
visit of young Lawton's was a dramatic proof of Samuel's
importance, and of the importance of the matter in hand. The
august occasion demanded etiquette, and etiquette said that a
wife should depart from her husband when he had to transact
affairs beyond the grasp of a wife.

The idea of a petition to the Home Secretary took shape at
this interview, and before the day was out it had spread over
the town and over the Five Towns, and it was in the *Signal*.
The *Signal* spoke of Daniel Povey as "the condemned man."
And the phrase startled the whole district into an indignant
agitation for his reprieve. The district woke up to the fact
that a Town Councillor, a figure in the world, an honest tradesman of unspotted character, was cooped solitary in a little
cell at Stafford, waiting to be hanged by the neck till he was
dead. The district determined that this must not and should
not be. Why! Dan Povey had actually once been Chairman
of the Bursley Society for the Prosecution of Felons, that
association for annual eating and drinking, whose members
humorously called each other "felons"! Impossible, monstrous,
that an ex-chairman of the "Felons" should be a sentenced
criminal!

However, there was nothing to fear. No Home Secretary

would dare to run counter to the jury's recommendation and the expressed wish of the whole district. Besides, the Home Secretary's nephew was M.P. for the Knype division. Of course a verdict of guilty had been inevitable. Everybody recognized that now. Even Samuel and all the hottest partisans of Daniel Povey recognized it. They talked as if they had always foreseen it, directly contradicting all that they had said on only the previous day. Without any sense of any inconsistency or of shame, they took up an absolutely new position. The structure of blind faith had once again crumbled at the assault of realities, and unhealthy, un-English truths, the statement of which would have meant ostracism twenty-four hours earlier, became suddenly the platitudes of the Square and the market-place.

Despatch was necessary in the affair of the petition, for the condemned man had but three Sundays. But there was delay at the beginning, because neither young Lawton nor any of his colleagues was acquainted with the proper formula of a petition to the Home Secretary for the reprieve of a criminal condemned to death. No such petition had been made in the district within living memory. And at first, young Lawton could not get sight or copy of any such petition anywhere, in the Five Towns or out of them. Of course there must exist a proper formula, and of course that formula and no other could be employed. Nobody was bold enough to suggest that young Lawton should commence the petition, "To the Most Noble the Marquis of Welwyn, K.C.B., May it please your Lordship," and end it, "And your petitioners will ever pray!" and insert between those phrases a simple appeal for the reprieve, with a statement of reasons. No! the formula consecrated by tradition must be found. And, after Daniel had arrived a day and a half nearer death, it was found. A lawyer at Alnwick had the draft of a petition which had secured for a murderer in Northumberland twenty years' penal servitude instead of sudden death, and on request he lent it to young Lawton. The prime movers in the petition felt that Daniel Povey was now as good as saved. Hundreds of forms were printed to receive signatures, and these forms, together with copies of the petition, were laid on the counters of all the principal shops, not merely in Bursley, but in the other towns. They were also to be found at the offices of the *Signal*, in railway waiting-rooms, and in the various reading-rooms; and on the second of Daniel's three Sundays they were exposed in the porches of churches and chapels. Chapel-keepers and vergers would come to Samuel and ask with the heavy inertia of their stupidity: "About pens and ink, sir?" These officials had the air of audaciously disturbing the sacrosanct routine of centuries in order to confer a favour.

Samuel continued to improve. His cough shook him less, and his appetite increased. Constance allowed him to establish himself in the drawing-room, which was next to the bedroom, and of which the grate was particularly efficient. Here, in an old winter overcoat, he directed the vast affair of the petition, which grew daily to vaster proportions. Samuel dreamed of twenty thousand signatures. Each sheet held twenty signatures, and several times a day he counted the sheets; the supply of forms actually failed once, and Constance herself had to hurry to the printers to order more. Samuel was put into a passion by this carelessness of the printers. He offered Cyril sixpence for every sheet of signatures which the boy would obtain. At first Cyril was too shy to canvass, but his father made him blush, and in a few hours Cyril had developed into an eager canvasser. One whole day he stayed away from school to canvass. Altogether he earned over fifteen shillings, quite honestly except that he got a companion to forge a couple of signatures with addresses lacking at the end of a last sheet, generously rewarding him with sixpence, the value of the entire sheet.

When Samuel had received a thousand sheets with twenty thousand signatures, he set his heart on twenty-five thousand signatures. And he also announced his firm intention of accompanying young Lawton to London with the petition. The petition had, in fact, become one of the most remarkable petitions of modern times. So the *Signal* said. The *Signal* gave a daily account of its progress, and its progress was astonishing. In certain streets every householder had signed it. The first sheets had been reserved for the signatures of members of Parliament, ministers of religion, civic dignitaries, justices of the peace, etc. These sheets were nobly filled. The aged Rector of Bursley signed first of all; after him the Mayor of Bursley, as was right; then sundry M.P.'s.

Samuel emerged from the drawing-room. He went into the parlour, and, later, into the shop; and no evil consequence followed. His cough was nearly, but not quite, cured. The

weather was extraordinarily mild for the season. He repeated
that he should go with the petition to London; and he went;
Constance could not validly oppose the journey. She, too, was
a little intoxicated by the petition. It weighed considerably
over a hundredweight. The crowning signature, that of the
M.P. for Knype, was duly obtained in London, and Samuel's
one disappointment was that his hope of twenty-five thousand
signatures had fallen short of realization—by only a few score.
The few score could have been got had not time urgently
pressed. He returned from London a man of mark, full of confidence; but his cough was worse again.

His confidence in the power of public opinion and the inherent virtue of justice might have proved to be well placed,
had not the Home Secretary happened to be one of your
humane officials. The Marquis of Welwyn was celebrated
through every stratum of the governing classes for his humane
instincts, which were continually fighting against his sense of
duty. Unfortunately his sense of duty, which he had inherited
from several centuries of ancestors, made havoc among his
humane instincts on nearly every occasion of conflict. It was
reported that he suffered horribly in consequence. Others also
suffered, for he was never known to advise a remission of a
sentence of flogging. Certain capital sentences he had com-
muted, but he did not commute Daniel Povey's. He could not
permit himself to be influenced by a wave of popular sentiment, and assuredly not by his own nephew's signature. He
gave to the case the patient, remorseless examination which he
gave to every case. He spent a sleepless night in trying to discover a reason for yielding to his humane instincts, but without
success. As Judge Lindley remarked in his confidential report,
the sole arguments in favour of Daniel were provocation and
his previous high character; and these were no sort of an argument. The provocation was utterly inadequate, and the previous high character was quite too ludicrously beside the point.
So once more the Marquis's humane instincts were routed and
he suffered horribly.

v

On the Sunday morning after the day on which the *Signal*
had printed the menu of Daniel Povey's supreme breakfast,
and the exact length of the "drop" which the executioner had

administered to him, Constance and Cyril stood together at the window of the large bedroom. The boy was in his best clothes; but Constance's garments gave no sign of the Sabbath. She wore a large apron over an old dress that was rather tight for her. She was pale and looked ill.

"Oh, mother!" Cyril exclaimed suddenly. "Listen! I'm sure I can hear the band."

She checked him with a soundless movement of her lips; and they both glanced anxiously at the silent bed, Cyril with a gesture of apology for having forgotten that he must make no noise.

The strains of the band came from down King Street, in the direction of St. Luke's Church. The music appeared to linger a long time in the distance, and then it approached, growing louder, and the Bursley Town Silver Prize Band passed under the window at the solemn pace of Handel's "Dead March." The effect of that requiem, heavy with its own inherent beauty and with the vast weight of harrowing tradition, was to wring the tears from Constance's eyes; they fell on her aproned bosom, and she sank into a chair. And though the cheeks of the trumpeters were puffed out, and though the drummer had to protrude his stomach and arch his spine backwards lest he should tumble over his drum, there was majesty in the passage of the band. The boom of the drum, desolating the interruptions of the melody, made sick the heart, but with a lofty grief; and the dirge seemed to be weaving a purple pall that covered every meanness.

The bandsmen were not all in black, but they all wore crape on their sleeves and their instruments were knotted with crape. They carried in their hats a black-edged card. Cyril held one of these cards in his hands. It ran thus:

SACRED TO THE MEMORY OF

DANIEL POVEY

A TOWN COUNCILLOR OF THIS TOWN

JUDICIALLY MURDERED AT 8 O'CLOCK IN THE MORNING

8TH FEBRUARY 1888

"HE WAS MORE SINNED AGAINST THAN SINNING."

In the wake of the band came the aged Rector, bare-headed, and wearing a surplice over his overcoat; his thin white hair was disarranged by the breeze that played in the chilly sunshine; his hands were folded on a gilt-edged book. A curate, churchwardens, and sidesmen followed. And after these, tramping through the dark mud in a procession that had apparently no end, wound the unofficial male multitude, nearly all in mourning, and all, save the more aristocratic, carrying the memorial card in their hats. Loafers, women, and children had collected on the drying pavements, and a window just opposite Constance was ornamented with the entire family of the landlord of the Sun Vaults. In the great bar of the Vaults a barman was craning over the pitchpine screen that secured privacy to drinkers. The procession continued without break, eternally rising over the verge of King Street "bank," and eternally vanishing round the corner into St. Luke's Square; at intervals it was punctuated by a clergyman, a Nonconformist minister, a town crier, a group of foremen, or a few Rifle Volunteers. The watching crowd grew as the procession lengthened. Then another band was heard, also playing the march from *Saul*. The first band had now reached the top of the Square, and was scarcely audible from King Street. The reiterated glitter in the sun of memorial cards in hats gave the fanciful illusion of an impossible whitish snake that was straggling across the town. Three-quarters of an hour elapsed before the tail of the snake came into view, and a rabble of unkempt boys closed in upon it, filling the street.

"I shall go to the drawing-room window, mother," said Cyril. She nodded. He crept out of the bedroom.

St. Luke's Square was a sea of hats and memorial cards. Most of the occupiers of the Square had hung out flags at half-mast, and a flag at half-mast was flying over the Town Hall in the distance. Sightseers were at every window. The two bands had united at the top of the Square; and behind them, on a North Staffordshire Railway lorry, stood the white-clad Rector and several black figures. The Rector was speaking; but only those close to the lorry could hear his feeble treble voice.

Such was the massive protest of Bursley against what Bursley regarded as a callous injustice. The execution of Daniel Povey had most genuinely excited the indignation of the town. That execution was not only an injustice; it was an insult, a humiliating snub. And the worst was that the rest of the country had really discovered no sympathetic interest in the affair. Certain London papers, indeed, in commenting casually on the execution, had slurred the morals and manners of the Five Towns, professing to regard the district as notoriously beyond the realm of the Ten Commandments. This had helped to render furious the townsmen. This, as much as anything, had encouraged the spontaneous outburst of feeling which had culminated in a St. Luke's Square full of people with memorial cards in their hats. The demonstration had scarcely been organized; it had somehow organized itself, employing the places of worship and a few clubs as centres of gathering. And it proved an immense success. There were seven or eight thousand people in the Square, and the pity was that England as a whole could not have had a glimpse of the spectacle. Since the execution of the elephant, nothing had so profoundly agitated Bursley. Constance, who left the bedroom momentarily for the drawing-room, reflected that the death and burial of Cyril's honoured grandfather, though a resounding event, had not caused one-tenth of the stir which she beheld. But then John Baines had killed nobody.

The Rector spoke too long; every one felt that. But at length he finished. The bands performed the Doxology, and the immense multitudes began to disperse by the eight streets that radiate from the Square. At the same time one o'clock struck, and the public-houses opened with their customary admirable promptitude. Respectable persons, of course, ignored the public-houses and hastened homewards to a delayed dinner. But in a town of over thirty thousand souls there are sufficient dregs to fill all the public-houses on an occasion of ceremonial excitement. Constance saw the bar of the Vaults crammed with individuals whose sense of decent fitness was imperfect. The barman and the landlord and the principal members of the landlord's family were hard put to it to quench that funeral thirst. Constance, as she ate a little meal in the bedroom, could not but witness the orgy. A bandsman with his silver instrument was prominent at the counter. At five minutes to three the Vaults spewed forth a squirt of roysterers who walked on the pavement as on a tight-rope; among them was the bandsman, his silver instrument only half enveloped in its bag of green serge. He established an equilibrium in the gutter. It would not have mattered so seriously if he had not been a bandsman. The barman and the landlord pushed the ultimate sot by force into the street and bolted the door (till six o'clock) just as a policeman strolled along, the first policeman of the day. It became known that similar scenes were enacting at the thresholds of other inns. And the judicious were sad.

vi

When the altercation between the policeman and the musician in the gutter was at its height, Samuel Povey became restless; but since he had scarcely stirred through the performances of the bands, it was probably not the cries of the drunkard that had aroused him.

He had shown very little interest in the preliminaries of the great demonstration. The flame of his passion for the case of Daniel Povey seemed to have shot up on the day before the execution, and then to have expired. On that day he went to Stafford in order, by permit of the prison governor, to see his cousin for the last time. His condition then was undoubtedly not far removed from monomania. "Unhinged" was the conventional expression which frequently rose in Constance's mind as a description of the mind of her husband; but she fought it down; she would not have it; it was too crude—with its associations. She would only admit that the case had "got on" his mind. A startling proof of this was that he actually suggested taking Cyril with him to see the condemned man. He wished Cyril to see Daniel; he said gravely that he thought Cyril ought to see him. The proposal was monstrous, inexplicable—or explicable only by the assumption that his mind, while not unhinged, had temporarily lost its balance. Constance opposed an absolute negative, and Samuel being in every way enfeebled, she overcame. As for Cyril, he was divided between fear and curiosity. On the whole, perhaps Cyril regretted that he would not be able to say at school that he had had speech with the most celebrated killer of the age on the day before his execution.

Samuel returned hysterical from Stafford. His account of the scene, which he gave in a very loud voice, was a most absurd and yet pathetic recital, obviously distorted by memory. When he came to the point of the entrance of Dick Povey, who was still at the hospital, and who had been specially driven to Stafford and carried into the prison, he wept without restraint. His hysteria was painful in a very high degree.

He went to bed—of his own accord, for his cough had improved again. And on the following day, the day of the execution, he remained in bed till the afternoon. In the evening the Rector sent for him to the Rectory to discuss the proposed demonstration. On the next day, Saturday, he said he should not get up. Icy showers were sweeping the town, and his cough was worse after the evening visit to the Rector. Constance had no apprehensions about him. The most dangerous part of the winter was over, and there was nothing now to force him into indiscretions. She said to herself calmly that he should stay in bed as long as he liked, that he could not have too much repose after the cruel fatigues, physical and spiritual, which he had suffered. His cough was short, but not as troublesome as in the past; his face flushed, dusky, and settled in gloom; and he was slightly feverish, with quick pulse and quick breathing— the symptoms of a renewed cold. He passed a wakeful night, broken by brief dreams in which he talked. At dawn he had some hot food, asked what day it was, frowned, and seemed to doze off at once. At eleven o'clock he had refused food. And he had intermittently dozed during the progress of the demonstration and its orgiastic sequel.

Constance had food ready for his waking, and she approached the bed and leaned over him. The fever had increased somewhat, the breathing was more rapid, and his lips were covered with tiny purple pimples. He feebly shook his head, with a disgusted air, at her mention of food. It was this obstinate refusal of food which first alarmed her. A little uncomfortable suspicion shot up in her: Surely there's nothing the *matter* with him?

Something—impossible to say what—caused her to bend still lower, and put her ear to his chest. She heard within that mysterious box a rapid succession of thin, dry, crackling sounds: sounds such as she would have produced by rubbing her hair between her fingers close to her ear. The crepitation ceased, then recommenced, and she perceived that it coincided with the intake of his breath. He coughed; the sounds were intensified; a spasm of pain ran over his face; and he put his damp hand to his side.

"Pain in my side!" he whispered with difficulty.

Constance stepped into the drawing-room, where Cyril was sketching by the fire.

"Cyril," she said, "go across and ask Dr. Harrop to come round at once. And if he isn't in, then his new partner."

"Is it for father?"

"Yes."

"What's the matter?"

"Now do as I say, please," said Constance, sharply, adding: "I don't know what's the matter. Perhaps nothing. But I'm not satisfied."

The venerable Harrop pronounced the word "pneumonia." It was acute double pneumonia that Samuel had got. During the three worst months of the year, he had escaped the fatal perils which await a man with a flat chest and a chronic cough, who ignores his condition and defies the weather. But a journey of five hundred yards to the Rectory had been one journey too many. The Rectory was so close to the shop that he had not troubled to wrap himself up as for an excursion to Stafford. He survived the crisis of the disease and then died of toxæmia, caused by a heart that would not do its duty by the blood. A casual death, scarce noticed in the reaction after the great febrile demonstration! Besides, Samuel Povey never could impose himself on the burgesses. He lacked individuality. He was little. I have often laughed at Samuel Povey. But I liked and respected him. He was a very honest man. I have always been glad to think that, at the end of his life, destiny took hold of him and displayed, to the observant, the vein of greatness which runs through every soul without exception. He embraced a cause, lost it, and died of it.

CHAPTER VI
THE WIDOW

CONSTANCE, alone in the parlour, stood expectant by the set tea-table. She was not wearing weeds; her mother and she, on the death of her father, had talked of the various disadvantages of weeds; her mother had worn them unwillingly, and only because a public opinion not sufficiently advanced had intimidated her. Constance had said: "If ever I'm a widow I won't wear them," positively, in the tone of youth; and Mrs. Baines had replied: "I hope you won't, my dear." That was over twenty years ago, but Constance perfectly remembered. And now, she was a widow! How strange and how impressive was life! And she had kept her word; not positively, not without hesitations; for though times were changed, Bursley was still Bursley; but she had kept it.

This was the first Monday after Samuel's funeral. Existence in the house had been resumed on the plane which would henceforth be the normal plane. Constance had put on for tea a dress of black silk with a jet brooch of her mother's. Her hands, just meticulously washed, had that feeling of being dirty which comes from roughening of the epidermis caused by a day spent in fingering stuffs. She had been "going through" Samuel's things, and her own, and ranging all anew. It was astonishing how little the man had collected, of "things," in the course of over half a century. All his clothes were contained in two long drawers and a short one. He had the least possible quantity of haberdashery and linen, for he invariably took from the shop such articles as he required, when he required them, and he would never preserve what was done with. He possessed no jewellery save a set of gold studs, a scarf-ring, and a wedding-ring; the wedding-ring was buried with him. Once, when Constance had offered him her father's gold watch and chain, he had politely refused it, saying that he preferred his own—a silver watch (with a black cord) which kept excellent time; he had said later that she might save the gold watch and chain for Cyril when he was twenty-one. Beyond these trifles and a half-empty box of cigars and a pair of spectacles, he left nothing personal to himself. Some men leave behind them a litter which takes months to sift and distribute. But Samuel had not the mania for owning. Constance put his clothes in a box, to be given away gradually (all except an overcoat and handkerchiefs which might do for Cyril); she locked up the watch and its black cord, the spectacles and the scarf-ring; she gave the gold studs to Cyril; she climbed on a chair and hid the cigar-box on the top of her wardrobe; and scarce a trace of Samuel remained!

By his own wish the funeral had been as simple and private as possible. One or two distant relations, whom Constance scarcely knew and who would probably not visit her again until

she too was dead, came—and went. And lo! the affair was over.
The simple celerity of the funeral would have satisfied even
Samuel, whose tremendous self-esteem hid itself so effectually
behind such externals that nobody had ever fully perceived it.
Not even Constance quite knew Samuel's secret opinion of
Samuel. Constance was aware that he had a ridiculous side,
that his greatest lack had been a lack of spectacular dignity.
Even in the coffin, where nevertheless most people are finally
effective, he had not been imposing—with his finicky little
grey beard persistently sticking up.

The vision of him in his coffin—there in the churchyard,
just at the end of King Street!—with the lid screwed down on
that unimportant beard, recurred frequently in the mind of
the widow, as something untrue and misleading. She had to
say to herself: "Yes, he is really there! And that is why I have
this particular feeling in my heart." She saw him as an object
pathetic and wistful, not majestic. And yet she genuinely
thought that there could not exist another husband quite so
honest, quite so just, quite so reliable, quite so good, as Samuel
had been. What a conscience he had! How he would try, and
try, to be fair with her! Twenty years she could remember,
of ceaseless, constant endeavour on his part to behave rightly
to her! She could recall many an occasion when he had
obviously checked himself, striving against his tendency to cold
abruptness and to sullenness, in order to give her the respect
due to a wife. What loyalty was his! How she could *depend*
on him! How much better he was than herself (she thought
with modesty)!

His death was an amputation for her. But she faced it with
calmness. She was not bowed with sorrow. She did not nurse
the idea that her life was at an end; on the contrary, she
obstinately put it away from her, dwelling on Cyril. She did
not indulge in the enervating voluptuousness of grief. She had
begun in the first hours of bereavement by picturing herself as
one marked out for the blows of fate. She had lost her father
and her mother, and now her husband. Her career seemed to
be punctuated by interments. But after a while her gentle
commonsense came to insist that most human beings lose their
parents, and that every marriage must end in either a widower
or a widow, and that all careers are punctuated by interments.
Had she not had nearly twenty-one years of happy married
life? (Twenty-one years—rolled up! The sudden thought of

their naïve ignorance of life, hers and his, when they were first married, brought tears into her eyes. How wise and experienced she was now!) And had she not Cyril? Compared to many women, she was indeed very fortunate.

The one visitation which had been specially hers was the disappearance of Sophia. And yet even that was not worse than the death outright of Sophia, was perhaps not so bad. For Sophia might return out of the darkness. The blow of Sophia's flight had seemed unique when it was fresh, and long afterwards; had seemed to separate the Baines family from all other families in a particular shame. But at the age of forty-three Constance had learnt that such events are not uncommon in families, and strange sequels to them not unknown. Thinking often of Sophia, she hoped wildly and frequently.

She looked at the clock; she had a little spasm of nervousness lest Cyril might fail to keep his word on that first day of their new regular life together. And at the instant he burst into the room, invading it like an armed force, having previously laid waste the shop in his passage.

"I'm not late, mother! I'm not late!" he cried proudly.

She smiled warmly, happy in him, drawing out of him balm and solace. He did not know that in that stout familiar body before him was a sensitive, trembling soul that clutched at him ecstatically as the one reality in the universe. He did not know that that evening meal, partaken of without hurry after school had released him to her, was to be the ceremonial sign of their intimate unity and their interdependence, a tender and delicious proof that they were "all in all to each other": he saw only his tea, for which he was hungry—just as hungry as though his father were not scarcely yet cold in the grave.

But he saw obscurely that the occasion demanded something not quite ordinary, and so exerted himself to be boyishly charming to his mother. She said to herself "how good he was." He felt at ease and confident in the future, because he detected beneath her customary judicial, impartial mask a clear desire to spoil him.

After tea, she regretfully left him, at his home-lessons, in order to go into the shop. The shop was the great unsolved question. What was she to do with the shop? Was she to continue the business or to sell it? With the fortunes of her father and her aunt, and the economies of twenty years, she had more than sufficient means. She was indeed rich, according to the standards of the Square; nay, wealthy! Therefore she was under no material compulsion to keep the shop. Moreover, to keep it would mean personal superintendence and the burden of responsibility, from which her calm lethargy shrank. On the other hand, to dispose of the business would mean the breaking of ties and leaving the premises: and from this also she shrank. Young Lawton, without being asked, had advised her to sell. But she did not want to sell. She wanted the impossible: that matters should proceed in the future as in the past, that Samuel's death should change nothing save in her heart.

In the meantime Miss Insull was priceless. Constance thoroughly understood one side of the shop; but Miss Insull understood both, and the finance of it also. Miss Insull could have directed the establishment with credit, if not with brilliance. She was indeed directing it at that moment. Constance, however, felt jealous of Miss Insull; she was conscious of a slight antipathy towards the faithful one. She did not care to be in the hands of Miss Insull.

There were one or two customers at the millinery counter. They greeted her with a deplorable copiousness of tact. Most tactfully they avoided any reference to Constance's loss; but by their tone, their glances, at Constance and at each other, and their heroically restrained sighs, they spread desolation as though they had been spreading ashes instead of butter on bread. The assistants, too, had a special demeanour for the poor lone widow which was excessively trying to her. She wished to be natural, and she would have succeeded, had they not all of them apparently conspired together to make her task impossible.

She moved away to the other side of the shop, to Samuel's desk, at which he used to stand, staring absently out of the little window into King Street while murmurously casting figures. She lighted the gas-jet there, arranged the light exactly to suit her, and then lifted the large flap of the desk and drew forth some account books.

"Miss Insull!" she called, in a low, clear voice, with a touch of haughtiness and a touch of command in it. The pose, a comical contradiction of Constance's benevolent character, was deliberately adopted; it illustrated the effects of jealousy on even the softest disposition.

Miss Insull responded. She had no alternative but to re-

spond. And she gave no sign of resenting her employer's attitude. But then Miss Insull seldom did give any sign of being
human.

The customers departed, one after another, obsequiously
sped by the assistants, who thereupon lowered the gases somewhat, according to sæcular rule; and in the dim eclipse, as
they restored boxes to shelves, they could hear the tranquil,
regular, half-whispered conversation of the two women at the
desk, discussing accounts; and then the chink of gold.

Suddenly there was an irruption. One of the assistants
sprang instinctively to the gas; but on perceiving that the
disturber of peace was only a slatternly girl, hatless and imperfectly clean, she decided to leave the gas as it was, and put
on a condescending, suspicious demeanour.

"If you please, can I speak to the missis?" said the girl,
breathlessly.

She seemed to be about eighteen years of age, fat and plain.
Her blue frock was torn, and over it she wore a rough brown
apron, caught up at one corner to the waist. Her bare fore-
arms were of brick-red colour.

"What is it?" demanded the assistant.

Miss Insull looked over her shoulder across the shop. "It
must be Maggie's—Mrs. Hollins's daughter!" said Miss Insull
under her breath.

"What can she want?" said Constance, leaving the desk instantly; and to the girl, who stood sturdily holding her own
against the group of assistants: "You are Mrs. Hollins's
daughter, aren't you?"

"Yes, mum."

"What's your name?"

"Maggie, mum. And, if you please, mother's sent me to ask
if you'll kindly give her a funeral card."

"A funeral card?"

"Yes. Of Mr. Povey. She's been expecting of one, and she
thought as how perhaps you'd forgotten it, especially as she
wasn't asked to the funeral."

The girl stopped.

Constance perceived that by mere negligence she had seriously wounded the feelings of Maggie, senior. The truth was,
she had never thought of Maggie. She ought to have remembered that funeral cards were almost the sole ornamentation
of Maggie's abominable cottage.

"Certainly," she replied after a pause. "Miss Insull, there are a few cards left in the desk, aren't there? Please put me one in an envelope for Mrs. Hollins."

She gave the heavily bordered envelope to the ruddy wench, who enfolded it in her apron, and with hurried, shy thanks ran off.

"Tell your mother I send her a card with pleasure," Constance called after the girl.

The strangeness of the hazards of life made her thoughtful. She, to whom Maggie had always seemed an old woman, was a widow, but Maggie's husband survived as a lusty invalid. And she guessed that Maggie, vilely struggling in squalor and poverty, was somehow happy in her frowzy, careless way.

She went back to the accounts, dreaming.

ii

When the shop had been closed, under her own critical and precise superintendence, she extinguished the last gas in it and returned to the parlour, wondering where she might discover some entirely reliable man or boy to deal with the shutters night and morning. Samuel had ordinarily dealt with the shutters himself, and on extraordinary occasions and during holidays Miss Insull and one of her subordinates had struggled with their unwieldiness. But the extraordinary occasion had now become ordinary, and Miss Insull could not be expected to continue indefinitely in the functions of a male. Constance had a mind to engage an errand-boy, a luxury against which Samuel had always set his face. She did not dream of asking the herculean Cyril to open and shut shop.

He had apparently finished his home-lessons. The books were pushed aside, and he was sketching in lead-pencil on a drawing-block. To the right of the fireplace, over the sofa, there hung an engraving after Landseer, showing a lonely stag paddling into a lake. The stag at eve had drunk or was about to drink his fill, and Cyril was copying him. He had already indicated a flight of birds in the middle distance; vague birds on the wing being easier than detailed stags, he had begun with the birds.

Constance put a hand on his shoulder. "Finished your lessons?" she murmured caressingly.

Before speaking, Cyril gazed up at the picture with a frowning, busy expression, and then replied in an absent-minded voice:

"Yes." And after a pause: "Except my arithmetic. I shall do that in the morning before breakfast."

"Oh, Cyril!" she protested.

It had been a positive ordinance, for a long time past, that there should be no sketching until lessons were done. In his father's lifetime Cyril had never dared to break it.

He bent over his block, feigning an intense absorption. Constance's hand slipped from his shoulder. She wanted to command him formally to resume his lessons. But she could not. She feared an argument; she mistrusted herself. And, moreover, it was so soon after his father's death!

"You know you won't have time to-morrow morning!" she said weakly.

"Oh, mother!" he retorted superiorly. "Don't worry." And then, in a cajoling tone: "I've wanted to do that stag for ages."

She sighed and sat down in her rocking-chair. He went on sketching, rubbing out, and making queer expostulatory noises against his pencil, or against the difficulties needlessly invented by Sir Edwin Landseer. Once he rose and changed the position of the gas-bracket, staring fiercely at the engraving as though it had committed a sin.

Amy came to lay the supper. He did not acknowledge that she existed.

"Now, Master Cyril, after you with that table, if you please!" She announced herself brusquely, with the privilege of an old servant and a woman who would never see thirty again.

"What a nuisance you are, Amy!" he gruffly answered. "Look here, mother, can't Amy lay the cloth on that half of the table? I'm right in the middle of my drawing. There's plenty of room there for two."

He seemed not to be aware that, in the phrase "plenty of room for two," he had made a callous reference to their loss. The fact was, there *was* plenty of room for two.

Constance said quickly: "Very well, Amy. For this once."

Amy grunted, but obeyed.

Constance had to summon him twice from art to nourishment. He ate with rapidity, frequently regarding the picture with half-shut, searching eyes. When he had finished, he refilled his glass with water, and put it next to his sketching-block.

"You surely aren't thinking of beginning to paint at this time of night!" Constance exclaimed, astonished.

"Oh *yes*, mother!" he fretfully appealed. "It's not late."

Another positive ordinance of his father's had been that there should be nothing after supper except bed. Nine o'clock was the latest permissible moment for going to bed. It was now less than a quarter to.

"It only wants twelve minutes to nine," Constance pointed out.

"Well, what if it does?"

"Now, Cyril," she said, "I do hope you are going to be a good boy, and not cause your mother anxiety."

But she said it too kindly.

He said sullenly: "I do think you might let me finish it. I've begun it. It won't take me long."

She made the mistake of leaving the main point. "How can you possibly choose your colours properly by gas-light?" she said.

"I'm going to do it in sepia," he replied in triumph.

"It mustn't occur again," she said.

He thanked God for a good supper, and sprang to the harmonium, where his paint-box was. Amy cleared away. Constance did crochet-work. There was silence. The clock struck nine, and it also struck half-past nine. She warned him repeatedly. At ten minutes to ten she said persuasively:

"Now, Cyril, when the clock strikes ten I shall really put the gas out."

The clock struck ten.

"Half a mo, half a mo!" he cried. "I've done! I've done!"

Her hand was arrested.

Another four minutes elapsed, and then he jumped up. "There you are!" he said proudly, showing her the block. And all his gestures were full of grace and cajolery.

"Yes, it's very good," Constance said, rather indifferently.

"I don't believe you care for it!" he accused her, but with a bright smile.

"I care for your health," she said. "Just look at that clock!"

He sat down in the other rocking-chair, deliberately.

"Now, Cyril!"

"Well, mother, I suppose you'll let me take my boots off !" He said it with teasing good-humour.

When he kissed her good night, she wanted to cling to him, so affectionate was his kiss; but she could not throw off the habits of restraint which she had been originally taught and had all her life practised. She keenly regretted the inability.

In her bedroom, alone, she listened to his movements as he undressed. The door between the two rooms was unlatched. She had to control a desire to open it ever so little and peep at him. He would not have liked that. He could have enriched her heart beyond all hope, and at no cost to himself; but he did not know his power. As she could not cling to him with her hands, she clung to him with that heart of hers, while moving sedately up and down the room, alone. And her eyes saw him through the solid wood of the door. At last she got heavily into bed. She thought with placid anxiety, in the dark: "I shall have to be firm with Cyril." And she thought also, simultaneously: "He really must be a good boy. He *must*." And clung to him passionately, without shame! Lying alone there in the dark, she could be as unrestrained and girlish as her heart chose. When she loosed her hold she instantly saw the boy's father arranged in his coffin, or flitting about the room. Then she would hug that vision too, for the pleasure of the pain it gave her.

iii

She was reassured as to Cyril during the next few days. He did not attempt to repeat his ingenious naughtiness of the Monday evening, and he came directly home for tea; moreover, he had, as a kind of miracle performed to dazzle her, actually arisen early on the Tuesday morning and done his arithmetic. To express her satisfaction she had manufactured a specially elaborate straw-frame for the sketch after Sir Edwin Landseer, and had hung it in her bedroom: an honour which Cyril appreciated. She was as happy as a woman suffering from a recent amputation can be; and compared with the long nightmare created by Samuel's monomania and illness, her existence seemed to be now a beneficent calm.

Cyril, she thought, had realized the importance in her eyes of tea, of that evening hour and that companionship which

were for her the flowering of the day. And she had such confidence in his goodness that she would pour the boiling water
on the Horniman tea-leaves even before he arrived: certainty
could not be more sure. And then, on the Friday of the first
week, he was late! He bounded in, after dark, and the state
of his clothes indicated too clearly that he had been playing
football in the mud that was a grassy field in summer.

"Have you been kept in, my boy?" she asked, for the sake
of form.

"No, mother," he said casually. "We were just kicking the
ball about a bit. Am I late?"

"Better go and tidy yourself," she said, not replying to his
question. "You can't sit down in that state. And I'll have
some fresh tea made. This is spoilt."

"Oh, very well!"

Her sacred tea—the institution which she wanted to hallow
by long habit, and which was to count before everything with
both of them—had been carelessly sacrificed to the kicking of
a football in mud! And his father buried not ten days! She was
wounded: a deep, clean, dangerous wound that would not bleed.
She tried to be glad that he had not lied; he might easily have
lied, saying that he had been detained for a fault and could
not help being late. No! He was not given to lying; he would
lie, like any human being, when a great occasion demanded
such prudence, but he was not a liar; he might fairly be called
a truthful boy. She tried to be glad, and did not succeed. She
would have preferred him to have lied.

Amy, grumbling, had to boil more water.

When he returned to the parlour, superficially cleaned, Constance expected him to apologize in his roundabout boyish
way; at any rate to woo and wheedle her, to show by some
gesture that he was conscious of having put an affront on her.
But his attitude was quite otherwise. His attitude was rather
brusque and overbearing and noisy. He ate a very considerable amount of jam, far too quickly, and then asked for more,
in a tone of a monarch who calls for his own. And ere tea was
finished he said boldly, apropos of nothing:

"I say, mother, you'll just have to let me go to the School
of Art after Easter."

And stared at her with a fixed challenge in his eyes.

He meant, by the School of Art, the evening classes at the
School of Art. His father had decided absolutely against the

project. His father had said that it would interfere with his lessons, would keep him up too late at night, and involve absence from home in the evening. The last had always been the real objection. His father had not been able to believe that Cyril's desire to study art sprang purely from his love of art; he could not avoid suspecting that it was a plan to obtain freedom in the evenings—that freedom which Samuel had invariably forbidden. In all Cyril's suggestions Samuel had been ready to detect the same scheme lurking. He had finally said that when Cyril left school and took to a vocation, then he could study art at night if he chose, but not before.

"You know what your father said!" Constance replied.

"But, mother! That's all very well! I'm sure father would have agreed. If I'm going to take up drawing I ought to do it at once. That's what the drawing-master says, and I suppose he ought to know." He finished on a tone of insolence.

"I can't allow you to do it yet," said Constance, quietly. "It's quite out of the question. Quite!"

He pouted and then he sulked. It was war between them. At times he was the image of his Aunt Sophia. He would not leave the subject alone; but he would not listen to Constance's reasoning. He openly accused her of harshness. He asked her how she could expect him to get on if she thwarted him in his most earnest desires. He pointed to other boys whose parents were wiser.

"It's all very fine of you to put it on father!" he observed sarcastically.

He gave up his drawing entirely.

When she hinted that if he attended the School of Art she would be condemned to solitary evenings, he looked at her as though saying: "Well, and if you are——?" He seemed to have no heart.

After several weeks of intense unhappiness she said: "How many evenings do you want to go?"

The war was over.

He was charming again. When she was alone she could cling to him again. And she said to herself: "If we can be happy together only when I give way to him, I must give way to him." And there was ecstasy in her yielding. "After all," she said to herself, "perhaps it's very important that he should go to the School of Art." She solaced herself with such thoughts on three solitary evenings a week, waiting for him to come home.

CHAPTER VII
Bricks and Mortar

In the summer of that year the occurrence of a white rash of posters on hoardings and on certain houses and shops, was symptomatic of organic change in the town. The posters were iterations of a mysterious announcement and summons, which began with the august words: "By Order of the Trustees of the late William Clews Mericarp, Esq." Mericarp had been a considerable owner of property in Bursley. After a prolonged residence at Southport, he had died, at the age of eighty-two, leaving his property behind. For sixty years he had been a name, not a figure; and the news of his death, which was assuredly an event, incited the burgesses to gossip, for they had come to regard him as one of the invisible immortals. Constance was shocked, though she had never seen Mericarp. ("Everybody dies nowadays!" she thought.) He owned the Baines-Povey shop, and also Mr. Critchlow's shop. Constance knew not how often her father and, later, her husband, had renewed the lease of those premises that were now hers; but from her earliest recollections rose a vague memory of her father talking to her mother about "Mericarp's rent," which was and always had been a hundred a year. Mericarp had earned the reputation of being "a good landlord." Constance said sadly: "We shall never have another as good!" When a lawyer's clerk called and asked her to permit the exhibition of a poster in each of her shop-windows, she had misgivings for the future; she was worried; she decided that she would determine the lease next year, so as to be on the safe side; but immediately afterwards she decided that she could decide nothing.

The posters continued: "To be sold by auction, at the Tiger Hotel at six-thirty for seven o'clock precisely." What six-thirty had to do with seven o'clock precisely no one knew. Then, after stating the name and credentials of the auctioneer, the posters at length arrived at the objects to be sold: "All those freehold messuages and shops and copyhold tenements namely." Houses were never sold by auction in Bursley. At moments of auction burgesses were reminded that the erections they lived in were not houses, as they had falsely sup-

posed, but messuages. Having got as far as "namely" the posters ruled a line and began afresh: "Lot 1. All that extensive
and commodious shop and messuage with the offices and appurtenances thereto belonging situate and being No. 4 St.
Luke's Square in the parish of Bursley in the County of
Stafford and at present in the occupation of Mrs. Constance
Povey widow under a lease expiring in September 1889." Thus
clearly asserting that all Constance's shop was for sale, its
whole entirety, and not a fraction or slice of it merely, the
posters proceeded: "Lot 2. All that extensive and commodious
shop and messuage with the offices and appurtenances thereto
belonging situate and being No. 3 St. Luke's Square in the
parish of Bursley in the County of Stafford and at present in
the occupation of Charles Critchlow chemist under an agreement for a yearly tenancy." The catalogue ran to fourteen
lots. The posters, lest any one should foolishly imagine that a
non-legal intellect could have achieved such explicit and comprehensive clarity of statement, were signed by a powerful
firm of solicitors in Hanbridge. Happily in the Five Towns
there were no metaphysicians; otherwise the firm might have
been expected to explain, in the "further particulars and conditions" which the posters promised, how even a messuage
could "be" the thing at which it was "situate."

Within a few hours of the outbreak of the rash, Mr. Critchlow abruptly presented himself before Constance at the millinery counter; he was waving a poster.

"Well!" he exclaimed grimly. "What next, eh?"

"Yes, indeed!" Constance responded.

"Are ye thinking o' buying?" he asked. All the assistants,
including Miss Insull, were in hearing, but he ignored their
presence.

"Buying!" repeated Constance. "Not me! I've got quite
enough house property as it is."

Like all owners of real property, she usually adopted
towards her possessions an attitude implying that she would be
willing to pay somebody to take them from her.

"Shall *you*?" she added, with Mr. Critchlow's own brusqueness.

"Me! Buy property in St. Luke's Square!" Mr. Critchlow
sneered. And then left the shop as suddenly as he had entered it.

The sneer at St. Luke's Square was his characteristic ex-

pression of an opinion which had been slowly forming for some
years. The Square was no longer what it had been, though individual businesses might be as good as ever. For nearly twelve
months two shops had been to let in it. And once, bankruptcy
had stained its annals. The tradesmen had naturally searched
for a cause in every direction save the right one, the obvious
one; and naturally they had found a cause. According to the
tradesmen, the cause was "this football." The Fursley Football Club had recently swollen into a genuine rival of the
ancient supremacy of the celebrated Knype Club. It had transformed itself into a limited company, and rented a ground up
the Moorthorne Road, and built a grand stand. The Bursley
F.C. had "tied" with the Knype F.C. on the Knype ground—
a prodigious achievement, an achievement which occupied a
column of the *Athletic News* one Monday morning! But were
the tradesmen civically proud of this glory? No! They said
that "this football" drew people out of the town on Saturday
afternoons, to the complete abolition of shopping. They said
also that people thought of nothing but "this football;" and,
nearly in the same breath, that only roughs and good-for-
nothings could possibly be interested in such a barbarous
game. And they spoke of gate-money, gambling, and profes-
sionalism, and the end of all true sport in England. In brief,
something new had come to the front and was submitting to the
ordeal of the curse.

The sale of the Mericarp estate had a particular interest for
respectable stake-in-the-town persons. It would indicate to
what extent, if at all, "this football" was ruining Bursley.

Constance mentioned to Cyril that she fancied she might like
to go to the sale, and as it was dated for one of Cyril's off-
nights Cyril said that he fancied he might like to go too. So
they went together; Samuel used to attend property sales, but
he had never taken his wife to one. Constance and Cyril arrived
at the Tiger shortly after seven o'clock, and were directed
to a room furnished and arranged as for a small public meeting of philanthropists. A few gentlemen were already present,
but not the instigating trustees, solicitors, and auctioneers. It
appeared that "six-thirty for seven o'clock precisely" meant
seven-fifteen. Constance took a Windsor chair in the corner
nearest the door, and motioned Cyril to the next chair; they
dared not speak; they moved on tiptoe; Cyril inadvertently
dragged his chair along the floor, and produced a scrunching

sound; he blushed, as though he had desecrated a church, and his mother made a gesture of horror. The remainder of the company glanced at the corner, apparently pained by this negligence. Some of them greeted Constance, but self-consciously, with a sort of shamed air; it might have been that they had all nefariously gathered together there for the committing of a crime. Fortunately Constance's widowhood had already lost its touching novelty, so that the greetings, if self-conscious, were at any rate given without unendurable commiseration and did not cause awkwardness.

When the official world arrived, fussy, bustling, bearing documents and a hammer, the general feeling of guilty shame was intensified. Useless for the auctioneer to try to dissipate the gloom by means of bright gestures and quick, cheerful remarks to his supporters! Cyril had an idea that the meeting would open with a hymn, until the apparition of a tapster with wine showed him his error. The auctioneer very particularly enjoined the tapster to see to it that no one lacked for his thirst, and the tapster became self-consciously energetic. He began by choosing Constance for service. In refusing wine, she blushed; then the fellow offered a glass to Cyril, who went scarlet, and mumbled "No" with a lump in his throat; when the tapster's back was turned, he smiled sheepishly at his mother. The majority of the company accepted and sipped. The auctioneer sipped and loudly smacked, and said: "Ah!"

Mr. Critchlow came in.

And the auctioneer said again: "Ah! I'm always glad when the tenants come. That's always a good sign."

He glanced round for approval of this sentiment. But everybody seemed too stiff to move. Even the auctioneer was self-conscious.

"Waiter! Offer wine to Mr. Critchlow!" he exclaimed bullyingly, as if saying: "Man! what on earth are you thinking of, to neglect Mr. Critchlow?"

"Yes, sir; yes, sir," said the waiter, who was dispensing wine as fast as a waiter can.

The auction commenced.

Seizing the hammer, the auctioneer gave a short biography of William Clews Mericarp, and, this pious duty accomplished, called upon a solicitor to read the conditions of sale. The solicitor complied and made a distressing exhibition of self-consciousness. The conditions of sale were very lengthy, and apparently composed in a foreign tongue; and the audience listened to this elocution with a stoical pretence of breathless interest.

Then the auctioneer put up all that extensive and commodious messuage and shop situate and being No. 4, St. Luke's Square. Constance and Cyril moved their limbs surreptitiously, as though being at last found out. The auctioneer referred to John Baines and to Samuel Povey, with a sense of personal loss, and then expressed his pleasure in presence of "the ladies;" he meant Constance, who once more had to blush.

"Now, gentlemen," said the auctioneer, "what do you say for these famous premises? I think I do not exaggerate when I use the word 'famous.' "

Some one said a thousand pounds, in the terrorized voice of a delinquent.

"A thousand pounds," repeated the auctioneer, paused, sipped, and smacked.

"Guineas," said another voice self-accused of iniquity.

"A thousand and fifty," said the auctioneer.

Then there was a long interval, an interval that tightened the nerves of the assembly.

"Now, ladies and gentlemen," the auctioneer adjured.

The first voice said sulkily: "Eleven hundred."

And thus the bids rose to fifteen hundred, lifted bit by bit, as it were, by the magnetic force of the auctioneer's personality. The man was now standing up, in domination. He bent down to the solicitor's head; they whispered together.

"Gentlemen," said the auctioneer, "I am happy to inform you that the sale is now open." His tone translated better than words his calm professional beatitude. Suddenly in a voice of wrath he hissed at the waiter: "Waiter, why don't you serve these gentlemen?"

"Yes, sir; yes, sir."

The auctioneer sat down and sipped at leisure, chatting with his clerk and the solicitor and the solicitor's clerk.

When he rose it was as a conqueror. "Gentlemen, fifteen hundred is bid. Now, Mr. Critchlow."

Mr. Critchlow shook his head. The auctioneer threw a courteous glance at Constance, who avoided it.

After many adjurations, he reluctantly raised his hammer, pretended to let it fall, and saved it several times.

And then Mr. Critchlow said: "And fifty."

"Fifteen hundred and fifty is bid," the auctioneer informed the company, electrifying the waiter once more. And when he had sipped he said, with feigned sadness: "Come, gentlemen, you surely don't mean to let this magnificent lot go for fifteen hundred and fifty pounds?"

But they did mean that.

The hammer fell, and the auctioneer's clerk and the solicitor's clerk took Mr. Critchlow aside and wrote with him.

Nobody was surprised when Mr. Critchlow bought Lot No. 2, his own shop.

Constance whispered then to Cyril that she wished to leave. They left, with unnatural precautions, but instantly regained their natural demeanour in the dark street.

"Well, I never! Well, I never!" she murmured outside, astonished and disturbed.

She hated the prospect of Mr. Critchlow as a landlord. And yet she could not persuade herself to leave the place, in spite of decisions.

The sale demonstrated that football had not entirely undermined the commercial basis of society in Bursley; only two Lots had to be withdrawn.

ii

On Thursday afternoon of the same week the youth whom Constance had ended by hiring for the manipulation of shutters and other jobs unsuitable for fragile women, was closing the shop. The clock had struck two. All the shutters were up except the last one, in the midst of the doorway. Miss Insull and her mistress were walking about the darkened interior, putting dust-sheets well over the edges of exposed goods; the other assistants had just left. The bull-terrier had wandered into the shop as he almost invariably did at closing time—for he slept there, an efficient guard—and had lain down by the dying stove; though not venerable, he was stiffening into age.

"You can shut," said Miss Insull to the youth.

But as the final shutter was ascending to its position, Mr. Critchlow appeared on the pavement.

"Hold on, young fellow!" Mr. Critchlow commanded, and stepped slowly, lifting up his long apron, over the horizontal shutter on which the perpendicular shutters rested in the doorway.

"Shall you be long, Mr. Critchlow?" the youth asked, posing the shutter. "Or am I to shut?"

"Shut, lad," said Mr. Critchlow, briefly. "I'll go out by th' side door."

"Here's Mr. Critchlow!" Miss Insull called out to Constance, in a peculiar tone. And a flush, scarcely perceptible, crept very slowly over her dark features. In the twilight of the shop, lit only by a few starry holes in the shutters, and by the small side-window, not the keenest eye could have detected that flush.

"Mr. Critchlow!" Constance murmured the exclamation. She resented his future ownership of her shop. She thought he was come to play the landlord, and she determined to let him see that her mood was independent and free, that she would as lief give up the business as keep it. In particular she meant to accuse him of having deliberately deceived her as to his intentions on his previous visit.

"Well, missis!" the aged man greeted her. "We've made it up between us. Happen some folk'll think we've taken our time, but I don't know as that's their affair."

His little blinking eyes had a red border. The skin of his pale small face was wrinkled in millions of minute creases. His arms and legs were marvellously thin and sharply angular. The corners of his heliotrope lips were turned down, as usual, in mysterious comment on the world; and his smile, as he fronted Constance with his excessive height, crowned the mystery.

Constance stared, at a loss. It surely could not after all be true, the substance of the rumours that had floated like vapours in the Square for eight years and more!

"What . . . ?" she began.

"Me, and her!" He jerked his head in the direction of Miss Insull.

The dog had leisurely strolled forward to inspect the edges of the *fiancé's* trousers. Miss Insull summoned the animal with a noise of fingers, and then bent down and caressed it. A strange gesture proving the validity of Charles Critchlow's discovery that in Maria Insull a human being was buried!

Miss Insull was, as near as any one could guess, forty years of age. For twenty-five years she had served in the shop, passing about twelve hours a day in the shop; attending regularly at least three religious services at the Wesleyan Chapel or School on Sundays, and sleeping with her mother, whom she kept. She had never earned more than thirty shillings a week, and yet her situation was considered to be exceptionally good. In the eternal fusty dusk of the shop she had gradually lost such sexual characteristics and charms as she had once possessed. She was as thin and flat as Charles Critchlow himself. It was as though her bosom had suffered from a prolonged drought at a susceptible period of development, and had never recovered. The one proof that blood ran in her veins was the pimply quality of her ruined complexion, and the pimples of that brickish expanse proved that the blood was thin and bad. Her hands and feet were large and ungainly; the skin of the fingers was roughened by coarse contacts to the texture of emery-paper. On six days a week she wore black; on the seventh a kind of discreet half-mourning. She was honest, capable, and industrious; and beyond the confines of her occupation she had no curiosity, no intelligence, no ideas. Superstitions and prejudices, deep and violent, served her for ideas; but she could incomparably sell silks and bonnets, braces and oilcloth; in widths, lengths, and prices she never erred; she never annoyed a customer, nor foolishly promised what could not be performed, nor was late nor negligent, nor disrespectful. No one knew anything about her, because there was nothing to know. Subtract the shop-assistant from her, and naught remained. Benighted and spiritually dead, she existed by habit.

But for Charles Critchlow she happened to be an illusion. He had cast eyes on her and had seen youth, innocence, virginity. During eight years the moth Charles had flitted round the lamp of her brilliance, and was now singed past escape. He might treat her with what casualness he chose; he might ignore her in public; he might talk brutally about women; he might leave her to wonder dully what he meant, for months at a stretch: but there emerged indisputable from the sum of his conduct the fact that he wanted her. He desired her; she charmed him; she was something ornamental and luxurious for which he was ready to pay—and to commit follies. He had been a widower since before she was born; to him she was a slip of a girl. All is relative in this world. As for her, she was too indifferent to refuse him. Why refuse him? Oysters do not refuse.

"I'm sure I congratulate you both," Constance breathed, realizing the import of Mr. Critchlow's laconic words. "I'm sure I hope you'll be happy."

"That'll be all right," said Mr. Critchlow.

"Thank you, Mrs. Povey," said Maria Insull.

Nobody seemed to know what to say next. "It's rather sudden," was on Constance's tongue, but did not achieve utterance, being patently absurd.

"Ah!" exclaimed Mr. Critchlow, as though himself contemplating anew the situation.

Miss Insull gave the dog a final pat.

"So that's settled," said Mr. Critchlow. "Now, missis, ye want to give up this shop, don't ye?"

"I'm not so sure about that," Constance answered uneasily.

"Don't tell me!" he protested. "Of course ye want to give up the shop."

"I've lived here all my life," said Constance.

"Ye've not lived in th' shop all ye're life. I said th' shop. Listen here!" he continued. "I've got a proposal to make to you. You can keep on the house, and I'll take the shop off ye're hands. Now?" He looked at her inquiringly.

Constance was taken aback by the brusqueness of the suggestion, which, moreover, she did not understand.

"But how——" she faltered.

"Come here," said Mr. Critchlow, impatiently, and he moved towards the house-door of the shop, behind the till.

"Come where? What do you want?" Constance demanded in a maze.

"Here!" said Mr. Critchlow, with increasing impatience. "Follow me, will ye?"

Constance obeyed. Miss Insull sidled after Constance, and the dog after Miss Insull. Mr. Critchlow went through the doorway and down the corridor, past the cutting-out room to his right. The corridor then turned at a right-angle to the left and ended at the parlour door, the kitchen steps being to the left.

Mr. Critchlow stopped short of the kitchen steps, and extended his arms, touching the walls on either side.

"Here!" he said, tapping the walls with his bony knuckles. "Here! Suppose I brick ye this up, and th' same upstairs between th' showroom and th' bedroom passage, ye've got your house to yourself. Ye say ye've lived here all your life. Well, what's to prevent ye finishing up here? The fact is," he added, "it would only be making into two houses again what was two houses to start with, afore your time, missis."

"And what about the shop?" cried Constance.

"Ye can sell us th' stock at a valuation."

Constance suddenly comprehended the scheme. Mr. Critchlow would remain the chemist, while Mrs. Critchlow became the head of the chief drapery business in the town. Doubtless they would knock a hole through the separating wall on the other side, to balance the bricking-up on this side. They must have thought it all out in detail. Constance revolted.

"Yes!" she said, a little disdainfully. "And my goodwill? Shall you take that at a valuation too?"

Mr. Critchlow glanced at the creature for whom he was ready to scatter thousands of pounds. She might have been a Phryne and he the infatuated fool. He glanced at her as if to say: "We expected this, and this is where we agreed it was to stop."

"Ay!" he said to Constance. "Show me your goodwill. Lap it up in a bit of paper and hand it over, and I'll take it at a valuation. But not afore, missis! Not afore! I'm making ye a very good offer. Twenty pound a year, I'll let ye th' house for. And take th' stock at a valuation. Think it over, my lass."

Having said what he had to say, Charles Critchlow departed, according to his custom. He unceremoniously let himself out by the side door, and passed with wavy apron round the corner of King Street into the Square and so to his own shop, which ignored the Thursday half-holiday. Miss Insull left soon afterwards.

iii

Constance's pride urged her to refuse the offer. But in truth her sole objection to it was that she had not thought of the scheme herself. For the scheme really reconciled her wish to remain where she was with her wish to be free of the shop.

"I shall make him put me in a new window in the parlour —one that will open!" she said positively to Cyril, who accepted Mr. Critchlow's idea with fatalistic indifference.

After stipulating for the new window, she closed with the offer. Then there was the stock-taking, which endured for weeks. And then a carpenter came and measured for the window. And a builder and a mason came and inspected doorways, and Constance felt that the end was upon her. She took up the carpet in the parlour and protected the furniture by dust-sheets. She and Cyril lived between bare boards and dust-sheets for twenty days, and neither carpenter nor mason reappeared. Then one surprising day the old window was removed by the carpenter's two journeymen, and late in the afternoon the carpenter brought the new window, and the three men worked till ten o'clock at night, fixing it. Cyril wore his cap and went to bed in his cap, and Constance wore a Paisley shawl. A painter had bound himself beyond all possibility of failure to paint the window on the morrow. He was to begin at six a.m., and Amy's alarm-clock was altered so that she might be up and dressed to admit him. He came a week later, administered one coat, and vanished for another ten days.

Then two masons suddenly came with heavy tools, and were shocked to find that all was not prepared for them. (After three carpetless weeks Constance had relaid her floors.) They tore off wall-paper, sent cascades of plaster down the kitchen steps, withdrew alternate courses of bricks from the walls, and, sated with destruction, hastened away. After four days new red bricks began to arrive, carried by a quite guiltless hodman who had not visited the house before. The hodman met the full storm of Constance's wrath. It was not a vicious wrath, rather a good-humoured wrath; but it impressed the hodman. "My house hasn't been fit to live in for a month," she said in fine. "If these walls aren't built to-morrow, upstairs *and* down— to-morrow, mind!—don't let any of you dare to show your noses here again, for I won't have you. Now you've brought your bricks. Off with you, and tell your master what I say!"

It was effective. The next day subdued and plausible workmen of all sorts awoke the house with knocking at six-thirty precisely, and the two doorways were slowly bricked up. The curious thing was that, when the barrier was already a foot high on the ground-floor Constance remembered small possessions of her own which she had omitted to remove from the cutting-out room. Picking up her skirts, she stepped over into the region that was no more hers, and stepped back with the goods. She had a bandanna round her head to keep the thick dust out of her hair. She was very busy, very preoccupied with nothings. She had no time for sentimentalities. Yet when the men arrived at the topmost course and were at last hidden behind their own erection, and she could see only rough bricks and mortar, she was disconcertingly overtaken by a misty blindness and could not even see bricks and mortar. Cyril found her, with her absurd bandanna, weeping in a sheet-covered rocking-chair in the sacked parlour. He whistled uneasily, remarked: "I say, mother, what about tea?" and then, hearing the heavy voices of workmen above, ran with relief upstairs. Tea had been set in the drawing-room, he was glad to learn that from Amy, who informed him also that she should "never get used to them there new walls," not as long as she lived.

He went to the School of Art that night. Constance, alone, could find nothing to do. She had willed that the walls should be built, and they had been built; but days must elapse before they could be plastered, and after the plaster still more days before the papering. Not for another month, perhaps, would her house be free of workmen and ripe for her own labours. She could only sit in the dust-drifts and contemplate the havoc of change, and keep her eyes as dry as she could. The legal transactions were all but complete; little bills announcing the transfer of the business lay on the counters in the shop at the disposal of customers. In two days Charles Critchlow would pay the price of a desire realized. The sign was painted out and new letters sketched thereon in chalk. In future she would be compelled, if she wished to enter the shop, to enter it as a customer and from the front. Yes, she saw that, though the house remained hers, the root of her life had been wrenched up.

And the mess! It seemed inconceivable that the material mess could ever be straightened away!

Yet, ere the fields of the county were first covered with snow that season, only one sign survived of the devastating revolution, and that was a loose sheet of wall-paper that had been too soon pasted on to new plaster and would not stick. Maria Insull was Maria Critchlow. Constance had been out into the Square and seen the altered sign, and seen Mrs. Critchlow's taste in window-curtains, and seen—most impressive sight of all—that the grimy window of the abandoned room at the top of the abandoned staircase next to the bedroom of her girlhood, had been cleaned and a table put in front of it. She knew that the chamber, which she herself had never entered, was to be employed as a storeroom, but the visible proof of its conversion so strangely affected her that she had not felt able to go boldly into the shop, as she had meant to do, and make a few purchases in the way of friendliness. "I'm a silly woman!" she muttered.

Later, she did venture, timidly abrupt, into the shop, and was received with fitting state by Mrs. Critchlow (as desiccated as ever), who insisted on allowing her the special trade discount. And she carried her little friendly purchases round to her own door in King Street. Trivial, trivial event! Constance, not knowing whether to laugh or cry, did both. She accused herself of developing a hysterical faculty in tears, and strove sagely against it.

CHAPTER VIII

THE PROUDEST MOTHER

IN THE year 1893 there was a new and strange man living at No. 4, St. Luke's Square. Many people remarked on the phenomenon. Very few of his like had ever been seen in Bursley before. One of the striking things about him was the complex way in which he secured himself by means of glittering chains. A chain stretched across his waistcoat, passing through a special button-hole, without a button, in the middle. To this cable were firmly linked a watch at one end and a pencil-case at the other; the chain also served as a protection against a thief who might attempt to snatch the fancy waistcoat entire. Then there were longer chains, beneath the waistcoat, partly designed, no doubt, to deflect bullets, but serving mainly to enable the owner to haul up penknives, cigarette-cases, match-boxes, and key-rings from the profundities of hip-pockets. An essential portion of the man's braces, visible sometimes when he played at tennis, consisted of chain, and the upper and nether halves of his cuff-links were connected by chains. Occasionally he was to be seen chained to a dog.

A reversion, conceivably, to a mediæval type! Yes, but also the exemplar of the excessively modern! Externally he was a consequence of the fact that, years previously, the leading tailor in Bursley had permitted his son to be apprenticed in London. The father died; the son had the wit to return and make a fortune while creating a new type in the town, a type of which multiple chains were but one feature, and that the least expensive if the most salient. For instance, up to the historic year in which the young tailor created the type, any cap was a cap in Bursley, and any collar was a collar. But thencefor-

ward no cap was a cap, and no collar was a collar, which did
not exactly conform in shape and material to certain sacred
caps and collars guarded by the young tailor in his back shop.
None knew why these sacred caps and collars were sacred, but
they were; their sacredness endured for about six months, and
then suddenly—again none knew why—they fell from their
estate and became lower than offal for dogs, and were supplanted on the altar. The type brought into existence by the
young tailor was to be recognized by its caps and collars, and
in a similar manner by every other article of attire, except
its boots. Unfortunately the tailor did not sell boots, and so
imposed on his creatures no mystical creed as to boots. This
was a pity, for the boot-makers of the town happened not to
be inflamed by the type-creating passion as the tailor was, and
thus the new type finished abruptly at the edges of the tailor's
trousers.

The man at No. 4, St. Luke's Square had comparatively
small and narrow feet, which gave him an advantage; and as
he was endowed with a certain vague general physical distinction he managed, despite the eternal untidiness of his hair, to
be eminent among the type. Assuredly the frequent sight of
him in her house flattered the pride of Constance's eye, which
rested on him almost always with pleasure. He had come into
the house with startling abruptness soon after Cyril left school
and was indentured to the head-designer at "Peel's," that
classic earthenware manufactory. The presence of a man in her
abode disconcerted Constance at the beginning; but she soon
grew accustomed to it, perceiving that a man would behave as
a man, and must be expected to do so. This man, in truth, did
what he liked in all things. Cyril having always been regarded
by both his parents as enormous, one would have anticipated a
giant in the new man; but, queerly, he was slim, and little above
the average height. Neither in enormity nor in many other particulars did he resemble the Cyril whom he had supplanted.
His gestures were lighter and quicker; he had nothing of
Cyril's ungainliness; he had not Cyril's limitless taste for
sweets, nor Cyril's terrific hatred of gloves, barbers, and soap.
He was much more dreamy than Cyril, and much busier. In
fact, Constance only saw him at meal-times. He was at Peel's
in the day and at the School of Art every night. He would
dream during a meal, even; and, without actually saying so,
he gave the impression that he was the busiest man in Bursley,

wrapped in occupations and preoccupations as in a blanket—a blanket which Constance had difficulty in penetrating.

Constance wanted to please him; she lived for nothing but to please him; he was, however, exceedingly difficult to please, not in the least because he was hypercritical and exacting, but because he was indifferent. Constance, in order to satisfy her desire of pleasing, had to make fifty efforts, in the hope that he might chance to notice one. He was a good man, amazingly industrious—when once Constance had got him out of bed in the morning; with no vices, kind, save when Constance mistakenly tried to thwart him; charming, with a curious strain of humour that Constance only half understood. Constance was unquestionably vain about him, and she could honestly find in him little to blame. But whereas he was the whole of her universe, she was merely a dim figure in the background of his. Every now and then, with his gentle, elegant raillery, he would apparently rediscover her, as though saying: "Ah! You're still there, are you?" Constance could not meet him on the plane where his interests lay, and he never knew the passionate intensity of her absorption in that minor part of his life which moved on her plane. He never worried about her solitude, or guessed that in throwing her a smile and a word at supper he was paying her meagrely for three hours of lone rocking in a rocking-chair.

The worst of it was that she was quite incurable. No experience would suffice to cure her trick of continually expecting him to notice things which he never did notice. One day he said, in the midst of a silence: "By the way, didn't father leave any boxes of cigars?" She had the steps up into her bedroom and reached down from the dusty top of the wardrobe the box which she had put there after Samuel's funeral. In handing him the box she was doing a great deed. His age was nineteen and she was ratifying his precocious habit of smoking by this solemn gift. He entirely ignored the box for several days. She said timidly: "Have you tried those cigars?" "Not yet," he replied. "I'll try 'em one of these days." Ten days later, on a Sunday, when he chanced not to have gone out with his aristocratic friend Matthew Peel-Swynnerton, he did at length open the box and take out a cigar. "Now," he observed roguishly, cutting the cigar, "we shall see, Mrs. Plover!" He often called her Mrs. Plover, for fun. Though she liked him to be sufficiently interested in her to tease her, she did not like being

called Mrs. Plover, and she never failed to say: "I'm not Mrs.
Plover." He smoked the cigar slowly, in the rocking-chair,
throwing his head back and sending clouds to the ceiling. And
afterwards he remarked: "The old man's cigars weren't so
bad." "Indeed!" she answered tartly, as if maternally resenting
this easy patronage. But in secret she was delighted. There
was something in her son's favourable verdict on her husband's
cigars that thrilled her.

And she looked at him. Impossible to see in him any resemblance to his father! Oh! He was a far more brilliant, more
advanced, more complicated, more seductive being than his
homely father! She wondered where he had come from. And
yet . . . ! If his father had lived, what would have occurred
between them? Would the boy have been openly smoking cigars
in the house at nineteen?

She laboriously interested herself, so far as he would allow,
in his artistic studies and productions. A back attic on the
second floor was now transformed into a studio—a naked apartment which smelt of oil and of damp clay. Often there were
traces of clay on the stairs. For working in clay he demanded
of his mother a smock, and she made a smock, on the model of
a genuine smock which she obtained from a country-woman who
sold eggs and butter in the Covered Market. Into the shoulders
of the smock she put a week's fancy-stitching, taking the pattern from an old book of embroidery. One day when he had seen
her stitching morn, noon, and afternoon, at the smock, he said,
as she rocked idly after supper: "I suppose you haven't forgotten all about the smock I asked you for, have you, mater?"
She knew that he was teasing her; but, while perfectly realizing
how foolish she was, she nearly always acted as though his teasing was serious; she picked up the smock again from the sofa.
When the smock was finished he examined it intently; then exclaimed with an air of surprise: "By Jove! That's beautiful!
Where did you get this pattern?" He continued to stare at it,
smiling in pleasure. He turned over the tattered leaves of the
embroidery-book with the same naïve, charmed astonishment,
and carried the book away to the studio. "I must show that
to Swynnerton," he said. As for her, the epithet "beautiful"
seemed a strange epithet to apply to a mere piece of honest
stitchery done in a pattern, and a stitch with which she had
been familiar all her life. The fact was she understood his "art"
less and less. The sole wall decoration of his studio was a

Japanese print, which struck her as being entirely preposterous, considered as a picture. She much preferred his own early drawings of moss-roses and picturesque castles—things that he now mercilessly contemned. Later, he discovered her cutting out another smock. "What's that for?" he inquired. "Well," she said, "you can't manage with one smock. What shall you do when that one has to go to the wash?" "Wash!" he repeated vaguely. "There's no need for it to go to the wash." "Cyril," she replied, "don't try my patience! I was thinking of making you half-a-dozen." He whistled. "With all that stitching?" he questioned, amazed at the undertaking. "Why not?" she said. In her young days, no sempstress ever made fewer than half-a-dozen of anything, and it was usually a dozen; it was sometimes half-a-dozen dozen. "Well," he murmured, "you have got a nerve! I'll say that."

Similar things happened whenever he showed that he was pleased. If he said of a dish, in the local tongue: "I could do a bit of that!" or if he simply smacked his lips over it, she would surfeit him with that dish.

ii

On a hot day in August, just before they were to leave Bursley for a month in the Isle of Man, Cyril came home, pale and perspiring, and dropped on to the sofa. He wore a grey alpaca suit, and, except his hair, which in addition to being very untidy was damp with sweat, he was a masterpiece of slim elegance, despite the heat. He blew out great sighs, and rested his head on the antimacassared arm of the sofa.

"Well, mater," he said, in a voice of factitious calm, "I've got it." He was looking up at the ceiling.

"Got what?"

"The National Scholarship. Swynnerton says it's a sheer fluke. But I've got it. Great glory for the Bursley School of Art!"

"National Scholarship?" she said. "What's that? What is it?"

"Now, mother!" he admonished her, not without testiness. "Don't go and say I've never breathed a word about it!"

He lit a cigarette, to cover his self-consciousness, for he perceived that she was moved far beyond the ordinary.

Never, in fact, not even by the death of her husband, had she received such a frightful blow as that which the dreamy Cyril had just dealt her.

It was not a complete surprise, but it was nearly a complete surprise. A few months previously he certainly had mentioned, in his incidental way, the subject of a National Scholarship. Apropos of a drinking-cup which he had designed, he had said that the director of the School of Art had suggested that it was good enough to compete for the National, and that as he was otherwise qualified for the competition he might as well send the cup to South Kensington. He had added that Peel-Swynnerton had laughed at the notion as absurd. On that occasion she had comprehended that a National Scholarship involved residence in London. She ought to have begun to live in fear, for Cyril had a most disturbing habit of making a mere momentary reference to matters which he deemed very important and which occupied a large share of his attention. He was secretive by nature, and the rigidity of his father's rule had developed this trait in his character. But really he had spoken of the competition with such an extreme casualness that with little effort she had dismissed it from her anxieties as involving a contingency so remote as to be negligible. She had, genuinely, almost forgotten it. Only at rare intervals had it wakened in her a dull transitory pain—like the herald of a fatal malady. And, as a woman in the opening stage of disease, she had hastily reassured herself: "How silly of me! This can't possibly be anything serious!"

And now she was condemned. She knew it. She knew there could be no appeal. She knew that she might as usefully have besought mercy from a tiger as from her good, industrious, dreamy son.

"It means a pound a week," said Cyril, his self-consciousness intensified by her silence and by the dreadful look on her face. "And of course free tuition."

"For how long?" she managed to say.

"Well," said he, "that depends. Nominally for a year. But if you behave yourself it's always continued for three years."

If he stayed for three years he would never come back: that was a certainty.

How she rebelled, furious and despairing, against the fortuitous cruelty of things! She was sure that he had not, till then, thought seriously of going to London. But the fact that the

Government would admit him free to its classrooms and give him a pound a week besides, somehow forced him to go to London. It was not the lack of means that would have prevented him from going. Why, then, should the presence of means induce him to go? There was no logical reason. The whole affair was disastrously absurd. The art-master at the Wedgwood Institution had chanced, merely chanced, to suggest that the drinking-cup should be sent to South Kensington. And the result of this caprice was that she was sentenced to solitude for life! It was too monstrously, too incredibly wicked!

With what futile and bitter execration she murmured in her heart the word "If." If Cyril's childish predilections had not been encouraged! If he had only been content to follow his father's trade! If she had flatly refused to sign his indenture at Peel's and pay the premium! If he had not turned from colour to clay! If the art-master had not had that fatal "idea"! If the judges for the competition had decided otherwise! If only she had brought Cyril up in habits of obedience, sacrificing temporary peace to permanent security!

For after all he could not abandon her without her consent. He was not of age. And he would want a lot more money, which he could obtain from none but her. She could refuse. . . . No! She could not refuse. He was the master, the tyrant. For the sake of daily pleasantness she had weakly yielded to him at the start! She had behaved badly to herself and to him. He was spoiled. She had spoiled him. And he was about to repay her with lifelong misery, and nothing would deflect him from his course. The usual conduct of the spoilt child! Had she not witnessed it, and moralized upon it, in other families?

"You don't seem very chirpy over it, mater!" he said.

She went out of the room. His joy in the prospect of departure from the Five Towns, from her, though he masked it, was more manifest than she could bear.

The *Signal*, the next day, made a special item of the news. It appeared that no National Scholarship had been won in the Five Towns for eleven years. The citizens were exhorted to remember that Mr. Povey had gained his success in open competition with the cleverest young students of the entire kingdom —and in a branch of art which he had but recently taken up; and further, that the Government offered only eight scholarships each year. The name of Cyril Povey passed from lip to lip. And nobody who met Constance, in street or shop, could refrain from informing her that she ought to be a proud mother, to have such a son, but that truly they were not surprised . . . and how proud his poor father would have been! A few sympathetically hinted that maternal pride was one of those luxuries that may cost too dear.

iii

The holiday in the Isle of Man was of course ruined for her. She could scarcely walk because of the weight of a lump of lead that she carried in her bosom. On the brightest days the lump of lead was always there. Besides, she was so obese. In ordinary circumstances they might have stayed beyond the month. An indentured pupil is not strapped to the wheel like a common apprentice. Moreover, the indentures were to be cancelled. But Constance did not care to stay. She had to prepare for his departure to London. She had to lay the fagots for her own martyrdom.

In this business of preparation she showed as much silliness, she betrayed as perfect a lack of perspective, as the most superior son could desire for a topic of affectionate irony. Her preoccupation with petty things of no importance whatever was worthy of the finest traditions of fond motherhood. However, Cyril's careless satire had no effect on her, save that once she got angry, thereby startling him; he quite correctly and sagely laid this unprecedented outburst to the account of her wrought nerves, and forgave it. Happily for the smoothness of Cyril's translation to London, young Peel-Swynnerton was acquainted with the capital, had a brother in Chelsea, knew of reputable lodgings, was, indeed, an encyclopædia of the town, and would himself spend a portion of the autumn there. Otherwise, the preliminaries which his mother would have insisted on by means of tears and hysteria might have proved fatiguing to Cyril.

The day came when on that day week Cyril would be gone. Constance steadily fabricated cheerfulness against the prospect. She said:

"Suppose I come with you?"

He smiled in toleration of this joke as being a passable quality of joke. And then she smiled in the same sense, hastening to agree with him that as a joke it was not a bad joke.

In the last week he was very loyal to his tailor. Many a young man would have commanded new clothes after, not before, his arrival in London. But Cyril had faith in his creator.

On the day of departure the household, the very house itself, was in a state of excitation. He was to leave early. He would not listen to the project of her accompanying him as far as Knype, where the Loop Line joined the main. She might go to Bursley Station and no further. When she rebelled he disclosed the merest hint of his sullen-churlish side, and she at once yielded. During breakfast she did not cry, but the aspect of her face made him protest.

"Now, look here, mater! Just try to remember that I shall be back for Christmas. It's barely three months." And he lit a cigarette.

She made no reply.

Amy lugged a Gladstone bag down the crooked stairs. A trunk was already close to the door; it had wrinkled the carpet and deranged the mat.

"You didn't forget to put the hair-brush in, did you, Amy?" he asked.

"N—no, Mr. Cyril," she blubbered.

"Amy!" Constance sharply corrected her, as Cyril ran upstairs, "I wonder you can't control yourself better than that."

Amy weakly apologized. Although treated almost as one of the family, she ought not to have forgotten that she was a servant. What right had she to weep over Cyril's luggage? This question was put to her in Constance's tone.

The cab came. Cyril tumbled downstairs with exaggerated carelessness, and with exaggerated carelessness he joked at the cabman.

"Now, mother!" he cried, when the luggage was stowed. "Do you want me to miss this train?" But he knew that the margin of time was ample. It was his fun!

"Nay, I can't be hurried!" she said, fixing her bonnet. "Amy, as soon as we are gone you can clear this table."

She climbed heavily into the cab.

"That's it! Smash the springs!" Cyril teased her.

The horse got a stinging cut to recall him to the seriousness of life. It was a fine, bracing autumn morning, and the driver felt the need of communicating his abundant energy to some one or something. They drove off, Amy staring after them from the door. Matters had been so marvellously well arranged that they arrived at the station twenty minutes before the train was due.

"Never mind!" Cyril mockingly comforted his mother. "You'd rather be twenty minutes too soon than one minute too late, wouldn't you?"

His high spirits had to come out somehow.

Gradually the minutes passed, and the empty slate-tinted platform became dotted with people to whom that train was nothing but a Loop Line train, people who took that train every week-day of their lives and knew all its eccentricities.

And they heard the train whistle as it started from Turnhill. And Cyril had a final word with the porter who was in charge of the luggage. He made a handsome figure, and he had twenty pounds in his pocket. When he returned to Constance she was sniffing, and through her veil he could see that her eyes were circled with red. But through her veil she could see nothing. The train rolled in, rattling to a standstill. Constance lifted her veil and kissed him; and kissed her life out. He smelt the odour of her crape. He was, for an instant, close to her, close; and he seemed to have an overwhelmingly intimate glimpse into her secrets; he seemed to be choked in the sudden strong emotion of that crape. He felt queer.

"Here you are, sir! Second smoker!" called the porter.

The daily frequenters of the train boarded it with their customary disgust.

"I'll write as soon as ever I get there!" said Cyril, of his own accord. It was the best he could muster.

With what grace he raised his hat!

A sliding-away; clouds of steam; and she shared the dead platform with milk-cans, two porters, and Smith's noisy boy!

She walked home, very slowly and painfully. The lump of lead was heavier than ever before. And the townspeople saw the proudest mother in Bursley walking home.

"After all," she argued with her soul angrily, petulantly, "could you expect the boy to do anything else? He is a serious student, he has had a brilliant success, and is he to be tied to your apron-strings? The idea is preposterous. It isn't as if he was an idler, or a bad son. No mother could have a better son. A nice thing, that he should stay all his life in Bursley simply because you don't like being left alone!"

Unfortunately one might as well argue with a mule as with

one's soul. Her soul only kept on saying monotonously: "I'm a lonely old woman now. I've nothing to live for any more, and I'm no use to anybody. Once I was young and proud. And this is what my life has come to! This is the end!"

When she reached home, Amy had not touched the breakfast things; the carpet was still wrinkled, and the mat still out of place. And, through the desolating atmosphere of reaction after a terrific crisis, she marched directly upstairs, entered his plundered room, and beheld the disorder of the bed in which he had slept.

CHAPTER I

THE ELOPEMENT

HER soberly rich dress had a countrified air, as she waited, ready for the streets, in the bedroom of the London hotel on the afternoon of the first of July, 1866; but there was nothing of the provincial in that beautiful face, nor in that bearing at once shy and haughty; and her eager heart soared beyond geographical boundaries.

It was the Hatfield Hotel, in Salisbury Street, between the Strand and the river. Both street and hotel are now gone, lost in the vast foundations of the Savoy and the Cecil; but the type of the Hatfield lingers with ever-increasing shabbiness in Jermyn Street. In 1866, with its dark passages and crooked stairs, its candles, its carpets and stuffs which had outlived their patterns, its narrow dining-room where a thousand busy flies ate together at one long table, its acrid stagnant atmosphere, and its disturbing sensation of dirt everywhere concealing itself, it stood forth in rectitude as a good average modern hotel. The patched and senile drabness of the bedroom made an environment that emphasized Sophia's flashing youth. She alone in it was unsullied.

There was a knock at the door, apparently gay and jaunty. But she thought, truly: "He's nearly as nervous as I am!" And in her sick nervousness she coughed, and then tried to take full possession of herself. The moment had at last come which would divide her life as a battle divides the history of a nation. Her mind in an instant swept backwards through an incredible three months.

The schemings to obtain and to hide Gerald's letters at the shop, and to reply to them! The far more complex and dangerous duplicity practised upon her majestic aunt at Axe! The visits to the Axe post-office! The three divine meetings with Gerald at early morning by the canal-feeder, when he had told her of his inheritance and of the harshness of his uncle Boldero, and with a rush of words had spread before her the prospect of eternal bliss! The nights of fear! The sudden, dizzy acquiescence in his plan, and the feeling of universal unreality which obsessed her! The audacious departure from her aunt's, showering a cascade of appalling lies! Her dismay at Knype Station! Her blush as she asked for a ticket to London! The ironic, sympathetic glance of the porter, who took charge of her trunk! And then the thunder of the incoming train! Her renewed dismay when she found that it was very full, and her distracted plunge into a compartment with six people already in it! And the abrupt reopening of the carriage-door and that curt inquisition from an inspector: "Where for, please? Where for? Where for?" Until her turn was reached: "Where for, miss?" and her weak little reply: "Euston"! And more violent blushes! And then the long, steady beating of the train over the rails, keeping time to the rhythm of the unanswerable voice within her breast: "Why are you here? Why are you here?" And then Rugby; and the awful ordeal of meeting Gerald, his entry into the compartment, the rearrangement of seats, and their excruciatingly painful attempts at commonplace conversation in the publicity of the carriage! (She had felt that that part of the enterprise had not been very well devised by Gerald.) And at last London; the thousands of cabs, the fabulous streets, the general roar, all dream-surpassing, intensifying to an extraordinary degree the obsession of unreality, the illusion that she could not really have done what she had done, that she was not really doing what she was doing!

Supremely and finally, the delicious torture of the clutch of terror at her heart as she moved by Gerald's side through the impossible adventure! Who was this rash, mad Sophia? Surely not herself!

The knock at the door was impatiently repeated.

"Come in," she said timidly.

Gerald Scales came in. Yes, beneath that mien of a commercial traveller who has been everywhere and through everything, he was very nervous. It was her privacy that, with her consent, he had invaded. He had engaged the bedroom only with the intention of using it as a retreat for Sophia until the evening, when they were to resume their travels. It ought not to have had any disturbing significance. But the mere disorder on the washstand, a towel lying on one of the cane chairs, made himself feel that he was affronting decency, and so increased his jaunty nervousness. The moment was painful; the moment was difficult beyond his skill to handle it naturally.

Approaching her with factitious ease, he kissed her through her veil, which she then lifted with an impulsive movement, and he kissed her again, more ardently, perceiving that her ardour was exceeding his. This was the first time they had been alone together since her flight from Axe. And yet, with his worldly experience, he was naïve enough to be surprised that he could not put all the heat of passion into his embrace, and he wondered why he was not thrilled at the contact with her! However, the powerful clinging of her lips somewhat startled his senses, and also delighted him by its silent promise. He could smell the stuff of her veil, the sarsenet of her bodice, and, as it were wrapped in these odours as her body was wrapped in its clothes, the faint fleshly perfume of her body itself. Her face, viewed so close that he could see the almost imperceptible down on those fruit-like cheeks, was astonishingly beautiful; the dark eyes were exquisitely misted; and he could feel the secret loyalty of her soul ascending to him. She was very slightly taller than her lover; but somehow she hung from him, her body curved backwards, and her bosom pressed against his, so that instead of looking up at her gaze he looked down at it. He preferred that; perfectly proportioned though he was, his stature was a delicate point with him. His spirits rose by the uplift of his senses. His fears slipped away; he began to be very satisfied with himself. He was the inheritor of twelve thousand pounds, and he had won this unique creature. She was his capture; he held her close, permittedly scanning the minutiæ of her skin, permittedly crushing her flimsy silks. Something in him had forced her to lay her modesty on the altar of his desire. And the sun brightly shone. So he kissed her yet more ardently, and with the slightest touch of a victor's condescension; and her burning response more than restored the self-confidence which he had been losing.

"I've got no one but you now," she murmured in a melting voice.

She fancied in her ignorance that the expression of this sentiment would please him. She was not aware that a man is usually rather chilled by it, because it proves to him that the other is thinking about his responsibilities and not about his privileges. Certainly it calmed Gerald, though without imparting to him her sense of his responsibilities. He smiled vaguely. To Sophia his smile was a miracle continually renewed; it mingled dashing gaiety with a hint of wistful appeal in a manner that never failed to bewitch her. A less innocent girl than Sophia might have divined from that adorable half-feminine smile that she could do anything with Gerald except rely on him. But Sophia had to learn.

"Are you ready?" he asked, placing his hands on her shoulders and holding her away from him.

"Yes," she said, nerving herself. Their faces were still very near together.

"Well, would you like to go and see the Doré pictures?"

A simple enough question! A proposal felicitous enough! Doré was becoming known even in the Five Towns, not, assuredly, by his illustrations to the *Contes Drolatiques* of Balzac— but by his shuddering Biblical conceits. In pious circles Doré was saving art from the reproach of futility and frivolity. It was indubitably a tasteful idea on Gerald's part to take his love of a summer's afternoon to gaze at the originals of those prints which had so deeply impressed the Five Towns. It was an idea that sanctified the profane adventure.

Yet Sophia showed signs of affliction. Her colour went and came; her throat made the motion of swallowing; there was a muscular contraction over her whole body. And she drew herself from him. Her glance, however, did not leave him, and his eyes fell before hers.

"But what about the—wedding?" she breathed.

That sentence seemed to cost all her pride; but she was obliged to utter it, and to pay for it.

"Oh," he said lightly and quickly, just as though she had reminded him of a detail that might have been forgotten, "I was just going to tell you. It can't be done here. There's been some change in the rules. I only found out for certain late last night. But I've ascertained that it'll be as simple as A B C before the English Consul at Paris; and as I've got the tickets for us to go over to-night, as we arranged . . ." He stopped.

She sat down on the towel-covered chair, staggered. She believed what he said. She did not suspect that he was using the classic device of the seducer. It was his casualness that staggered her. Had it really been his intention to set off on an excursion and remark as an afterthought: "*By the way*, we can't be married as I told you at half-past two to-day"? Despite her extreme ignorance and innocence, Sophia held a high opinion of her own commonsense and capacity for looking after herself, and she could scarcely believe that he was expecting her to go to Paris, and at night, without being married. She looked pitiably young, virgin, raw, unsophisticated; helpless in the midst of dreadful dangers. Yet her head was full of a blank astonishment at being mistaken for a simpleton! The sole explanation could be that Gerald, in some matters, must himself be a confiding simpleton. He had not reflected. He had not sufficiently realized the immensity of her sacrifice in flying with him even to London. She felt sorry for him. She had the woman's first glimpse of the necessity for some adjustment of outlook as an essential preliminary to uninterrupted happiness.

"It'll be all right!" Gerald persuasively continued.

He looked at her, as she was not looking at him. She was nineteen. But she seemed to him utterly mature and mysterious. Her face baffled him; her mind was a foreign land. Helpless in one sense she might be; yet she, and not he, stood for destiny; the future lay in the secret and capricious workings of that mind.

"Oh no!" she exclaimed curtly. "Oh no!"

"Oh no what?"

"We can't possibly go like that," she said.

"But don't I tell you it'll be all right?" he protested. "If we stay here and they come after you . . . . ! Besides, I've got the tickets and all."

"Why didn't you tell me sooner?" she demanded.

"But how could I?" he grumbled. "Have we had a single minute alone?"

This was nearly true. They could not have discussed the formalities of marriage in the crowded train, nor during the hurried lunch with a dozen cocked ears at the same table. He saw himself on sure ground here.

"Now, could we?" he pressed.

"And you talk about going to see pictures!" was her reply.

Undoubtedly this had been a grave error of tact. He recognized that it was a stupidity. And so he resented it, as though she had committed it and not he.

"My dear girl," he said, hurt, "I acted for the best. It isn't my fault if rules are altered and officials silly."

"You ought to have told me before," she persisted sullenly.

"But how *could* I?"

He almost believed in that moment that he had really intended to marry her, and that the ineptitudes of red-tape had prevented him from achieving his honourable purpose. Whereas he had done nothing whatever towards the marriage.

"Oh no! Oh no!" she repeated, with heavy lip and liquid eye. "Oh no!"

He gathered that she was flouting his suggestion of Paris. Slowly and nervously he approached her. She did not stir nor look up. Her glance was fixed on the washstand. He bent down and murmured:

"Come, now. It'll be all right. You'll travel in the ladies' saloon on the steam-packet."

She did not stir. He bent lower and touched the back of her neck with his lips. And she sprang up, sobbing and angry. Because she was mad for him she hated him furiously. All tenderness had vanished.

"I'll thank you not to touch me!" she said fiercely. She had given him her lips a moment ago, but now to graze her neck was an insult.

He smiled sheepishly. "But really you must be reasonable," he argued. "What have I done?"

"It's what you haven't done, I think!" she cried. "Why didn't you tell me while we were in the cab?"

"I didn't care to begin worrying you just then," he replied: which was exactly true.

The fact was, he had of course shirked telling her that no marriage would occur that day. Not being a professional seducer of young girls, he lacked skill to do a difficult thing simply.

"Now come along, little girl," he went on, with just a trifle of impatience. "Let's go out and enjoy ourselves. I assure you that everything will be all right in Paris."

"That's what you said about coming to London," she retorted sarcastically through her sobs. "And look at you!"

Did he imagine for a single instant that she would have come to London with him save on the understanding that she was to be married immediately upon arrival? This attitude of an indignant question was not to be reconciled with her belief that his excuses for himself were truthful. But she did not remark the discrepancy.

Her sarcasm wounded his vanity.

"Oh, very well!" he muttered. "If you don't choose to believe what I say!" He shrugged his shoulders.

She said nothing; but the sobs swept at intervals through her frame, shaking it.

Reading hesitation in her face, he tried again. "Come along, little girl. And wipe your eyes." And he approached her. She stepped back.

"No, no!" she denied him, passionately. He had esteemed her too cheaply. And she did not care to be called "little girl."

"Then what shall you do?" he inquired, in a tone which blended mockery and bullying. She was making a fool of him.

"I can tell you what I shan't do," she said. "I shan't go to Paris." Her sobs were less frequent.

"That's not my question," he said icily. "I want to know what you will do."

There was now no pretence of affectionateness either on her part or on his. They might, to judge from their attitudes, have been nourished from infancy on mutual hatred.

"What's that got to do with you?" she demanded.

"It's got everything to do with me," he said.

"Well, you can go and find out!" she said.

It was girlish; it was childish; it was scarcely according to the canons for conducting a final rupture; but it was not the less tragically serious. Indeed, the spectacle of this young girl absurdly behaving like one, in a serious crisis, increased the tragicalness of the situation even if it did not heighten it. The idea that ran through Gerald's brain was the ridiculous folly of having anything to do with young girls. He was quite blind to her beauty.

" 'Go'?" he repeated her word. "You mean that?"

"Of course I mean it," she answered promptly.

The coward in him urged him to take advantage of her ignorant, helpless pride, and leave her at her word. He remembered the scene she had made at the pit shaft, and he said to himself that her charm was not worth her temper, and that he was a fool ever to have dreamed that it was, and that he would be doubly a fool now not to seize the opportunity of withdrawing from an insane enterprise.

"I am to go?" he asked, with a sneer.

She nodded.

"Of course if you order me to leave you, I must. Can I do anything for you?"

She signified that he could not.

"Nothing? You're sure?"

She frowned.

"Well, then, good-bye." He turned towards the door.

"I suppose you'd leave me without money or anything?" she said in a cold, cutting voice. And her sneer was far more destructive than his. It destroyed in him the last trace of compassion for her.

"Oh, I beg pardon!" he said, and swaggeringly counted out five sovereigns on to a chest of drawers.

She rushed at them. "Do you think I'll take your odious money?" she snarled, gathering the coins in her gloved hand.

Her first impulse was to throw them in his face; but she paused and then flung them into a corner of the room.

"Pick them up!" she commanded him.

"No, thanks," he said briefly; and left, shutting the door.

Only a very little while, and they had been lovers, exuding tenderness with every gesture, like a perfume! Only a very little while, and she had been deciding to telegraph condescendingly to her mother that she was "all right"! And now the dream was utterly dissolved. And the voice of that hard commonsense which spake to her in her wildest moods grew loud in asserting that the enterprise could never have come to any good, that it was from its inception an impossible enterprise, unredeemed by the slightest justification. An enormous folly! Yes, an elopement; but not like a real elopement; always unreal! She had always known that it was only an imitation of an elopement, and must end in some awful disappointment. She had never truly wanted to run away; but something within her had pricked her forward in spite of her protests. The strict notions of her elderly relatives were right after all. It was she who had been wrong. And it was she who would have to pay.

"I've been a wicked girl," she said to herself grimly, in the midst of her ruin.

She faced the fact. But she would not repent; at any rate

she would never sit on that stool. She would not exchange the remains of her pride for the means of escape from the worst misery that life could offer. On that point she knew herself. And she set to work to repair and renew her pride.

Whatever happened she would not return to the Five Towns. She could not, because she had stolen money from her Aunt Harriet. As much as she had thrown back at Gerald, she had filched from her aunt, but in the form of a note. A prudent, mysterious instinct had moved her to take this precaution. And she was glad. She would never have been able to dart that sneer at Gerald about money if she had really needed money. So she rejoiced in her crime; though, since Aunt Harriet would assuredly discover the loss at once, the crime eternally prevented her from going back to her family. Never, never would she look at her mother with the eyes of a thief!

(In truth Aunt Harriet did discover the loss, and very creditably said naught about it to anybody. The knowledge of it would have twisted the knife in the maternal heart.)

Sophia was also glad that she had refused to proceed to Paris. The recollection of her firmness in refusing flattered her vanity as a girl convinced that she could take care of herself. To go to Paris unmarried would have been an inconceivable madness. The mere thought of the enormity did outrage to her moral susceptibilities. No, Gerald had most perfectly mistaken her for another sort of girl; as, for instance, a shop-assistant or a barmaid!

With this the catalogue of her satisfactions ended. She had no idea at all as to what she ought to do, or could do. The mere prospect of venturing out of the room intimidated her. Had Gerald left her trunk in the hall? Of course he had. What a question! But what would happen to her? London . . . London had merely dazed her. She could do nothing for herself. She was as helpless as a rabbit in London. She drew aside the window-curtain and had a glimpse of the river. It was inevitable that she should think of suicide; for she could not suppose that any girl had ever got herself into a plight more desperate than hers. "I could slip out at night and drown myself," she thought seriously. "A nice thing that would be for Gerald!"

Then loneliness, like a black midnight, overwhelmed her, swiftly wasting her strength, disintegrating her pride in its horrid flood. She glanced about for support, as a woman in the open street who feels she is going to faint, and went blindly to the bed, falling on it with the upper part of her body, in an attitude of abandonment. She wept, but without sobbing.

ii

Gerald Scales walked about the Strand, staring up at its high narrow houses, crushed one against another as though they had been packed, unsorted, by a packer who thought of nothing but economy of space. Except by Somerset House, King's College, and one or two theatres and banks, the monotony of mean shops, with several storeys unevenly perched over them, was unbroken. Then Gerald encountered Exeter Hall, and examined its prominent façade with a provincial's eye; for despite his travels he was not very familiar with London. Exeter Hall naturally took his mind back to his Uncle Boldero, that great and ardent Nonconformist, and his own godly youth. It was laughable to muse upon what his uncle would say and think, did the old man know that his nephew had run away with a girl, meaning to seduce her in Paris. It was enormously funny!

However, he had done with all that. He was well out of it. She had told him to go, and he had gone. She had money to get home; she had nothing to do but use the tongue in her head. The rest was her affair. He would go to Paris alone, and find another amusement. It was absurd to have supposed that Sophia would ever have suited him. Not in such a family as the Baineses could one reasonably expect to discover an ideal mistress. No! there had been a mistake. The whole business was wrong. She had nearly made a fool of him. But he was not the man to be made a fool of. He had kept his dignity intact.

So he said to himself. Yet all the time his dignity, and his pride also, were bleeding, dropping invisible blood along the length of the Strand pavements.

He was at Salisbury Street again. He pictured her in the bedroom. Damn her! He wanted her. He wanted her with an excessive desire. He hated to think that he had been baulked. He hated to think that she would remain immaculate. And he continued to picture her in the exciting privacy of that cursed bedroom.

Now he was walking down Salisbury Street. He did not wish to be walking down Salisbury Street; but there he was!

"Oh, hell!" he murmured. "I suppose I must go through with it."

He felt desperate. He was ready to pay any price in order to be able to say to himself that he had accomplished what he had set his heart on.

"My wife hasn't gone out, has she?" he asked of the hall-porter.

"I'm not sure, sir; I think not," said the hall-porter.

The fear that Sophia had already departed made him sick. When he noticed her trunk still there, he took hope and ran upstairs.

He saw her, a dark crumpled, sinuous piece of humanity, half on and half off the bed, silhouetted against the bluish-white counterpane; her hat was on the floor, with the spotted veil trailing away from it. This sight seemed to him to be the most touching that he had ever seen, though her face was hidden. He forgot everything except the deep and strange emotion which affected him. He approached the bed. She did not stir.

Having heard the entry and knowing that it must be Gerald who had entered, Sophia forced herself to remain still. A wild, splendid hope shot up in her. Constrained by all the power of her will not to move, she could not stifle a sob that had lain in ambush in her throat.

The sound of the sob fetched tears to the eyes of Gerald.

"Sophia!" he appealed to her.

But she did not stir. Another sob shook her.

"Very well, then," said Gerald. "We'll stay in London till we can be married. I'll arrange it. I'll find a nice boarding-house for you, and I'll tell the people you're my cousin. I shall stay on at this hotel, and I'll come and see you every day."

A silence.

"Thank you!" she blubbered. "Thank you!"

He saw that her little gloved hand was stretching out towards him, like a feeler; and he seized it, and knelt down and took her clumsily by the waist. Somehow he dared not kiss her yet.

An immense relief surged very slowly through them both.

"I—I—really——" She began to say something, but the articulation was lost in her sobs.

"What? What do you say, dearest?" he questioned eagerly.

And she made another effort. "I really couldn't have gone to Paris with you without being married," she succeeded at last. "I really couldn't."

"No, no!" he soothed her. "Of course you couldn't. It was I who was wrong. But you didn't know how I felt. . . . Sophia, it's all right now, isn't it?"

She sat up and kissed him fairly.

It was so wonderful and startling that he burst openly into tears. She saw in the facile intensity of his emotion a guarantee of their future happiness. And as he had soothed her, so now she soothed him. They clung together, equally surprised at the sweet, exquisite, blissful melancholy which drenched them through and through. It was remorse for having quarrelled, for having lacked faith in the supreme rightness of the high adventure. Everything was right, and would be right; and they had been criminally absurd. It was remorse; but it was pure bliss, and worth the quarrel! Gerald resumed his perfection again in her eyes! He was the soul of goodness and honour! And for him she was again the ideal mistress, who would, however, be also a wife. As in his mind he rapidly ran over the steps necessary to their marriage, he kept saying to himself, far off in some remote cavern of the brain: "I shall have her! I shall have her!" He did not reflect that this fragile slip of the Baines stock, unconsciously drawing upon the accumulated strength of generations of honest living, had put a defeat upon him.

After tea, Gerald, utterly content with the universe, redeemed his word and found an irreproachable boarding-house for Sophia in Westminster, near the Abbey. She was astonished at the glibness of his lies to the landlady about her, and about their circumstances generally. He also found a church and a parson, close by, and in half an hour the formalities preliminary to a marriage were begun. He explained to her that as she was now resident in London, it would be simpler to recommence the business entirely. She sagaciously agreed. As she by no means wished to wound him again, she made no inquiry about those other formalities which, owing to red-tape, had so unexpectedly proved abortive! She knew she was going to be married, and that sufficed. The next day she carried out her filial idea of telegraphing to her mother.

CHAPTER II

SUPPER

THEY had been to Versailles and had dined there. A tram had sufficed to take them out; but for the return, Gerald, who had been drinking champagne, would not be content with less than a carriage. Further, he insisted on entering Paris by way of the Bois and the Arc de Triomphe. Thoroughly to appease his conceit, it would have been necessary to swing open the gates of honour in the Arc and allow his fiacre to pass through; to be forced to drive round the monument instead of under it hurt the sense of fitness which champagne engenders. Gerald was in all his pride that day. He had been displaying the wonders to Sophia, and he could not escape the cicerone's secret feeling: that he himself was somehow responsible for the wonders. Moreover, he was exceedingly satisfied with the effect produced by Sophia.

Sophia, on arriving in Paris with the ring on her triumphant finger, had timidly mentioned the subject of frocks. None would have guessed from her tone that she was possessed by the desire for French clothes as by a devil. She had been surprised and delighted by the eagerness of Gerald's response. Gerald, too, was possessed by a devil. He thirsted to see her in French clothes. He knew some of the shops and ateliers in the Rue de la Paix, the Rue de la Chaussée d'Antin, and the Palais Royal. He was much more skilled in the lore of frocks than she, for his previous business in Paris had brought him into relations with the great firms; and Sophia suffered a brief humiliation in the discovery that his private opinion of her dresses was that they were not dresses at all. She had been aware that they were not Parisian, nor even of London; but she had thought them pretty good. It healed her wound, however, to reflect that Gerald had so marvellously kept his own counsel in order to spare her self-love. Gerald had taken her to an establishment in the Chaussée d'Antin. It was not one of what Gerald called *les grandes maisons*, but it was on the very fringe of them, and the real *haute couture* was practised therein; and Gerald was remembered there by name.

Sophia had gone in trembling and ashamed, yet in her heart

courageously determined to emerge uncompromisingly French. But the models frightened her. They surpassed even the most fantastic things that she had seen in the streets. She recoiled before them and seemed to hide for refuge in Gerald, as it were appealing to him for moral protection, and answering to him instead of to the saleswoman when the saleswoman offered remarks in stiff English. The prices also frightened her. The simplest trifle here cost sixteen pounds; and her mother's historic "silk," whose elaborateness had cost twelve pounds, was supposed to have approached the inexpressible! Gerald said that she was not to think about prices. She was, however, forced by some instinct to think about prices—she who at home had scorned the narrowness of life in the Square. In the Square she was understood to be quite without commonsense, hopelessly imprudent; yet here, a spring of sagacity seemed to be welling up in her all the time, a continual antidote against the general madness in which she found herself. With extraordinary rapidity she had formed a habit of preaching moderation to Gerald. She hated to "see money thrown away," and her notion of the boundary line between throwing money away and judiciously spending it was still the notion of the Square.

Gerald would laugh. But she would say, piqued and blushing, but self-sure: "You can laugh!" It was all deliciously agreeable.

On this evening she wore the first of the new costumes. She had worn it all day. Characteristically she had chosen something which was not too special for either afternoon or evening, for either warm or cold weather. It was of pale blue taffetas striped in a darker blue, with the corsage cut in basques, and the underskirt of a similar taffetas, but unstriped. The effect of the ornate overskirt falling on the plain underskirt with its small double *volant* was, she thought, and Gerald too, adorable. The waist was higher than any she had had before, and the crinoline expansive. Tied round her head with a large bow and flying blue ribbons under the chin, was a fragile flat *capote* like a baby's bonnet, which allowed her hair to escape in front and her great chignon behind. A large spotted veil flew out from the *capote* over the chignon. Her double skirts waved amply over Gerald's knees in the carriage, and she leaned back against the hard cushions and put an arrogant look into her face, and thought of nothing but the intense throbbing joy of life, longing with painful ardour for more and more pleasure, then and for ever.

As the carriage slipped downwards through the wide, empty gloom of the Champs Elysées into the brilliant Paris that was waiting for them, another carriage drawn by two white horses flashed upwards and was gone in dust. Its only occupant, except the coachman and footman, was a woman. Gerald stared after it.

"By Jove!" he exclaimed. "That's Hortense!"

It might have been Hortense, or it might not. But he instantly convinced himself that it was. Not every evening did one meet Hortense driving alone in the Champs Elysées, and in August too!

"Hortense?" Sophia asked simply.

"Yes. Hortense Schneider."

"Who is she?"

"You've never heard of Hortense Schneider?"

"No!"

"Well! Have you ever heard of Offenbach?"

"I—I don't know. I don't think so."

He had the mien of utter incredulity. "You don't mean to say you've never heard of *Bluebeard?*"

"I've heard of Bluebeard, of course," said she. "Who hasn't?"

"I mean the opera—Offenbach's."

She shook her head, scarce knowing even what an opera was.

"Well, well! What next?"

He implied that such ignorance stood alone in his experience. Really he was delighted at the cleanness of the slate on which he had to write. And Sophia was not a bit alarmed. She relished instruction from his lips. It was a pleasure to her to learn from that exhaustless store of worldly knowledge. To the world she would do her best to assume omniscience in its ways, but to him, in her present mood, she liked to play the ignorant, uninitiated little thing.

"Why," he said, "the Schneider has been the rage since last year but one. Absolutely the *rage.*"

"I do wish I'd noticed her!" said Sophia.

"As soon as the Variétés reopens we'll go and see her," he replied, and then gave his detailed version of the career of Hortense Schneider.

More joys for her in the near future! She had yet scarcely

penetrated the crust of her bliss. She exulted in the dazzling destiny which comprised freedom, fortune, eternal gaiety, and the exquisite Gerald.

As they crossed the Place de la Concorde, she inquired, "Are we going back to the hotel?"

"No," he said. "I thought we'd go and have supper somewhere, if it isn't too early."

"After all that dinner?"

"All what dinner? You ate about five times as much as me, anyhow!"

"Oh, *I'm* ready!" she said.

She was. This day, because it was the first day of her French frock, she regarded as her *début* in the dizzy life of capitals. She existed in a rapture of bliss, an ecstasy which could feel no fatigue, either of body or spirit.

ii

It was after midnight when they went into the Restaurant Sylvain; Gerald, having decided not to go to the hotel, had changed his mind and called there, and having called there, had remained a long time: this of course! Sophia was already accustoming herself to the idea that, with Gerald, it was impossible to predict accurately more than five minutes of the future.

As the *chasseur* held open the door for them to enter, and Sophia passed modestly into the glowing yellow interior of the restaurant, followed by Gerald in his character of man-of-the-world, they drew the attention of Sylvain's numerous and glittering guests. No face could have made a more provocative contrast to the women's faces in those screened rooms than the face of Sophia, so childlike between the baby's bonnet and the huge bow of ribbon, so candid, so charmingly conscious of its own pure beauty and of the fact that she was no longer a virgin, but the equal in knowledge of any woman alive. She saw around her, clustered about the white tables, multitudes of violently red lips, powdered cheeks, cold, hard eyes, self-possessed arrogant faces, and insolent bosoms. What had impressed her more than anything else in Paris, more even than the three-horsed omnibuses, was the extraordinary self-assurance of all the women, their unashamed posing, their calm acceptance of the public gaze. They seemed to say: "We are the renowned Parisiennes." They frightened her: they appeared to her so corrupt and so proud in their corruption. She had already seen a dozen women in various situations of conspicuousness apply powder to their complexions with no more ado than if they had been giving a pat to their hair. She could not understand such boldness. As for them, they marvelled at the phenomena presented in Sophia's person; they admired; they admitted the style of the gown; but they envied neither her innocence nor her beauty; they envied nothing but her youth and the fresh tint of her cheeks.

"Encore des Anglais!" said some of them, as if that explained all.

Gerald had a very curt way with waiters; and the more obsequious they were, the haughtier he became; and a headwaiter was no more to him than a scullion. He gave loud-voiced orders in French of which both he and Sophia were proud, and a table was laid for them in a corner near one of the large windows. Sophia settled herself on the bench of green velvet, and began to ply the ivory fan which Gerald had given her. It was very hot; all the windows were wide open, and the sounds of the street mingled clearly with the tinkle of the supper-room. Outside, against a sky of deepest purple, Sophia could discern the black skeleton of a gigantic building; it was the new opera house.

"All sorts here!" said Gerald, contentedly, after he had ordered iced soup and sparkling Moselle. Sophia did not know what Moselle was, but she imagined that anything would be better than champagne.

Sylvain's was then typical of the Second Empire, and particularly famous as a supper-room. Expensive and gay, it provided, with its discreet decorations, a sumptuous scene where lorettes, actresses, respectable women, and an occasional grirette in luck, could satisfy their curiosity as to each other. In its catholicity it was highly correct as a resort; not many other restaurants in the centre could have successfully fought against the rival attractions of the Bois and the dim groves of the Champs Elysées on a night in August. The complicated richness of the dresses, the yards and yards of fine stitchery, the endless ruching, the hints, more or less incautious, of nether treasures of embroidered linen; and, leaping over all this to the eye, the vivid colourings of silks and muslins, veils, plumes and flowers, piled as it were pell-mell in heaps on the universal green cushions to the furthest vista of the restaurant, and all multiplied in gilt mirrors—the spectacle intoxicated Sophia. Her eyes gleamed. She drank the soup with eagerness, and tasted the wine, though no desire on her part to like wine could make her like it; and then, seeing pineapples on a large table covered with fruits, she told Gerald that she should like some pineapple, and Gerald ordered one.

She gathered her self-esteem and her wits together, and began to give Gerald her views on the costumes. She could do so with impunity, because her own was indubitably beyond criticism. Some she wholly condemned, and there was not one which earned her unreserved approval. All the absurd fastidiousness of her schoolgirlish provinciality emerged in that eager, affected torrent of remarks. However, she was clever enough to read, after a time, in Gerald's tone and features, that she was making a tedious fool of herself. And she adroitly shifted her criticism from the taste to the *work*—she put a strong accent on the word—and pronounced that to be miraculous beyond description. She reckoned that she knew what dressmaking and millinery were, and her little fund of expert knowledge caused her to picture a whole necessary cityful of girls stitching, stitching, and stitching day and night. She had wondered, during the few odd days that they had spent in Paris, between visits to Chantilly and other places, at the massed luxury of the shops; she had wondered, starting with St. Luke's Square as a standard, how they could all thrive. But now in her first real glimpse of the banal and licentious profusion of one among a hundred restaurants, she wondered that the shops were so few. She thought how splendid was all this expensiveness for trade. Indeed, the notions chasing each other within that lovely and foolish head were a surprising medley.

"Well, what do you think of Sylvain's?" Gerald asked, impatient to be assured that his Sylvain's had duly overwhelmed her.

"Oh, Gerald!" she murmured, indicating that speech was inadequate. And she just furtively touched his hand with hers. The ennui due to her critical disquisition on the shortcomings of Parisian costume cleared away from Gerald's face.

"What do you suppose those people there are talking about?" he said with a jerk of the head towards a chattering group of three gorgeous lorettes and two middle-aged men at the next table but one.

"What are they talking about?"

"They're talking about the execution of the murderer Rivain that takes place at Auxerre the day after to-morrow. They're arranging to make up a party and go and see it."

"Oh, what a horrid idea!" said Sophia.

"Guillotine, you know!" said Gerald.

"But can people see it?"

"Yes, of course."

"Well, I think it's horrible."

"Yes, that's why people like to go and see it. Besides, the man isn't an ordinary sort of criminal at all. He's very young and good-looking, and well connected. And he killed the celebrated Claudine . . ."

"Claudine?"

"Claudine Jacquinot. Of course you wouldn't know. She was a tremendous—er—wrong 'un here in the forties. Made a lot of money, and retired to her native town."

Sophia, in spite of her efforts to maintain the *rôle* of a woman who has nothing to learn, blushed.

"Then she was older than he is."

"Thirty-five years older, if a day."

"What did he kill her for?"

"She wouldn't give him enough money. She was his mistress —or rather one of 'em. He wanted money for a young lady friend, you see. He killed her and took all the jewels she was wearing. Whenever he went to see her she always wore all her best jewels—and you may bet a woman like that had a few. It seems she had been afraid for a long time that he meant to do for her."

"Then why did she see him? And why did she wear her jewels?"

"Because she liked being afraid, goose! Some women only enjoy themselves when they're terrified. Queer, isn't it?"

Gerald insisted on meeting his wife's gaze as he finished these revelations. He pretended that such stories were the commonest things on earth, and that to be scandalized by them was infantile. Sophia, thrust suddenly into a strange civilization perfectly frank in its sensuality and its sensuousness, under the guidance of a young man to whom her half-formed intelligence was a most diverting toy—Sophia felt mysteriously uncomfortable, disturbed by sinister, flitting phantoms of ideas which she only dimly apprehended. Her eyes fell. Gerald laughed self-consciously. She would not eat any more pineapple.

Immediately afterwards there came into the restaurant an apparition which momentarily stopped every conversation in the room. It was a tall and mature woman who wore over a dress of purplish-black silk a vast flowing *sortie de bal* of vermilion velvet, looped and tasselled with gold. No other costume could live by the side of that garment, Arab in shape, Russian in colour, and Parisian in style. It blazed. The woman's heavy coiffure was bound with fillets of gold braid and crimson rosettes. She was followed by a young Englishman in evening dress and whiskers of the most exact correctness. The woman sailed, a little breathlessly, to a table next to Gerald's and took possession of it with an air of use, almost of tedium. She sat down, threw the cloak from her majestic bosom, and expanded her chest. Seeming to ignore the Englishman, who superciliously assumed the seat opposite to her, she let her large scornful eyes travel round the restaurant, slowly and imperiously meeting the curiosity which she had evoked. Her beauty had undoubtedly been dazzling, it was still effulgent; but the blossom was about to fall. She was admirably rouged and powdered; her arms were glorious; her lashes were long. There was little fault, save the excessive ripeness of a blonde who fights in vain against obesity. And her clothes combined audacity with the propriety of fashion. She carelessly deposed costly trinkets on the table, and then, having intimidated the whole company, she accepted the menu from the head-waiter and began to study it.

"That's one of 'em!" Gerald whispered to Sophia.

"One of what?" Sophia whispered.

Gerald raised his eyebrows warningly, and winked. The Englishman had overheard; and a look of frigid displeasure passed across his proud face. Evidently he belonged to a rank much higher than Gerald's; and Gerald, though he could always comfort himself by the thought that he had been to a university with the best, felt his own inferiority and could not hide that he felt it. Gerald was wealthy; he came of a wealthy family; but he had not the habit of wealth. When he spent money furiously, he did it with bravado, too conscious of grandeur and too conscious of the difficulties of acquiring that which he threw away. For Gerald had earned money. This whiskered Englishman had never earned money, never known the value of it, never imagined himself without as much of it as he might happen to want. He had the face of one accustomed to give orders and to look down upon inferiors. He was absolutely sure of himself. That his companion chiefly ignored him did not appear to incommode him in the least. She spoke to him in French. He replied in English, very briefly; and then, in English, he commanded the supper. As soon as the champagne was served he began to drink; in the intervals of drinking he gently stroked his whiskers. The woman spoke no more.

Gerald talked more loudly. With that aristocratic Englishman observing him, he could not remain at ease. And not only did he talk more loudly; he brought into his conversation references to money, travels, and worldly experiences. While seeking to impress the Englishman, he was merely becoming ridiculous to the Englishman; and obscurely he was aware of this. Sophia noticed and regretted it. Still, feeling very unimportant herself, she was reconciled to the superiority of the whiskered Englishman as to a natural fact. Gerald's behaviour slightly lowered him in her esteem. Then she looked at him—at his well-shaped neatness, his vivacious face, his excellent clothes, and decided that he was much to be preferred to any heavy-jawed, long-nosed aristocrat alive.

The woman whose vermilion cloak lay around her like a fortification spoke to her escort. He did not understand. He tried to express himself in French, and failed. Then the woman recommenced, talking at length. When she had done he shook his head. His acquaintance with French was limited to the vocabulary of food.

"Guillotine!" he murmured, the sole word of her discourse that he had understood.

"Oui, oui! Guillotine. Enfin . . . !" cried the woman excitedly. Encouraged by her success in conveying even one word of her remarks, she began a third time.

"Excuse me," said Gerald. "Madame is talking about the execution at Auxerre the day after to-morrow. N'est-ce-pas, madame, que vous parliez de Rivain?"

The Englishman glared angrily at Gerald's officious interruption. But the woman smiled benevolently on Gerald, and insisted on talking to her friend through him. And the Englishman had to make the best of the situation.

"There isn't a restaurant in Paris to-night where they aren't talking about that execution," said Gerald on his own account.

"Indeed!" observed the Englishman.

Wine affected them in different ways.

Now a fragile, short young Frenchman, with an extremely pale face ending in a thin black imperial, appeared at the entrance. He looked about, and, recognizing the woman of the scarlet cloak, very discreetly saluted her. Then he saw Gerald, and his worn, fatigued features showed a sudden, startled smile. He came rapidly forward, hat in hand, seized Gerald's palm and greeted him effusively.

"My wife," said Gerald, with the solemn care of a man who is determined to prove that he is entirely sober.

The young man became grave and excessively ceremonious. He bowed low over Sophia's hand and kissed it. Her impulse was to laugh, but the gravity of the young man's deference stopped her. She glanced at Gerald, blushing, as if to say: "This comedy is not my fault." Gerald said something, the young man turned to him and his face resumed its welcoming smile.

"This is Monsieur Chirac," Gerald at length completed the introduction, "a friend of mine when I lived in Paris."

He was proud to have met by accident an acquaintance in a restaurant. It demonstrated that he was a Parisian, and improved his standing with the whiskered Englishman and the vermilion cloak.

"It is the first time you come Paris, madame?" Chirac addressed himself to Sophia, in limping, timorous English.

"Yes," she giggled. He bowed again.

Chirac, with his best compliments, felicitated Gerald upon his marriage.

"Don't mention it!" said the humorous Gerald in English, amused at his own wit; and then: "What about this execution?"

"Ah!" replied Chirac, breathing out a long breath, and smiling at Sophia. "Rivain! Rivain!" He made a large, important gesture with his hand.

It was at once to be seen that Gerald had touched the topic which secretly ravaged the supper-world as a subterranean fire ravages a mine.

"I go!" said Chirac, with pride, glancing at Sophia, who smiled self-consciously.

Chirac entered upon a conversation with Gerald in French. Sophia comprehended that Gerald was surprised and impressed by what Chirac told him and that Chirac in turn was surprised. Then Gerald laboriously found his pocket-book, and after some fumbling with it handed it to Chirac so that the latter might write in it.

"Madame!" murmured Chirac, resuming his ceremonious stiffness in order to take leave. "Alors, c'est entendu, mon cher ami!" he said to Gerald, who nodded phlegmatically. And Chirac went away to the next table but one, where were the three lorettes and the two middle-aged men. He was received there with enthusiasm.

Sophia began to be teased by a little fear that Gerald was not quite his usual self. She did not think of him as tipsy. The idea of his being tipsy would have shocked her. She did not think clearly at all. She was lost and dazed in the labyrinth of new and vivid impressions into which Gerald had led her. But her prudence was awake.

"I think I'm tired," she said in a low voice.

"You don't want to go, do you?" he asked, hurt.

"Well——"

"Oh, wait a bit!"

The owner of the vermilion cloak spoke again to Gerald, who showed that he was flattered. While talking to her he ordered a brandy-and-soda. And then he could not refrain from displaying to her his familiarity with Parisian life, and he related how he had met Hortense Schneider behind a pair of white horses. The vermilion cloak grew even more sociable at the mention of this resounding name, and chattered with the most agreeable vivacity. Her friend stared inimically.

"Do you hear that?" Gerald explained to Sophia, who was sitting silent. "About Hortense Schneider—you know, we met her to-night. It seems she made a bet of a louis with some fellow, and when he lost he sent her the louis set in diamonds worth a hundred thousand francs. That's how they go on here."

"Oh!" cried Sophia, further than ever in the labyrinth.

" 'Scuse me," the Englishman put in heavily. He had heard the words "Hortense Schneider," "Hortense Schneider," repeating themselves in the conversation, and at last it occurred to him that the conversation was about Hortense Schneider.

" 'Scuse me," he began again. "Are you—do you mean Hortense Schneider?"

"Yes," said Gerald. "We met her to-night."

"She's in Trouville," said the Englishman, flatly.

Gerald shook his head positively.

"I gave a supper to her in Trouville last night," said the Englishman. "And she plays at the Casino Theatre to-night."

Gerald was repulsed but not defeated. "What is she playing in to-night? Tell me that!" he sneered.

"I don't see why I sh'd tell you."

"H'm!" Gerald retorted. "If what you say is true, it's a very strange thing I should have seen her in the Champs Elysées to-night, isn't it?"

The Englishman drank more wine. "If you want to insult me, sir——" he began coldly.

"Gerald!" Sophia urged in a whisper.

"Be quiet!" Gerald snapped.

A fiddler in fancy costume plunged into the restaurant at that moment and began to play wildly. The shock of his strange advent momentarily silenced the quarrel; but soon it leaped up again, under the shelter of the noisy music,—the common, tedious, tippler's quarrel. It rose higher and higher. The fiddler looked askance at it over his fiddle. Chirac cautiously observed it. Instead of attending to the music, the festal company attended to the quarrel. Three waiters in a group watched it with an impartial sporting interest. The English voices grew more menacing.

Then suddenly the whiskered Englishman, jerking his head towards the door, said more quietly:

"Hadn't we better settle thish outside?"

"At your service!" said Gerald, rising.

The owner of the vermilion cloak lifted her eyebrows to Chirac in fatigued disgust, but she said nothing. Nor did Sophia say anything. Sophia was overcome by terror.

The swain of the cloak, dragging his coat after him across the floor, left the restaurant without offering any apology or explanation to his lady.

"Wait here for me," said Gerald defiantly to Sophia. "I shall be back in a minute."

"But, Gerald!" She put her hand on his sleeve.

He snatched his arm away. "Wait here for me, I tell you," he repeated.

The doorkeeper obsequiously opened the door to the two unsteady carousers, for whom the fiddler drew back, still playing.

Thus Sophia was left side by side with the vermilion cloak. She was quite helpless. All the pride of a married woman had abandoned her. She stood transfixed by intense shame, staring painfully at a pillar, to avoid the universal assault of eyes. She felt like an indiscreet little girl, and she looked like one. No youthful radiant beauty of features, no grace and style of a Parisian dress, no certificate of a ring, no premature initiation into the mysteries, could save her from the appearance of a raw fool whose foolishness had been her undoing. Her face changed to its reddest, and remained at that, and all the fundamental innocence of her nature, which had been overlaid by the violent experiences of her brief companionship with Gerald, rose again to the surface with that blush. Her situation drew pity from a few hearts and a careless contempt from the rest. But since once more it was a question of *ces Anglais*, nobody could be astonished.

Without moving her head, she twisted her eyes to the clock: half-past two. The fiddler ceased his dance and made a collection in his tasselled cap. The vermilion cloak threw a coin into the cap. Sophia stared at it moveless, until the fiddler, tired of waiting, passed to the next table and relieved her agony. She had no money at all. She set herself to watch the clock; but its fingers would not stir.

With an exclamation the lady of the cloak got up and peered out of the window, chatted with waiters, and then removed herself and her cloak to the next table, where she was received with amiable sympathy by the three lorettes, Chirac, and the other two men. The party surreptitiously examined Sophia from time to time. Then Chirac went outside with the head-waiter, returned, consulted with his friends, and finally approached Sophia. It was twenty minutes past three.

He renewed his magnificent bow. "Madame," he said carefully, "will you allow me to bring you to your hotel?"

He made no reference to Gerald, partly, doubtless, because his English was treacherous on difficult ground.

Sophia had not sufficient presence of mind to thank her saviour.

"But the bill?" she stammered. "The bill isn't paid."

He did not instantly understand her. But one of the waiters had caught the sound of a familiar word, and sprang forward with a slip of paper on a plate.

"I have no money," said Sophia, with a feeble smile.

"Je vous arrangerai ça," he said. "What name of the hotel? Meurice, is it not?"

"Hotel Meurice," said Sophia. "Yes."

He spoke to the head-waiter about the bill, which was carried away like something obscene; and on his arm, which he punctiliously offered and she could not refuse, Sophia left the scene of her ignominy. She was so distraught that she could not manage her crinoline in the doorway. No sign anywhere outside of Gerald or his foe!

He put her into an open carriage, and in five minutes they had clattered down the brilliant silence of the Rue de la Paix, through the Place Vendôme into the Rue de Rivoli; and the night-porter of the hotel was at the carriage-step.

"I tell them at the restaurant where you gone," said Chirac, bare-headed under the long colonnade of the street. "If your husband is there, I tell him. Till to-morrow . . . !"

His manners were more wonderful than any that Sophia had ever imagined. He might have been in the dark Tuileries on the opposite side of the street, saluting an empress, instead of taking leave of a raw little girl, who was still too disturbed even to thank him.

She fled candle in hand up the wide, many-cornered stairs; Gerald might be already in the bedroom, . . . drunk! There was a chance. But the gilt-fringed bedroom was empty. She sat down at the velvet-covered table and the shadows cast by the candle that wavered in the draught from the open window. And she set her teeth and a cold fury possessed her in the hot and languorous night. Gerald was an imbecile. That he should have allowed himself to get tipsy was bad enough, but that he should have exposed her to the horrible situation from which Chirac had extricated her, was unspeakably disgraceful. He was an imbecile. He had no common sense. With all his captivating charm, he could not be relied upon not to make himself and her ridiculous, tragically ridiculous. Compare him with Mr. Chirac! She leaned despairingly on the table. She would not undress. She would not move. She had to realize her position; she had to see it.

Folly! Folly! Fancy a commercial traveller throwing a compromising piece of paper to the daughter of his customer in the shop itself: that was the incredible folly with which their relations had begun! And his mad gesture at the pit shaft! And his scheme for bringing her to Paris unmarried! And then to-night! Monstrous folly! Alone in the bedroom she was a wise and a disillusioned woman, wiser than any of those dolls in the restaurant.

And had she not gone to Gerald, as it were, over the dead body of her father, through lies and lies and again lies? That was how she phrased it to herself. . . . Over the dead body of her father! How could such a venture succeed? How could she ever have hoped that it would succeed? In that moment she saw her acts with the terrible vision of a Hebrew prophet.

She thought of the Square and of her life there with her mother and Constance. Never would her pride allow her to return to that life, not even if the worst happened to her that could happen. She was one of those who are prepared to pay without grumbling for what they have had.

There was a sound outside. She noticed that the dawn had begun. The door opened and disclosed Gerald.

They exchanged a searching glance, and Gerald shut the door. Gerald infected the air, but she perceived at once that he was sobered. His lip was bleeding.

"Mr. Chirac brought me home," she said.

"So it seems," said Gerald, curtly. "I asked you to wait for me. Didn't I say I should come back?"

He was adopting the injured magisterial tone of the man who is ridiculously trying to conceal from himself and others that he has recently behaved like an ass.

She resented the injustice. "I don't think you need talk like that," she said.

"Like what?" he bullied her, determined that she should be in the wrong.

And what a hard look on his pretty face!

Her prudence bade her accept the injustice. She was his. Rapt away from her own world, she was utterly dependent on his good nature.

"I knocked my chin against the damned balustrade, coming upstairs," said Gerald, gloomily.

She knew that was a lie. "Did you?" she replied kindly. "Let me bathe it."

CHAPTER III

An Ambition Satisfied

SHE went to sleep in misery. All the glory of her new life had been eclipsed. But when she woke up, a few hours later, in the large, velvety stateliness of the bedroom for which Gerald was paying so fantastic a price per day, she was in a brighter mood, and very willing to reconsider her verdicts. Her pride induced her to put Gerald in the right and herself in the wrong, for she was too proud to admit that she had married a charming and irresponsible fool. And, indeed, ought she not to put herself in the wrong? Gerald had told her to wait, and she had not waited. He had said that he should return to the restaurant, and he had returned. Why had she not waited? She had not waited because she had behaved like a simpleton. She had been terrified about nothing. Had she not been frequenting restaurants now for a month past? Ought not a married woman to be capable of waiting an hour in a restaurant for her lawful husband without looking a ninny? And as for Gerald's behaviour, how could he have acted differently? The other Englishman was obviously a brute and had sought a quarrel. His contradiction of Gerald's statements was extremely offensive. On being invited by the brute to go outside, what could Gerald do but comply? Not to have complied might have meant a fight in the restaurant, as the brute was certainly drunk. Compared to the brute, Gerald was not at all drunk, merely a little gay and talkative. Then Gerald's fib about his chin was natural; he simply wished to minimize the fuss and to spare her feelings. It was, in fact, just like Gerald to keep perfect silence as to what had passed between himself and the brute. However, she was convinced that Gerald, so lithe and quick, had given that great brute with his supercilious ways as good as he received, if not better.

And if she were a man and had asked her wife to wait in a restaurant, and the wife had gone home under the escort of another man, she would most assuredly be much more angry than Gerald had been. She was very glad that she had controlled herself and exercised a meek diplomacy. A quarrel had thus been avoided. Yes, the finish of the evening could not be called

a quarrel; after her nursing of his chin, nothing but a slight
coolness on his part had persisted.

She arose silently and began to dress, full of a determination
to treat Gerald as a good wife ought to treat a husband. Gerald did not stir; he was an excellent sleeper: one of those
organisms that never want to go to bed and never want to get
up. When her toilet was complete save for her bodice, there
was a knock at the door. She started.

"Gerald!" She approached the bed, and leaned her nude
bosom over her husband, and put her arms round his neck.
This method of being brought back to consciousness did not
displease him.

The knock was repeated. He gave a grunt.

"Some one's knocking at the door," she whispered.

"Then why don't you open it?" he asked dreamily.

"I'm not dressed, darling."

He looked at her. "Stick something on your shoulders, girl!"
said he. "What does it matter?"

There she was, being a simpleton again, despite her resolution!

She obeyed, and cautiously opened the door, standing behind it.

A middle-aged whiskered servant, in a long white apron,
announced matters in French which passed her understanding.
But Gerald had heard from the bed, and he replied.

"Bien, monsieur!" The servant departed, with a bow, down
the obscure corridor.

"It's Chirac," Gerald explained when she had shut the door.
"I was forgetting I asked him to come and have lunch with us,
early. He's waiting in the drawing-room. Just put your bodice
on, and go and talk to him till I come."

He jumped out of bed, and then, standing in his night-garb,
stretched himself and terrifically yawned.

"Me?" Sophia questioned.

"Who else?" said Gerald, with that curious satiric dryness
which he would sometimes import into his tone.

"But I can't speak French!" she protested.

"I didn't suppose you could," said Gerald, with an increase
of dryness; "but you know as well as I do that he can speak
English."

"Oh, very well, then!" she murmured with agreeable alacrity.

Evidently Gerald had not yet quite recovered from his legitimate displeasure of the night. He minutely examined his mouth in the glass of the Louis Philippe wardrobe. It showed scarcely a trace of battle.

"I say!" he stopped her, as, nervous at the prospect before her, she was leaving the room. "I was thinking of going to Auxerre to-day."

"Auxerre?" she repeated, wondering under what circumstances she had recently heard that name. Then she remembered: it was the place of execution of the murderer Rivain.

"Yes," he said. "Chirac has to go. He's on a newspaper now. He was an architect when I knew him. He's got to go and he thinks himself jolly lucky. So I thought I'd go with him."

The truth was that he had definitely arranged to go.

"Not to see the execution?" she stammered.

"Why not? I've always wanted to see an execution, especially with the guillotine. And executions are public in France. It's quite the proper thing to go to them."

"But why do you want to see an execution?"

"It just happens that I do want to see an execution. It's a fancy of mine, that's all. I don't know that any reason is necessary," he said, pouring out water into the diminutive ewer.

She was aghast. "And shall you leave me here alone?"

"Well," said he, "I don't see why my being married should prevent me from doing something that I've always wanted to do. Do you?"

"Oh no!" she eagerly concurred.

"That's all right," he said. "You can do exactly as you like. Either stay here, or come with me. If you go to Auxerre there's no need at all for you to see the execution. It's an interesting old town—cathedral and so on. But of course if you can't bear to be in the same town as a guillotine, I'll go alone. I shall come back to-morrow."

It was plain where his wish lay. She stopped the phrases that came to her lips, and did her best to dismiss the thoughts which prompted them.

"Of course I'll go," she said quietly. She hesitated, and then went up to the washstand and kissed a part of his cheek that was not soapy. That kiss, which comforted and somehow reassured her, was the expression of a surrender whose monstrousness she would not admit to herself.

In the rich and dusty drawing-room, Chirac and Chirac's exquisite formalities awaited her. Nobody else was there.

"My husband . . ." she began, smiling and blushing. She liked Chirac.

It was the first time she had had the opportunity of using that word to other than a servant. It soothed her and gave her confidence. She perceived after a few moments that Chirac did genuinely admire her; more, that she inspired him with something that resembled awe. Speaking very slowly and distinctly she said that she should travel with her husband to Auxerre, as he saw no objection to that course; implying that if he saw no objection she was perfectly satisfied. Chirac was concurrence itself. In five minutes it seemed to be the most natural and proper thing in the world that, on her honeymoon, she should be going with her husband to a particular town because a notorious murderer was about to be decapitated there in public.

"My husband has always wanted to see an execution," she said, later. "It would be a pity to . . ."

"As psychological experience," replied Chirac, pronouncing the *p* of the adjective, "it will be very *interessant*. . . . To observe one's self, in such circumstances . . ." He smiled enthusiastically.

She thought how strange even nice Frenchmen were. Imagine going to an execution in order to observe yourself!

ii

What continually impressed Sophia as strange, in the behaviour not only of Gerald but of Chirac and other people with whom she came into contact, was its quality of casualness. She had all her life been accustomed to see enterprises, even minor ones, well pondered and then carefully schemed beforehand. In St. Luke's Square there was always, in every head, a sort of time-table of existence prepared at least one week in advance. But in Gerald's world nothing was prearranged. Elaborate affairs were decided in a moment and undertaken with extraordinary lightness. Thus the excursion to Auxerre! During lunch scarcely a word was said as to it; the conversation, in English for Sophia's advantage, turning, as usual under such circumstances, upon the difficulty of languages and the differences between countries. Nobody would have guessed that any member of the party had any preoccupation whatever for the rest of the day. The meal was delightful to Sophia; not merely did she find Chirac comfortingly kind and sincere, but Gerald was restored to the perfection of his charm and his good humour. Then suddenly, in the midst of coffee, the question of trains loomed up like a swift crisis. In five minutes Chirac had departed—whether to his office or his home Sophia did not understand, and within a quarter of an hour she and Gerald were driving rapidly to the Gare de Lyon, Gerald stuffing into his pocket a large envelope full of papers which he had received by registered post. They caught the train by about a minute, and Chirac by a few seconds. Yet neither he nor Gerald seemed to envisage the risk of inconvenience and annoyance which they had incurred and escaped. Chirac chattered through the window with another journalist in the next compartment. When she had leisure to examine him, Sophia saw that he must have called at his home to put on old clothes. Everybody except herself and Gerald seemed to travel in his oldest clothes.

The train was hot, noisy, and dusty. But, one after another, all three of them fell asleep and slept heavily, calmly, like healthy and exhausted young animals. Nothing could disturb them for more than a moment. To Sophia it appeared to be by simple chance that Chirac aroused himself and them at Laroche and sleepily seized her valise and got them all out on the platform, where they yawned and smiled, full of the deep, half-realized satisfaction of repose. They drank nectar from a wheeled buffet, drank it eagerly, in thirsty gulps, and sighed with pleasure and relief, and Gerald threw down a coin, refusing change with a lord's gesture. The local train to Auxerre was full, and with a varied and sinister cargo. At length they were in the zone of the waiting guillotine. The rumour ran that the executioner was on the train. No one had seen him; no one was sure of recognizing him, but everyone hugged the belief that he was on the train. Although the sun was sinking the heat seemed not to abate. Attitudes grew more limp, more abandoned. Soot and prickly dust flew in unceasingly at the open windows. The train stopped at Bonnard, Chemilly, and Moneteau, each time before a waiting crowd that invaded it. And at last, in the great station at Auxerre, it poured out an incredible mass of befouled humanity that spread over everything like an inundation. Sophia was frightened. Gerald left the initiative to Chirac, and Chirac took her arm and led her forward, looking behind him to see that Gerald followed with the valise. Frenzy seemed to reign in Auxerre.

The driver of a cab demanded ten francs for transporting them to the Hotel de l'Epée.

"Bah!" scornfully exclaimed Chirac, in his quality of experienced Parisian who is not to be exploited by heavy-witted provincials.

But the driver of the next cab demanded twelve francs.

"Jump in," said Gerald to Sophia. Chirac lifted his eyebrows.

At the same moment a tall, stout man with the hard face of a flourishing scoundrel, and a young, pallid girl on his arm, pushed aside both Gerald and Chirac and got into the cab with his companion.

Chirac protested, telling him that the cab was already engaged.

The usurper scowled and swore, and the young girl laughed boldly.

Sophia, shrinking, expected her escort to execute justice heroic and final; but she was disappointed.

"Brute!" murmured Chirac, and shrugged his shoulders, as the carriage drove off, leaving them foolish on the kerb.

By this time all the other cabs had been seized. They walked to the Hotel de l'Epée, jostled by the crowd, Sophia and Chirac in front, and Gerald following with the valise, whose weight caused him to lean over to the right and his left arm to rise. The avenue was long, straight, and misty with a floating dust. Sophia had a vivid sense of the romantic. They saw towers and spires, and Chirac talked to her slowly and carefully of the cathedral and the famous churches. He said that the stained glass was marvellous, and with much care he catalogued for her all the things she must visit. They crossed a river. She felt as though she was stepping into the middle age. At intervals Gerald changed the valise from hand to hand; obstinately, he would not let Chirac touch it. They struggled upwards, through narrow curving streets.

"Voilà!" said Chirac.

They were in front of the Hotel de l'Epée. Across the street was a café crammed with people. Several carriages stood in front. The Hotel de l'Epée had a reassuring air of mellow respectability, such as Chirac had claimed for it. He had suggested this hotel for Madame Scales because it was not near

the place of execution. Gerald had said, "Of course! Of course!"
Chirac, who did not mean to go to bed, required no room for
himself.

The Hotel de l'Epée had one room to offer, at the price of
twenty-five francs.

Gerald revolted at the attempted imposition. "A nice thing!"
he grumbled, "that ordinary travellers can't get a decent room
at a decent price just because some one's going to be guillo-
tined to-morrow! We'll try elsewhere!"

His features expressed disgust, but Sophia fancied that he
was secretly pleased.

They swaggered out of the busy stir of the hotel, as those
must who, having declined to be swindled, wish to preserve their
importance in the face of the world. In the street a cabman
solicited them, and filled them with hope by saying that he
knew of a hotel that might suit them and would drive them
there for five francs. He furiously lashed his horse. The mere
fact of being in a swiftly moving carriage which wayfarers had
to avoid nimbly, maintained their spirits. They had a near
glimpse of the cathedral. The cab halted with a bump, in a
small square, in front of a repellent building which bore the
sign, "Hotel de Vezelay." The horse was bleeding. Gerald instructed Sophia to remain where she was, and he and Chirac
went up four stone steps into the hotel. Sophia, stared at by
loose crowds that were promenading, gazed about her, and saw
that all the windows of the square were open and most of them
occupied by people who laughed and chattered. Then there
was a shout: Gerald's voice. He had appeared at a window on
the second floor of the hotel with Chirac and a very fat woman.
Chirac saluted, and Gerald laughed carelessly, and nodded.

"It's all right," said Gerald, having descended.

"How much do they ask?" Sophia inquired indiscreetly.

Gerald hesitated, and looked self-conscious. "Thirty-five
francs," he said. "But I've had enough of driving about. It
seems we're lucky to get it even at that."

And Chirac shrugged his shoulders as if to indicate that the
situation and the price ought to be accepted philosophically.
Gerald gave the driver five francs. He examined the piece and
demanded a pourboire.

"Oh! Damn!" said Gerald, and, because he had no smaller
change, parted with another two francs.

"Is any one coming out for this damned valise?" Gerald

demanded, like a tyrant whose wrath would presently fall if the populace did not instantly set about minding their p's and q's.

But nobody emerged, and he was compelled to carry the bag himself.

The hotel was dark and malodorous, and every room seemed to be crowded with giggling groups of drinkers.

"We can't both sleep in this bed, surely," said Sophia when, Chirac having remained downstairs, she faced Gerald in a small, mean bedroom.

"You don't suppose I shall go to bed, do you?" said Gerald, rather brusquely. "It's for you. We're going to eat now. Look sharp."

iii

It was night. She lay in the narrow, crimson-draped bed. The heavy crimson curtains had been drawn across the dirty lace curtains of the window, but the lights of the little square faintly penetrated through chinks into the room. The sounds of the square also penetrated, extraordinarily loud and clear, for the unabated heat had compelled her to leave the window open. She could not sleep. Exhausted though she was, there was no hope of her being able to sleep.

Once again she was profoundly depressed. She remembered the dinner with horror. The long, crowded table, with semi-circular ends, in the oppressive and reeking dining-room lighted by oil-lamps! There must have been at least forty people at that table. Most of them ate disgustingly, as noisily as pigs, with the ends of the large coarse napkins tucked in at their necks. All the service was done by the fat woman whom she had seen at the window with Gerald, and a young girl whose demeanour was candidly brazen. Both these creatures were slatterns. Everything was dirty. But the food was good. Chirac and Gerald were agreed that the food was good, as well as the wine. "Remarquable!" Chirac had said, of the wine. Sophia, however, could neither eat nor drink with relish. She was afraid. The company shocked her by its gestures alone. It was very heterogeneous in appearance, some of the diners being well dressed, approaching elegance, and others shabby. But all the faces, to the youngest, were brutalized, corrupt, and shameless. The juxtaposition of old men and young women was odious to her, especially when those pairs kissed, as they did frequently towards the end of the meal. Happily she was placed between Chirac and Gerald. That situation seemed to shelter her even from the conversation. She would have comprehended nothing of the conversation, had it not been for the presence of a middle-aged Englishman who sat at the opposite end of the table with a youngish, stylish Frenchwoman whom she had seen at Sylvain's on the previous night. The Englishman was evidently under a promise to teach English to the Frenchwoman. He kept translating for her into English, slowly and distinctly, and she would repeat the phrases after him, with strange contortions of the mouth.

Thus Sophia gathered that the talk was exclusively about assassinations, executions, criminals, and executioners. Some of the people there made a practice of attending every execution. They were fountains of interesting gossip, and the lions of the meal. There was a woman who could recall the dying words of all the victims of justice for twenty years past. The table roared with hysteric laughter at one of this woman's anecdotes. Sophia learned that she had related how a criminal had said to the priest who was good-naturedly trying to screen the sight of the guillotine from him with his body: "Stand away now, parson. Haven't I paid to see it?" Such was the Englishman's rendering. The wages of the executioners and their assistants were discussed, and differences of opinions led to ferocious arguments. A young and dandiacal fellow told, as a fact which he was ready to vouch for with a pistol, how Cora Pearl, the renowned English courtesan, had through her influence over a prefect of police succeeded in visiting a criminal alone in his cell during the night preceding his execution, and had only quitted him an hour before the final summons. The tale won the honours of the dinner. It was regarded as truly impressive, and inevitably it led to the general inquiry: what could the highest personages in the empire see to admire in that red-haired Englishwoman? And of course Rivain himself, the handsome homicide, the centre and hero of the fête, was never long out of the conversation. Several of the diners had seen him; one or two knew him and could give amazing details of his prowess as a man of pleasure. Despite his crime, he seemed to be the object of sincere idolatry. It was said positively that a niece of his victim had been promised a front place at the execution.

Apropos of this, Sophia gathered, to her intense astonish-

ment and alarm, that the prison was close by and that the
execution would take place at the corner of the square itself
in which the hotel was situated. Gerald must have known; he
had hidden it from her. She regarded him sideways, with distrust. As the dinner finished, Gerald's pose of calm, disinterested, scientific observer of humanity gradually broke down.
He could not maintain it in front of the increasing license of
the scene round the table. He was at length somewhat ashamed
of having exposed his wife to the view of such an orgy; his
restless glance carefully avoided both Sophia and Chirac. The
latter, whose unaffected simplicity of interest in the affair had
more than anything helped to keep Sophia in countenance, observed the change in Gerald and Sophia's excessive discomfort,
and suggested that they should leave the table without waiting
for the coffee. Gerald agreed quickly. Thus had Sophia been
released from the horror of the dinner. She did not understand how a man so thoughtful and kindly as Chirac—he had
bidden her good night with the most distinguished courtesy—
could tolerate, much less pleasurably savour, the gluttonous,
drunken, and salacious debauchery of the Hotel de Vezelay;
but his theory was, so far as she could judge from his imperfect English, that whatever existed might be admitted and
examined by serious persons interested in the study of human
nature. His face seemed to say: "Why not?" His face seemed
to say to Gerald and to herself: "If this incommodes you, what
did you come for?"

Gerald had left her at the bedroom door with a self-conscious
nod. She had partly undressed and lain down, and instantly
the hotel had transformed itself into a kind of sounding-box.
It was as if, beneath and within all the noises of the square,
every movement in the hotel reached her ears through cardboard walls: distant shoutings and laughter below; rattlings
of crockery below; stampings up and down stairs; stealthy
creepings up and down stairs; brusque calls; fragments of
song, whisperings; long sighs suddenly stifled; mysterious
groans as of torture, broken by a giggle; quarrels and bicker-
ing,—she was spared nothing in the strangely resonant darkness.

Then there came out of the little square a great uproar and
commotion, with shrieks, and under the shrieks a confused din.
In vain she pressed her face into the pillow and listened to the
irregular, prodigious noise of her eyelashes as they scraped the

rough linen. The thought had somehow introduced itself into her head that she must arise and go to the window and see all that was to be seen. She resisted. She said to herself that the idea was absurd, that she did not *wish* to go to the window. Nevertheless, while arguing with herself, she well knew that resistance to the thought was useless and that ultimately her legs would obey its command.

When ultimately she yielded to the fascination and went to the window and pulled aside one of the curtains, she had a feeling of relief.

The cool, grey beginnings of dawn were in the sky, and every detail of the square was visible. Without exception all the windows were wide open and filled with sightseers. In the background of many windows were burning candles or lamps that the far distant approach of the sun was already killing. In front of these, on the frontier of two mingling lights, the attentive figures of the watchers were curiously silhouetted. On the red-tiled roofs, too, was a squatted population. Below, a troop of gendarmes, mounted on caracoling horses stretched in line across the square, was gradually sweeping the entire square of a packed, gesticulating, cursing crowd. The operation of this immense besom was very slow. As the spaces of the square were cleared they began to be dotted by privileged persons, journalists or law officers or their friends, who walked to and fro in conscious pride; among them Sophia descried Gerald and Chirac, strolling arm-in-arm and talking to two elaborately clad girls, who were also arm-in-arm.

Then she saw a red reflection coming from one of the side streets of which she had a vista; it was the swinging lantern of a waggon drawn by a gaunt grey horse. The vehicle stopped at the end of the square from which the besom had started, and it was immediately surrounded by the privileged, who, however, were soon persuaded to stand away. The crowd amassed now at the principal inlets of the square, gave a formidable cry and burst into the refrain—

> "Le voilà!
> Nicolas!
> Ah! Ah! Ah!"

The clamour became furious as a group of workmen in blue blouses drew piece by piece all the components of the guillotine from the waggon and laid them carefully on the ground, under the superintendence of a man in a black frock-coat and a silk hat with broad flat brims; a little fussy man of nervous gestures. And presently the red columns had risen upright from the ground and were joined at the top by an acrobatic climber. As each part was bolted and screwed to the growing machine the man in the high hat carefully tested it. In a short time that seemed very long, the guillotine was finished save for the triangular steel blade which lay shining on the ground, a cynosure. The executioner pointed to it, and two men picked it up and slipped it into its groove, and hoisted it to the summit of the machine. The executioner peered at it interminably amid a universal silence. Then he actuated the mechanism, and the mass of metal fell with a muffled, reverberating thud. There were a few faint shrieks, blended together, and then an overpowering racket of cheers, shouts, hootings, and fragments of song. The blade was again lifted, instantly reproducing silence, and again it fell, liberating a new bedlam. The executioner made a movement of satisfaction. Many women at the windows clapped enthusiastically, and the gendarmes had to fight brutally against the fierce pressure of the crowd. The workmen doffed their blouses and put on coats, and Sophia was disturbed to see them coming in single file towards the hotel, followed by the executioner in the silk hat.

iv

There was a tremendous opening of doors in the Hotel de Vezelay, and much whispering on thresholds, as the executioner and his band entered solemnly. Sophia heard them tramp upstairs; they seemed to hesitate, and then apparently went into a room on the same landing as hers. A door banged. But Sophia could hear the regular sound of new voices talking, and then the rattling of glasses on a tray. The conversation which came to her from the windows of the hotel now showed a great increase of excitement. She could not see the people at these neighbouring windows without showing her own head, and this she would not do. The boom of a heavy bell striking the hour vibrated over the roofs of the square; she supposed that it might be the cathedral clock. In a corner of the square she saw Gerald talking vivaciously alone with one of the two girls who had been together. She wondered vaguely how such a girl had been brought up, and what her parents thought—or knew! And she was conscious of an intense pride in herself, of a measureless haughty feeling of superiority.

Her eye caught the guillotine again, and was held by it. Guarded by gendarmes, that tall and simple object did most menacingly dominate the square with its crude red columns. Tools and a large open box lay on the ground beside it. The enfeebled horse in the waggon had an air of dozing on his twisted legs. Then the first rays of the sun shot lengthwise across the square at the level of the chimneys; and Sophia noticed that nearly all the lamps and candles had been extinguished. Many people at the windows were yawning; they laughed foolishly after they had yawned. Some were eating and drinking. Some were shouting conversations from one house to another. The mounted gendarmes were still pressing back the feverish crowds that growled at all the inlets to the square. She saw Chirac walking to and fro alone. But she could not find Gerald. He could not have left the square. Perhaps he had returned to the hotel and would come up to see if she was comfortable or if she needed anything. Guiltily she sprang back into bed. When last she had surveyed the room it had been dark; now it was bright and every detail stood clear. Yet she had the sensation of having been at the window only a few minutes.

She waited. But Gerald did not come. She could hear chiefly the steady hum of the voices of the executioner and his aids. She reflected that the room in which they were must be at the back. The other sounds in the hotel grew less noticeable. Then, after an age, she heard a door open, and a low voice say something commandingly in French, and then a "Oui, monsieur," and a general descent of the stairs. The executioner and his aids were leaving. "You," cried a drunken English voice from an upper floor—it was the middle-aged Englishman translating what the executioner had said—"you, you will take the head." Then a rough laugh, and the repeating voice of the Englishman's girl, still pursuing her studies in English: "You will take ze 'ead. Yess, sair." And another laugh. At length quiet reigned in the hotel. Sophia said to herself: "I won't stir from this bed till it's all over and Gerald comes back!"

She dozed, under the sheet, and was awakened by a tremendous shrieking, growling, and yelling: a phenomenon of human bestiality that far surpassed Sophia's narrow experiences. Shut up though she was in a room, perfectly secure, the mad fury of that crowd, balked at the inlets to the square, thrilled and intimidated her. It sounded as if they would be capable of tearing the very horses to pieces. "I must stay where I am," she murmured. And even while saying it she rose and went to the window again and peeped out. The torture involved was extreme, but she had not sufficient force within her to resist the fascination. She stared greedily into the bright square. The first thing she saw was Gerald coming out of a house opposite, followed after a few seconds by the girl with whom he had previously been talking. Gerald glanced hastily up at the façade of the hotel, and then approached as near as he could to the red columns, in front of which were now drawn a line of gendarmes with naked swords. A second and larger waggon, with two horses, waited by the side of the other one. The racket beyond the square continued and even grew louder. But the couple of hundred persons within the cordons, and all the inhabitants of the windows, drunk and sober, gazed in a fixed and sinister enchantment at the region of the guillotine, as Sophia gazed. "I cannot stand this!" she told herself in horror, but she could not move; she could not move even her eyes.

At intervals the crowd would burst out in a violent staccato—

"Le voilà!
Nicolas!
Ah! Ah! Ah!"

And the final "Ah" was devilish.

Then a gigantic passionate roar, the culmination of the mob's fierce savagery, crashed against the skies. The line of maddened horses swerved and reared, and seemed to fall on the furious multitude while the statue-like gendarmes rocked over them. It was a last effort to break the cordon, and it failed.

From the little street at the rear of the guillotine appeared a priest, walking backwards, and holding a crucifix high in his right hand, and behind him came the handsome hero, his body all crossed with cords, between two wardens, who pressed against him and supported him on either side. He was certainly very young. He lifted his chin gallantly, but his face was incredibly white. Sophia discerned that the priest was trying to hide the sight of the guillotine from the prisoner with his body, just as in the story which she had heard at dinner.

Except the voice of the priest, indistinctly rising and falling in the prayer for the dying, there was no sound in the square or its environs. The windows were now occupied by groups turned to stone with distended eyes fixed on the little procession. Sophia had a tightening of the throat, and the hand trembled by which she held the curtain. The central figure did not seem to her to be alive; but rather a doll, a marionette wound up to imitate the action of a tragedy. She saw the priest offer the crucifix to the mouth of the marionette, which with a clumsy unhuman shoving of its corded shoulders butted the thing away. And as the procession turned and stopped she could plainly see that the marionette's nape and shoulders were bare, his shirt having been slit. It was horrible. "Why do I stay here?" she asked herself hysterically. But she did not stir. The victim had disappeared now in the midst of a group of men. Then she perceived him prone under the red column, between the grooves. The silence was now broken only by the tinkling of the horses' bits in the corners of the square. The line of gendarmes in front of the scaffold held their swords tightly and looked over their noses, ignoring the privileged groups that peered almost between their shoulders.

And Sophia waited, horror-struck. She saw nothing but the gleaming triangle of metal that was suspended high above the prone, attendant victim. She felt like a lost soul, torn too soon from shelter, and exposed for ever to the worst hazards of destiny. Why was she in this strange, incomprehensible town, foreign and inimical to her, watching with agonized glance this cruel, obscene spectacle? Her sensibilities were all a bleeding mass of wounds. Why? Only yesterday, and she had been an innocent, timid creature in Bursley, in Axe, a foolish creature who deemed the concealment of letters a supreme excitement. Either that day or this day was not real. Why was she imprisoned alone in that odious, indescribably odious hotel, with no one to soothe and comfort her, and carry her away?

The distant bell boomed once. Then a monosyllabic voice sounded, sharp, low, nervous; she recognized the voice of the executioner, whose name she had heard but could not remember. There was a clicking noise . . .

She shrank down to the floor in terror and loathing, and hid her face, and shuddered. Shriek after shriek, from various

windows, rang on her ears in a fusillade; and then the mad
yell of the penned crowd, which, like herself, had not seen but
had heard, extinguished all other noise. Justice was done. The
great ambition of Gerald's life was at last satisfied.

v

Later, amid the stir of the hotel, there came a knock at her
door, impatient and nervous. Forgetting, in her tribulation,
that she was without her bodice, she got up from the floor in a
kind of miserable dream, and opened. Chirac stood on the
landing, and he had Gerald by the arm. Chirac looked worn
out, curiously fragile and pathetic; but Gerald was the very
image of death. The attainment of ambition had utterly destroyed his equilibrium; his curiosity had proved itself stronger
than his stomach. Sophia would have pitied him had she in
that moment been capable of pity. Gerald staggered past her
into the room, and sank with a groan on to the bed. Not long
since he had been proudly conversing with impudent women.
Now, in swift collapse, he was as flaccid as a sick hound and as
disgusting as an aged drunkard.

"He is some little *souffrant*," said Chirac, weakly.

Sophia perceived in Chirac's tone the assumption that of
course her present duty was to devote herself to the task of
restoring her shamed husband to his manly pride.

"And what about me?" she thought bitterly.

The fat woman ascended the stairs like a tottering blanc-
mange, and began to gabble to Sophia, who understood nothing
whatever.

"She wants sixty francs," Chirac said, and in answer to
Sophia's startled question, he explained that Gerald had agreed
to pay a hundred francs for the room, which was the landlady's
own—fifty francs in advance and the fifty after the execution.
The other ten was for the dinner. The landlady, distrusting
the whole of her *clientèle*, was collecting her accounts instantly
on the completion of the spectacle.

Sophia made no remark as to Gerald's lie to her. Indeed,
Chirac had heard it. She knew Gerald for a glib liar to others,
but she was naïvely surprised when he practised upon herself.

"Gerald! Do you hear?" she said coldly.

The amateur of severed heads only groaned.

With a movement of irritation she went to him and felt in his pockets for his purse; he acquiesced, still groaning. Chirac helped her to choose and count the coins.

The fat woman, appeased, pursued her way.

"Good-bye, madame!" said Chirac, with his customary courtliness, transforming the landing of the hideous hotel into some imperial antechamber.

"Are you going away?" she asked, in surprise. Her distress was so obvious that it tremendously flattered him. He would have stayed if he could. But he had to return to Paris to write and deliver his article.

"To-morrow, I hope!" he murmured sympathetically, kissing her hand. The gesture atoned somewhat for the sordidness of her situation, and even corrected the faults of her attire. Always afterwards it seemed to her that Chirac was an old and intimate friend; he had successfully passed through the ordeal of seeing "the wrong side" of the stuff of her life.

She shut the door on him with a lingering glance, and reconciled herself to her predicament.

Gerald slept. Just as he was, he slept heavily.

This was what he had brought her to, then! The horrors of the night, of the dawn, and of the morning! Ineffable suffering and humiliation; anguish and torture that could never be forgotten! And after a fatuous vigil of unguessed license, he had tottered back, an offensive beast, to sleep the day away in that filthy chamber! He did not possess even enough spirit to play the *rôle* of roysterer to the end. And she was bound to him; far, far from any other human aid; cut off irrevocably by her pride from those who perhaps would have protected her from his dangerous folly. The deep conviction henceforward formed a permanent part of her general consciousness that he was simply an irresponsible and thoughtless fool! He was without *sense*. Such was her brilliant and godlike husband, the man who had given her the right to call herself a married woman! He was a fool. With all her ignorance of the world she could see that nobody but an arrant imbecile could have brought her to the present pass. Her native sagacity revolted. Gusts of feeling came over her in which she could have thrashed him into the realization of his responsibilities.

Sticking out of the breast-pocket of his soiled coat was the packet which he had received on the previous day. If he had not already lost it, he could only thank his luck. She took it.

There were English bank-notes in it for two hundred pounds, a letter from a banker, and other papers. With precautions against noise she tore the envelope and the letters and papers into small pieces, and then looked about for a place to hide them. A cupboard suggested itself. She got on a chair, and pushed the fragments out of sight on the topmost shelf, where they may well be to this day. She finished dressing, and then sewed the notes into the lining of her skirt. She had no silly, delicate notions about stealing. She obscurely felt that, in the care of a man like Gerald, she might find herself in the most monstrous, the most impossible dilemmas. Those notes, safe and secret in her skirt, gave her confidence, reassured her against the perils of the future, and endowed her with independence. The act was characteristic of her enterprise and of her fundamental prudence. It approached the heroic. And her conscience hotly defended its righteousness.

She decided that when he discovered his loss, she would merely deny all knowledge of the envelope, for he had not spoken a word to her about it. He never mentioned the details of money; he had a fortune. However, the necessity for this untruth did not occur. He made no reference whatever to his loss. The fact was, he thought he had been careless enough to let the envelope be filched from him during the excesses of the night.

All day till evening Sophia sat on a dirty chair, without food, while Gerald slept. She kept repeating to herself, in amazed resentment: "A hundred francs for this room! A hundred francs! And he hadn't the pluck to tell me!" She could not have expressed her contempt.

Long before sheer ennui forced her to look out of the window again, every sign of justice had been removed from the square. Nothing whatever remained in the heavy August sunshine save gathered heaps of filth where the horses had reared and caracoled.

CHAPTER IV

A CRISIS FOR GERALD

For a time there existed in the minds of both Gerald and Sophia the remarkable notion that twelve thousand pounds

represented the infinity of wealth, that this sum possessed
special magical properties which rendered it insensible to the
process of subtraction. It seemed impossible that twelve thousand pounds, while continually getting less, could ultimately
quite disappear. The notion lived longer in the mind of Gerald
than in that of Sophia; for Gerald would never look at a disturbing fact, whereas Sophia's gaze was morbidly fascinated
by such phenomena. In a life devoted to travel and pleasure
Gerald meant not to spend more than six hundred a year, the
interest on his fortune. Six hundred a year is less than two
pounds a day, yet Gerald never paid less than two pounds a
day in hotel bills alone. He hoped that he was living on a thousand a year, had a secret fear that he might be spending fifteen
hundred, and was really spending about two thousand five
hundred. Still, the remarkable notion of the inexhaustibility
of twelve thousand pounds always reassured him. The faster
the money went, the more vigorously this notion flourished in
Gerald's mind. When twelve had unaccountably dwindled to
three, Gerald suddenly decided that he must act, and in a few
months he lost two thousand on the Paris Bourse. The adventure frightened him, and in his panic he scattered a couple of
hundred in a frenzy of high living.

But even with only twenty thousand francs left out of three
hundred thousand, he held closely to the belief that natural
laws would in his case somehow be suspended. He had heard of
men who were once rich begging bread and sweeping crossings,
but he felt quite secure against such risks, by simple virtue of
the axiom that he was he. However, he meant to assist the axiom
by efforts to earn money. When these continued to fail, he
tried to assist the axiom by borrowing money; but he found
that his uncle had definitely done with him. He would have
assisted the axiom by stealing money, but he had neither the
nerve nor the knowledge to be a swindler; he was not even
sufficiently expert to cheat at cards.

He had thought in thousands. Now he began to think in
hundreds, in tens, daily and hourly. He paid two hundred
francs in railway fares in order to live economically in a village, and shortly afterwards another two hundred francs in
railway fares in order to live economically in Paris. And to
celebrate the arrival in Paris and the definite commencement
of an era of strict economy and serious search for a livelihood,
he spent a hundred francs on a dinner at the Maison Dorée and

two balcony stalls at the Gymnase. In brief, he omitted nothing —no act, no resolve, no self-deception—of the typical fool in his situation; always convinced that his difficulties and his wisdom were quite exceptional.

In May, 1870, on an afternoon, he was raging nervously to and fro in a three-cornered bedroom of a little hotel at the angle of the Rue Fontaine and the Rue Laval (now the Rue Victor Massé), within half a minute of the Boulevard de Clichy. It had come to that—an exchange of the "grand boulevard" for the "boulevard extérieur!" Sophia sat on a chair at the grimy window, glancing down in idle disgust of life at the Clichy-Odéon omnibus which was casting off its tip-horse at the corner of the Rue Chaptal. The noise of petty, hurried traffic over the bossy paving stones was deafening. The locality was not one to correspond with an ideal. There was too much humanity crowded into those narrow hilly streets; humanity seemed to be bulging out at the windows of the high houses. Gerald healed his pride by saying that this was, after all, the real Paris, and that the cookery was as good as could be got anywhere, pay what you would. He seldom ate a meal in the little salons on the first floor without becoming ecstatic upon the cookery. To hear him, he might have chosen the hotel on its superlative merits, without regard to expense. And with his air of use and custom, he did indeed look like a connoisseur of Paris who knew better than to herd with vulgar tourists in the pens of the Madeleine quarter. He was dressed with some distinction; good clothes, when put to the test, survive a change of fortune, as a Roman arch survives the luxury of departed empire. Only his collar, large V-shaped front, and wristbands, which bore the ineffaceable signs of cheap laundering, reflected the shadow of impending disaster.

He glanced sideways, stealthily, at Sophia. She, too, was still dressed with distinction; in the robe of black *faille*, the cashmere shawl, and the little black hat with its falling veil, there was no apparent symptom of beggary. She would have been judged as one of those women who content themselves with few clothes but good, and, greatly aided by nature, make a little go a long way. Good black will last for eternity; it discloses no secrets of modification and mending, and it is not transparent.

At last Gerald, resuming a suspended conversation, said as it were doggedly:

"I tell you I haven't got five francs altogether! and you can feel my pockets if you like," added the habitual liar in him, fearing incredulity.

"Well, and what do you expect *me* to do?" Sophia inquired. The accent, at once ironic and listless, in which she put this question, showed that strange and vital things had happened to Sophia in the four years which had elapsed since her marriage. It did really seem to her, indeed, that the Sophia whom Gerald had espoused was dead and gone, and that another Sophia had come into her body: so intensely conscious was she of a fundamental change in herself under the stress of continuous experience. And though this was but a seeming, though she was still the same Sophia more fully disclosed, it was a true seeming. Indisputably more beautiful than when Gerald had unwillingly made her his legal wife, she was now nearly twenty-four, and looked perhaps somewhat older than her age. Her frame was firmly set, her waist thicker, neither slim nor stout. The lips were rather hard, and she had a habit of tightening her mouth, on the same provocation as sends a snail into its shell. No trace was left of immature gawkiness in her gestures or of simplicity in her intonations. She was a woman of commanding and slightly arrogant charm, not in the least degree the charm of innocence and ingenuousness. Her eyes were the eyes of one who has lost her illusions too violently and too completely. Her gaze, coldly comprehending, implied familiarity with the abjectness of human nature. Gerald had begun and had finished her education. He had not ruined her, as a bad professor may ruin a fine voice, because her moral force immeasurably exceeded his; he had unwittingly produced a masterpiece, but it was a tragic masterpiece. Sophia was such a woman as, by a mere glance as she utters an opinion, will make a man say to himself, half in desire and half in alarm lest she reads him too: "By jove! she must have been through a thing or two. She knows what people are!"

The marriage was, of course, a calamitous folly. From the very first, from the moment when the commercial traveller had with incomparable rash fatuity thrown the paper pellet over the counter, Sophia's awakening commonsense had told her that in yielding to her instinct she was sowing misery and shame for herself; but she had gone on, as if under a spell. It had needed the irretrievableness of flight from home to begin the breaking of the trance. Once fully awakened out of the trance, she had recognized her marriage for what it was. She had made neither the best nor the worst of it. She had accepted Gerald as one accepts a climate. She saw again and again that he was irreclaimably a fool and a prodigy of irresponsibleness. She tolerated him, now with sweetness, now bitterly; accepting always his caprices, and not permitting herself to have wishes of her own. She was ready to pay the price of pride and of a moment's imbecility with a lifetime of self-repression. It was high, but it was the price. She had acquired nothing but an exceptionally good knowledge of the French language (she soon learnt to scorn Gerald's glib maltreatment of the tongue), and she had conserved nothing but her dignity. She knew that Gerald was sick of her, that he would have danced for joy to be rid of her; that he was constantly unfaithful; that he had long since ceased to be excited by her beauty. She knew also that at bottom he was a little afraid of her; here was her sole moral consolation. The thing that sometimes struck her as surprising was that he had not abandoned her, simply and crudely walked off one day and forgotten to take her with him.

They hated each other, but in different ways. She loathed him, and he resented her.

"What do I expect you to do?" he repeated after her. "Why don't you write home to your people and get some money out of them?"

Now that he had said what was in his mind, he faced her with a bullying swagger. Had he been a bigger man he might have tried to effect a physical bullying on her. One of his numerous reasons for resenting her was that she was the taller of the two. She made no reply.

"Now you needn't turn pale and begin all that fuss over again. What I'm suggesting is a perfectly reasonable thing. If I haven't got money I haven't got it. I can't invent it."

She perceived that he was ready for one of their periodical tempestuous quarrels. But that day she felt too tired and unwell to quarrel. His warning against a repetition of "fuss" had reference to the gastric dizziness from which she had been suffering for two years. It would take her usually after a meal. She did not swoon, but her head swam and she could not stand. She would sink down wherever she happened to be, and, her face alarmingly white, murmur faintly: "My salts." Within five minutes the attack had gone and left no trace. She had been through one just after lunch. He resented this affection. He detested being compelled to hand the smelling-bottle to her, and he would have avoided doing so if her pallor did not always alarm him. Nothing but this pallor convinced him that the attacks were not a deep ruse to impress him. His attitude invariably implied that she could cure the malady if she chose, but that through obstinacy she did not choose.

"Are you going to have the decency to answer my question, or aren't you?"

"What question?" Her vibrating voice was low and restrained.

"Will you write to your people?"

"For money?"

The sarcasm of her tone was diabolic. She could not have kept the sarcasm out of her tone; she did not attempt to keep it out. She cared little if it whipped him to fury. Did he imagine, seriously, that she would be capable of going on her knees to her family? She? Was he unaware that his wife was the proudest and the most obstinate woman on earth, that all her behaviour to him was the expression of her pride and her obstinacy? Ill and weak though she felt, she marshalled together all the forces of her character to defend her resolve never, never to eat the bread of humiliation. She was absolutely determined to be dead to her family. Certainly, one December, several years previously, she had seen English Christmas cards in an English shop in the Rue de Rivoli, and in a sudden gush of tenderness towards Constance, she had despatched a coloured greeting to Constance and her mother. And having initiated the custom, she had continued it. That was not like asking a kindness; it was bestowing a kindness. But except for the annual card, she was dead to St. Luke's Square. She was one of those daughters who disappear and are not discussed in the family circle. The thought of her immense foolishness, the little tender thoughts of Constance, some flitting souvenir, full of unwilling admiration, of a regal gesture of her mother,—these things only steeled her against any sort of resurrection after death.

And he was urging her to write home for money! Why, she would not even have paid a visit in splendour to St. Luke's Square. Never should they know what she had suffered! And especially her Aunt Harriet, from whom she had stolen!

"Will you write to your people?" he demanded yet again, emphasizing and separating each word.

"No," she said shortly, with terrific disdain.

"Why not?"

"Because I won't." The curling line of her lips, as they closed on each other, said all the rest; all the cruel truths about his unspeakable, inane, coarse follies, his laziness, his excesses, his lies, his deceptions, his bad faith, his truculence, his improvidence, his shameful waste and ruin of his life and hers. She doubted whether he realized his baseness and her wrongs, but if he could not read them in her silent contumely, she was too proud to recite them to him. She had never complained, save in uncontrolled moments of anger.

"If that's the way you're going to talk—all right!" he snapped, furious. Evidently he was baffled.

She kept silence. She was determined to see what he would do in the face of her inaction.

"You know, I'm not joking," he pursued. "We shall starve."

"Very well," she agreed. "We shall starve."

She watched him surreptitiously, and she was almost sure that he really had come to the end of his tether. His voice, which never alone convinced, carried a sort of conviction now. He was penniless. In four years he had squandered twelve thousand pounds, and had nothing to show for it except an enfeebled digestion and a tragic figure of a wife. One small point of satisfaction there was—and all the Baines in her clutched at it and tried to suck satisfaction from it—their manner of travelling about from hotel to hotel had made it impossible for Gerald to run up debts. A few debts he might have, unknown to her, but they could not be serious.

So they looked at one another, in hatred and despair. The inevitable had arrived. For months she had fronted it in bravado, not concealing from herself that it lay in waiting. For years he had been sure that though the inevitable might happen to others it could not happen to him. There it was! He was conscious of a heavy weight in his stomach, and she of a general numbness, enwrapping her fatigue. Even then he could not believe that it was true, this disaster. As for Sophia she was reconciling herself with bitter philosophy to the eccentricities of fate. Who would have dreamed that she, a young girl brought up, etc.? Her mother could not have improved the occasion more uncompromisingly than Sophia did—behind that disdainful mask.

"Well—if that's it . . . !" Gerald exploded at length, puffing. And he puffed out of the room and was gone in a second.

ii

She languidly picked up a book, the moment Gerald had departed, and tried to prove to herself that she was sufficiently in command of her nerves to read. For a long time reading had been her chief solace. But she could not read. She glanced round the inhospitable chamber, and thought of the hundreds of rooms—some splendid and some vile, but all arid in their unwelcoming aspect—through which she had passed in her progress from mad exultation to calm and cold disgust. The ceaseless din of the street annoyed her jaded ears. And a great wave of desire for peace, peace of no matter what kind, swept through her. And then her deep distrust of Gerald reawakened; in spite of his seriously desperate air, which had a quality of sincerity quite new in her experience of him, she could not be entirely sure that, in asserting utter penury, he was not after all merely using a trick to get rid of her.

She sprang up, threw the book on the bed, and seized her gloves. She would follow him, if she could. She would do what she had never done before—she would spy on him. Fighting against her lassitude, she descended the long winding stairs, and peeped forth from the doorway into the street. The ground floor of the hotel was a wine-shop; the stout landlord was lightly flicking one of the three little yellow tables that stood on the pavement. He smiled with his customary benevolence, and silently pointed in the direction of the Rue Notre Dame de Lorette. She saw Gerald down there in the distance. He was smoking a cigar.

He seemed to be a little man without a care. The smoke of the cigar came first round his left cheek and then round his right, sailing away into nothing. He walked with a gay spring, but not quickly, flourishing his cane as freely as the traffic of the pavement would permit, glancing into all the shop windows and into the eyes of all the women under forty. This was not at all the same man as had a moment ago been spitting angry menaces at her in the bedroom of the hotel. It was a fellow of blithe charm, ripe for any adventurous joys that destiny had to offer.

Supposing he turned round and saw her?

If he turned round and saw her and asked her what she was doing there in the street, she would tell him plainly: "I'm following you, to find out what you do."

But he did not turn. He went straight forward, deviating at the church, where the crowd became thicker, into the Rue du Faubourg Montmartre, and so to the boulevard, which he crossed. The whole city seemed excited and vivacious. Cannons boomed in slow succession, and flags were flying. Sophia had no conception of the significance of those guns, for, though she read a great deal, she never read a newspaper; the idea of opening a newspaper never occurred to her. But she was accustomed to the feverish atmosphere of Paris. She had lately seen regiments of cavalry flashing and prancing in the Luxembourg Gardens, and had much admired the fine picture. She accepted the booming as another expression of the high spirits that had to find vent somehow in this feverish empire. She so accepted it and forgot it, using all the panorama of the capital as a dim background for her exacerbated egoism.

She was obliged to walk slowly, because Gerald walked slowly. A beautiful woman, or any woman not positively haglike or venerable, who walks slowly in the streets of Paris becomes at once the cause of inconvenient desires, as representing the main objective on earth, always transcending in importance politics and affairs. Just as a true patriotic Englishman cannot be too busy to run after a fox, so a Frenchman is always ready to forsake all in order to follow a woman whom he has never before set eyes on. Many men thought twice about her, with her romantic Saxon mystery of temperament, and her Parisian clothes; but all refrained from affronting her, not in the least out of respect for the gloom in her face, but from an expert conviction that those rapt eyes were fixed immovably on another male. She walked unscathed amid the frothing hounds as though protected by a spell.

On the south side of the boulevard, Gerald proceeded down the Rue Montmartre, and then turned suddenly into the Rue Croissant. Sophia stopped and asked the price of some combs which were exposed outside a little shop. Then she went on, boldly passing the end of the Rue Croissant. No shadow of Gerald! She saw the signs of newspapers all along the street, *Le Bien Public, La Presse Libre, La Patrie.* There was a creamery at the corner. She entered it, asked for a cup of chocolate, and sat down. She wanted to drink coffee, but every doctor had forbidden coffee to her, on account of her attacks of dizziness. Then, having ordered chocolate, she felt that, on this occasion, when she had need of strength in her great fatigue, only coffee could suffice her, and she changed the order. She was close to the door, and Gerald could not escape her vigilance if he emerged at that end of the street. She drank the coffee with greedy satisfaction, and waited in the creamery till she began to feel conspicuous there. And then Gerald went by the door, within six feet of her. He turned the corner and continued his descent of the Rue Montmartre. She paid for her coffee and followed the chase. Her blood seemed to be up. Her lips were tightened, and her thought was: "Wherever he goes, I'll go, and I don't care what happens." She despised him. She felt herself above him. She felt that somehow, since quitting the hotel, he had been gradually growing more and more vile and meet to be exterminated. She imagined infamies as to the Rue Croissant. There was no obvious ground for this intensifying of her attitude towards him; it was merely the result of the chase. All that could be definitely charged against him was the smoking of a cigar.

He stepped into a tobacco-shop, and came out with a longer cigar than the first one, a more expensive article, stripped off its collar, and lighted it as a millionaire might have lighted it. This was the man who swore that he did not possess five francs.

She tracked him as far as the Rue de Rivoli, and then lost him. There were vast surging crowds in the Rue de Rivoli, and much bunting, and soldiers and gesticulatory policemen. The general effect of the street was that all things were brightly waving in the breeze. She was caught in the crowd as in the current of a stream, and when she tried to sidle out of it into a square, a row of smiling policemen barred her passage; she was a part of the traffic that they had to regulate. She drifted till the Louvre came into view. After all, Gerald had only strolled forth to see the sight of the day, whatever it might be! She knew not what it was. She had no curiosity about it. In the middle of all that thickening mass of humanity, staring with one accord at the vast monument of royal and imperial vanities, she thought, with her characteristic grimness, of the sacrifice of her whole career as a school-teacher for the chance of seeing Gerald once a quarter in the shop. She gloated over that, as a sick appetite will gloat over tainted food. And she saw the shop, and the curve of the stairs up to the showroom, and the pier-glass in the showroom.

Then the guns began to boom again, and splendid carriages swept one after another from under a majestic archway and glittered westward down a lane of spotless splendid uniforms. The carriages were laden with still more splendid uniforms, and with enchanting toilets. Sophia, in her modestly stylish black, mechanically noticed how much easier it was for attired women to sit in a carriage now that crinolines had gone. That was the sole impression made upon her by this glimpse of the last fête of the Napoleonic Empire. She knew not that the supreme pillars of imperialism were exhibiting themselves before her; and that the eyes of those uniforms and those toilettes were full of the legendary beauty of Eugénie, and their ears echoing to the long phrases of Napoleon the Third about his gratitude to his people for their confidence in him as shown by the plebiscite, and about the ratification of constitutional reforms guaranteeing order, and about the empire having been strengthened at its base, and about showing force by moderation and envisaging the future without fear, and about the bosom of peace and liberty, and the eternal continuance of his dynasty.

She just wondered vaguely what was afoot.

When the last carriage had rolled away, and the guns and acclamations had ceased, the crowd at length began to scatter. She was carried by it into the Place du Palais Royal, and in a few moments she managed to withdraw into the Rue des Bons Enfants and was free.

The coins in her purse amounted to three sous, and therefore, though she felt exhausted to the point of illness, she had to return to the hotel on foot. Very slowly she crawled upwards in the direction of the Boulevard, through the expiring gaiety of the city. Near the Bourse a fiacre overtook her, and in the fiacre were Gerald and a woman. Gerald had not seen her; he was talking eagerly to his ornate companion. All his body was alive. The fiacre was out of sight in a moment, but Sophia judged instantly the grade of the woman, who was evidently of the discreet class that frequented the big shops of an afternoon with something of their own to sell.

Sophia's grimness increased. The pace of the fiacre, her fatigued body, Gerald's delightful, careless vivacity, the attractive streaming veil of the nice, modest courtesan—everything conspired to increase it.

iii

Gerald returned to the bedroom which contained his wife and all else that he owned in the world at about nine o'clock that evening. Sophia was in bed. She had been driven to bed by weariness. She would have preferred to sit up to receive her husband, even if it had meant sitting up all night, but her body was too heavy for her spirit. She lay in the dark. She had eaten nothing. Gerald came straight into the room. He struck a match, which burned blue, with a stench, for several seconds, and then gave a clear, yellow flame. He lit a candle; and saw his wife.

"Oh!" he said; "you're there, are you?"

She offered no reply.

"Won't speak, eh?" he said. "Agreeable sort of wife! Well, have you made up your mind to do what I told you? I've come back especially to know."

She still did not speak.

He sat down, with his hat on, and stuck out his feet, wagging them to and fro on the heels.

"I'm quite without money," he went on. "And I'm sure your people will be glad to lend us a bit till I get some. Especially as it's a question of you starving as well as me. If I had enough to pay your fares to Bursley I'd pack you off. But I haven't."

She could only hear his exasperating voice. The end of the bed was between her eyes and his.

"Liar!" she said, with uncompromising distinctness. The word reached him barbed with all the poison of her contempt and disgust.

There was a pause.

"Oh! I'm a liar, am I? Thanks. I lied enough to get you, I'll admit. But you never complained of that. I remember beginning the New Year well with a thumping lie just to have a sight of you, my vixen. But you didn't complain then. I took you with only the clothes on your back. And I've spent every cent I had on you. And now I'm spun, you call me a liar."

She said nothing.

"However," he went on, "this is going to come to an end, this is!"

He rose, changed the position of the candle, putting it on a chest of drawers, and then drew his trunk from the wall, and knelt in front of it.

She gathered that he was packing his clothes. At first she did not comprehend his reference to beginning the New Year. Then his meaning revealed itself. That story to her mother about having been attacked by ruffians at the bottom of King Street had been an invention, a ruse to account plausibly for his presence on her mother's doorstep! And she had never suspected that the story was not true. In spite of her experience of his lying, she had never suspected that that particular statement was a lie. What a simpleton she was!

There was a continual movement in the room for about a quarter of an hour. Then a key turned in the lock of the trunk.

His head popped up over the foot of the bed. "This isn't a joke, you know," he said.

She kept silence.

"I give you one more chance. Will you write to your mother —or Constance if you like—or won't you?"

She scorned to reply in any way.

"I'm your husband," he said. "And it's your duty to obey me, particularly in an affair like this. I order you to write to your mother."

The corners of her lips turned downwards.

Angered by her mute obstinacy, he broke away from the bed with a sudden gesture.

"You do as you like," he cried, putting on his overcoat, "and I shall do as I like. You can't say I haven't warned you. It's your own deliberate choice, mind you! Whatever happens to you you've brought on yourself." He lifted and shrugged his shoulders to get the overcoat exactly into place on his shoulders.

She would not speak a word, not even to insist that she was indisposed.

He pushed his trunk outside the door, and returned to the bed.

"You understand," he said menacingly; "I'm off."

She looked up at the foul ceiling.

"Hm!" he sniffed, bringing his reserves of pride to combat the persistent silence that was damaging his dignity. And he went off, sticking his head forward like a pugilist.

"Here!" she muttered. "You're forgetting this."

He turned.

She stretched her hand to the night-table and held up a red circlet.

"What is it?"

"It's the bit of paper off the cigar you bought in the Rue Montmartre this afternoon," she answered, in a significant tone.

He hesitated, then swore violently, and bounced out of the room. He had made her suffer, but she was almost repaid for everything by that moment of cruel triumph. She exulted in it and never forgot it.

Five minutes later, the gloomy menial in felt slippers and alpaca jacket, who seemed to pass the whole of his life flitting in and out of bedrooms like a rabbit in a warren, carried Gerald's trunk downstairs. She recognized the peculiar tread of his slippers.

Then there was a knock at the door. The landlady entered, actuated by a legitimate curiosity.

"Madame is suffering?" the landlady began.

Sophia refused offers of food and nursing.

"Madame knows without doubt that monsieur has gone away?"

"Has he paid the bill?" Sophia asked bluntly.

"But yes, madame, till to-morrow. Then madame has want of nothing?"

"If you will extinguish the candle," said Sophia.

He had deserted her, then!

"All this," she reflected, listening in the dark to the ceaseless rattle of the street, "because mother and Constance wanted to see the elephant, and I had to go into father's room! I should never have caught sight of him from the drawing-room window!"

iv

She passed a night of physical misery, exasperated by the tireless rattling vitality of the street. She kept saying to herself: "I'm all alone now, and I'm going to be ill. I am ill."

She saw herself dying in Paris, and heard the expressions of
facile sympathy and idle curiosity drawn forth by the sight
of the dead body of this foreign woman in a little Paris hotel.
She reached the stage, in the gradual excruciation of her
nerves, when she was obliged to concentrate her agonized
mind on an intense and painful expectancy of the next new
noise, which when it came increased her torture and decreased
her strength to support it. She went through all the interminable dilatoriness of the dawn, from the moment when she
could scarcely discern the window to the moment when she
could read the word "Bock" on the red circlet of paper which
had tossed all night on the sea of the counterpane. She knew
she would never sleep again. She could not imagine herself
asleep; and then she was startled by a sound that seemed to
clash with the rest of her impressions. It was a knocking at
the door. With a start she perceived that she must have been
asleep.

"Enter," she murmured.

There entered the menial in alpaca. His waxen face showed
a morose commiseration. He noiselessly approached the bed
—he seemed to have none of the characteristics of a man, but
to be a creature infinitely mysterious and aloof from humanity
—and held out to Sophia a visiting card in his grey hand.

It was Chirac's card.

"Monsieur asked for monsieur," said the waiter. "And then,
as monsieur had gone away he demanded to see madame. He
says it is very important."

Her heart jumped, partly in vague alarm, and partly with
a sense of relief at this chance of speaking to some one whom
she knew. She tried to reflect rationally.

"What time is it?" she inquired.

"Eleven o'clock, madame."

This was surprising. The fact that it was eleven o'clock
destroyed the remains of her self-confidence. How could it
be eleven o'clock, with the dawn scarcely finished?

"He says it is very important," repeated the waiter, imperturbably and solemnly. "Will madame see him an instant?"

Between resignation and anticipation she said: "Yes."

"It is well, madame," said the waiter, disappearing without
a sound.

She sat up and managed to drag her *matinée* from a chair
and put it around her shoulders. Then she sank back from

weakness, physical and spiritual. She hated to receive Chirac in a bedroom, and particularly in that bedroom. But the hotel had no public room except the dining-room, which began to be occupied after eleven o'clock. Moreover, she could not possibly get up. Yes, on the whole she was pleased to see Chirac. He was almost her only acquaintance, assuredly the only being whom she could by any stretch of meaning call a friend, in the whole of Europe. Gerald and she had wandered to and fro, skimming always over the real life of nations, and never penetrating into it. There was no place for them, because they had made none. With the exception of Chirac, whom an accident of business had thrown into Gerald's company years before, they had no social relations. Gerald was not a man to make friends; he did not seem to need friends, or at any rate to feel the want of them. But, as chance had given him Chirac, he maintained the connection whenever they came to Paris. Sophia, of course, had not been able to escape from the solitude imposed by existence in hotels. Since her marriage she had never spoken to a woman in the way of intimacy. But once or twice she had approached intimacy with Chirac, whose wistful admiration for her always aroused into activity her desire to charm.

Preceded by the menial, he came into the room hurriedly, apologetically, with an air of acute anxiety. And as he saw her lying on her back, with flushed features, her hair disarranged, and only the grace of the silk ribbons of her *matinée* to mitigate the melancholy repulsiveness of her surroundings, that anxiety seemed to deepen.

"Dear madame," he stammered, "all my excuses!" He hastened to the bedside and kissed her hand—a little peck, according to his custom. "You are ill?"

"I have my migraine," she said. "You want Gerald?"

"Yes," he said diffidently. "He had promised——"

"He has left me," Sophia interrupted him in her weak and fatigued voice. She closed her eyes as she uttered the words.

"Left you?" He glanced round to be sure that the waiter had retired.

"Quitted me! Abandoned me! Last night!"

"Not possible!" he breathed.

She nodded. She felt intimate with him. Like all secretive persons, she could be suddenly expansive at times.

"It is serious?" he questioned.

"All that is most serious," she replied.

"And you ill! Ah, the wretch! Ah, the wretch! That, for example!" He waved his hat about.

"What is it you want, Chirac?" she demanded, in a confidential tone.

"Eh, well," said Chirac. "You do not know where he has gone?"

"No. What do you want?" she insisted.

He was nervous. He fidgeted. She guessed that, though warm with sympathy for her plight, he was preoccupied by interests and apprehensions of his own. He did not refuse her request temporarily to leave the astonishing matter of her situation in order to discuss the matter of his visit.

"Eh, well! He came to me yesterday afternoon in the Rue Croissant to borrow some money."

She understood then the object of Gerald's stroll on previous afternoon.

"I hope you didn't lend him any," she said.

"Eh, well! It was like this. He said he ought to have received five thousand francs yesterday morning, but that he had had a telegram that it would not arrive till to-day. And he had need of five hundred francs at once. I had not five hundred francs"—he smiled sadly, as if to insinuate that he did not handle such sums—"but I borrowed it from the cashbox of the journal. It is necessary, absolutely, that I should return it this morning." He spoke with increased seriousness. "Your husband said he would take a cab and bring me the money immediately on the arrival of the post this morning—about nine o'clock. Pardon me for deranging you with such a——"

He stopped. She could see that he really was grieved to "derange" her, but that circumstances pressed.

"At my paper," he murmured, "it is not so easy as that to—in fine——!"

Gerald had genuinely been at his last francs. He had not lied when she thought he had lied. The nakedness of his character showed now. Instantly upon the final and definite cessation of the lawful supply of money, he had set his wits to obtain money unlawfully. He had, in fact, simply stolen it from Chirac, with the ornamental addition of endangering Chirac's reputation and situation—as a sort of reward to Chirac for the kindness! And, further, no sooner had he got hold of the money than it had intoxicated him, and he had yielded to the first fatuous temptation. He had no sense of responsibility, no scruple. And as for common prudence—had he not risked permanent disgrace and even prison for a paltry sum which he would certainly squander in two or three days? Yes, it was indubitable that he would stop at nothing, at nothing whatever.

"You did not know that he was coming to me?" asked Chirac, pulling his short, silky brown beard.

"No," Sophia answered.

"But he said that you had charged him with your friendlinesses to me!" He nodded his head once or twice, sadly but candidly accepting, in his quality of a Latin, the plain facts of human nature—reconciling himself to them at once.

Sophia revolted at this crowning detail of the structure of Gerald's rascality.

"It is fortunate that I can pay you," she said.

"But——" he tried to protest.

"I have quite enough money."

She did not say this to screen Gerald, but merely from *amour-propre.* She would not let Chirac think that she was the wife of a man bereft of all honour. And so she clothed Gerald with the rag of having, at any rate, not left her in destitution as well as in sickness. Her assertion seemed a strange one, in view of the fact that he had abandoned her on the previous evening—that is to say, immediately after the borrowing from Chirac. But Chirac did not examine the statement.

"Perhaps he has the intention to send me the money. Perhaps, after all, he is now at the offices——"

"No," said Sophia. "He is gone. Will you go downstairs and wait for me. We will go together to Cook's office. It is English money I have."

"Cook's?" he repeated. The word now so potent had then little significance. "But you are ill. You cannot——"

"I feel better."

She did. Or rather, she felt nothing except the power of her resolve to remove the painful anxiety from that wistful brow. The shame of the trick played on Chirac awakened new forces in her. She dressed in a physical torment which, however, had no more reality than a nightmare. She searched in a place where even an inquisitive husband would not think of looking, and then, painfully, she descended the long stairs, holding to

the rail, which swam round and round her, carrying the whole
staircase with it. "After all," she thought, "I can't be seriously
ill, or I shouldn't have been able to get up and go out like this.
I never guessed early this morning that I could do it! I can't
possibly be as ill as I thought I was!"

And in the vestibule she encountered Chirac's face, lighten-
ing at the sight of her, which proved to him that his deliver-
ance was really to be accomplished.

"Permit me——"

"I'm all right," she smiled, tottering. "Get a cab." It suddenly occurred to her that she might quite as easily have given
him the money in English notes; he could have changed them.
But she had not thought. Her brain would not operate. She
was dreaming and waking together.

He helped her into the cab.

v

In the *bureau de change* there was a little knot of English
people, with naïve, romantic, and honest faces, quite different
from the faces outside in the street. No corruption in those
faces, but a sort of wondering and infantile sincerity, rather
out of its element and lost in a land too unsophisticated, seeming to belong to an earlier age! Sophia liked their tourist
stare, and their plain and ugly clothes. She longed to be back
in England, longed for a moment with violence, drowning in
that desire.

The English clerk behind his brass bars took her notes, and
carefully examined them one by one. She watched him, not
entirely convinced of his reality, and thought vaguely of the
detestable morning when she had abstracted the notes from
Gerald's pocket. She was filled with pity for the simple, ignorant Sophia of those days, the Sophia who still had a few
ridiculous illusions concerning Gerald's character. Often, since,
she had been tempted to break into the money, but she had
always withstood the temptation, saying to herself that an
hour of more urgent need would come. It had come. She was
proud of her firmness, of the force of will which had enabled
her to reserve the fund intact. The clerk gave her a keen look,
and then asked her how she would take the French money. And
she saw the notes falling down one after another on to the

counter as the clerk separated them with a snapping sound of
the paper.

Chirac was beside her.

"Does that make the count?" she said, having pushed
towards him five hundred-franc notes.

"I should not know how to thank you," he said, accepting
the notes. "Truly——"

His joy was unmistakably eager. He had had a shock and
a fright, and he saw the danger past. He could return to the
cashier of his newspaper, and fling down the money with a
lordly and careless air, as if to say: "When it is a question of
these English, one can always be sure!" But first he would
escort her to the hotel. She declined—she did not know why,
for he was her sole point of moral support in all France. He
insisted. She yielded. So she turned her back, with regret, on
that little English oasis in the Sahara of Paris, and staggered
to the fiacre.

And now that she had done what she had to do, she lost control of her body, and reclined flaccid and inert. Chirac was
evidently alarmed. He did not speak, but glanced at her from
time to time with eyes full of fear. The carriage appeared to
her to be swimming amid waves over great depths. Then she
was aware of a heavy weight against her shoulder; she had
slipped down upon Chirac, unconscious.

CHAPTER V
Fever

THEN she was lying in bed in a small room, obscure because
it was heavily curtained; the light came through the inner pair
of curtains of *écru* lace, with a beautiful soft silvery quality.
A man was standing by the side of the bed—not Chirac.

"Now, madame," he said to her, with kind firmness, and
speaking with a charming exaggerated purity of the vowels.
"You have the mucous fever. I have had it myself. You will be
forced to take baths, very frequently. I must ask you to reconcile yourself to that, to be good."

She did not reply. It did not occur to her to reply. But she certainly thought that this doctor—he was probably a doctor—was overestimating her case. She felt better than she had felt for two days. Still, she did not desire to move, nor was she in the least anxious as to her surroundings. She lay quiet.

A woman in a rather coquettish deshabille watched over her with expert skill.

Later, Sophia seemed to be revisiting the sea on whose waves the cab had swum; but now she was under the sea, in a watery gulf, terribly deep; and the sounds of the world came to her through the water, sudden and strange. Hands seized her and forced her from the subaqueous grotto where she had hidden into new alarms. And she briefly perceived that there was a large bath by the side of the bed, and that she was being pushed into it. The water was icy cold. After that her outlook upon things was for a time clearer and more precise. She knew from fragments of talk which she heard that she was put into the cold bath by her bed every three hours, night and day, and that she remained in it for ten minutes. Always, before the bath, she had to drink a glass of wine, and sometimes another glass while she was in the bath. Beyond this wine, and occasionally a cup of soup, she took nothing, had no wish to take anything. She grew perfectly accustomed to these extraordinary habits of life, to this merging of night and day into one monotonous and endless repetition of the same rite amid the same circumstances on exactly the same spot. Then followed a period during which she objected to being constantly wakened up for this annoying immersion. And she fought against it even in her dreams. Long days seemed to pass when she could not be sure whether she had been put into the bath or not, when all external phenomena were disconcertingly interwoven with matters which she knew to be merely fanciful. And then she was overwhelmed by the hopeless gravity of her state. She felt that her state was desperate. She felt that she was dying. Her unhappiness was extreme, not because she was dying, but because the veils of sense were so puzzling, so exasperating, and because her exhausted body was so vitiated, in every fibre, by disease. She was perfectly aware that she was going to die. She cried aloud for a pair of scissors. She wanted to cut off her hair, and to send part of it to Constance and part of it to her mother, in separate packages. She insisted upon separate packages. Nobody would give her a pair of scissors. She implored, meekly, haughtily, furiously, but nobody would satisfy her. It seemed to her shocking that all her hair should go with her into her coffin while Constance and her mother had nothing by which to remember her, no tangible souvenir of her beauty. Then she fought for the scissors. She clutched at some one—always through those baffling veils—who was putting her into the bath by the bedside, and fought frantically. It appeared to her that this some one was the rather stout woman who had supped at Sylvain's with the quarrelsome Englishman four years ago. She could not rid herself of this singular conceit, though she knew it to be absurd. . . .

A long time afterwards—it seemed like a century—she did actually and unmistakably see the woman sitting by her bed, and the woman was crying.

"Why are you crying?" Sophia asked wonderingly.

And the other, younger, woman, who was standing at the foot of the bed, replied:

"You do well to ask! It is you who have hurt her, in your delirium, when you so madly demanded the scissors."

The stout woman smiled with the tears on her cheeks; but Sophia wept, from remorse. The stout woman looked old, worn, and untidy. The other one was much younger. Sophia did not trouble to inquire from them who they were.

That little conversation formed a brief interlude in the delirium, which overtook her again and distorted everything. She forgot, however, that she was destined to die.

One day her brain cleared. She could be sure that she had gone to sleep in the morning and not wakened till the evening. Hence she had not been put into the bath.

"Have I had my baths?" she questioned.

It was the doctor who faced her.

"No," he said, "the baths are finished."

She knew from his face that she was out of danger. Moreover, she was conscious of a new feeling in her body, as though the fount of physical energy within her, long interrupted, had recommenced to flow—but very slowly, a trickling. It was a rebirth. She was not glad, but her body itself was glad; her body had an existence of its own.

She was now often left by herself in the bedroom. To the right of the foot of the bed was a piano in walnut, and to the left a chimney-piece with a large mirror. She wanted to look at herself in the mirror. But it was a very long way off. She tried to sit up, and could not. She hoped that one day she would be able to get as far as the mirror. She said not a word about this to either of the two women.

Often they would sit in the bedroom and talk without ceasing. Sophia learnt that the stout woman was named Foucault, and the other Laurence. Sometimes Laurence would address Madame Foucault as Aimée, but usually she was more formal. Madame Foucault always called the other Laurence.

Sophia's curiosity stirred and awoke. But she could not obtain any very exact information as to where she was, except that the house was in the Rue Bréda, off the Rue Notre Dame de Lorette. She recollected vaguely that the reputation of the street was sinister. It appeared that, on the day when she had gone out with Chirac, the upper part of the Rue Notre Dame de Lorette was closed for repairs—(this she remembered)—and that the cabman had turned up the Rue Bréda in order to make a détour, and that it was just opposite to the house of Madame Foucault that she had lost consciousness. Madame Foucault happened to be getting into a cab at the moment; but she had told Chirac nevertheless to carry Sophia into the house, and a policeman had helped. Then, when the doctor came, it was discovered that she could not be moved, save to a hospital, and both Madame Foucault and Laurence were determined that no friend of Chirac's should be committed to the horrors of a Paris hospital. Madame Foucault had suffered in one as a patient, and Laurence had been a nurse in another. . . .

Chirac was now away. The women talked loosely of a war.

"How kind you have been!" murmured Sophia, with humid eyes.

But they silenced her with gestures. She was not to talk. They seemed to have nothing further to tell her. They said Chirac would be returning perhaps soon, and that she could talk to him. Evidently they both held Chirac in affection. They said often that he was a charming boy.

Bit by bit Sophia comprehended the length and the seriousness of her illness, and the immense devotion of the two women, and the terrific disturbance of their lives, and her own debility. She saw that the women were strongly attached to her, and she could not understand why, as she had never done anything for them, whereas they had done everything for her. She had not

learnt that benefits rendered, not benefits received, are the
cause of such attachments.

All the time she was plotting, and gathering her strength to
disobey orders and get as far as the mirror. Her preliminary
studies and her preparations were as elaborate as those of a
prisoner arranging to escape from a fortress. The first attempt
was a failure. The second succeeded. Though she could not
stand without support, she managed by clinging to the bed
to reach a chair, and to push the chair in front of her until it
approached the mirror. The enterprise was exciting and terrific. Then she saw a face in the glass: white, incredibly emaciated, with great, wild, staring eyes; and the shoulders were
bent as though with age. It was a painful, almost a horrible
sight. It frightened her, so that in her alarm she recoiled from
it. Not attending sufficiently to the chair, she sank to the
ground. She could not pick herself up, and she was caught
there, miserably, by her angered jailers. The vision of her face
taught her more efficiently than anything else the gravity of
her adventure. As the women lifted her inert, repentant mass
into the bed, she reflected, "How queer my life is!" It seemed
to her that she ought to have been trimming hats in the showroom instead of being in that curtained, mysterious, Parisian
interior.

ii

One day Madame Foucault knocked at the door of Sophia's
little room (this ceremony of knocking was one of the indications that Sophia, convalescent, had been reinstated in her
rights as an individual), and cried:

"Madame, one is going to leave you all alone for some time."

"Come in," said Sophia, who was sitting up in an armchair,
and reading.

Madame Foucault opened the door. "One is going to leave
you all alone for some time," she repeated in a low, confidential voice, sharply contrasting with her shriek behind the door.
Sophia nodded and smiled, and Madame Foucault also nodded
and smiled. But Madame Foucault's face quickly resumed its
anxious expression.

"The servant's brother marries himself to-day, and she implored me to accord her two days—what would you? Madame

Laurence is out. And I must go out. It is four o'clock. I shall re-enter at six o'clock striking. Therefore . . ."

"Perfectly," Sophia concurred.

She looked curiously at Madame Foucault, who was carefully made up and arranged for the street, in a dress of yellow tussore with blue ornaments, bright lemon-coloured gloves, a little blue bonnet, and a little white parasol not wider when opened than her shoulders. Cheeks, lips, and eyes were heavily charged with rouge, powder, or black. And that too abundant waist had been most cunningly confined in a belt that descended beneath, instead of rising above, the lower masses of the vast torso. The general effect was worthy of the effort that must have gone to it. Madame Foucault was not rejuvenated by her toilette, but it almost procured her pardon for the crime of being over forty, fat, creased, and worn out. It was one of those defeats that are a triumph.

"You are very chic," said Sophia, uttering her admiration.

"Ah!" said Madame Foucault, shrugging the shoulders of disillusion. "Chic! What does that do?"

But she was pleased.

The front-door banged. Sophia, by herself for the first time in the flat into which she had been carried unconscious and which she had never since left, had the disturbing sensation of being surrounded by mysterious rooms and mysterious things. She tried to continue reading, but the sentences conveyed nothing to her. She rose—she could walk now a little—and looked out of the window, through the interstices of the pattern of the lace curtains. The window gave on the courtyard, which was about sixteen feet below her. A low wall divided the courtyard from that of the next house. And the windows of the two houses, only to be distinguished by the different tints of their yellow paint, rose tier above tier in level floors, continuing beyond Sophia's field of vision. She pressed her face against the glass, and remembered the St. Luke's Square of her childhood; and just as there from the showroom window she could not even by pressing her face against the glass see the pavement, so here she could not see the roof; the courtyard was like the bottom of a well. There was no end to the windows; six storeys she could count, and the sills of a seventh were the limit of her view. Every window was heavily curtained, like her own. Some of the upper ones had green sun-blinds. Scarcely any sound! Mysteries brooded without as well as within the flat of Madame Foucault. Sophia saw a bodiless hand twitch at a curtain and vanish. She noticed a green bird in a tiny cage on a sill in the next house. A woman whom she took to be the concierge appeared in the courtyard, deposited a small plant in the track of a ray of sunshine that lighted a corner for a couple of hours in the afternoon, and disappeared again. Then she heard a piano—somewhere. That was all. The feeling that secret and strange lives were being lived behind those baffling windows, that humanity was everywhere intimately pulsing around her, oppressed her spirit yet not quite unpleasantly. The environment softened her glance upon the spectacle of existence, insomuch that sadness became a voluptuous pleasure. And the environment threw her back on herself, into a sensuous contemplation of the fundamental fact of Sophia Scales, formerly Sophia Baines.

She turned to the room, with the marks of the bath on the floor by the bed, and the draped piano that was never opened, and her two trunks filling up the corner opposite the door. She had the idea of thoroughly examining those trunks, which Chirac or somebody else must have fetched from the hotel. At the top of one of them was her purse, tied up with old ribbon and ostentatiously sealed! How comical these French people were when they deemed it necessary to be serious! She emptied both trunks, scrutinizing minutely all her goods, and thinking of the varied occasions upon which she had obtained them. Then she carefully restored them, her mind full of souvenirs newly awakened.

She sighed as she straightened her back. A clock struck in another room. It seemed to invite her towards discoveries. She had been in no other room of the flat. She knew nothing of the rest of the flat save by sound. For neither of the other women had ever described it, nor had it occurred to them that Sophia might care to leave her room though she could not leave the house.

She opened her door, and glanced along the dim corridor, with which she was familiar. She knew that the kitchen lay next to her little room, and that next to the kitchen came the front-door. On the opposite side of the corridor were four double-doors. She crossed to the pair of doors facing her own little door, and quietly turned the handle, but the doors were locked; the same with the next pair. The third pair yielded, and she was in a large bedroom, with three windows on the street. She

saw that the second pair of doors, which she had failed to unfasten, also opened into this room. Between the two pairs of
doors was a wide bed. In front of the central window was a
large dressing-table. To the left of the bed, half hiding the
locked doors, was a large screen. On the marble mantelpiece,
reflected in a huge mirror, that ascended to the ornate cornice,
was a gilt-and-basalt clock, with pendants to match. On the
opposite side of the room from this was a long wide couch. The
floor was of polished oak, with a skin on either side of the bed.
At the foot of the bed was a small writing-table, with a penny
bottle of ink on it. A few coloured prints and engravings—representing, for example, Louis Philippe and his family, and
people perishing on a raft—broke the tedium of the walls. The
first impression on Sophia's eye was one of sombre splendour.
Everything had the air of being richly ornamented, draped,
looped, carved, twisted, brocaded into gorgeousness. The dark
crimson bed-hangings fell from massive rosettes in majestic
folds. The counterpane was covered with lace. The window-
curtains had amplitude beyond the necessary, and they were
suspended from behind fringed and pleated valances. The
green sofa and its sateen cushions were stiff with applied embroidery. The chandelier hanging from the middle of the ceiling, modelled to represent cupids holding festoons, was a
glittering confusion of gilt and lustres: the lustres tinkled
when Sophia stood on a certain part of the floor. The cane-
seated chairs were completely gilded. There was an effect of
spaciousness. And the situation of the bed between the two
double-doors, with the three windows in front and other pairs
of doors communicating with other rooms on either hand, produced in addition an admirable symmetry.

But Sophia, with the sharp gaze of a woman brought up in
the traditions of a modesty so proud that it scorns ostentation,
quickly tested and condemned the details of this chamber that
imitated every luxury. Nothing in it, she found, was "good."
And in St. Luke's Square "goodness" meant honest workmanship, permanence, the absence of pretence. All the stuffs were
cheap and showy and shabby; all the furniture was cracked,
warped, or broken. The clock showed five minutes past twelve
at five o'clock. And further, dust was everywhere, except in
those places where even the most perfunctory cleaning could
not have left it. In the obscurer pleatings of draperies it lay
thick. Sophia's lip curled, and instinctively she lifted her

peignoir. One of her mother's phrases came into her head: "a lick and a promise." And then another: "If you want to leave dirt, leave it where everybody can see it, not in the corners."

She peeped behind the screen, and all the horrible welter of a *cabinet de toilette* met her gaze: a repulsive medley of foul waters, stained vessels and cloths, brushes, sponges, powders, and pastes. Clothes were hung up in disorder on rough nails; among them she recognized a dressing-gown of Madame Foucault's, and, behind affairs of later date, the dazzling scarlet cloak in which she had first seen Madame Foucault, dilapidated now. So this was Madame Foucault's room! This was the bower from which that elegance emerged, the filth from which had sprung the mature blossom!

She passed from that room direct to another, of which the shutters were closed, leaving it in twilight. This room too was a bedroom, rather smaller than the middle one, and having only one window, but furnished with the same dubious opulence. Dust covered it everywhere, and small footmarks were visible in the dust on the floor. At the back was a small door, papered to match the wall, and within this door was a *cabinet de toilette*, with no light and no air; neither in the room nor in the closet was there any sign of individual habitation. She traversed the main bedroom again and found another bedroom to balance the second one, but open to the full light of day, and in a state of extreme disorder; the double-pillowed bed had not even been made; clothes and towels draped all the furniture; shoes were about the floor, and on a piece of string tied across the windows hung a single white stocking, wet. At the back was a *cabinet de toilette*, as dark as the other one, a vile malodorous mess of appliances whose familiar forms loomed vague and extraordinarily sinister in the dense obscurity. Sophia turned away with the righteous disgust of one whose preparations for the gaze of the world are as candid and simple as those of a child. Concealed dirt shocked her as much as it would have shocked her mother; and as for the trickeries of the toilet table, she contemned them as harshly as a young saint who has never been tempted contemns moral weakness. She thought of the strange flaccid daily life of those two women, whose hours seemed to slip unprofitably away without any result of achievement. She had actually witnessed nothing; but since the beginning of her convalescence her ears had heard, and she could piece the evidences together. There was never any sound in the flat, outside the kitchen, until noon. Then vague noises and smells would commence. And about one o'clock Madame Foucault, disarrayed, would come to inquire if the servant had attended to the needs of the invalid. Then the odours of cookery would accentuate themselves; bells rang; fragments of conversations escaped through doors ajar; occasionally a man's voice or a heavy step; then the fragrance of coffee; sometimes the sound of a kiss, the banging of the front-door, the noise of brushing, or of the shaking of a carpet, a little scream as at some trifling domestic contretemps. Laurence, still in a dressing-gown, would lounge into Sophia's room, dirty, haggard, but polite with a curious stiff ceremony, and would drink her coffee there. This wandering in peignoirs would continue till three o'clock, and then Laurence might say, as if nerving herself to an unusual and immense effort: "I must be dressed by five o'clock. I have not a moment." Often Madame Foucault did not dress at all; on such days she would go to bed immediately after dinner, with the remark that she didn't know what was the matter with her, but she was exhausted. And then the servant would retire to her seventh floor, and there would be silence until, now and then, faint creepings were heard at midnight or after. Once or twice, through the chinks of her door, Sophia had seen a light at two o'clock in the morning, just before the dawn.

Yet these were the women who had saved her life, who between them had put her into a cold bath every three hours night and day for weeks! Surely it was impossible after that to despise them for shiftlessness and talkative idling in peignoirs; impossible to despise them for anything whatever! But Sophia, conscious of her inheritance of strong and resolute character, did despise them as poor things. The one point on which she envied them was their formal manners to her, which seemed to become more dignified and graciously distant as her health improved. It was always "Madame," "Madame," to her, with an intonation of increasing deference. They might have been apologizing to her for themselves.

She prowled into all the corners of the flat; but she discovered no more rooms, nothing but a large cupboard crammed with Madame Foucault's dresses. Then she went back to the large bedroom, and enjoyed the busy movement and rattle of the sloping street, and had long, vague yearnings for strength and for freedom in wide, sane places. She decided that on the morrow she would dress herself "properly," and never again wear a peignoir; the peignoir and all that it represented, disgusted her. And while looking at the street she ceased to see it and saw Cook's office and Chirac helping her into the carriage. Where was he? Why had he brought her to this impossible abode? What did he mean by such conduct? . . . But could he have acted otherwise? He had done the one thing that he could do. . . . Chance! . . . Chance! And why an impossible abode? Was one place more impossible than another? . . . All this came of running away from home with Gerald. It was remarkable that she seldom thought of Gerald. He had vanished from her life as he had come into it—madly, preposterously. She wondered what the next stage in her career would be. She certainly could not forecast it. Perhaps Gerald was starving, or in prison. . . . Bah! That exclamation expressed her appalling disdain of Gerald and of the Sophia who had once deemed him the paragon of men. Bah!

A carriage stopping in front of the house awakened her from her meditation. Madame Foucault and a man very much younger than Madame Foucault got out of it. Sophia fled. After all, this prying into other people's rooms was quite inexcusable. She dropped on to her own bed and picked up a book, in case Madame Foucault should come in.

iii

In the evening, just after night had fallen, Sophia on the bed heard the sound of raised and acrimonious voices in Madame Foucault's room. Nothing except dinner had happened since the arrival of Madame Foucault and the young man. These two had evidently dined informally in the bedroom on a dish or so prepared by Madame Foucault, who had herself served Sophia with her invalid's repast. The odours of cookery still hung in the air.

The noise of virulent discussion increased and continued, and then Sophia could hear sobbing, broken by short and fierce phrases from the man. Then the door of the bedroom opened brusquely. "J'en ai soupé!" exclaimed the man, in tones of angry disgust. "Laisse-moi, pe je prie!" And then a soft muffled sound, as of a struggle, a quick step, and the very violent banging of the front door. After that there was a notice-

able silence, save for the regular sobbing. Sophia wondered
when it would cease, that monotonous sobbing.

"What is the matter?" she called out from her bed.

The sobbing grew louder, like the sobbing of a child who
has detected an awakening of sympathy and instinctively begins to practise upon it. In the end Sophia arose and put on
the peignoir which she had almost determined never to wear
again.

The broad corridor was lighted by a small, smelling oil-
lamp with a crimson globe. That soft, transforming radiance
seemed to paint the whole corridor with voluptuous luxury: so
much so that it was impossible to believe that the smell came
from the lamp. Under the lamp lay Madame Foucault on the
floor, a shapeless mass of lace, frilled linen, and corset; her light
brown hair was loose and spread about the floor. At the first
glance, the creature abandoned to grief made a romantic and
striking picture, and Sophia thought for an instant that she
had at length encountered life on a plane that would correspond to her dreams of romance. And she was impressed, with
a feeling somewhat akin to that of a middling commoner when
confronted with a viscount. There was, in the distance, something imposing and sensational about that prone, trembling
figure. The tragic works of love were therein apparently manifest, in a sort of dignified beauty. But when Sophia bent over
Madame Foucault, and touched her flabbiness, this illusion at
once vanished; and instead of being dramatically pathetic the
woman was ridiculous. Her face, especially as damaged by
tears, could not support the ordeal of inspection; it was horrible; not a picture, but a palette; or like the coloured design
of a pavement artist after a heavy shower. Her great, relaxed
eyelids alone would have rendered any face absurd; and there
were monstrous details far worse than the eyelids. Then she
was amazingly fat; her flesh seemed to be escaping at all ends
from a corset strained to the utmost limit. And above her
boots—she was still wearing dainty, high-heeled, tightly laced
boots—the calves bulged suddenly out.

As a woman of between forty and fifty, the obese sepulchre
of a dead vulgar beauty, she had no right to passions and tears
and homage, or even the means of life; she had no right to expose herself picturesquely beneath a crimson glow in all the
panoply of ribboned garters and lacy seductiveness. It was
silly; it was disgraceful. She ought to have known that only

youth and slimness have the right to appeal to the feelings by indecent abandonments.

Such were the thoughts that mingled with the sympathy of the beautiful and slim Sophia as she bent down to Madame Foucault. She was sorry for her landlady, but at the same time she despised her, and resented her woe.

"What is the matter?" she asked quietly.

"He has chucked me!" stammered Madame Foucault. "And he's the last. I have no one now!"

She rolled over in the most grotesque manner, kicking up her legs, with a fresh outburst of sobs. Sophia felt quite ashamed for her.

"Come and lie down. Come now!" she said, with a touch of sharpness. "You mustn't lie there like that."

Madame Foucault's behaviour was really too outrageous. Sophia helped her, morally rather than physically, to rise, and then persuaded her into the large bedroom. Madame Foucault fell on the bed, of which the counterpane had been thrown over the foot. Sophia covered the lower part of her heaving body with the counterpane.

"Now, calm yourself, please!"

This room too was lit in crimson, by a small lamp that stood on the night-table, and though the shade of the lamp was cracked, the general effect of the great chamber was incontestably romantic. Only the pillows of the wide bed and a small semi-circle of floor were illuminated, all the rest lay in shadow. Madame Foucault's head had dropped between the pillows. A tray containing dirty plates and glasses and a wine-bottle was speciously picturesque on the writing-table.

Despite her genuine gratitude to Madame Foucault for astounding care during her illness, Sophia did not like her landlady, and the present scene made her coldly wrathful. She saw the probability of having another's troubles piled on the top of her own. She did not, in her mind, actively object, because she felt that she could not be more hopelessly miserable than she was; but she passively resented the imposition. Her reason told her that she ought to sympathize with this ageing, ugly, disagreeable, undignified woman; but her heart was reluctant; her heart did not want to know anything at all about Madame Foucault, nor to enter in any way into her private life.

"I have not a single friend now," stammered Madame Foucault.

"Oh, yes, you have," said Sophia, cheerfully. "You have Madame Laurence."

"Laurence—that is not a friend. You know what I mean."

"And me! I am your friend!" said Sophia, in obedience to her conscience.

"You are very kind," replied Madame Foucault, from the pillow. "But you know what I mean."

The fact was that Sophia did know what she meant. The terms of their intercourse had been suddenly changed. There was no pretentious ceremony now, but the sincerity that disaster brings. The vast structure of make-believe, which between them they had gradually built, had crumbled to nothing.

"I never treated badly any man in my life," whimpered Madame Foucault. "I have always been a good girl. There is not a man·who can say I have not been a good girl. Never was I a girl like the rest. And every one has said so. Ah! when I tell you that once I had a hotel in the Avenue de la Reine Hortense. Four horses . . . I have sold a horse to Madame Musard. . . . You know Madame Musard. . . . But one cannot make economies. Impossible to make economies! Ah! In 'fifty-six I was spending a hundred thousand francs a year. That cannot last. Always I have said to myself: 'That cannot last.' Always I had the intention. . . . But what would you? I installed myself here, and borrowed money to pay for the furniture. There did not remain to me one jewel. The men are poltroons, all! I could let three bedrooms for three hundred and fifty francs a month, and with serving meals and so on I could live."

"Then that," Sophia interrupted, pointing to her own bedroom across the corridor, "is your room?"

"Yes," said Madame Foucault. "I put you in it because at the moment all these were let. They are so no longer. Only one—Laurence—and she does not pay me always. What would you? Tenants—that does not find itself at the present hour. . . . I have nothing, and I owe. And he quits me. He chooses this moment to quit me! And why? For nothing. For nothing. That is not for his money that I regret him. No, no! You know, at his age—he is twenty-five—and with a woman like me—one is not generous! No. I loved him. And then a man is a moral support, always. I loved him. It is at my age, mine, that one knows how to love. Beauty goes always, but not the temperament! Ah, that—No! . . . I loved him. I love him."

Sophia's face tingled with a sudden emotion caused by the repetition of those last three words, whose spell no usage can mar. But she said nothing.

"Do you know what I shall become? There is nothing but that for me. And I know of such, who are there already. A charwoman! Yes, a charwoman! More soon or more late. Well, that is life. What would you? One exists always." Then in a different tone: "I demand your pardon, madame, for talking like this. I ought to have shame."

And Sophia felt that in listening she also ought to be ashamed. But she was not ashamed. Everything seemed very natural, and even ordinary. And, moreover, Sophia was full of the sense of her superiority over the woman on the bed. Four years ago, in the Restaurant Sylvain, the ingenuous and ignorant Sophia had shyly sat in awe of the resplendent courtesan, with her haughty stare, her large, easy gestures, and her imperturbable contempt for the man who was paying. And now Sophia knew that she, Sophia, knew all that was to be known about human nature. She had not merely youth, beauty, and virtue, but knowledge—knowledge enough to reconcile her to her own misery. She had a vigorous, clear mind, and a clean conscience. She could look any one in the face, and judge every one too as a woman of the world. Whereas this obscene wreck on the bed had nothing whatever left. She had not merely lost her effulgent beauty, she had become repulsive. She could never have had any commonsense, nor any force of character. Her haughtiness in the day of glory was simply fatuous, based on stupidity. She had passed the years in idleness, trailing about all day in stuffy rooms, and emerging at night to impress nincompoops; continually meaning to do things which she never did, continually surprised at the lateness of the hour, continually occupied with the most foolish trifles. And here she was at over forty writhing about on the bare floor because a boy of twenty-five (who *must* be a worthless idiot) had abandoned her after a scene of ridiculous shoutings and stampings. She was dependent on the caprices of a young scamp, the last donkey to turn from her with loathing! Sophia thought: "Goodness! If I had been in her place I shouldn't have been

like that. I should have been rich. I should have saved like a
miser. I wouldn't have been dependent on anybody at that
age. If I couldn't have made a better courtesan than this
pitiable woman, I would have drowned myself."

In the harsh vanity of her conscious capableness and young
strength she thought thus, half forgetting her own follies, and
half excusing them on the ground of inexperience.

Sophia wanted to go round the flat and destroy every crimson lampshade in it. She wanted to shake Madame Foucault
into self-respect and sagacity. Moral reprehension, though
present in her mind, was only faint. Certainly she felt the immense gulf between the honest woman and the wanton, but she
did not feel it as she would have expected to feel it. "What a
fool you have been!" she thought; not: "What a sinner!" With
her precocious cynicism, which was somewhat unsuited to the
lovely northern youthfulness of that face, she said to herself
that the whole situation and their relative attitudes would have
been different if only Madame Foucault had had the wit to
amass a fortune, as (according to Gerald) some of her rivals
had succeeded in doing.

And all the time she was thinking, in another part of her
mind: "I ought not to be here. It's no use arguing. I ought
not to be here. Chirac did the only thing for me there was to do.
But I must go now."

Madame Foucault continued to recite her woes, chiefly financial, in a weak voice damp with tears; she also continued to
apologize for mentioning herself. She had finished sobbing,
and lay looking at the wall, away from Sophia, who stood
irresolute near the bed, ashamed for her companion's weakness
and incapacity.

"You must not forget," said Sophia, irritated by the unrelieved darkness of the picture drawn by Madame Foucault,
"that at least I owe you a considerable sum, and that I am
only waiting for you to tell me how much it is. I have asked you
twice already, I think."

"Oh, you are still suffering!" said Madame Foucault.

"I am quite well enough to pay my debts," said Sophia.

"I do not like to accept money from you," said Madame
Foucault.

"But why not?"

"You will have the doctor to pay."

"Please do not talk in that way," said Sophia. "I have

money, and I can pay for everything, and I shall pay for everything."

She was annoyed because she was sure that Madame Foucault was only making a pretence of delicacy, and that in any case her delicacy was preposterous. Sophia had remarked this on the two previous occasions when she had mentioned the subject of bills. Madame Foucault would not treat her as an ordinary lodger, now that the illness was past. She wanted, as it were, to complete brilliantly what she had begun, and to live in Sophia's memory as a unique figure of lavish philanthropy. This was a sentiment, a luxury that she desired to offer herself : the thought that she had played providence to a respectable married lady in distress ; she frequently hinted at Sophia's misfortunes and helplessness. But she could not afford the luxury. She gazed at it as a poor woman gazes at costly stuffs through the glass of a shop-window. The truth was, she wanted the luxury for nothing. For a double reason Sophia was exasperated : by Madame Foucault's absurd desire, and by a natural objection to the *rôle* of a subject for philanthropy. She would not admit that Madame Foucault's devotion as a nurse entitled her to the satisfaction of being a philanthropist when there was no necessity for philanthropy.

"How long have I been here?" asked Sophia.

"I don't know," murmured Madame Foucault. "Eight weeks —or is it nine?"

"Suppose we say nine," said Sophia.

"Very well," agreed Madame Foucault, apparently reluctant.

"Now, how much must I pay you per week?"

"I don't want anything—I don't want anything! You are a friend of Chirac's. You——"

"Not at all!" Sophia interrupted, tapping her foot and biting her lip. "Naturally I must pay."

Madame Foucault wept quietly.

"Shall I pay you seventy-five francs a week?" said Sophia, anxious to end the matter.

"It is too much!" Madame Foucault protested, insincerely.

"What? For all you have done for me?"

"I speak not of that," Madame Foucault modestly replied.

If the devotion was not to be paid for, then seventy-five francs a week was assuredly too much, as during more than half the time Sophia had had almost no food. Madame Foucault was therefore within the truth when she again protested, at sight of the bank-notes which Sophia brought from her trunk:

"I am sure that it is too much."

"Not at all!" Sophia repeated. "Nine weeks at seventy-five. That makes six hundred and seventy-five. Here are seven hundreds."

"I have no change," said Madame Foucault. "I have nothing."

"That will pay for the hire of the bath," said Sophia.

She laid the notes on the pillow. Madame Foucault looked at them gluttonously, as any other person would have done in her place. She did not touch them. After an instant she burst into wild tears.

"But why do you cry?" Sophia asked, softened.

"I—I don't know!" spluttered Madame Foucault. "You are so beautiful. I am so content that we saved you." Her great wet eyes rested on Sophia.

It was sentimentality. Sophia ruthlessly set it down as sentimentality. But she was touched. She was suddenly moved. Those women, such as they were in their foolishness, probably had saved her life—and she a stranger! Flaccid as they were, they had been capable of resolute perseverance there. It was possible to say that chance had thrown them upon an enterprise which they could not have abandoned till they or death had won. It was possible to say that they hoped vaguely to derive advantage from their labours. But even then? Judged by an ordinary standard, those women had been angels of mercy. And Sophia was despising them, cruelly taking their motives to pieces, accusing them of incapacity when she herself stood a supreme proof of their capacity in, at any rate, one direction! In a rush of emotion she saw her hardness and her injustice.

She bent down. "Never can I forget how kind you have been to me. It is incredible! Incredible!" She spoke softly, in tones loaded with genuine feeling. It was all she said. She could not embroider on the theme. She had no talent for thanksgiving.

Madame Foucault made the beginning of a gesture, as if she meant to kiss Sophia with those thick, marred lips; but refrained. Her head sank back, and then she had a recurrence of the fit of nervous sobbing. Immediately afterwards there was the sound of a latchkey in the front-door of the flat; the bedroom door was open. Still sobbing very violently, she cocked her ear, and pushed the bank-notes under the pillow.

Madame Laurence—as she was called: Sophia had never heard her surname—came straight into the bedroom, and beheld the scene with astonishment in her dark twinkling eyes. She was usually dressed in black, because people said that black suited her, and because black was never out of fashion; black was an expression of her idiosyncrasy. She showed a certain elegance, and by comparison with the extreme disorder of Madame Foucault and the deshabille of Sophia her appearance, all fresh from a modish restaurant, was brilliant; it gave her an advantage over the other two—that moral advantage which ceremonial raiment always gives.

"What is it that passes?" she demanded.

"He has chucked me, Laurence!" exclaimed Madame Foucault, in a sort of hysteric scream which seemed to force its way through her sobs. From the extraordinary freshness of Madame Foucault's woe, it might have been supposed that her young man had only that instant strode out.

Laurence and Sophia exchanged a swift glance; and Laurence, of course, perceived that Sophia's relations with her landlady and nurse were now of a different, a more candid order. She indicated her perception of the change by a single slight movement of the eyebrows.

"But listen, Aimée," she said authoritatively. "You must not let yourself go like that. He will return."

"Never!" cried Madame Foucault. "It is finished. And he is the last!"

Laurence, ignoring Madame Foucault, approached Sophia. "You have an air very fatigued," she said, caressing Sophia's shoulder with her gloved hand. "You are pale like everything. All this is not for you. It is not reasonable to remain here, you still suffering! At this hour! Truly not reasonable!"

Her hands persuaded Sophia towards the corridor. And, in fact, Sophia did then notice her own exhaustion. She departed from the room with the ready obedience of physical weakness, and shut her door.

After about half an hour, during which she heard confused noises and murmurings, her door half opened.

"May I enter, since you are not asleep?" It was Laurence's voice. Twice, now, she had addressed Sophia without adding the formal "madame."

"Enter, I beg you," Sophia called from the bed. "I am reading."

Laurence came in. Sophia was both glad and sorry to see her. She was eager to hear gossip which, however, she felt she ought to despise. Moreover, she knew that if they talked that night they would talk as friends, and that Laurence would ever afterwards treat her with the familiarity of a friend. This she dreaded. Still, she knew that she would yield, at any rate, to the temptation to listen to gossip.

"I have put her to bed," said Laurence, in a whisper, as she cautiously closed the door. "The poor woman! Oh, what a charming bracelet! It is a true pearl, naturally?"

Her roving eye had immediately, with an infallible instinct, caught sight of a bracelet which, in taking stock of her possessions, Sophia had accidentally left on the piano. She picked it up, and then put it down again.

"Yes," said Sophia. She was about to add: "It's nearly all the jewellery I possess;" but she stopped.

Laurence moved towards Sophia's bed, and stood over it as she had often done in her quality as nurse. She had taken off her gloves, and she made a piquant, pretty show, with her thirty years, and her agreeable, slightly roguish face, in which were mingled the knowingness of a street boy and the confidence of a woman who has ceased to be surprised at the influence of her snub nose on a highly intelligent man.

"Did she tell you what they had quarrelled about?" Laurence inquired abruptly. And not only the phrasing of the question, but the assured tone in which it was uttered, showed that Laurence meant to be the familiar of Sophia.

"Not a word!" said Sophia.

In this brief question and reply, all was crudely implied that had previously been supposed not to exist. The relations between the two women were altered irretrievably in a moment.

"It must have been her fault!" said Laurence. "With men she is insupportable. I have never understood how that poor woman has made her way. With women she is charming. But she seems to be incapable of not treating men like dogs. Some men adore that, but they are few. Is it not?"

Sophia smiled.

"I have told her! How many times have I told her! But it is useless. It is stronger than she is, and if she finishes on straw one will be able to say that it was because of that. But truly she ought not to have asked him here! Truly that was too much! If he knew . . . . !"

"Why not?" asked Sophia, awkwardly. The answer startled her.

"Because her room has not been disinfected."

"But I thought all the flat had been disinfected?".

"All except her room."

"But why not her room?"

Laurence shrugged her shoulders. "She did not want to disturb her things! Is it that I know, I? She is like that. She takes an idea—and then, there you are!"

"She told me every room had been disinfected."

"She told the same to the police and the doctor."

"Then all the disinfection is useless?"

"Perfectly! But she is like that. This flat might be very remunerative; but with her, never! She has not even paid for the furniture—after two years!"

"But what will become of her?" Sophia asked.

"Ah—that!" Another shrug of the shoulders. "All that I know is that it will be necessary for me to leave here. The last time I brought Monsieur Cerf here, she was excessively rude to him. She has doubtless told you about Monsieur Cerf?"

"No. Who is Monsieur Cerf?"

"Ah! She has not told you? That astonishes me. Monsieur Cerf, that is my friend, you know."

"Oh!" murmured Sophia.

"Yes," Laurence proceeded, impelled by a desire to impress Sophia and to gossip at large. "That is my friend. I knew him at the hospital. It was to please him that I left the hospital. After that we quarrelled for two years; but at the end he gave me right. I did not budge. Two years! It is long. And I had left the hospital. I could have gone back. But I would not. That is not a life, to be nurse in a Paris hospital! No, I drew myself out as well as I could. . . . He is the most charming boy you can imagine! And rich now; that is to say, relatively. He has a cousin infinitely more rich than he. I dined with them both to-night at the Maison Dorée. For a luxurious boy, he is a luxurious boy—the cousin I mean. It appears that he has made a fortune in Canada."

"Truly!" said Sophia, with politeness. Laurence's hand was playing on the edge of the bed, and Sophia observed for the first time that it bore a wedding-ring.

"You remark my ring?" Laurence laughed. "That is he—the cousin. 'What!' he said, 'you do not wear an *alliance?* An *alliance* is more proper. We are going to arrange that after dinner.' I said that all the jewellers' shops would be closed. 'That is all the same to me,' he said. 'We will open one.' And in effect . . . it passed like that. He succeeded! Is it not beautiful?" She held forth her hand.

"Yes," said Sophia. "It is very beautiful."

"Yours also is beautiful," said Laurence, with an extremely puzzling intonation.

"It is just the ordinary English wedding-ring," said Sophia. In spite of herself she blushed.

" 'Now I have married you. It is I, the curé,' said he—the cousin—when he put the ring on my finger. Oh, he is excessively amusing! He pleases me much. And he is all alone. He asked me whether I knew among my friends a sympathetic, pretty girl, to make four with us three for a picnic. I said I was not sure, but I thought not. Whom do I know? Nobody. I'm not a woman like the rest. I am always discreet. I do not like casual relations. . . . But he is very well, the cousin. Brown eyes. . . . It is an idea—will you come, one day? He speaks English. He loves the English. He is all that is most correct, the perfect gentleman. He would arrange a dazzling fête. I am sure he would be enchanted to make your acquaintance. Enchanted! . . . As for my Charles, happily he is completely mad about me—otherwise I should have fear."

She smiled, and in her smile was a genuine respect for Sophia's face.

"I fear I cannot come," said Sophia. She honestly endeavoured to keep out of her reply any accent of moral superiority, but she did not quite succeed. She was not at all horrified by Laurence's suggestion. She meant simply to refuse it; but she could not do so in a natural voice.

"It is true you are not yet strong enough," said the imperturbable Laurence, quickly, and with a perfect imitation of naturalness. "But soon you must make a little promenade." She stared at her ring. "After all, it is more proper," she observed judicially. "With a wedding-ring one is less likely to be annoyed. What is curious is that the idea never before came to me. Yet . . ."

"You like jewellery?" said Sophia.

"If I like jewellery!"—with a gesture of the hands.

"Will you pass me that bracelet?"

Laurence obeyed, and Sophia clasped it round the girl's wrist.

"Keep it," Sophia said.

"For me?" Laurence exclaimed, ravished. "It is too much."

"It is not enough," said Sophia. "And when you look at it, you must remember how kind you were to me, and how grateful I am."

"How nicely you say that!" Laurence said ecstatically.

And Sophia felt that she had indeed said it rather nicely. This giving of the bracelet, souvenir of one of the few capricious follies that Gerald had committed for her and not for himself, pleased Sophia very much.

"I am afraid your nursing of me forced you to neglect Monsieur Cerf," she added.

"Yes, a little!" said Laurence, impartially, with a small pout of haughtiness. "It is true that he used to complain. But I soon put him straight. What an idea! He knows there are things upon which I do not joke. It is not he who will quarrel a second time! Believe me!"

Laurence's absolute conviction of her power was what impressed Sophia. To Sophia she seemed to be a vulgar little piece of goods, with dubious charm and a glance that was far too brazen. Her movements were vulgar. And Sophia wondered how she had established her empire and upon what it rested.

"I shall not show this to Aimée," whispered Laurence, indicating the bracelet.

"As you wish," said Sophia.

"By the way, have I told you that war is declared?" Laurence casually remarked.

"No," said Sophia. "What war?"

"The scene with Aimée made me forget it. . . . With Germany. The city is quite excited. An immense crowd in front of the new Opéra. They say we shall be at Berlin in a month— or at most two months."

"Oh!" Sophia muttered. "Why is there a war?"

"Ah! It is I who asked that. Nobody knows. It is those Prussians."

"Don't you think we ought to begin again with the disinfecting?" Sophia asked anxiously. "I must speak to Madame Foucault."

Laurence told her not to worry, and went off to show the

bracelet to Madame Foucault. She had privately decided that this was a pleasure which, after all, she could not deny herself.

iv

About a fortnight later—it was a fine Saturday in early August—Sophia, with a large pinafore over her dress, was finishing the portentous preparations for disinfecting the flat. Part of the affair was already accomplished, her own room and the corridor having been fumigated on the previous day, in spite of the opposition of Madame Foucault, who had taken amiss Laurence's tale-bearing to Sophia. Laurence had left the flat—under exactly what circumstances Sophia knew not, but she guessed that it must have been in consequence of a scene elaborating the tiff caused by Madame Foucault's resentment against Laurence. The brief, factitious friendliness between Laurence and Sophia had gone like a dream, and Laurence had gone like a dream. The servant had been dismissed; in her place Madame Foucault employed a charwoman each morning for two hours. Finally, Madame Foucault had been suddenly called away that morning by a letter to her sick father at St. Mammès-sur-Seine. Sophia was delighted at the chance. The disinfecting of the flat had become an obsession with Sophia—the obsession of a convalescent whose perspective unconsciously twists things to the most wry shapes. She had had trouble on the day before with Madame Foucault, and she was expecting more serious trouble when the moment arrived for ejecting Madame Foucault as well as all her movable belongings from Madame Foucault's own room. Nevertheless, Sophia had been determined, whatever should happen, to complete an honest fumigation of the entire flat. Hence the eagerness with which, urging Madame Foucault to go to her father, Sophia had protested that she was perfectly strong and could manage by herself for a couple of days. Owing to the partial suppression of the ordinary railway services in favour of military needs, Madame Foucault could not hope to go and return on the same day. Sophia had lent her a louis.

Pans of sulphur were mysteriously burning in each of the three front rooms, and two pairs of doors had been pasted over with paper, to prevent the fumes from escaping. The charwoman had departed. Sophia, with brush, scissors, flour-paste, and news-sheets, was sealing the third pair of doors, when there was a ring at the front-door.

She had only to cross the corridor in order to open.

It was Chirac. She was not surprised to see him. The outbreak of the war had induced even Sophia and her landlady to look through at least one newspaper during the day, and she had in this way learnt, from an article signed by Chirac, that he had returned to Paris after a mission into the Vosges country for his paper.

He started on seeing her. "Ah!" He breathed out the exclamation slowly. And then smiled, seized her hand, and kissed it.

The sight of his obvious extreme pleasure in meeting her again was the sweetest experience that had fallen to Sophia for years.

"Then you are cured?"

"Quite."

He sighed. "You know, this is an enormous relief to me, to know, veritably, that you are no longer in danger. You gave me a fright . . . but a fright, my dear madame!"

She smiled in silence.

As he glanced inquiringly up and down the corridor, she said——

"I'm all alone in the flat. I'm disinfecting it."

"Then that is sulphur that I smell?"

She nodded. "Excuse me while I finish this door," she said.

He closed the front-door. "But you seem to be quite at home here!" he observed.

"I ought to be," said she.

He glanced again inquiringly up and down the corridor. "And you are really all alone now?" he asked, as though to be doubly sure.

She explained the circumstances.

"I owe you my most sincere excuses for bringing you here," he said confidentially.

"But why?" she replied, looking intently at her door. "They have been most kind to me. Nobody could have been kinder. And Madame Laurence being such a good nurse——"

"It is true," said he. "That was a reason. In effect they are both very good-natured little women. . . . You comprehend,

as journalist it arrives to me to know all kinds of people . . ."
He snapped his fingers . . . . "And as we were opposite the
house. In fine, I pray you to excuse me . . ."

"Hold me this paper," she said. "It is necessary that every
crack should be covered; also between the floor and the door."

"You English are wonderful," he murmured, as he took the
paper. "Imagine you doing that! Then," he added, resuming
the confidential tone, "I suppose you will leave the Foucault
now, hein?"

"I suppose so," she said carelessly.

"You go to England?"

She turned to him, as she patted the creases out of a strip of
paper with a duster, and shook her head.

"Not to England?"

"No."

"If it is not indiscreet, where are you going?"

"I don't know," she said candidly.

And she did not know. She was without a plan. Her brain
told her that she ought to return to Bursley, or, at the least,
write. But her pride would not hear of such a surrender. Her
situation would have to be far more desperate than it was before she could confess her defeat to her family even in a letter.
A thousand times no! That was a point which she had for ever
decided. She would face any disaster, and any other shame,
rather than the shame of her family's forgiving reception of
her.

"And you?" she asked. "How does it go? This war?"

He told her, in a few words, a few leading facts about himself. "It must not be said," he added of the war, "but that will
turn out ill! I—I know, you comprehend."

"Truly?" she answered with casualness.

"You have heard nothing of him?" Chirac asked.

"Who? Gerald?"

He gave a gesture.

"Nothing! Not a word! Nothing!"

"He will have gone back to England!"

"Never!" she said positively.

"But why not?"

"Because he prefers France. He really does like France. I
think it is the only real passion he ever had."

"It is astonishing," reflected Chirac, "how France is loved!
And yet . . . ! But to live, what will he do? Must live!"

Sophia merely shrugged her shoulders.

"Then it is finished between you two?" he muttered awkwardly.

She nodded. She was on her knees, at the lower crack of the doors.

"There!" she said, rising. "It's well done, isn't it? That is all."

She smiled at him, facing him squarely, in the obscurity of the untidy and shabby corridor. Both felt that they had become very intimate. He was intensely flattered by her attitude, and she knew it.

"Now," she said, "I will take off my pinafore. Where can I niche you? There is only my bedroom, and I want that. What are we to do?"

"Listen," he suggested diffidently. "Will you do me the honour to come for a drive? That will do you good. There is sunshine. And you are always very pale."

"With pleasure," she agreed cordially.

While dressing, she heard him walking up and down the corridor; occasionally they exchanged a few words. Before leaving, Sophia pulled off the paper from one of the key-holes of the sealed suite of rooms, and they peered through, one after the other, and saw the green glow of the sulphur, and were troubled by its uncanniness. And then Sophia refixed the paper.

In descending the stairs of the house she felt the infirmity of her knees; but in other respects, though she had been out only once before since her illness, she was conscious of a sufficient strength. A disinclination for any enterprise had prevented her from taking the air as she ought to have done, but within the flat she had exercised her limbs in many small tasks. The little Chirac, nervously active and restless, wanted to take her arm, but she would not allow it.

The concierge and part of her family stared curiously at Sophia as she passed under the archway, for the course of her illness had excited the interest of the whole house. Just as the carriage was driving off, the concierge came across the pavement and paid her compliments, and then said:

"You do not know by hazard why Madame Foucault has not returned for lunch, madame?"

"Returned for lunch!" said Sophia. "She will not come back till to-morrow."

The concierge made a face. "Ah! How curious it is! She told my husband that she would return in two hours. It is very grave! Question of business."

"I know nothing, madame," said Sophia. She and Chirac looked at each other. The concierge murmured thanks and went off muttering indistinctly.

The fiacre turned down the Rue Laferrière, the horse slipping and sliding as usual over the cobblestones. Soon they were on the boulevard, making for the Champs Elysées and the Bois de Boulogne.

The fresh breeze and bright sunshine and the large freedom of the streets quickly intoxicated Sophia—intoxicated her, that is to say, in quite a physical sense. She was almost drunk, with the heady savour of life itself. A mild ecstasy of well-being overcame her. She saw the flat as a horrible, vile prison, and blamed herself for not leaving it sooner and oftener. The air was medicine, for body and mind too. Her perspective was instantly corrected. She was happy, living neither in the past nor in the future, but in and for that hour. And beneath her happiness moved a wistful melancholy for the Sophia who had suffered such a captivity and such woes. She yearned for more and yet more delight, for careless orgies of passionate pleasure, in the midst of which she would forget all trouble. Why had she refused the offer of Laurence? Why had she not rushed at once into the splendid fire of joyous indulgence, ignoring everything but the crude, sensuous instinct? Acutely aware as she was of her youth, her beauty, and her charm, she wondered at her refusal. She did not regret her refusal. She placidly observed it as the result of some tremendously powerful motive in herself, which could not be questioned or reasoned with— which was, in fact, the essential *her*.

"Do I look like an invalid?" she asked, leaning back luxuriously in the carriage among the crowd of other vehicles.

Chirac hesitated. "My faith! Yes!" he said at length. "But it becomes you. If I did not know that you have little love for compliments, I——"

"But I adore compliments!" she exclaimed. "What made you think that?"

"Well, then," he youthfully burst out, "you are more ravishing than ever."

She gave herself up deliciously to his admiration.

After a silence, he said: "Ah! if you knew how disquieted

I was about you, away there . . . . ! I should not know how to tell you. Veritably disquieted, you comprehend! What could I do? Tell me a little about your illness."

She recounted details.

As the fiacre entered the Rue Royale, they noticed a crowd of people in front of the Madeleine shouting and cheering.

The cabman turned towards them. "It appears there has been a victory!" he said.

"A victory! If only it was true!" murmured Chirac, cynically.

In the Rue Royale people were running frantically to and fro, laughing and gesticulating in glee. The customers in the cafés stood on their chairs, and even on tables, to watch, and occasionally to join in, the sudden fever. The fiacre was slowed to a walking pace. Flags and carpets began to show from the upper storeys of houses. The crowd grew thicker and more febrile. "Victory! Victory!" rang hoarsely, shrilly, and hoarsely again in the air.

"My God!" said Chirac, trembling. "It must be a true victory! We are saved! We are saved! . . . Oh yes, it is true!"

"But naturally it is true! What are you saying?" demanded the driver.

At the Place de la Concorde the fiacre had to stop altogether. The immense square was a sea of white hats and flowers and happy faces, with carriages anchored like boats on its surface. Flag after flag waved out from neighbouring roofs in the breeze that tempered the August sun. Then hats began to go up, and cheers rolled across the square like echoes of firing in an enclosed valley. Chirac's driver jumped madly on to his seat, and cracked his whip.

"Vive la France!" he bawled with all the force of his lungs.

A thousand throats answered him.

Then there was a stir behind them. Another carriage was being slowly forced to the front. The crowd was pushing it, and crying, "Marseillaise! Marseillaise!" In the carriage was a woman alone; not beautiful, but distinguished, and with the assured gaze of one who is accustomed to homage and multitudinous applause.

"It is Gueymard!" said Chirac to Sophia. He was very pale. And he too shouted, "Marseillaise!" All his features were distorted.

The woman rose and spoke to her coachman, who offered his

hand and she climbed to the box seat, and stood on it and bowed several times.

"Marseillaise!" The cry continued. Then a roar of cheers, and then silence spread round the square like an inundation. And amid this silence the woman began to sing the Marseillaise. As she sang, the tears ran down her cheeks. Everybody in the vicinity was weeping or sternly frowning. In the pauses of the first verse could be heard the rattle of horses' bits, or a whistle of a tug on the river. The refrain, signalled by a proud challenging toss of Gueymard's head, leapt up like a tropical tempest, formidable, overpowering. Sophia, who had no warning of the emotion gathering within her, sobbed violently. At the close of the hymn Gueymard's carriage was assaulted by worshippers. All around, in the tumult of shouting, men were kissing and embracing each other; and hats went up continually in fountains. Chirac leaned over the side of the carriage and wrung the hand of a man who was standing by the wheel.

"Who is that?" Sophia asked, in an unsteady voice, to break the inexplicable tension within her.

"I don't know," said Chirac. He was weeping like a child. And he sang out: "Victory! To Berlin! Victory!"

v

Sophia walked alone, with tired limbs, up the damaged oak stairs to the flat. Chirac had decided that, in the circumstances of the victory, he would do well to go to the offices of his paper rather earlier than usual. He had brought her back to the Rue Bréda. They had taken leave of each other in a sort of dream or general enchantment due to their participation in the vast national delirium which somehow dominated individual feelings. They did not define their relations. They had been conscious only of emotion.

The stairs, which smelt of damp even in summer, disgusted Sophia. She thought of the flat with horror and longed for green places and luxury. On the landing were two stoutish, ill-dressed men, of middle age, apparently waiting. Sophia found her key and opened the door.

"Pardon, madame!" said one of the men, raising his hat, and they both pushed into the flat after her. They stared, puzzled, at the strips of paper pasted on the doors.

"What do you want?" she asked haughtily. She was very frightened. The extraordinary irruption brought her down with a shock to the scale of the individual.

"I am the concierge," said the man who had addressed her. He had the air of a superior artisan. "It was my wife who spoke to you this afternoon. This," pointing to his companion, "this is the law. I regret it, but . . ."

The law saluted and shut the front-door. Like the concierge, the law emitted an odour—the odour of uncleanliness on a hot August day.

"The rent?" exclaimed Sophia.

"No, madame, not the rent: the furniture!"

Then she learnt the history of the furniture. It had belonged to the concierge, who had acquired it from a previous tenant and sold it on credit to Madame Foucault. Madame Foucalt had signed bills and had not met them. She had made promises and broken them. She had done everything except discharge her liabilities. She had been warned and warned again. That day had been fixed as the last limit, and she had solemnly assured her creditor that on that day she would pay. On leaving the house she had stated precisely and clearly that she would return before lunch with all the money. She had made no mention of a sick father.

Sophia slowly perceived the extent of Madame Foucault's duplicity and moral cowardice. No doubt the sick father was an invention. The woman, at the end of a tether which no ingenuity of lies could further lengthen, had probably absented herself solely to avoid the pain of witnessing the seizure. She would do anything, however silly, to avoid an immediate unpleasantness. Or perhaps she had absented herself without any particular aim, but simply in the hope that something fortunate might occur. Perhaps she had hoped that Sophia, taken unawares, would generously pay. Sophia smiled grimly.

"Well," she said. "I can't do anything. I suppose you must do what you have to do. You will let me pack up my own affairs?"

"Perfectly, madame!"

She warned them as to the danger of opening the sealed rooms. The man of the law seemed prepared to stay in the corridor indefinitely. No prospect of delay disturbed him.

Strange and disturbing, the triumph of the concierge! He was a locksmith by trade. He and his wife and their children lived in two little dark rooms by the archway—an insignificant fragment of the house. He was away from home about fourteen hours every day, except Sundays, when he washed the courtyard. All the other duties of the concierge were performed by the wife. The pair always looked poor, untidy, dirty, and rather forlorn. But they were steadily levying toll on everybody in the big house. They amassed money in forty ways. They lived for money, and all men have what they live for. With what arrogant gestures Madame Foucault would descend from a carriage at the great door! What respectful attitudes and tones the ageing courtesan would receive from the wife and children of the concierge! But beneath these conventional fictions the truth was that the concierge held the whip. At last he was using it. And he had given himself a half-holiday in order to celebrate his second acquirement of the ostentatious furniture and the crimson lampshades. This was one of the dramatic crises in his career as a man of substance. The national thrill of victory had not penetrated into the flat with the concierge and the law. The emotions of the concierge were entirely independent of the Napoleonic foreign policy.

As Sophia, sick with a sudden disillusion, was putting her things together, and wondering where she was to go, and whether it would be politic to consult Chirac, she heard a fluster at the front door: cries, protestations, implorings. Her own door was thrust open, and Madame Foucault burst in.

"Save me!" exclaimed Madame Foucault, sinking to the ground.

The feeble theatricality of the gesture offended Sophia's taste. She asked sternly what Madame Foucault expected her to do. Had not Madame Foucault knowingly exposed her, without the least warning, to the extreme annoyance of this visit of the law, a visit which meant practically that Sophia was put into the street?

"You must not be hard!" Madame Foucault sobbed.

Sophia learnt the complete history of the woman's efforts to pay for the furniture; a farrago of folly and deceptions. Madame Foucault confessed too much. Sophia scorned confession for the sake of confession. She scorned the impulse which forces a weak creature to insist on its weakness, to revel in remorse, and to find an excuse for its conduct in the very fact that there is no excuse. She gathered that Madame Foucault had in fact gone away in the hope that Sophia, trapped, would pay; and that in the end, she had not even had the courage of her own trickery, and had run back, driven by panic into audacity, to fall at Sophia's feet, lest Sophia might not have yielded and the furniture have been seized. From beginning to end the conduct of Madame Foucault had been fatuous and despicable and wicked. Sophia coldly condemned Madame Foucault for having allowed herself to be brought into the world with such a weak and maudlin character, and for having allowed herself to grow old and ugly. As a sight the woman was positively disgraceful.

"Save me!" she exclaimed again. "I did what I could for you!"

Sophia hated her. But the logic of the appeal was irresistible.

"But what can I do?" she asked reluctantly.

"Lend me the money. You can. If you don't, this will be the end for me."

"And a good thing, too!" thought Sophia's hard sense.

"How much is it?" Sophia glumly asked.

"It isn't a thousand francs!" said Madame Foucault with eagerness. "All my beautiful furniture will go for less than a thousand francs! Save me!"

She was nauseating Sophia.

"Please rise," said Sophia, her hands fidgeting undecidedly.

"I shall repay you, surely!" Madame Foucault asseverated. "I swear!"

"Does she take me for a fool?" thought Sophia, "with her oaths!"

"No!" said Sophia. "I won't lend you the money. But I tell you what I will do. I will buy the furniture at that price; and I will promise to re-sell it to you as soon as you can pay me. Like that, you can be tranquil. But I have very little money. I must have a guarantee. The furniture must be mine till you pay me."

"You are an angel of charity!" cried Madame Foucault, embracing Sophia's skirts. "I will do whatever you wish. Ah! You Englishwomen are astonishing."

Sophia was not an angel of charity. What she had promised to do involved sacrifice and anxiety without the prospect of reward. But it was not charity. It was part of the price

Sophia paid for the exercise of her logical faculty; she paid it unwillingly. "I did what I could for you!" Sophia would have died sooner than remind any one of a benefit conferred, and Madame Foucault had committed precisely that enormity. The appeal was inexcusable to a fine mind; but it was effective.

The men were behind the door, listening. Sophia paid out of her stock of notes. Needless to say, the total was more and not less than a thousand francs. Madame Foucault grew rapidly confidential with the man. Without consulting Sophia, she asked the bailiff to draw up a receipt transferring the ownership of all the furniture to Sophia; and the bailiff, struck into obligingness by glimpses of Sophia's beauty, consented to do so. There was much conferring upon forms of words, and flourishing of pens between thick, vile fingers, and scattering of ink.

Before the men left Madame Foucault uncorked a bottle of wine for them, and helped them to drink it. Throughout the evening she was insupportably deferential to Sophia, who was driven to bed. Madame Foucault contentedly went up to the sixth floor to occupy the servant's bedroom. She was glad to get so far away from sulphur, of which a few faint fumes had penetrated into the corridor.

The next morning, after a stifling night of bad dreams, Sophia was too ill to get up. She looked round at the furniture in the little room, and she imagined the furniture in the other rooms, and dismally thought: "All this furniture is mine. She will never pay me! I am saddled with it."

It was cheaply bought, but she probably could not sell it for even what she had paid. Still, the sense of ownership was reassuring.

The charwoman brought her coffee, and Chirac's newspaper; from which she learnt that the news of the victory which had sent the city mad on the previous day was utterly false. Tears came into her eyes as she gazed absently at all the curtained windows of the courtyard. She had youth and loveliness; according to the rules she ought to have been irresponsible, gay, and indulgently watched over by the wisdom of admiring age. But she felt towards the French nation as a mother might feel towards adorable, wilful children suffering through their own charming foolishness. She saw France personified in Chirac. How easily, despite his special knowledge, he had yielded to the fever! Her heart bled for France and Chirac on that morning of reaction and of truth. She could not bear to recall the scene in the Place de la Concorde. Madame Foucault had not descended.

CHAPTER VI

THE SIEGE

MADAME FOUCAULT came into Sophia's room one afternoon with a peculiar guilty expression on her large face, and she held her peignoir close to her exuberant body in folds consciously majestic, as though endeavouring to prove to Sophia by her carriage that despite her shifting eyes she was the most righteous and sincere woman that ever lived.

It was Saturday, the third of September, a beautiful day. Sophia, suffering from an unimportant relapse, had remained in a state of inactivity, and had scarcely gone out at all. She loathed the flat, but lacked the energy to leave it every day. There was no sufficiently definite object in leaving it. She could not go out and look for health as she might have looked for flowers. So she remained in the flat, and stared at the courtyard and the continual mystery of lives hidden behind curtains that occasionally moved. And the painted yellow walls of the house, and the papered walls of her room pressed upon her and crushed her. For a few days Chirac had called daily, animated by the most adorable solicitude. Then he had ceased to call. She had tired of reading the journals; they lay unopened. The relations between Madame Foucault and herself, and her status in the flat of which she now legally owned the furniture,—these things were left unsettled. But the question of her board was arranged on the terms that she halved the cost of food and service with Madame Foucault; her expenses were thus reduced to the lowest possible—about eighteen francs a week. An idea hung in the air—like a scientific discovery on the point of being made by several independent investigators simultaneously—that she and Madame Foucault should cooperate in order to let furnished rooms at a remunerative profit. Sophia felt the nearness of the idea and she wanted to be shocked at the notion of any avowed association between herself and Madame Foucault; but she could not be.

"Here are a lady and a gentleman who want a bedroom," began Madame Foucault, "a nice large bedroom, furnished."

"Oh!" said Sophia; "who are they?"

"They will pay a hundred and thirty francs a month, in advance, for the middle bedroom."

"You've shown it to them already?" said Sophia. And her tone implied that somehow she was conscious of a right to overlook the affair of Madame Foucault.

"No," said the other. "I said to myself that first I would ask you for a counsel."

"Then will they pay all that for a room they haven't seen?"

"The fact is," said Madame Foucault, sheepishly. "The lady has seen the room before. I know her a little. It is a former tenant. She lived here some weeks."

"In that room?"

"Oh no! She was poor enough then."

"Where are they?"

"In the corridor. She is very well, the lady. Naturally one must live, she like all the world; but she is veritably well. Quite respectable! One would never say . . . Then there would be the meals. We could demand one franc for the *café au lait*, two and a half francs for the lunch, and three francs for the dinner. Without counting other things. That would mean over five hundred francs a month, at least. And what would they cost us? Almost nothing! By what appears, he is a plutocrat . . . I could thus quickly repay you."

"Is it a married couple?"

"Ah! You know, one cannot demand the marriage certificate." Madame Foucault indicated by a gesture that the Rue Bréda was not the paradise of saints.

"When she came before, this lady, was it with the same man?" Sophia asked coldly.

"Ah, my faith, no!" exclaimed Madame Foucault, bridling. "It was a bad sort, the other, a . . . ! Ah, no."

"Why do you ask my advice?" Sophia abruptly questioned, in a hard, inimical voice. "Is it that it concerns me?"

Tears came at once into the eyes of Madame Foucault. "Do not be unkind," she implored.

"I'm not unkind," said Sophia, in the same tone.

"Shall you leave me if I accept this offer?"

There was a pause.

"Yes," said Sophia, bluntly. She tried to be large-hearted,

large-minded, and sympathetic; but there was no sign of these
qualities in her speech.

"And if you take with you the furniture which is yours . . . !"

Sophia kept silence.

"How am I to live, I demand of you?" Madame Foucault
asked weakly.

"By being respectable and dealing with respectable people!"
said Sophia, uncompromisingly, in tones of steel.

"I am unhappy!" murmured the elder woman. "However,
you are more strong than I!"

She brusquely dabbed her eyes, gave a little sob, and ran
out of the room. Sophia listened at the door, and heard her
dismiss the would-be tenants of the best bedroom. She wondered that she should possess such moral ascendancy over the
woman, she so young and ingenuous! For, of course, she had
not meant to remove the furniture. She could hear Madame
Foucault sobbing quietly in one of the other rooms; and her
lips curled.

Before evening a truly astonishing event happened. Perceiving that Madame Foucault showed no signs of bestirring
herself, Sophia, with good nature in her heart but not on her
tongue, went to her, and said:

"Shall I occupy myself with the dinner?"

Madame Foucault sobbed more loudly.

"That would be very amiable on your part," Madame Foucault managed at last to reply, not very articulately.

Sophia put a hat on and went to the grocer's. The grocer,
who kept a busy establishment at the corner of the Rue Clausel, was a middle-aged and wealthy man. He had sent his young
wife and two children to Normandy until victory over the
Prussians should be more assured, and he asked Sophia
whether it was true that there was a good bedroom to let in
the flat where she lived. His servant was ill of smallpox; he
was attacked by anxieties and fears on all sides; he would not
enter his own flat on account of possible infection; he liked
Sophia, and Madame Foucault had been a customer of his,
with intervals, for twenty years. Within an hour he had arranged to rent the middle bedroom at eighty francs a month,
and to take his meals there. The terms were modest, but the
respectability was prodigious. All the glory of this tenancy
fell upon Sophia.

Madame Foucault was deeply impressed. Characteristically

she began at once to construct a theory that Sophia had only to walk out of the house in order to discover ideal tenants for the rooms. Also she regarded the advent of the grocer as a reward from Providence for her self-denial in refusing the profits of sinfulness. Sophia felt personally responsible to the grocer for his comfort, and so she herself undertook the preparation of the room. Madame Foucault was amazed at the thoroughness of her housewifery, and at the ingenuity of her ideas for the arrangement of furniture. She sat and watched with admiration sycophantic but real.

That night, when Sophia was in bed, Madame Foucault came into the room, and dropped down by the side of the bed, and begged Sophia to be her moral support for ever. She confessed herself generally. She explained how she had always hated the negation of respectability; how respectability was the one thing that she had all her life passionately desired. She said that if Sophia would be her partner in the letting of furnished rooms to respectable persons, she would obey her in everything. She gave Sophia a list of all the traits in Sophia's character which she admired. She asked Sophia to influence her, to stand by her. She insisted that she would sleep on the sixth floor in the servant's tiny room; and she had a vision of three bedrooms let to successful tradesmen. She was in an ecstasy of repentance and good intentions.

Sophia consented to the business proposition; for she had nothing else whatever in prospect, and she shared Madame Foucault's rosy view about the remunerativeness of the bedrooms. With three tenants who took meals the two women would be able to feed themselves for nothing and still make a profit on the food; and the rents would be clear gain.

And she felt very sorry for the ageing, feckless Madame Foucault, whose sincerity was obvious. The association between them would be strange; it would have been impossible to explain it to St. Luke's Square. . . . And yet, if there was anything at all in the virtue of Christian charity, what could properly be urged against the association?

"Ah!" murmured Madame Foucault, kissing Sophia's hands, "it is to-day, then, that I recommence my life. You will see— you will see! You have saved me!"

It was a strange sight, the time-worn, disfigured courtesan, half prostrate before the beautiful young creature proud and unassailable in the instinctive force of her own character. It was almost a didactic tableau, fraught with lessons for the vicious. Sophia was happier than she had been for years. She had a purpose in existence; she had a fluid soul to mould to her will according to her wisdom; and there was a large compassion to her credit. Public opinion could not intimidate her, for in her case there was no public opinion; she knew nobody; nobody had the right to question her doings.

The next day, Sunday, they both worked hard at the bedrooms from early morning. The grocer was installed in his chamber, and the two other rooms were cleansed as they had never been cleansed. At four o'clock, the weather being more magnificent than ever, Madame Foucault said:

"If we took a promenade on the boulevard?"

Sophia reflected. They were partners. "Very well," she agreed.

The boulevard was crammed with gay, laughing crowds. All the cafés were full. None, who did not know, could have guessed that the news of Sedan was scarcely a day old in the capital. Delirious joy reigned in the glittering sunshine. As the two women strolled along, content with their industry and their resolves, they came to a National Guard, who, perched on a ladder, was chipping away the "N" from the official sign of a court-tradesman. He was exchanging jokes with a circle of open mouths. It was in this way that Madame Foucault and Sophia learnt of the establishment of a republic.

"Vive la république!" cried Madame Foucault, incontinently, and then apologized to Sophia for the lapse.

They listened a long while to a man who was telling strange histories of the Empress.

Suddenly Sophia noticed that Madame Foucault was no longer at her elbow. She glanced about, and saw her in earnest conversation with a young man whose face seemed familiar. She remembered it was the young man with whom Madame Foucault had quarrelled on the night when Sophia found her prone in the corridor; the last remaining worshipper of the courtesan.

The woman's face was quite changed by her agitation. Sophia drew away, offended. She watched the pair from a distance for a few moments, and then, furious in disillusion, she escaped from the fever of the boulevards and walked quietly home. Madame Foucault did not return. Apparently Madame Foucault was doomed to be the toy of chance. Two

days later Sophia received a scrawled letter from her, with the
information that her lover had required that she should accompany him to Brussels, as Paris would soon be getting dangerous. "He adores me always. He is the most delicious boy. As
I have always said, this is the grand passion of my life. I am
happy. He would not permit me to come to you. He has spent
two thousand francs on clothes for me, since naturally I had
nothing." And so on. No word of apology. Sophia, in reading
the letter, allowed for a certain exaggeration and twisting of
the truth.

"Young fool! Fool!" she burst out angrily. She did not
mean herself; she meant the fatuous adorer of that dilapidated,
horrible woman. She never saw her again. Doubtless Madame
Foucault fulfilled her own prediction as to her ultimate destiny, but in Brussels.

ii

Sophia still possessed about a hundred pounds, and had she
chosen to leave Paris and France, there was nothing to prevent
her from doing so. Perhaps if she had chanced to visit the
Gare St. Lazare or the Gare du Nord, the sight of tens of
thousands of people flying seawards might have stirred in her
the desire to flee also from the vague coming danger. But she
did not visit those termini; she was too busy looking after M.
Niepce, her grocer. Moreover, she would not quit her furniture, which seemed to her to be a sort of rock. With a flat full
of furniture she considered that she ought to be able to devise
a livelihood; the enterprise of becoming independent was already indeed begun. She ardently wished to be independent, to
utilize in her own behalf the gifts of organization, foresight,
commonsense and tenacity which she knew she possessed and
which had lain idle. And she hated the idea of flight.

Chirac returned as unexpectedly as he had gone; an expedition for his paper had occupied him. With his lips he urged
her to go, but his eyes spoke differently. He had, one afternoon, a mood of candid despair, such as he would have dared
to show only to one in whom he felt great confidence. "They
will come to Paris," he said; "nothing can stop them. And
. . . then . . . !" He gave a cynical laugh. But when he
urged her to go she said:

"And what about my furniture? And I've promised M. Niepce to look after him."

Then Chirac informed her that he was without a lodging, and that he would like to rent one of her rooms. She agreed.

Shortly afterwards he introduced a middle-aged acquaintance named Carlier, the secretary-general of his newspaper, who wished to rent a bedroom. Thus by good fortune Sophia let all her rooms immediately, and was sure of over two hundred francs a month, apart from the profit on meals supplied. On this latter occasion Chirac (and his companion too) was quite optimistic, reiterating an absolute certitude that Paris could never be invested. Briefly, Sophia did not believe him. She believed the candidly despairing Chirac. She had no information, no wide theory, to justify her pessimism; nothing but the inward conviction that the race capable of behaving as she had seen it behave in the Place de la Concorde, was bound to be defeated. She loved the French race; but all the practical Teutonic sagacity in her wanted to take care of it in its difficulties, and was rather angry with it for being so unfitted to take care of itself.

She let the men talk, and with careless disdain of their discussions and their certainties she went about her business of preparation. At this period, overworked and harassed by novel responsibilities and risks, she was happier, for days together, than she had ever been, simply because she had a purpose in life and was depending upon herself. Her ignorance of the military and political situation was complete; the situation did not interest her. What interested her was that she had three men to feed wholly or partially, and that the price of eatables was rising. She bought eatables. She bought fifty pecks of potatoes at a franc a peck, and another fifty pecks at a franc and a quarter—double the normal price; ten hams at two and a half francs a pound; a large quantity of tinned vegetables and fruits, a sack of flour, rice, biscuits, coffee, Lyons sausage, dried prunes, dried figs, and much wood and charcoal. But the chief of her purchases was cheese, of which her mother used to say that bread and cheese and water made a complete diet. Many of these articles she obtained from her grocer. All of them, except the flour and the biscuits, she stored in the cellar belonging to the flat; after several days' delay, for the Parisian workmen were too elated by the advent of a republic to stoop to labour, she caused a new lock to be fixed on the cellar-door. Her activities were the sensation of the house. Everybody admired, but no one imitated.

One morning, on going to do her marketing, she found a notice across the shuttered windows of her creamery in the Rue Notre Dame de Lorette: "Closed for want of milk." The siege had begun. It was in the closing of the creamery that the siege was figured for her; in this, and in eggs at five sous a piece. She went elsewhere for her milk and paid a franc a litre for it. That evening she told her lodgers that the price of meals would be doubled, and that if any gentleman thought that he could get equally good meals elsewhere, he was at liberty to get them elsewhere. Her position was strengthened by the appearance of another candidate for a room, a friend of Niepce. She at once offered him her own room, at a hundred and fifty francs a month.

"You see," she said, "there is a piano in it."

"But I don't play the piano," the man protested, shocked at the price.

"That is not my fault," she said.

He agreed to pay the price demanded for the room because of the opportunity of getting good meals much cheaper than in the restaurants. Like M. Niepce, he was a "siege-widower," his wife having been put under shelter in Brittany. Sophia took to the servant's bedroom on the sixth floor. It measured nine feet by seven, and had no window save a skylight; but Sophia was in a fair way to realize a profit of at least four pounds a week, after paying for everything.

On the night when she installed herself in that chamber, amid a world of domestics and poor people, she worked very late, and the rays of her candles shot up intermittently through the skylight into a black heaven; at intervals she flitted up and down the stairs with a candle. Unknown to her a crowd gradually formed opposite the house in the street, and at about one o'clock in the morning a file of soldiers woke the concierge and invaded the courtyard, and every window was suddenly populated with heads. Sophia was called upon to prove that she was not a spy signalling to the Prussians. Three quarters of an hour passed before her innocence was established and the staircases cleared of uniforms and dishevelled curiosity. The childish, impossible unreason of the suspicion against her completed in Sophia's mind the ruin of the reputation of the French people as a sensible race. She was extremely caustic the next day to her boarders. Except for this episode, the frequency of military uniforms in the streets, the price of food, and the fact that at least one house in four was flying either the ambulance flag or the flag of a foreign embassy (in an absurd hope of immunity from the impending bombardment) the siege did not exist for Sophia. The men often talked about their guard-duty, and disappeared for a day or two to the ramparts, but she was too busy to listen to them. She thought of nothing but her enterprise, which absorbed all her powers. She arose at six a.m. in the dark, and by seven-thirty M. Niepce and his friend had been served with breakfast, and much general work was already done. At eight o'clock she went out to market. When asked why she continued to buy at a high price, articles of which she had a store, she would reply: "I am keeping all that till things are much dearer." This was regarded as astounding astuteness.

On the fifteenth of October she paid the quarter's rent of the flat, four hundred francs, and was accepted as tenant. Her ears were soon quite accustomed to the sound of cannon, and she felt that she had always been a citizeness of Paris, and that Paris had always been besieged. She did not speculate about the end of the siege; she lived from day to day. Occasionally she had a qualm of fear, when the firing grew momentarily louder, or when she heard that battles had been fought in such and such a suburb. But then she said it was absurd to be afraid when you were with a couple of million people, all in the same plight as yourself. She grew reconciled to everything. She even began to like her tiny bedroom, partly because it was so easy to keep warm (the question of artificial heat was growing acute in Paris), and partly because it ensured her privacy. Down in the flat, whatever was done or said in one room could be more or less heard in all the others, owing to the prevalence of doors.

Her existence, in the first half of November, had become regular with a monotony almost absolute. Only the number of meals served to her boarders varied slightly from day to day. All these repasts, save now and then one in the evening, were carried into the bedrooms by the charwoman. Sophia did not allow herself to be seen much, except in the afternoons. Though Sophia continued to increase her prices, and was now selling her stores at an immense profit, she never approached the prices current outside. She was very indignant against the ex-

ploitation of Paris by its shopkeepers, who had vast supplies
of provender, and were hoarding for the rise. But the force of
their example was too great for her to ignore it entirely; she
contented herself with about half their gains. Only to M.
Niepce did she charge more than to the others, because he was
a shopkeeper. The four men appreciated their paradise. In
them developed that agreeable feeling of security which solitary males find only under the roof of a landlady who is at once
prompt, honest, and a votary of cleanliness. Sophia hung a
slate near the front-door, and on this slate they wrote their re-
quests for meals, for being called, for laundry-work, etc.
Sophia never made a mistake, and never forgot. The perfection of the domestic machine amazed these men, who had been
accustomed to something quite different, and who every day
heard harrowing stories of discomfort and swindling from their
acquaintances. They even admired Sophia for making them
pay, if not too high, still high. They thought it wonderful that
she should tell them the price of all things in advance, and even
show them how to avoid expense, particularly in the matter of
warmth. She arranged rugs for each of them, so that they
could sit comfortably in their rooms with nothing but a small
charcoal heater for the hands. Quite naturally they came to
regard her as the paragon and miracle of women. They endowed her with every fine quality. According to them there
had never been such a woman in the history of mankind; there
could not have been! She became legendary among their
friends: a young and elegant creature, surpassingly beautiful,
proud, queenly, unapproachable, scarcely visible, a marvellous manager, a fine cook and artificer of strange English
dishes, utterly reliable, utterly exact and with habits of order
. . . . ! They adored the slight English accent which gave a
touch of the exotic to her very correct and freely idiomatic
French. In short, Sophia was perfect for them, an impossible
woman. Whatever she did was right.

And she went up to her room every night with limbs exhausted, but with head clear enough to balance her accounts
and go through her money. She did this in bed with thick gloves
on. If often she did not sleep well, it was not because of the distant guns, but because of her preoccupation with the subject
of finance. She was making money, and she wanted to make
more. She was always inventing ways of economy. She was so
anxious to achieve independence that money was always in her

mind. She began to love gold, to love hoarding it, and to hate paying it away.

One morning her charwoman, who by good fortune was nearly as precise as Sophia herself, failed to appear. When the moment came for serving M. Niepce's breakfast, Sophia hesitated, and then decided to look after the old man personally. She knocked at his door, and went boldly in with the tray and candle. He started at seeing her; she was wearing a blue apron, as the charwoman did, but there could be no mistaking her for the charwoman. Niepce looked older in bed than when dressed. He had a rather ridiculous, undignified appearance, common among old men before their morning toilette is achieved; and a nightcap did not improve it. His rotund paunch lifted the bedclothes, upon which, for the sake of extra warmth, he had spread unmajestic garments. Sophia smiled to herself; but the contempt implied by that secret smile was softened by the thought: "Poor old man!" She told him briefly that she supposed the charwoman to be ill. He coughed and moved nervously. His benevolent and simple face beamed on her paternally as she fixed the tray by the bed.

"I really must open the window for one little second," she said, and did so. The chill air of the street came through the closed shutters, and the old man made a noise as of shivering. She pushed back the shutters, and closed the window, and then did the same with the other two windows. It was almost day in the room.

"You will no longer need the candle," she said, and came back to the bedside to extinguish it.

The benign and fatherly old man put his arm round her waist. Fresh from the tonic of pure air, and with the notion of his ridiculousness still in her mind, she was staggered for an instant by this gesture. She had never given a thought to the temperament of the old grocer, the husband of a young wife. She could not always imaginatively keep in mind the effect of her own radiance, especially under such circumstances. But after an instant her precocious cynicism, which had slept, sprang up. "Naturally! I might have expected it!" she thought with blasting scorn.

"Take away your hand!" she said bitterly to the amiable old fool. She did not stir.

He obeyed, sheepishly.

"Do you wish to remain with me?" she asked, and as he did

not immediately answer, she said in a most commanding tone: "Answer, then!"

"Yes," he said feebly.

"Well, behave properly."

She went towards the door.

"I wished only——" he stammered.

"I do not wish to know what you wished," she said.

Afterwards she wondered how much of the incident had been overheard. The other breakfasts she left outside the respective doors; and in future Niepce's also.

The charwoman never came again. She had caught smallpox and she died of it, thus losing a good situation. Strange to say, Sophia did not replace her; the temptation to save her wages and food was too strong. She could not, however, stand waiting for hours at the door of the official baker and the official butcher, one of a long line of frozen women, for the daily rations of bread and tri-weekly rations of meat. She employed the concierge's boy, at two sous an hour, to do this. Sometimes he would come in with his hands so blue and cold that he could scarcely hold the precious cards which gave the right to the rations and which cost Chirac an hour or two of waiting at the mayoral offices each week. Sophia might have fed her flock without resorting to the official rations, but she would not sacrifice the economy which they represented. She demanded thick clothes for the concierge's boy, and received boots from Chirac, gloves from Carlier, and a great overcoat from Niepce. The weather increased in severity, and provisions in price. One day she sold to the wife of a chemist who lived on the first floor, for a hundred and ten francs, a ham for which she had paid less than thirty francs. She was conscious of a thrill of joy in receiving a beautiful banknote and a gold coin in exchange for a mere ham. By this time her total cash resources had grown to nearly five thousand francs. It was astounding. And the reserves in the cellar were still considerable, and the sack of flour that encumbered the kitchen was still more than half full. The death of the faithful charwoman, when she heard of it, produced but little effect on Sophia, who was so overworked and so completely absorbed in her own affairs that she had no nervous energy to spare for sentimental regrets. The charwoman by whose side she had regularly passed many hours in the kitchen, so that she knew every crease in her face and fold of her dress, vanished out of Sophia's memory.

Sophia cleaned and arranged two of the bedrooms in the morning, and two in the afternoon. She had stayed in hotels where fifteen bedrooms were in charge of a single chambermaid, and she thought it would be hard if she could not manage four in the intervals of cooking and other work! This she said to herself by way of excuse for not engaging another charwoman. One afternoon she was rubbing the brass knobs of the numerous doors in M. Niepce's room, when the grocer unexpectedly came in.

She glanced at him sharply. There was a self-conscious look in his eye. He had entered the flat noiselessly. She remembered having told him, in response to a question, that she now did his room in the afternoon. Why should he have left his shop? He hung up his hat behind the door, with the meticulous care of an old man. Then he took off his overcoat and rubbed his hands.

"You do well to wear gloves, madame," he said. "It is dog's weather."

"I do not wear them for the cold," she replied. "I wear them so as not to spoil my hands."

"Ah! truly! Very well! Very well! May I demand some wood? Where shall I find it? I do not wish to derange you."

She refused his help, and brought wood from the kitchen, counting the logs audibly before him.

"Shall I light the fire now?" she asked.

"I will light it," he said.

"Give me a match, please."

As she was arranging the wood and paper, he said: "Madame, will you listen to me?"

"What is it?"

"Do not be angry," he said. "Have I not proved that I am capable of respecting you? I continue in that respect. It is with all that respect that I say to you that I love you, madame. . . . No, remain calm, I implore you!" The fact was that Sophia showed no sign of not remaining calm. "It is true that I have a wife. But what do you wish . . . ? She is far away. I love you madly," he proceeded with dignified respect. "I know I am old; but I am rich. I understand your character. You are a lady, you are decided, direct, sincere, and a woman of business. I have the greatest respect for you. One can talk to you as one could not to another woman. You prefer directness and sincerity. Madame, I will give you two thousand francs a month, and all you require from my shop, if you will be amiable to me. I am very solitary, I need the society of a charming creature who would be sympathetic. Two thousand francs a month. It is money."

He wiped his shiny head with his hand.

Sophia was bending over the fire. She turned her head towards him.

"Is that all?" she said quietly.

"You could count on my discretion," he said in a low voice. "I appreciate your scruples. I would come, very late, to your room on the sixth. One could arrange . . . You see, I am direct, like you."

She had an impulse to order him tempestuously out of the flat; but it was not a genuine impulse. He was an old fool. Why not treat him as such? To take him seriously would be absurd. Moreover, he was a very remunerative boarder.

"Do not be stupid," she said with cruel tranquillity. "Do not be an old fool."

And the benign but fatuous middle-aged lecher saw the enchanting vision of Sophia, with her natty apron and her amusing gloves, sweep and fade from the room. He left the house, and the expensive fire warmed an empty room.

Sophia was angry with him. He had evidently planned the proposal. If capable of respect, he was evidently also capable of chicane. But she supposed these Frenchmen were all alike: disgusting; and decided that it was useless to worry over a universal fact. They had simply no shame, and she had been very prudent to establish herself far away on the sixth floor. She hoped that none of the other boarders had overheard Niepce's outrageous insolence. She was not sure if Chirac was not writing in his room.

That night there was no sound of cannon in the distance, and Sophia for some time was unable to sleep. She woke up with a start, after a doze, and struck a match to look at her watch. It had stopped. She had forgotten to wind it up, which omission indicated that the grocer had perturbed her more than she thought. She could not be sure how long she had slept. The hour might be two o'clock or it might be six o'clock. Impossible for her to rest! She got up and dressed (in case it should be as late as she feared) and crept down the interminable creaking stairs with the candle. As she descended, the conviction that it was the middle of the night grew upon her, and she

stepped more softly. There was no sound save that caused by
her footfalls. With her latchkey she cautiously opened the
front-door of the flat and entered. She could then hear the noisy
ticking of the small, cheap clock in the kitchen. At the same
moment another door creaked, and Chirac, with hair all
tousled, but fully dressed, appeared in the corridor.

"So you have decided to sell yourself to him!" Chirac whispered.

She drew away instinctively, and she could feel herself blushing. She was at a loss. She saw that Chirac was in a furious
rage, tremendously moved. He crept towards her, half crouching. She had never seen anything so theatrical as his movement,
and the twitching of his face. She felt that she too ought to
be theatrical, that she ought nobly to scorn his infamous suggestion, his unwarrantable attack. Even supposing that she
had decided to sell herself to the old pasha, did that concern
him? A dignified silence, an annihilating glance, were all that
he deserved. But she was not capable of this heroic behaviour.

"What time is it?" she added weakly.

"Three o'clock," Chirac sneered.

"I forgot to wind up my watch," she said. "And so I came
down to see."

"In effect!" He spoke sarcastically, as if saying: "I've
waited for you, and here you are."

She said to herself that she owed him nothing, but all the
time she felt that he and she were the only young people in
that flat, and that she did owe to him the proof that she was
guiltless of the supreme dishonour of youth. She collected her
forces and looked at him.

"You should be ashamed," she said. "You will wake the
others."

"And M. Niepce—will he need to be wakened?"

"M. Niepce is not here," she said.

Niepce's door was unlatched. She pushed it open, and went
into the room, which was empty and bore no sign of having
been used.

"Come and satisfy yourself!" she insisted.

Chirac did so. His face fell.

She took her watch from her pocket.

"And now wind my watch, and set it, please."

She saw that he was in anguish. He could not take the watch.
Tears came into his eyes. Then he hid his face, and dashed

away. She heard a sob-impeded murmur that sounded like, "Forgive me!" and the banging of a door. And in the stillness she heard the regular snoring of M. Carlier. She too cried. Her vision was blurred by a mist, and she stumbled into the kitchen and seized the clock, and carried it with her upstairs, and shivered in the intense cold of the night. She wept gently for a very long time. "What a shame! What a shame!" she said to herself. Yet she did not quite blame Chirac. The frost drove her into bed, but not to sleep. She continued to cry. At dawn her eyes were inflamed with weeping. She was back in the kitchen then. Chirac's door was wide open. He had left the flat. On the slate was written, "I shall not take meals to-day."

iii

Their relations were permanently changed. For several days they did not meet at all; and when at the end of the week Chirac was obliged at last to face Sophia in order to pay his bill, he had a most grievous expression. It was obvious that he considered himself a criminal without any defence to offer for his crime. He seemed to make no attempt to hide his state of mind. But he said nothing. As for Sophia, she preserved a mien of amiable cheerfulness. She exerted herself to convince him by her attitude that she bore no resentment, that she had determined to forget the incident, that in short she was the forgiving angel of his dreams. She did not, however, succeed entirely in being quite natural. Confronted by his misery, it would have been impossible for her to be quite natural, and at the same time quite cheerful!

A little later the social atmosphere of the flat began to grow querulous, disputatious and perverse. The nerves of everybody were seriously strained. This applied to the whole city. Days of heavy rains followed the sharp frosts, and the town was, as it were, sodden with woe. The gates were closed. And though nine-tenths of the inhabitants never went outside the gates, the definite and absolute closing of them demoralized all hearts. Gas was no longer supplied. Rats, cats, and thorough-bred horses were being eaten and pronounced "not bad." The siege had ceased to be a novelty. Friends did not invite one another to a "siege-dinner" as to a picnic. Sophia, fatigued by regular overwork, became weary of the situation. She was angry with the Prussians for dilatoriness, and with the French for inaction, and she poured out her English spleen on her boarders. The boarders told each other in secret that the *patronne* was growing formidable. Chiefly she bore a grudge against the shopkeepers; and when, upon a rumour of peace, the shop-windows one day suddenly blossomed with prodigious quantities of all edibles, at highest prices, thus proving that the famine was artificially created, Sophia was furious. M. Niepce in particular, though he sold goods to her at a special discount, suffered indignities. A few days later that benign and fatherly man put himself lamentably in the wrong by attempting to introduce into his room a charming young creature who knew how to be sympathetic. Sophia, by an accident unfortunate for the grocer, caught them in the corridor. She was beside herself, but the only outward symptoms were a white face and a cold steely voice that grated like a rasp on the susceptibilities of the adherents of Aphrodite. At this period Sophia had certainly developed into a termagant—without knowing it!

She would often insist now on talking about the siege, and hearing everything that the men could tell her. Her comments, made without the least regard for the justifiable delicacy of their feelings as Frenchmen, sometimes led to heated exchanges. When all Montmartre and the Quartier Bréda was impassioned by the appearance from outside of the Thirty-second battalion, she took the side of the populace, and would not credit the solemn statement of the journalists, proved by documents, that these maltreated soldiers were not cowards in fight. She supported the women who had spit in the faces of the Thirty-second. She actually said that if she had met them, she would have spit too. Really, she was convinced of the innocence of the Thirty-second, but something prevented her from admitting it. The dispute ended with high words between herself and Chirac.

The next day Chirac came home at an unusual hour, knocked at the kitchen door, and said:

"I must give notice to leave you."

"Why?" she demanded curtly.

She was kneading flour and water for a potato-cake. Her potato-cakes were the joy of the household.

"My paper has stopped!" said Chirac.

"Oh!" she added thoughtfully, but not looking at him. "That is no reason why you should leave."

"Yes," he said. "This place is beyond my means. I do not need to tell you that in ceasing to appear the paper has omitted to pay its debts. The house owes me a month's salary. So I must leave."

"No!" said Sophia. "You can pay me when you have money."

He shook his head. "I have no intention of accepting your kindness."

"Haven't you got any money?" she abruptly asked.

"None," said he. "It is the disaster—quite simply!"

"Then you will be forced to get into debt somewhere."

"Yes, but not here! Not to you!"

"Truly, Chirac," she exclaimed, with a cajoling voice, "you are not reasonable."

"Nevertheless it is like that!" he said with decision.

"Eh, well!" she turned on him menacingly. "It will not be like that! You understand me? You will stay. And you will pay me when you can. Otherwise we shall quarrel. Do you imagine I shall tolerate your childishness? Just because you were angry last night——"

"It is not that," he protested. "You ought to know it is not that." (She did.) "It is solely that I cannot permit myself to——"

"Enough!" she cried peremptorily, stopping him. And then in a quieter tone, "And what about Carlier? Is he also in the ditch?"

"Ah! he has money," said Chirac, with sad envy.

"You also, one day," said she. "You stop—in any case until after Christmas, or we quarrel. Is it agreed?" Her accent had softened.

"You are too good!" he yielded. "I cannot quarrel with you. But it pains me to accept——"

"Oh!" she snapped, dropping into the vulgar idiom, "you make me sweat with your stupid pride. Is it that that you call friendship? Go away now. How do you wish that I should succeed with this cake while you station yourself there to distract me?"

iv

But in three days Chirac, with amazing luck, fell into another situation, and on the *Journal des Débats*. It was the

Prussians who had found him a place. The celebrated Payenneville, second greatest *chroniqueur* of his time, had caught a
cold while doing his duty as a national guard, and had died of
pneumonia. The weather was severe again; soldiers were being frozen to death at Aubervilliers. Payenneville's position
was taken by another man, whose post was offered to Chirac.
He told Sophia of his good fortune with unconcealed vanity.

"You with your smile!" she said impatiently. "One can refuse you nothing!"

She behaved just as though Chirac had disgusted her. She
humbled him. But with his fellow-lodgers his airs of importance as a member of the editorial staff of the *Débats* were comical in their ingenuousness. On the very same day Carlier gave
notice to leave Sophia. He was comparatively rich; but the
habits which had enabled him to arrive at independence in the
uncertain vocation of a journalist would not allow him, while
he was earning nothing, to spend a sou more than was absolutely necessary. He had decided to join forces with a widowed sister, who was accustomed to parsimony as parsimony is
understood in France, and who was living on hoarded potatoes
and wine.

"There!" said Sophia, "you have lost me a tenant!"

And she insisted, half jocularly and half seriously, that
Carlier was leaving because he could not stand Chirac's infantile conceit. The flat was full of acrimonious words.

On Christmas morning Chirac lay in bed rather late; the
newspapers did not appear that day. Paris seemed to be in a
sort of stupor. About eleven o'clock he came to the kitchen
door.

"I must speak with you," he said. His tone impressed
Sophia.

"Enter," said she.

He went in, and closed the door like a conspirator. "We
must have a little fête," he said. "You and I."

"Fête!" she repeated. "What an idea! How can I leave?"

If the idea had not appealed to the secrecies of her heart,
stirring desires and souvenirs upon which the dust of time lay
thick, she would not have begun by suggesting difficulties; she
would have begun by a flat refusal.

"That is nothing," he said vigorously. "It is Christmas, and
I must have a chat with you. We cannot chat here. I have not

had a true little chat with you since you were ill. You will come with me to a restaurant for lunch."

She laughed. "And the lunch of my lodgers?"

"You will serve it a little earlier. We will go out immediately afterwards, and we will return in time for you to prepare dinner. It is quite simple."

She shook her head. "You are mad," she said crossly.

"It is necessary that I should offer you something," he went on scowling. "You comprehend me? I wish you to lunch with me to-day. I demand it, and you are not going to refuse me."

He was very close to her in the little kitchen, and he spoke fiercely, bullyingly, exactly as she had spoken to him when insisting that he should live on credit with her for a while.

"You are very rude," she parried.

"If I am rude, it is all the same to me," he held out uncompromisingly. "You will lunch with me; I hold to it."

"How can I be dressed?" she protested.

"That does not concern me. Arrange that as you can."

It was the most curious invitation to a Christmas dinner imaginable.

At a quarter past twelve they issued forth side by side, heavily clad, into the mournful streets. The sky, slate-coloured, presaged snow. The air was bitterly cold, and yet damp. There were no fiacres in the little three-cornered place which forms the mouth of the Rue Clausel. In the Rue Notre Dame de Lorette, a single empty omnibus was toiling up the steep glassy slope, the horses slipping and recovering themselves in response to the whip-cracking, which sounded in the streets as in an empty vault. Higher up, in the Rue Fontaine, one of the few shops that were open displayed this announcement: "*A large selection of cheeses for New Year's gifts.*" They laughed.

"Last year at this moment," said Chirac, "I was thinking of only one thing—the masked ball at the opera. I could not sleep after it. This year even the churches are not open. And you?"

She put her lips together. "Do not ask me," she said.

They proceeded in silence.

"We are triste, we others," he said. "But the Prussians, in their trenches, they cannot be so gay, either! Their families and their Christmas trees must be lacking to them. Let us laugh!"

The Place Blanche and the Boulevard de Clichy were no

more lively than the lesser streets and squares. There was no
life anywhere, scarcely a sound; not even the sound of cannon.
Nobody knew anything; Christmas had put the city into a
lugubrious trance of hopelessness. Chirac took Sophia's arm
across the Place Blanche, and a few yards up the Rue Lepic
he stopped at a small restaurant, famous among the initiated,
and known as "The Little Louis." They entered, descending by
two steps into a confined and sombrely picturesque interior.

Sophia saw that they were expected. Chirac must have paid
a previous visit to the restaurant that morning. Several disordered tables showed that people had already lunched, and
left; but in the corner was a table for two, freshly laid in the
best manner of such restaurants; that is to say, with a red-and-
white checked cloth, and two other red-and-white cloths, almost as large as the table-cloth, folded as serviettes and
arranged flat on two thick plates between solid steel cutlery; a
salt-cellar, out of which one ground rock-salt by turning a
handle, a pepper-castor, two knife-rests, and two common
tumblers. The phenomena which differentiated this table from
the ordinary table were a champagne bottle and a couple of
champagne glasses. Champagne was one of the few items which
had not increased in price during the siege.

The landlord and his wife were eating in another corner, a
fat, slatternly pair, whom no privations of a siege could have
emaciated. The landlord rose. He was dressed as a chef, all in
white, with the sacred cap; but a soiled white. Everything in
the place was untidy, unkempt and more or less unclean, except just the table upon which champagne was waiting. And
yet the restaurant was agreeable, reassuring. The landlord
greeted his customers as honest friends. His greasy face was
honest, and so was the pale, weary, humorous face of his wife.
Chirac saluted her.

"You see," said she, across from the other corner, indicating a bone on her plate. "This is Diane!"

"Ah! the poor animal!" exclaimed Chirac, sympathetically.
"What would you?" said the landlady. "It cost too dear to
feed her. And she was so *mignonne!* One could not watch her
grow thin!"

"I was saying to my wife," the landlord put in, "how she
would have enjoyed that bone—Diane!" He roared with laughter.

Sophia and the landlady exchanged a curious sad smile at

this pleasantry, which had been re-discovered by the landlord for perhaps the thousandth time during the siege, but which he evidently regarded as quite new and original.

"Eh, well!" he continued confidentially to Chirac. "I have found for you something very good—half a duck." And in a still lower tone: "And it will not cost you too dear."

No attempt to realize more than a modest profit was ever made in that restaurant. It possessed a regular clientèle who knew the value of the little money they had, and who knew also how to appreciate sincere and accomplished cookery. The landlord was the chef, and he was always referred to as the chef, even by his wife.

"How did you get that?" Chirac asked.

"Ah!" said the landlord, mysteriously. "I have one of my friends, who comes from Villeneuve St. Georges—refugee, you know. In fine . . ." A wave of the fat hands, suggesting that Chirac should not inquire too closely.

"In effect!" Chirac commented. "But it is very chic, that!"

"I believe you that it is *chic!*" said the landlady, sturdily.

"It is charming," Sophia murmured politely.

"And then a quite little salad!" said the landlord.

"But that—that is still more striking!" said Chirac.

The landlord winked. The fact was that the commerce which resulted in fresh green vegetables in the heart of a beleagured town was notorious.

"And then also a quite little cheese!" said Sophia, slightly imitating the tone of the landlord, as she drew from the inwardness of her cloak a small round parcel. It contained a Brie cheese, in fairly good condition. It was worth at least fifty francs, and it had cost Sophia less than two francs. The landlady joined the landlord in inspecting this wondrous jewel. Sophia seized a knife and cut a slice for the landlady's table.

"Madame is too good!" said the landlady, confused by this noble generosity, and bearing the gift off to her table as a fox-terrier will hurriedly seek solitude with a sumptuous morsel. The landlord beamed. Chirac was enchanted. In the intimate and unaffected cosiness of that interior the vast, stupefied melancholy of the city seemed to be forgotten, to have lost its sway.

Then the landlord brought a hot brick for the feet of madame. It was more an acknowledgment of the slice of cheese than a necessity, for the restaurant was very warm; the tiny kitchen opened directly into it, and the door between the two was open; there was no ventilation whatever.

"It is a friend of mine," said the landlord, proudly, in the way of gossip, as he served an undescribed soup, "a butcher in the Faubourg St. Honoré, who has bought the three elephants of the Jardin des Plantes for twenty-seven thousand francs."

Eyebrows were lifted. He uncorked the champagne.

As she drank the first mouthful (she had long lost her youthful aversion for wine), Sophia had a glimpse of herself in a tilted mirror hung rather high on the opposite wall. It was several months since she had attired herself with ceremoniousness. The sudden unexpected vision of elegance and pallid beauty pleased her. And the instant effect of the champagne was to renew in her mind a forgotten conception of the goodness of life and of the joys which she had so long missed.

v

At half-past two they were alone in the little salon of the restaurant, and vaguely in their dreamy and feverish minds that were too preoccupied to control with precision their warm, relaxed bodies, there floated the illusion that the restaurant belonged to them and that in it they were at home. It was no longer a restaurant, but a retreat and shelter from hard life. The chef and his wife were dozing in an inner room. The champagne was drunk; the adorable cheese was eaten; and they were sipping Marc de Bourgogne. They sat at right angles to one another, close to one another, with brains aswing; full of good nature and quick sympathy; their flesh content and yet expectant. In a pause of the conversation (which, entirely banal and fragmentary, had seemed to reach the acme of agreeableness), Chirac put his hand on the hand of Sophia as it rested limp on the littered table. Accidentally she caught his eye; she had not meant to do so. They both became self-conscious. His thin, bearded face had more than ever that wistfulness which always softened towards him the uncompromisingness of her character. He had the look of a child. For her, Gerald had sometimes shown the same look. But indeed she was now one of those women for whom all men, and especially all men in a tender mood, are invested with a certain incurable quality of childishness. She had not withdrawn her hand at once, and so she could not withdraw it at all.

He gazed at her with timid audacity. Her eyes were liquid. "What are you thinking about?" she asked.

"I was asking myself what I should have done if you had refused to come."

"And what *should* you have done?"

"Assuredly something terribly inconvenient," he replied, with the large importance of a man who is in the domain of pure supposition. He leaned towards her. "My very dear friend," he said in a different voice, getting bolder.

It was infinitely sweet to her, voluptuously sweet, this basking in the heat of temptation. It certainly did seem to her, then, the one real pleasure in the world. Her body might have been saying to his: "See how ready I am!" Her body might have been saying to his: "Look into my mind. For you I have no modesty. Look and see all that is there." The veil of convention seemed to have been rent. Their attitude to each other was almost that of lover and mistress, between whom a single glance may be charged with the secrets of the past and promises for the future. Morally she was his mistress in that moment.

He released her hand and put his arm round her waist.

"I love thee," he whispered with great emotion.

Her face changed and hardened. "You must not do that," she said, coldly, unkindly, harshly. She scowled. She would not abate one crease in her forehead to the appeal of his surprised glance. Yet she did not want to repulse him. The instinct which repulsed him was not within her control. Just as a shy man will obstinately refuse an invitation which he is hungering to accept, so, though not from shyness, she was compelled to repulse Chirac. Perhaps if her desires had not been laid to sleep by excessive physical industry and nervous strain, the sequel might have been different.

Chirac, like most men who have once found a woman weak, imagined that he understood women profoundly. He thought of women as the Occidental thinks of the Chinese, as a race apart, mysterious but capable of being infallibly comprehended by the application of a few leading principles of psychology. Moreover he was in earnest; he was hard driven, and he was honest. He continued, respectfully obedient in withdrawing his arm:

"Very dear friend," he urged with undaunted confidence, "you must know that I love you."

She shook her head impatiently, all the time wondering what it was that prevented her from slipping into his arms. She knew that she was treating him badly by this brusque change of front; but she could not help it. Then she began to feel sorry for him.

"We have been very good friends," he said. "I have always admired you enormously. I did not think that I should dare to love you until that day when I overheard that old villain Niepce make his advances. Then, when I perceived my acute jealousy, I knew that I was loving you. Ever since, I have thought only of you. I swear to you that if you will not belong to me, it is already finished for me! Altogether! Never have I seen a woman like you! So strong, so proud, so kind, and so beautiful! You are astonishing, yes, astonishing! No other woman could have drawn herself out of an impossible situation as you have done, since the disappearance of your husband. For me, you are a woman unique. I am very sincere. Besides, you know it. . . . Dear friend!"

She shook her head passionately.

She did not love him. But she was moved. And she wanted to love him. She wanted to yield to him, only liking him, and to love afterwards. But this obstinate instinct held her back.

"I do not say, now," Chirac went on. "Let me hope."

The Latin theatricality of his gestures and his tone made her sorrowful for him.

"My poor Chirac!" she plaintively murmured, and began to put on her gloves.

"I shall hope!" he persisted.

She pursed her lips. He seized her violently by the waist. She drew her face away from his, firmly. She was not hard, not angry now. Disconcerted by her compassion, he loosed her.

"My poor Chirac," she said, "I ought not to have come. I must go. It is perfectly useless. Believe me."

"No, no!" he whispered fiercely.

She stood up and the abrupt movement pushed the table gratingly across the floor. The throbbing spell of the flesh was snapped like a stretched string, and the scene over. The landlord, roused from his doze, stumbled in. Chirac had nothing but the bill as a reward for his pains. He was baffled.

They left the restaurant, silently, with a foolish air.

Dusk was falling on the mournful streets, and the lamplighters were lighting the miserable oil lamps that had replaced gas. They two, and the lamplighters, and an omnibus were alone in the streets. The gloom was awful; it was desolating. The universal silence seemed to be the silence of despair. Steeped in woe, Sophia thought wearily upon the hopeless problem of existence. For it seemed to her that she and Chirac had created this woe out of nothing, and yet it was an incurable woe!

CHAPTER VII

SUCCESS

SOPHIA lay awake one night in the room lately quitted by Carlier. That silent negation of individuality had come and gone, and left scarcely any record of himself either in his room or in the memories of those who had surrounded his existence in the house. Sophia had decided to descend from the sixth floor, partly because the temptation of a large room, after months in a cubicle, was rather strong; but more because of late she had been obliged to barricade the door of the cubicle with a chest of drawers, owing to the propensities of a new tenant of the sixth floor. It was useless to complain to the concierge; the sole effective argument was the chest of drawers, and even that was frailer than Sophia could have wished. Hence, finally, her retreat.

She heard the front-door of the flat open; then it was shut with nervous violence. The resonance of its closing would have certainly wakened less accomplished sleepers than M. Niepce and his friend, whose snores continued with undisturbed regularity. After a pause of shuffling, a match was struck, and feet crept across the corridor with the most exaggerated precautions against noise. There followed the unintentional bang of another door. It was decidedly the entry of a man without the slightest natural aptitude for furtive irruptions. The clock in M. Niepce's room, which the grocer had persuaded to exact time-keeping, chimed three with its delicate *ting*.

For several days past Chirac had been mysteriously engaged very late at the bureaux of the *Débats*. No one knew the nature of his employment; he said nothing, except to inform Sophia that he would continue to come home about three o'clock until further notice. She had insisted on leaving in his room the materials and apparatus for a light meal. Naturally he had protested, with the irrational obstinacy of a physically weak man who sticks to it that he can defy the laws of nature. But he had protested in vain.

His general conduct since Christmas Day had frightened Sophia, in spite of her tendency to stifle facile alarms at their birth. He had eaten scarcely anything at all, and he went about with the face of a man dying of a broken heart. The change in him was indeed tragic. And instead of improving, he grew worse. "Have I done this?" Sophia asked herself. "It is impossible that I should have done this! It is absurd and ridiculous that he should behave so!" Her thoughts were employed alternately in sympathizing with him and in despising him, in blaming herself and in blaming him. When they spoke, they spoke awkwardly, as though one or both of them had committed a shameful crime, which could not even be mentioned. The atmosphere of the flat was tainted by the horror. And Sophia could not offer him a bowl of soup without wondering how he would look at her or avoid looking, and without carefully arranging in advance her own gestures and speech. Existence was a nightmare of self-consciousness.

"At last they have unmasked their batteries!" he had exclaimed with painful gaiety two days after Christmas, when the besiegers had recommenced their cannonade. He tried to imitate the strange, general joy of the city, which had been roused from apathy by the recurrence of a familiar noise; but the effort was a deplorable failure. And Sophia condemned not merely the failure of Chirac's imitation, but the thing imitated. "Childish!" she thought. Yet, despite the feebleness of Chirac's behaviour as she might, she was deeply impressed, genuinely astonished, by the gravity and persistence of the symptoms. "He must have been getting himself into a state about me for a long time," she thought. "Surely he could not have gone mad like this all in a day or two! But I never noticed anything. No; honestly I never noticed anything!" And just as her behaviour in the restaurant had shaken Chirac's confidence in his knowledge of the other sex, so now the singular behaviour of Chirac shook hers. She was taken aback. She was frightened, though she pretended not to be frightened.

She had lived over and over again the scene in the restaurant. She asked herself over and over again if really she had not beforehand expected him to make love to her in the restaurant. She could not decide exactly when she had begun to expect a declaration; but probably a long time before the meal was finished. She had foreseen it, and might have stopped it. But she had not chosen to stop it. Curiosity concerning not merely him, but also herself, had tempted her tacitly to encourage him. She asked herself over and over again why she had repulsed him. It struck her as curious that she had repulsed him. Was it because she was a married woman? Was it because she had moral scruples? Was it at bottom because she did not care for him? Was it because she could not care for anybody? Was it because his fervid manner of love-making offended her English phlegm? And did she feel pleased or displeased by his forbearance in not renewing the assault? She could not answer. She did not know.

But all the time she knew that she wanted love. Only, she conceived a different kind of love: placid, regular, somewhat stern, somewhat above the plane of whims, moods, caresses, and all mere fleshly contacts. Not that she considered that she despised these things (though she did)! What she wanted was a love that was too proud, too independent, to exhibit frankly either its joy or its pain. She hated a display of sentiment. And even in the most intimate abandonments she would have made reserves, and would have expected reserves, trusting to a lover's powers of divination, and to her own! The foundation of her character was a haughty moral independence, and this quality was what she most admired in others.

Chirac's inability to draw from his own pride strength to sustain himself against the blow of her refusal gradually killed in her the sexual desire which he had aroused, and which during a few days flickered up under the stimulus of fancy and of regret. Sophia saw with increasing clearness that her unreasoning instinct had been right in saying him nay. And when, in spite of this, regrets still visited her, she would comfort herself in thinking: "I cannot be bothered with all that sort of thing. It is not worth while. What does it lead to? Is not life complicated enough without that? No, no! I will stay as I am. At any rate I know what I am in for, as things are!" And she would reflect upon her hopeful financial situation, and the approaching prospect of a constantly sufficient income. And a little thrill of impatience against the interminable and gigantic foolishness of the siege would take her.

But her self-consciousness in presence of Chirac did not abate.

As she lay in bed she awaited accustomed sounds which should have connoted Chirac's definite retirement for the night. Her ear, however, caught no sound whatever from his room. Then she imagined that there was a smell of burning in the flat. She sat up, and sniffed anxiously, of a sudden wideawake and apprehensive. And then she was sure that the smell of burning was not in her imagination. The bedroom was in perfect darkness. Feverishly she searched with her right hand for the matches on the night-table, and knocked candlestick and matches to the floor. She seized her dressing-gown, which was spread over the bed, and put it on, aiming for the door. Her feet were bare. She discovered the door. In the passage she could discern nothing at first, and then she made out a thin line of light, which indicated the bottom of Chirac's door. The smell of burning was strong and unmistakable. She went towards the faint light, fumbled for the door-handle with her palm, and opened. It did not occur to her to call out and ask what was the matter.

The house was not on fire; but it might have been. She had left on the table at the foot of Chirac's bed a small cooking-lamp, and a saucepan of bouillon. All that Chirac had to do was to ignite the lamp and put the saucepan on it. He had ignited the lamp, having previously raised the double wicks, and had then dropped into the chair by the table just as he was, and sunk forward and gone to sleep with his head lying sideways on the table. He had not put the saucepan on the lamp; he had not lowered the wicks, and the flames, capped with thick black smoke, were waving slowly to and fro within a few inches of his loose hair. His hat had rolled along the floor; he was wearing his great overcoat and one woollen glove; the other glove had lodged on his slanting knee. A candle was also burning.

Sophia hastened forward, as it were surreptitiously, and with a forward-reaching movement turned down the wicks of the lamp; black specks were falling on the table; happily the saucepan was covered, or the bouillon would have been ruined.

Chirac made a heart-rending spectacle, and Sophia was

aware of deep and painful emotion in seeing him thus. He must have been utterly exhausted and broken by loss of sleep. He was a man incapable of regular hours, incapable of treating his body with decency. Though going to bed at three o'clock, he had continued to rise at his usual hour. He looked like one dead; but more sad, more wistful. Outside in the street a fog reigned, and his thin draggled beard was jewelled with the moisture of it. His attitude had the unconsidered and violent prostration of an overspent dog. The beaten animal in him was expressed in every detail of that posture. It showed even in his white, drawn eyelids, and in the falling of a finger. All his face was very sad. It appealed for mercy as the undefended face of sleep always appeals; it was so helpless, so exposed, so simple. It recalled Sophia to a sense of the inner mysteries of life, reminding her somehow that humanity walks ever on a thin crust over terrific abysses. She did not physically shudder; but her soul shuddered.

She mechanically placed the saucepan on the lamp, and the noise awakened Chirac. He groaned. At first he did not perceive her. When he saw that some one was looking down at him, he did not immediately realize who this some one was. He rubbed his eyes with his fists, exactly like a baby, and sat up, and the chair cracked.

"What then?" he demanded. "Oh, madame, I ask pardon. What?"

"You have nearly destroyed the house," she said. "I smelt fire, and I came in. I was just in time. There is no danger now. But please be careful." She made as if to move towards the door.

"But what did I do?" he asked, his eyelids wavering.

She explained.

He rose from his chair unsteadily. She told him to sit down again, and he obeyed as though in a dream.

"I can go now," she said.

"Wait one moment," he murmured. "I ask pardon. I should not know how to thank you. You are truly too good. Will you wait one moment?"

His tone was one of supplication. He gazed at her, a little dazzled by the light and by her. The lamp and the candle illuminated the lower part of her face, theatrically, and showed the texture of her blue flannel peignoir; the pattern of a part of the lace collar was silhouetted in shadow on her cheek. Her face was flushed, and her hair hung down unconfined. Evidently he could not recover from his excusable astonishment at the apparition of such a figure in his room.

"What is it—now?" she said. The faint, quizzical emphasis which she put on the "now" indicated the essential of her thought. The sight of him touched her and filled her with a womanly sympathy. But that sympathy was only the envelope of her disdain of him. She could not admire weakness. She could but pity it with a pity in which scorn was mingled. Her instinct was to treat him as a child. He had failed in human dignity. And it seemed to her as if she had not previously been quite certain whether she could not love him, but that now she was quite certain. She was close to him. She saw the wounds of a soul that could not hide its wounds, and she resented the sight. She was hard. She would not make allowances. And she revelled in her hardness. Contempt—a good-natured, kindly, forgiving contempt—that was the kernel of the sympathy which exteriorly warmed her! Contempt for the lack of self-control which had resulted in this swift degeneration of a man into a tortured victim! Contempt for the lack of perspective which magnified a mere mushroom passion till it filled the whole field of life! Contempt for this feminine slavery to sentiment! She felt that she might have been able to give herself to Chirac as one gives a toy to an infant. But of loving him . . . ! No! She was conscious of an immeasurable superiority to him, for she was conscious of the freedom of a strong mind.

"I wanted to tell you," said he, "I am going away."

"Where?" she asked.

"Out of Paris."

"Out of Paris? How?"

"By balloon! My journal . . . ! It is an affair of great importance. You understand. I offered myself. What would you?"

"It is dangerous," she observed, waiting to see if he would put on the silly air of one who does not understand fear.

"Oh!" the poor fellow muttered with a fatuous intonation and snapping of the fingers. "That is all the same to me. Yes, it is dangerous. Yes, it is dangerous!" he repeated. "But what would you . . . ? For me . . . !"

She wished that she had not mentioned danger. It hurt her to watch him incurring her ironic disdain.

"It will be the night after to-morrow," he said. "In the

courtyard of the Gare du Nord. I want you to come and see me go. I particularly want you to come and see me go. I have asked Carlier to escort you."

He might have been saying, "I am offering myself to martyrdom, and you must assist at the spectacle."

She despised him yet more.

"Oh! Be tranquil," he said. "I shall not worry you. Never shall I speak to you again of my love. I know you. I know it would be useless. But I hope you will come and wish me bon voyage."

"Of course, if you really wish it," she replied with cheerful coolness.

He seized her hand and kissed it.

Once it had pleased her when he kissed her hand. But now she did not like it. It seemed hysterical and foolish to her. She felt her feet to be stone-cold on the floor.

"I'll leave you now," she said. "Please eat your soup."

She escaped, hoping he would not espy her feet.

ii

The courtyard of the Nord Railway Station was lighted by oil-lamps taken from locomotives; their silvered reflectors threw dazzling rays from all sides on the under portion of the immense yellow mass of the balloon; the upper portion was swaying to and fro with gigantic ungainliness in the strong breeze. It was only a small balloon, as balloons are measured, but it seemed monstrous as it wavered over the human forms that were agitating themselves beneath it. The cordage was silhouetted against the yellow taffetas as high up as the widest diameter of the balloon, but above that all was vague, and even spectators standing at a distance could not clearly separate the summit of the great sphere from the darkly moving sky. The car, held by ropes fastened to stakes, rose now and then a few inches uneasily from the ground. The sombre and severe architecture of the station-buildings enclosed the balloon on every hand; it had only one way of escape. Over the roofs of that architecture, which shut out the sounds of the city, came the irregular booming of the bombardment. Shells were falling in the southern quarters of Paris, doing perhaps not a great deal of damage, but still plunging occasionally into the midst of some domestic interior and making a sad mess of it. The Parisians were convinced that the shells were aimed maliciously at hospitals and museums; and when a child happened to be blown to pieces their unspoken comments upon the Prussian savagery were bitter. Their faces said: "Those barbarians cannot even spare our children!" They amused themselves by creating a market in shells, paying more for a live shell than a dead one, and modifying the tariff according to the supply. And as the cattle-market was empty, and the vegetable-market was empty, and beasts no longer pastured on the grass of the parks, and the twenty-five million rats of the metropolis were too numerous to furnish interest to spectators, and the Bourse was practically deserted, the traffic in shells sustained the starving mercantile instinct during a very dull period. But the effect on the nerves was deleterious. The nerves of everybody were like nothing but a raw wound. Violent anger would spring up magically out of laughter, and blows out of caresses. This indirect consequence of the bombardment was particularly noticeable in the group of men under the balloon. Each behaved as if he were controlling his temper in the most difficult circumstances. Constantly they all gazed upwards into the sky, though nothing could possibly be distinguished there save the blurred edge of a flying cloud. But the booming came from that sky; the shells that were dropping on Montrouge came out of that sky; and the balloon was going up into it; the balloon was ascending into its mysteries, to brave its dangers, to sweep over the encircling ring of fire and savages.

Sophia stood apart with Carlier. Carlier had indicated a particular spot, under the shelter of the colonnade, where he said it was imperative that they should post themselves. Having guided Sophia to this spot, and impressed upon her that they were not to move, he seemed to consider that the activity of his *rôle* was finished, and spoke no word. With the very high silk hat which he always wore, and a thin old-fashioned overcoat whose collar was turned up, he made a rather grotesque figure. Fortunately the night was not very cold, or he might have passively frozen to death on the edge of that feverish group. Sophia soon ignored him. She watched the balloon. An aristocratic old man leaned against the car, watch in hand; at intervals he scowled, or stamped his foot. An old sailor, tranquilly smoking a pipe, walked round and round the balloon, staring at it; once he climbed up into the rigging, and once he jumped into the car and angrily threw out of it a bag, which some one had placed in it. But for the most part he was calm. Other persons of authority hurried about, talking and gesticulating; and a number of workmen waited idly for orders.

"Where is Chirac?" suddenly cried the old man with the watch.

Several voices deferentially answered, and a man ran away into the gloom on an errand.

Then Chirac appeared, nervous, self-conscious, restless. He was enveloped in a fur coat that Sophia had never seen before, and he carried dangling in his hand a cage containing six pigeons whose whiteness stirred uneasily within it. The sailor took the cage from him and all the persons of authority gathered round to inspect the wonderful birds upon which, apparently, momentous affairs depended. When the group separated, the sailor was to be seen bending over the edge of the car to deposit the cage safely. He then got into the car, still smoking his pipe, and perched himself negligently on the wickerwork. The man with the watch was conversing with Chirac; Chirac nodded his head frequently in acquiescence, and seemed to be saying all the time: "Yes, sir! Perfectly, sir! I understand, sir! Yes, sir!"

Suddenly Chirac turned to the car and put a question to the sailor, who shook his head. Whereupon Chirac gave a gesture of submissive despair to the man with the watch. And in an instant the whole throng was in a ferment.

"The victuals!" cried the man with the watch. "The victuals, name of God! Must one be indeed an idiot to forget the victuals! Name of God—of God!"

Sophia smiled at the agitation, and at the inefficient management which had never thought of food. For it appeared that the food had not merely been forgotten; it was a question which had not even been considered. She could not help despising all that crowd of self-important and fussy males to whom the idea had not occurred that even balloonists must eat. And she wondered whether everything was done like that. After a delay that seemed very long, the problem of victuals was solved, chiefly, as far as Sophia could judge, by means of cakes of chocolate and bottles of wine.

"It is enough! It is enough!" Chirac shouted passionately several times to a knot of men who began to argue with him.

Then he gazed round furtively, and with an inflation of the

chest and a patting of his fur coat he came directly towards Sophia. Evidently Sophia's position had been prearranged between him and Carlier. They could forget food, but they could think of Sophia's position!

All eyes followed him. Those eyes could not, in the gloom, distinguish Sophia's beauty, but they could see that she was young and slim and elegant, and of foreign carriage. That was enough. The very air seemed to vibrate with the intense curiosity of those eyes. And immediately Chirac grew into the hero of some brilliant and romantic adventure. Immediately he was envied and admired by every man of authority present. What was she? Who was she? Was it a serious passion or simply a caprice? Had she flung herself at him? It was undeniable that lovely creatures did sometimes fling themselves at lucky mediocrities. Was she a married woman? An artiste? A girl? Such queries thumped beneath overcoats, while the correctness of a ceremonious demeanour was strictly observed.

Chirac uncovered, and kissed her hand. The wind disarranged his hair. She saw that his face was very pale and anxious beneath the swagger of a sincere desire to be brave.

"Well, it is the moment!" he said.

"Did you all forget the food?" she asked.

He shrugged his shoulders. "What will you? One cannot think of everything."

"I hope you will have a safe voyage," she said.

She had already taken leave of him once, in the house, and heard all about the balloon and the sailor-aeronaut and the preparations; and now she had nothing to say, nothing whatever.

He shrugged his shoulders again. "I hope so!" he murmured, but in a tone to convey that he had no such hope.

"The wind isn't too strong?" she suggested.

He shrugged his shoulders again. "What would you?"

"Is it in the direction you want?"

"Yes, nearly," he admitted unwillingly. Then rousing himself: "Eh, well, madame. You have been extremely amiable to come. I held to it very much—that you should come. It is because of you I quit Paris."

She resented the speech by a frown.

"Ah!" he implored in a whisper. "Do not do that. Smile on me. After all, it is not my fault. Remember that this may be the last time I see you, the last time I regard your eyes."

She smiled. She was convinced of the genuineness of the emotion which expressed itself in all this flamboyant behaviour. And she had to make excuses to herself on behalf of Chirac. She smiled to give him pleasure. The hard commonsense in her might sneer, but indubitably she was the centre of a romantic episode. The balloon darkly swinging there! The men waiting! The secrecy of the mission! And Chirac, bareheaded in the wind that was to whisk him away, telling her in fatalistic accents that her image had devastated his life, while envious aspirants watched their colloquy! Yes, it was romantic. And she was beautiful! Her beauty was an active reality that went about the world playing tricks in spite of herself. The thoughts that passed through her mind were the large, splendid thoughts of romance. And it was Chirac who had aroused them! A real drama existed, then, triumphing over the accidental absurdities and pettiness of the situation. Her final words to Chirac were tender and encouraging.

He hurried back to the balloon, resuming his cap. He was received with the respect due to one who comes fresh from conquest. He was sacred.

Sophia rejoined Carlier, who had withdrawn, and began to talk to him with a self-conscious garrulity. She spoke without reason and scarcely noticed what she was saying. Already Chirac was snatched out of her life, as other beings, so many of them, had been snatched. She thought of their first meetings, and of the sympathy which had always united them. He had lost his simplicity, now, in the self-created crisis of his fate, and had sunk in her esteem. And she was determined to like him all the more because he had sunk in her esteem. She wondered whether he really had undertaken this adventure from sentimental disappointment. She wondered whether, if she had not forgotten to wind her watch one night, they would still have been living quietly under the same roof in the Rue Bréda.

The sailor climbed definitely into the car; he had covered himself with a large cloak. Chirac had got one leg over the side of the car, and eight men were standing by the ropes, when a horse's hoofs clattered through the guarded entrance to the courtyard, amid an uproar of sudden excitement. The shiny chest of the horse was flecked with the classic foam.

"A telegram from the Governor of Paris!"

As the orderly, checking his mount, approached the group, even the old man with the watch raised his hat. The orderly responded, bent down to make an inquiry, which Chirac answered, and then, with another exchange of salutes, the official telegram was handed over to Chirac, and the horse backed away from the crowd. It was quite thrilling. Carlier was thrilled.

"He is never too prompt, the Governor. It is a quality!" said Carlier, with irony.

Chirac entered the car. And then the old man with the watch drew a black bag from the shadow behind him and entrusted it to Chirac, who accepted it with a profound deference and hid it. The sailor began to issue commands. The men at the ropes were bending down now. Suddenly the balloon rose about a foot and trembled. The sailor continued to shout. All the persons of authority gazed motionless at the balloon. The moment of suspense was eternal.

"Let go all!" cried the sailor, standing up, and clinging to the cordage. Chirac was seated in the car, a mass of dark fur with a small patch of white in it. The men at the ropes were a knot of struggling confused figures.

One side of the car tilted up, and the sailor was nearly pitched out. Three men at the other side had failed to free the ropes.

"Let go, corpses!" the sailor yelled at them.

The balloon jumped, as if it were drawn by some terrific impulse from the skies.

"Adieu!" called Chirac, pulling his cap off and waving it. "Adieu!"

"Bon voyage! Bon voyage!" the little crowd cheered. And then, "Vive la France!" Throats tightened, including Sophia's.

But the top of the balloon had leaned over, destroying its pear-shape, and the whole mass swerved violently towards the wall of the station, the car swinging under it like a toy, and an anchor under the car. There was a cry of alarm. Then the great ball leaped again, and swept over the high glass roof, escaping by inches the spouting. The cheers expired instantly. . . . The balloon was gone. It was spirited away as if by some furious and mighty power that had grown impatient in waiting for it. There remained for a few seconds on the collective retina of the spectators a vision of the inclined car swinging near the roof like the tail of a kite. And then nothing! Blankness! Blackness! Already the balloon was lost to sight in the vast stormy ocean of the night, a plaything of the winds. The spectators became once more aware of the dull booming of the cannonade. The balloon was already perhaps flying unseen amid the wrack over those guns.

Sophia involuntarily caught her breath. A chill sense of loneliness, of purposelessness, numbed her being.

Nobody ever saw Chirac or the old sailor again. The sea must have swallowed them. Of the sixty-five balloons that left Paris during the siege, two were not heard of. This was the first of the two. Chirac had, at any rate, not magnified the peril, though his intention was undoubtedly to magnify it.

iii

This was the end of Sophia's romantic adventures in France. Soon afterwards the Germans entered Paris, by mutual agreement, and made a point of seeing the Louvre, and departed, amid the silence of a city. For Sophia the conclusion of the siege meant chiefly that prices went down. Long before supplies from outside could reach Paris, the shop-windows were suddenly full of goods which had arrived from the shopkeepers alone knew where. Sophia, with the stock in her cellar, could have held out for several weeks more, and it annoyed her that she had not sold more of her good things while good things were worth gold. The signing of a treaty at Versailles reduced the value of Sophia's two remaining hams from about five pounds apiece to the usual price of hams. However, at the end of January she found herself in possession of a capital of about eight thousand francs, all the furniture of the flat, and a reputation. She had earned it all. Nothing could destroy the structure of her beauty, but she looked worn and appreciably older. She wondered often when Chirac would return. She might have written to Carlier or to the paper; but she did not. It was Niepce who discovered in a newspaper that Chirac's balloon had miscarried. At the moment the news did not affect her at all; but after several days she began to feel her loss in a dull sort of way; and she felt it more and more, though never acutely. She was perfectly convinced that Chirac could never have attracted her powerfully. She continued to dream, at rare intervals, of the kind of passion that would have satisfied her, glowing but banked down like a fire in some fine chamber of a rich but careful household.

She was speculating upon what her future would be, and

whether by inertia she was doomed to stay for ever in the Rue
Bréda, when the Commune caught her. She was more vexed
than frightened by the Commune; vexed that a city so in need
of repose and industry should indulge in such antics. For many
people the Commune was a worse experience than the siege; but
not for Sophia. She was a woman and a foreigner. Niepce was
infinitely more disturbed than Sophia; he went in fear of his
life. Sophia would go out to market and take her chances. It
is true that during one period the whole population of the
house went to live in the cellars, and orders to the butcher and
other tradesmen were given over the party-wall into the adjoining courtyard, which communicated with an alley. A
strange existence, and possibly perilous! But the women who
passed through it and had also passed through the siege, were
not very much intimidated by it, unless they happened to have
husbands or lovers who were active politicians.

Sophia did not cease, during the greater part of the year
1871, to make a living and to save money. She watched every
sou, and she developed a tendency to demand from her tenants
all that they could pay. She excused this to herself by ostentatiously declaring every detail of her prices in advance. It came
to the same thing in the end, with this advantage, that the bills
did not lead to unpleasantness. Her difficulties commenced
when Paris at last definitely resumed its normal aspect and
life, when all the women and children came back to those city
termini which they had left in such huddled, hysterical throngs,
when flats were re-opened that had long been shut, and men
who for a whole year had had the disadvantages and the advantages of being without wife and family, anchored themselves
once more to the hearth. Then it was that Sophia failed to
keep all her rooms let. She could have let them easily and constantly and at high rents; but not to men without encumbrances.
Nearly every day she refused attractive tenants in pretty hats,
or agreeable gentlemen who only wanted a room on condition
that they might offer hospitality to a dashing petticoat. It was
useless to proclaim aloud that her house was "serious." The
ambition of the majority of these joyous persons was to live
in a "serious" house, because each was sure that at bottom he
or she was a "serious" person, and quite different from the rest
of the joyous world. The character of Sophia's flat, instead of
repelling the wrong kind of aspirant, infallibly drew just that
kind. Hope was inextinguishable in these bosoms. They heard

that there would be no chance for them at Sophia's; but they
tried nevertheless. And occasionally Sophia would make a mistake, and grave unpleasantness would occur before the mistake
could be rectified. The fact was that the street was too much
for her. Few people would credit that there was a serious
boarding-house in the Rue Bréda. The police themselves would
not credit it. And Sophia's beauty was against her. At that
time the Rue Bréda was perhaps the most notorious street in
the centre of Paris; at the height of its reputation as a warren
of individual improprieties; most busily creating that prejudice against itself which, over thirty years later, forced the
authorities to change its name in obedience to the wish of its
tradesmen. When Sophia went out at about eleven o'clock in
the morning with her reticule to buy, the street was littered
with women who had gone out with reticules to buy. But whereas Sophia was fully dressed, and wore headgear, the others were
in dressing-gown and slippers, or opera-cloak and slippers,
having slid directly out of unspeakable beds and omitted to
brush their hair out of their puffy eyes. In the little shops of
the Rue Bréda, the Rue Notre Dame de Lorette, and the Rue
des Martyrs, you were very close indeed to the primitive instincts of human nature. It was wonderful; it was amusing; it
was excitingly picturesque; and the universality of the manners rendered moral indignation absurd. But the neighbourhood was certainly not one in which a woman of Sophia's race,
training, and character, could comfortably earn a living, or
even exist. She could not fight against the entire street. She,
and not the street, was out of place and in the wrong. Little
wonder that the neighbours lifted their shoulders when they
spoke of her! What beautiful woman but a mad Englishwoman
would have had the idea of establishing herself in the Rue
Bréda with the intention of living like a nun and compelling
others to do the same?

By dint of continual ingenuity, Sophia contrived to win
somewhat more than her expenses, but she was slowly driven
to admit to herself that the situation could not last.

Then one day she saw in *Galignani's Messenger* an advertisement of an English pension for sale in the Rue Lord Byron,
in the Champs Elysées quarter. It belonged to some people
named Frensham, and had enjoyed a certain popularity before
the war. The proprietor and his wife, however, had not sufficiently allowed for the vicissitudes of politics in Paris. Instead

of saving money during their popularity they had put it on the back and on the fingers of Mrs. Frensham. The siege and the Commune had almost ruined them. With capital they might have restored themselves to their former pride; but their capital was exhausted. Sophia answered the advertisement. She impressed the Frenshams, who were delighted with the prospect of dealing in business with an honest English face. Like many English people abroad they were most strangely obsessed by the notion that they had quitted an island of honest men to live among thieves and robbers. They always implied that dishonesty was unknown in Britain. They offered, if she would take over the lease, to sell all their furniture and their renown for ten thousand francs. She declined, the price seeming absurd to her. When they asked her to name a price, she said that she preferred not to do so. Upon entreaty, she said four thousand francs. They then allowed her to see that they considered her to have been quite right in hesitating to name a price so ridiculous. And their confidence in the honest English face seemed to have been shocked. Sophia left. When she got back to the Rue Bréda she was relieved that the matter had come to nothing. She did not precisely foresee what her future was to be, but at any rate she knew she shrank from the responsibility of the Pension Frensham. The next morning she received a letter offering to accept six thousand. She wrote and declined. She was indifferent and she would not budge from four thousand. The Frenshams gave way. They were pained, but they gave way. The glitter of four thousand francs in cash, and freedom, was too tempting.

Thus Sophia became the proprietress of the Pension Frensham in the cold and correct Rue Lord Byron. She made room in it for nearly all her other furniture, so that instead of being under-furnished, as pensions usually are, it was over-furnished. She was extremely timid at first, for the rent alone was four thousand francs a year; and the prices of the quarter were alarmingly different from those of the Rue Bréda. She lost a lot of sleep. For some nights, after she had been installed in the Rue Lord Byron about a fortnight, she scarcely slept at all, and she ate no more than she slept. She cut down expenditure to the very lowest, and frequently walked over to the Rue Bréda to do her marketing. With the aid of a charwoman at six sous an hour she accomplished everything. And though clients were few, the feat was in the nature of a miracle; for Sophia had to cook.

The articles which George Augustus Sala wrote under the title "Paris herself again" ought to have been paid for in gold by the hotel and pension-keepers of Paris. They awakened English curiosity and the desire to witness the scene of terrible events. Their effect was immediately noticeable. In less than a year after her adventurous purchase, Sophia had acquired confidence, and she was employing two servants, working them very hard at low wages. She had also acquired the landlady's manner. She was known as Mrs. Frensham. Across the balconies of two windows the Frenshams had left a gilded sign, "Pension Frensham," and Sophia had not removed it. She often explained that her name was not Frensham; but in vain. Every visitor inevitably and persistently addressed her according to the sign. It was past the general comprehension that the proprietress of the Pension Frensham might bear another name than Frensham. But later there came into being a class of persons, habitués of the Pension Frensham, who knew the real name of the proprietress and were proud of knowing it, and by this knowledge were distinguished from the herd. What struck Sophia was the astounding similarity of her guests. They all asked the same questions, made the same exclamations, went out on the same excursions, returned with the same judgments, and exhibited the same unimpaired assurance that foreigners were really very peculiar people. They never seemed to advance in knowledge. There was a constant stream of explorers from England who had to be set on their way to the Louvre or the Bon Marché.

Sophia's sole interest was in her profits. The excellence of her house was firmly established. She kept it up, and she kept the modest prices up. Often she had to refuse guests. She naturally did so with a certain distant condescension. Her manner to guests increased in stiff formality; and she was excessively firm with undesirables. She grew to be seriously convinced that no pension as good as hers existed in the world, or ever had existed, or ever could exist. Hers was the acme of niceness and respectability. Her preference for the respectable rose to a passion. And there were no faults in her establishment. Even the once despised showy furniture of Madame Foucault had mysteriously changed into the best conceivable furniture; and its cracks were hallowed.

She never heard a word of Gerald nor of her family. In the thousands of people who stayed under her perfect roof, not one mentioned Bursley nor disclosed a knowledge of anybody that Sophia had known. Several men had the wit to propose marriage to her with more or less skilfulness, but none of them was skilful enough to perturb her heart. She had forgotten the face of love. She was a landlady. She was *the* landlady: efficient, stylish, diplomatic, and tremendously experienced. There was no trickery, no baseness of Parisian life that she was not acquainted with and armed against. She could not be startled and she could not be swindled.

Years passed, until there was a vista of years behind her. Sometimes she would think, in an unoccupied moment, "How strange it is that I should be here, doing what I am doing!" But the regular ordinariness of her existence would instantly seize her again. At the end of 1878, the Exhibition Year, her Pension consisted of two floors instead of one, and she had turned the two hundred pounds stolen from Gerald into over two thousand.

BOOK IV

WHAT LIFE IS

CHAPTER I

FRENSHAM'S

MATTHEW PEEL-SWYNNERTON sat in the long dining-room of the Pension Frensham, Rue Lord Byron, Paris; and he looked out of place there. It was an apartment about thirty feet in length, and of the width of two windows, which sufficiently lighted one half of a very long table with round ends. The gloom of the other extremity was illuminated by a large mirror in a tarnished gilt frame, which filled a good portion of the wall opposite the windows. Near the mirror was a high folding-screen of four leaves, and behind this screen could be heard the sound of a door continually shutting and opening. In the long wall to the left of the windows were two doors, one dark and important, a door of state, through which a procession of hungry and a procession of sated solemn self-conscious persons passed twice daily, and the other, a smaller door, glazed, its glass painted with wreaths of roses, not an original door of the house, but a late breach in the wall, that seemed to lead to the dangerous and to the naughty. The wall-paper and the window drapery were rich and forbidden, dark in hue, mysterious of pattern. Over the state-door was a pair of antlers. And at intervals, so high up as to defy inspection, engravings and oil-paintings made oblong patches on the walls. They were hung from immense nails with porcelain heads, and they appeared to depict the more majestic aspect of man and nature. One engraving, over the mantelpiece and nearer earth than the rest, unmistakably showed Louis Philippe and his family in attitudes of virtue. Beneath this royal group, a vast gilt clock, flanked by pendants of the same period, gave the right time—a quarter past seven.

And down the room, filling it, ran the great white table, bordered with bowed heads and the backs of chairs. There were over thirty people at the table, and the peculiarly restrained noisiness of their knives and forks on the plates proved that they were a discreet and a correct people. Their clothes—

blouses, bodices, and jackets—did not flatter the lust of the eye. Only two or three were in evening dress. They spoke little, and generally in a timorous tone, as though silence had been enjoined. Somebody would half-whisper a remark, and then his neighbour, absently fingering her bread and lifting gaze from her plate into vacancy, would conscientiously weigh the remark and half-whisper in reply: "I dare say." But a few spoke loudly and volubly, and were regarded by the rest, who envied them, as underbred.

Food was quite properly the chief preoccupation. The diners ate as those eat who are paying a fixed price per day for as much as they can consume while observing the rules of the game. Without moving their heads they glanced out of the corners of their eyes, watching the manœuvres of the three starched maids who served. They had no conception of food save as portions laid out in rows on large silver dishes, and when a maid bent over them deferentially, balancing the dish, they summed up the offering in an instant, and in an instant decided how much they could decently take, and to what extent they could practise the theoretic liberty of choice. And if the food for any reason did not tempt them, or if it egregiously failed to coincide with their aspirations, they considered themselves aggrieved. For, according to the game, they might not command; they had the right to seize all that was presented under their noses, like genteel tigers; and they had the right to refuse; that was all. The dinner was thus a series of emotional crises for the diners, who knew only that full dishes and clean plates came endlessly from the banging door behind the screen, and that ravaged dishes and dirty plates vanished endlessly through the same door. They were all eating similar food simultaneously; they began together and they finished together. The flies that haunted the paper-bunches which hung from the chandeliers to the level of the flower-vases, were more free. The sole event that chequered the exact regularity of the repast was the occasional arrival of a wine-bottle for one of the guests. The receiver of the wine-bottle signed a small paper in exchange for it and wrote largely a number on the label of the bottle; then, staring at the number and fearing that after all it might be misread by a stupid or an unscrupulous compeer, he would re-write the number on another part of the label, even more largely.

Matthew Peel-Swynnerton obviously did not belong to this

world. He was a young man of twenty-five or so, not hand-some, but elegant. Though he was not in evening dress, though he was, as a fact, in a very light grey suit, entirely improper to a dinner, he was elegant. The suit was admirably cut, and nearly new; but he wore it as though he had never worn any-thing else. Also his demeanour, reserved yet free from self-consciousness, his method of handling a knife and fork, the niceties of his manner in transferring food from the silver dishes to his plate, the tone in which he ordered half a bottle of wine—all these details infallibly indicated to the company that Matthew Peel-Swynnerton was their superior. Some folks hoped that he was the son of a lord, or even a lord. He hap-pened to be fixed at the end of the table, with his back to the window, and there was a vacant chair on either side of him; this situation favoured the hope of his high rank. In truth, he was the son, the grandson, and several times the nephew, of earth-enware manufacturers. He noticed that the large "compote" (as it was called in his trade) which marked the centre of the table, was the production of his firm. This surprised him, for Peel, Swynnerton and Co., known and revered throughout the Five Towns as "Peels," did not cater for cheap markets.

A late guest startled the room, a fat, flabby, middle-aged man whose nose would have roused the provisional hostility of those who have convinced themselves that Jews are not as other men. His nose did not definitely brand him as a usurer and a murderer of Christ, but it was suspicious. His clothes hung loose, and might have been anybody's clothes. He advanced with brisk assurance to the table, bowed, somewhat too effu-sively, to several people, and sat down next to Peel-Swynner-ton. One of the maids at once brought him a plate of soup, and he said: "Thank you, Marie," smiling at her. He was evidently a habitué of the house. His spectacled eyes beamed the supe-riority which comes of knowing girls by their names. He was seriously handicapped in the race for sustenance, being two and a half courses behind, but he drew level with speed and then, having accomplished this, he sighed, and pointedly en-gaged Peel-Swynnerton with his sociable glance.

"Ah!" he breathed out. "Nuisance when you come in late, sir!"

Peel-Swynnerton gave a reluctant affirmative.

"Doesn't only upset you! It upsets the house! Servants don't like it!"

"No," murmured Peel-Swynnerton, "I suppose not."

"However, it's not often *I'm* late," said the man. "Can't help it sometimes. Business! Worst of these French business people is that they've no notion of time. Appointments . . . ! God bless my soul!"

"Do you come here often?" asked Peel-Swynnerton. He detested the fellow, quite inexcusably, perhaps because his serviette was tucked under his chin; but he saw that the fellow was one of your determined talkers, who always wins in the end. Moreover, as being clearly not an ordinary tourist in Paris, the fellow mildly excited his curiosity.

"I live here," said the other. "Very convenient for a bachelor, you know. Have done for years. My office is just close by. You may know my name—Lewis Mardon."

Peel-Swynnerton hesitated. The hesitation convicted him of not "knowing his Paris" well.

"House-agent," said Lewis Mardon, quickly.

"Oh yes," said Peel-Swynnerton, vaguely recalling a vision of the name among the advertisements on newspaper kiosks.

"I expect," Mr. Mardon went on, "my name is as well known as anybody's in Paris."

"I suppose so," assented Peel-Swynnerton.

The conversation fell for a few moments.

"Staying here long?" Mr. Mardon demanded, having added up Peel-Swynnerton as a man of style and of means, and being puzzled by his presence at that table.

"I don't know," said Peel-Swynnerton.

This was a lie, justified in the utterer's opinion as a repulse to Mr. Mardon's vulgar inquisitiveness, such inquisitiveness as might have been expected from a fellow who tucked his serviette under his chin. Peel-Swynnerton knew exactly how long he would stay. He would stay until the day after the morrow; he had only about fifty francs in his pocket. He had been making a fool of himself in another quarter of Paris, and he had descended to the Pension Frensham as a place where he could be absolutely sure of spending not more than twelve francs a day. Its reputation was high, and it was convenient for the Galliera Museum, where he was making some drawings which he had come to Paris expressly to make, and without which he could not reputably return to England. He was capable of foolishness, but he was also capable of wisdom, and scarcely any pressure of need would have induced him to write home for money to replace the money spent on making himself into a fool.

Mr. Mardon was conscious of a check. But, being of an accommodating disposition, he at once tried another direction.

"Good food here, eh?" he suggested.

"Very," said Peel-Swynnerton, with sincerity. "I was quite——"

At that moment, a tall straight woman of uncertain age pushed open the principal door and stood for an instant in the doorway. Peel-Swynnerton had just time to notice that she was handsome and pale, and that her hair was black, and then she was gone again, followed by a clipped poodle that accompanied her. She had signed with a brief gesture to one of the servants, who at once set about lighting the gas-jets over the table.

"Who is that?" asked Peel-Swynnerton, without reflecting that it was now he who was making advances to the fellow whose napkin covered all his shirt-front.

"That's the missis, that is," said Mr. Mardon, in a lower and semi-confidential voice.

"Oh! Mrs. Frensham?"

"Yes. But her real name is Scales," said Mr. Mardon, proudly.

"Widow, I suppose?"

"Yes."

"And she runs the whole show?"

"She runs the entire contraption," said Mardon, solemnly; "and don't you make any mistake!" He was getting familiar.

Peel-Swynnerton beat him off once more, glancing with careful, uninterested nonchalance at the gas-burners which exploded one after another with a little plop under the application of the maid's taper. The white table gleamed more whitely than ever under the flaring gas. People at the end of the room away from the window instinctively smiled, as though the sun had begun to shine. The aspect of the dinner was changed, ameliorated; and with the reiterated statement that the evenings were drawing in though it was only July, conversation became almost general. In two minutes Mr. Mardon was genially talking across the whole length of the table. The meal finished in a state that resembled conviviality.

Matthew Peel-Swynnerton might not go out into the crepuscular delights of Paris. Unless he remained within the shelter

of the Pension, he could not hope to complete successfully his
re-conversion from folly to wisdom. So he bravely passed
through the small rose-embroidered door into a small glass-
covered courtyard, furnished with palms, wicker armchairs,
and two small tables; and he lighted a pipe and pulled out of
his pocket a copy of *The Referee*. That retreat was called the
Lounge; it was the only part of the Pension where smoking
was not either a positive crime or a transgression against good
form. He felt lonely. He said to himself grimly in one breath
that pleasure was all rot, and in the next he sullenly demanded
of the universe how it was that pleasure could not go on for
ever, and why he was not Mr. Barney Barnato. Two old men
entered the retreat and burnt cigarettes with many precautions. Then Mr. Lewis Mardon appeared and sat down boldly
next to Matthew, like a privileged friend. After all, Mr. Mardon was better than nobody whatever, and Matthew decided
to suffer him, especially as he began without preliminary
skirmishing to talk about life in Paris. An irresistible subject!
Mr. Mardon said in a worldly tone that the existence of a
bachelor in Paris might easily be made agreeable. But that,
of course, for himself—well, he preferred, as a general rule,
the Pension Frensham sort of thing; and it was excellent for
his business. Still he could not . . . he knew . . . He compared the advantages of what he called "knocking about" in
Paris, with the equivalent in London. His information about
London was out of date, and Peel-Swynnerton was able to set
him right on important details. But his information about
Paris was infinitely precious and interesting to the younger
man, who saw that he had hitherto lived under strange mis-
conceptions.

"Have a whiskey?" asked Mr. Mardon, suddenly. "Very
good here!" he added.

"Thanks!" drawled Peel-Swynnerton.

The temptation to listen to Mr. Mardon as long as Mr. Mardon would talk was not to be overcome. And presently, when
the old men had departed, they were frankly telling each other
stories in the dimness of the retreat. Then, when the supply of
stories came to an end, Mr. Mardon smacked his lips over the
last drop of whiskey and ejaculated: "Yes!" as if giving a general confirmation to all that had been said.

"Do have one with me," said Matthew, politely. It was the
least he could do.

The second supply of whiskies was brought into the Lounge by Mr. Mardon's Marie. He smiled on her familiarly, and remarked that he supposed she would soon be going to bed after a hard day's work. She gave a *moue* and a flounce in reply, and swished out.

"Carries herself well, doesn't she?" observed Mr. Mardon, as though Marie had been an exhibit at an agricultural show. "Ten years ago she was very fresh and pretty, but of course it takes it out of 'em, a place like this!"

"But still," said Peel-Swynnerton, "they must like it or they wouldn't stay—that is, unless things are very different here from what they are in England."

The conversation seemed to have stimulated him to examine the woman question in all its bearings, with philosophic curiosity.

"Oh! They *like* it," Mr. Mardon assured him, as one who knew. "Besides, Mrs. Scales treats 'em very well. I know *that*. She's told me. She's very particular"—he looked around to see if walls had ears—"and, by jove, you've got to be: but she treats 'em well. You'd scarcely believe the wages they get, and pickings. Now at the Hotel Moscow—know the Hotel Moscow?"

Happily Peel-Swynnerton did. He had been advised to avoid it because it catered exclusively for English visitors, but in the Pension Frensham he had accepted something even more exclusively British than the Hotel Moscow. Mr. Mardon was quite relieved at his affirmative.

"The Hotel Moscow is a limited company now," said he; "English."

"Really?"

"Yes. I floated it. It was my idea. A great success! That's how I know all about the Hotel Moscow." He looked at the walls again. "I wanted to do the same here," he murmured, and Peel-Swynnerton had to show that he appreciated this confidence. "But she never would agree. I've tried her all ways. No go! It's a thousand pities."

"Paying thing, eh?"

"This place? I should say it was! And I ought to be able to judge, I reckon. Mrs. Scales is one of the shrewdest women you'd meet in a day's march. She's made a lot of money here, a lot of money. And there's no reason why a place like this shouldn't be five times as big as it is. Ten times. The scope's unlimited, my dear sir. All that's wanted is capital. Naturally she has capital of her own, and she could get more. But then, as she says, she doesn't want the place any bigger. She says it's now just as big as she can handle. That isn't so. She's a woman who could handle anything—a born manager—but even if it was so, all she would have to do would be to retire—only leave us the place and the name. It's the name that counts. And she's made the name of Frensham worth something, I can tell you!"

"Did she get the place from her husband?" asked Peel-Swynnerton. Her own name of Scales intrigued him.

Mr. Mardon shook his head. "Bought it on her own, after the husband's time, for a song—a song! I know, because I knew the original Frenshams."

"You must have been in Paris a long time," said Peel-Swynnerton.

Mr. Mardon could never resist an opportunity to talk about himself. His was a wonderful history. And Peel-Swynnerton, while scorning the man for his fatuity, was impressed. And when that was finished—

"Yes!" said Mr. Mardon after a pause, reaffirming everything in general by a single monosyllable.

Shortly afterwards he rose, saying that his habits were regular.

"Good-night," he said with a mechanical smile.

"G-good-night," said Peel-Swynnerton, trying to force the tone of fellowship and not succeeding. Their intimacy, which had sprung up like a mushroom, suddenly fell into dust. Peel-Swynnerton's unspoken comment to Mr. Mardon's back was: "Ass!" Still, the sum of Peel-Swynnerton's knowledge had indubitably been increased during the evening. And the hour was yet early. Half-past ten! The Folies-Marigny, with its beautiful architecture and its crowds of white toilettes, and its frothing of champagne and of beer, and its musicians in tight red coats, was just beginning to be alive—and at a distance of scarcely a stone's-throw! Peel-Swynnerton pictured the terraced, glittering hall, which had been the prime origin of his exceeding foolishness. And he pictured all the other resorts, great and small, garlanded with white lanterns, in the Champs Elysées; and the sombre aisles of the Champs Elysées where mysterious pale figures walked troublingly under the shade of trees, while snatches of wild song or absurd brassy music floated up from the resorts and restaurants. He wanted to go out and spend those fifty francs that remained in his pocket. After all, why not telegraph to England for more money? "Oh, damn it!" he said savagely, and stretched his arms and got up. The Lounge was very small, gloomy and dreary.

One brilliant incandescent light burned in the hall, crudely illuminating the wicker fauteuils, a corded trunk with a blue-and-red label on it, a Fitzroy barometer, a map of Paris, a coloured poster of the Compagnie Transatlantique, and the mahogany retreat of the hall-portress. In that retreat was not only the hall-portress—an aged woman with a white cap above her wrinkled pink face—but the mistress of the establishment. They were murmuring together softly; they seemed to be well disposed to one another. The portress was respectful, but the mistress was respectful also. The hall, with its one light tranquilly burning, was bathed in an honest calm, the calm of a day's work accomplished, of gradual relaxation from tension, of growing expectation of repose. In its simplicity it affected Peel-Swynnerton as a medicine tonic for nerves might have affected him. In that hall, though exterior nocturnal life was but just stirring into activity, it seemed that the middle of the night had come, and that these two women alone watched in a mansion full of sleepers. And all the recitals which Peel-Swynnerton and Mr. Mardon had exchanged sank to the level of pitiably foolish gossip. Peel-Swynnerton felt that his duty to the house was to retire to bed. He felt, too, that he could not leave the house without saying that he was going out, and that he lacked the courage deliberately to tell these two women that he was going out—at that time of night! He dropped into one of the chairs and made a second attempt to peruse *The Referee*. Useless! Either his mind was outside in the Champs Elysées, or his gaze would wander surreptitiously to the figure of Mrs. Scales. He could not well distinguish her face because it was in the shadow of the mahogany.

Then the portress came forth from her box, and, slightly bent, sped actively across the hall, smiling pleasantly at the guest as she passed him, and disappeared up the stairs. The mistress was alone in the retreat. Peel-Swynnerton jumped up brusquely, dropping the paper with a rustle, and approached her.

"Excuse me," he said deferentially. "Have any letters come for me to-night?"

He knew that the arrival of letters for him was impossible, since nobody knew his address.

"What name?" The question was coldly polite, and the questioner looked him full in the face. Undoubtedly she was a handsome woman. Her hair was greying at the temples, and the skin was withered and crossed with lines. But she was handsome. She was one of those women of whom to their last on earth the stranger will say: "When she was young she must have been worth looking at!"—with a little transient regret that beautiful young women cannot remain for ever young. Her voice was firm and even, sweet in tone, and yet morally harsh from incessant traffic with all varieties of human nature. Her eyes were the impartial eyes of one who is always judging. And evidently she was a proud, even a haughty creature, with her careful, controlled politeness. Evidently she considered herself superior to no matter what guest. Her eyes announced that she had lived and learnt, that she knew more about life than any one whom she was likely to meet, and that having pre-eminently succeeded in life, she had tremendous confidence in herself. The proof of her success was the unique Frensham's. A consciousness of the uniqueness of Frensham's was also in those eyes. Theoretically Matthew Peel-Swynnerton's mental attitude towards lodging-house keepers was condescending, but here it was not condescending. It had the real respectfulness of a man who for the moment at any rate is impressed beyond his calculation. His glance fell as he said—

"Peel-Swynnerton." Then he looked up again.

He said the words awkwardly, and rather fearfully, as if aware that he was playing with fire. If this Mrs. Scales was the long-vanished aunt of his friend, Cyril Povey, she must know those two names, locally so famous. Did she start? Did she show a sign of being perturbed? At first he thought he detected a symptom of emotion, but in an instant he was sure that he had detected nothing of the sort, and that it was silly to suppose that he was treading on the edge of a romance. Then she turned towards the letter-rack at her side, and he saw her face in profile. It bore a sudden and astonishing likeness to the profile of Cyril Povey; a resemblance unmistakable and finally decisive. The nose, and the curve of the upper lip were absolutely Cyril's. Matthew Peel-Swynnerton felt very queer. He felt like a criminal in peril of being caught in the act, and he could not understand why he should feel so. The landlady looked in the "P" pigeon-hole, and in the "S" pigeon-hole.

"No," she said quietly, "I see nothing for you."

Taken with a swift rash audacity, he said: "Have you had any one named Povey here recently?"

"Povey?"

"Yes. Cyril Povey, of Bursley—in the Five Towns."

He was very impressionable, very sensitive, was Matthew Peel-Swynnerton. His voice trembled as he spoke. But hers also trembled in reply.

"Not that I remember! No! Were you expecting him to be here?"

"Well, it wasn't at all sure," he muttered. "Thank you. Good-night."

"Good-night," she said, apparently with the simple perfunctoriness of the landlady who says good-night to dozens of strangers every evening.

He hurried away upstairs, and met the portress coming down. "Well, well!" he thought. "Of all the queer things——!" And he kept nodding his head. At last he had encountered something *really* strange in the spectacle of existence. It had fallen to him to discover the legendary woman who had fled from Bursley before he was born, and of whom nobody knew anything. What news for Cyril! What a staggering episode! He had scarcely any sleep that night. He wondered whether he would be able to meet Mrs. Scales without self-consciousness on the morrow. However, he was spared the curious ordeal of meeting her. She did not appear at all on the following day; nor did he see her before he left. He could not find a pretext for asking why she was invisible.

ii

The hansom of Matthew Peel-Swynnerton drew up in front of No. 26, Victoria Grove, Chelsea; his kit-bag was on the roof of the cab. The cabman had a red flower in his buttonhole. Matthew leaped out of the vehicle, holding his straw hat on his head with one hand. On reaching the pavement he checked himself suddenly and became carelessly calm. Another straw-hatted and grey-clad figure was standing at the side-gate of No. 26 in the act of lighting a cigarette.

"Hello, Matt!" exclaimed the second figure, languidly, and in a veiled voice due to the fact that he was still holding the match to the cigarette and puffing. "What's the meaning of all this fluster? You're just the man I want to see."

He threw away the match with a wave of the arm, and took Matthew's hand for a moment, blowing a double shaft of smoke through his nose.

"I want to see you, too," said Matthew. "And I've only got a minute. I'm on my way to Euston. I must catch the twelve-five."

He looked at his friend, and could positively see no feature of it that was not a feature of Mrs. Scales's face. Also, the elderly woman held her body in exactly the same way as the young man. It was entirely disconcerting.

"Have a cigarette," answered Cyril Povey, imperturbably. He was two years younger than Matthew, from whom he had acquired most of his vast and intricate knowledge of life and art, with certain leading notions of deportment; whose pupil indeed he was in all the things that matter to young men. But he had already surpassed his professor. He could pretend to be old much more successfully than Matthew could.

The cabman approvingly watched the ignition of the second cigarette, and then the cabman pulled out a cigar, and showed his large, white teeth, as he bit the end off it. The appearance and manner of his fare, the quality of the kit-bag, and the opening gestures of the interview between the two young dukes, had put the cabman in an optimistic mood. He had no apprehensions of miserly and ungentlemanly conduct by his fare upon the arrival at Euston. He knew the language of the tilt of a straw hat. And it was a magnificent day in London. The group of the two elegances dominated by the perfection of the cabman made a striking tableau of triumphant masculinity, content with itself, and needing nothing.

Matthew lightly took Cyril's arm and drew him further down the street, past the gate leading to the studio (hidden behind a house) which Cyril rented.

"Look here, my boy," he began, "I've found your aunt."

"Well, that's very nice of you," said Cyril, solemnly. "That's a friendly act. May I ask what aunt?"

"Mrs. Scales," said Matthew. "You know——"

"Not the——" Cyril's face changed.

"Yes, precisely!" said Matthew, feeling that he was not being cheated of the legitimate joy caused by making a sensation. Assuredly he had made a sensation in Victoria Grove.

When he had related the whole story, Cyril said: "Then she doesn't know you know?"

"I don't think so. No, I'm sure she doesn't. She may guess."

"But how can you be certain you haven't made a mistake? It may be that——"

"Look here, my boy," Matthew interrupted him. "I've not made any mistake."

"But you've no proof."

"Proof be damned!" said Matthew, nettled. "I tell you it's *her!*"

"Oh! All right! All right! What puzzles me most is what the devil you were doing in a place like that. According to your description of it, it must be a——"

"I went there because I was broke," said Matthew.

"Razzle?"

Matthew nodded.

"Pretty stiff, that!" commented Cyril, when Matthew had narrated the prologue to Frensham's.

"Well, she absolutely swore she never took less than two hundred francs. And she looked it, too! And she was worth it! I had the time of my life with that woman. I can tell you one thing— no more English for me! They simply aren't in it."

"How old was she?"

Matthew reflected judicially. "I should say she was thirty." The gaze of admiration and envy was upon him. He had the legitimate joy of making a second sensation. "I'll let you know more about that when I come back," he added. "I can open your eyes, my child."

Cyril smiled sheepishly. "Why can't you stay now?" he asked. "I'm going to take the cast of that Verrall girl's arm this afternoon, and I know I can't do it alone. And Robson's no good. You're just the man I want."

"Can't!" said Matthew.

"Well, come into the studio a minute, anyhow."

"Haven't time; I shall miss my train."

"I don't care if you miss forty trains. You must come in. You've got to see that fountain," Cyril insisted crossly.

Matthew yielded. When they emerged into the street again, after six minutes of Cyril's savage interest in his own work, Matthew remembered Mrs. Scales.

"Of course you'll write to your mother?" he said.

"Yes," said Cyril, "I'll write; but if you happen to see her, you might tell her."

"I will," said Matthew. "Shall you go over to Paris?"

"What! To see Auntie?" He smiled. "I don't know. Depends. If the mater will fork out all my exes . . . it's an idea," he said lightly, and then without any change of tone, "Naturally, if you're going to idle about here all morning you aren't likely to catch the twelve-five."

Matthew got into the cab, while the driver, the stump of a cigar between his exposed teeth, leaned forward and lifted the reins away from the tilted straw hat.

"By-the-by, lend me some silver," Matthew demanded. "It's a good thing I've got my return ticket. I've run it as fine as ever I did in my life."

Cyril produced eight shillings in silver. Secure in the possession of these riches, Matthew called to the driver—

"Euston—like hell!"

"Yes, sir," said the driver, calmly.

"Not coming my way I suppose?" Matthew shouted as an afterthought, just when the cab began to move.

"No. Barber's," Cyril shouted in answer, and waved his hand.

The horse rattled into Fulham Road.

iii

Three days later Matthew Peel-Swynnerton was walking along Bursley Market Place when, just opposite the Town Hall, he met a short, fat, middle-aged lady dressed in black, with a black embroidered mantle, and a small bonnet tied with black ribbon and ornamented with jet fruit and crape leaves. As she stepped slowly and carefully forward she had the dignified, important look of a provincial woman who has always been accustomed to deference in her native town, and whose income is ample enough to extort obsequiousness from the vulgar of all ranks. But immediately she caught sight of Matthew, her face changed. She became simple and naïve. She blushed slightly, smiling with a timid pleasure. For her, Matthew belonged to a superior race. He bore the almost sacred name of Peel. His family had been distinguished in the district for generations. "Peel!" You could without impropriety utter it in the same breath with "Wedgwood." And "Swynnerton" stood not much lower. Neither her self-respect, which was great, nor her commonsense, which far exceeded the average, could enable her to extend as far as the Peels the theory that one man is as good as another. The Peels never shopped in St. Luke's Square. Even in its golden days the Square could not have expected such a condescension. The Peels shopped in London or in Stafford; at a pinch, in Oldcastle. That was the distinction for the ageing stout lady in black. Why, she had not in six years recovered from her surprise that her son and Matthew Peel-Swynnerton treated each other rudely as equals! She and Matthew did not often meet, but they liked each other. Her involuntary meekness flattered him. And his rather elaborate homage flattered her. He admired her fundamental goodness, and her occasional raps at Cyril seemed to put him into ecstasies of joy.

"Well, Mrs. Povey," he greeted her, standing over her with his hat raised. (It was a fashion he had picked up in Paris.) "Here I am, you see."

"You're quite a stranger, Mr. Matthew. I needn't ask you how you are. Have you been seeing anything of my boy lately?"

"Not since Wednesday," said Matthew. "Of course he's written to you?"

"There's no 'of course' about it," she laughed faintly. "I had a short letter from him on Wednesday morning. He said you were in Paris."

"But since that—hasn't he written?"

"If I hear from him on Sunday I shall be lucky, bless ye!" said Constance, grimly. "It's not letter-writing that will kill Cyril."

"But do you mean to say he hasn't——" Matthew stopped.

"Whatever's amiss?" asked Constance.

Matthew was at a loss to know what to do or say. "Oh, nothing."

"Now, Mr. Matthew, do please——" Constance's tone had suddenly quite changed. It had become firm, commanding, and gravely suspicious. The conversation had ceased to be small-talk for her.

Matthew saw how nervous and how fragile she was. He had never noticed before that she was so sensitive to trifles, though it was notorious that nobody could safely discuss Cyril with her in terms of chaff. He was really astounded at that youth's carelessness, shameful carelessness. That Cyril's attitude to his mother was marked by a certain benevolent negligence—this Matthew knew; but not to have written to her with the important news concerning Mrs. Scales was utterly inexcusable; and Matthew determined that he would tell Cyril so. He felt very sorry for Mrs. Povey. She seemed pathetic to him, standing there in ignorance of a tremendous fact which she ought to have been aware of. He was very content that he had said nothing about Mrs. Scales to anybody except his own mother, who had prudently enjoined silence upon him, saying that his one duty, having told Cyril, was to keep his mouth shut until the Poveys talked. Had it not been for his mother's advice he would assuredly have spread the amazing tale, and Mrs. Povey might have first heard of it from a stranger's gossip, which would have been too cruel upon her.

"Oh!" Matthew tried to smile gaily, archly. "You're bound to hear from Cyril to-morrow."

He wanted to persuade her that he was concealing merely some delightful surprise from her. But he did not succeed. With all his experience of the world and of women he was not clever enough to deceive that simple woman.

"I'm waiting, Mr. Matthew," she said, in a tone that flattened the smile out of Matthew's sympathetic face. She was ruthless. The fact was, she had in an instant convinced herself that Cyril had met some girl and was engaged to be married. She could think of nothing else. "What has Cyril been doing?" she added, after a pause.

"It's nothing to do with Cyril," said he.

"Then what is it?"

"It was about—Mrs. Scales," he murmured, nearly trembling. As she offered no response, merely looking around her in a peculiar fashion, he said: "Shall we walk along a bit?" And he turned in the direction in which she had been going. She obeyed the suggestion.

"What did ye say?" she asked. The name of Scales for a moment had no significance for her. But when she comprehended it she was afraid, and so she said vacantly, as though wishing to postpone a shock: "What did ye say?"

"I said it was about Mrs. Scales. You know I m-met her in Paris." And he was saying to himself: "I ought not to be telling this poor old thing here in the street. But what can I do?"

"Nay, nay!" she muttered.

She stopped and looked at him with a worried expression. Then he observed that the hand that carried her reticule was making strange purposeless curves in the air, and her rosy face went the colour of cream, as though it had been painted with one stroke of an unseen brush. Matthew was very much put about.

"Hadn't you better——" he began.

"Eh," she said; "I must sit me——" Her bag dropped.

He supported her to the door of Allman's shop, the iron-monger's. Unfortunately, there were two steps up into the shop, and she could not climb them. She collapsed like a sack of flour on the first step. Young Edward Allman ran to the door. He was wearing a black apron and fidgeting with it in his excitement.

"Don't lift her up—don't try to lift her up, Mr. Peel-Swyn-nerton!" he cried, as Matthew instinctively began to do the wrong thing.

Matthew stopped, looking a fool and feeling one, and he and young Allman contemplated each other helpless for a second across the body of Constance Povey. A part of the Market Place now perceived that the unusual was occurring. It was Mr. Shawcross, the chemist next door to Allman's who dealt adequately with the situation. He had seen all, while selling a Kodak to a young lady, and he ran out with salts. Constance recovered very rapidly. She had not quite swooned. She gave a long sigh, and whispered weakly that she was all right. The three men helped her into the lofty dark shop, which smelt of nails and of stove-polish, and she was balanced on a rickety chair.

"My word!" exclaimed young Allman, in his loud voice, when she could smile and the pink was returning reluctantly to her cheeks. "You mustn't frighten us like that, Mrs. Povey!"

Matthew said nothing. He had at last created a genuine sensation. Once again he felt like a criminal, and could not understand why.

Constance announced that she would walk slowly home, down the Cock-yard and along Wedgwood Street. But when, glancing round in her returned strength, she saw the hedge of faces at the doorway, she agreed with Mr. Shawcross that she would do better to have a cab. Young Allman went to the door and whistled to the unique cab that stands for ever at the grand entrance to the Town Hall.

"Mr. Matthew will come with me," said Constance.

"Certainly, with pleasure," said Matthew.

And she passed through the little crowd of gapers on Mr. Shawcross's arm.

"Just take care of yourself, missis," said Mr. Shawcross to her, through the window of the cab. "It's fainting weather, and we're none of us any younger, seemingly."

She nodded.

"I'm awfully sorry I upset you, Mrs. Povey," said Matthew, when the cab moved.

She shook her head, refusing his apology as unnecessary. Tears filled her eyes. In less than a minute the cab had stopped in front of Constance's light-grained door. She demanded her reticule from Matthew, who had carried it since it fell. She would pay the cabman. Never before had Matthew permitted a woman to pay for a cab in which he had ridden; but there was no arguing with Constance. Constance was dangerous.

Amy Bates, still inhabiting the cave, had seen the cab-wheels through the grating of her window and had panted up the kitchen stairs to open the door ere Constance had climbed the steps. Amy, decidedly over forty, was a woman of authority. She wanted to know what was the matter, and Constance had to tell her that she had "felt unwell." Amy took the hat and mantle and departed to prepare a cup of tea. When they were alone Constance said to Matthew:

"Now, Mr. Matthew, will you please tell me?"

"It's only this," he began.

And as he told it, in quite a few words, it indeed had the air of being "only that." And yet his voice shook, in sympathy with the ageing woman's controlled but visible emotion. It seemed to him that gladness should have filled the absurd little parlour, but the spirit that presided had no name; it was certainly not joy. He himself felt very sad, desolated. He would have given much money to have been spared the experience. He knew simply that in the memory of the stout, comical, nice woman in the rocking-chair he had stirred old, old things, wakened slumbers that might have been eternal. He did not know that he was sitting on the very spot where the sofa had

been on which Samuel Povey lay when a beautiful and shameless young creature of fifteen extracted his tooth. He did not
know that Constance was sitting in the very chair in which
the memorable Mrs. Baines had sat in vain conflict with that
same unconquerable girl. He did not know ten thousand
matters that were rushing violently about in the vast heart of
Constance.

She cross-questioned him in detail. But she did not put the
questions which he in his innocence expected; such as, if her
sister looked old, if her hair was grey, if she was stout or thin.
And until Amy, mystified and resentful, had served the tea, on
a little silver tray, she remained comparatively calm. It was in
the middle of a gulp of tea that she broke down, and Matthew
had to take the cup from her.

"I can't thank you, Mr. Matthew," she wept. "I couldn't
thank you enough."

"But I've done nothing," he protested.

She shook her head. "I never hoped for this. Never hoped
for it!" she went on. "It makes me so happy—in a way.
. . . You mustn't take any notice of me. I'm silly. You
must kindly write down that address for me. And I must write
to Cyril at once. And I must see Mr. Critchlow."

"It's really very funny that Cyril hasn't written to you,"
said Matthew.

"Cyril has not been a good son," she said with sudden, solemn
coldness. "To think that he should have kept that . . . !"
She wept again.

At length Matthew saw the possibility of leaving. He felt
her warm, soft, crinkled hand round his fingers.

"You've behaved very nicely over this," she said. "And very
cleverly. In *every* thing—both over there and here. Nobody
could have shown a nicer feeling than you've shown. It's a
great comfort to me that my son has got you for a friend."

When he thought of his escapades, and of all the knowledge,
unutterable in Bursley, fantastically impossible in Bursley,
which he had imparted to her son, he marvelled that the
maternal instinct should be so deceived. Still, he felt that her
praise of him was deserved.

Outside, he gave vent to a "Phew" of relief. He smiled, in
his worldiest manner. But the smile was a sham. A pretence
to himself! A childish attempt to disguise from himself how
profoundly he had been moved by a natural scene!

iv

On the night when Matthew Peel-Swynnerton spoke to Mrs. Scales, Matthew was not the only person in the Pension Frensham who failed to sleep. When the old portress came downstairs from her errand, she observed that her mistress was leaving the mahogany retreat.

"She is sleeping tranquilly, the poor one!" said the portress, discharging her commission, which had been to learn the latest news of the mistress's indisposed dog, Fossette. In saying this her ancient, vibrant voice was rich with sympathy for the suffering animal. And she smiled. She was rather like a figure out of an almshouse, with her pink, apparently brittle skin, her tight black dress, and frilled white cap. She stooped habitually, and always walked quickly, with her head a few inches in advance of her feet. Her grey hair was scanty. She was old; nobody perhaps knew exactly how old. Sophia had taken her with the Pension, over a quarter of a century before, because she was old and could not easily have found another place. Although the clientèle was almost exclusively English, she spoke only French, explaining herself to Britons by means of benevolent smiles.

"I think I shall go to bed, Jacqueline," said the mistress, in reply.

A strange reply, thought Jacqueline. The unalterable custom of Jacqueline was to retire at midnight and to rise at five-thirty. Her mistress also usually retired about midnight, and during the final hour mistress and portress saw a good deal of each other. And considering that Jacqueline had just been sent up into the mistress's own bedroom to glance at Fossette, and that the bulletin was satisfactory, and that madame and Jacqueline had several customary daily matters to discuss, it seemed odd that madame should thus be going instantly to bed. However, Jacqueline said nothing but:

"Very well, madame. And the number 32?"

"Arrange yourself as you can," said the mistress, curtly.

"It is well, madame. Good evening, madame, and a good night."

Jacqueline, alone in the hall, re-entered her box and set upon one of those endless, mysterious tasks which occupied her when she was not rushing to and fro or whistling up the tubes.

Sophia, scarcely troubling even to glance into Fossette's round basket, undressed, put out the light, and got into bed. She felt extremely and inexplicably gloomy. She did not wish to reflect; she strongly wished not to reflect; but her mind insisted on reflection—a monotonous, futile, and distressing reflection. Povey! Povey! Could this be Constance's Povey, the unique Samuel Povey? That is to say, not he, but his son, Constance's son. Had Constance a grown-up son? Constance must be over fifty now, perhaps a grandmother! Had she really married Samuel Povey? Possibly she was dead. Certainly her mother must be dead, and Aunt Harriet and Mr. Critchlow. If alive, her mother must be at least eighty years of age.

The cumulative effect of merely remaining inactive when one ought to be active, was terrible. Undoubtedly she should have communicated with her family. It was silly not to have done so. After all, even if she had, as a child, stolen a trifle of money from her wealthy aunt, what would that have mattered? She had been proud. She was criminally proud. That was her vice. She admitted it frankly. But she could not alter her pride. Everybody had some weak spot. Her reputation for sagacity, for commonsense, was, she knew, enormous; she always felt, when people were talking to her, that they regarded her as a very unusually wise woman. And yet she had been guilty of the capital folly of cutting herself off from her family. She was ageing, and she was alone in the world. She was enriching herself; she had the most perfectly managed and the most respectable Pension in the world (she sincerely believed), and she was alone in the world. Acquaintances she had—French people who never offered nor accepted hospitality other than tea or wine, and one or two members of the English commercial colony—but her one friend was Fossette, aged three years! She was the most solitary person on earth. She had heard no word of Gerald, no word of anybody. Nobody whatever could truly be interested in her fate. This was what she had achieved after a quarter of a century of ceaseless labour and anxiety, during which she had not once been away from the Rue Lord Byron for more than thirty hours at a stretch. It was appalling—the passage of years; and the passage of years would grow more appalling. Ten years hence, where would she be? She pictured herself dying. Horrible!

Of course there was nothing to prevent her from going back to Bursley and repairing the grand error of her girlhood. No, nothing except the fact that her whole soul recoiled from the mere idea of any such enterprise! She was a fixture in the Rue Lord Byron. She was a part of the street. She knew all that happened or could happen there. She was attached to it by the heavy chains of habit. In the chill way of long use she loved it. There! The incandescent gas-burner of the street-lamp outside had been turned down, as it was turned down every night! If it is possible to love such a phenomenon, she loved that phenomenon. That phenomenon was a portion of her life, dear to her.

An agreeable young man, that Peel-Swynnerton! Then, evidently, since her days in Bursley, the Peels and the Swynnertons, partners in business, must have intermarried, or there must have been some affair of a will. Did he suspect who she was? He had had a very self-conscious, guilty look. No! He could not have suspected who she was. The idea was ridiculous. Probably he did not even know that her name was Scales. And even if he knew her name, he had probably never heard of Gerald Scales, or the story of her flight. Why, he could not have been born until after she had left Bursley! Besides, the Peels were always quite aloof from the ordinary social life of the town. No! He could not have suspected her identity. It was infantile to conceive such a thing.

And yet, she inconsequently proceeded in the tangle of her afflicted mind, supposing he had suspected it! Supposing by some queer chance, he had heard her forgotten story, and casually put two and two together! Supposing even that he were merely to mention in the Five Towns that the Pension Frensham was kept by a Mrs. Scales. "Scales? Scales?" people might repeat. "Now, what does that remind me of?" And the ball might roll and roll till Constance or somebody picked it up! And then . . . .

Moreover—a detail of which she had at first unaccountably failed to mark the significance—this Peel-Swynnerton was a friend of the Mr. Povey as to whom he had inquired. . . . In that case it could not be the same Povey. Impossible that the Peels should be on terms of friendship with Samuel Povey or his connections! But supposing after all they were! Supposing something utterly unanticipated and revolutionary had happened in the Five Towns!

She was disturbed. She was insecure. She foresaw inquiries being made concerning her. She foresaw an immense family

fuss, endless tomfoolery, the upsetting of her existence, the destruction of her calm. And she sank away from that prospect.
She could not face it. She did not want to face it. "No," she
cried passionately in her soul, "I've lived alone, and I'll stay as
I am. I can't change at my time of life." And her attitude
towards a possible invasion of her solitude became one of resentment. "I won't have it! I won't have it! I will be left alone.
Constance! What can Constance be to me, or I to her, now?"
The vision of any change in her existence was in the highest degree painful to her. And not only painful! It frightened her.
It made her shrink. But she could not dismiss it. . . . She
could not argue herself out of it. The apparition of Matthew
Peel-Swynnerton had somehow altered the very stuff of her
fibres.

And surging on the outskirts of the central storm of her
brain were ten thousand apprehensions about the management
of the Pension. All was black, hopeless. The Pension might
have been the most complete business failure that gross carelessness and incapacity had ever provoked. Was it not the fact
that she had to supervise everything herself, that she could
depend on no one? Were she to be absent even for a single day
the entire structure would inevitably fall. Instead of working
less she worked harder. And who could guarantee that her
investments were safe?

When dawn announced itself, slowly discovering each object
in the chamber, she was ill. Fever seemed to rage in her head.
And in and round her mouth she had strange sensations. Fossette stirred in the basket near the large desk on which multifarious files and papers were ranged with minute particularity.

"Fossette!" she tried to call out; but no sound issued from
her lips. She could not move her tongue. She tried to protrude
it, and could not. For hours she had been conscious of a headache. Her heart sank. She was sick with fear. Her memory
flashed to her father and his seizure. She was his daughter!
Paralysis! "Ça serait le comble!" she thought in French, horrified. Her fear became abject! "Can I move at all?" she
thought, and madly jerked her head. Yes, she could move her
head slightly on the pillow, and she could stretch her right arm,
both arms. Absurd cowardice! Of course it was not a seizure!
She reassured herself. Still, she could not put her tongue out.
Suddenly she began to hiccough, and she had no control over
the hiccough. She put her hand to the bell, whose ringing

would summon the man who slept in a pantry off the hall, and suddenly the hiccough ceased. Her hand dropped. She was better. Besides, what use in ringing for a man if she could not speak to him through the door? She must wait for Jacqueline. At six o'clock every morning, summer and winter, Jacqueline entered her mistress's bedroom to release the dog for a moment's airing under her own supervision. The clock on the mantelpiece showed five minutes past three. She had three hours to wait. Fossette pattered across the room, and sprang on to the bed and nestled down. Sophia ignored her, but Fossette, being herself unwell and torpid, did not seem to care.

Jacqueline was late. In the quarter of an hour between six o'clock and a quarter past, Sophia suffered the supreme pangs of despair and verged upon insanity. It appeared to her that her cranium would blow off under pressure from within. Then the door opened silently, a few inches. Usually Jacqueline came into the room, but sometimes she stood behind the door and called in her soft, trembling voice, "Fossette! Fossette!" And on this morning she did not come into the room. The dog did not immediately respond. Sophia was in an agony. She marshalled all her volition, all her self-control and strength, to shout:

"*Jacqueline!*"

It came out of her, a horribly difficult and misshapen birth, but it came. She was exhausted.

"Yes, madame." Jacqueline entered.

As soon as she had a glimpse of Sophia she threw up her hands. Sophia stared at her, wordless.

"I will fetch the doctor—myself," whispered Jacqueline, and fled.

"*Jacqueline!*" The woman stopped. Then Sophia determined to force herself to make a speech, and she braced her muscles to an unprecedented effort. "Say not a word to the others." She could not bear that the whole household should know of her illness. Jacqueline nodded and vanished, the dog following. Jacqueline understood. She lived in the place with her mistress as with a fellow-conspirator.

Sophia began to feel better. She could get into a sitting posture, though the movement made her dizzy. By working to the foot of the bed she could see herself in the glass of the wardrobe. And she saw that the lower part of her face was twisted out of shape.

The doctor, who knew her, and who earned a lot of money in her house, told her frankly what had happened. *Paralysie glosso-labio-laryngée* was the phrase he used. She understood. A very slight attack; due to overwork and worry. He ordered absolute rest and quiet.

"Impossible!" she said, genuinely convinced that she alone was indispensable.

"Repose the most absolute!" he repeated.

She marvelled that a few words with a man who chanced to be named Peel-Swynnerton could have resulted in such a disaster, and drew a curious satisfaction from this fearful proof that she was so highly-strung. But even then she did not realize how profoundly she had been disturbed.

v

"My darling Sophia——"

The inevitable miracle had occurred. Her suspicions concerning that Mr. Peel-Swynnerton were well-founded, after all! Here was a letter from Constance! The writing on the envelope was not Constance's; but even before examining it she had had a peculiar qualm. She received letters from England nearly every day asking about rooms and prices (and on many of them she had to pay threepence excess postage, because the writers carelessly or carefully forgot that a penny stamp was not sufficient); there was nothing to distinguish this envelope, and yet her first glance at it had startled her; and when, deciphering the smudged post-mark, she made out the word "Bursley," her heart did literally seem to stop, and she opened the letter in quite violent tremulation, thinking to herself: "The doctor would say this is very bad for me." Six days had elapsed since her attack, and she was wonderfully better; the distortion of her face had almost disappeared. But the doctor was grave; he ordered no medicine, merely a tonic; and monotonously insisted on "repose the most absolute," on perfect mental calm. He said little else, allowing Sophia to judge from his silences the seriousness of her condition. Yes, the receipt of such a letter must be bad for her!

She controlled herself while she read it, lying in her dressing-gown against several pillows on the bed; a mist did not form in her eyes, nor did she sob, nor betray physically that she was not reading an order for two rooms for a week. But the expenditure of nervous force necessary to self-control was terrific.

Constance's handwriting had changed; it was, however, easily recognizable as a development of the neat calligraphy of the girl who could print window-tickets. The "S" of Sophia was formed in the same way as she had formed it in the last letter which she had received from her at Axe!

"My Darling Sophia,

"I cannot tell you how overjoyed I was to learn that after all these years you are alive and well, and doing so well too. I long to see you, my dear sister. It was Mr. Peel-Swynnerton who told me. He is a friend of Cyril's. Cyril is the name of my son. I married Samuel in 1867. Cyril was born in 1874 at Christmas. He is now twenty-two, and doing very well in London as a student of sculpture, though so young. He won a National Scholarship. There were only eight, of which he won one, in all England. Samuel died in 1888. If you read the papers you must have seen about the Povey affair. I mean of course Mr. Daniel Povey, Confectioner. It was that that killed poor Samuel. Poor mother died in 1875. It doesn't seem so long. Aunt Harriet and Aunt Maria are both dead. Old Dr. Harrop is dead, and his son has practically retired. He has a partner, a Scotchman. Mr. Critchlow has married Miss Insull. Did you ever hear of such a thing? They have taken over the shop, and I live in the house part, the other being bricked up. Business in the Square is not what it used to be. The steam trams take all the custom to Hanbridge, and they are talking of electric trams, but I dare say it is only talk. I have a fairly good servant. She has been with me a long time, but servants are not what they were. I keep pretty well, except for my sciatica and palpitation. Since Cyril went to London I have been very lonely. But I try to cheer up and count my blessings. I am sure I have a great deal to be thankful for. And now this news of you! Please write to me a long letter, and tell me all about yourself. It is a long way to Paris. But surely now you know I am still here, you will come and pay me a visit—at least. Everybody would be *most* glad to see you. And I should be so proud and glad. As I say, I am all alone. Mr. Critchlow says I am to say there is a deal of money waiting for you. You know he is the trustee. There is the half-share of mother's and also of Aunt Harriet's, and it has been accumulating. By the way, they are getting up a subscription for Miss Chetwynd, poor old thing. Her sister is dead, and she is in poverty. I have put myself down for £20. Now, my dear sister, please do write to me at once. You see it is still the old address. I remain, my darling Sophia, with much love, your affectionate sister,

"CONSTANCE POVEY.

"P.S.—I should have written yesterday, but I was not fit. Every time I sat down to write, I cried."

"Of course," said Sophia to Fossette, "she expects me to go to her, instead of her coming to me! And yet who's the busiest?"

But this observation was not serious. It was merely a trifle of affectionate malicious embroidery that Sophia put on the edge of her deep satisfaction. The very spirit of simple love seemed to emanate from the paper on which Constance had written. And this spirit woke suddenly and completely Sophia's love for Constance. Constance! At that moment there was assuredly for Sophia no creature in the world like Constance. Constance personified for her the qualities of the Baines family. Constance's letter was a great letter, a perfect letter, perfect in its artlessness; the natural expression of the Baines character at its best. Not an awkward reference in the whole of it! No clumsy expression of surprise at anything that she, Sophia, had done, or failed to do! No mention of Gerald! Just a sublime acceptance of the situation as it was, and the assurance of undiminished love! Tact? No; it was something finer than tact! Tact was conscious, skilful. Sophia was certain that the notion of tactfulness had not entered Constance's head. Constance had simply written out of her heart. And that was what made the letter so splendid. Sophia was convinced that no one but a Baines could have written such a letter.

She felt that she must rise to the height of that letter, that she too must show her Baines blood. And she went primly to her desk, and began to write (on private notepaper) in that imperious large hand of hers that was so different from Constance's. She began a little stiffly, but after a few lines her generous and passionate soul was responding freely to the appeal of Constance. She asked that Mr. Critchlow should pay £20 for her to the Miss Chetwynd fund. She spoke of her

Pension and of Paris, and of her pleasure in Constance's letter. But she said nothing as to Gerald, nor as to the possibility of a visit to the Five Towns. She finished the letter in a blaze of love, and passed from it as from a dream to the sterile banality of the daily life of the Pension Frensham, feeling that, compared to Constance's affection, nothing else had any worth.

But she would not consider the project of going to Bursley. Never, never would she go to Bursley. If Constance chose to come to Paris and see her, she would be delighted, but she herself would not budge. The mere notion of any change in her existence intimidated her. And as for returning to Bursley itself . . . no, no!

Nevertheless, at the Pension Frensham, the future could not be as the past. Sophia's health forbade that. She knew that the doctor was right. Every time that she made an effort, she knew intimately and speedily that the doctor was right. Only her will-power was unimpaired; the machinery by which will-power is converted into action was mysteriously damaged. She was aware of the fact. But she could not face it yet. Time would have to elapse before she could bring herself to face that fact. She was getting an old woman. She could no longer draw on reserves. Yet she persisted to every one that she was quite recovered, and was abstaining from her customary work simply from an excess of prudence. Certainly her face had recovered. And the Pension, being a machine all of whose parts were in order, continued to run, apparently, with its usual smoothness. It is true that the excellent chef began to peculate, but as his cuisine did not suffer, the result was not noticeable for a long period. The whole staff and many of the guests knew that Sophia had been indisposed; and they knew no more.

When by hazard Sophia observed a fault in the daily conduct of the house, her first impulse was to go to the root of it and cure it, her second was to leave it alone, or to palliate it by some superficial remedy. Unperceived, and yet vaguely suspected by various people, the decline of the Pension Frensham had set in. The tide, having risen to its highest, was receding, but so little that no one could be sure that it had turned. Every now and then it rushed up again and washed the furthest stone.

Sophia and Constance exchanged several letters. Sophia said repeatedly that she could not leave Paris. At length she roundly asked Constance to come and pay her a visit. She made the suggestion with fear—for the prospect of actually seeing her beloved Constance alarmed her—but she could do no less than make it. And in a few days she had a reply to say that Constance would have come, under Cyril's charge, but that her sciatica was suddenly much worse, and she was obliged to lie down every day after dinner to rest her legs. Travelling was impossible for her. The fates were combining against Sophia's decision.

And now Sophia began to ask herself about her duty to Constance. The truth was that she was groping round to find an excuse for reversing her decision. She was afraid to reverse it, yet tempted. She had the desire to do something which she objected to doing. It was like the desire to throw one's self over a high balcony. It drew her, drew her, and she drew back against it. The Pension was now tedious to her. It bored her even to pretend to be the supervising head of the Pension. Throughout the house discipline had loosened.

She wondered when Mr. Mardon would renew his overtures for the transformation of her enterprise into a limited company. In spite of herself she would deliberately cross his path and give him opportunities to begin on the old theme. He had never before left her in peace for so long a period. No doubt she had, upon his last assault, absolutely convinced him that his efforts had no smallest chance of success, and he had made up his mind to cease them. With a single word she could wind him up again. The merest hint, one day when he was paying his bill, and he would be beseeching her. But she could not utter the word.

Then she began to say openly that she did not feel well, that the house was too much for her, and that the doctor had imperatively commanded rest. She said this to every one except Mardon. And every one somehow persisted in not saying it to Mardon. The doctor having advised that she should spend more time in the open air, she would take afternoon drives in the Bois with Fossette. It was October. But Mr. Mardon never seemed to hear of those drives.

One morning he met her in the street outside the house.

"I'm sorry to hear you're so unwell," he said confidentially, after they had discussed the health of Fossette.

"So unwell!" she exclaimed as if resenting the statement. "Who told you I was so unwell?"

"Jacqueline. She told me you often said that what you

needed was a complete change. And it seems the doctor says so, too."

"Oh! doctors!" she murmured, without however denying the truth of Jacqueline's assertion. She saw hope in Mr. Mardon's eyes.

"Of course, you know," he said, still more confidentially, "if you *should* happen to change your mind, I'm always ready to form a little syndicate to take this"—he waved discreetly at the Pension—"off your hands."

She shook her head violently, which was strange, considering that for weeks she had been wishing to hear such words from Mr. Mardon.

"You needn't give it up altogether," he said. "You could retain your hold on it. We'd make you manageress, with a salary and a share in the profits. You'd be mistress just as much as you are now."

."Oh!" said she carelessly. "*If I gave it up, I should give it up entirely.* No half measures for me."

With the utterance of that sentence, the history of Frensham's as a private understanding was brought to a close. Sophia knew it. Mr. Mardon knew it. Mr. Mardon's heart leapt. He saw in his imagination the formation of the preliminary syndicate, with himself at its head, and then the resale by the syndicate to a limited company at a profit. He saw a nice little profit for his own private personal self of a thousand or so—gained in a moment. The plant, his hope, which he had deemed dead, blossomed with miraculous suddenness.

"Well," he said. "Give it up entirely, then! Take a holiday for life. You've deserved it, Mrs. Scales."

She shook her head once again.

"Think it over," he said.

"I gave you my answer years ago," she said obstinately, while fearing lest he should take her at her word.

"Oblige me by thinking it over," he said. "I'll mention it to you again in a few days."

"It will be no use," she said.

He took his leave, waddling down the street in his vague clothes, conscious of his fame as Lewis Mardon, the great house-agent of the Champs Elysées, known throughout Europe and America.

In a few days he did mention it again.

"There's only one thing that makes me dream of it even for a moment," said Sophia. "And that is my sister's health."

"Your sister!" he exclaimed. He did not know she had a sister. Never had she spoken of her family.

"Yes. Her letters are beginning to worry me."

"Does she live in Paris?"

"No. In Staffordshire. She has never left home."

And to preserve her pride intact she led Mr. Mardon to think that Constance was in a most serious way, whereas in truth Constance had nothing worse than her sciatica, and even that was somewhat better.

Thus she yielded.

CHAPTER II

THE MEETING

SOON after dinner one day in the following spring, Mr. Critchlow knocked at Constance's door. She was seated in the rocking-chair in front of the fire in the parlour. She wore a large "rough" apron, and with the outlying parts of the apron she was rubbing the moisture out of the coat of a young wire-haired fox-terrier, for whom no more original name had been found than "Spot." It is true that he had a spot. Constance had more than once called the world to witness that she would never have a young dog again, because, as she said, she could not be always running about after them, and they ate the stuffing out of the furniture. But her last dog had lived too long; a dog can do worse things than eat furniture; and, in her natural reaction against age in dogs, and also in the hope of postponing as long as possible the inevitable sorrow and upset which death causes when it takes off a domestic pet, she had not known how to refuse the very desirable fox-terrier aged ten months that an acquaintance had offered to her. Spot's beautiful pink skin could be seen under his disturbed hair; he was exquisitely soft to the touch, and to himself he was loathsome. His eyes continually peeped forth between corners of the agitated towel, and they were full of inquietude and shame.

Amy was assisting at this performance, gravely on the watch to see that Spot did not escape into the coal-cellar. She opened the door to Mr. Critchlow's knock. Mr. Critchlow entered without any formalities, as usual. He did not seem to have changed. He had the same quantity of white hair, he wore the same long white apron, and his voice (which showed however an occasional tendency to shrillness) had the same grating quality. He stood fairly straight. He was carrying a newspaper in his vellum hand.

"Well, missis!" he said.

"That will do, thank you, Amy," said Constance, quietly. Amy went slowly.

"So ye're washing him for her!" said Mr. Critchlow.

"Yes," Constance admitted. Spot glanced sharply at the aged man.

"An' ye seen this bit in the paper about Sophia?" he asked, holding the *Signal* for her inspection.

"About Sophia?" cried Constance. "What's amiss?"

"Nothing's amiss. But they've got it. It's in the 'Staffordshire day by day' column. Here! I'll read it ye." He drew a long wooden spectacle-case from his waistcoat pocket, and placed a second pair of spectacles on his nose. Then he sat down on the sofa, his knees sticking out pointedly, and read: " 'We understand that Mrs. Sophia Scales, proprietress of the famous Pension Frensham in the Rue Lord Byron, Paris' —it's that famous that nobody in th' Five Towns has ever heard of it—'is about to pay a visit to her native town, Bursley, after an absence of over thirty years. Mrs. Scales belonged to the well-known and highly respected family of Baines. She has recently disposed of the Pension Frensham to a limited company, and we are betraying no secret in stating that the price paid ran well into five figures.' So ye see!" Mr. Critchlow commented.

"How do those *Signal* people find out things?" Constance murmured.

"Eh, bless ye, I don't know," said Mr. Critchlow.

This was an untruth. Mr. Critchlow had himself given the information to the new editor of the *Signal*, who had soon been made aware of Critchlow's passion for the press, and who knew how to make use of it.

"I wish it hadn't appeared just to-day," said Constance.

"Why?"

"Oh! I don't know, I wish it hadn't."

"Well, I'll be touring on, missis," said Mr. Critchlow, meaning that he would go.

He left the paper, and descended the steps with senile deliberation. It was characteristic that he had shown no curiosity whatever as to the details of Sophia's arrival.

Constance removed her apron, wrapped Spot up in it, and put him in a corner of the sofa. She then abruptly sent Amy out to buy a penny time-table.

"I thought you were going by tram to Knype," Amy observed.

"I have decided to go by train," said Constance, with cold dignity, as if she had decided the fate of nations. She hated such observations from Amy, who unfortunately lacked, in an increasing degree, the supreme gift of unquestioning obedience.

When Amy came breathlessly back, she found Constance in her bedroom, withdrawing crumpled balls of paper from the sleeves of her second-best mantle. Constance scarcely ever wore this mantle. In theory it was destined for chapel on wet Sundays; in practice it had remained long in the wardrobe, Sundays having been obstinately fine for weeks and weeks together. It was a mantle that Constance had never really liked. But she was not going to Knype to meet Sophia in her everyday mantle; and she had no intention of donning her best mantle for such an excursion. To make her first appearance before Sophia in the best mantle she had—this would have been a sad mistake of tactics! Not only would it have led to an anticlimax on Sunday, but it would have given to Constance the air of being in awe of Sophia. Now Constance was in truth a little afraid of Sophia; in thirty years Sophia might have grown into anything, whereas Constance had remained just Constance. Paris was a great place; and it was immensely far off. And the mere sound of that limited company business was intimidating. Imagine Sophia having by her own efforts created something which a real limited company wanted to buy and had bought! Yes, Constance was afraid, but she did not mean to show her fear in her mantle. After all, she was the elder. And she had her dignity too—and a lot of it—tucked away in her secret heart, hidden within the mildness of that soft exterior. So she had decided on the second-best mantle, which, being seldom used, had its sleeves stuffed with paper to the end that they might keep their shape and their "fall." The little balls of paper were strewed over the bed.

"There's a train at a quarter to three, gets to Knype at ten minutes past," said Amy, officiously. "But supposing it was only three minutes late and the London train was prompt, then you might miss her. Happen you'd better take the two fifteen to be on the safe side."

"Let me look," said Constance, firmly. "Please put all this paper in the wardrobe."

She would have preferred not to follow Amy's suggestion, but it was so incontestably wise that she was obliged to accept it.

"Unless ye go by tram," said Amy. "That won't mean starting quite so soon."

But Constance would not go by tram. If she took the tram she would be bound to meet people who had read the *Signal*, and who would say, with their stupid vacuity: "Going to meet your sister at Knype?" And then tiresome conversations would follow. Whereas, in the train, she would choose a compartment, and would be far less likely to encounter chatterers.

There was now not a minute to lose. And the excitement which had been growing in that house for days past, under a pretence of calm, leapt out swiftly into the light of the sun, and was unashamed. Amy had to help her mistress make herself as comely as she could be made without her best dress, mantle, and bonnet. Amy was frankly consulted as to effects. The barrier of class was lowered for a space. Many years had elapsed since Constance had been conscious of a keen desire to look smart. She was reminded of the days when, in full fig for chapel, she would dash downstairs on a Sunday morning, and, assuming a pose for inspection at the threshold of the parlour, would demand of Samuel: "Shall I do?" Yes, she used to dash downstairs, like a child, and yet in those days she had thought herself so sedate and mature! She sighed, half with lancinating regret, and half in gentle disdain of that mercurial creature aged less than thirty. At fifty-one she regarded herself as old. And she was old. And Amy had the tricks and manners of an old spinster. Thus the excitement in the house was an "old" excitement, and, like Constance's desire to look smart, it had its ridiculous side, which was also its tragic side, the side that would have made a boor guffaw, and a hysterical fool cry, and a wise man meditate sadly upon the earth's fashion of renewing itself.

At half-past one Constance was dressed, with the exception of her gloves. She looked at the clock a second time to make sure that she might safely glance round the house without fear of missing the train. She went up into the bedroom on the second-floor, her and Sophia's old bedroom, which she had prepared with enormous care for Sophia. The airing of that room had been an enterprise of days, for, save by a minister during the sittings of the Wesleyan Methodist Conference at Bursley, it had never been occupied since the era when Maria Insull used occasionally to sleep in the house. Cyril clung to his old room on his visits. Constance had an ample supply of solid and stately furniture, and the chamber destined for Sophia was lightened in every corner by the reflections of polished mahogany. It was also fairly impregnated with the odour of furniture paste—an odour of which no housewife need be ashamed. Further, it had been re-papered in a delicate blue, with one of the new "art" patterns. It was a "Baines" room. And Constance did not care where Sophia came from, nor what Sophia had been accustomed to, nor into what limited company Sophia had been transformed—that room was adequate! It could not have been improved upon. You had only to look at the crocheted mats—even those on the washstand under the white-and-gold ewer and other utensils. It was folly to expose such mats to the splashings of a washstand, but it was sublime folly. Sophia might remove them if she cared. Constance was house-proud; house-pride had slumbered within her; now it blazed forth.

A fire brightened the drawing-room, which was a truly magnificent apartment, a museum of valuables collected by the Baines and the Maddack families since the year 1840, tempered by the latest novelties in antimacassars and cloths. In all Bursley there could have been few drawing-rooms to compare with Constance's. Constance knew it. She was not afraid of her drawing-room being seen by anybody.

She passed for an instant into her own bedroom, where Amy was patiently picking balls of paper from the bed.

"Now you quite understand about tea?" Constance asked.

"Oh yes, 'm," said Amy, as if to say: "How much oftener are you going to ask me that question?" "Are you off now, 'm?"

"Yes," said Constance. "Come and fasten the front-door after me."

They descended together to the parlour. A white cloth for tea lay folded on the table. It was of the finest damask that skill could choose and money buy. It was fifteen years old, and had never been spread. Constance would not have produced it for the first meal, had she not possessed two other of equal eminence. On the harmonium were ranged several jams and cakes, a Bursley pork-pie, and some pickled salmon; with the necessary silver. All was there. Amy could not go wrong. And crocuses were in the vases on the mantelpiece. Her "garden," in the phrase which used to cause Samuel to think how extraordinary feminine she was! It was a long time since she had had a "garden" on the mantelpiece. Her interest in her chronic sciatica and in her palpitations had grown at the expense of her interest in gardens. Often, when she had finished the complicated processes by which her furniture and other goods were kept in order, she had strength only to "rest." She was rather a fragile, small, fat woman, soon out of breath, easily marred. This business of preparing for the advent of Sophia had appeared to her genuinely colossal. However, she had come through it very well. She was in pretty good health; only a little tired, and more than a little anxious and nervous, as she gave the last glance.

"Take away that apron, do," she said to Amy, pointing to the rough apron in the corner of the sofa. "By the way, where is Spot?"

"Spot, m'm?" Amy ejaculated.

Both their hearts jumped. Amy instinctively looked out of the window. He was there, sure enough, in the gutter, studying the indescribabilities of King Street. He had obviously escaped when Amy came in from buying the time-table. The woman's face was guilty.

"Amy, I wonder *at* you!" exclaimed Constance, tragically. She opened the door.

"Well, I never did see the like of that dog!" murmured Amy.

"Spot!" his mistress commanded. "Come here at once. Do you hear me?"

Spot turned sharply and gazed motionless at Constance. Then with a toss of the head he dashed off to the corner of the Square, and gazed motionless again. Amy went forth to catch him. After an age she brought him in, squealing. He was in a state exceedingly offensive to the eye and to the nose. He had effectively got rid of the smell of soap, which he loathed. Constance could have wept. It did really appear to her that nothing had gone right that day. And Spot had the most innocent, trustful air. Impossible to make him realize that his aunt Sophia was coming. He would have sold his entire family into servitude in order to buy ten yards of King Street gutter.

"You must wash him in the scullery, that's all there is for it," said Constance, controlling herself. "Put that apron on, and don't forget one of your new aprons when you open the door. Better shut him up in Mr. Cyril's bedroom when you've dried him."

And she went, charged with worries, clasping her bag and her umbrella and smoothing her gloves, and spying downwards at the folds of her mantle.

"That's a funny way to go to Bursley Station, that is," said Amy, observing that Constance was descending King Street instead of crossing it into Wedgwood Street. And she caught Spot "a fair clout on the head," to indicate to him that she had him alone in the house now.

Constance was taking a round-about route to the station, so that, if stopped by acquaintances, she should not be too obviously going to the station. Her feelings concerning the arrival of Sophia, and concerning the town's attitude towards it, were very complex.

She was forced to hurry. And she had risen that morning with plans perfectly contrived for the avoidance of hurry. She disliked hurry because it always "put her about."

ii

The express from London was late, so that Constance had three-quarters of an hour of the stony calmness of Knype platform when it is waiting for a great train. At last the porters began to cry, "Macclesfield, Stockport, and Manchester train"; the immense engine glided round the curve, dwarfing the carriages behind it, and Constance had a supreme tremor. The calmness of the platform was transformed into a *mêlée*. Little Constance found herself left on the fringe of a physically agitated crowd which was apparently trying to scale a precipice surmounted by windows and doors from whose apertures looked forth defenders of the train. Knype platform

seemed as if it would never be reduced to order again. And
Constance did not estimate highly the chances of picking out
an unknown Sophia from that welter. She was very seriously
perturbed. All the muscles of her face were drawn as her gaze
wandered anxiously from end to end of the train.

Presently she saw a singular dog. Other people also saw it.
It was of the colour of chocolate; it had a head and shoulders
richly covered with hair that hung down in thousands of tufts
like the tufts of a modern mop such as is bought in shops.
This hair stopped suddenly rather less than halfway along the
length of the dog's body, the remainder of which was naked
and as smooth as marble. The effect was to give to the inhabitants of the Five Towns the impression that the dog had
forgotten an essential part of its attire and was outraging
decency. The ball of hair which had been allowed to grow on
the dog's tail, and the circles of hair which ornamented its
ankles, only served to intensify the impression of indecency.
A pink ribbon round its neck completed the outrage. The
animal had absolutely the air of a decked trollop. A chain ran
taut from the creature's neck into the middle of a small crowd
of persons gesticulating over trunks, and Constance traced it
to a tall and distinguished woman in a coat and skirt with a
rather striking hat. A beautiful and aristocratic woman, Constance thought, at a distance! Then the strange idea came to
her: "That's Sophia!" She was sure. . . . She was not sure.
. . . She was sure. The woman emerged from the crowd.
Her eye fell on Constance. They both hesitated, and, as it
were, wavered uncertainly towards each other.

"I should have known you anywhere," said Sophia, with
apparently careless tranquillity, as she stooped to kiss Constance, raising her veil.

Constance saw that this marvellous tranquillity must be
imitated, and she imitated it very well. It was a "Baines"
tranquillity. But she noticed a twitching of her sister's lips.
The twitching comforted Constance, proving to her that she
was not alone in foolishness. There was also something queer
about the permanent lines of Sophia's mouth. That must be
due to the "attack" about which Sophia had written.

"Did Cyril meet you?" asked Constance. It was all that
she could think of to say.

"Oh yes!" said Sophia, eagerly. "And I went to his studio,

and he saw me off at Euston. He is a *very* nice boy. I love him."

She said "I love him" with the intonation of Sophia aged fifteen. Her tone and imperious gesture sent Constance flying back to the 'sixties. "She hasn't altered one bit," Constance thought with joy. "Nothing could change Sophia." And at the back of that notion was a more general notion: "Nothing could change a Baines." It was true that Constance's Sophia had not changed. Powerful individualities remain undisfigured by no matter what vicissitudes. After this revelation of the original Sophia, arising as it did out of praise of Cyril, Constance felt easier, felt reassured.

"This is Fossette," said Sophia, pulling at the chain.

Constance knew not what to reply. Surely Sophia could not be aware what she did in bringing such a dog to a place where people were so particular as they are in the Five Towns.

"Fossette!" She repeated the name in an endearing accent, half stooping towards the dog. After all, it was not the dog's fault. Sophia had certainly mentioned a dog in her letters, but she had not prepared Constance for the spectacle of Fossette.

All that happened in a moment. A porter appeared with two trunks belonging to Sophia. Constance observed that they were superlatively "good" trunks; also that Sophia's clothes, though "on the showy side," were superlatively "good." The getting of Sophia's ticket to Bursley occupied them next, and soon the first shock of meeting had worn off.

In a second-class compartment of the Loop Line train, with Sophia and Fossette opposite to her, Constance had leisure to "take in" Sophia. She came to the conclusion that, despite her slenderness and straightness and the general effect of the long oval of her face under the hat, Sophia looked her age. She saw that Sophia must have been through a great deal; her experiences were damagingly printed in the details of feature. Seen at a distance, she might have passed for a woman of thirty, even for a girl, but seen across a narrow railway carriage she was a woman whom suffering had aged. Yet obviously her spirit was unbroken. Hear her tell a doubtful porter that of course she should take Fossette with her into the carriage! See her shut the carriage door with the expressed intention of keeping other people out! She was accustomed to command. At the same time her face had an almost set smile, as though she had said to herself: "I will die smiling." Constance felt sorry for her. While recognizing in Sophia a superior in charm, in experience, in knowledge of the world and in force of personality, she yet with a kind of undisturbed, fundamental superiority felt sorry for Sophia.

"What do you think?" said Sophia, absently fingering Fossette. "A man came up to me at Euston, while Cyril was getting my ticket, and said, 'Eh, Miss Baines, I haven't seen ye for over thirty years, but I know you're Miss Baines, or *were*—and you're looking bonny.' Then he went off. I think it must have been Holl, the grocer."

"Had he got a long white beard?"

"Yes."

"Then it was Mr. Holl. He's been Mayor twice. He's an alderman, you know."

"Really!" said Sophia. "But wasn't it queer?"

"Eh! Bless us!" exclaimed Constance. "Don't talk about queer! It's terrible how time flies."

The conversation stopped, and it refused to start again. Two women who are full of affectionate curiosity about each other, and who have not seen each other for thirty years, and who are anxious to confide in each other, ought to discover no difficulty in talking; but somehow these two could not talk. Constance perceived that Sophia was impeded by the same awkwardness as herself.

"Well I never!" cried Sophia, suddenly. She had glanced out of the window and had seen two camels and an elephant in a field close to the line, amid manufactories and warehouses and advertisements of soap.

"Oh!" said Constance. "That's Barnum's, you know. They have what they call a central depôt here, because it's the middle of England." Constance spoke proudly. (After all, there can be only one middle.) It was on her tongue to say, in her "tart" manner, that Fossette ought to be with the camels, but she refrained. Sophia hit on the excellent idea of noting all the buildings that were new to her and all the landmarks that she remembered. It was surprising how little the district had altered.

"Same smoke!" said Sophia.

"Same smoke!" Constance agreed.

"It's even worse," said Sophia.

"Do you think so?" Constance was slightly piqued. "But they're doing something now for smoke abatement."

"I must have forgotten how dirty it was!" said Sophia. "I suppose that's it. I'd no *idea* . . . !"

"Really!" said Constance. Then, in candid admission, "The fact is, it *is* dirty. You can't imagine what work it makes, especially with window-curtains."

As the train puffed under Trafalgar Road, Constance pointed to a new station that was being built there, to be called "Trafalgar Road" station.

"Won't it be strange?" said she, accustomed to the eternal sequence of Loop Line stations—Turnhill, Bursley, Bleakridge, Hanbridge, Cauldon, Knype, Trent Vale, and Longshaw. A "Trafalgar Road" inserting itself between Bleakridge and Hanbridge seemed to her excessively curious.

"Yes, I suppose it will," Sophia agreed.

"But of course it's not the same to you," said Constance, dashed. She indicated the glories of Bursley Park, as the train slackened for Bursley, with modesty. Sophia gazed, and vaguely recognized the slopes where she had taken her first walk with Gerald Scales.

Nobody accosted them at Bursley Station, and they drove to the Square in a cab. Amy was at the window; she held up Spot, who was in a plenary state of cleanliness, rivalling the purity of Amy's apron.

"Good afternoon, m'm," said Amy, officiously, to Sophia, as Sophia came up the steps.

"Good afternoon, Amy," Sophia replied. She flattered Amy in thus showing that she was acquainted with her name; but if ever a servant was put into her place by mere tone, Amy was put into her place on that occasion. Constance trembled at Sophia's frigid and arrogant politeness. Certainly Sophia was not used to being addressed first by servants. But Amy was not quite the ordinary servant. She was much older than the ordinary servant, and she had acquired a partial moral dominion over Constance, though Constance would have warmly denied it. Hence Constance's apprehension. However, nothing happened. Amy apparently did not feel the snub.

"Take Spot and put him in Mr. Cyril's bedroom," Constance murmured to her, as if implying: "Have I not already told you to do that?" The fact was, she was afraid for Spot's life.

"Now, Fossette!" She welcomed the incoming poodle kindly; the poodle began at once to sniff.

The fat, red cabman was handling the trunks on the pavement, and Amy was upstairs. For a moment the sisters were alone together in the parlour.

"So here I am!" exclaimed the tall, majestic woman of fifty. And her lips twitched again as she looked round the room—so small to her.

"Yes, here you are!" Constance agreed. She bit her lip, and, as a measure of prudence to avoid breaking down, she bustled out to the cabman. A passing instant of emotion, like a fleck of foam on a wide and calm sea!

The cabman blundered up and downstairs with trunks, and saluted Sophia's haughty generosity, and then there was quietness. Amy was already brewing the tea in the cave. The prepared tea-table in front of the fire made a glittering array.

"Now, what about Fossette?" Constance voiced anxieties that had been growing on her.

"Fossette will be quite right with me," said Sophia, firmly.

They ascended to the guest's room, which drew Sophia's admiration for its prettiness. She hurried to the window and looked out into the Square.

"Would you like a fire?" Constance asked, in a rather perfunctory manner. For a bedroom fire, in seasons of normal health, was still regarded as absurd in the Square.

"Oh, no!" said Sophia; but with a slight failure to rebut the suggestion as utterly ridiculous.

"Sure?" Constance questioned.

"Quite, thank you," said Sophia.

"Well, I'll leave you. I expect Amy will have tea ready directly." She went down into the kitchen. "Amy," she said, "as soon as we've finished tea, light a fire in Mrs. Scales's bedroom."

"In the top bedroom, m'm?"

"Yes."

Constance climbed again to her own bedroom, and shut the door. She needed a moment to herself, in the midst of this terrific affair. She sighed with relief as she removed her mantle. She thought: "At any rate we've met, and I've got her here. She's very nice. No, she's isn't a bit altered." She hesitated to admit that to her Sophia was the least in the world formidable. And so she said once more: "She's very nice. She isn't a bit altered." And then: "Fancy her being here! She really is here." With her perfect simplicity it did not occur to Constance to speculate as to what Sophia thought of her.

Sophia was downstairs first, and Constance found her looking at the blank wall beyond the door leading to the kitchen steps.

"So this is where you had it bricked up?" said Sophia.

"Yes," said Constance. "That's the place."

"It makes me feel like people feel when they have tickling in a limb that's been cut off!" said Sophia.

"Oh, Sophia!"

The tea received a great deal of praise from Sophia, but neither of them ate much. Constance found that Sophia was like herself: she had to be particular about her food. She tasted dainties for the sake of tasting, but it was a bird's pecking. Not the twelfth part of the tea was consumed. They dared not indulge caprices. Only their eyes could feed.

After tea they went up to the drawing-room, and in the corridor had the startling pleasure of seeing two dogs who scurried about after each other in amity. Spot had found Fossette, with the aid of Amy's incurable carelessness, and had at once examined her with great particularity. She seemed to be of an amiable disposition, and not averse from the lighter distractions. For a long time the sisters sat chatting together in the lit drawing-room to the agreeable sound of happy dogs playing in the dark corridor. Those dogs saved the situation, because they needed constant attention. When the dogs dozed, the sisters began to look through photograph albums, of which Constance had several, bound in plush or morocco. Nothing will sharpen the memory, evoke the past, raise the dead, rejuvenate the ageing, and cause both sighs and smiles, like a collection of photographs gathered together during long years of life. Constance had an astonishing menagerie of unknown cousins and their connections, and of townspeople; she had Cyril at all ages; she had weird daguerreotypes of her parents and their parents. The strangest of all was a portrait of Samuel Povey as an infant in arms. Sophia checked an impulse to laugh at it. But when Constance said: "Isn't it funny?" she did allow herself to laugh. A photograph of Samuel in the year before his death was really imposing. Sophia stared at it, impressed. It was the portrait of an honest man.

"How long have you been a widow?" Constance asked in a low voice, glancing at upright Sophia over her spectacles, a leaf of the album raised against her finger.

Sophia unmistakably flushed. "I don't know that I am a widow," said she, with an air. "My husband left me in 1870, and I've never seen nor heard of him since."

"Oh, my dear!" cried Constance, alarmed and deafened as by a clap of awful thunder. "I thought ye were a widow. Mr. Peel-Swynnerton said he was told positively ye were a widow. That's why I never. . . ." She stopped. Her face was troubled.

"Of course I always passed for a widow, over there," said Sophia.

"Of course," said Constance quickly. "I see. . . ."

"And I may be a widow," said Sophia.

Constance made no remark. This was a blow. Bursley was such a particular place. Doubtless, Gerald Scales had behaved like a scoundrel. That was sure!

When, immediately afterwards, Amy opened the drawing-room door (having first knocked—the practice of encouraging a servant to plunge without warning of any kind into a drawing-room had never been favoured in that house) she saw the sisters sitting rather near to each other at the walnut oval table, Mrs. Scales very upright, and staring into the fire, and Mrs. Povey "bunched up" and staring at the photograph album; both seeming to Amy aged and apprehensive; Mrs. Povey's hair was quite grey, though Mrs. Scales' hair was nearly as black as Amy's own. Mrs. Scales started at the sound of the knock, and turned her head.

"Here's Mr. and Mrs. Critchlow, m'm," announced Amy.

The sisters glanced at one another, with lifted foreheads. Then Mrs. Povey spoke to Amy as though visits at half-past eight at night were a customary phenomenon of the household. Nevertheless, she trembled to think what outrageous thing Mr. Critchlow might say to Sophia after thirty years' absence. The occasion was great, and it might also be terrible.

"Ask them to come up," she said calmly.

But Amy had the best of that encounter. "I have done," she replied, and instantly produced them out of the darkness of the corridor. It was providential: the sisters had made no remark that the Critchlows might not hear.

Then Maria Critchlow, simpering, had to greet Sophia. Mrs. Critchlow was very agitated, from sheer nervousness. She curvetted; she almost pranced; and she made noises with her mouth as though she saw some one eating a sour apple.

She wanted to show Sophia how greatly she had changed from the young, timid apprentice. Certainly since her marriage she had changed. As manager of other people's business she had not felt the necessity of being effusive to customers, but as proprietress, anxiety to succeed had dragged her out of her capable and mechanical indifference. It was a pity. Her consistent dullness had had a sort of dignity; but genial, she was merely ridiculous. Animation cruelly displayed her appalling commonness and physical shabbiness. Sophia's demeanour was not chilly; but it indicated that Sophia had no wish to be eyed over as a freak of nature.

Mr. Critchlow advanced very slowly into the room. "Ye still carry your head on a stiff neck," said he, deliberately examining Sophia. Then with great care he put out his long thin arm and took her hand. "Well, I'm rare and glad to see ye!"

Every one was thunderstruck at this expression of joy. Mr. Critchlow had never been known to be glad to see anybody.

"Yes," twittered Maria, "Mr. Critchlow would come in to-night. Nothing would do but he must come in to-night."

"You didn't tell me this afternoon," said Constance, "that you were going to give us the pleasure of your company like this."

He looked momentarily at Constance. "No," he grated, "I don't know as I did."

His gaze flattered Sophia. Evidently he treated this experienced and sad woman of fifty as a young girl. And in presence of his extreme age she felt like a young girl, remembering the while how as a young girl she had hated him. Repulsing the assistance of his wife, he arranged an armchair in front of the fire and meticulously put himself into it. Assuredly he was much older in a drawing-room than behind the counter of his shop. Constance had noticed that in the afternoon. A live coal fell out of the fire. He bent forward, wet his fingers, picked up the coal and threw it back into the fire.

"Well," said Sophia. "I wouldn't have done that."

"I never saw Mr. Critchlow's equal for picking up hot cinders," Maria giggled.

Mr. Critchlow deigned no remark. "When did ye leave this Paris?" he demanded of Sophia, leaning back, and putting his hands on the arms of the chair.

"Yesterday morning," said Sophia.

"And what'n ye been doing with yerself since yesterday morning?"

"I spent last night in London," Sophia replied.

"Oh, in London, did ye?"

"Yes. Cyril and I had an evening together."

"Eh? Cyril! What's yer opinion o' Cyril, Sophia?"

"I'm very proud to have Cyril for a nephew," said Sophia.

"Oh! Are ye?" The old man was obviously ironic.

"Yes I am," Sophia insisted sharply. "I'm not going to hear a word said against Cyril."

She proceeded to an enthusiastic laudation of Cyril which rather overwhelmed his mother. Constance was pleased; she was delighted. And yet somewhere in her mind was an uncomfortable feeling that Cyril, having taken a fancy to his brilliant aunt, had tried to charm her as he seldom or never tried to charm his mother. Cyril and Sophia had dazzled and conquered each other; they were of the same type; whereas she, Constance, being but a plain person, could not glitter.

She rang the bell and gave instructions to Amy about food —fruit cakes, coffee and hot milk, on a tray; and Sophia also spoke to Amy murmuring a request as to Fossette.

"Yes, Mrs. Scales," said Amy, with eager deference.

Mrs. Critchlow smiled vaguely from a low chair near the curtained window. Then Constance lit another burner of the chandelier. In doing so, she gave a little sigh; it was a sigh of relief. Mr. Critchlow had behaved himself. Now that he and Sophia had met, the worst was over. Had Constance known beforehand that he would pay a call, she would have been agonized by apprehensions, but now that he had actually come she was glad he had come.

When he had silently sipped some hot milk, he drew a thick bunch of papers, white and blue, from his bulging breast-pocket.

"Now, Maria Critchlow," he called, edging round his chair slightly. "Ye'd best go back home."

Maria Critchlow was biting at a bit of walnut cake, while in her right hand, all seamed with black lines, she held a cup of coffee.

"But, Mr. Critchlow——!" Constance protested.

"I've got business with Sophia, and I must get it done. I've got for to render an account of my stewardship to

Sophia, under her father's will, and her mother's will, and her aunt's will, and it's nobody's business but mine and Sophia's, I reckon. Now then," he glanced at his wife, "off with ye!"

Maria rose, half-kittenish and half-ashamed.

"Surely you don't want to go into all that to-night," said Sophia. She spoke softly, for she had already fully perceived that Mr. Critchlow must be managed with the tact which the capricious obstinacies of advanced age demanded. "Surely you can wait a day or two. I'm in no hurry."

"*Haven't I waited long enough?*" he retorted fiercely.

There was a pause. Maria Critchlow moved.

"As for you being in no hurry, Sophia," the old man went on, "nobody can say as *you've* been in a hurry."

Sophia had suffered a check. She glanced hesitatingly at Constance.

"Mrs. Critchlow and I will go down into the parlour," said Constance, quickly. "There is a bit of fire there."

"Oh no. I won't hear of such a thing!"

"Yes, we will, won't we, Mrs. Critchlow?" Constance insisted, cheerfully but firmly. She was determined that in her house Sophia should have all the freedom and conveniences that she could have had in her own. If a private room was needed for discussions between Sophia and her trustee, Constance's pride was piqued to supply that room. Further, Constance was glad to get Maria out of Sophia's sight. She was accustomed to Maria; with her it did not matter; but she did not care that the teeth of Sophia should be set on edge by the ridiculous demeanour of Maria. So those two left the drawing-room, and the old man began to open the papers which he had been preparing for weeks.

There was very little fire in the parlour, and Constance, in addition to being bored by Mrs. Critchlow's inane and inquisitive remarks, felt chilly, which was bad for her sciatica. She wondered whether Sophia would have to confess to Mr. Critchlow that she was not certainly a widow. She thought that steps ought to be taken to ascertain, through Birkinshaws, if anything was known of Gerald Scales. But even that course was set with perils. Supposing that he still lived, an unspeakable villain (Constance could only think of him as an unspeakable villain), and supposing that he molested Sophia,—what scenes! What shame in the town! Such frightful thoughts ran endlessly through Constance's mind as she bent over the fire endeavouring to keep alive a silly conversation with Maria Critchlow.

Amy passed through the parlour to go to bed. There was no other way of reaching the upper part of the house.

"Are you going to bed, Amy?"

"Yes'm."

"Where is Fossette?"

"In the kitchen, m'm," said Amy, defending herself. "Mrs. Scales told me the dog might sleep in the kitchen with Spot, as they was such good friends. I've opened the bottom drawer, and Fossit is lying in that."

"Mrs. Scales has brought a dog with her!" exclaimed Maria.

"Yes'm!" said Amy, drily, before Constance could answer. She implied everything in that affirmative.

"You *are* a family for dogs," said Maria. "What sort of dog is it?"

"Well," said Constance. "I don't know exactly what they call it. It's a French dog, one of those French dogs." Amy was lingering at the stairfoot. "Good night, Amy, thank you."

Amy ascended, shutting the door.

"Oh! I see!" Maria muttered. "Well, I never!"

It was ten o'clock before sounds above indicated that the first interview between trustee and beneficiary was finished.

"I'll be going on to open our side-door," said Maria. "Say good night to Mrs. Scales for me." She was not sure whether Charles Critchlow had really meant her to go home, or whether her mere absence from the drawing-room had contented him. So she departed. He came down the stairs with the most tiresome slowness, went through the parlour in silence, ignoring Constance, and also Sophia, who was at his heels, and vanished.

As Constance shut and bolted the front-door, the sisters looked at each other, Sophia faintly smiling. It seemed to them that they understood each other better when they did not speak. With a glance, they exchanged their ideas on the subject of Charles Critchlow and Maria, and learnt that their ideas were similar. Constance said nothing as to the private interview. Nor did Sophia. At present, on this the first day, they could only achieve intimacy by intermittent flashes.

"What about bed?" asked Sophia.

"You must be tired," said Constance.

Sophia got to the stairs, which received a little light from the corridor gas, before Constance, having tested the window-fastening, turned out the gas in the parlour. They climbed the lower flight of stairs together.

"I must just see that your room is all right," Constance said.

"Must you?" Sophia smiled.

They climbed the second flight, slowly. Constance was out of breath.

"Oh, a fire! How nice!" cried Sophia. "But why did you go to all that trouble? I told you not to."

"It's no trouble at all," said Constance, raising the gas in the bedroom. Her tone implied that bedroom fires were a quite ordinary incident of daily life in a place like Bursley.

"Well, my dear, I hope you'll find everything comfortable," said Constance.

"I'm sure I shall. Good night, dear."

"Good night, then."

They looked at each other again, with timid affectionateness. They did not kiss. The thought in both their minds was: "We couldn't keep on kissing every day." But there was a vast amount of quiet, restrained affection, of mutual confidence and respect, even of tenderness, in their tones.

About half an hour later a dreadful hullabaloo smote the ear of Constance. She was just getting into bed. She listened intently, in great alarm. It was undoubtedly those dogs fighting, and fighting to the death. She pictured the kitchen as a battlefield, and Spot slain. Opening the door, she stepped out into the corridor.

"Constance," said a low voice above her. She jumped. "Is that you?"

"Yes."

"Well, don't bother to go down to the dogs; they'll stop in a moment. Fossette won't bite. I'm so sorry she's upsetting the house."

Constance stared upwards, and discerned a pale shadow. The dogs did soon cease their altercation. This short colloquy in the dark affected Constance strangely.

iii

The next morning, after a night varied by periods of wakefulness not unpleasant, Sophia arose and, taking due precautions against cold, went to the window. It was Saturday; she had left Paris on the Thursday. She looked forth upon the Square, holding aside the blind. She had expected, of course, to find that the Square had shrunk in size; but nevertheless she was startled to see how small it was. It seemed to her scarcely bigger than a courtyard. She could remember a winter morning when from the window she had watched the Square under virgin snow in the lamplight, and the Square had been vast, and the first wayfarer, crossing it diagonally and leaving behind him the irregular impress of his feet, had appeared to travel for hours over an interminable white waste before vanishing past Holl's shop in the direction of the Town Hall. She chiefly recalled the Square under snow; cold mornings, and the coldness of the oil-cloth at the window, and the draught of cold air through the ill-fitting sash (it was put right now)! These visions of herself seemed beautiful to her; her childish existence seemed beautiful; the storms and tempests of her girlhood seemed beautiful; even the great sterile expanse of tedium when, after giving up a scholastic career, she had served for two years in the shop—even this had a strange charm in her memory.

And she thought that not for millions of pounds would she live her life over again.

In its contents the Square had not surprisingly changed during the immense, the terrifying interval that separated her from her virginity. On the east side, several shops had been thrown into one, and forced into a semblance of eternal unity by means of a coat of stucco. And there was a fountain at the north end which was new to her. No other constructional change! But the moral change, the sad declension from the ancient proud spirit of the Square—this was painfully depressing. Several establishments lacked tenants, had obviously lacked tenants for a long time; "To let" notices hung in their stained and dirty upper windows, and clung insecurely to their closed shutters. And on the sign-boards of these establishments were names that Sophia did not know. The character of most of the shops seemed to have worsened; they had become pettifogging little holes, unkempt, shabby, poor; they had no brightness, no feeling of vitality. And the floor of the Square was littered with nondescript refuse. The whole scene, paltry, confined, and dull, reached for her the extreme of provinciality. It was what the French called, with a pregnant intonation, *la province.* This being said, there was nothing else to say. Bursley, of course, was in the provinces; Bursley must, in the nature of things, be typically provincial. But in her mind it had always been differentiated from the common *province*; it had always had an air, a distinction, and especially St. Luke's Square! That illusion was now gone. Still, the alteration was not wholly in herself; it was not wholly subjective. The Square really had changed for the worse; it might not be smaller, but it had deteriorated. As a centre of commerce it had assuredly approached very near to death. On a Saturday morning thirty years ago it would have been covered with linen-roofed stalls, and chattering country-folk, and the stir of bargains. Now, Saturday morning was like any other morning in the Square, and the glass-roof of St. Luke's market in Wedgwood Street, which she could see from her window, echoed to the sounds of noisy commerce. In that instance business had simply moved a few yards to the east; but Sophia knew, from hints in Constance's letters and in her talk, that business in general had moved more than a few yards, it had moved a couple of miles—to arrogant and pushing Hanbridge, with its electric light and its theatres and its big, advertising shops. The heaven of thick smoke over the Square, the black deposit on painted woodwork, the intermittent hooting of steam syrens, showed that the wholesale trade of Bursley still flourished. But Sophia had no memories of the wholesale trade of Bursley; it meant nothing to the youth of her heart; she was attached by intimate links to the retail traffic of Bursley, and as a mart old Bursley was done for.

She thought: "It would kill me if I had to live here. It's deadening. It weighs on you. And the dirt, and the horrible ugliness! And the way they talk, and the way they think! I felt it first at Knype station. The Square is rather picturesque, but it's such a poor, poor little thing! Fancy having to look at it every morning of one's life! No!" She almost shuddered.

For the time being she had no home. To Constance she was "paying a visit."

Constance did not appear to realize the awful conditions of dirt, decay, and provinciality in which she was living. Even Constance's house was extremely inconvenient, dark, and no doubt unhealthy. Cellar-kitchen, no hall, abominable stairs, and as to hygiene, simply mediæval. She could not understand why Constance had remained in the house. Constance had plenty of money and might live where she liked, and in a good modern house. Yet she stayed in the Square. "I daresay she's got used to it," Sophia thought leniently. "I daresay I should be just the same in her place." But she did not really think so, and she could not understand Constance's state of mind.

Certainly she could not claim to have "added up" Constance yet. She considered that her sister was in some respects utterly provincial—what they used to call in the Five Towns a "body." Somewhat too diffident, not assertive enough, not erect enough; with curious provincial pronunciations, accents, gestures, mannerisms, and inarticulate ejaculations; with a curious narrowness of outlook! But at the same time Constance was very shrewd, and she was often proving by some bit of a remark that she knew what was what, despite her provinciality. In judgments upon human nature they undoubtedly thought alike, and there was a strong natural general sympathy between them. And at the bottom of Constance was something fine. At intervals Sophia discovered herself secretly patronizing Constance, but reflection would always cause her to cease from patronage and to examine her own defences. Constance, besides being the essence of kindness, was no fool. Constance could see through a pretence, an absurdity, as quickly as any one. Constance did honestly appear to Sophia to be superior to any Frenchwoman that she had ever encountered. She saw supreme in Constance that quality which she had recognized in the porters at Newhaven on landing—the quality of an honest and naïve goodwill, of powerful simplicity. That quality presented itself to her as the greatest in the world, and it seemed to be in the very air of England. She could even detect it in Mr. Critchlow, whom, for the rest, she liked, admiring the brutal force of his character. She pardoned his brutality to his wife. She found it proper. "After all," she said, "supposing he hadn't married her, what would she have been? Nothing but a slave! She's infinitely better off as his wife. In fact she's lucky. And it would be absurd for him to treat her otherwise than he does treat her." (Sophia did not divine that her masterful Critchlow had once wanted Maria as one might want a star.)

But to be always with such people! To be always with Constance! To be always in the Bursley atmosphere, physical and mental!

She pictured Paris as it would be on that very morning—

bright, clean, glittering; the neatness of the Rue Lord Byron, and the magnificent slanting splendour of the Champs Elysées. Paris had always seemed beautiful to her; but the life of Paris had not seemed beautiful to her. Yet now it did seem beautiful. She could delve down into the earlier years of her ownership of the Pension, and see a regular, placid beauty in her daily life there. Her life there, even so late as a fortnight ago, seemed beautiful; sad, but beautiful. It had passed into history. She sighed when she thought of the innumerable interviews with Mardon, the endless formalities required by the English and the French law and by the particularity of the Syndicate. She had been through all that. She had actually been through it and it was over. She had bought the Pension for a song and sold it for great riches. She had developed from a nobody into the desired of Syndicates. And after long, long, monotonous, strenuous years of possession the day had come, the emotional moment had come, when she had yielded up the keys of ownership to Mr. Mardon and a man from the Hotel Moscow, and had paid her servants for the last time and signed the last receipted bill. The men had been very gallant, and had requested her to stay in the Pension as their guest until she was ready to leave Paris. But she had declined that. She could not have borne to remain in the Pension under the reign of another. She had left at once and gone to a hotel with her few goods while finally disposing of certain financial questions. And one evening Jacqueline had come to see her, and had wept.

Her exit from the Pension Frensham struck her now as poignantly pathetic, in its quickness and its absence of ceremonial. Ten steps, and her career was finished, closed. Astonishing, with what liquid tenderness she turned and looked back on that hard, fighting, exhausting life in Paris! For, even if she had unconsciously liked it, she had never enjoyed it. She had always compared France disadvantageously with England, always resented the French temperament in business, always been convinced that "you never knew where you were" with French tradespeople. And now they flitted before her endowed with a wondrous charm; so polite in their lying, so eager to spare your feelings and to reassure you, so neat and prim. And the French shops, so exquisitely arranged! Even a butcher's shop in Paris was a pleasure to the eye, whereas the butcher's shop in Wedgwood Street, which she remembered of old, and which she had glimpsed from the cab—what a bloody shambles! She longed for Paris again. She longed to stretch her lungs in Paris. These people in Bursley did not suspect what Paris was. They did not appreciate and they never would appreciate the marvels that she had accomplished in a theatre of marvels. They probably never realized that the whole of the rest of the world was not more or less like Bursley. They had no curiosity. Even Constance was a thousand times more interested in relating trifles of Bursley gossip than in listening to details of life in Paris. Occasionally she had expressed a mild, vapid surprise at things told to her by Sophia; but she was not really impressed, because her curiosity did not extend beyond Bursley. She, like the rest, had the formidable, thrice-callous egotism of the provinces. And if Sophia had informed her that the heads of Parisians grew out of their navels she would have murmured: "Well, well! Bless us! I never heard of such things! Mrs. Brindley's second boy has got his head quite crooked, poor little fellow!"

Why should Sophia feel sorrowful? She did not know. She was free; free to go where she liked and do what she liked. She had no responsibilities, no cares. The thought of her husband had long ago ceased to rouse in her any feeling of any kind. She was rich. Mr. Critchlow had accumulated for her about as much money as she had herself acquired. Never could she spend her income! She did not know how to spend it. She lacked nothing that was procurable. She had no desires except the direct desire for happiness. If thirty thousand pounds or so could have bought a son like Cyril, she would have bought one for herself. She bitterly regretted that she had no child. In this, she envied Constance. A child seemed to be the one commodity worth having. She was too free, too exempt from responsibilities. In spite of Constance she was alone in the world. The strangeness of the hazards of life overwhelmed her. Here she was at fifty, alone.

But the idea of leaving Constance, having once rejoined her, did not please Sophia. It disquieted her. She could not see herself living away from Constance. She was alone—but Constance was there.

She was downstairs first, and she had a little conversation with Amy. And she stood on the step of the front-door while Fossette made a preliminary inspection of Spot's gutter. She found the air nipping.

Constance, when she descended, saw stretching across one

side of the breakfast-table an umbrella, Sophia's present to her from Paris. It was an umbrella such that a better could not be bought. It would have impressed even Aunt Harriet. The handle was of gold, set with a circlet of opalines. The tips of the ribs were also of gold. It was this detail which staggered Constance. Frankly, this development of luxury had been unknown and unsuspected in the Square. That the tips of the ribs should match the handle . . . that did truly beat everything! Sophia said calmly that the device was quite common. But she did not conceal that the umbrella was strictly of the highest class and that it might be shown to queens without shame. She intimated that the frame (a "Fox's Paragon"), handle, and tips, would outlast many silks. Constance was childish with pleasure.

They decided to go out marketing together. The unspoken thought in their minds was that as Sophia would have to be introduced to the town sooner or later, it might as well be sooner. Constance looked at the sky. "It can't possibly rain," she said. "I shall take my umbrella."

CHAPTER III

TOWARDS HOTEL LIFE

SOPHIA wore list slippers in the morning. It was a habit which she had formed in the Rue Lord Byron—by accident rather than with an intention to utilize list slippers for the effective supervision of servants. These list slippers were the immediate cause of important happenings in St. Luke's Square. Sophia had been with Constance one calendar month—it was, of course, astonishing how quickly the time had passed!—and she had become familiar with the house. Restraint had gradually ceased to mark the relations of the sisters. Constance, in particular, hid nothing from Sophia, who was made aware of the minor and major defects of Amy and all the other creakings of the household machine. Meals were eaten off the ordinary table-cloths, and on the days for "turning out" the parlour, Constance assumed, with a little laugh, that Sophia would excuse Amy's apron, which she had not had time to change. In brief, Sophia was no longer a stranger, and nobody felt bound to pre-

tend that things were not exactly what they were. In spite of
the foulness and the provinciality of Bursley, Sophia enjoyed
the intimacy with Constance. As for Constance, she was enchanted. The inflections of their voices, when they were talking
to each other very privately, were often tender, and these sudden surprising tendernesses secretly thrilled both of them.

On the fourth Sunday morning Sophia put on her dressing-
gown and those list slippers very early, and paid a visit to
Constance's bedroom. She was somewhat concerned about Constance, and her concern was pleasurable to her. She made the
most of it. Amy, with her lifelong carelessness about doors,
had criminally failed to latch the street-door of the parlour on
the previous morning, and Constance had only perceived the
omission by the phenomenon of frigidity in her legs at breakfast. She always sat with her back to the door, in her mother's
fluted rocking-chair; and Sophia on the spot, but not in the
chair, occupied by John Baines in the forties, and in the seventies and later by Samuel Povey. Constance had been alarmed
by that frigidity. "I shall have a return of my sciatica!" she
had exclaimed, and Sophia was startled by the apprehension in
her tone. Before evening the sciatica had indeed revisited Constance's sciatic nerve, and Sophia for the first time gained an
idea of what a pulsating sciatica can do in the way of torturing
its victim. Constance, in addition to the sciatica, had caught a
sneezing cold, and the act of sneezing caused her the most acute
pain. Sophia had soon stopped the sneezing. Constance was got
to bed. Sophia wished to summon the doctor, but Constance
assured her that the doctor would have nothing new to advise.
Constance suffered angelically. The weak and exquisite sweetness of her smile, as she lay in bed under the stress of twinging
pain amid hot-water bottles, was amazing to Sophia. It made
her think upon the reserves of Constance's character, and upon
the variety of the manifestations of the Baines' blood.

So on the Sunday morning she had arisen early, just after
Amy.

She discovered Constance to be a little better, as regards the
neuralgia, but exhausted by the torments of a sleepless night.
Sophia, though she had herself not slept well, felt somehow con-
science-stricken for having slept at all.

"You poor dear!" she murmured, brimming with sympathy.
"I shall make you some tea at once, myself."

"Oh, Amy will do it," said Constance.

Sophia repeated with a resolute intonation: "I shall make it myself." And after being satisfied that there was no instant need for a renewal of hot-water bottles, she went further downstairs in those list slippers.

As she was descending the dark kitchen steps she heard Amy's voice in pettish exclamation: "Oh, get out, *you!*" followed by a yelp from Fossette. She had a swift movement of anger, which she controlled. The relations between her and Fossette were not marked by transports, and her rule over dogs in general was severe; even when alone she very seldom kissed the animal passionately, according to the general habit of people owning dogs. But she loved Fossette. And, moreover, her love for Fossette had been lately sharpened by the ridicule which Bursley had showered upon that strange beast. Happily for Sophia's *amour propre*, there was no means of getting Fossette shaved in Bursley, and thus Fossette was daily growing less comic to the Bursley eye. Sophia could therefore without loss of dignity yield to force of circumstances what she would not have yielded to popular opinion. She guessed that Amy had no liking for the dog, but the accent which Amy had put upon the "*you*" seemed to indicate that Amy was making distinctions between Fossette and Spot, and this disturbed Sophia much more than Fossette's yelp.

Sophia coughed, and entered the kitchen.

Spot was lapping his morning milk out of a saucer, while Fossette stood wistfully, an amorphous mass of thick hair, under the table.

"Good morning Amy," said Sophia, with dreadful politeness.

"Good morning, m'm," said Amy, glumly.

Amy knew that Sophia had heard that yelp, and Sophia knew that she knew. The pretence of politeness was horrible. Both the women felt as though the kitchen was sanded with gunpowder and there were lighted matches about. Sophia had a very proper grievance against Amy on account of the open door of the previous day. Sophia thought that, after such a sin, the least Amy could do was to show contrition and amiability and an anxiety to please: which things Amy had not shown. Amy had a grievance against Sophia because Sophia had recently thrust upon her a fresh method of cooking green vegetables. Amy was a strong opponent of new or foreign methods. Sophia was not aware of this grievance, for Amy had hidden it under her customary cringing politeness to Sophia.

They surveyed each other like opposing armies.

"What a pity you have no gas-stove here! I want to make some tea at once for Mrs. Povey," said Sophia, inspecting the just-born fire.

"Gas-stove, m'm?" said Amy, hostilely. It was Sophia's list slippers which had finally decided Amy to drop the mask of deference.

She made no effort to aid Sophia; she gave no indication as to where the various necessaries for tea were to be found. Sophia got the kettle, and washed it out. Sophia got the smallest teapot, and, as the tea-leaves had been left in it, she washed out the teapot also, with exaggerated noise and meticulousness. Sophia got the sugar and the other trifles, and Sophia blew up the fire with the bellows. And Amy did nothing in particular except encourage Spot to drink.

"Is that all the milk you give to Fossette?" Sophia demanded coldly, when it had come to Fossette's turn. She was waiting for the water to boil. The saucer for the bigger dog, who would have made two of Spot, was not half full.

"It's all there is to spare, m'm," Amy rasped.

Sophia made no reply. Soon afterwards she departed, with the tea successfully made. If Amy had not been a mature woman of over forty she would have snorted as Sophia went away. But Amy was scarcely the ordinary silly girl.

Save for a certain primness as she offered the tray to her sister, Sophia's demeanour gave no sign whatever that the Amazon in her was aroused. Constance's eager trembling pleasure in the tea touched her deeply, and she was exceedingly thankful that Constance had her, Sophia, as a succour in time of distress.

A few minutes later, Constance, having first asked Sophia what time it was by the watch in the watch-case on the chest of drawers (the Swiss clock had long since ceased to work), pulled the red tassel of the bell-cord over her bed. A bell tinkled far away in the kitchen.

"Anything I can do?" Sophia inquired.

"Oh no, thanks," said Constance. "I only want my letters, if the postman has come. He ought to have been here long ago."

Sophia had learned during her stay that Sunday morning

was the morning on which Constance expected a letter from Cyril. It was a definite arrangement between mother and son that Cyril should write on Saturdays, and Constance on Sundays. Sophia knew that Constance set store by this letter, becoming more and more preoccupied about Cyril as the end of the week approached. Since Sophia's arrival Cyril's letter had not failed to come, but once it had been naught save a scribbled line or two, and Sophia gathered that it was never a certainty, and that Constance was accustomed, though not reconciled, to disappointments. Sophia had been allowed to read the letters. They left a faint impression on her mind that her favourite was perhaps somewhat negligent in his relations with his mother.

There was no reply to the bell. Constance rang again without effect.

With a brusque movement Sophia left the bedroom by way of Cyril's room.

"Amy," she called over the banisters, "do you not hear your mistress's bell?"

"I'm coming as quick as I can, m'm." The voice was still very glum.

Sophia murmured something inarticulate, staying till assured that Amy really was coming, and then she passed back into Cyril's bedroom. She waited there, hesitant, not exactly on the watch, not exactly unwilling to assist at an interview between Amy and Amy's mistress; indeed, she could not have surely analyzed her motive for remaining in Cyril's bedroom, with the door ajar between that room and Constance's.

Amy reluctantly mounted the stairs and went into her mistress's bedroom with her chin in the air. She thought that Sophia had gone up to the second storey, where she "belonged." She stood in silence by the bed, showing no sympathy with Constance, no curiosity as to the indisposition. She objected to Constance's attack of sciatica, as being a too permanent reproof of her carelessness as to doors.

Constance also waited, for the fraction of a second, as if expectant.

"Well, Amy," she said at length in her voice weakened by fatigue and pain. "The letters?"

"There ain't no letters," said Amy, grimly. "You might have known, if there'd been any, I should have brought 'em up. Postman went past twenty minutes agone. I'm always being interrupted, and it isn't as if I hadn't got enough to do—now!"

She turned to leave, and was pulling the door open.

"Amy!" said a voice sharply. It was Sophia's.

The servant jumped, and in spite of herself obeyed the implicit, imperious command to stop.

"You will please not speak to your mistress in that tone, at any rate while I'm here," said Sophia, icily. "You know she is ill and weak. You ought to be ashamed of yourself."

"I never——" Amy began.

"I don't want to argue," Sophia said angrily. "Please leave the room."

Amy obeyed. She was cowed, in addition to being staggered.

To the persons involved in it, this episode was intensely dramatic. Sophia had surmised that Constance permitted liberties of speech to Amy; she had even guessed that Amy sometimes took licence to be rude. But that the relations between them were such as to allow the bullying of Constance by an Amy downright insolent—this had shocked and wounded Sophia, who suddenly had a vision of Constance as the victim of a reign of terror. "If the creature will do this while I'm here," said Sophia to herself, "what does she do when they are alone together in the house?"

"Well," she exclaimed, "I never heard of such goings-on! And you let her talk to you in that style! My dear Constance!"

Constance was sitting up in bed, the small tea-tray on her knees. Her eyes were moist. The tears had filled them when she knew that there was no letter. Ordinarily the failure of Cyril's letter would not have made her cry, but weakness had impaired her self-control. And the tears having once got into her eyes, she could not dismiss them. There they were!

"She's been with me such a long time," Constance murmured. "She takes liberties. I've corrected her once or twice."

"Liberties!" Sophia repeated the word. "Liberties!"

"Of course I really ought not to allow it," said Constance. "I ought to have put a stop to it long since."

"Well," said Sophia, rather relieved by this symptom of Constance's secret mind, "I do hope you won't think I'm meddlesome, but truly it was too much for me. The words were out of my mouth before I——" She stopped.

"You were quite right, quite right," said Constance, seeing before her in the woman of fifty the passionate girl of fifteen.

"I've had a good deal of experience of servants," said Sophia.

"I know you have," Constance put in.

"And I'm convinced that it never pays to stand any sauce. Servants don't understand kindness and forbearance. And this sort of thing grows and grows till you can't call your soul your own."

"You are quite right," Constance said again, with even more positiveness.

Not merely the conviction that Sophia was quite right, but the desire to assure Sophia that Sophia was not meddlesome, gave force to her utterance. Amy's allusion to extra work shamed Amy's mistress as a hostess, and she was bound to make amends.

"Now as to that woman," said Sophia in a lower voice, as she sat down confidentially on the edge of the bed. And she told Constance about Amy and the dogs, and about Amy's rudeness in the kitchen. "I should never have *dreamt* of mentioning such things," she finished. "But under the circumstances I feel it right that you should know. I feel you ought to know."

And Constance nodded her head in thorough agreement. She did not trouble to go into articulate apologies to her guest for the actual misdeeds of her servant. The sisters were now on a plane of intimacy where such apologies would have been supererogatory. Their voices fell lower and lower, and the case of Amy was laid bare and discussed to the minutest detail.

Gradually they realized that what had occurred was a crisis. They were both very excited, apprehensive, and rather too consciously defiant. At the same time they were drawn very close to each other, by Sophia's generous indignation and by Constance's absolute loyalty.

A long time passed before Constance said, thinking about something else:

"I expect it's been delayed in the post."

"Cyril's letter? Oh, no doubt! If you knew the posts in France, my word!"

Then they determined, with little sighs, to face the crisis cheerfully.

In truth it was a crisis, and a great one. The sensation of the crisis affected the atmosphere of the entire house. Constance got up for tea and managed to walk to the drawing-room. And when Sophia, after an absence in her own room,

came down to tea and found the tea all served, Constance
whispered:

"She's given notice! And Sunday too!"

"What did she say?"

"She didn't say much," Constance replied vaguely, hiding
from Sophia that Amy had harped on the too great profusion
of mistresses in that house. "After all, it's just as well. She'll be
all right. She's saved a good bit of money, and she has friends."

"But how foolish of her to give up such a good place!"

"She simply doesn't care," said Constance, who was a little
hurt by Amy's defection. "When she takes a thing into her
head she simply doesn't care. She's got no common sense. I've
always known that."

"So you're going to leave, Amy?" said Sophia that evening,
as Amy was passing through the parlour on her way to bed.
Constance was already arranged for the night.

"I am, m'm," answered Amy, precisely.

Her tone was not rude, but it was firm. She had apparently
reconnoitred her position in calmness.

"I'm sorry I was obliged to correct you this morning," said
Sophia, with cheerful amicableness, pleased in spite of herself
with the woman's tone. "But I think you will see that I had
reason to."

"I've been thinking it over, m'm," said Amy, with dignity,
"and I see as I must leave."

There was a pause.

"Well, you know best. . . . Good night, Amy."

"Good night, m'm."

"She's a decent woman," thought Sophia, "but hopeless for
this place now."

The sisters were fronted with the fact that Constance had a
month in which to find a new servant, and that a new servant
would have to be trained in well-doing and might easily prove
disastrous. Both Constance and Amy were profoundly disturbed
by the prospective dissolution of a bond which dated from the
seventies. And both were decided that there was no alternative
to the dissolution. Outsiders knew merely that Mrs. Povey's old
servant was leaving. Outsiders merely saw Mrs. Povey's advertisement in the *Signal* for a new servant. They could not
read hearts. Some of the younger generation even said
superiorly that old-fashioned women like Mrs. Povey seemed
to have servants on the brain, etc., etc.

ii

"Well, have you got your letter?" Sophia demanded cheerfully of Constance when she entered the bedroom the next morning.

Constance merely shook her head. She was very depressed. Sophia's cheerfulness died out. As she hated to be insincerely optimistic, she said nothing. Otherwise she might have remarked: "Perhaps the afternoon post will bring it." Gloom reigned. To Constance particularly, as Amy had given notice and as Cyril was "remiss," it seemed really that the time was out of joint and life unworth living. Even the presence of Sophia did not bring her much comfort. Immediately Sophia left the room Constance's sciatica began to return, and in a severe form. She had regretted this, less for the pain than because she had just assured Sophia, quite honestly, that she was not suffering; Sophia had been sceptical. After that it was of course imperative that Constance should get up as usual. She had said that she would get up as usual. Besides, there was the immense enterprise of obtaining a new servant! Worries loomed mountainous. Suppose Cyril were dangerously ill, and unable to write! Suppose something had happened to him! Supposing she never did obtain a new servant!

Sophia, up in her room, was endeavouring to be philosophical, and to see the world brightly. She was saying to herself that she must take Constance in hand, that what Constance lacked was energy, that Constance must be stirred out of her groove. And in the cavernous kitchen Amy, preparing the nine-o'clock breakfast, was meditating upon the ingratitude of employers and wondering what the future held for her. She had a widowed mother in the picturesque village of Sneyd, where the mortal and immortal welfare of every inhabitant was watched over by God's vicegerent, the busy Countess of Chell; she possessed about two hundred pounds of her own; her mother for years had been begging Amy to share her home free of expense. But nevertheless Amy's mind was black with foreboding and vague dejection. The house was a house of sorrow, and these three women, each solitary, the devotees of sorrow. And the two dogs wandered disconsolate up and down, aware of the necessity for circumspection, never guessing that the highly peculiar state of the atmosphere had been brought about by nothing but a half-shut door and an incorrect tone.

As Sophia, fully dressed this time, was descending to breakfast, she heard Constance's voice, feebly calling her, and found the convalescent still in bed. The truth could not be concealed. Constance was once more in great pain, and her moral condition was not favourable to fortitude.

"I wish you had told me, to begin with," Sophia could not help saying, "then I should have known what to do."

Constance did not defend herself by saying that the pain had only recurred since their first interview that morning. She just wept.

"I'm very low!" she blubbered.

Sophia was surprised. She felt that this was not "being a Baines."

During the progress of that interminable April morning, her acquaintance with the possibilities of sciatica as an agent destructive of moral fibre was further increased. Constance had no force at all to resist its activity. The sweetness of her resignation seemed to melt into nullity. She held to it that the doctor could do nothing for her.

About noon, when Sophia was moving anxiously around her, she suddenly screamed.

"I feel as if my leg was going to burst!" she cried.

That decided Sophia. As soon as Constance was a little easier she went downstairs to Amy.

"Amy," she said, "it's a Doctor Stirling that your mistress has when she's ill, isn't it?"

"Yes, m'm."

"Where is his surgery?"

"Well, m'm, he did live just opposite, with Dr. Harrop, but latterly he's gone to live at Bleakridge."

"I wish you would put your things on, and run up there and ask him to call as soon as he can."

"I will, m'm," said Amy, with the greatest willingness. "I thought I heard missis cry out." She was not effusive. She was better than effusive: kindly and helpful with a certain reserve.

"There's something about that woman I like," said Sophia, to herself. For a proved fool, Amy was indeed holding her own rather well.

Dr. Stirling drove down about two o'clock. He had now been

established in the Five Towns for more than a decade, and the
stamp of success was on his brow and on the proud forehead of
his trotting horse. He had, in the phrase of the *Signal*, "identified himself with the local life of the district." He was liked,
being a man of broad sympathies. In his rich Scotch accent he
could discuss with equal ability the flavour of whisky or of a
sermon, and he had more than sufficient tact never to discuss
either whiskies or sermons in the wrong place. He had made a
speech (responding for the learned professions) at the annual
dinner of the Society for the Prosecution of Felons, and this
speech (in which praise of red wine was rendered innocuous by
praise of books—his fine library was notorious) had classed
him as a wit with the American consul, whose post-prandial
manner was modelled on Mark Twain's. He was thirty-five
years of age, tall and stoutish, with a chubby boyish face that
the razor left chiefly blue every morning.

The immediate effect of his arrival on Constance was miraculous. His presence almost cured her for a moment, just as
though her malady had been toothache and he a dentist. Then,
when he had finished his examination, the pain resumed its
sway over her.

In talking to her and to Sophia, he listened very seriously to
all that they said; he seemed to regard the case as the one case
that had ever aroused his genuine professional interest; but as
it unfolded itself, in all its difficulty and urgency, so he seemed,
in his mind, to be discovering wondrous ways of dealing with
it; these mysterious discoveries seemed to give him confidence,
and his confidence was communicated to the patient by means
of faint sallies of humour. He was a highly skilled doctor. This
fact, however, had no share in his popularity, which was due
solely to his rare gift of taking a case very seriously while remaining cheerful.

He said he would return in a quarter of an hour, and he returned in thirteen minutes with a hypodermic syringe, with
which he attacked the pain in its central strongholds.

"What is it?" asked Constance, breathing gratitude for the
relief.

He paused, looking at her roguishly from under lowered eyelids.

"I'd better not tell ye," he said. "It might lead ye into mischief."

"Oh, but you must tell me, doctor," Constance insisted,

anxious that he should live up to his reputation for Sophia's benefit.

"It's hydrochloride of cocaine," he said, and lifted a finger. "Beware of the cocaine habit. It's ruined many a respectable family. But if I hadn't had a certain amount of confidence in yer strength of character, Mrs. Povey, I wouldn't have risked it."

"He will have his joke, will the doctor!" Constance smiled, in a brighter world.

He said he should come again about half-past five, and he arrived about half-past six, and injected more cocaine. The special importance of the case was thereby established. On this second visit, he and Sophia soon grew rather friendly. When she conducted him downstairs again he stopped chatting with her in the parlour for a long time, as though he had nothing else on earth to do, while his coachman walked the horse to and fro in front of the door.

His attitude to her flattered Sophia, for it showed that he took her for no ordinary woman. It implied a continual assumption that she must be a mine of interest for any one who was privileged to delve into her memory. So far, among Constance's acquaintance, Sophia had met no one who showed more than a perfunctory curiosity as to her life. Her return was accepted with indifference. Her escapade of thirty years ago had entirely lost its dramatic quality. Many people indeed had never heard that she had run away from home to marry a commercial traveller; and to those who remembered, or had been told, it seemed a sufficiently banal exploit—after thirty years! Her fear, and Constance's, that the town would be murmurous with gossip was ludicrously unfounded. The effect of time was such that even Mr. Critchlow appeared to have forgotten even that she had been indirectly responsible for her father's death. She had nearly forgotten it herself; when she happened to think of it she felt no shame, no remorse, seeing the death as purely accidental, and not altogether unfortunate. On two points only was the town inquisitive: as to her husband, and as to the precise figure at which she had sold the pension. The town knew that she was probably not a widow, for she had been obliged to tell Mr. Critchlow, and Mr. Critchlow in some hour of tenderness had told Maria. But nobody had dared to mention the name of Gerald Scales to her. With her fashionable clothes, her striking mien of command, and the legend of her wealth, she inspired respect, if not awe, in the townsfolk. In the doctor's attitude there was something of amaze; she felt it. Though the dull apathy of the people she had hitherto met was assuredly not without its advantageous side for her tranquillity of mind, it had touched her vanity, and the gaze of the doctor soothed the smart. He had so obviously divined her interestingness; he so obviously wanted to enjoy it.

"I've just been reading Zola's 'Downfall,' " he said.

Her mind searched backwards, and recalled a poster.

"Oh!" she replied. " 'La Débâcle'?"

"Yes. What do ye think of it?" His eyes lighted at the prospect of a talk. He was even pleased to hear her give him the title in French.

"I haven't read it," she said, and she was momentarily sorry that she had not read it, for she could see that he was dashed. The doctor had supposed that residence in a foreign country involved a knowledge of the literature of that country. Yet he had never supposed that residence in England involved a knowledge of English literature. Sophia had read practically nothing since 1870; for her the latest author was Cherbuliez. Moreover, her impression of Zola was that he was not at all nice, and that he was the enemy of his race, though at that date the world had scarcely heard of Dreyfus. Dr. Stirling had too hastily assumed that the opinions of the burgeois upon art differ in different countries.

"And ye actually were in the siege of Paris?" he questioned, trying again.

"Yes."

"*And* the commune?"

"Yes, the commune too."

"Well!" he exclaimed. "It's incredible! When I was reading the 'Downfall' the night before last, I said to myself that you must have been through a lot of all that. I didn't know I was going to have the pleasure of a chat with ye so soon."

She smiled. "But how did you know I was in the siege of Paris?" she asked, curious.

"How do I know? I know because I've seen that birthday card ye sent to Mrs. Povey in 1871, after it was over. It's one of her possessions, that card is. She showed it me one day when she told me ye were coming."

Sophia started. She had quite forgotten that card. It had

not occurred to her that Constance would have treasured all those cards that she had despatched during the early years of her exile. She responded as well as she could to his eagerness for personal details concerning the siege and the commune. He might have been disappointed at the prose of her answers, had he not been determined not to be disappointed.

"Ye seem to have taken it all very quietly," he observed.

"Eh yes!" she agreed, not without pride. "But it's a long time since."

Those events, as they existed in her memory, scarcely warranted the tremendous fuss subsequently made about them. What were they, after all? Such was her secret thought. Chirac himself was now nothing but a faint shadow. Still, were the estimate of those events true or false, she was a woman who had been through them, and Dr. Stirling's high appreciation of that fact was very pleasant to her. Their friendliness approached intimacy. Night had fallen. Outside could be heard the champing of a bit.

"I must be getting on," he said at last; but he did not move.

"Then there is nothing else I am to do for my sister?" Sophia inquired.

"I don't think so," said he. "It isn't a question of medicine."

"Then what is it a question of?" Sophia demanded bluntly.

"Nerves," he said. "It's nearly all nerves. I know something about Mrs. Povey's constitution now, and I was hoping that your visit would do her good."

"She's been quite well—I mean what you may call quite well—until the day before yesterday, when she sat in that draught. She was better last night, and then this morning I find her ever so much worse."

"No worries?" The doctor looked at her confidentially.

"What *can* she have in the way of worries?" exclaimed Sophia. "That's to say—real worries."

"Exactly!" the doctor agreed.

"I tell her she doesn't know what worry is," said Sophia.

"So do I!" said the doctor, his eyes twinkling.

"She was a little upset because she didn't receive her usual Sunday letter from Cyril yesterday. But then she was weak and low."

"Clever youth, Cyril!" mused the doctor.

"I think he's a particularly nice boy," said Sophia, eagerly. "So you've seen him?"

"Of course," said Sophia, rather stiffly. Did the doctor suppose that she did not know her own nephew? She went back to the subject of her sister. "She is also a little bothered, I think, because the servant is going to leave."

"Oh! So Amy is going to leave, is she?" He spoke still lower. "Between you and me, it's no bad thing."

"I'm so glad you think so."

"In another few years the servant would have been the mistress here. One can see these things coming on, but it's so difficult to do anything. In fact ye can't do anything."

"I did something," said Sophia, sharply. "I told the woman straight that it shouldn't go on while I was in the house. I didn't suspect it at first—but when I found it out . . . I can tell you!" She let the doctor imagine what she could tell him.

He smiled. "No," he said. "I can easily understand that ye didn't suspect anything at first. When she's well and bright Mrs. Povey could hold her own—so I'm told. But it was certainly slowly getting worse."

"Then people talk about it?" said Sophia, shocked.

"As a native of Bursley, Mrs. Scales," said the doctor, "ye ought to know what people in Bursley do!" Sophia put her lips together. The doctor rose, smoothing his waistcoat. "What does she bother with servants at all for?" he burst out. "She's perfectly free. She hasn't got a care in the world, if she only knew it. Why doesn't she go out and about, and enjoy herself? She wants stirring up, that's what your sister wants."

"You're quite right," Sophia burst out in her turn. "That's precisely what I say to myself; precisely! I was thinking it over only this morning. She wants stirring up. She's got into a rut."

"She needs to be jolly. Why doesn't she go to some seaside place, and live in a hotel, and enjoy herself? Is there anything to prevent her?"

"Nothing whatever."

"Instead of being dependent on a servant! I believe in enjoying one's self—when ye've got the money to do it with! Can ye imagine anybody living in Bursley, for pleasure? And especially in St. Luke's Square, right in the thick of it all! Smoke! Dirt! No air! No light! No scenery! No amusements! What does she do it for? She's in a rut."

"Yes, she's in a rut," Sophia repeated her own phrase which he had copied.

"My word!" said the doctor. "Wouldn't I clear out and enjoy myself if I could! Your sister's a young woman."

"Of course she is!" Sophia concurred, feeling that she herself was even younger. "Of course she is!"

"And except that she's nervously organized, and has certain predispositions, there's nothing the matter with her. This sciatica—I don't say it would be cured, but it might be, by a complete change and throwing off all these ridiculous worries. Not only does she live in the most depressing conditions, but she suffers tortures for it, and there's absolutely no need for her to be here at all."

"Doctor," said Sophia, solemnly, impressed, "you are quite right. I agree with every word you say."

"Naturally she's attached to the place," he continued, glancing round the room. "I know all about that. After living here all her life! But she's got to break herself of her attachment. It's her duty to do so. She ought to show a little energy. I'm deeply attached to my bed in the morning, but I have to leave it."

"Of course," said Sophia, in an impatient tone, as though disgusted with every person who could not perceive, or would not subscribe to, these obvious truths that the doctor was uttering. "Of course!"

"What she needs is the bustle of life in a good hotel, a good hydro, for instance. Among jolly people. Parties! Games! Excursions! She wouldn't be the same woman. You'd see. Wouldn't I do it, if I could? Strathpeffer. She'd soon forget her sciatica. I don't know what Mrs. Povey's annual income is, but I expect that if she took it into her head to live in the dearest hotel in England, there would be no reason why she shouldn't."

Sophia lifted her head and smiled in calm amusement. "I expect so," she said superiorly.

"A hotel—that's the life. No worries. If ye want anything ye ring a bell. If a waiter gives notice, it's some one else who has the worry, not you. But you know all about that, Mrs. Scales."

"No one better," murmured Sophia.

"Good evening," he said abruptly, sticking out his hand. "I'll be down in the morning."

"Did you ever mention this to my sister?" Sophia asked him, rising.

"Yes," said he. "But it's no use. Oh yes, I've told her. But she does really think it's quite impossible. She wouldn't even hear of going to live in London with her beloved son. She won't listen."

"I never thought of that," said Sophia. "Good night."

Their hand-grasp was very intimate and mutually comprehending. He was pleased by the quick responsiveness of her temperament, and the masterful vigour which occasionally flashed out in her replies. He noticed the hardly perceptible distortion of her handsome, worn face, and he said to himself: "She's been through a thing or two," and: "She'll have to mind her p's and q's." Sophia was pleased because he admired her, and because with her he dropped his bedside jocularities, and talked plainly as a sensible man will talk when he meets an uncommonly wise woman, and because he echoed and amplified her own thoughts. She honoured him by standing at the door till he had driven off.

For a few moments she mused solitary in the parlour, and then, lowering the gas, she went upstairs to her sister, who lay in the dark. Sophia struck a match.

"You've been having quite a long chat with the doctor," said Constance. "He's very good company, isn't he? What did he talk about this time?"

"He wanted to know about Paris and so on," Sophia answered.

"Oh! I believe he's a rare student."

Lying there in the dark, the simple Constance never suspected that those two active and strenuous ones had been arranging her life for her, so that she should be jolly and live for twenty years yet. She did not suspect that she had been tried and found guilty of sinful attachments, and of being in a rut, and of lacking the elements of ordinary sagacity. It had not occurred to her that if she was worried and ill, the reason was to be found in her own blind and stupid obstinacy. She had thought herself a fairly sensible kind of creature.

iii

The sisters had an early supper together in Constance's bedroom. Constance was much easier. Having a fancy that a little movement would be beneficial, she had even got up for a few moments and moved about the room. Now she sat ensconced in pillows. A fire burned in the old-fashioned ineffectual grate. From the Sun Vaults opposite came the sound of a phonograph singing an invitation to God to save its gracious queen. This phonograph was a wonderful novelty, and filled the Sun nightly. For a few evenings it had interested the sisters, in spite of themselves, but they had soon sickened of it and loathed it. Sophia became more and more obsessed by the monstrous absurdity of the simple fact that she and Constance were there, in that dark inconvenient house, wearied by the gaiety of public-houses, blackened by smoke, surrounded by mud, instead of being luxuriously installed in a beautiful climate, amid scenes of beauty and white cleanliness. Secretly she became more and more indignant.

Amy entered, bearing a letter in her coarse hand. As Amy unceremoniously handed the letter to Constance, Sophia thought: "If she was my servant she would hand letters on a tray." (An advertisement had already been sent to the *Signal*.)

Constance took the letter trembling. "Here it is at last," she cried.

When she had put on her spectacles and read it, she exclaimed:

"Bless us! Here's news! He's coming down! That's why he didn't write on Saturday as usual."

She gave the letter to Sophia to read. It ran——

"Sunday midnight.

"DEAR MOTHER,

"Just a line to say I am coming down to Bursley on Wednesday, on business with Peels. I shall get to Knype at 5.28, and take the Loop. I've been very busy, and as I was coming down I didn't write on Saturday. I hope you didn't worry. Love to yourself and Aunt Sophia.

"Yours, C."

"I must send him a line," said Constance, excitedly.

"What? To-night?"

"Yes. Amy can easily catch the last post with it. Otherwise he won't know that I've got his letter."

She rang the bell.

Sophia thought: "His coming down is really no excuse for his not writing on Saturday. How could she guess that he was coming down? I shall have to put in a little word to that young man. I wonder Constance is so blind. She is quite satisfied now that his letter has come." On behalf of the elder generation she rather resented Constance's eagerness to write in answer.

But Constance was not so blind. Constance thought exactly as Sophia thought. In her heart she did not at all justify or excuse Cyril. She remembered separately almost every instance of his carelessness in her regard. "Hope I didn't worry, indeed!" she said to herself with a faint touch of bitterness, apropos of the phrase in his letter.

Nevertheless she insisted on writing at once. And Amy had to bring the writing materials.

"Mr. Cyril is coming down on Wednesday," she said to Amy with great dignity.

Amy's stony calmness was shaken, for Mr. Cyril was a great deal to Amy. Amy wondered how she would be able to look Mr. Cyril in the face when he knew that she had given notice.

In the middle of writing, on her knee, Constance looked up at Sophia, and said, as though defending herself against an accusation: "I didn't write to him yesterday, you know, or to-day."

"No," Sophia murmured assentingly.

Constance rang the bell yet again, and Amy was sent out to the post.

Soon afterwards the bell was rung for a fourth time, and not answered.

"I suppose she hasn't come back yet. But I thought I heard the door. What a long time she is!"

"What do you want?" Sophia asked.

"I just want to speak to her," said Constance.

When the bell had been rung seven or eight times, Amy at length re-appeared, somewhat breathless.

"Amy," said Constance, "let me examine those sheets, will you?"

"Yes'm," said Amy, apparently knowing what sheets, of all the various and multitudinous sheets in that house.

"And the pillow-cases," Constance added as Amy left the room.

So it continued. The next day the fever heightened. Constance was up early, before Sophia, and trotting about the

house like a girl. Immediately after breakfast Cyril's bedroom
was invested and revolutionized; not till evening was order restored in that chamber. And on the Wednesday morning it had
to be dusted afresh. Sophia watched the preparations, and the
increasing agitation of Constance's demeanour, with an astonishment which she had real difficulty in concealing. "Is the
woman absolutely mad?" she asked herself. The spectacle was
ludicrous: or it seemed so to Sophia, whose career had not
embraced much experience of mothers. It was not as if the manifestations of Constance's anxiety were dignified or original or
splendid. They were just silly, ordinary fussinesses; they had
no sense in them. Sophia was very careful to make no observation. She felt that before she and Constance were very much
older she had a very great deal to do, and that a subtle diplomacy and wary tactics would be necessary. Moreover, Constance's angelic temper was slightly affected by the strain of
expectation. She had a tendency to rasp. After the high-tea
was set she suddenly sprang on to the sofa and lifted down the
"Stag at Eve" engraving. The dust on the top of the frame incensed her.

"What are you going to do?" Sophia asked, in a final marvel.

"I'm going to change it with that one," said Constance,
pointing to another engraving opposite the fireplace. "He said
the effect would be very much better if they were changed.
And his lordship is very particular."

Constance did not go to Bursley station to meet her son. She
explained that it upset her to do so, and that also Cyril preferred her not to come.

"Suppose I go to meet him," said Sophia, at half-past five.
The idea had visited her suddenly. She thought: "Then I could
talk to him before any one else."

"Oh, *do!*" Constance agreed.

Sophia put her things on with remarkable expedition. She
arrived at the station a minute before the train came in. Only
a few persons emerged from the train, and Cyril was not among
them. A porter said that there was not supposed to be any
connection between the Loop Line trains and the main line
expresses, and that probably the express had missed the Loop.
She waited thirty-five minutes for the next Loop, and Cyril did
not emerge from that train either.

Constance opened the front-door to her, and showed a telegram—

          "Sorry prevented last moment. Writing. CYRIL."

Sophia had known it. Somehow she had known that it was useless to wait for the second train. Constance was silent and calm; Sophia also.

"What a shame! What a shame!" thumped Sophia's heart.

It was the most ordinary episode. But beneath her calm she was furious against her favourite. She hesitated.

"I'm just going out a minute," she said.

"Where?" asked Constance. "Hadn't we better have tea? I suppose we must have tea."

"I shan't be long. I want to buy something."

Sophia went to the post-office and despatched a telegram. Then, partially eased, she returned to the arid and painful desolation of the house.

iv

The next evening Cyril sat at the tea-table in the parlour with his mother and his aunt. To Constance his presence there had something of the miraculous in it. He had come, after all! Sophia was in a rich robe, and for ornament wore an old silver-gilt neck-chain, which was clasped at the throat, and fell in double to her waist, where it was caught in her belt. This chain interested Cyril. He referred to it once or twice, and then he said: "Just let me have a *look* at that chain," and put out his hand; and Sophia leaned forward so that he could handle it. His fingers played with it thus for some seconds; the picture strikingly affected Constance. At length he dropped it, and said: "H'm!" After a pause he said: "Louis Sixteenth, eh?" and Sophia said:

"They told me so. But it's nothing; it only cost thirty francs, you know." And Cyril took her up sharply:

"What does that matter?" Then after another pause he asked: "How often do you break a link of it?"

"Oh, often," she said. "It's always getting shorter."

And he murmured mysteriously: "H'm!"

He was still mysterious, withdrawn within himself extraordinarily uninterested in his physical surroundings. But that evening he talked more than he usually did. He was benevolent, and showed a particular benevolence towards his mother, apparently exerting himself to answer her questions with fullness and heartiness, as though admitting frankly her right to be curious. He praised the tea; he seemed to notice what he was eating. He took Spot on his knee, and gazed in admiration at Fossette.

"By Jove!" he said, "that's a dog, that is! . . . All the same. . . . ." And he burst out laughing.

"I won't have Fossette laughed at," Sophia warned him.

"No, seriously," he said, in his quality of an amateur of dogs; "she is very fine." Even then he could not help adding: "What you can see of her!"

Whereupon Sophia shook her head, deprecating such wit. Sophia was very lenient towards him. Her leniency could be perceived in her eyes, which followed his movements all the time. "Do you think he is like me, Constance?" she asked.

"I wish I was half as good-looking," said Cyril, quickly; and Constance said:

"As a baby he was very like you. He was a handsome baby. He wasn't at all like you when he was at school. These last few years he's begun to be like you again. He's very much changed since he left school; he was rather heavy and clumsy then."

"Heavy and clumsy!" exclaimed Sophia. "Well, I should never have believed it!"

"Oh, but he was!" Constance insisted.

"Now, mater," said Cyril, "it's a pity you don't want that cake cutting into. I think I could have eaten a bit of that cake. But of course if it's only for show . . . !"

Constance sprang up, seizing a knife.

"You shouldn't tease your mother," Sophia told him. "He doesn't really want any, Constance; he's regularly stuffed himself."

And Cyril agreed, "No, no, mater, don't cut it; I really couldn't. I was only gassing."

But Constance could never clearly see through humour of that sort. She cut three slices of cake, and she held the plate towards Cyril.

"I tell you I really couldn't!" he protested.

"Come!" she said obstinately. "I'm waiting! How much longer must I hold this plate?"

And he had to take a slice. So had Sophia. When she was roused, they both of them had to yield to Constance.

With the dogs, and the splendour of the tea-table under the gas, and the distinction of Sophia and Cyril, and the conversation, which on the whole was gay and free, rising at times to jolly garrulity, the scene in her parlour ought surely to have satisfied Constance utterly. She ought to have been quite happy, as her sciatica had raised the siege for a space. But she was not quite happy. The circumstances of Cyril's arrival had disturbed her; they had in fact wounded her, though she would scarcely admit the wound. In the morning she had received a brief letter from Cyril to say that he had not been able to come, and vaguely promising, or half-promising, to run down at a later date. That letter had the cardinal defects of all Cyril's relations with his mother; it was casual, and it was not candid. It gave no hint of the nature of the obstacle which had prevented him from coming. Cyril had always been too secretive. She was gravely depressed by the letter, which she did not show to Sophia, because it impaired her dignity as a mother, and displayed her son in a bad light. Then about eleven o'clock a telegram had come for Sophia.

"That's all right," Sophia had said, on reading it. "He'll be here this evening!" And she had handed over the telegram, which read—

"Very well. Will come same train to-day."

And Constance learned that when Sophia had rushed out just before tea on the previous evening, it was to telegraph to Cyril.

"What did you say to him?" Constance asked.

"Oh!" said Sophia, with a careless air, "I told him I thought he ought to come. After all, you're more important than any *business*, Constance! And I don't like him behaving like that. I was determined he should come!"

Sophia had tossed her proud head.

Constance had pretended to be pleased and grateful. But the existence of a wound was incontestable. Sophia, then, could do more with Cyril than she could! Sophia had only met him once, and could simply twist him round her little finger. He would never have done so much for his mother. A fine sort of an obstacle it must have been, if a single telegram from Sophia could overcome it . . . ! And Sophia, too, was secretive. She had gone out and had telegraphed, and had not breathed a word until she got the reply, sixteen hours later. She was secretive, and Cyril was secretive. They resembled one another. They had taken to one another. But Sophia was a curious mixture. When Constance had asked her if she should go to the station again to meet Cyril, she had replied scornfully: "No, indeed! I've done going to meet Cyril. People who don't arrive must not expect to be met."

When Cyril drove up to the door, Sophia had been in attendance. She hurried down the steps. "Don't say anything about my telegram," she had rapidly whispered to Cyril; there was no time for further explanation. Constance was at the top of the steps. Constance had not heard the whisper, but she had seen it; and she saw a guilty, puzzled look on Cyril's face, afterwards an ineffectively concealed conspiratorial look on both their faces. They had "something between them," from which she, the mother, was shut out! Was it not natural that she should be wounded? She was far too proud to mention the telegrams. And as neither Cyril nor Sophia mentioned them, the circumstances leading to Cyril's change of plan were not referred to at all, which was very curious. Then Cyril was more sociable than he had ever been; he was different, under his aunt's gaze. Certainly he treated his mother faultlessly. But Constance said to herself: "It is because she is here that he is so specially nice to me."

When tea was finished and they were going upstairs to the drawing-room, she asked him, with her eye on the "Stag at Eve" engraving:

"Well, is it a success?"

"What?" His eye followed hers. "Oh, you've changed it! What did you do that for, mater?"

"You said it would be better like that," she reminded him.

"Did I?" He seemed genuinely surprised. "I don't remember. I believe it is better, though," he added. "It might be even better still if you turned it the other way up."

He pulled a face to Sophia, and screwed up his shoulders, as if to indicate: "I've done it, this time!"

"How? The other way up?" Constance queried. Then as she comprehended that he was teasing her, she said: "Get away with you!" and pretended to box his ears. "You were fond enough of that picture at one time!" she said ironically.

"Yes, I was, mater," he submissively agreed. "There's no getting over that." And he pressed her cheeks between his hands and kissed her.

In the drawing-room he smoked cigarettes and played the piano—waltzes of his own composition. Constance and Sophia did not entirely comprehend those waltzes. But they agreed that all were wonderful and that one was very pretty indeed. (It soothed Constance that Sophia's opinion coincided with hers.) He said that that waltz was the worst of the lot. When he had finished with the piano, Constance informed him about Amy. "Oh! She told me," he said, "when she brought me my water. I didn't mention it because I thought it would be rather a sore subject." Beneath the casualness of his tone there lurked a certain curiosity, a willingness to hear details. He heard them.

At five minutes to ten, when Constance had yawned, he threw a bomb among them on the hearthrug.

"Well," he said, "I've got an appointment with Matthew at the Conservative Club at ten o'clock. I must go. Don't wait up for me."

Both women protested, Sophia the more vivaciously. It was Sophia now who was wounded.

"It's business," he said, defending himself. "He's going away early to-morrow, and it's my only chance." And as Constance did not brighten he went on: "Business has to be attended to. You mustn't think I've got nothing to do but enjoy myself."

No hint of the nature of the business! He never explained. As to business, Constance knew only that she allowed him three hundred a year, and paid his local tailor. The sum had at first seemed to her enormous, but she had grown accustomed to it.

"I should have preferred you to see Mr. Peel-Swynnerton here," said Constance. "You could have had a room to yourselves. I do not like you going out at ten o'clock at night to a club."

"Well, good night, mater," he said, getting up. "See you to-morrow. I shall take the key out of the door. It's true my pocket will never be the same again."

Sophia saw Constance into bed, and provided her with two hot-water bottles against sciatica. They did not talk much.

v

Sophia sat waiting on the sofa in the parlour. It appeared to her that, though little more than a month had elapsed since her arrival in Bursley, she had already acquired a new set of interests and anxieties. Paris and her life there had receded in the strangest way. Sometimes for hours she would absolutely forget Paris. Thoughts of Paris were disconcerting; for either Paris or Bursley must surely be unreal! As she sat waiting on the sofa Paris kept coming into her mind. Certainly it was astonishing that she should be just as preoccupied with her schemes for the welfare of Constance as she had ever been preoccupied with schemes for the improvement of the Pension Frensham. She said to herself: "My life has been so queer— and yet every part of it separately seemed ordinary enough— how will it end?"

Then there were footfalls on the steps outside, and a key was put into the door, which she at once opened.

"Oh!" exclaimed Cyril, startled, and also somewhat out of countenance. "You're still up! Thanks." He came in, smoking the end of a cigar. "Fancy having to cart that about!" he murmured, holding up the great old-fashioned key before inserting it in the lock on the inside.

"I stayed up," said Sophia, "because I wanted to talk to you about your mother, and it's so difficult to get a chance."

Cyril smiled, not without self-consciousness, and dropped into his mother's rocking-chair, which he had twisted round with his feet to face the sofa.

"Yes," he said. "I was wondering what was the real meaning of your telegram. What was it?" He blew out a lot of smoke and waited for her reply.

"I thought you ought to come down," said Sophia, cheerfully but firmly. "It was a fearful disappointment to your mother that you didn't come yesterday. And when she's expecting a letter from you and it doesn't come, it makes her ill."

"Oh, well!" he said. "I'm glad it's no worse. I thought from your telegram there was something seriously wrong. And then when you told me not to mention it—when I came in . . . !"

She saw that he failed to realize the situation, and she lifted her head challengingly.

"You neglect your mother, young man," she said.

"Oh, come now, auntie!" he answered quite gently. "You mustn't talk like that. I write to her every week. I've never missed a week. I come down as often as———"

"You miss the Sunday sometimes," Sophia interrupted him.

"Perhaps," he said doubtfully. "But what———"

"Don't you understand that she simply lives for your letters? And if one doesn't come, she's very upset indeed—can't eat! And it brings on her sciatica, and I don't know what!"

He was taken aback by her boldness, her directness.

"But how silly of her! A fellow can't always———"

"It may be silly. But there it is. You can't alter her. And, after all, what would it cost you to be more attentive, even to write to her twice a week? You aren't going to tell me you're so busy as all that! I know a great deal more about young men than your mother does." She smiled like an aunt.

He answered her smile sheepishly.

"If you'll only put yourself in your mother's place . . . !"

"I expect you're quite right," he said at length. "And I'm much obliged to you for telling me. How was I to know?" He threw the end of the cigar, with a large sweeping gesture, into the fire.

"Well, anyhow, you know now!" she said curtly; and she thought: "You *ought* to have known. It was your business to know." But she was pleased with the way in which he had accepted her criticism, and the gesture with which he threw away the cigar-end struck her as very distinguished.

"That's all right!" he said dreamily, as if to say: "That's done with." And he rose.

Sophia, however, did not stir.

"Your mother's health is not what it ought to be," she went on, and gave him a full account of her conversation with the doctor.

"Really!" Cyril murmured, leaning on the mantel-piece with his elbow and looking down at her. "Stirling said that, did he? I should have thought she would have been better where she is, in the Square."

"Why better in the Square?"

"Oh, I don't know!"

"Neither do I!"

"She's always been here."

"Yes," said Sophia, "she's been here a great deal too long."

"What do *you* suggest?" Cyril asked, with impatience in his voice against this new anxiety that was being thrust upon him.

"Well," said Sophia, "what should you say to her coming to London and living with you?" .

Cyril started back. Sophia could see that he was genuinely shocked. "I don't think that would do at all," he said.

"Why?"

"Oh! I don't think it would. London wouldn't suit her. She's not that sort of woman. I really thought she was quite all right down here. She wouldn't like London." He shook his head, looking up at the gas; his eyes had a dangerous glare.

"But supposing she said she did?"

"Look here," Cyril began in a new and brighter tone. "Why don't you and she keep house together somewhere? That would be the very——"

He turned his head sharply. There was a noise on the staircase, and the staircase door opened with its eternal creak.

"Yes," said Sophia. "The Champs Elysées begins at the Place de la Concorde, and ends——. Is that you, Constance?"

The figure of Constance filled the doorway. Her face was troubled. She had heard Cyril in the street, and had come down to see why he remained so long in the parlour. She was astounded to find Sophia with him. There they were, as intimate as cronies, chattering about Paris! Undoubtedly she was jealous! Never did Cyril talk like that to her!

"I thought you were in bed and asleep, Sophia," she said weakly. "It's nearly one o'clock."

"No," said Sophia. "I didn't seem to feel like going to bed; and then Cyril happened to come in."

But neither she nor Cyril could look innocent. And Constance glanced from one to the other apprehensively.

The next morning Cyril received a letter which, he said—with no further explanation—forced him to leave at once. He intimated that there had been danger in his coming just then, and that matters had turned out as he had feared.

"You think over what I said," he whispered to Sophia when they were alone for an instant, "and let me know."

vi

A week before Easter the guests of the Rutland Hotel in the Broad Walk, Buxton, being assembled for afternoon tea in the "lounge" of that establishment, witnessed the arrival of two middle-aged ladies and two dogs. Critically to examine newcomers was one of the amusements of the occupants of the lounge. This apartment, furnished "in the oriental style," made a pretty show among the photographs in the illustrated brochure of the hotel, and, though draughty, it was of all the public rooms the favourite. It was draughty because only separated from the street (if the Broad Walk can be called a street) by two pairs of swinging-doors—in charge of two page-boys. Every visitor entering the hotel was obliged to pass through the lounge, and for newcomers the passage was an ordeal; they were made to feel that they had so much to learn, so much to get accustomed to; like passengers who join a ship at a port of call, they felt that the business lay before them of creating a niche for themselves in a hostile and haughty society. The two ladies produced a fairly favourable impression at the outset by reason of their two dogs. It is not every one who has the courage to bring dogs into an expensive private hotel; to bring one dog indicates that you are not accustomed to deny yourself small pleasures for the sake of a few extra shillings; to bring two indicates that you have no fear of hotel-managers and that you are in the habit of regarding your own whim as nature's law. The shorter and stouter of the two ladies did not impose herself with much force on the collective vision of the Rutland; she was dressed in black, not fashionably, though with a certain unpretending richness; her gestures were timid and nervous; evidently she relied upon her tall companion to shield her in the first trying contacts of hotel life. The tall lady was of a different stamp. Handsome, stately, deliberate, and handsomely dressed in colours, she had the assured hard gaze of a person who is thoroughly habituated to the inspection of strangers. She curtly asked one of the page-boys for the manager, and the manager's wife tripped rapidly down the stairs in response, and was noticeably deferential. Her voice was quiet and commanding, the voice of one who gives orders that are obeyed. The opinion of the lounge was divided as to whether or not they were sisters.

They vanished quietly upstairs in convoy of the manager's wife, and they did not re-appear for the lounge tea, which in any case would have been undrinkably stewed. It then became known, by the agency of one of those guests, to be found in every hotel, who acquire all the secrets of the hotel by the exercise of unabashed curiosity on the personnel, that the two ladies had engaged two bedrooms, Nos. 17 and 18, and the sumptuous private parlour with a balcony on the first floor, styled "C" in the nomenclature of rooms. This fact definitely established the position of the new arrivals in the moral fabric of the hotel. They were wealthy. They had money to throw away. For even in a select hotel like the Rutland it is not everybody who indulges in a private sitting-room; there were only four such apartments in the hotel, as against fifty bedrooms.

At dinner they had a small table to themselves in a corner. The short lady wore a white shawl over her shoulders. Her almost apologetic manner during the meal confirmed the view that she must be a very simple person, unused to the world and its ways. The other continued to be imperial. She ordered half-a-bottle of wine and drank two glasses. She stared about her quite self-unconsciously, whereas the little woman divided her glances between her companion and her plate. They did not talk much. Immediately after dinner they retired. "Widows in easy circumstances" was the verdict; but the contrast between the pair held puzzles that piqued the inquisitive.

Sophia had conquered again. Once more Sophia had resolved to accomplish a thing and she had accomplished it. Events had fallen out thus. The advertisement for a general servant in the *Signal* had been a disheartening failure. A few answers were received, but of an entirely unsatisfactory character. Constance, a great deal more than Sophia, had been astounded by the bearing and the demands of modern servants. Constance was in despair. If Constance had not had an immense pride she would have been ready to suggest to Sophia that Amy should be asked to "stay on." But Constance would have accepted a modern impudent wench first. It was Maria Critchlow who got Constance out of her difficulty by giving her particulars of a reliable servant who was about to leave a situation in which she had stayed for eight years. Constance did not imagine that a servant recommended by Maria Critchlow would suit her, but, being in a quandary, she arranged to see the servant, and both she and Sophia were very pleased with the girl— Rose Bennion by name. The mischief was that Rose would not be free until about a month after Amy had left. Rose would have left her old situation, but she had a fancy to go and spend a fortnight with a married sister at Manchester before settling into new quarters. Constance and Sophia felt that this caprice of Rose's was really very tiresome and unnecessary. Of course Amy might have been asked to "stay on" just for a month. Amy would probably have volunteered to do so had she been aware of the circumstances. She was not, however, aware of the circumstances. And Constance was determined not to be beholden to Amy for anything. What could the sisters do? Sophia, who conducted all the interviews with Rose and other candidates, said that it would be a grave error to let Rose slip. Besides, they had no one to take her place, no one who could come at once.

The dilemma was appalling. At least, it seemed appalling to Constance, who really believed that no mistress had ever been so "awkwardly fixed." And yet, when Sophia first proposed her solution, Constance considered it to be a quite impossible solution. Sophia's idea was that they should lock up the house and leave it on the same day as Amy left it, to spend a few weeks in some holiday resort. To begin with, the idea of leaving the house empty seemed to Constance a mad idea. The house had never been left empty. And then—going for a holiday in April! Constance had never been for a holiday except in the month of August. No! The project was beset with difficulties and dangers which could not be overcome nor provided against. For example, "We can't come back to a dirty house," said Constance. "And we can't have a strange servant coming here before us." To which Sophia had replied: "Then what *shall* you do?" And Constance, after prodigious reflection on the frightful pass to which destiny had brought her, had said that she supposed she would have to manage with a charwoman until Rose's advent. She asked Sophia if she remembered old Maggie. Sophia, of course, perfectly remembered. Old Maggie was dead, as well as the drunken, amiable Hollins, but there was a young Maggie (wife of a bricklayer) who went out charing in the spare time left from looking after seven children. The more Constance meditated upon young Maggie, the more was she convinced that young Maggie would meet the case. Constance felt she could trust young Maggie.

This expression of trust in Maggie was Constance's undoing. Why should they not go away, and arrange with Maggie to come to the house a few days before their return, to clean and ventilate? The weight of reason overbore Constance. She yielded unwillingly, but she yielded. It was the mention of Buxton that finally moved her. She knew Buxton. Her old landlady at Buxton was dead, and Constance had not visited the place since before Samuel's death; nevertheless its name had a reassuring sound to her ears, and for sciatica its waters and climate were admitted to be the best in England. Gradually Constance permitted herself to be embarked on this perilous enterprise of shutting up the house for twenty-five days. She imparted the information to Amy, who was astounded. Then she commenced upon her domestic preparations. She wrapped Samuel's Family Bible in brown paper; she put Cyril's straw-framed copy of Sir Edwin Landseer away in a drawer, and she took ten thousand other precautions. It was grotesque; it was farcical; it was what you please. And when, with the cab at the door and the luggage on the cab, and the dogs chained together, and Maria Critchlow waiting on the pavement to receive the key, Constance put the key into the door on the outside, and locked up the empty house, Constance's face was tragic with innumerable apprehensions. And Sophia felt that she had performed a miracle. She had.

On the whole the sisters were well received in the hotel, though they were not at an age which commands popularity. In the criticism which was passed upon them—the free, realistic and relentless criticism of private hotels—Sophia was at first set down as overbearing. But in a few days this view was modified, and Sophia rose in esteem. The fact was that Sophia's behaviour changed after forty-eight hours. The Rutland Hotel was very good. It was so good as to disturb Sophia's profound beliefs that there was in the world only one truly high-class pension, and that nobody could teach the creator of that unique pension anything about the art of management. The food was excellent; the attendance in the bedrooms was excellent (and Sophia knew how difficult of attainment was excellent bedroom attendance); and to the eye the interior of the Rutland presented a spectacle far richer than the Pension Frensham could show. The standard of comfort was higher. The guests had a more distinguished appearance. It is true that the prices were much higher. Sophia was humbled. She had enough sense to adjust her perspective. Further, she found herself ignorant of many matters which by the other guests were taken for granted and used as a basis for conversation. Prolonged residence in Paris would not justify this ignorance; it seemed rather to intensify its strangeness. Thus, when someone of cosmopolitan experience, having learnt that she had lived in

Paris for many years, asked what had been going on lately at the Comédie Française, she had to admit that she had not been in a French theatre for nearly thirty years. And when, on a Sunday, the same person questioned her about the English chaplain in Paris, lo! she knew nothing but his name, had never even seen him. Sophia's life, in its way, had been as narrow as Constance's. Though her experience of human nature was wide, she had been in a groove as deep as Constance's. She had been utterly absorbed in doing one single thing.

By tacit agreement she had charge of the expedition. She paid all the bills. Constance protested against the expensiveness of the affair several times, but Sophia quietened her by sheer force of individuality. Constance had one advantage over Sophia. She knew Buxton and its neighbourhood intimately, and she was therefore in a position to show off the sights and to deal with local peculiarities. In all other respects Sophia led.

They very soon became acclimatized to the hotel. They moved easily between Turkey carpets and sculptured ceilings; their eyes grew used to the eternal vision of themselves and other slow-moving dignities in gilt mirrors, to the heaviness of great oil-paintings of picturesque scenery, to the indications of surreptitious dirt behind massive furniture, to the grey-brown of the shirt-fronts of the waiters, to the litter of trays, boots and pails in long corridors; their ears were always awake to the sounds of gongs and bells. They consulted the barometer and ordered the daily carriage with the perfunctoriness of habit. They discovered what can be learnt of other people's needlework in a hotel on a wet day. They performed co-operative outings with fellow-guests. They invited fellow-guests into their sitting-room. When there was an entertainment they did not avoid it. Sophia was determined to do everything that could with propriety be done, partly as an outlet for her own energy (which since she left Paris had been accumulating), but more on Constance's account. She remembered all that Dr. Stirling had said, and the heartiness of her own agreement with his opinions. It was a great day when, under tuition of an aged lady and in the privacy of their parlour, they both began to study the elements of Patience. Neither had ever played at cards. Constance was almost afraid to touch cards, as though in the very cardboard there had been something unrighteous and perilous. But the respectability of a luxurious private hotel makes proper every act that passes within its walls. And Constance plausibly argued that no harm could come from a game which you played by yourself. She acquired with some aptitude several varieties of Patience. She said: "I think I could enjoy that, if I kept at it. But it does make my head whirl."

Nevertheless Constance was not happy in the hotel. She worried the whole time about her empty house. She anticipated difficulties and even disasters. She wondered again and again whether she could trust the second Maggie in her house alone, whether it would not be better to return home earlier and participate personally in the cleaning. She would have decided to do so had it not been that she hesitated to subject Sophia to the inconvenience of a house upside down. The matter was on her mind, always. Always she was restlessly anticipating the day when they would leave. She had carelessly left her heart behind in St. Luke's Square. She had never stayed in a hotel before, and she did not like it. Sciatica occasionally harassed her. Yet when it came to the point she would not drink the waters. She said she never had drunk them, and seemed to regard that as a reason why she never should. Sophia had achieved a miracle in getting her to Buxton for nearly a month, but the ultimate grand effect lacked brilliance.

Then came the fatal letter, the desolating letter, which vindicated Constance's dark apprehensions. Rose Bennion calmly wrote to say that she had decided not to come to St. Luke's Square. She expressed regret for any inconvenience which might possibly be caused; she was polite. But the monstrousness of it! Constance felt that this actually and truly was the deepest depth of her calamities. There she was, far from a dirty home, with no servant and no prospect of a servant! She bore herself bravely, nobly; but she was stricken. She wanted to return to the dirty home at once.

Sophia felt that the situation created by this letter would demand her highest powers of dealing with situations, and she determined to deal with it adequately. Great measures were needed, for Constance's health and happiness were at stake. She alone could act. She knew that she could not rely upon Cyril. She still had an immense partiality for Cyril; she thought him the most charming young man she had ever known; she knew him to be industrious and clever; but in his relations with his mother there was a hardness, a touch of callousness. She explained it vaguely by saying that "they did not get on well together"; which was strange, considering Constance's sweet affectionateness. Still, Constance could be a little trying —at times. Anyhow, it was soon clear to Sophia that the idea of mother and son living together in London was entirely impracticable. No! If Constance was to be saved from herself, there was no one but Sophia to save her.

After half a morning spent chiefly in listening to Constance's hopeless comments on the monstrous letter, Sophia said suddenly that she must take the dogs for an airing. Constance did not feel equal to walking out, and she would not drive. She did not want Sophia to "venture," because the sky threatened. However, Sophia did venture, and she returned a few minutes late for lunch, full of vigour, with two happy dogs. Constance was moodily awaiting her in the dining-room. Constance could not eat. But Sophia ate, and she poured out cheerfulness and energy as from a source inexhaustible. After lunch it began to rain. Constance said she thought she should retire directly to the sitting-room. "I'm coming too," said Sophia, who was still wearing her hat and coat and carried her gloves in her hand. In the pretentious and banal sitting-room they sat down on either side the fire. Constance put a little shawl round her shoulders, pushed her spectacles into her grey hair, folded her hands, and sighed an enormous sigh: "Oh, dear!" She was the tragic muse, aged, and in black silk.

"I tell you what I've been thinking," said Sophia, folding up her gloves.

"What?" asked Constance, expecting some wonderful solution to come out of Sophia's active brain.

"There's no earthly reason why you should go back to Bursley. The house won't run away, and it's costing nothing but the rent. Why not take things easy for a bit?"

"And stay here?" said Constance, with an inflection that enlightened Sophia as to the intensity of her dislike of the existence at the Rutland.

"No, not here," Sophia answered with quick depreciation. "There are plenty of other places we could go to."

"I don't think I should be easy in my mind," said Constance. "What with nothing being settled, the house——"

"What does it matter about the house?"

"It matters a great deal," said Constance, seriously, and slightly hurt. "I didn't leave things as if we were going to be away for a long time. It wouldn't do."

"I don't see that anything could come to any harm, I really

don't!" said Sophia, persuasively. "Dirt can always be cleaned, after all. I think you ought to go about more. It would do you good—all the good in the world. And there is no reason why you shouldn't go about. You are perfectly free. Why shouldn't we go abroad together, for instance, you and I? I'm sure you would enjoy it very much."

"Abroad?" murmured Constance, aghast, recoiling from the proposition as from a grave danger.

"Yes," said Sophia, brightly and eagerly. She was determined to take Constance abroad. "There are lots of places we could go to, and live very comfortably among nice English people." She thought of the resorts she had visited with Gerald in the sixties. They seemed to her like cities of a dream. They came back to her as a dream recurs.

"I don't think going abroad would suit me," said Constance.

"But why not? You don't know. You've never tried, my dear." She smiled encouragingly. But Constance did not smile. Constance was inclined to be grim.

"I don't think it would," said she, obstinately. "I'm one of your stay-at-homes. I'm not like you. We can't all be alike," she added, with her "tart" accent.

Sophia suppressed a feeling of irritation. She knew that she had a stronger individuality than Constance's.

"Well, then," she said, with undiminished persuasiveness, "in England or Scotland. There are several places I should like to visit—Torquay, Tunbridge Wells. I've always understood that Tunbridge Wells is a very nice town indeed, with very superior people, and a beautiful climate."

"I think I shall have to be getting back to St. Luke's Square," said Constance, ignoring all that Sophia had said. "There's so much to be done."

Then Sophia looked at Constance with a more serious and resolute air; but still kindly, as though looking thus at Constance for Constance's own good.

"You are making a mistake, Constance," she said, "if you will allow me to say so."

"A mistake!" exclaimed Constance, startled.

"A very great mistake," Sophia insisted, observing that she was creating an effect.

"I don't see how I can be making a mistake," Constance said, gaining confidence in herself, as she thought the matter over.

"No," said Sophia, "I'm sure you don't see it. But you are.

You know, you are just a little apt to let yourself be a slave to that house of yours. Instead of the house existing for you, you exist for the house."

"Oh! Sophia!" Constance muttered awkwardly. "What ideas you do have, to be sure!" In her nervousness she rose and picked up some embroidery, adjusting her spectacles and coughing. When she sat down she said: "No one could take things easier than I do as regards housekeeping. I can assure you I let dozens of little matters go, rather than bother myself."

"Then why do you bother now?" Sophia posed her.

"I can't leave the place like that." Constance was hurt.

"There's one thing I can't understand," said Sophia, raising her head and gazing at Constance again, "and that is, why you live in St. Luke's Square at all."

"I must live somewhere. And I'm sure it's very pleasant."

"In all that smoke! And with that dirt! And the house is very old."

"It's a great deal better built than a lot of those new houses by the Park," Constance sharply retorted. In spite of herself she resented any criticism of her house. She even resented the obvious truth that it was old.

"You'll never get a servant to stay in that cellar-kitchen, for one thing," said Sophia, keeping calm.

"Oh! I don't know about that! I don't know about that! That Bennion woman didn't object to it, anyway. It's all very well for you, Sophia, to talk like that. But I know Bursley perhaps better than you do." She was tart again. "And I can assure you that my house is looked upon as a very good house indeed."

"Oh! I don't say it isn't; I don't say it isn't. But you would be better away from it. Every one says that."

"Every one?" Constance looked up, dropping her work. "Who? Who's been talking about me?"

"Well," said Sophia, "the doctor, for instance."

"Dr. Stirling? I like that! He's always saying that Bursley is one of the healthiest climates in England. He's always sticking up for Bursley."

"Dr. Stirling thinks you ought to go away more—not stay always in that dark house." If Sophia had sufficiently reflected she would not have used the adjective "dark." It did not help her cause.

"Oh, does he!" Constance fairly snorted. "Well, if it's of any interest to Dr. Stirling, I like my dark house."

"Hasn't he ever told you you ought to go away more?" Sophia persisted.

"He may have mentioned it," Constance reluctantly admitted.

"When he was talking to me he did a good deal more than mention it. And I've a good mind to tell you what he said."

"Do!" said Constance, politely.

"You don't realize how serious it is, I'm afraid," said Sophia. "You can't see yourself." She hesitated a moment. Her blood being stirred by Constance's peculiar inflection of the phrase "my dark house," her judgment was slightly obscured. She decided to give Constance a fairly full version of the conversation between herself and the doctor.

"It's a question of your health," she finished. "I think it's my duty to talk to you seriously, and I have done. I hope you'll take it as it's meant."

"Oh, of course!" Constance hastened to say. And she thought: "It isn't yet three months that we've been together, and she's trying already to get me under her thumb."

A pause ensued. Sophia at length said: "There's no doubt that both your sciatica and your palpitations are due to nerves. And you let your nerves get into a state because you worry over trifles. A change would do you a tremendous amount of good. It's just what you need. Really, you must admit, Constance, that the idea of living always in a place like St. Luke's Square, when you are perfectly free to do what you like and go where you like—you must admit it's rather too much."

Constance put her lips together and bent over her embroidery.

"Now, what do you say?" Sophia gently entreated.

"There's some of us like Bursley, black as it is!" said Constance. And Sophia was surprised to detect tears in her sister's voice.

"Now, my dear Constance," she remonstrated.

"It's no use!" cried Constance, flinging away her work, and letting her tears flow suddenly. Her face was distorted. She was behaving just like a child. "It's no use! I've got to go back home and look after things. It's no use. Here we are pitching money about in this place. It's perfectly sinful. Drives, carriages, extras! A shilling a day extra for each dog. I never heard of such goings-on. And I'd sooner be at home. That's it. I'd sooner be at home." This was the first reference that Constance had made for a long time to the question of expense, and incomparably the most violent. It angered Sophia.

"We will count it that you are here as my guest," said Sophia, loftily, "if that is how you look at it."

"Oh no!" said Constance. "It isn't the money I grudge. Oh no, we won't." And her tears were falling thick.

"Yes, we will," said Sophia, coldly. "I've only been talking to you for your own good. I——"

"Well," Constance interrupted her despairingly, "I wish you wouldn't try to domineer over me!"

"Domineer!" exclaimed Sophia, aghast. "Well, Constance, I do think——"

She got up and went to her bedroom, where the dogs were imprisoned. They escaped to the stairs. She was shaking with emotion. This was what came of trying to help other people! Imagine Constance . . . ! Truly Constance was most unjust, and quite unlike her usual self! And Sophia encouraged in her breast the feeling of injustice suffered. But a voice kept saying to her: "You've made a mess of this. You've not conquered this time. You're beaten. And the situation is unworthy of you, of both of you. Two women of fifty quarreling like this! It's undignified. You've made a mess of things." And to strangle the voice, she did her best to encourage the feeling of injustice suffered.

"Domineer!"

And Constance was absolutely in the wrong. She had not argued at all. She had merely stuck to her idea like a mule! How difficult and painful would be the next meeting with Constance, after this grievous miscarriage!

As she was reflecting thus the door burst open, and Constance stumbled, as it were blindly, into the bedroom. She was still weeping.

"Sophia!" she sobbed, supplicatingly, and all her fat body was trembling. "You mustn't kill me. . . . I'm like that—you can't alter me. I'm like that. I know I'm silly. But it's no use!" She made a piteous figure.

Sophia was aware of a lump in her throat.

"It's all right, Constance; it's all right. I quite understand. Don't bother any more."

Constance, catching her breath at intervals, raised her wet, worn face and kissed her.

Sophia remembered the very words, "You can't alter her," which she had used in remonstrating with Cyril. And now she had been guilty of precisely the same unreason as that with which she had reproached Cyril! She was ashamed, both for herself and for Constance. Assuredly it had not been such a scene as women of their age would want to go through often. It was humiliating. She wished that it could have been blotted out as though it had never happened. Neither of them ever forgot it. They had had a lesson. And particularly Sophia had had a lesson. Having learnt, they left the Rutland, amid due ceremonies, and returned to St. Luke's Square.

CHAPTER IV
END OF SOPHIA

THE kitchen steps were as steep, dark, and difficult as ever. Up those steps Sophia Scales, nine years older than when she had failed to persuade Constance to leave the Square, was carrying a large basket, weighted with all the heaviness of Fossette. Sophia, despite her age, climbed the steps violently, and burst with equal violence into the parlour, where she deposited the basket on the floor near the empty fireplace. She was triumphant and breathless. She looked at Constance, who had been standing near the door in the attitude of a shocked listener.

"There!" said Sophia. "Did you hear how she talked?"

"Yes," said Constance. "What shall you do?"

"Well," said Sophia. "I had a very good mind to order her out of the house at once. But then I thought I would take no notice. Her time will be up in three weeks. It's best to be indifferent. If once they see they can upset you . . . However, I wasn't going to leave Fossette down there to her tender mercies a moment longer. She's simply not looked after her at all."

Sophia went on her knees to the basket, and, pulling aside the dog's hair, round about the head, examined the skin. Fossette was a sick dog and behaved like one. Fossette, too, was

nine years older, and her senility was offensive. She was to no
sense a pleasant object.

"See here," said Sophia.

Constance also knelt to the basket.

"And here," said Sophia. "And here."

The dog sighed, the insincere and pity-seeking sigh of a
spoilt animal. Fossette foolishly hoped by such appeals to be
spared the annoying treatment prescribed for her by the vet-
erinary surgeon.

While the sisters were coddling her, and protecting her from
her own paws, and trying to persuade her that all was for the
best, another aged dog wandered vaguely into the room: Spot.
Spot had very few teeth, and his legs were stiff. He had only
one vice, jealousy. Fearing that Fossette might be receiving
the entire attention of his mistresses, he had come to inquire
into the situation. When he found the justification of his
gloomiest apprehensions, he nosed obstinately up to Constance,
and would not be put off. In vain Constance told him at length
that he was interfering with the treatment. In vain Sophia
ordered him sharply to go away. He would not listen to reason,
being furious with jealousy. He got his foot into the basket.

"Will you!" exclaimed Sophia angrily, and gave him a clout
on his old head. He barked snappishly, and retired to the
kitchen again, disillusioned, tired of the world, and nursing his
terrific grievance. "I do declare," said Sophia, "that dog gets
worse and worse."

Constance said nothing.

When everything was done that could be done for the aged
virgin in the basket, the sisters rose from their knees, stiffly;
and they began to whisper to each other about the prospects of
obtaining a fresh servant. They also debated whether they
could tolerate the criminal eccentricities of the present occupant of the cave for yet another three weeks. Evidently they
were in the midst of a crisis. To judge from Constance's face
every imaginable woe had been piled on them by destiny without the slightest regard for their powers of resistance. Her
eyes had the permanent look of worry, and there was in them
also something of the self-defensive. Sophia had a bellicose air,
as though the creature in the cave had squarely challenged her,
and she was decided to take up the challenge. Sophia's tone
seemed to imply an accusation of Constance. The general tension was acute.

Then suddenly their whispers expired, and the door opened and the servant came in to lay the supper. Her nose was high, her gaze cruel, radiant, and conquering. She was a pretty and an impudent girl of about twenty-three. She knew she was torturing her old and infirm mistresses. She did not care. She did it purposely. Her motto was: War on employers, get all you can out of them, for they will get all they can out of you. On principle—the sole principle she possessed—she would not stay in a place more than six months. She liked change. And employers did not like change. She was shameless with men. She ignored all orders as to what she was to eat and what she was not to eat. She lived up to the full resources of her employers. She could be to the last degree slatternly. Or she could be as neat as a pin, with an apron that symbolized purity and propriety, as to-night. She could be idle during a whole day, accumulating dirty dishes from morn till eve. On the other hand she could, when she chose, work with astonishing celerity and even thoroughness. In short, she was born to infuriate a mistress like Sophia and to wear out a mistress like Constance. Her strongest advantage in the struggle was that she enjoyed altercation; she revelled in a brawl; she found peace tedious. She was perfectly calculated to convince the sisters that times had worsened, and that the world would never again be the beautiful, agreeable place it once had been.

Her gestures as she laid the table were very graceful, in the pert style. She dropped forks into their appointed positions with disdain; she made slightly too much noise; when she turned she manœuvred her swelling hips as though for the benefit of a soldier in a handsome uniform.

Nothing but the servant had been changed in that house. The harmonium on which Mr. Povey used occasionally to play was still behind the door; and on the harmonium was the tea-caddy of which Mrs. Baines used to carry the key on her bunch. In the corner to the right of the fireplace still hung the cupboard where Mrs. Baines stored her pharmacopœia. The rest of the furniture was arranged as it had been arranged when the death of Mrs. Baines endowed Mr. and Mrs. Povey with all the treasures of the house at Axe. And it was as good as ever; better than ever. Dr. Stirling often expressed the desire for a corner cupboard like Mrs. Baines's corner cupboard. One item had been added: the "Peel" compote which Matthew Peel-Swynnerton had noticed in the dining-room of the Pension

Frensham. This majestic piece, which had been reserved by Sophia in the sale of the pension, stood alone on a canterbury in the drawing-room. She had stored it, with a few other trifles, in Paris, and when she sent for it and the packing-case arrived, both she and Constance became aware that they were united for the rest of their lives. Of worldly goods, except money, securities, and clothes, that compote was practically all that Sophia owned. Happily it was a first-class item, doing no shame to the antique magnificence of the drawing-room.

In yielding to Constance's terrible inertia, Sophia had meant nevertheless to work her own will on the interior of the house. She had meant to bully Constance into modernizing the dwelling. She did bully Constance, but the house defied her. Nothing could be done to that house. If only it had had a hall or lobby a complete transformation would have been possible. But there was no access to the upper floor except through the parlour. The parlour could not therefore be turned into a kitchen and the basement suppressed, and the ladies of the house could not live entirely on the upper floor. The disposition of the rooms had to remain exactly as it had always been. There was the same draught under the door, the same darkness on the kitchen stairs, the same difficulties with tradesmen in the distant backyard, the same twist in the bedroom stairs, the same eternal ascending and descending of pails. An efficient cooking-stove, instead of the large and capacious range, alone represented the twentieth century in the fixtures of the house.

Buried at the root of the relations between the sisters was Sophia's grudge against Constance for refusing to leave the Square. Sophia was loyal. She would not consciously give with one hand while taking away with the other, and in accepting Constance's decision she honestly meant to close her eyes to its stupidity. But she could not entirely succeed. She could not avoid thinking that the angelic Constance had been strangely and monstrously selfish in refusing to quit the Square. She marvelled that a woman of Constance's sweet and calm disposition should be capable of so vast and ruthless an egotism. Constance must have known that Sophia would not leave her, and that the habitation of the Square was a continual irk to Sophia. Constance had never been able to advance a single argument for remaining in the Square. And yet she would not budge. It was so inconsistent with the rest of Constance's behaviour. See Sophia sitting primly there by the table, a woman approaching sixty, with immense experience written on the fine hardness of her worn and distinguished face! Though her hair is not yet all grey, nor her figure bowed, you would imagine that she would, in her passage through the world, have learnt better than to expect a character to be consistent. But no! She was ever disappointed and hurt by Constance's inconsistency! And see Constance, stout and bowed, looking more than her age with hair nearly white and slightly trembling hands! See that face whose mark is meekness and the spirit of conciliation, the desire for peace—you would not think that that placid soul could, while submitting to it, inly rage against the imposed weight of Sophia's individuality. "Because I wouldn't turn out of my house to please her," Constance would say to herself, "she fancies she is entitled to do just as she likes." Not often did she secretly rebel thus, but it occurred sometimes. They never quarrelled. They would have regarded separation as a disaster. Considering the difference of their lives, they agreed marvellously in their judgment of things. But that buried question of domicile prevented a complete unity between them. And its subtle effect was to influence both of them to make the worst, instead of the best, of the trifling mishaps that disturbed their tranquillity. When annoyed, Sophia would meditate upon the mere fact that they lived in the Square for no reason whatever, until it grew incredibly shocking to her. After all it was scarcely conceivable that they should be living in the very middle of a dirty, ugly, industrial town simply because Constance mulishly declined to move. Another thing that curiously exasperated both of them upon occasion was that, owing to a recurrence of her old complaint of dizziness after meals, Sophia had been strictly forbidden to drink tea, which she loved. Sophia chafed under the deprivation, and Constance's pleasure was impaired because she had to drink it alone.

While the brazen and pretty servant, mysteriously smiling to herself, dropped food and utensils on to the table, Constance and Sophia attempted to converse with negligent ease upon indifferent topics, as though nothing had occurred that day to mar the beauty of ideal relations between employers and employed. The pretence was ludicrous. The young wench saw through it instantly, and her mysterious smile developed almost into a laugh.

"Please shut the door after you, Maud," said Sophia, as the girl picked up her empty tray.

"Yes, ma'am," replied Maud, politely.

She went out and left the door open.

It was a defiance, offered from sheer, youthful, wanton mischief.

The sisters looked at each other, their faces gravely troubled, aghast, as though they had glimpsed the end of civilized society, as though they felt that they had lived too long into an age of decadence and open shame. Constance's face showed despair—she might have been about to be pitched into the gutter without a friend and without a shilling—but Sophia's had the reckless courage that disaster breeds.

Sophia jumped up, and stepped to the door. "Maud," she called out.

No answer.

"Maud, do you hear me?"

The suspense was fearful.

Still no answer.

Sophia glanced at Constance. "Either she shuts this door, or she leaves this house at once, even if I have to fetch a policeman!"

And Sophia disappeared down the kitchen steps. Constance trembled with painful excitement. The horror of existence closed in upon her. She could imagine nothing more appalling than the pass to which they had been brought by the modern change in the lower classes.

In the kitchen, Sophia, conscious that the moment held the future of at least the next three weeks, collected her forces.

"Maud," she said, "did you not hear me call you?"

Maud looked up from a book—doubtless a wicked book.

"No, ma'am."

"You liar!" thought Sophia. And she said: "I asked you to shut the parlour door, and I shall be obliged if you will do so."

Now Maud would have given a week's wages for the moral force to disobey Sophia. There was nothing to compel her to obey. She could have trampled on the fragile and weak Sophia. But something in Sophia's gaze compelled her to obey. She flounced; she bridled; she mumbled; she unnecessarily disturbed the venerable Spot; but she obeyed. Sophia had risked all, and she had won something.

"And you should light the gas in the kitchen," said Sophia

magnificently, as Maud followed her up the steps. "Your young eyes may be very good now, but you are not going the way to preserve them. My sister and I have often told you that we do not grudge you gas."

With stateliness she rejoined Constance, and sat down to the cold supper. And as Maud clicked the door to, the sisters breathed relief. They envisaged new tribulations, but for a brief instant there was surcease.

Yet they could not eat. Neither of them, when it came to the point, could swallow. The day had been too exciting, too distressing. They were at the end of their resources. And they did not hide from each other that they were at the end of their resources. The illness of Fossette, without anything else, had been more than enough to ruin their tranquillity. But the illness of Fossette was as nothing to the ingenious naughtiness of the servant. Maud had a sense of temporary defeat, and was planning fresh operations; but really it was Maud who had conquered. Poor old things, they were in such a "state" that they could not eat!

"I'm not going to let her think she can spoil my appetite!" said Sophia, dauntless. Truly that woman's spirit was unquenchable.

She cut a couple of slices off the cold fowl; she cut a tomato into slices; she disturbed the butter; she crumbled bread on the cloth, and rubbed bits of fowl over the plates, and dirtied knives and forks. Then she put the slices of fowl and bread and tomato into a piece of tissue paper, and silently went upstairs with the parcel and came down again a moment afterwards empty-handed.

After an interval she rang the bell, and lighted the gas.

"We've finished, Maud. You can clear away."

Constance thirsted for a cup of tea. She felt that a cup of tea was the one thing that would certainly keep her alive. She longed for it passionately. But she would not demand it from Maud. Nor would she mention it to Sophia, lest Sophia, flushed by the victory of the door, should incur new risks. She simply did without. On empty stomachs they tried pathetically to help each other in games of Patience. And when the blithe Maud passed through the parlour on the way to bed, she saw two dignified and apparently calm ladies, apparently absorbed in a delightful game of cards, apparently without a worry in the world. They said "Good night, Maud," cheerfully, politely, and coldly. It was a heroic scene. Immediately afterwards Sophia carried Fossette up to her own bedroom.

ii

The next afternoon the sisters, in the drawing-room, saw Dr. Stirling's motor-car speeding down the Square. The doctor's partner, young Harrop, had died a few years before at the age of over seventy, and the practice was much larger than it had ever been, even in the time of old Harrop. Instead of two or three horses, Stirling kept a car, which was a constant spectacle in the streets of the district.

"I do hope he'll call in," said Mrs. Povey, and sighed.

Sophia smiled to herself with a little scorn. She knew that Constance's desire for Dr. Stirling was due simply to the need which she felt of telling some one about the great calamity that had happened to them that morning. Constance was utterly absorbed by it, in the most provincial way. Sophia had said to herself at the beginning of her sojourn in Bursley, and long afterwards, that she should never get accustomed to the exasperating provinciality of the town, exemplified by the childish preoccupation of the inhabitants with their own two-penny affairs. No characteristic of life in Bursley annoyed her more than this. None had oftener caused her to yearn in a brief madness for the desert-like freedom of great cities. But she had got accustomed to it. Indeed, she had almost ceased to notice it. Only occasionally, when her nerves were more upset than usual, did it strike her.

She went into Constance's bedroom to see whether the doctor's car halted in King Street. It did.

"He's here," she called out to Constance.

"I wish you'd go down, Sophia," said Constance. "I can't trust that minx——"

So Sophia went downstairs to superintend the opening of the door by the minx.

The doctor was radiant, according to custom.

"I thought I'd just see how that dizziness was going on," said he as he came up the steps.

"I'm glad you've come," said Sophia, confidentially. Since the first days of their acquaintanceship they had always been confidential. "You'll do my sister good to-day."

Just as Maud was closing the door a telegraph-boy arrived, with a telegram addressed to Mrs. Scales. Sophia read it and then crumpled it in her hand.

"What's wrong with Mrs. Povey to-day?" the doctor asked, when the servant had withdrawn.

"She only wants a bit of your society," said Sophia. "Will you go up? You know the way to the drawing-room. I'll follow."

As soon as he had gone she sat down on the sofa, staring out of the window. Then with a grunt: "Well, that's no use, anyway!" she went upstairs after the doctor. Already Constance had begun upon her recital.

"Yes," Constance was saying. "And when I went down this morning to keep an eye on the breakfast, I thought Spot was very quiet——" She paused. "He was dead in the drawer. She pretended she didn't know, but I'm sure she did. Nothing will convince me that she didn't poison that dog with the mice-poison we had last year. She was vexed because Sophia took her up sharply about Fossette last night, and she revenged herself on the other dog. It would just be like her. Don't tell me! I know. I should have packed her off at once, but Sophia thought better not. We couldn't *prove* anything, as Sophia says. Now, what do you think of it, doctor?"

Constance's eyes suddenly filled with tears.

"Ye'd had Spot a long time, hadn't ye?" he said sympathetically.

She nodded. "When I was married," said she, "the first thing my husband did was to buy a fox-terrier, and ever since we've always had a fox-terrier in the house." This was not true, but Constance was firmly convinced of its truth.

"It's very trying," said the doctor. "I know when my Airedale died, I said to my wife I'd never have another dog—unless she could find me one that would live for ever. Ye remember my Airedale?"

"Oh, quite well!"

"Well, my wife said I should be bound to have another one sooner or later, and the sooner the better. She went straight off to Oldcastle and bought me a spaniel pup, and there was such a to-do training it that we hadn't too much time to think about Piper."

Constance regarded this procedure as somewhat callous, and she said so, tartly. Then she recommenced the tale of Spot's

death from the beginning, and took it as far as his burial, that
afternoon, by Mr. Critchlow's manager, in the yard. It had
been necessary to remove and replace paving-stones.

"Of course," said Dr. Sterling, "ten years is a long time. He
was an old dog. Well, you've still got the celebrated Fossette."
He turned to Sophia.

"Oh yes," said Constance, perfunctorily. "Fossette's ill. The
fact is that if Fossette hadn't been ill, Spot would probably
have been alive and well now."

Her tone exhibited a grievance. She could not forget that
Sophia had harshly dismissed Spot to the kitchen, thus practically sending him to his death. It seemed very hard to her that
Fossette, whose life had once been despaired of, should continue to exist, while Spot, always healthy and unspoilt, should
die untended, and by treachery. For the rest, she had never
liked Fossette. On Spot's behalf she had always been jealous of
Fossette.

"Probably alive and well now!" she repeated, with a peculiar
accent.

Observing that Sophia maintained a strange silence, Dr.
Stirling suspected a slight tension in the relations of the sisters, and he changed the subject. One of his great qualities was
that he refrained from changing a subject introduced by a patient unless there was a professional reason for changing it.

"I've just met Richard Povey in the town," said he. "He told
me to tell ye that he'll be round in about an hour or so to take
you for a spin. He was in a new car, which he did his best to
sell to me, but he didn't succeed."

"It's very kind of Dick," said Constance. "But this afternoon really we're not——"

"I'll thank ye to take it as a prescription, then," replied the
doctor. "I told Dick I'd see that ye went. Splendid June weather. No dust after all that rain. It'll do ye all the good in the
world. I must exercise my authority. The truth is, I've gradually been losing all control over ye. Ye do just as ye like."

"Oh, doctor, how you do run on!" murmured Constance, not
quite well pleased to-day by his tone.

After the scene between Sophia and herself at Buxton, Constance had always, to a certain extent, in the doctor's own
phrase, "got her knife into him." Sophia had, then, in a manner betrayed him. Constance and the doctor discussed that matter with frankness, the doctor humorously accusing her of be-

ing "hard" on him. Nevertheless the little cloud between them was real, and the result was often a faint captiousness on Constance's part in judging the doctor's behaviour.

"He's got a surprise for ye, has Dick!" the doctor added.

Dick Povey, after his father's death and his own partial recovery, had set up in Hanbridge as a bicycle agent. He was permanently lamed, and he hopped about with a thick stick. He had succeeded with bicycles and had taken to automobiles, and he was succeeding with automobiles. People were at first startled that he should advertise himself in the Five Towns. There was an obscure general feeling that because his mother had been a drunkard and his father a murderer, Dick Povey had no right to exist. However, when it had recovered from the shock of seeing Dick Povey's announcement of bargains in the *Signal*, the district most sensibly decided that there was no reason why Dick Povey should not sell bicycles as well as a man with normal parents. He was now supposed to be acquiring wealth rapidly. It was said that he was a marvellous chauffeur, at once daring and prudent. He had one day, several years previously, overtaken the sisters in the rural neighbourhood of Sneyd, where they had been making an afternoon excursion. Constance had presented him to Sophia, and he had insisted on driving the ladies home. They had been much impressed by his cautious care of them, and their natural prejudice against anything so new as a motor-car had been conquered instantly. Afterwards he had taken them out for occasional runs. He had a great admiration for Constance, founded on gratitude to Samuel Povey; and as for Sophia, he always said to her that she would be an ornament to any car.

"You haven't heard his latest, I suppose?" said the doctor, smiling.

"What is it?" Sophia asked perfunctorily.

"He wants to take to ballooning. It seems he's been up once."

Constance made a deprecating noise with her lips.

"However, that's not his surprise," the doctor added, smiling again at the floor. He was sitting on the music-stool, and saying to himself, behind his mask of effulgent good-nature: "It gets more and more uphill work, cheering up these two women. I'll try them on Federation."

Federation was the name given to the scheme for blending the Five Towns into one town, which would be the twelfth largest town in the kingdom. It aroused fury in Bursley, which saw in the suggestion nothing but the extinction of its ancient glory to the aggrandizement of Hanbridge. Hanbridge had already, with the assistance of electric cars that whizzed to and fro every five minutes, robbed Bursley of two-thirds of its retail trade—as witness the steady decadence of the Square!—and Bursley had no mind to swallow the insult and become a mere ward of Hanbridge. Bursley would die fighting. Both Constance and Sophia were bitter opponents of Federation. They would have been capable of putting Federationists to the torture. Sophia in particular, though so long absent from her native town, had adopted its cause with characteristic vigour. And when Dr. Stirling wished to practise his curative treatment of taking the sisters "out of themselves," he had only to start the hare of Federation and the hunt would be up in a moment. But this afternoon he did not succeed with Sophia, and only partially with Constance. When he stated that there was to be a public meeting that very night, and that Constance as a ratepayer ought to go to it and vote, if her convictions were genuine, she received his chaff with a mere murmur to the effect that she did not think she should go. Had the man forgotten that Spot was dead? At length he became grave, and examined them both as to their ailments, and nodded his head, and looked into vacancy while meditating upon each case. And then, when he had inquired where they meant to go for their summer holidays, he departed.

"Aren't you going to see him out?" Constance whispered to Sophia, who had shaken hands with him at the drawing-room door. It was Sophia who did the running about, owing to the state of Constance's sciatic nerve. Constance had, indeed, become extraordinarily inert, leaving everything to Sophia.

Sophia shook her head. She hesitated; then approached Constance, holding out her hand and disclosing the crumpled telegram.

"Look at that!" said she.

Her face frightened Constance, who was always expectant of new anxieties and troubles. Constance straightened out the paper with difficulty, and read—

"Mr. Gerald Scales is dangerously ill here. Boldero, 49, Deansgate, Manchester."

All through the inexpressibly tedious and quite unnecessary

call of Dr. Stirling—(Why had he chosen to call just then?
Neither of them was ill)—Sophia had held that telegram concealed in her hand and its information concealed in her heart.
She had kept her head up, offering a calm front to the world.
She had given no hint of the terrible explosion—for an explosion it was. Constance was astounded at her sister's self-control,
which entirely passed her comprehension. Constance felt that
worries would never cease, but would rather go on multiplying
until death ended all. First, there had been the frightful worry
of the servant; then the extremely distressing death and burial
of Spot—and now it was Gerald Scales turning up again!
With what violence was the direction of their thoughts now
shifted! The wickedness of maids was a trifle; the death of pets
was a trifle. But the reappearance of Gerald Scales! . . .
That involved the possibility of consequences which could not
even be named, so afflictive was the mere prospect to them. Constance was speechless, and she saw that Sophia was also speechless.

Of course the event had been bound to happen. People do
not vanish never to be heard of again. The time surely arrives
when the secret is revealed. So Sophia said to herself—now!

She had always refused to consider the effect of Gerald's
reappearance. She had put the idea of it away from her, determined to convince herself that she had done with him finally
and for ever. She had forgotten him. It was years since he had
ceased to disturb her thoughts—many years. "He *must* be
dead," she had persuaded herself. "It is inconceivable that he
should have lived on and never come across me. If he had been
alive and learnt that I had made money, he would assuredly
have come to me. No, he must be dead!"

And he was not dead! The brief telegram overwhelmingly
shocked her. Her life had been calm, regular, monotonous. And
now it was thrown into an indescribable turmoil by five words
of a telegram, suddenly, with no warning whatever. Sophia had
the right to say to herself: "I have had my share of trouble,
and more than my share!" The end of her life promised to be
as awful as the beginning. The mere existence of Gerald Scales
was a menace to her. But it was the simple impact of the blow
that affected her supremely, beyond ulterior things. One might
have pictured fate as a cowardly brute who had struck this
ageing woman full in the face, a felling blow, which however
had not felled her. She staggered, but she stuck on her legs.

It seemed a shame—one of those crude, spectacular shames which make the blood boil—that the gallant, defenceless creature should be so maltreated by the bully, destiny.

"Oh, Sophia!" Constance moaned. "What trouble is this?"

Sophia's lip curled with a disgusted air. Under that she hid her suffering.

She had not seen him for thirty-six years. He must be over seventy years of age, and he had turned up again like a bad penny, doubtless a disgrace! What had he been doing in those thirty-six years? He was an old, enfeebled man now! He must be a pretty sight! And he lay at Manchester, not two hours away!

Whatever feelings were in Sophia's heart, tenderness was not among them. As she collected her wits from the stroke, she was principally aware of the sentiment of fear. She recoiled from the future.

"What shall you do?" Constance asked. Constance was weeping.

Sophia tapped her foot, glancing out of the window.

"Shall you go to see him?" Constance continued.

"Of course," said Sophia. "I must!"

She hated the thought of going to see him. She flinched from it. She felt herself under no moral obligation to go. Why should she go? Gerald was nothing to her, and had no claim on her of any kind. This she honestly believed. And yet she knew that she must go to him. She knew it to be impossible that she should not go.

"Now?" demanded Constance.

Sophia nodded.

"What about the trains? . . . Oh, you poor dear!" The mere idea of the journey to Manchester put Constance out of her wits, seeming a business of unparalleled complexity and difficulty.

"Would you like me to come with you?"

"Oh no! I must go by myself."

Constance was relieved by this. They could not have left the servant in the house alone, and the idea of shutting up the house without notice or preparation presented itself to Constance as too fantastic.

By a common instinct they both descended to the parlour.

"Now, what about a time-table? What about a time-table?" Constance mumbled on the stairs. She wiped her eyes resolutely. "I wonder whatever in this world has brought him at last to that Mr. Boldero's in Deansgate?" she asked the walls.

As they came into the parlour, a great motor-car drove up before the door, and when the pulsations of its engine had died away, Dick Povey hobbled from the driver's seat to the pavement. In an instant he was hammering at the door in his lively style. There was no avoiding him. The door had to be opened. Sophia opened it. Dick Povey was over forty, but he looked considerably younger. Despite his lameness, and the fact that his lameness tended to induce corpulence, he had a dashing air, and his face, with its short, light moustache, was boyish. He seemed to be always upon some joyous adventure.

"Well, aunties," he greeted the sisters, having perceived Constance behind Sophia; he often so addressed them. "Has Dr. Stirling warned you that I was coming? Why haven't you got your things on?"

Sophia observed a young woman in the car.

"Yes," said he, following her gaze, "you may as well look. Come down, miss. Come down, Lily. You've got to go through with it." The young woman, delicately confused and blushing, obeyed. "This is Miss Lily Holl," he went on. "I don't know whether you would remember her. I don't think you do. It's not often she comes to the Square. But, of course, she knows you by sight. Granddaughter of your old neighbour, Alderman Holl! We are engaged to be married, if you please."

Constance and Sophia could not decently pour out their griefs on the top of such news. The betrothed pair had to come in and be congratulated upon their entry into the large realms of mutual love. But the sisters, even in their painful quandary, could not help noticing what a nice, quiet, ladylike girl Lily Holl was. Her one fault appeared to be that she was too quiet. Dick Povey was not the man to pass time in formalities, and he was soon urging departure.

"I'm sorry we can't come," said Sophia. "I've got to go to Manchester now. We are in great trouble."

"Yes, in great trouble," Constance weakly echoed.

Dick's face clouded sympathetically. And both the affianced began to see that to which the egotism of their happiness had blinded them. They felt that long, long years had elapsed since these ageing ladies had experienced the delights which they were feeling.

"Trouble? I'm sorry to hear that!" said Dick.

"Can you tell me the trains to Manchester?" asked Sophia.

"No," said Dick, quickly, "But I can drive you there quicker than any train, if it's urgent. Where do you want to go to?"

"Deansgate," Sophia faltered.

"Look here," said Dick, "it's half-past three. Put yourself in my hands; I'll guarantee at Deansgate you shall be before half-past five. I'll look after you."

"But——"

"There isn't any 'but.' I'm quite free for the afternoon and evening."

At first the suggestion seemed absurd, especially to Constance. But really it was too tempting to be declined. While Sophia made ready for the journey, Dick and Lily Holl and Constance conversed in low, solemn tones. The pair were waiting to be enlightened as to the nature of the trouble; Constance, however, did not enlighten them. How could Constance say to them: "Sophia has a husband that she hasn't seen for thirty-six years, and he's dangerously ill, and they've telegraphed for her to go?" Constance could not. It did not even occur to Constance to order a cup of tea.

iii

Dick Povey kept his word. At a quarter-past five he drew up in front of No. 49, Deansgate, Manchester. "There you are!" he said, not without pride. "Now, we'll come back in about a couple of hours or so, just to take your orders, whatever they are." He was very comforting, with his suggestion that in him Sophia had a sure support in the background.

Without many words Sophia went straight into the shop. It looked like a jeweller's shop, and a shop for bargains generally. Only the conventional sign over the side-entrance showed that at heart it was a pawnbroker's. Mr. Till Boldero did a nice business in the Five Towns, and in other centres near Manchester, by selling silver-ware second-hand, or nominally second-hand, to persons who wished to make presents to other persons or to themselves. He would send anything by post on approval. Occasionally he came to the Five Towns, and he had once, several years before, met Constance. They had talked. He was the son of a cousin of the late great and wealthy Boldero, sleeping partner in Birkinshaw's and Gerald's uncle.

It was from Constance that he had learnt of Sophia's return to Bursley. Constance had often remarked to Sophia what a superior man Mr. Till Boldero was.

The shop was narrow and lofty. It seemed like a menagerie for trapped silver-ware. In glass cases right up to the dark ceiling silver vessels and instruments of all kinds lay confined. The top of the counter was a glass prison containing dozens of gold watches, together with snuff-boxes, enamels, and other antiquities. The front of the counter was also glazed, showing vases and large pieces of porcelain. A few pictures in heavy gold frames were perched about. There was a case of umbrellas with elaborate handles and rich tassels. There were a couple of statuettes. The counter, on the customers' side, ended in a glass screen on which were the words "Private Office." On the seller's side the prospect was closed by a vast safe. A tall young man was fumbling in this safe. Two women sat on customers' chairs, leaning against the crystal counter. The young man came towards them from the safe, bearing a tray.

"How much is that goblet?" asked one of the women, raising her parasol dangerously among such fragility and pointing to one object among many in a case high up from the ground.

"That, madam?"

"Yes."

"Thirty-five pounds."

The young man disposed his tray on the counter. It was packed with more gold watches, adding to the extraordinary glitter and shimmer of the shop. He chose a small watch from the regiment.

"Now, this is something I can recommend," he said. "It's made by Cuthbert Butler of Blackburn. I can guarantee you that for five years." He spoke as though he were the accredited representative of the Bank of England, with calm and absolute assurance.

The effect upon Sophia was mysteriously soothing. She felt that she was among honest men. The young man raised his head towards her with a questioning, deferential gesture.

"Can I see Mr. Boldero?" she asked. "Mrs. Scales."

The young man's face changed instantly to a sympathetic comprehension.

"Yes, madam. I'll fetch him at once," said he, and he disappeared behind the safe. The two customers discussed the watch. Then the door opened in the glass screen, and a portly, middle-aged man showed himself. He was dressed in blue broad-cloth, with a turned-down collar and a small black tie. His waistcoat displayed a plain but heavy gold watch-chain, and his cuff-links were of plain gold. His eye-glasses were gold-rimmed. He had grey hair, beard and moustache, but on the backs of his hands grew a light brown hair. His appearance was strangely mild, dignified, and confidence-inspiring. He was, in fact, one of the most respected tradesmen in Manchester.

He peered forward, looking over his eye-glasses, which he then took off, holding them up in the air by their short handle. Sophia had approached him.

"Mrs. Scales?" he said, in a very quiet, very benevolent voice. Sophia nodded. "Please come this way." He took her hand, squeezing it commiseratingly, and drew her into the sanctum. "I didn't expect you so soon," he said. "I looked up th' trains, and I didn't see how you could get here before six."

Sophia explained.

He led her further, through the private office, into a sort of parlour, and asked her to sit down. And he too sat down. Sophia waited, as it were, like a suitor.

"I'm afraid I've got bad news for you, Mrs. Scales," he said, still in that mild, benevolent voice.

"He's dead?" Sophia asked.

Mr. Till Boldero nodded. "He's dead. I may as well tell you that he had passed away before I telegraphed. It all hap-pened very, very suddenly." He paused. "Very, very sud-denly!"

"Yes," said Sophia, weakly. She was conscious of a pro-found sadness which was not grief, though it resembled grief. And she had also a feeling that she was responsible to Mr. Till Boldero for anything untoward that might have occurred to him by reason of Gerald.

"Yes," said Mr. Till Boldero, deliberately and softly. "He came in last night just as we were closing. We had very heavy rain here. I don't know how it was with you. He was wet, in a dreadful state, simply dreadful. Of course, I didn't recognize him. I'd never seen him before, so far as my recollection goes. He asked me if I was the son of Mr. Till Boldero that had this shop in 1866. I said I was. 'Well,' he says, 'you're the only connection I've got. My name's Gerald Scales. My mother was your father's cousin. Can you do anything for me?' he

says. I could see he was ill. I had him in here. When I found
he couldn't eat nor drink I thought I'd happen better send for
th' doctor. The doctor got him to bed. He passed away at one
o'clock this afternoon. I was very sorry my wife wasn't here
to look after things a bit better. But she's at Southport, not
well at all."

"What was it?" Sophia asked briefly.

Mr. Boldero indicated the enigmatic. "Exhaustion, I suppose," he replied.

"He's here?" demanded Sophia, lifting her eyes to possible
bedrooms.

"Yes," said Mr. Boldero. "I suppose you would wish to see
him?"

"Yes," said Sophia.

"You haven't seen him for a long time, your sister told me?"
Mr. Boldero murmured, sympathetically.

"Not since 'seventy," said Sophia.

"Eh, dear! Eh, dear!" ejaculated Mr. Boldero. "I fear it's
been a sad business for ye, Mrs. Scales. Not since 'seventy!"
He sighed. "You must take it as well as you can. I'm not one
as talks much, but I sympathize with you. I do that! I wish
my wife had been here to receive you."

Tears came into Sophia's eyes.

"Nay, nay!" he said. "You must bear up now!"

"It's you that make me cry," said Sophia, gratefully. "You
were very good to take him in. It must have been exceedingly
trying for you."

"Oh," he protested, "you mustn't talk like that. I couldn't
leave a Boldero on the pavement, and an old man at that!
. . . Oh, to think that if he'd only managed to please his
uncle he might ha' been one of the richest men in Lancashire.
But then there'd ha' been no Boldero Institute at Strange-
ways!" he added.

They both sat silent a moment.

"Will you come now? Or will you wait a bit?" asked Mr.
Boldero, gently. "Just as you wish. I'm sorry as my wife's
away, that I am!"

"I'll come now," said Sophia, firmly. But she was stricken.

He conducted her up a short, dark flight of stairs, which
gave on a passage, and at the end of the passage was a door
ajar. He pushed the door open.

"I'll leave you for a moment," he said, always in the same

very restrained tone. "You'll find me downstairs, there, if you want me." And he moved away with hushed, deliberate tread.

Sophia went into the room, of which the white blind was drawn. She appreciated Mr. Boldero's consideration in leaving her. She was trembling. But when she saw, in the pale gloom, the face of an aged man peeping out from under a white sheet on a naked mattress, she started back, trembling no more—rather transfixed into an absolute rigidity. That was no conventional, expected shock that she had received. It was a genuine unforeseen shock, the most violent that she had ever had. In her mind she had not pictured Gerald as a very old man. She knew that he was old; she had said to herself that he must be very old, well over seventy. But she had not pictured him. This face on the bed was painfully, pitiably old. A withered face, with the shiny skin all drawn into wrinkles! The stretched skin under the jaw was like the skin of a plucked fowl. The cheek-bones stood up, and below them were deep hollows, almost like egg-cups. A short, scraggy white beard covered the lower part of the face. The hair was scanty, irregular, and quite white; a little white hair grew in the ears. The shut mouth obviously hid toothless gums, for the lips were sucked in. The eyelids were as if pasted down over the eyes, fitting them like kid. All the skin was extremely pallid; it seemed brittle. The body, whose outlines were clear under the sheet, was very small, thin, shrunk, pitiable as the face. And on the face was a general expression of final fatigue, of tragic and acute exhaustion; such as made Sophia pleased that the fatigue and exhaustion had been assuaged in rest, while all the time she kept thinking to herself horribly: "Oh! how tired he must have been!"

Sophia then experienced a pure and primitive emotion, uncoloured by any moral or religious quality. She was not sorry that Gerald had wasted his life, nor that he was a shame to his years and to her. The manner of his life was of no importance. What affected her was that he had once been young, and that he had grown old, and was now dead. That was all. Youth and vigour had come to that. Youth and vigour always came to that. Everything came to that. He had ill-treated her; he had abandoned her; he had been a devious rascal; but how trivial were such accusations against him! The whole of her huge and bitter grievance against him fell to pieces and crumbled. She saw him young, and proud, and strong, as for instance when he had kissed her lying on the bed in that London hotel—she forgot the name—in 1866; and now he was old, and worn, and horrible, and dead. It was the riddle of life that was puzzling and killing her. By the corner of her eye, reflected in the mirror of a wardrobe near the bed, she glimpsed a tall, forlorn woman, who had once been young and now was old; who had once exulted in abundant strength, and trodden proudly on the neck of circumstance, and now was old. He and she had once loved and burned and quarrelled in the glittering and scornful pride of youth. But time had worn them out. "Yet a little while," she thought, "and I shall be lying on a bed like that! And what shall I have lived for? What is the meaning of it?" The riddle of life itself was killing her, and she seemed to drown in a sea of inexpressible sorrow.

Her memory wandered hopelessly among those past years. She saw Chirac with his wistful smile. She saw him whipped over the roof of the Gare du Nord at the tail of a balloon. She saw old Niepce. She felt his lecherous arm round her. She was as old now as Niepce had been then. Could she excite lust now? Ah! the irony of such a question! To be young and seductive, to be able to kindle a man's eye—that seemed to her the sole thing desirable. Once she had been so! . . . Niepce must certainly have been dead for years. Niepce, the obstinate and hopeful voluptuary, was nothing but a few bones in a coffin now!

She was acquainted with affliction in that hour. All that she had previously suffered sank into insignificance by the side of that suffering.

She turned to the veiled window and idly pulled the blind and looked out. Huge red and yellow cars were swimming in thunder along Deansgate; lorries jolted and rattled; the people of Manchester hurried along the pavements, apparently unconscious that all their doings were vain. Yesterday he too had been in Deansgate, hungry for life, hating the idea of death! What a figure he must have made! Her heart dissolved in pity for him. She dropped the blind.

"My life has been too terrible!" she thought. "I wish I was dead. I have been through too much. It is monstrous, and I cannot stand it. I do not want to die, but I wish I was dead."

There was a discreet knock on the door.

"Come in," she said, in a calm, resigned, cheerful voice.

The sound had recalled her with the swiftness of a miracle to the unconquerable dignity of human pride.

Mr. Till Boldero entered.

"I should like you to come downstairs and drink a cup of tea," he said. He was a marvel of tact and good nature. "My wife is unfortunately not here, and the house is rather at sixes and sevens; but I have sent out for some tea."

She followed him downstairs into the parlour. He poured out a cup of tea.

"I was forgetting," she said. "I am forbidden tea. I mustn't drink it."

She looked at the cup, tremendously tempted. She longed for tea. An occasional transgression could not harm her. But no! She would not drink it.

"Then what can I get you?"

"If I could have just milk and water," she said meekly.

Mr. Boldero emptied the cup into the slop basin, and began to fill it again.

"Did he tell you anything?" she asked, after a considerable silence.

"Nothing," said Mr. Boldero in his low, soothing tones. "Nothing except that he had come from Liverpool. Judging from his shoes I should say he must have walked a good bit of the way."

"At his age!" murmured Sophia, touched.

"Yes," sighed Mr. Boldero. "He must have been in great straits. You know, he could scarcely talk at all. By the way, here are his clothes. I have had them put aside."

Sophia saw a small pile of clothes on a chair. She examined the suit, which was still damp, and its woeful shabbiness pained her. The linen collar was nearly black, its stud of bone. As for the boots, she had noticed such boots on the feet of tramps. She wept now. These were the clothes of him who had once been a dandy living at the rate of fifty pounds a week.

"No luggage or anything, of course?" she muttered.

"No," said Mr. Boldero. "In the pockets there was nothing whatever but this."

He went to the mantelpiece and picked up a cheap, cracked letter case, which Sophia opened. In it were a visiting card— "Senorita Clemenzia Borja"—and a bill-head of the Hotel of the Holy Spirit, Concepcion del Uruguay, on the back of which a lot of figures had been scrawled.

"One would suppose," said Mr. Boldero, "that he had come from South America."

"Nothing else?"

"Nothing."

Gerald's soul had not been compelled to abandon much in the haste of its flight.

A servant announced that Mrs. Scales's friends were waiting for her outside in the motor-car. Sophia glanced at Mr. Till Boldero with an exacerbated anxiety on her face.

"Surely they don't expect me to go back with them to-night!" she said. "And look at all there is to be done!"

Mr. Till Boldero's kindness was then redoubled. "You can do nothing for *him* now," he said. "Tell me your wishes about the funeral. I will arrange everything. Go back to your sister to-night. She will be nervous about you. And return to-morrow or the day after. . . . No! It's no trouble, I assure you!"

She yielded.

Thus towards eight o'clock, when Sophia had eaten a little under Mr. Boldero's superintendence, and the pawnshop was shut up, the motor-car started again for Bursley, Lily Holl being beside her lover and Sophia alone in the body of the car. Sophia had told them nothing of the nature of her mission. She was incapable of talking to them. They saw that she was in a condition of serious mental disturbance. Under cover of the noise of the car, Lily said to Dick that she was sure Mrs. Scales was ill, and Dick, putting his lips together, replied that he meant to be in King Street at nine-thirty at the latest. From time to time Lily surreptitiously glanced at Sophia—a glance of apprehensive inspection, or smiled at her silently; and Sophia vaguely responded to the smile.

In half an hour they had escaped from the ring of Manchester and were on the county roads of Cheshire, polished, flat, sinuous. It was the season of the year when there is no night—only daylight and twilight; When the last silver of dusk remains obstinately visible for hours. And in the open country, under the melancholy arch of evening, the sadness of the earth seemed to possess Sophia anew. Only then did she realize the intensity of the ordeal through which she was passing.

To the south of Congleton one of the tyres softened, immediately after Dick had lighted his lamps. He stopped the car and got down again. They were two miles from Astbury, the nearest village. He had just, with the resignation of experience, reached for the tool-bag, when Lily exclaimed: "Is she asleep, or what?" Sophia was not asleep, but she was apparently not conscious.

It was a difficult and a trying situation for two lovers. Their voices changed momentarily to the tone of alarm and consternation, and then grew firm again. Sophia showed life but not reason. Lily could feel the poor old lady's heart.

"Well, there's nothing for it!" said Dick, briefly, when all their efforts failed to rouse her.

"What—shall you do?"

"Go straight home as quick as I can on three tyres. We must get her over to this side, and you must hold her. Like that we shall keep the weight off the other side."

He pitched back the tool-bag into its box. Lily admired his decision.

It was in this order, no longer under the spell of the changing beauty of nocturnal landscapes, that they finished the journey. Constance had opened the door before the car came to a stop in the gloom of King Street. The young people considered that she bore the shock well, though the carrying into the house of Sophia's inert, twitching body, with its hat forlornly awry, was a sight to harrow a soul sturdier than Constance.

When that was done, Dick said curtly: "I'm off. You stay here, of course."

"Where are you going?" asked Lily.

"Doctor!" snapped Dick, hobbling rapidly down the steps.

iv

The extraordinary violence of the turn in affairs was what chiefly struck Constance, though it did not overwhelm her. Less than twelve hours before—nay, scarcely six hours before—she and Sophia had been living their placid and monotonous existence, undisturbed by anything worse than the indisposition or death of dogs, or the perversity of a servant. And now, the menacing Gerald Scales having reappeared, Sophia's form lay mysterious and affrightening on the sofa; and she and Lily Holl, a girl whom she had not met till that day, were staring at Sophia side by side, intimately sharing the same alarm. Constance rose to the crisis. She no longer had Sophia's energy and decisive peremptoriness to depend on, and the Baines in her was awakened. All her daily troubles sank away to their proper scale of unimportance. Neither the young woman nor the old one knew what to do. They could loosen clothes, vainly offer restoratives to the smitten mouth: that was all. Sophia was not unconscious, as could be judged from her eyes; but she could not speak, nor make signs; her body was frequently convulsed. So the two women waited, and the servant waited in the background. The sight of Sophia had effected an astonishing transformation in Maud. Maud was a changed girl. Constance could not recognize, in her eager deferential anxiety to be of use, the pert naughtiness of the minx. She was altered as a wanton of the middle ages would have been altered by some miraculous visitation. It might have been the turning-point in Maud's career!

Doctor Stirling arrived in less than ten minutes. Dick Povey had had the wit to look for him at the Federation meeting in the Town Hall. And the advent of the doctor and Dick, noisily, at breakneck speed in the car, provided a second sensation. The doctor inquired quickly what had occurred. Nobody could tell him anything. Constance had already confided to Lily Holl the reason of the visit to Manchester; but that was the extent of her knowledge. Not a single person in Bursley, except Sophia, knew what had happened in Manchester. But Constance conjectured that Gerald Scales was dead—or Sophia would never have returned so soon. Then the doctor suggested that on the contrary Gerald Scales might be out of danger. And all then pictured to themselves this troubling Gerald Scales, this dark and sinister husband that had caused such a violent upheaval.

Meanwhile the doctor was at work. He sent Dick Povey to knock up Critchlow's, if the shop should be closed, and obtain a drug. Then, after a time, he lifted Sophia, just as she was, like a bundle on his shoulder, and carried her single-handed upstairs to the second floor. He had recently been giving a course of instruction to enthusiasts of the St. John's Ambulance Association in Bursley. The feat had an air of the superhuman. Above all else it remained printed on Constance's mind: the burly doctor treading delicately and carefully on the crooked, creaking stairs, his precautions against damaging Sophia by brusque contacts, his stumble at the two steps in the middle of the corridor; Sophia's horribly limp head and loosened hair; and then the tender placing of her on the bed, and the doctor's long breath and flourish of his large handkerchief, all that under the crude lights and shadows of gas jets! The doctor was nonplussed. Constance gave him a second-hand account of Sophia's original attack in Paris, roughly as she had heard it from Sophia. He at once said that it could not have been what the French doctor had said it was. Constance shrugged her shoulders. She was not surprised. For her there was necessarily something of the charlatan about a French doctor. She said she only knew what Sophia had told her. After a time Dr. Stirling determined to try electricity, and Dick Povey drove him up to the surgery to fetch his apparatus. The women were left alone again. Constance was very deeply impressed by Lily Holl's sensible, sympathetic attitude. "Whatever I should have done without Miss Lily I don't know!" she used to exclaim afterwards. Even Maud was beyond praise. It seemed to be the middle of the night when Dr. Stirling came back, but it was barely eleven o'clock, and people were only just returning from Hanbridge Theatre and Hanbridge Music Hall. The use of the electrical apparatus was a dead spectacle. Sophia's inertness under it was agonizing. They waited, as it were, breathless for the result. And there was no result. Both injections and electricity had entirely failed to influence the paralysis of Sophia's mouth and throat. Everything had failed. "Nothing to do but wait a bit!" said the doctor quietly. They waited in the chamber. Sophia seemed to be in a kind of coma. The distortion of her handsome face was more marked as time passed. The doctor spoke now and then in a low voice. He said that the attack had ultimately been determined by cold produced by rapid motion in the automobile. Dick Povey whispered that he must run over to Hanbridge and let Lily's parents know that there was no cause for alarm on her account, and that he would return at once. He was very devoted. On the landing outside the bedroom, the doctor murmured to him: "U. P." And Dick nodded. They were great friends.

At intervals the doctor, who never knew when he was beaten, essayed new methods of dealing with Sophia's case. New symptoms followed. It was half-past twelve when, after gazing with prolonged intensity at the patient, and after having tested her mouth and heart, he rose slowly and looked at Constance.

"It's over?" said Constance.

And he very slightly moved his head. "Come downstairs,

please," he enjoined her, in a pause that ensued. Constance was amazingly courageous. The doctor was very solemn and very kind; Constance had never before seen him to such heroic advantage. He led her with infinite gentleness out of the room. There was nothing to stay for; Sophia had gone. Constance wanted to stay by Sophia's body; but it was the rule that the stricken should be led away, the doctor observed this classic rule, and Constance felt that he was right and that she must obey. Lily Holl followed. The servant, learning the truth by the intuition accorded to primitive natures, burst into loud sobs, yelling that Sophia had been the most excellent mistress that servant ever had. The doctor angrily told her not to stand blubbering there, but to go into her kitchen and shut the door if she couldn't control herself. All his accumulated nervous agitation was discharged on Maud like a thunderclap. Constance continued to behave wonderfully. She was the admiration of the doctor and Lily Holl. Then Dick Povey came back. It was settled that Lily should pass the night with Constance. At last the doctor and Dick departed together, the doctor undertaking the mortuary arrangements. Maud was hunted to bed.

Early in the morning Constance rose up from her own bed. It was five o'clock, and there had been daylight for two hours already. She moved noiselessly and peeped over the foot of the bed at the sofa. Lily was quietly asleep there, breathing with the softness of a child. Lily would have deemed that she was a very mature woman, who had seen life and much of it. Yet to Constance her face and attitude had the exquisite quality of a child's. She was not precisely a pretty girl, but her features, the candid expression of her disposition, produced an impression that was akin to that of beauty. Her abandonment was complete. She had gone through the night unscathed, and was now renewing herself in calm, oblivious sleep. Her ingenuous girlishness was apparent then. It seemed as if all her wise and sweet behaviour of the evening could have been nothing but so many imitative gestures. It seemed impossible that a being so young and fresh could have really experienced the mood of which her gestures had been the expression. Her strong virginal simplicity made Constance vaguely sad for her.

Creeping out of the room, Constance climbed to the second floor in her dressing-gown, and entered the other chamber. She was obliged to look again upon Sophia's body. Incredible swiftness of calamity! Who could have foreseen it? Constance was less desolated than numbed. She was as yet only touching the fringe of her bereavement. She had not begun to think of herself. She was drenched, as she gazed at Sophia's body, not by pity for herself, but by compassion for the immense disaster of her sister's life. She perceived fully now for the first time the greatness of that disaster. Sophia's charm and Sophia's beauty —what profit had they been to their owner? She saw pictures of Sophia's career, distorted and grotesque images formed in her untravelled mind from Sophia's own rare and compressed recitals. What a career! A brief passion, and then nearly thirty years in a boarding-house! And Sophia had never had a child; had never known either the joy or the pain of maternity. She had never even had a true home till, in all her sterile splendour, she came to Bursley. And she had ended—thus! This was the piteous, ignominious end of Sophia's wondrous gifts of body and soul. Hers had not been a life at all. And the reason? It is strange how fate persists in justifying the harsh generalizations of Puritan morals, of the morals in which Constance had been brought up by her stern parents! Sophia had sinned. It was therefore inevitable that she should suffer. An adventure such as she had in wicked and capricious pride undertaken with Gerald Scales, could not conclude otherwise than it had concluded. It could have brought nothing but evil. There was no getting away from these verities, thought Constance. And she was to be excused for thinking that all modern progress and cleverness was as naught, and that the world would be forced to return upon its steps and start again in the path which it had left.

Up to within a few days of her death people had been wont to remark that Mrs. Scales looked as young as ever, and that she was as bright and as energetic as ever. And truly, regarding Sophia from a little distance—that handsome oval, that erect carriage of a slim body, that challenging eye!—no one would have said that she was in her sixtieth year. But look at her now, with her twisted face, her sightless orbs, her worn skin—she did not seem sixty, but seventy! She was like something used, exhausted, and thrown aside! Yes, Constance's heart melted in an anguished pity for that stormy creature. And mingled with the pity was a stern recognition of the handiwork of divine justice. To Constance's lips came the same phrase as had come to the lips of Samuel Povey on a different occasion: God is not mocked! The ideas of her parents and her grandparents had survived intact in Constance. It is true that Constance's father would have shuddered in Heaven could he have seen Constance solitarily playing cards of a night. But in spite of cards, and of a son who never went to chapel, Constance, under the various influences of destiny, had remained essentially what her father had been. Not in her was the force of evolution manifest. There are thousands such.

Lily, awake, and reclothed with that unreal mien of a grown and comprehending woman, stepped quietly into the room, searching for the poor old thing, Constance. The layer-out had come.

By the first post was delivered a letter addressed to Sophia by Mr. Till Boldero. From its contents the death of Gerald Scales was clear. There seemed then to be nothing else for Constance to do. What had to be done was done for her. And stronger wills than hers put her to bed. Cyril was telegraphed for. Mr. Critchlow called, Mrs. Critchlow following—a fussy infliction, but useful in certain matters. Mr. Critchlow was not allowed to see Constance. She could hear his high grating voice in the corridor. She had to lie calm, and the sudden tranquillity seemed strange after the feverish violence of the night. Only twenty-four hours since, and she had been worrying about the death of a dog! With a body crying for sleep, she dozed off, thoughts of the mystery of life merging into the incoherence of dreams.

The news was abroad in the Square before nine o'clock. There were persons who had witnessed the arrival of the motor-car, and the transfer of Sophia to the house. Untruthful rumours had spread as to the manner of Gerald Scales's death. Some said that he had dramatically committed suicide. But the town, though titillated, was not moved as it would have been moved by a similar event twenty years, or even ten years earlier. Times had changed in Bursley. Bursley was more sophisticated than in the old days.

Constance was afraid lest Cyril, despite the seriousness of the occasion, might exhibit his customary tardiness in coming. She had long since learnt not to rely upon him. But he came the same evening. His behaviour was in every way perfect. He showed quiet but genuine grief for the death of his aunt, and he was a model of consideraton for his mother. Further, he at once assumed charge of all the arrangements, in regard both to Sophia and to her husband. Constance was surprised at the ease which he displayed in the conduct of practical affairs, and the assurance with which he gave orders. She had never seen him direct anything before. He said, indeed, that he had never directed anything before, but that there appeared to him to be no difficulties. Whereas Constance had figured a tiresome series of varied complications. As to the burial of Sophia, Cyril was vigorously in favour of an absolutely private funeral; that is to say, a funeral at which none but himself should be present. He seemed to have a passionate objection to any sort of parade. Constance agreed with him. But she said that it would be impossible not to invite Mr. Critchlow, Sophia's trustee, and that if Mr. Critchlow were invited certain others must be invited. Cyril asked: "Why impossible?" Constance said: "Because it *would* be impossible. Because Mr. Critchlow would be hurt." Cyril asked: "What does it matter if he is hurt?" and suggested that Mr. Critchlow would get over his damage. Constance grew more serious. The discussion threatened to be warm. Suddenly Cyril yielded. "All right, Mrs. Plover, all right! It shall be exactly as you choose," he said, in a gentle, humouring tone. He had not called her "Mrs. Plover" for years. She thought the hour badly chosen for verbal pleasantry, but he was so kind that she made no complaint. Thus there were six people at Sophia's funeral, including Mr. Critchlow. No refreshments were offered. The mourners separated at the church. When both funerals were accomplished Cyril sat down and played the harmonium softly, and said that it had kept well in tune. He was extraordinarily soothing.

He had now reached the age of thirty-three. His habits were as industrious as ever, his preoccupation with his art as keen. But he had achieved no fame, no success. He earned nothing, living in comfort on an allowance from his mother. He seldom spoke of his plans and never of his hopes. He had in fact settled down into a dilletante, having learnt gently to scorn the triumphs which he lacked the force to win. He imagined that industry and a regular existence were sufficient justification in themselves for any man's life. Constance had dropped the habit of expecting him to astound the world. He was rather grave and precise in manner, courteous and tepid, with a touch of condescension towards his environment; as though he were continually permitting the perspicacious to discern that he had nothing to learn—if the truth were known! His humour had assumed a modified form. He often smiled to himself. He was unexceptionable.

On the day after Sophia's funeral he set to work to design a simple stone for his aunt's tomb. He said he could not tolerate the ordinary gravestone, which always looked, to him, as if the wind might blow it over, thus negativing the idea of solidity. His mother did not in the least understand him. She thought the lettering of his tombstone affected and finicking. But she let it pass without comment, being secretly very flattered that he should have deigned to design a stone at all.

Sophia had left all her money to Cyril, and had made him the sole executor of her will. This arrangement had been agreed with Constance. The sisters thought it was the best plan. Cyril ignored Mr. Critchlow entirely, and went to a young lawyer at Hanbridge, a friend of his and of Matthew Peel-Swynnerton's. Mr. Critchlow, aged and unaccustomed to interference, had to render accounts of his trusteeship to this young man, and was incensed. The estate was proved at over thirty-five thousand pounds. In the main, Sophia had been careful, and had even been parsimonious. She had often told Constance that they ought to spend money much more freely, and she had had a few brief fits of extravagance. But the habit of stern thrift, begun in 1870 and practised without any intermission till she came to England in 1897, had been too strong for her theories. The squandering of money pained her. And she could not, in her age, devise expensive tastes.

Cyril showed no emotion whatever on learning himself the inheritor of thirty-five thousand pounds. He did not seem to care. He spoke of the sum as a millionaire might have spoken of it. In justice to him it is to be said that he cared nothing for wealth, except in so far as wealth could gratify his eye and ear trained to artistic voluptuousness. But, for his mother's sake, and for the sake of Bursley, he might have affected a little satisfaction. His mother was somewhat hurt. His behaviour caused her to revert in meditation again and again to the futility of Sophia's career, and the waste of her attributes. She had grown old and hard in joyless years in order to amass this money which Cyril would spend coldly and ungratefully, never thinking of the immense effort and endless sacrifice which had gone to its collection. He would spend it as carelessly as though he had picked it up in the street. As the days went by and Constance realized her own grief, she also realized more and more the completeness of the tragedy of Sophia's life. Headstrong Sophia had deceived her mother, and for the deception had paid with thirty years of melancholy and the entire frustration of her proper destiny.

After haunting Bursley for a fortnight in elegant black, Cyril said, without any warning, one night: "I must go the day after to-morrow, mater." And he told her of a journey to Hungary which he had long since definitely planned with Matthew Peel-Swynnerton, and which could not be postponed, as it comprised "business." He had hitherto breathed no word of this. He was as secretive as ever. As to her holiday, he suggested that she should arrange to go away with the Holls and Dick Povey. He approved of Lily Holl and of Dick Povey. Of Dick Povey he said: "He's one of the most remarkable chaps in the Five Towns." And he had the air of having made Dick's reputation. Constance, knowing there was no appeal, accepted the sentence of loneliness. Her health was singularly good.

When he was gone she said to herself: "Scarcely a fortnight and Sophia was here at this table!" She would remember every now and then, with a faint shock, that poor, proud, masterful Sophia was dead.

CHAPTER V

End of Constance

When, on a June afternoon about twelve months later, Lily Holl walked into Mrs. Povey's drawing-room overlooking the Square, she found a calm, somewhat optimistic old lady—older than her years—which were little more than sixty—whose chief enemies were sciatica and rheumatism. The sciatica was a dear enemy of long standing, always affectionately referred to by the forgiving Constance as "*my* sciatica"; the rheumatism was a new-comer, unprivileged, spoken of by its victim apprehensively and yet disdainfully as "this *rheumatism*." Constance was now very stout. She sat in a low easy-chair between the oval table and the window, arrayed in black silk. As the girl

Lily came in, Constance lifted her head with a bland smile, and Lily kissed her, contentedly. Lily knew that she was a welcome visitor. These two had become as intimate as the difference between their ages would permit; of the two, Constance was the more frank. Lily as well as Constance was in mourning. A few months previously her aged grandfather, "Holl, the grocer," had died. The second of his two sons, Lily's father, had then left the business established by the brothers at Hanbridge in order to manage, for a time, the parent business in St. Luke's Square. Alderman Holl's death had delayed Lily's marriage. Lily took tea with Constance, or at any rate paid a call, four or five times a week. She listened to Constance.

Everybody considered that Constance had "come splendidly through" the dreadful affair of Sophia's death. Indeed, it was observed that she was more philosophic, more cheerful, more sweet, than she had been for many years. The truth was that, though her bereavement had been the cause of a most genuine and durable sorrow, it had been a relief to her. When Constance was over fifty, the energetic and masterful Sophia had burst in upon her lethargic tranquillity and very seriously disturbed the flow of old habits. Certainly Constance had fought Sophia on the main point, and won; but on a hundred minor points she had either lost or had not fought. Sophia had been "too much" for Constance, and it had been only by a wearying expenditure of nervous force that Constance had succeeded in holding a small part of her own against the unconscious domination of Sophia. The death of Mrs. Scales had put an end to all the strain, and Constance had been once again mistress in Constance's house. Constance would never have admitted these facts, even to herself; and no one would ever have dared to suggest them to her. For with all her temperamental mildness she had her formidable side.

She was slipping a photograph into a plush-covered photograph album.

"More photographs?" Lily questioned. She had almost exactly the same benignant smile that Constance had. She seemed to be the personification of gentleness—one of those feather-beds that some capricious men occasionally have the luck to marry. She was capable, with a touch of honest, simple stupidity. All her character was displayed in the tone in which she said: "More photographs?" It showed an eager responsive sympathy with Constance's cult for photographs, also a slight

personal fondness for photographs, also a dim perception that
a cult for photographs might be carried to the ridiculous, and
a kind desire to hide all trace of this perception. The voice was
thin, and matched the pale complexion of her delicate face.

Constance's eyes had a quizzical gleam behind her spectacles
as she silently held up the photograph for Lily's inspection.

Lily, sitting down, lowered the corners of her soft lips when
she beheld the photograph, and nodded her head several times,
scarce perceptibly.

"Her ladyship has just given it to me," whispered Constance.

"Indeed!" said Lily, with an extraordinary accent.

"Her ladyship" was the last and best of Constance's servants, a really excellent creature of thirty, who had known misfortune, and who must assuredly have been sent to Constance
by the old watchful Providence. They "got on together" nearly
perfectly. Her name was Mary. After ten years of turmoil
Constance in the matter of servants was now at rest.

"Yes," said Constance. "She's named it to me several times
—about having her photograph taken, and last week I let her
go. I told you, didn't I? I always consider her in every way,
all her little fancies and everything. And the copies came to-
day. I wouldn't hurt her feelings for anything. You may be
sure she'll take a look into the album next time she cleans the
room."

Constance and Lily exchanged a glance agreeing that Constance had affably stretched a point in deciding to put the photograph of a servant between the same covers with photographs
of her family and friends. It was doubtful whether such a thing
had ever been done before.

One photograph usually leads to another, and one photograph album to another photograph album.

"Pass me that album on the second shelf of the Canterbury,
my dear," said Constance.

Lily rose vivaciously, as though to see the album on the second shelf of the Canterbury had been the ambition of her life.

They sat side by side at the table, Lily turning over the
pages. Constance, for all her vast bulk, continually made little
nervous movements. Occasionally she would sniff and occasionally a mysterious noise would occur in her chest; she always
pretended that this noise was a cough, and would support the
pretence by emitting a real cough immediately after it.

"Why!" exclaimed Lily. "Have I seen that before?"

"I don't know, my dear," said Constance. "*Have* you?"

It was a photograph of Sophia taken a few years previously by "a very nice gentleman," whose acquaintance the sisters had made during a holiday at Harrogate. It portrayed Sophia on a knoll, fronting the weather.

"It's Mrs. Scales to the life—I can see that," said Lily.

"Yes," said Constance. "Whenever there was a wind she always stood like that, and took long deep breaths of it."

This recollection of one of Sophia's habits recalled the whole woman to Constance's memory, and drew a picture of her character for the girl who had scarcely known her.

"It's not like ordinary photographs. There's something special about it," said Lily, enthusiastically. "I don't think I ever saw a photograph like that."

"I've got another copy of it in my bedroom," said Constance. "I'll give you this one."

"Oh, Mrs. Povey! I couldn't think——!"

"Yes, yes!" said Constance, removing the photograph from the page.

"Oh, *thank* you!" said Lily.

"And that reminds me," said Constance, getting up with great difficulty from her chair.

"Can I find anything for you?" Lily asked.

"No, no!" said Constance, leaving the room.

She returned in a moment with her jewel-box, a receptacle of ebony with ivory ornamentations.

"I've always meant to give you this," said Constance, taking from the box a fine cameo brooch. "I don't seem to fancy wearing it myself. And I should like to see you wearing it. It was mother's. I believe they're coming into fashion again. I don't see why you shouldn't wear it while you're in mourning. They aren't half so strict now about mourning as they used to be."

"Truly!" murmured Lily, ecstatically. They kissed. Constance seemed to breathe out benevolence, as with trembling hands she pinned the brooch at Lily's neck. She lavished the warm treasure of her heart on Lily, whom she regarded as an almost perfect girl, and who had become the idol of her latter years.

"What a magnificent old watch!" said Lily, as they delved together in the lower recesses of the box. "*And* the chain to it!"

"That was father's," said Constance. "He always used to

swear by it. When it didn't agree with the Town Hall, he used
to say: 'Then th' Town Hall's wrong.' And it's curious, the
Town Hall *was* wrong. You know the Town Hall clock has
never been a good timekeeper. I've been thinking of giving
that watch and chain to Dick."

"*Have* you?" said Lily.

"Yes. It's just as good as it was when father wore it. My
husband never would wear it. He preferred his own. He had
little fancies like that. And Cyril takes after his father." She
spoke in her "dry" tone. "I've almost decided to give it to Dick
—that is, if he behaves himself. Is he still on with this ballooning?"

Lily smiled guiltily: "Oh yes!"

"Well," said Constance, "I never heard the like! If he's been
up and come down safely, that ought to be enough for him.
I wonder you let him do it, my dear."

"But how can I stop him? I've no control over him."

"But do you mean to say that he'd still do it if you told him
seriously you didn't want him to?"

"Yes," said Lily; and added: "So I shan't tell him."

Constance nodded her head, musing over the secret nature
of men. She remembered too well the cruel obstinacy of Samuel
who had nevertheless loved her. And Dick Povey was a thousand times more bizarre than Samuel. She saw him vividly, a
little boy, whizzing down King Street on a boneshaker, and his
cap flying off. Afterwards it had been motor-cars! Now it was
balloons! She sighed. She was struck by the profound instinctive wisdom just enunciated by the girl.

"Well," she said, "I shall see. I've not made up my mind
yet. What's the young man doing this afternoon, by the way?"

"He's gone to Birmingham to try to sell two motor-lorries.
He won't be back home till late. He's coming over here to-
morrow."

It was an excellant illustration of Dick Povey's methods that
at this very moment Lily heard in the Square the sound of a
motor-car, which happened to be Dick's car. She sprang up to
look.

"Why!" she cried, flushing. "Here he is now!"

"Bless us, bless us!" muttered Constance, closing the box.

When Dick, having left his car in King Street, limped tempestuously into the drawing-room, galvanizing it by his abundant vitality into a new life, he cried joyously: "Sold my lorries

Sold my lorries!" And he explained that by a charming accident he had disposed of them to a chance buyer in Hanbridge, just before starting for Birmingham. So he had telephoned to Birmingham that the matter was "off," and then, being "at a loose end," he had come over to Bursley in search of his betrothed. At Holl's shop they had told him that she was with Mrs. Povey. Constance glanced at him, impressed by his jolly air of success. He seemed exactly like his breezy and self-confident advertisements in the *Signal*. He was absolutely pleased with himself. He triumphed over his limp—that ever-present reminder of a tragedy. Who would dream, to look at his blond, laughing, scintillating face, astonishingly young for his years, that he had once passed through such a night as that on which his father had killed his mother while he lay immovable and cursing, with a broken knee, in bed? Constance had heard all about that scene from her husband, and she paused in wonder at the contrasting hazards of existence.

Dick Povey brought his hands together with a resounding smack, and then rubbed them rapidly.

"*And* a good price, too!" he exclaimed blithely. "Mrs. Povey, I don't mind telling you that I've netted seventy pounds odd this afternoon."

Lily's eyes expressed her proud joy.

"I hope pride won't have a fall," said Constance, with a calm smile out of which peeped a hint of a rebuke. "That's what I hope. I must just go and see about tea."

"I can't stay for tea—really," said Dick.

"Of course you can," said Constance, positively. "Suppose you'd been at Birmingham? It's weeks since you stayed to tea."

"Oh, well, thanks!" Dick yielded, rather snubbed.

"Can't I save you a journey, Mrs. Povey?" Lily asked, eagerly thoughtful.

"No, thank you, my dear. There are one or two little things that need my attention." And Constance departed with her jewel-box.

Dick, having assured himself that the door was closed, assaulted Lily with a kiss.

"Been here long?" he inquired.

"About an hour and a half."

"Glad to see me?"

"Oh, Dick!" she protested.

"Old lady's in one of her humours, eh?"

"No, no! Only she was just talking about balloons—you know. She's very much up in arms."

"You ought to keep her off balloons. Balloons may be the ruin of her wedding-present to us, my child."

"Dick! How can you talk like that? . . . It's all very well saying I ought to keep her off balloons. You try to keep her off balloons when once she begins, and see!"

"What started her?"

"She said she was thinking of giving you old Mr. Baines' gold watch and chain—if you behaved yourself."

"Thank you for nothing!" said Dick. "I don't want it."

"Have you seen it?"

"Have I seen it? I should say I had seen it. She's mentioned it once or twice before."

"Oh! I didn't know."

"I don't see myself carting that thing about. I much prefer my own. What do you think of it?"

"Of course it is rather clumsy," said Lily. "But if she offered it to you, you couldn't refuse it, and you'd simply have to wear it."

"Well, then," said Dick, "I must try to behave myself just badly enough to keep off the watch, but not badly enough to upset her notions about wedding-presents."

"Poor old thing!" Lily murmured, compassionately.

Then Lily put her hand silently to her neck.

"What's that?"

"She's just given it to me."

Dick approached very near to examine the cameo brooch. "Hm!" he murmured. It was an adverse verdict. And Lily coincided with it by a lift of the eyebrows.

"And I suppose you'll have to wear that!" said Dick.

"She values it as much as anything she's got, poor old thing!" said Lily. "It belonged to her mother. And she says cameos are coming into fashion again. It really is rather good, you know."

"I wonder where she learnt that!" said Dick, drily. "I see you've been suffering from the photographs again."

"Well," said Lily, "I much prefer the photographs to helping her to play Patience. The way she cheats herself—it's too silly! I——"

She stopped. The door which had after all not been latched

was pushed open, and the antique Fossette introduced herself painfully into the room. Fossette had an affection for Dick Povey.

"Well, Methusaleh!" he greeted the animal loudly. She could scarcely wag her tail, nor shake the hair out of her dim eyes in order to look up at him. He stooped to pat her.

"That dog does smell," said Lily, bluntly.

"What do you expect? What she wants is the least dose of prussic acid. She's a burden to herself."

"It's funny that if you venture to hint to Mrs. Povey that the dog is offensive she gets quite peppery," said Lily.

"Well, that's very simple," said Dick. "Don't hint, that's all! Hold your nose and your tongue too."

"Dick, I do wish you wouldn't be so absurd."

Constance returned into the room, cutting short the conversation.

"Mrs. Fovey," said Dick, in a voice full of gratitude, "Lily has just been showing me her brooch——"

He noticed that she paid no heed to him, but passed hurriedly to the window.

"What's amiss in the Square?" Constance exclaimed. "When I was in the parlour just now I saw a man running along Wedgwood Street, and I said to myself, what's amiss?"

Dick and Lily joined her at the window.

Several people were hurrying down the Square, and then a man came running with a doctor from the market-place. All these persons disappeared from view under the window of Mrs. Povey's drawing-room, which was over part of Mrs. Critchlow's shop. As the windows of the shop projected beyond the walls of the house it was impossible, from the drawing-room window, to see the pavement in front of the shop.

"It must be something on the pavement—or in the shop!" murmured Constance.

"Oh, ma'am!" said a startled voice behind the three. It was Mary, original of the photograph, who had run unperceived into the drawing-room. "They say as Mrs. Critchlow has tried to commit suicide!"

Constance started back. Lily went towards her, with an instinctive gesture of supporting consolation.

"Maria Critchlow tried to commit suicide!" Constance muttered.

"Yes, ma'am! But they say she's not done it."

"By Jove! I'd better go and see if I can help, hadn't I?" cried Dick Povey, hobbling off, excited and speedy. "Strange, isn't it?" he exclaimed afterwards, "how I manage to come in for things? Sheer chance that I was here to-day! But it's always like that! Somehow something extraordinary is always happening where I am." And this too ministered to his satisfaction, and to his zest for life.

ii

When, in the evening, after all sorts of comings and goings, he finally returned to the old lady and the young one, in order to report the upshot, his demeanour was suitably toned to Constance's mood. The old lady had been very deeply disturbed by the tragedy, which, as she said, had passed under her very feet while she was calmly talking to Lily.

The whole truth came out in a short space of time. Mrs. Critchlow was suffering from melancholia. It appeared that for long she had been depressed by the failing trade of the shop, which was none of her fault. The state of the Square had steadily deteriorated. Even the "Vaults" were not what they once were. Four or five shops had been shut up, as it were definitely, the landlords having given up hope of discovering serious tenants. And, of those kept open, the majority were struggling desperately to make ends meet. Only Holl's and a new upstart draper, who had widely advertised his dress-making department, were really flourishing. The confectionery half of Mr. Brindley's business was disappearing. People would not go to Hanbridge for their bread or for their groceries, but they would go for their cakes. These electric trams had simply carried to Hanbridge the cream, and much of the milk, of Bursley's retail trade. There were unprincipled tradesmen in Hanbridge ready to pay the car-fares of any customer who spent a crown in their establishments. Hanbridge was the geographical centre of the Five Towns, and it was alive to its situation. Useless for Bursley to compete! If Mrs. Critchlow had been a philosopher, if she had known that geography had always made history, she would have given up her enterprise a dozen years ago. But Mrs. Critchlow was merely Maria Insull. She had seen Baines's in its magnificent prime, when

Baines's almost conferred a favour on customers in serving them. At the time when she took over the business under the wing of her husband, it was still a good business. But from that instant the tide had seemed to turn. She had fought, and she kept on fighting, stupidly. She was not aware that she was fighting against evolution, not aware that evolution had chosen her for one of its victims! She could understand that all the other shops in the Square should fail, but not that Baines's should fail! She was as industrious as ever, as good a buyer, as good a seller, as keen for novelties, as economical, as methodical! And yet the returns dropped and dropped.

She naturally had no sympathy from Charles, who now took small interest even in his own business, or what was left of it, and who was coldly disgusted at the ultimate cost of his marriage. Charles gave her no money that he could avoid giving her. The crisis had been slowly approaching for years. The assistants in the shop had said nothing, or had only whispered among themselves, but now that the crisis had flowered suddenly in an attempted self-murder, they all spoke at once, and the evidences were pieced together into a formidable proof of the strain which Mrs. Critchlow had suffered. It appeared that for many months she had been depressed and irritable, that sometimes she would sit down in the midst of work and declare, with every sign of exhaustion, that she could do no more. Then with equal briskness she would arise and force herself to labour. She did not sleep for whole nights. One assistant related how she had complained of having had no sleep whatever for four nights consecutively. She had noises in the ears and a chronic headache. Never very plump, she had grown thinner and thinner. And she was for ever taking pills: this information came from Charles's manager. She had had several outrageous quarrels with the redoubtable Charles, to the stupefaction of all who heard or saw them. . . . Mrs. Critchlow standing up to her husband! Another strange thing was that she thought the bills of several of the big Manchester firms were unpaid, when as a fact they had been paid. Even when shown the receipts she would not be convinced, though she pretended to be convinced. She would recommence the next day. All this was sufficiently disconcerting for female assistants in the drapery. But what could they do?

Then Maria Critchlow had gone a step further. She had

summoned the eldest assistant to her corner and had informed her, with all the solemnity of a confession made to assuage a conscience which has been tortured too long, that she had on many occasions been guilty of sexual irregularity with her late employer, Samuel Povey. There was no truth whatever in this accusation (which everybody, however, took care not to mention to Constance); it merely indicated, perhaps, the secret aspirations of Maria Insull, the virgin. The assistant was properly scandalized, more by the crudity of Mrs. Critchlow's language than by the alleged sin buried in the past. Goodness knows what the assistant would have done! But two hours later Maria Critchlow tried to commit suicide by stabbing herself with a pair of scissors. There was blood in the shop.

With as little delay as possible she had been driven away to the asylum. Charles Critchlow, enveloped safely in the armour of his senile egotism, had shown no emotion, and very little activity. The shop was closed. And as a general draper's it never opened again. That was the end of Baines's. Two assistants found themselves without a livelihood. The small tumble with the great.

Constance's emotion was more than pardonable; it was justified. She could not eat and Lily could not persuade her to eat. In an unhappy moment Dick Povey mentioned—he never could remember how, afterwards—the word Federation! And then Constance, from a passive figure of grief became a menace. She overwhelmed Dick Povey with her anathema of Federation, for Dick was a citizen of Hanbridge, where this detestable movement for Federation had had its birth. All the misfortunes of St. Luke's Square were due to that great, busy, grasping, unscrupulous neighbour. Had not Hanbridge done enough, without wanting to merge all the Five Towns into one town, of which of course itself would be the centre? For Constance, Hanbridge was a borough of unprincipled adventurers, bent on ruining the ancient "Mother of the Five Towns" for its own glory and aggrandizement. Let Constance hear no more of Federation! Her poor sister Sophia had been dead against Federation, and she had been quite right! All really respectable people were against it! The attempted suicide of Mrs. Critchlow sealed the fate of Federation and damned it for ever, in Constance's mind. Her hatred of the idea of it was intensified into violent animosity; insomuch that in the result she died a martyr to the cause of Bursley's municipal independence.

iii

It was on a muddy day in October that the first great battle for and against Federation was fought in Bursley. Constance was suffering severely from sciatica. She was also suffering from disgust with the modern world.

Unimaginable things had happened in the Square. For Constance, the reputation of the Square was eternally ruined. Charles Critchlow, by that strange good fortune which always put him in the right when fairly he ought to have been in the wrong, had let the Baines shop and his own shop and house to the Midland Clothiers Company, which was establishing branches throughout Staffordshire, Warwickshire, Leicestershire, and adjacent counties. He had sold his own chemist's stock and gone to live in a little house at the bottom of King Street. It is doubtful whether he would have consented to retire had not Alderman Holl died earlier in the year, thus ending a long rivalry between the old men for the patriarchate of the Square. Charles Critchlow was as free from sentiment as any man, but no man is quite free from it, and the ancient was in a position to indulge sentiment had he chosen. His business was not a source of loss, and he could still trust his skinny hands and peering eyes to make up a prescription. However, the offer of the Midland Clothiers Company tempted him, and as the undisputed "father" of the Square he left the Square in triumph.

The Midland Clothiers Company had no sense of the proprieties of trade. Their sole idea was to sell goods. Having possessed themselves of one of the finest sites in a town which, after all was said and done, comprised nearly forty thousand inhabitants, they set about to make the best of that site. They threw the two shops into one, and they caused to be constructed a sign compared to which the spacious old "Baines" sign was a postcard. They covered the entire frontage with posters of a theatrical description—coloured posters! They occupied the front page of the *Signal*, and from that pulpit they announced that winter was approaching, and that they meant to sell ten thousand overcoats at their new shop in Bursley at the price of twelve and sixpence each. The tailoring of the world was loudly and coarsely defied to equal the value of those overcoats. On the day of opening they arranged an orchestra or artillery of phonographs upon the leads over the window of that part of the shop which had been Mr. Critchlow's. They also carpeted the Square with handbills, and flew flags from their upper storeys. The immense shop proved to be full of overcoats; overcoats were shown in all the three great windows; in one window an overcoat was disposed as a receptacle for water, to prove that the Midland twelve-and-sixpenny overcoats were impermeable by rain. Overcoats flapped in the two doorways. These devices woke and drew the town, and the town found itself received by bustling male assistants very energetic and rapid, instead of by demure anæmic virgins. At moments towards evening the shop was populous with custom; the number of overcoats sold was prodigious. On another day the Midland sold trousers in a like manner, but without the phonographs. Unmistakably the Midland had shaken the Square and demonstrated that commerce was still possible to fearless enterprise.

Nevertheless the Square was not pleased. The Square was conscious of shame, of dignity departed. Constance was divided between pain and scornful wrath. For her, what the Midland had done was to desecrate a shrine. She hated those flags, and those flaring, staring posters on the honest old brick walls, and the enormous gilded sign, and the windows all filled with a monotonous repetition of the same article, and the bustling assistants. As for the phonographs, she regarded them as a grave insult; they had been within twenty feet of her drawing-room window! Twelve-and-sixpenny overcoats! It was monstrous, and equally monstrous was the gullibility of the people. How could an overcoat at twelve and sixpence be "good." She remembered the overcoats made and sold in the shop in the time of her father and her husband, overcoats of which the inconvenience was that they would not wear out! The Midland, for Constance, was not a trading concern, but something between a cheap-jack and a circus. She could scarcely bear to walk down the Square, to such a degree did the ignoble frontage of the Midland offend her eye and outrage her ancestral pride. She even said that she would give up her house.

But when, on the twenty-ninth of September, she received six months' notice, signed in Critchlow's shaky hand, to quit the house—it was wanted for the Midland's manager, the Midland having taken the premises on condition that they might eject Constance if they chose—the blow was an exceedingly severe one. She had sworn to go—but to be turned out, to be turned out of the house of her birth and out of her father's home, that was different! Her pride, injured as it was, had a great deal to support. It became necessary for her to recollect that she was a Baines. She affected magnificently not to care. But she could not refrain from telling all her acquaintances that she was being turned out of her house, and asking them what they thought of *that;* and when she met Charles Critchlow in the street she seared him with the heat of her resentment. The enterprise of finding a new house and moving into it loomed before her gigantic, terrible, the idea of it was alone sufficient to make her ill.

Meanwhile, in the matter of Federation, preparations for the pitched battle had been going forward, especially in the columns of the *Signal,* where the scribes of each one of the Five Towns had proved that all the other towns were in the clutch of unscrupulous gangs of self-seekers. After months of argument and recrimination, all the towns except Bursley were either favourable or indifferent to the prospect of becoming a part of the twelfth largest town in the United Kingdom. But in Bursley the opposition was strong, and the twelfth largest town in the United Kingdom could not spring into existence without the consent of Bursley. The United Kingdom itself was languidly interested in the possibility of suddenly being endowed with a new town of a quarter of a million inhabitants. The Five Towns were frequently mentioned in the London dailies, and London journalists would write such sentences as: 'The Five Towns, which are of course, *as everybody knows,* Hanbridge, Bursley, Knype, Longshaw, and Turnhill. . . ." This was renown at last, for the most maligned district in the country! And then a Cabinet Minister had visited the Five Towns, and assisted at an official inquiry, and stated in his hammering style that he meant personally to do everything possible to accomplish the Federation of the Five Towns: an incautious remark, which infuriated, while it flattered, the opponents of Federation in Bursley. Constance, with many other sensitive persons, asked angrily what right a Cabinet Minister had to take sides in a purely local affair. But the partiality of the official world grew flagrant. The Mayor of Bursley openly proclaimed himself a Federationist, though there was a majority on the Council against him. Even ministers of religion permitted themselves to think and to express opinions. Well might the indignant Old Guard imagine that the end of public decency had come! The Federationists were very ingenious individuals. They contrived to enrol in their ranks a vast number of leading men. Then they hired the Covered Market, and put a platform in it, and put all these leading men on the platform, and made them all speak eloquently on the advantages of moving with the times. The meeting was crowded and enthusiastic, and readers of the *Signal* next day could not but see that the battle was won in advance, and that anti-Federation was dead. In the following week, however, the anti-Federationists held in the Covered Market an exactly similar meeting (except that the display of leading men was less brilliant), and demanded of a floor of serried heads whether the old Mother of the Five Towns was prepared to put herself into the hands of a crew of highly-paid bureaucrats at Hanbridge, and was answered by a wild defiant "No," that could be heard on Duck Bank. Readers of the *Signal* next day were fain to see that the battle had not been won in advance. Bursley was lukewarm on the topics of education, slums, water, gas, electricity. But it meant to fight for that mysterious thing, its identity. Was the name of Bursley to be lost to the world? To ask the question was to give the answer.

Then dawned the day of battle, the day of the Poll, when the burgesses were to indicate plainly by means of a cross on a voting paper whether or not they wanted Federation. And on this day Constance was almost incapacitated by sciatica. It was a heroic day. The walls of the town were covered with literature, and the streets dotted with motor-cars and other vehicles at the service of the voters. The greater number of these vehicles bore large cards with the words, "Federation this time." And hundreds of men walked briskly about with circular cards tied to their lapels, as though Bursley had been a race-course, and these cards too had the words, "Federation this time." (The reference was to a light poll which had been taken several years before, when no interest had been aroused and the immature project yet defeated by a six to one majority.) All partisans of Federation sported a red ribbon; all Anti-Federationists sported a blue ribbon. The schools were closed and the Federationists displayed their characteristic lack of scruple in appropriating the children. The Federationists, with devilish skill, had hired the Bursley Town Silver

Prize Band, an organization of terrific respectability, and had set it to march playing through the town followed by wagon-ettes crammed with children, who sang:

> Vote, vote, vote for Federation,
> Don't be stupid, old and slow,
> We are sure that it will be
> Good for the communitie,
> So vote, vote, vote, and make it go.

How this performance could affect the decision of grave burgesses at the polls was not apparent; but the Anti-Federationists feared that it might, and before noon was come they had engaged two bands and had composed in committee, the following lyric in reply to the first one:

> Down, down, down, with Federation,
> As we are we'd rather stay;
> When the vote on Saturday's read
> Federation will be dead,
> Good old Bursley's sure to win the day.

They had also composed another song, entitled "Dear old Bursley," which, however, they made the fatal error of setting to the music of "Auld Lang Syne." The effect was that of a dirge, and it perhaps influenced many voters in favour of the more cheerful party. The Anti-Federationists, indeed, never regained the mean advantage filched by unscrupulous Federationists with the help of the Silver Prize Band and a few hundred infants. The odds were against the Anti-Federationists. The mayor had actually issued a letter to the inhabitants accusing the Anti-Federationists of unfair methods! This was really too much! The impudence of it knocked the breath out of its victims, and breath is very necessary in a polling contest. The Federationists, as one of their prominent opponents admitted, "had it all their own way," dominating both the streets and the walls. And when, early in the afternoon, Mr. Dick Povey sailed over the town in a balloon that was plainly decorated with the crimson of Federation, it was felt that the cause of Bursley's separate identity was for ever lost. Still, Bursley, with the willing aid of the public-houses, maintained its gaiety.

iv

Towards dusk a stout old lady, with grey hair, and a dowdy bonnet, and an expensive mantle, passed limping, very slowly, along Wedgwood Street and up the Cock Yard towards the Town Hall. Her wrinkled face had an anxious look, but it was also very determined. The busy, joyous Federationists and Anti-Federationists who knew her not saw merely a stout old lady fussing forth, and those who knew her saw merely Mrs. Povey and greeted her perfunctorily, a woman of her age and gait being rather out of place in that feverish altercation of opposed principles. But it was more than a stout old lady, it was more than Mrs. Povey, that waddled with such painful deliberation through the streets—it was a miracle.

In the morning Constance had been partially incapacitated by her sciatica; so much so, at any rate, that she had perceived the advisability of remaining on the bedroom floor instead of descending to the parlour. Therefore Mary had lighted the drawing-room fire, and Constance had ensconced herself by it, with Fossette in a basket. Lily Holl had called early, and had been very sympathetic, but rather vague. The truth was that she was concealing the imminent balloon ascent which Dick Povey, with his instinct for the picturesque, had somehow arranged, in conjunction with a well-known Manchester aeronaut, for the very day of the poll. That was one of various matters that had to be "kept from" the old lady. Lily herself was much perturbed about the balloon ascent. She had to run off and see Dick before he started, at the Football Ground at Bleakridge, and then she had to live through the hours till she should receive a telegram to the effect that Dick had come down safely or that Dick had broken his leg in coming down, or that Dick was dead. It was a trying time for Lily. She had left Constance after a brief visit, with a preoccupied unusual air, saying that as the day was a special day, she should come in again "if she could." And she did not forget to assure Constance that Federation would beyond any question whatever be handsomely beaten at the poll; for this was another matter as to which it was deemed advisable to keep the old lady "in the dark," lest the foolish old lady should worry and commit indiscretions.

After that Constance had been forgotten by the world of Bursley, which could pay small heed to sciatical old ladies confined to sofas and firesides. She was in acute pain, as Mary could see when at intervals she hovered round her. Assuredly it was one of Constance's bad days, one of those days on which she felt that the tide of life had left her stranded in utter neglect. The sound of the Bursley Town Silver Prize Band aroused her from her mournful trance of suffering. Then the high treble of children's voices startled her. She defied her sciatica, and, grimacing, went to the window. And at the first glimpse she could see that the Federation Poll was going to be a much more exciting affair than she had imagined. The great cards swinging from the wagonettes showed her that Federation was at all events still sufficiently alive to make a formidable impression on the eye and the ear. The Square was transformed by this clamour in favour of Federation; people cheered, and sang also, as the procession wound down the Square. And she could distinctly catch the tramping, martial syllables, *"Vote, vote, vote."* She was indignant. The pother, once begun, continued. Vehicles flashed frequently across the Square, most of them in the crimson livery. Little knots and processions of excited wayfarers were a recurring feature of the unaccustomed traffic, and the large majority of them flaunted the colours of Federation. Mary, after some errands of shopping, came upstairs and reported that "it was simply 'Federation' everywhere," and that Mr. Brindley, a strong Federationist, was "above a bit above himself"; further, that the interest in the poll was tremendous and universal. She said there were "crowds and crowds" round the Town Hall. Even Mary, generally a little placid and dull, had caught something of the contagious vivacity.

Constance remained at the window till dinner, and after dinner she went to it again. It was fortunate that she did not think of looking up into the sky when Dick's balloon sailed westwards; she would have guessed instantly that Dick was in that balloon, and her grievances would have been multiplied. The vast grievance of the Federation scheme weighed on her to the extremity of her power to bear. She was not a politician; she had no general ideas; she did not see the cosmic movement in large curves. She was incapable of perceiving the absurdity involved in perpetuating municipal divisions which the growth of the district had rendered artificial, vexatious, and harmful. She saw nothing but Bursley, and in Bursley nothing but the Square. She knew nothing except that the people of Bursley, who once shopped in Bursley, now shopped in Hanbridge, and that the Square was a desert infested by cheap-jacks. And there were actually people who wished to bow the neck to Hanbridge, who were ready to sacrifice the very name of Bursley to the greedy humour of that pushing Chicago! She could not understand such people. Did they know that poor Maria Critchlow was in a lunatic asylum because Hanbridge was so grasping? Ah, poor Maria was already forgotten! Did they know that, as a further indirect consequence, she, the daughter of Bursley's chief tradesman, was to be thrown out of the house in which she was born? She wished, bitterly, as she stood there at the window, watching the triumph of Federation, that she had bought the house and shop at the Mericarp sale years ago. She would have shown them, as owner, what was what! She forgot that the property which she already owned in Bursley was a continual annoyance to her, and that she was always resolving to sell it at no matter what loss.

She said to herself that she had a vote, and that if she had been "at all fit to stir out" she would certainly have voted. She said to herself that it had been her duty to vote. And then by an illusion of her wrought nerves, tightened minute by minute throughout the day, she began to fancy that her sciatica was easier. She said: "If only I could go out!" She might have a cab, or any of the parading vehicles would be glad to take her to the Town Hall, and, perhaps, as a favour, to bring her back again. But no! She dared not go out. She was afraid, really afraid that even the mild Mary might stop her. Otherwise, she could have sent Mary for a cab. And supposing that Lily returned, and caught her going out or coming in! She ought not to go out. Yet her sciatica was strangely better. It was folly to think of going out. Yet . . . ! And Lily did not come. She was rather hurt that Lily had not paid her a second visit. Lily was neglecting her. . . . She *would* go out. It was not four minutes' walk for her to the Town Hall, and she was better. And there had been no shower for a long time, and the wind was drying the mud in the roadways. Yes, she would go.

Like a thief she passed into her bedroom and put on her things; and like a thief she crept downstairs, and so, without a word to Mary, into the street. It was a desperate adventure. As soon as she was in the street she felt all her weakness, all the fatigue which the effort had already cost her. The pain returned. The streets were still wet and foul, the wind cold, and the sky menacing. She ought to go back. She ought to admit that she had been a fool to dream of the enterprise. The Town Hall seemed to be miles off, at the top of a mountain. She went forward, however, steeled to do her share in the killing of Federation. Every step caused her a gnashing of her old teeth. She chose the Cock Yard route, because if she had gone up the Square she would have had to pass Holl's shop, and Lily might have spied her.

This was the miracle that breezy politicians witnessed without being aware that it was a miracle. To have impressed them, Constance ought to have fainted before recording her vote, and made herself the centre of a crowd of gapers. But she managed, somehow, to reach home again on her own tortured feet, and an astounded and protesting Mary opened the door to her. Rain was descending. She was frightened, then, by the hardihood of her adventure, and by its atrocious results on her body. An appalling exhaustion rendered her helpless. But the deed was done.

v

The next morning, after a night which she could not have described, Constance found herself lying flat in bed, with all her limbs stretched out straight. She was conscious that her face was covered with perspiration. The bell-rope hung within a foot of her head, but she had decided that, rather than move in order to pull it, she would prefer to wait for assistance until Mary came of her own accord. Her experiences of the night had given her a dread of the slightest movement; anything was better than movement. She felt vaguely ill, with a kind of subdued pain, and she was very thirsty and somewhat cold. She knew that her left arm and leg were extraordinarily tender to the touch. When Mary at length entered, clean and fresh and pale in all her mildness, she found the mistress the colour of a duck's egg, with puffed features, and a strangely anxious expression.

"Mary," said Constance, "I feel so queer. Perhaps you'd

better run up and tell Miss Holl, and ask her to telephone for Dr. Stirling."

This was the beginning of Constance's last illness. Mary most impressively informed Miss Holl that her mistress had been out on the previous afternoon in spite of her sciatica, and Lily telephoned the fact to the Doctor. Lily then came down to take charge of Constance. But she dared not upbraid the invalid.

"Is the result out?" Constance murmured.

"Oh yes," said Lily, lightly. "There's a majority of over twelve hundred against Federation. Great excitement last night! I told you yesterday morning that Federation was bound to be beaten."

Lily spoke as though the result throughout had been a certainty; her tone to Constance indicated: "Surely you don't imagine that I should have told you untruths yesterday morning merely to cheer you up!" The truth was, however, that towards the end of the day nearly every one had believed Federation to be carried. The result had caused great surprise. Only the profoundest philosophers had not been surprised to see that the mere blind, deaf, inert forces of reaction, with faulty organization, and quite deprived of the aid of logic, had proved far stronger than all the alert enthusiasm arrayed against them. It was a notable lesson to reformers.

"Oh!" murmured Constance, startled. She was relieved; but she would have liked the majority to be smaller. Moreover, her interest in the question had lessened. It was her limbs that preoccupied her now.

"You look tired," she said feebly to Lily.

"Do I?" said Lily, shortly, hiding the fact that she had spent half the night in tending Dick Povey, who, in a sensational descent near Macclesfield, had been dragged through the tops of a row of elm trees to the detriment of an elbow-joint; the professional aeronaut had broken a leg.

Then Dr. Stirling came.

"I'm afraid my sciatica's worse, Doctor," said Constance, apologetically.

"Did you expect it to be better?" said he, gazing at her sternly. She knew then that some one had saved her the trouble of confessing her escapade.

However, her sciatica was not worse. Her sciatica had not

behaved basely. What she was suffering from was the preliminary advances of an attack of acute rheumatism. She had indeed selected the right month and weather for her escapade! Fatigued by pain, by nervous agitation, and by the immense moral and physical effort needed to carry her to the Town Hall and back, she had caught a chill, and had got her feet damp. In such a subject as herself it was enough. The doctor used only the phrase "acute rheumatism." Constance did not know that acute rheumatism was precisely the same thing as that dread disease, rheumatic fever, and she was not informed. She did not surmise for a considerable period that her case was desperately serious. The doctor explained the summoning of two nurses, and the frequency of his own visits, by saying that his chief anxiety was to minimise the fearful pain as much as possible, and that this end could only be secured by incessant watchfulness. The pain was certainly formidable. But then Constance was well habituated to formidable pain. Sciatica, at its most active, cannot be surpassed even by rheumatic fever. Constance had been in nearly continuous pain for years. Her friends, however sympathetic, could not appreciate the intensity of her torture. They were just as used to it as she was. And the monotony and particularity of her complaints (slight though the complaints were in comparison with their cause) necessarily blunted the edge of compassion. "Mrs. Povey and her sciatica again! Poor thing, she really is a little tedious!" They were apt not to realise that sciatica is even more tedious than complaints about sciatica.

She asked one day that Dick should come to see her. He came with his arm in a sling, and told her charily that he had hurt his elbow through dropping his stick and slipping downstairs.

"Lily never told me," said Constance, suspiciously.

"Oh, it's simply nothing!" said Dick. Not even the sick room could chasten him of his joy in the magnificent balloon adventure.

"I do hope you won't go running any risks!" said Constance.

"Never you fear!" said he. "I shall die in my bed."

And he was absolutely convinced that he would, and not as the result of any accident, either! The nurse would not allow him to remain in the room.

Lily suggested that Constance might like her to write to

Cyril. It was only in order to make sure of Cyril's correct address. He had gone on a tour through Italy with some friends
of whom Constance knew nothing. The address appeared to be
very uncertain; there were several addresses, *poste restante* in
various towns. Cyril had sent postcards to his mother. Dick
and Lily went to the post-office and telegraphed to foreign
parts.

Though Constance was too ill to know how ill she was,
though she had no conception of the domestic confusion caused
by her illness, her brain was often remarkably clear, and she
could reflect in long, sane meditations above the uneasy sea of
her pain. In the earlier hours of the night, after the nurses had
been changed, and Mary had gone to bed exhausted with stair-
climbing, and Lily Holl was recounting the day to Dick up at
the grocer's, and the day-nurse was already asleep, and the
night-nurse had arranged the night, then, in the faintly-lit
silence of the chamber, Constance would argue with herself for
an hour at a time. She frequently thought of Sophia. In spite
of the fact that Sophia was dead she still pitied Sophia as a
woman whose life had been wasted. This idea of Sophia's wasted
and sterile life, and of the far-reaching importance of adher-
ing to principles, recurred to her again and again. "Why did
she run away with him? If only she had not run away!" she
would repeat. And yet there had been something so fine about
Sophia! Which made Sophia's case all the more pitiable! Constance never pitied herself. She did not consider that Fate had
treated her very badly. She was not very discontented with
herself. The invincible commonsense of a sound nature prevented her, in her best moments, from feebly dissolving in self-
pity. She had lived in honesty and kindliness for a fair number of years, and she had tasted triumphant hours. She was
justly respected, she had a position, she had dignity, she was
well-off. She possessed, after all, a certain amount of quiet self-
conceit. There existed nobody to whom she would "knuckle
down," or could be asked to "knuckle down." True, she was
old! So were thousands of other people in Bursley. She was in
pain. So there were thousands of other people. With whom
would she be willing to exchange lots? She had many dissatis-
factions. But she rose superior to them. When she surveyed her
life, and life in general, she would think, with a sort of tart but
not sour cheerfulness: "*Well, that is what life is!*" Despite her

habit of complaining about domestic trifles, she was, in the essence of her character, "a great body for making the best of things." Thus she did not unduly bewail her excursion to the Town Hall to vote, which the sequel had proved to be ludicrously supererogatory. "How was I to know?" she said.

The one matter in which she had gravely to reproach herself was her indulgent spoiling of Cyril after the death of Samuel Povey. But the end of her reproaches always was: "I expect I should do the same again! And probably it wouldn't have made any difference if I hadn't spoiled him!" And she had paid tenfold for the weakness. She loved Cyril, but she had no illusions about him; she saw both sides of him. She remembered all the sadness and all the humiliations which he had caused her. Still, her affection was unimpaired. A son might be worse than Cyril was; he had admirable qualities. She did not resent his being away from England while she lay ill. "If it was serious," she said, "he would not lose a moment." And Lily and Dick were a treasure to her. In those two she really had been lucky. She took great pleasure in contemplating the splendour of the gift with which she would mark her appreciation of them at their approaching wedding. The secret attitude of both of them towards her was one of good-natured condescension, expressed in the tone in which they would say to each other, "the old lady." Perhaps they would have been startled to know that Constance lovingly looked down on both of them. She had unbounded admiration for their hearts; but she thought that Dick was a little too brusque, a little too clownish, to be quite a gentleman. And though Lily was perfectly ladylike, in Constance's opinion she lacked backbone, or grit, or independence of spirit. Further, Constance considered that the disparity of age between them was excessive. It is to be doubted whether, when all was said, Constance had such a very great deal to learn from the self-confident wisdom of these young things.

After a period of self-communion, she would sometimes fall into a shallow delirium. In all her delirium she was invariably wandering to and fro, lost, in the long underground passage leading from the scullery past the coal-cellar and the cinder-cellar to the backyard. And she was afraid of the vast-obscure of those regions, as she had been in her infancy.

It was not acute rheumatism, but a supervening pericarditis that in a few days killed her. She died in the night, alone with the night-nurse. By a curious chance the Wesleyan minister, hearing that she was seriously ill, had called on the previous day. She had not asked for him; and this pastoral visit, from a man who had always said that the heavy duties of the circuit rendered pastoral visits almost impossible, made her think. In the evening she had requested that Fossette should be brought upstairs.

Thus she was turned out of her house, but not by the Midland Clothiers Company. Old people said to one another: "Have you heard that Mrs. Povey is dead? Eh, dear me! There'll be no one left soon." These old people were bad prophets. Her friends genuinely regretted her, and forgot the tediousness of her sciatica. They tried, in their sympathetic grief, to picture to themselves all that she had been through in her life. Possibly they imagined that they succeeded in this imaginative attempt. But they did not succeed. No one but Constance could realize all that Constance had been through, and all that life had meant to her.

Cyril was not at the funeral. He arrived three days later. (As he had no interest in the love affairs of Dick and Lily, the couple were robbed of their wedding-present. The will, fifteen years old, was in Cyril's favour.) But the immortal Charles Critchlow came to the funeral, full of calm, sardonic glee, and without being asked. Though fabulously senile, he had preserved and even improved his faculty for enjoying a catastrophe. He now went to funerals with gusto, contentedly absorbed in the task of burying his friends one by one. It was he who said, in his high, trembling, rasping, deliberate voice: "It's a pity her didn't live long enough to hear as Federation is going on after all! That would ha' worritted her." (For the unscrupulous advocates of Federation had discovered a method of setting at naught the decisive result of the referendum, and that day's *Signal* was fuller than ever of Federation.)

When the short funeral procession started, Mary and the infirm Fossette (sole relic of the connection between the Baines family and Paris) were left alone in the house. The tearful servant prepared the dog's dinner and laid it before her in the customary soup-plate in the customary corner. Fossette sniffed at it, and then walked away and lay down with a dog's sigh in front of the kitchen fire. She had been deranged in her habits that day; she was conscious of neglect, due to events which passed her comprehension. And she did not like it. She was hurt, and her appetite was hurt. However, after a few minutes, she began to reconsider the matter. She glanced at the soup-plate, and, on the chance that it might after all contain some-thing worth inspection, she awkwardly balanced herself on her old legs and went to it again.

POEMS

SECTION II

In a previous section I offered the reader a small selection of the works of modern poets which, I ventured to suggest, had in them the possibility of becoming poems. Here he will find verses which time and the process of crystallisation to which I before referred have already made into poems. They are pieces that he will find in every anthology. This does not disturb me. It is partly because they are so well known that they have the quality proper to great poems. If there is anything in my notion an ode of Keats might be discovered among old papers which was intrinsically as good as the Grecian Urn, but it would not be so lovely a poem. It would not have the beauty which all its readers during a hundred years have given to the other.

But, alas, beauty does not last for ever. It has the transitoriness of all human things, for beauty is not an object, beauty is an emotion that certain objects can give man; and as men change, growing bored with one thing and desiring novelty, as in course of time they express from an object all the feeling it can give them, so beauty changes. The estheticians, seeking an absolute, will not face the fact that fashion is an element of beauty, but they are for the most part better acquainted with the products of art than with human nature; and they are more concerned with the dignity of their subject than with the humble truth that stares them in the face. It is not strange then that a poem should not have a life of indefinite duration. The verses that were instilled with the passion of all those lovers, the verses that possessed this strange power to inspire feeling, became a great poem; sometimes it really looks as though they possessed immortality; but sometimes things that one would have thought would last as long

1135

as the language in which they are written grow tired and old, and the day comes when the poem you read once is now again no more than agreeable verse. I suppose there was a time when people felt about Gray's elegy exactly as we feel now about Wordsworth's *Lucy*. In my own life I have seen Fitzgerald's Omar Khayyam lose its magic. It has become a period piece. It has a tinselly, meretricious air like a picture of Gustave Moreau. It has the Orientalism of the Victorian Age. Sometimes one can see the process going on before one's eyes. When I was young I thought no poem more beautiful than Matthew Arnold's *The Scholar Gypsy* and it is with dismay that I have seen the poetry ooze out of it. I am sadly conscious that it will not be a poem much longer but no more than scholarly and accomplished verse. Those lines that swung along with such a gallant and romantic bearing now trudge by a little wearily, like trades-unionists in a procession whose minds are no longer set on liberty and fraternity but on the tram home to tea. In two or three of the poems I have here collected I seem already to discern signs of dissolution, but they are hinted only; here and now, I think, they are poems. They have given me delight in the past and they give me delight still. How can I tell what the future will feel about them?

W. S. M.

Robert Bridges

A PASSER-BY

Whither, O splendid ship, thy white sails crowding,
   Leaning across the bosom of the urgent West,
That fearest nor sea rising, nor sky clouding,
   Whither away, fair rover, and what thy quest?
   Ah! soon, when Winter has all our vales opprest,
When skies are cold and misty, and hail is hurling,
   Wilt thóu glíde on the blue Pacific, or rest
In a summer haven asleep, thy white sails furling.

I there before thee, in the country that well thou knowest,
   Already arrived am inhaling the odorous air:
I watch thee enter unerringly where thou goest,
   And anchor queen of the strange shipping there,
   Thy sails for awnings spread, thy masts bare;
Nor is aught from the foaming reef to the snow-capped,
     grandest
   Peak, that is over the feathery palms more fair
Than thou, so upright, so stately, and still thou standest.

And yet, O splendid ship, unhailed and nameless,
   I know not if, aiming a fancy, I rightly divine
That thou hast a purpose joyful, a courage blameless,
   Thy port assured in a happier land than mine.
   But for all I have given thee, beauty enough is thine,
As thou, aslant with trim tackle and shrouding,
   From the proud nostril curve of a prow's line
In the offing scatterest foam, thy white sails crowding.

ON A DEAD CHILD

Perfect little body, without fault or stain on thee,
　With promise of strength and manhood full and fair!
　　　Though cold and stark and bare,
The bloom and the charm of life doth awhile remain on thee.

Thy mother's treasure wert thou;—alas! no longer
　To visit her heart with wondrous joy; to be
　　　Thy father's pride;—ah, he
Must gather his faith together, and his strength make stronger.

To me, as I move thee now in the last duty,
　Dost thou with a turn or gesture anon respond;
　　　Startling my fancy fond
With a chance attitude of the head, a freak of beauty.

Thy hand clasps, as 'twas wont, my finger, and holds it:
　But the grasp is the clasp of Death, heartbreaking and stiff
　　　Yet feels to my hand as if
'Twas still thy will, thy pleasure and trust that enfolds it.

So I lay thee there, thy sunken eyelids closing,—
　Go lie thou there in thy coffin, thy last little bed!—
　　　Propping thy wise, sad head,
Thy firm, pale hands across thy chest disposing.

So quiet! doth the change content thee?—Death, whither hath
　　he taken thee?
　To a world, do I think, that rights the disaster of this?
　　　The vision of which I miss,
Who weep for the body, and wish but to warm thee and
　　awaken thee?

Ah! little at best can all our hopes avail us
　To lift this sorrow, or cheer us, when in the dark,
　　　Unwilling, alone we embark,
And the things we have seen and have known and have heard
　　of, fail us.

NIGHTINGALES

Beautiful must be the mountains whence ye come,
And bright in the fruitful valleys the streams, wherefrom
　　　　Ye learn your song:
Where are those starry woods? O might I wander there,
　Among the flowers, which in that heavenly air
　　　　Bloom the year long!

Nay, barren are those mountains and spent the streams:
Our song is the voice of desire, that haunts our dreams,
　　　　A throe of the heart,
Whose pining visions dim, forbidden hopes profound,
　No dying cadence nor long sigh can sound,
　　　　For all our art.

Alone, aloud in the raptured ear of men
We pour our dark nocturnal secret; and then,
　　　　As night is withdrawn
From these sweet-springing meads and bursting boughs of
　　May,
　Dream, while the innumerable choir of day
　　　　Welcome the dawn.

Alice Meynell

RENOUNCEMENT

I must not think of thee; and, tired yet strong,
  I shun the thought that lurks in all delight—
  The thought of thee—and in the blue Heaven's height,
And in the sweetest passage of a song.

O just beyond the fairest thoughts that throng
  This breast, the thought of thee waits, hidden yet bright;
  But it must never, never come in sight;
I must stop short of thee the whole day long.

But when sleep comes to close each difficult day,
  When night gives pause to the long watch I keep,
  And all my bonds I needs must loose apart,

Must doff my will as raiment laid away,—
  With the first dream that comes with the first sleep
  I run, I run, I am gathered to thy heart.

Francis Thompson

THE HOUND OF HEAVEN

I fled Him, down the nights and down the days;
I fled Him, down the arches of the years;
I fled Him, down the labyrinthine ways
  Of my own mind; and in the mist of tears
I hid from Him, and under running laughter.
      Up vistaed hopes I sped;
      And shot, precipitated,
Adown Titanic glooms of chasmèd fears,
  From those strong Feet that followed, followed after.
      But with unhurrying chase,
      And unperturbèd pace,
  Deliberate speed, majestic instancy,
      They beat—and a Voice beat
      More instant than the Feet—
  "All things betray thee, who betrayest Me."

      I pleaded, outlaw-wise,
By many a hearted casement, curtained red,
  Trellised with intertwining charities;
(For, though I knew His love Who followèd,
      Yet was I sore adread
Lest, having Him, I must have naught beside.)
But, if one little casement parted wide,
  The gust of His approach would clash it to:
  Fear wist not to evade, as Love wist to pursue.
Across the margent of the world I fled,

1141

And troubled the gold gateways of the stars,
  Smiting for shelter on their clangèd bars;
      Fretted to dulcet jars
And silvern chatter the pale ports o' the moon.
I said to Dawn: Be sudden—to Eve: Be soon;
  With thy young skiey blossoms heap me over

      From this tremendous Lover—
Float thy vague veil about me, lest He see!
  I tempted all His servitors, but to find
My own betrayal in their constancy,
In faith to Him their fickleness to me,
  Their traitorous trueness, and their loyal deceit.
To all swift things for swiftness did I sue;
  Clung to the whistling mane of every wind.
     But whether they swept, smoothly fleet,
    The long savannahs of the blue;
      Or whether, Thunder-driven,
    They clanged his chariot 'thwart a heaven,
Plashy with flying lightnings round the spurn o' their feet:—
  Fear wist not to evade as Love wist to pursue.
      Still with unhurrying chase,
      And unperturbèd pace,
   Deliberate speed, majestic instancy,
     Came on the following Feet,
     And a Voice above their beat—
"Naught shelters thee, who wilt not shelter Me."

I sought no more that after which I strayed
     In face of man or maid;
But still within the little children's eyes
    Seems something, something that replies,
They at least are for me, surely for me!
I turned me to them very wistfully;
But just as their young eyes grew sudden fair
    With dawning answers there,
Their angel plucked them from me by the hair.
"Come then, ye other children, Nature's—share
With me" (said I) "your delicate fellowship;
   Let me greet you lip to lip,

Let me twine with you caresses,
    Wantoning
With our Lady-Mother's vagrant tresses,
    Banqueting
With her in her wind-walled palace,
    Underneath her azured daïs,
Quaffing, as your taintless way is,
    From a chalice
Lucent-weeping out of the dayspring."
    So it was done:
I in their delicate fellowship was one—
Drew the bolt of Nature's secrecies.
    I knew all the swift importings
    On the wilful face of skies;
    I knew how the clouds arise
    Spumèd of the wild sea-snortings;
        All that's born or dies
    Rose and drooped with; made them shapers
Of mine own moods, or wailful or divine;
    With them joyed and was bereaven.
    I was heavy with the even,
    When she lit her glimmering tapers
    Round the day's dead sanctities.
    I laughed in the morning's eyes.
I triumphed and I saddened with all weather,
    Heaven and I wept together,
And its sweet tears were salt with mortal mine;
Against the red throb of its sunset-heart
    I laid my own to beat,
    And share commingling heat;
But not by that, by that, was eased my human smart.
In vain my tears were wet on Heaven's grey cheek.
For ah! we know not what each other says,
    These things and I; in sound *I* speak—
Their sound is but their stir, they speak by silences.
Nature, poor stepdame, cannot slake my drouth;
    Let her, if she would owe me,
Drop yon blue bosom-veil of sky, and show me
    The breasts o' her tenderness:
Never did any milk of hers once bless
    My thirsting mouth.

Nigh and nigh draws the chase,
With unperturbèd pace,
Deliberate speed, majestic instancy;
And past those noisèd Feet
A voice comes yet more fleet—
"Lo! naught contents thee, who content'st not Me."

Naked I wait Thy love's uplifted stroke!
My harness piece by piece Thou hast hewn from me,
And smitten me to my knee;
I am defenceless utterly.
I slept, methinks, and woke,
And, slowly gazing, find me stripped in sleep.
In the rash lustihead of my young powers,
I shook the pillaring hours
And pulled my life upon me; grimed with smears,
I stand amid the dust o' the mounded years—
My mangled youth lies dead beneath the heap.
My days have crackled and gone up in smoke,
Have puffed and burst as sun-starts on a stream.
Yea, faileth now even dream
The dreamer, and the lute the lutanist;
Even the linked fantasies, in whose blossomy twist
I swung the earth a trinket at my wrist,
Are yielding; cords of all too weak account
For earth with heavy griefs so overplussed.
Ah! is Thy love indeed
A weed, albeit an amaranthine weed,
Suffering no flowers except its own to mount?
Ah! must—
Designer infinite!—
Ah! must Thou char the wood ere Thou canst limn with it?
My freshness spent its wavering shower i' the dust;
And now my heart is as a broken fount,
Wherein tear-drippings stagnate, spilt down ever
From the dank thoughts that shiver
Upon the sighful branches of my mind.
Such is; what is to be?
The pulp so bitter, how shall taste the rind?
I dimly guess what Time in mists confounds;
Yet ever and anon a trumpet sounds
From the hid battlements of Eternity;

Those shaken mists a space unsettle, then
Round the half-glimpsèd turrets slowly wash again.
      But not ever him who summoneth
      I first have seen, enwound
With glooming robes purpureal, cypress-crowned;
His name I know, and what his trumpet saith.
Whether man's heart or life it be which yields
      Thee harvest, must Thy harvest-fields
      Be dunged with rotten death?

      Now of that long pursuit
      Comes on at hand the bruit;
That Voice is round me like a bursting sea:
      "And is thy earth so marred,
      Shattered in shard on shard?
Lo, all things fly thee, for thou fliest Me!
Strange, piteous, futile thing!
Wherefore should any set thee love apart?
Seeing none but I makes much of naught" (He said),
"And human love needs human meriting:
      How hast thou merited—
Of all man's clotted clay the dingiest clot?
      Alack, thou knowest not
How little worthy of any love thou art!
Whom wilt thou find to love ignoble thee,
      Save Me, save only Me?
All which I took from thee I did but take,
      Not for thy harms,
But just that thou might'st seek it in My arms.
      All which thy child's mistake
Fancies as lost, I have stored for thee at home:
      Rise, clasp My hand, and come!"
  Halts by me that footfall:
  Is my gloom, after all,
Shade of His hand, outstretched caressingly?
  "Ah, fondest, blindest, weakest,
  I am He Whom thou seekest!
Thou dravest love from thee, who dravest Me."

THE KINGDOM OF GOD

"In no Strange Land"

O world invisible, we view thee,
O world intangible, we touch thee,
O world unknowable, we know thee,
Inapprehensible, we clutch thee!

Does the fish soar to find the ocean,
The eagle plunge to find the air—
That we ask of the stars in motion
If they have rumour of thee there?

Not where the wheeling systems darken,
And our benumbed conceiving soars!—
The drift of pinions, would we hearken,
Beats at our own clay-shuttered doors.

The angels keep their ancient places;—
Turn but a stone, and start a wing!
'Tis ye, 'tis your enstrangèd faces,
That miss the many-splendoured thing.

But (when so sad thou canst not sadder)
Cry;—and upon thy so sore loss
Shall shine the traffic of Jacob's ladder
Pitched betwixt Heaven and Charing Cross.

Yea, in the night, my Soul, my daughter,
Cry,—clinging Heaven by the hems;
And lo, Christ walking on the water
Not of Gennesareth, but Thames!

Rupert Brooke

THE SOLDIER

If I should die, think only this of me:
  That there's some corner of a foreign field
That is for ever England. There shall be
  In that rich earth a richer dust concealed;
A dust whom England bore, shaped, made aware,
  Gave, once, her flowers to love, her ways to roam,
A body of England's, breathing English air,
  Washed by the rivers, blest by suns of home.

And think, this heart, all evil shed away,
  A pulse in the eternal mind, no less
    Gives somewhere back the thoughts by England given;
Her sights and sounds; dreams happy as her days;
  And laughter, learnt of friends; and gentleness,
    In hearts at peace, under an English heaven.

THE HILL

Breathless, we flung us on the windy hill,
  Laughed in the sun, and kissed the lovely grass.
  You said, "Through glory and ecstasy we pass;
Wind, sun, and earth remain, the birds sing still,
When we are old, are old. . . ." "And when we die
  All's over that is ours; and life burns on
Through other lovers, other lips," said I,
—"Heart of my heart, our heaven is now, is won!"

"We are Earth's best, that learnt her lesson here.
Life is our cry. We have kept the faith!" we said;
   "We shall go down with unreluctant tread
Rose-crowned into the darkness!" . . . Proud we were,
And laughed, that had such brave true things to say.
—And then you suddenly cried, and turned away.

THE OLD VICARAGE, GRANTCHESTER

(*Café des Westens, Berlin, May 1912*)

Just now the lilac is in bloom,
All before my little room;
And in my flower-beds, I think,
Smile the carnation and the pink;
And down the borders, well I know,
The poppy and the pansy blow . . .
Oh! there the chestnuts, summer through,
Beside the river make for you
A tunnel of green gloom, and sleep
Deeply above; and green and deep
The stream mysterious glides beneath,
Green as a dream and deep as death.
—Oh, damn! I know it! and I know
How the May fields all golden show,
And when the day is young and sweet,
Gild gloriously the bare feet
That run to bathe . . .
                        Du lieber Gott!

Here am I, sweating, sick, and hot,
And there the shadowed waters fresh
Lean up to embrace the naked flesh.
Temperamentvoll German Jews
Drink beer around;—and *there* the dews
Are soft beneath a morn of gold.
Here tulips bloom as they are told;
Unkempt about those hedges blows
An English unofficial rose;
And there the unregulated sun
Slopes down to rest when day is done,

And wakes a vague unpunctual star,
A slippered Hesper; and there are
Meads towards Haslingfield and Coton
Where *das Betreten's* not *verboten*.

ε'ἴθε γενοίμην . . . would I were
In Grantchester, in Grantchester!—
Some, it may be, can get in touch
With Nature there, or Earth, or such.
And clever modern men have seen
A Faun a-peeping through the green,
And felt the Classics were not dead,
To glimpse a Naiad's reedy head,
Or hear the Goat-foot piping low: . . . . .
But these are things I do not know.
I only know that you may lie
Day long and watch the Cambridge sky,
And, flower-lulled in sleepy grass,
Hear the cool lapse of hours pass,
Until the centuries blend and blur
In Grantchester, in Grantchester. . . .
Still in the dawnlit waters cool
His ghostly Lordship swims his pool,
And tries the strokes, essays the tricks,
Long learnt on Hellespont, or Styx.
Dan Chaucer hears his river still
Chatter beneath a phantom mill.
Tennyson notes, with studious eye,
How Cambridge waters hurry by . . .
And in that garden, black and white,
Creep whispers through the grass all night;
And spectral dance, before the dawn,
A hundred Vicars down the lawn;
Curates, long dust, will come and go
On lissom, clerical, printless toe;
And oft between the boughs is seen
The sly shade of a Rural Dean . . .
Till, at a shiver in the skies,
Vanishing with Satanic cries,
The prim ecclesiastic rout

Leaves but a startled sleeper-out,
Grey heavens, the first bird's drowsy calls,
The falling house that never falls.

God! I will pack, and take a train,
And get me to England once again!
For England's the one land, I know,
Where men with Splendid Hearts may go;
And Cambridgeshire, of all England,
The shire for Men who Understand;
And of *that* district I prefer
The lovely hamlet Grantchester.
For Cambridge people rarely smile,
Being urban, squat, and packed with guile;
And Royston men in the far South
Are black and fierce and strange of mouth;
At Over they fling oaths at one,
And worse than oaths at Trumpington,
And Ditton girls are mean and dirty,
And there's none in Harston under thirty,
And folks in Shelford and those parts
Have twisted lips and twisted hearts,
And Barton men make Cockney rhymes,
And Coton's full of nameless crimes,
And things are done you'd not believe
At Madingley on Christmas Eve.
Strong men have run for miles and miles,
When one from Cherry Hinton smiles;
Strong men have blanched, and shot their wives,
Rather than send them to St. Ives;
Strong men have cried like babes, bydam,
To hear what happened at Babraham.
But Grantchester! ah, Grantchester!
There's peace and holy quiet there,
Great clouds along pacific skies,
And men and women with straight eyes,
Lithe children lovelier than a dream,
A bosky wood, a slumbrous stream,
And little kindly winds that creep
Round twilight corners, half asleep.

In Grantchester their skins are white;
They bathe by day, they bathe by night;
The women there do all they ought;
The men observe the Rules of Thought.
They love the Good; they worship Truth;
They laugh uproariously in youth;
(And when they get to feeling old,
They up and shoot themselves, I'm told) . . .

Ah God! to see the branches stir
Across the moon at Grantchester!
To smell the thrilling-sweet and rotten
Unforgettable, unforgotten
River-smell, and hear the breeze
Sobbing in the little trees.
Say, do the elm-clumps greatly stand
Still guardians of that holy land?
The chestnuts shade, in reverent dream,
The yet unacademic stream?
Is dawn a secret shy and cold
Anadyomene, silver-gold?
And sunset still a golden sea
From Haslingfield to Madingley?
And after, ere the night is born,
Do hares come out about the corn?
Oh, is the water sweet and cool,
Gentle and brown, above the pool?
And laughs the immortal river still
Under the mill, under the mill?
Say, is there Beauty yet to find?
And Certainty? and Quiet kind?
Deep meadows yet, for to forget
The lies, and truths, and pain? . . . oh! yet
Stands the Church clock at ten to three?
And is there honey still for tea?

HEAVEN

Fish (fly-replete, in depth of June,
Dawdling away their wat'ry noon)
Ponder deep wisdom, dark or clear,
Each secret fishy hope or fear.
Fish say, they have their Stream and Pond;
But is there anything Beyond?
This life cannot be All, they swear,
For how unpleasant, if it were!
One may not doubt that, somehow, Good
Shall come of Water and of Mud;
And, sure, the reverent eye must see
A Purpose in Liquidity.
We darkly know, by Faith we cry,
The future is not Wholly Dry.
Mud unto mud!—Death eddies near—
Not here the appointed End, not here!
But somewhere, beyond Space and Time
Is wetter water, slimier slime!
And there (they trust) there swimmith One
Who swam ere rivers were begun,
Immense, of fishy form and mind,
Squamous, omnipotent, and kind;
And under that Almighty Fin,
The littlest fish may enter in.
Oh! never fly conceals a hook,
Fish say, in the Eternal Brook,
But more than mundane weeds are there,
And mud, celestially fair;
Fat caterpillars drift around,
And Paradisal grubs are found;
Unfading moths, immortal flies,
And the worm that never dies.
And in that Heaven of all their wish,
There shall be no more land, say fish.

Walter de la Mare

AN EPITAPH

Here lies a most beautiful lady,
Light of step and heart was she;
I think she was the most beautiful lady
That ever was in the West Country.
But beauty vanishes; beauty passes;
However rare—rare it be;
And when I crumble, who will remember
This lady of the West Country?

THE THREE STRANGERS

Far are those tranquil hills,
  Dyed with fair evening's rose;
On urgent, secret errand bent,
  A traveller goes.

Approach him strangers three,
  Barefooted, cowled; their eyes
Scan the lone, hastening solitary
  With dumb surmise.

One instant in close speech
  With them he doth confer:
God-sped, he hasteneth on,
  That anxious traveller . . .

1153

I was that man—in a dream:
  And each world's night in vain
I patient wait on sleep to unveil
  Those vivid hills again.

Would that they three could know
  How yet burns on in me
Love—from one lost in Paradise—
  For their grave courtesy.

THE LITTLE SALAMANDER

To Margot

When I go free,
I think 'twill be
A night of stars and snow,
And the wild fires of frost shall light
My footsteps as I go;
Nobody—nobody will be there
With groping touch, or sight,
To see me in my bush of hair
Dance burning through the night.

ARABIA

Far are the shades of Arabia,
  Where the Princes ride at noon,
'Mid the verdurous vales and thickets,
  Under the ghost of the moon;
And so dark is that vaulted purple
  Flowers in the forest rise
And toss into blossom 'gainst the phantom stars
  Pale in the noonday skies.

Sweet is the music of Arabia
  In my heart, when out of dreams
I still in the thin clear mirk of dawn
  Descry her gliding streams;

Hear her strange lutes on the green banks
    Ring loud with the grief and delight
Of the dim-silked dark-haired Musicians
    In the brooding silence of night.

They haunt me—her lutes and her forests;
    No beauty on earth I see
But shadowed with that dreams recalls
    Her loveliness to me:
Still eyes look coldly upon me,
    Cold voices whisper and say—
"He is crazed with the spell of far Arabia,
    They have stolen his wits away."

THE LISTENERS

"Is there anybody there?" said the Traveller,
    Knocking on the moonlit door;
And his horse in the silence champed the grasses
    Of the forest's ferny floor:
And a bird flew up out of the turret,
    Above the Traveller's head:
And he smote upon the door again a second time;
    "Is there anybody there?" he said.
But no one descended to the Traveller;
    No head from the leaf-fringed sill
Leaned over and looked into his grey eyes,
    Where he stood perplexed and still.
But only a host of phantom listeners
    That dwelt in the lone house then
Stood listening in the quiet of the moonlight
    To that voice from the world of men:
Stood thronging the faint moonbeams on the dark stair,
    That goes down to the empty hall,
Hearkening in an air stirred and shaken
    By the lonely Traveller's call.
And he felt in his heart their strangeness,
    Their stillness answering his cry,
While his horse moved, cropping the dark turf,
    'Neath the starred and leafy sky;

For he suddenly smote on the door, even
    Louder, and lifted his head:—
"Tell them I came, and no one answered,
    That I kept my word," he said.
Never the least stir made the listeners,
    Though every word he spake
Fell echoing through the shadowiness of the still house
    From the one man left awake:
Ay, they heard his foot upon the stirrup,
    And the sound of iron on stone,
And how the silence surged softly backward,
    When the plunging hoofs were gone.

James Elroy Flecker

THE GOLDEN JOURNEY TO SAMARKAND
Prologue

WE WHO with songs beguile your pilgrimage
    And swear that Beauty lives though lilies die,
We Poets of the proud old lineage
    Who sing to find your hearts, we know not why,—

What shall we tell you? Tales, marvellous tales
    Of ships and stars and isles where good men rest,
Where nevermore the rose of sunset pales,
    And winds and shadows fall toward the West:

And there the world's first huge white-bearded kings
    In dim glades sleeping, murmur in their sleep,
And closer round their breasts the ivy clings,
    Cutting its pathway slow and red and deep.

II

And how beguile you? Death has no repose
    Warmer and deeper than that Orient sand
Which hides the beauty and bright faith of those
    Who made the Golden Journey to Samarkand.

And now they wait and whiten peaceably,
    Those conquerors, those poets, those so fair:
They know time comes, not only you and I,
    But the whole world shall whiten, here or there;

When those long caravans that cross the plain
    With dauntless feet and sound of silver bells
Put forth no more for glory or for gain,
    Take no more solace from the palm-girt wells.

When the great markets by the sea shut fast
    All that calm Sunday that goes on and on:
When even lovers find their peace at last,
    And Earth is but a star, that once had shone.

WAR SONG OF THE SARACENS

We are they who come faster than fate: we are they who ride
    early or late:
We storm at your ivory gate: Pale Kings of the Sunset, be-
    ware!
Not on silk nor in samet we lie, not in curtained solemnity die
Among women who chatter and cry, and children who mumble
    a prayer.
But we sleep by the ropes of the camp, and we rise with a
    shout, and we tramp
With the sun or the moon for a lamp, and the spray of the
    wind in our hair.

From the lands, where the elephants are, to the forts of Merou
    and Balghar,
Our steel we have brought and our star to shine on the ruins
    of Rum.
We have marched from the Indus to Spain, and by God we
    will go there again;
We have stood on the shore of the plain where the Waters of
    Destiny boom.
A mart of destruction we made at Jalula where men were
    afraid,
For death was a difficult trade, and the sword was a broker of
    doom;

And the Spear was a Desert Physician who cured not a few of
    ambition,
And drave not a few to perdition with medicine bitter and
    strong:

And the shield was a grief to the fool and as bright as a deso-
    late pool,
And as straight as the rock of Stamboul when their cavalry
    thundered along:
For the coward was drowned with the brave when our battle
    sheered up like a wave,
And the dead to the desert we gave, and the glory to God in
    our song.

THE OLD SHIPS

I have seen old ships sail like swans asleep
Beyond the village which men still call Tyre,
With leaden age o'ercargoed, dipping deep
For Famagusta and the hidden sun
That rings black Cyprus with a lake of fire;
And all those ships were certainly so old
Who knows how oft with squat and noisy gun,
Questing brown slaves or Syrian oranges,
The pirate Genoese
Hell-raked them till they rolled
Blood, water, fruit and corpses up the hold.
But now through friendly seas they softly run,
Painted the mid-sea blue or shore-sea green,
Still patterned with the vine and grapes in gold.

But I have seen,
Pointing her shapely shadows from the dawn
And image tumbled on a rose-swept bay,
A drowsy ship of some yet older day;
And, wonder's breath indrawn,
Thought I—who knows—who knows—but in that same
(Fished up beyond Ææa, patched up new
—Stern painted brighter blue—)
That talkative, bald-headed seaman came
(Twelve patient comrades sweating at the oar)
From Troy's doom-crimson shore,
And with great lies about his wooden horse
Set the crew laughing, and forgot his course.

It was so old a ship—who knows, who knows?
—And yet so beautiful, I watched in vain
To see the mast burst open with a rose,
And the whole deck put on its leaves again.

BRUMANA

Oh shall I never be home again?
Meadows of England shining in the rain
Spread wide your daisied lawns: your ramparts green
With briar fortify, with blossom screen
Till my far morning—and O streams that slow
And pure and deep through plains and playlands go,
For me your love and all your kingcups store,
And—dark militia of the southern shore,
Old fragrant friends—preserve me the last lines
Of that long saga which you sung me, pines,
When, lonely boy, beneath the chosen tree
I listened, with my eyes upon the sea.

O traitor pines, you sang what life has found
The falsest of fair tales.
Earth blew a far-horn prelude all around,
That native music of her forest home,
While from the sea's blue fields and syren dales
Shadows and light noon-spectres of the foam
Riding the summer gales
On aery viols plucked an idle sound.

Hearing you sing, O trees,
Hearing you murmur, "There are older seas,
That beat on vaster sands,
Where the wise snailfish move their pearly towers
To carven rocks and sculptured promont'ries,"
Hearing you whisper, "Lands
Where blaze the unimaginable flowers."

Beneath me in the valley waves the palm,
Beneath, beyond the valley, breaks the sea;
Beneath me sleep in mist and light and calm
Cities of Lebanon, dream-shadow-dim,

Where Kings of Tyre and Kings of Tyre did rule
In ancient days in endless dynasty,
And all around the snowy mountains swim
Like mighty swans afloat in heaven's pool.

But I will walk upon the wooded hill
Where stands a grove, O pines, of sister pines,
And when the downy twilight droops her wing
And no sea glimmers and no mountain shines
My heart shall listen still.
For pines are gossip pines the wide world through
And full of runic tales to sigh or sing.
'Tis ever sweet through pines to see the sky
Mantling a deeper gold or darker blue.
'Tis ever sweet to lie
On the dry carpet of the needles brown,
And though the fanciful green lizard stir
And windy odours light as thistledown
Breathe from the lavdanon and lavender,
Half to forget the wandering and pain,
Half to remember days that have gone by,
And dream and dream that I am home again!

HYALI

Στὸ Γυαλὶ, στὸ γαλἄζιο βρᾰχο

Island in blue of summer floating on,
    Little brave sister of the Sporades,
Hail and farewell! I pass, and thou art gone,
    So fast in fire the great boat beats the seas.

But slowly fade, soft Island! Ah to know
    Thy town and who the gossips of thy town,
What flowers flash in thy meadows, what winds blow
    Across thy mountain when the sun goes down.

There is thy market, where the fisher throws
    His gleaming fish that gasp in the death-bright dawn:
And there thy Prince's house, painted old rose,
    Beyond the olives, crowns its slope of lawn.

And is thy Prince so rich that he displays
　　At festal board the flesh of sheep and kine?
Or dare he—summer days are long hot days—
　　Load up with Asian snow his Coan wine?

Behind a rock, thy harbour, whence a noise
　　Of tarry sponge-boats hammered lustily:
And from that little rock thy naked boys
　　Like burning arrows shower upon the sea.

And there by the old Greek chapel—there beneath
　　A thousand poppies that each sea-wind stirs
And cyclamen, as honied and white as death,
　　Dwell deep in earth the elder islanders.

　　　　　*　　　　　*　　　　　*

Thy name I know not, Island, but *his* name
　　I know, and why so proud thy mountain stands,
And what thy happy secret, and Who came
　　Drawing his painted galley up thy sands.

For my Gods—Trident Gods who deep and pale
　　Swim in the Latmian Sound, have murmured thus:
"To such an island came with a pompous sail
　　On his first voyage young Herodotus."

Since then—tell me no tale how Romans built,
　　Saracens plundered—or that bearded lords
Rowed by to fight for Venice, and here spilt
　　Their blood across the bay that keeps their swords.

That old Greek day was all thy history:
　　For that did Ocean poise thee as a flower.
Farewell: this boat attends not such as thee:
　　Farewell: I was thy lover for an hour!

Farewell! But I who call upon thy caves
　　Am far like thee,—like thee, unknown and poor.
And yet my words are music as thy waves,
　　And like thy rocks shall down through time endure.

William Butler Yeats

DOWN BY THE SALLEY GARDENS

Down by the salley gardens my love and I did meet;
She passed the salley gardens with little snow-white feet.
She bid me take love easy, as the leaves grow on the tree;
But I, being young and foolish, with her would not agree.

In a field by the river my love and I did stand,
And on my leaning shoulder she laid her snow-white hand.
She bid me take life easy, as the grass grows on the weirs;
But I was young and foolish, and now am full of tears.

THE LAKE ISLE OF INNISFREE

I will arise and go now, and go to Innisfree,
And a small cabin build there, of clay and wattles made:
Nine bean rows will I have there, a hive for the honey bee,
And live alone in the bee-loud glade.

And I shall have some peace there, for peace comes dropping
   slow,
Dropping from the veils of the morning to where the cricket
   sings;
There midnight's all a glimmer, and noon a purple glow,
And evening full of the linnets' wings.

I will arise and go now, for always night and day
I hear lake water lapping with low sounds by the shore;
While I stand on the roadway, or on the pavements grey,
I hear it in the deep heart's core.

WHEN YOU ARE OLD

When you are old and grey and full of sleep,
And nodding by the fire, take down this book,
And slowly read and dream of the soft look
Your eyes had once and of their shadows deep.

How many loved your moments of glad grace,
And loved your beauty with love false or true;
But one man loved the pilgrim soul in you,
And loved the sorrows of your changing face.

And bending down beside the glowing bars
Murmur, a little sadly, how love fled
And paced upon the mountains overhead
And hid his face amid a crowd of stars.

TO A FRIEND WHOSE WORK HAS COME TO NOTHING

Now all the truth is out,
Be secret and take defeat
From any brazen throat,
For how can you compete,
Being honour bred, with one
Who, were it proved he lies,
Were neither shamed in his own
Nor in his neighbor's eyes?
Bred to a harder thing
Than Triumph, turn away
And like a laughing string
Whereon mad fingers play
Amid a place of stone,
Be secret and exult,
Because of all things known
That is most difficult.

THAT THE NIGHT COME

She lived in storm and strife,
Her soul had such desire
For what proud death may bring
That it could not endure
The common good of life,
But lived as 'twere a king
That packed his marriage day
With banneret and pennon,
Trumpet and kettledrum,
And the outrageous cannon,
To bundle time away
That the night come.

ESSAYS

SECTION II

THE following essays are somewhat different in character from those presented to the reader in the early part of this book. First comes Mr Lytton Strachey's *Florence Nightingale*. I know nothing more perfect in the modern literature of England. It is in the line of the great essayists of the Victorian era. It is informative, which I happen to like in this sort of writing, it has a pleasant humour, and it is written with elegance. Then I have put an essay by Mr Julian Huxley, which I have found extremely interesting, one by Professor Haldane on a subject which must be of moment to all reflective persons, and after that three by Lord Russell. A great mathematician, they say (for mathematics is a subject on which I am even less competent to speak than of any other) and a restless, nimble-witted philosopher, he writes with a lucidity that makes it easy to follow him even at his most abstruse. He is a proof that, however abstract your thought, if you know exactly what you mean you can say it in such a way that every intelligent person can understand you. Metaphysics is a subject that I can always read with pleasure, but I wish modern philosophers would take a leaf out of Lord Russell's book and learn to express themselves with distinction. The philosophers of the past did not disdain to write English with grace and whatever you think of Hobbes and Hume as philosophers you can still read their works with satisfaction for the excellence of their style. They portray themselves engagingly in their characteristic use of the language. In Lord Russell's essay entitled *A Free Man's Worship* there is a tragic beauty which I find deeply impressive. Finally, a delicate dish to set before a sated king, I have placed *A Night at Pietramela* by Mr Aldous Huxley. Here certainly is charm, and earlier on I confided to the reader (not expecting him to care one way or the other) that charm was a quality I could have enough of; but this is charm backed by an admirable education and a personality of power and originality. I think that there is no one writing in England just now who has a more comprehensive culture than Mr Huxley. His great gifts are supported by a knowledge which to anyone as ignorant as I seems encyclopedic. His attitude towards life is individual. He has humour, candour and courage. I think at present he is somewhat lacking in humanity; that is why he seems to me a better essayist than novelist; but Mr Huxley is still young. Youth when it is intelligent is apt to be ruthless, but life teaches one tolerance, and the advantage of being intelligent is that you can learn. Mr Huxley's English is cultured, but racy and vivid. It is an admirable instrument for his purposes and he uses it with the easy assurance of a craftsman accustomed to his tools. To those interested in such matters it is a great pleasure to notice his apt use of epithets. With many authors these seem to be written with a flowing, heedless pen, but with Mr Huxley you have the impression that they are chosen with deliberate and tender care. Often they come upon you with the joyful surprise of a wayside flower that you have never seen before. I have every confidence that one of these days Mr Huxley will write a very great novel.

W. S. M.

Lytton Strachey

FLORENCE NIGHTINGALE

Everyone knows the popular conception of Florence Nightingale. The saintly, self-sacrificing woman, the delicate maiden of high degree who threw aside the pleasures of a life of ease to succour the afflicted, the Lady with the Lamp, gliding through the horrors of the hospital at Scutari, and consecrating with the radiance of her goodness the dying soldier's couch— the vision is familiar to all. But the truth was different. The Miss Nightingale of fact was not as facile fancy painted her. She worked in another fashion, and towards another end; she moved under the stress of an impetus which finds no place in the popular imagination. A Demon possessed her. Now demons, whatever else they may be, are full of interest. And so it happens that in the real Miss Nightingale there was more that was interesting than in the legendary one; there was also less that was agreeable.

Her family was extremely well-to-do, and connected by marriage with a spreading circle of other well-to-do families. There was a large country house in Derbyshire; there was another in the New Forest; there were Mayfair rooms for the London season and all its finest parties; there were tours on the Continent with even more than the usual number of Italian operas and of glimpses at the celebrities of Paris. Brought up among such advantages, it was only natural to suppose that Florence would show a proper appreciation of them by doing her duty in that state of life unto which it had pleased God to call her—in other words, by marrying, after a fitting number of dances and dinner-parties, an eligible gentleman, and living happily ever afterwards. Her sister, her cousins, all the young ladies of her acquaintance, were either getting ready to do this or had already done it. It was inconceivable

that Florence should dream of anything else; yet dream she
did. Ah! To do her duty in that state of life unto which it had
pleased God to call her! Assuredly she would not be behindhand in doing her duty; but unto what state of life *had* it
pleased God to call her? That was the question. God's calls
are many, and they are strange. Unto what state of life had
it pleased Him to call Charlotte Corday, or Elizabeth of
Hungary? What was that secret voice in her ear, if it was not
a call? Why had she felt, from her earliest years, those mysterious promptings towards . . . she hardly knew what but
certainly towards something very different from anything
around her? Why, as a child in the nursery, when her sister
had shown a healthy pleasure in tearing her dolls to pieces, had
she shown an almost morbid one in sewing them up again? Why
was she driven now to minister to the poor in their cottages,
to watch by sick-beds, to put her dog's wounded paw into elaborate splints as if it was a human being? Why was her head
filled with queer imaginations of the country house at Embley
turned, by some enchantment, into a hospital, with herself as
matron moving about among the beds? Why was even her
vision of heaven itself filled with suffering patients to whom
she was being useful? So she dreamed and wondered, and, taking out her diary, she poured into it the agitations of her soul.
And then the bell rang, and it was time to go and dress for
dinner.

As the years passed, a restlessness began to grow upon her.
She was unhappy, and at last she knew it. Mrs. Nightingale, too, began to notice that there was something wrong.
It was very odd; what could be the matter with dear Flo? Mr.
Nightingale suggested that a husband might be advisable; but
the curious thing was that she seemed to take no interest in
husbands. And with her attractions, and her accomplishments,
too! There was nothing in the world to prevent her making
a really brilliant match. But no! She would think of nothing
but how to satisfy that singular craving of hers to be *doing*
something. As if there was not plenty to do in any case, in the
ordinary way, at home. There was the china to look after, and
there was her father to be read to after dinner. Mrs. Nightingale could not understand it; and then one day her perplexity was changed to consternation and alarm. Florence
announced an extreme desire to go to Salisbury Hospital for
several months as a nurse; and she confessed to some visionary

plan of eventually setting up in a house of her own in a neighbouring village, and there founding "something like a
Protestant Sisterhood, without vows, for women of educated
feelings." The whole scheme was summarily brushed aside as
preposterous; and Mrs. Nightingale, after the first shock of
terror, was able to settle down again more or less comfortably
to her embroidery. But Florence, who was now twenty-five
and felt that the dream of her life had been shattered, came
near to desperation.

And, indeed, the difficulties in her path were great. For not
only was it an almost unimaginable thing in those days for a
woman of means to make her own way in the world and to live
in independence, but the particular profession for which Florence was clearly marked out both by her instincts and her
capacities was at that time a peculiarly disreputable one. A
"nurse" meant then a coarse old woman, always ignorant,
usually dirty, often brutal, a Mrs. Gamp, in bunched-up
sordid garments, tippling at the brandy-bottle or indulging
in worse irregularities. The nurses in the hospitals were
especially notorious for immoral conduct; sobriety almost unknown among them; and they could hardly be trusted to carry
out the simplest medical duties. Certainly, things have changed
since those days; and that they *have* changed is due, far more
than to any other human being, to Miss Nightingale herself.
It is not to be wondered at that her parents should have shuddered at the notion of their daughter devoting her life to such
an occupation. "It was as if," she herself said afterwards, "I
had wanted to be a kitchen-maid." Yet the want, absurd, impracticable as it was, not only remained fixed immovably in
her heart, but grew in intensity day by day. Her wretchedness
deepened into a morbid melancholy. Everything about her
was vile, and she herself, it was clear, to have deserved such
misery, was even viler than her surroundings. Yes, she had
sinned—"standing before God's judgment seat." "No one,"
she declared, "has so grieved the Holy Spirit"; of that she was
quite certain. It was in vain that she prayed to be delivered
from vanity and hypocrisy, and she could not bear to smile
or to be gay, "because she hated God to hear her laugh, as if
she had not repented of her sin."

A weaker spirit would have been overwhelmed by the load
of such distresses—would have yielded or snapped. But this
extraordinary young woman held firm, and fought her way to

victory. With an amazing persistency, during the eight years that followed her rebuff over Salisbury Hospital, she struggled and worked and planned. While superficially she was carrying on the life of a brilliant girl in high society, while internally she was a prey to the tortures of regret and of remorse, she yet possessed the energy to collect the knowledge and to undergo the experience which alone could enable her to do what she had determined she would do in the end. In secret she devoured the reports of medical commissions, the pamphlets of sanitary authorities, the histories of hospitals and homes. She spent the intervals of the London season in ragged schools and work-houses. When she went abroad with her family, she used her spare time so well that there was hardly a great hospital in Europe with which she was not acquainted, hardly a great city whose slums she had not passed through. She managed to spend some days in a convent school in Rome, and some weeks as a "Sœur de Charité" in Paris. Then, while her mother and sister were taking the waters at Carlsbad, she succeeded in slipping off to a nursing institution at Kaiserswerth, where she remained for more than three months. This was the critical event of her life. The experience which she gained as a nurse at Kaiserswerth formed the foundation of all her future action and finally fixed her in her career.

But one other trial awaited her. The allurements of the world she had brushed aside with disdain and loathing; she had resisted the subtler temptation which, in her weariness, had sometimes come upon her, of devoting her baffled energies to art or literature; the last ordeal appeared in the shape of a desirable young man. Hitherto, her lovers had been nothing to her but an added burden and a mockery; but now—. For a moment, she wavered. A new feeling swept over her—a feeling which she had never known before, which she was never to know again. The most powerful and the profoundest of all the instincts of humanity laid claim upon her. But it rose before her, that instinct, arrayed—how could it be otherwise?—in the inevitable habiliments of a Victorian marriage; and she had the strength to stamp it underfoot.

I have an intellectual nature which requires satisfaction [she noted], and that would find it in him. I have a passional nature which requires satisfaction, and that would find it in him. I have a moral, an active nature which requires satisfaction, and that would not find it in his life. Sometimes I think that I will satisfy my passional nature at all events. . . .

But no, she knew in her heart that it could not be. "To be nailed to a continuation and exaggeration of my present life . . . to put it out of my power ever to be able to seize the chance of forming for myself a true and rich life"—that would be a suicide. She made her choice, and refused what was at least a certain happiness for a visionary good which might never come to her at all. And so she returned to her old life of waiting and bitterness.

The thoughts and feelings that I have now [she wrote] I can remember since I was six years old. A profession, a trade, a necessary occupation, something to fill and employ all my faculties, I have always felt essential to me, I have always longed for. The first thought I can remember, and the last, was nursing work; and in the absence of this, education work, but more the education of the bad than of the young. . . . Everything has been tried, foreign travel, kind friends, everything. My God! What is to become of me?

A desirable young man? Dust and ashes! What was there desirable in such a thing as that? "In my thirty-first year," she noted in her diary, "I see nothing desirable but death."

Three more years passed, and then at last the pressure of time told; her family seemed to realise that she was old enough and strong enough to have her way; and she became the superintendent of a charitable nursing home in Harley Street. She had gained her independence, though it was in a meagre sphere enough; and her mother was still not quite resigned: surely Florence might at least spend the summer in the country. At times, indeed, among her intimates, Mrs. Nightingale almost wept. "We are ducks," she said with tears in her eyes, "who have hatched a wild swan." But the poor lady was wrong; it was not a swan that they had hatched; it was an eagle.

ii

Miss Nightingale had been a year in her nursing home in Harley Street, when Fate knocked at the door. The Crimean War broke out; the battle of the Alma was fought; and the

terrible condition of our military hospitals at Scutari began
to be known in England. It sometimes happens that the plans
of Providence are a little difficult to follow, but on this occasion
all was plain; there was a perfect co-ordination of events. For
years Miss Nightingale had been getting ready; at last she
was prepared—experienced, free, mature, yet still young—
she was thirty-four—desirous to serve, accustomed to command: at that precise moment the desperate need of a great
nation came, and she was there to satisfy it. If the war had
fallen a few years earlier, she would have lacked the knowledge,
perhaps even the power, for such a work; a few years later
and she would, no doubt, have been fixed in the routine of some
absorbing task, and moreover, she would have been growing
old. Nor was it only the coincidence of Time that was remarkable. It so fell out that Sidney Herbert was at the War Office
and in the Cabinet; and Sidney Herbert was an intimate friend
of Miss Nightingale's, convinced, from personal experience in
charitable work, of her supreme capacity. After such premises,
it seems hardly more than a matter of course that her letter, in
which she offered her services for the East, and Sidney Herbert's letter, in which he asked for them, should actually have
crossed in the post. Thus it all happened, without a hitch. The
appointment was made, and even Mrs. Nightingale, overawed
by the magnitude of the venture, could only approve. A pair
of faithful friends offered themselves as personal attendants;
thirty-eight nurses were collected; and within a week of the
crossing of the letters Miss Nightingale, amid a great burst
of popular enthusiasm, left for Constantinople.

Among the numerous letters which she received on her departure was one from Dr. Manning, who at that time was
working in comparative obscurity as a Catholic priest in Bays-
water. "God will keep you," he wrote, "and my prayer for
you will be that your one object of Worship, Pattern of Imitation, and source of consolation and strength may be the Sacred
Heart of our Divine Lord."

To what extent Dr. Manning's prayer was answered must
remain a matter of doubt; but this much is certain, that, if
ever a prayer was needed, it was needed then for Florence
Nightingale. For dark as had been the picture of the state of
affairs at Scutari, revealed to the English public in the
despatches of the *Times* correspondent and in a multitude of
private letters, yet the reality turned out to be darker still.

What had occurred was, in brief, the complete break-down of our medical arrangements at the seat of war. The origins of this awful failure were complex and manifold; they stretched back through long years of peace and carelessness in England; they could be traced through endless ramifications of administrative incapacity—from the inherent faults of confused systems to the petty bunglings of minor officials, from the inevitable ignorance of Cabinet Ministers to the fatal exactitudes of narrow routine. In the inquiries which followed it was clearly shown that the evil was in reality that worst of all evils—one which has been caused by nothing in particular and for which no one in particular is to blame. The whole organization of the war machine was incompetent and out of date. The old Duke had sat for a generation at the Horse Guards repressing innovations with an iron hand. There was an extraordinary overlapping of authorities, an almost incredible shifting of responsibilities to and fro. As for such a notion as the creation and the maintenance of a really adequate medical service for the army—in that atmosphere of aged chaos, how could it have entered anybody's head? Before the war, the easy-going officials at Westminster were naturally persuaded that all was well—or at least as well as could be expected; when someone, for instance, actually had the temerity to suggest the formation of a corps of army nurses, he was at once laughed out of court. When the war had begun, the gallant British officers in control of affairs had other things to think about than the petty details of medical organisation. Who had bothered with such trifles in the Peninsula? And surely, on that occasion, we had done pretty well. Thus the most obvious precautions were neglected, the most necessary preparations put off from day to day. The principal medical officer of the army, Dr. Hall, was summoned from India at a moment's notice, and was unable to visit England before taking up his duties at the front. And it was not until after the battle of the Alma, when we had been at war for many months, that we acquired hospital accommodation at Scutari for more than a thousand men. Errors, follies, and vices on the part of individuals there doubtless were; but, in the general reckoning, they were of small account—insignificant symptoms of the deep disease of the body politic—the enormous calamity of administrative collapse.

Miss Nightingale arrived at Scutari—a suburb of Con-

stantinople, on the Asiatic side of the Bosphorus—on
November 4th, 1854; it was ten days after the battle of Balaclava, and the day before the battle of Inkerman. The
organisation of the hospitals, which had already given way
under the stress of the battle of the Alma, was now to be
subjected to the further pressure which these two desperate
and bloody engagements implied. Great detachments of
wounded were already beginning to pour in. The men, after
receiving such summary treatment as could be given them at
the smaller hospitals in the Crimea itself, were forthwith
shipped in batches of two hundred across the Black Sea to
Scutari. This voyage was in normal times one of four days
and a half; but the times were no longer normal, and now the
transit often lasted for a fortnight or three weeks. It received,
not without reason, the name of "the middle passage." Between, and sometimes on the decks, the wounded, the sick, and
the dying were crowded—men who had just undergone the
amputation of limbs, men in the clutches of fever or of frost-
bite, men in the last stages of dysentery and cholera—without
beds, sometimes without blankets, often hardly clothed. The
one or two surgeons on board did what they could; but medical
stores were lacking, and the only form of nursing available
was that provided by a handful of invalid soldiers, who were
usually themselves prostrate by the end of the voyage. There
was no other food beside the ordinary salt rations of ship
diet; and even the water was sometimes so stored that it was
out of reach of the weak. For many months, the average of
deaths during these voyages was seventy-four in the thousand; the corpses were shot out into the waters; and who shall
say that they were the most unfortunate? At Scutari, the
landing-stage, constructed with all the perverseness of Oriental
ingenuity, could only be approached with great difficulty,
and, in rough weather, not at all. When it was reached, what
remained of the men in the ships had first to be disembarked,
and then conveyed up a steep slope of a quarter of a mile to
the nearest of the hospitals. The most serious cases might be
put upon stretchers—for there were far too few for all; the
rest were carried or dragged up the hill by such convalescent
soldiers as could be got together, who were not too obviously
infirm for the work. At last the journey was accomplished;
slowly, one by one, living or dying, the wounded were carried

up into the hospital. And in the hospital what did they find?

Lasciate ogni speranza, voi ch'entrate: the delusive doors bore no such inscription; and yet behind them Hell yawned. Want, neglect, confusion, misery—in every shape and in every degree of intensity—filled the endless corridors and the vast apartments of the gigantic barrack-house, which, without forethought or preparation, had been hurriedly set aside as the chief shelter for the victims of the war. The very building itself was radically defective. Huge sewers underlay it, and cesspools loaded with filth wafted their poison into the upper rooms. The floors were in so rotten a condition that many of them could not be scrubbed; the walls were thick with dirt; incredible multitudes of vermin swarmed everywhere. And, enormous as the building was, it was yet too small. It contained four miles of beds, crushed together so close that there was but just room to pass between them. Under such conditions, the most elaborate system of ventilation might well have been at fault; but here there was no ventilation. The stench was indescribable. "I have been well acquainted," said Miss Nightingale, "with the dwellings of the worst parts of most of the great cities in Europe, but have never been in any atmosphere which I could compare with that of the Barrack Hospital at night." The structural defects were equalled by the deficiencies in the commonest objects of hospital use. There were not enough bedsteads; the sheets were of canvas, and so coarse that the wounded men recoiled from them, begging to be left in their blankets; there was no bedroom furniture of any kind, and empty beer-bottles were used for candlesticks. There were no basins, no towels, no soap, no brooms, no mops, no trays, no plates; there were neither slippers nor scissors, neither shoe-brushes nor blacking; there were no knives or forks or spoons. The supply of fuel was constantly deficient. The cooking arrangements were preposterously inadequate, and the laundry was a farce. As for purely medical materials, the tale was no better. Stretchers, splints, bandages—all were lacking; and so were the most ordinary drugs.

To replace such wants, to struggle against such difficulties, there was a handful of men overburdened by the strain of ceaseless work, bound down by the traditions of official routine, and enfeebled either by old age or inexperience or sheer incompetence. They had proved utterly unequal to their task.

The principal doctor was lost in the imbecilities of a senile optimism. The wretched official whose business it was to provide for the wants of the hospital was tied fast hand and foot by red tape. A few of the younger doctors struggled valiantly, but what could they do? Unprepared, disorganised, with such help only as they could find among the miserable band of convalescent soldiers drafted off to tend their sick comrades, they were faced with disease, mutilation, and death in all their most appalling forms, crowded multitudinously about them in an ever increasing mass. They were like men in a shipwreck, fighting, not for safety, but for the next moment's bare existence—to gain, by yet another frenzied effort, some brief respite from the waters of destruction.

In these surroundings, those who had been long inured to scenes of human suffering—surgeons with a world-wide knowledge of agonies, soldiers familiar with fields of carnage, missionaries with remembrances of famine and of plague—yet found a depth of horror which they had never known before. There were moments, there were places, in the Barrack Hospital at Scutari, where the strongest hand was struck with trembling, and the boldest eye would turn away its gaze.

Miss Nightingale came, and she, at any rate, in that Inferno, did not abandon hope. For one thing, she brought material succour. Before she left London she had consulted Dr. Andrew Smith, the head of the Army Medical Board, as to whether it would be useful to take out stores of any kind to Scutari; and Dr. Andrew Smith had told her that "nothing was needed." Even Sidney Herbert had given her similar assurances; possibly, owing to an oversight, there might have been some delay in the delivery of the medical stores, which, he said, had been sent out from England "in profusion," but "four days would have remedied this." She preferred to trust her own instincts, and at Marseilles purchased a large quantity of miscellaneous provisions, which were of the utmost use at Scutari. She came, too, amply provided with money—in all, during her stay in the East, about £7000 reached her from private sources; and, in addition, she was able to avail herself of another valuable means of help. At the same time as herself, Mr. Macdonald, of the *Times*, had arrived at Scutari, charged with the duty of administering the large sums of money collected through the agency of that newspaper in aid of the sick and wounded; and Mr. Macdonald had the sense to see that the best use he could make of the *Times* Fund was to put it at the disposal of Miss Nightingale.

I cannot conceive [wrote an eye-witness], as I now calmly look back on the first three weeks after the arrival of the wounded from Inkerman, how it could have been possible to have avoided a state of things too disastrous to contemplate, had not Miss Nightingale been there, with the means placed at her disposal by Mr. Macdonald.

But the official view was different. What! Was the public service to admit, by accepting outside charity, that it was unable to discharge its own duties without the assistance of private and irregular benevolence? Never! And accordingly when Lord Stratford de Redcliffe, our Ambassador at Constantinople, was asked by Mr. Macdonald to indicate how the *Times* Fund could best be employed, he answered that there was indeed one object to which it might very well be devoted —the building of an English Protestant Church at Pera.

Mr. Macdonald did not waste further time with Lord Stratford, and immediately joined forces with Miss Nightingale. But, with such a frame of mind in the highest quarters, it is easy to imagine the kind of disgust and alarm with which the sudden intrusion of a band of amateurs and females must have filled the minds of the ordinary officer and the ordinary military surgeon. They could not understand it; what had women to do with war? Honest Colonels relieved their spleen by the cracking of heavy jokes about "the Bird"; while poor Dr. Hall, a rough terrier of a man, who had worried his way to the top of his profession, was struck speechless with astonishment, and at last observed that Miss Nightingale's appointment was extremely droll.

Her position was, indeed, an official one, but it was hardly the easier for that. In the hospitals it was her duty to provide the services of herself and her nurses when they were asked for by the doctors, and not until then. At first some of the surgeons would have nothing to say to her, and, though she was welcomed by others, the majority were hostile and suspicious. But gradually she gained ground. Her good will could not be denied, and her capacity could not be disregarded. With consummate tact, with all the gentleness of supreme strength, she managed at last to impose her personality upon the susceptible, overwrought, discouraged, and helpless group of men in authority who surrounded her. She stood firm, she was a rock in the angry ocean; with her alone was safety, comfort, life. And so it was that hope dawned at Scutari. The reign of chaos and old night began to dwindle; order came upon the scene, and common sense, and forethought, and decision, radiating out from the little room off the great gallery in the Barrack Hospital where day and night the Lady Superintendent was at her task. Progress might be slow, but it was sure. The first sign of a great change came with the appearance of some of those necessary objects with which the hospitals had been unprovided for months. The sick men began to enjoy the use of towels and soap, knives and forks, combs and toothbrushes. Dr. Hall might snort when he heard of it, asking, with a growl, what a soldier wanted with a tooth-brush; but the good work went on. Eventually the whole business of purveying to the hospitals was, in effect, carried out by Miss Nightingale. She alone, it seemed, whatever the contingency, knew where to lay her hands on what was wanted; she alone could dispense her stores with readiness; above all she alone possessed the art of circumventing the pernicious influences of official etiquette. This was her greatest enemy, and sometimes even she was baffled by it. On one occasion 27,000 shirts sent out at her instance by the Home Government, arrived, were landed, and were only waiting to be unpacked. But the official "Purveyor" intervened; "he could not unpack them," he said, "without a Board." Miss Nightingale pleaded in vain; the sick and wounded lay half-naked shivering for want of clothing; and three weeks elapsed before the Board released the shirts. A little later, however, on a similar occasion, Miss Nightingale felt that she could assert her own authority. She ordered a Government consignment to be forcibly opened, while the miserable "Purveyor" stood by, wringing his hands in departmental agony.

Vast quantities of valuable stores sent from England lay, she found, engulfed in the bottomless abyss of the Turkish Customs House. Other ship-loads, buried beneath munitions of war destined for Balaclava, passed Scutari without a sign, and thus hospital materials were sometimes carried to and fro three times over the Black Sea, before they reached their destination. The whole system was clearly at fault, and Miss Nightingale suggested to the home authorities that a Government Store House should be instituted at Scutari for the reception and distribution of the consignments. Six months after her arrival this was done.

In the meantime she had reorganised the kitchens and the laundries in the hospitals. The ill-cooked hunks of meat, vilely served at irregular intervals, which had hitherto been the only diet for the sick men were replaced by punctual meals, well-prepared and appetising, while strengthening extra foods—soups and wines, and jellies ("preposterous luxuries," snarled Dr. Hall)—were distributed to those who needed them. One thing, however, she could not effect. The separation of the bones from the meat was no part of official cookery: the rule was that the food must be divided into equal portions, and if some of the portions were all bone—well, every man must take his chance. The rule, perhaps, was not a very good one; but there it was. "It would require a new Regulation of the Service," she was told, "to bone the meat." As for the washing arrangements, they were revolutionised. Up to the time of Miss Nightingale's arrival the number of shirts which the authorities had succeeded in washing was seven. The hospital bedding, she found, was "washed" in cold water. She took a Turkish house, had boilers installed, and employed soldiers' wives to do the laundry work. The expenses were defrayed from her own funds and that of the *Times;* and henceforward the sick and wounded had the comfort of clean linen.

Then she turned her attention to their clothing. Owing to military exigencies the greater number of the men had abandoned their kit; their knapsacks were lost for ever; they possessed nothing but what was on their persons, and that was usually only fit for speedy destruction. The "Purveyor," of course, pointed out that, according to the regulations, all soldiers should bring with them into hospital an adequate supply of clothing, and he declared that it was no business of his to make good their deficiencies. Apparently, it was the business of Miss Nightingale. She procured socks, boots, and shirts in enormous quantities; she had trousers made, she rigged up dressing-gowns. "The fact is," she told Sidney Herbert, "I am now clothing the British Army."

All at once, word came from the Crimea that a great new contingent of sick and wounded might shortly be expected. Where were they to go? Every available inch in the wards was occupied; the affair was serious and pressing, and the authorities stood aghast. There were some dilapidated rooms

in the Barrack Hospital, unfit for human habitation, but Miss
Nightingale believed that if measures were promptly taken
they might be made capable of accommodating several hundred beds. One of the doctors agreed with her; the rest of the
officials were irresolute: it would be a very expensive job, they
said; it would involve building; and who could take the responsibility? The proper course was that a representation
should be made to the Director-General of the Army Medical
Department in London; then the Director-General would
apply to the Horse Guards, the Horse Guards would move the
Ordnance, the Ordnance would lay the matter before the
Treasury, and, if the Treasury gave its consent, the work
might be correctly carried through, several months after the
necessity for it had disappeared. Miss Nightingale, however,
had made up her mind, and she persuaded Lord Stratford—
or thought she had persuaded him—to give his sanction to the
required expenditure. A hundred and twenty-five workmen
were immediately engaged, and the work was begun. The workmen struck; whereupon Lord Stratford washed his hands of
the whole business. Miss Nightingale engaged two hundred
other workmen on her own authority, and paid the bill out
of her own resources. The wards were ready by the required
date; five hundred sick men were received in them; and all the
utensils, including knives, forks, spoons, cans and towels, were
supplied by Miss Nightingale.

This remarkable woman was in truth performing the
function of an administrative chief. How had this come about?
Was she not in reality merely a nurse? Was it not her duty
simply to tend to the sick? And indeed, was it not as a ministering angel, a gentle "lady with a lamp" that she actually
impressed the minds of her contemporaries? No doubt that was
so; and yet it is no less certain that, as she herself said, the
specific business of nursing was "the least important of the
functions into which she had been forced." It was clear that
in the state of disorganisation into which the hospitals at
Scutari had fallen the most pressing, the really vital, need
was for something more than nursing; it was for the necessary
elements of civilised life—the commonest material objects, the
most ordinary cleanliness, the rudimentary habits of order and
authority. "Oh, dear Miss Nightingale," said one of her party
as they were approaching Constantinople, "when we land, let
there be no delays, let us get straight to nursing the poor

fellows!" "The strongest will be wanted at the wash-tub," was
Miss Nightingale's answer. And it was upon the wash-tub, and
all that the wash-tub stood for, that she expended her greatest
energies. Yet to say that is perhaps to say too much. For to
those who watched her at work among the sick, moving day and
night from bed to bed, with that unflinching courage, with
that indefatigable vigilance, it seemed as if the concentrated
force of an undivided and unparalleled devotion could hardly
suffice for that portion of her task alone. Wherever, in those
vast wards, suffering was at its worst and the need for help
was greatest, there, as if by magic, was Miss Nightingale.
Her superhuman equanimity would, at the moment of some
ghastly operation, nerve the victim to endure and almost to
hope. Her sympathy would assuage the pangs of dying and
bring back to those still living something of the forgotten
charm of life. Over and over again her untiring efforts rescued
those whom the surgeons had abandoned as beyond the possibility of cure. Her mere presence brought with it a strange
influence. A passionate idolatry spread among the men: they
kissed her shadow as it passed. They did more. "Before she
came," said a soldier, "there was cussin' and swearin', but
after that it was as 'oly as a church." The most cherished
privilege of the fighting man was abandoned for the sake of
Miss Nightingale. In those "lowest sinks of human misery,"
as she herself put it, she never heard the use of one expression
"which could distress a gentlewoman."

She was heroic; and these were the humble tributes paid
by those of grosser mould to that high quality. Certainly, she
was heroic. Yet her heroism was not of that simple sort so
dear to the readers of novels and the compilers of hagiologies
—the romantic sentimental heroism with which mankind loves
to invest its chosen darlings: it was made of sterner stuff. To
the wounded soldier on his couch of agony she might well
appear in the guise of a gracious angel of mercy; but the
military surgeons, and the orderlies, and her own nurses, and
the "Purveyor," and Dr. Hall, and even Lord Stratford himself could tell a different story. It was not by gentle sweetness
and womanly self-abnegation that she had brought order out
of chaos in the Scutari hospitals, that, from her own resources,
she had clothed the British Army, that she had spread her
dominion over the serried and reluctant powers of the official
world; it was by strict method, by stern discipline, by rigid

attention to detail, by ceaseless labour, by the fixed determination of an indomitable will. Beneath her cool and calm demeanour lurked fierce and passionate fires. As she passed through the wards in her plain dress, so quiet, so unassuming, she struck the casual observer simply as the pattern of a perfect lady; but the keener eye perceived something more than that—the serenity of high deliberation in the scope of the capacious brow, the sign of power in the dominating curve of the thin nose, and the traces of a harsh and dangerous temper —something peevish, something mocking, and yet something precise—in the small and delicate mouth. There was humour in the face; but the curious watcher might wonder whether it was humour of a very pleasant kind; might ask himself, even as he heard the laughter and marked the jokes with which she cheered the spirits of her patients, what sort of sardonic merriment this same lady might not give vent to, in the privacy of her chamber. As for her voice, it was true of it, even more than of her countenance, that it "had that in it one must fain call master." Those clear tones were in no need of emphasis: "I never heard her raise her voice," said one of her companions. Only, when she had spoken, it seemed as if nothing could follow but obedience. Once, when she had given some direction, a doctor ventured to remark that the thing could not be done. "But it must be done," said Miss Nightingale. A chance bystander, who heard the words, never forgot through all his life the irresistible authority of them. And they were spoken quietly—very quietly indeed.

Late at night, when the long miles of beds lay wrapped in darkness, Miss Nightingale would sit at work in her little room, over her correspondence. It was one of the most formidable of all her duties. There were hundreds of letters to be written to the friends and relations of soldiers; there was the enormous mass of official documents to be dealt with; there were her own private letters to be answered; and, most important of all, there was the composition of her long and confidential reports to Sidney Herbert. These were by no means official communications. Her soul, pent up all day in the restraint and reserve of a vast responsibility, now at last poured itself out in these letters with all its natural vehemence, like a swollen torrent through an open sluice. Here, at least, she did not mince matters. Here she painted in her darkest colours the hideous scenes which surrounded her; here she tore away remorselessly the last veils still shrouding the abominable truth. Then she would fill pages with recommendations and suggestions, with criticisms of the minutest details of organisation, with elaborate calculations of contingencies, with exhaustive analyses and statistical statements piled up in breathless eagerness one on the top of the other. And then her pen, in the virulence of its volubility, would rush on to the discussion of individuals, to the denunciation of an incompetent surgeon or the ridicule of a self-sufficient nurse. Her sarcasm searched the ranks of the officials with the deadly and unsparing precision of a machine-gun. Her nicknames were terrible. She respected no one: Lord Stratford, Lord Raglan, Lady Stratford, Dr. Andrew Smith, Dr. Hall, the Commissary-General, the Purveyor—she fulminated against them all. The intolerable futility of mankind obsessed her like a nightmare, and she gnashed her teeth against it. "I do well to be angry," was the burden of her cry. How many just men were there at Scutari? How many who cared at all for the sick, or had done anything for their relief? Were there ten? Were there five? Was there even one? She could not be sure.

At one time, during several weeks, her vituperations descended upon the head of Sidney Herbert himself. He had misinterpreted her wishes, he had traversed her positive instructions, and it was not until he had admitted his error and apologised in abject terms that he was allowed again into favour. While this misunderstanding was at its height an aristocratic young gentleman arrived at Scutari with a recommendation from the Minister. He had come out from England filled with a romantic desire to render homage to the angelic heroine of his dreams. He had, he said, cast aside his life of ease and luxury; he would devote his days and nights to the service of that gentle lady; he would perform the most menial offices, he would "fag" for her, he would be her footman—and feel requited by a single smile. A single smile, indeed, he had, but it was of an unexpected kind. Miss Nightingale at first refused to see him, and then, when she consented, believing that he was an emissary sent by Sidney Herbert to put her in the wrong over their dispute, she took notes of her conversation with him, and insisted on his signing them at the end of it. The young gentleman returned to England by the next ship.

This quarrel with Sidney Herbert was, however, an exceptional incident. Alike by him, and by Lord Panmure, his successor at the War Office, she was firmly supported; and the fact that during the whole of her stay at Scutari she had the Home Government at her back, was her trump card in her dealings with the hospital authorities. Nor was it only the Government that was behind her: public opinion in England early recognised the high importance of her mission, and its enthusiastic appreciation of her work soon reached an extraordinary height. The Queen herself was deeply moved. She made repeated inquiries as to the welfare of Miss Nightingale; she asked to see her accounts of the wounded, and made her the intermediary between the throne and the troops.

Let Mrs. Herbert know [she wrote to the War Minister] that I wish Miss Nightingale and the ladies would tell these poor noble, wounded, and sick men that *no one* takes a warmer interest or feels *more* for their sufferings or admires their courage and heroism *more* than their Queen. Day and night she thinks of her beloved troops. So does the Prince. Beg Mrs. Herbert to communicate these my words to those ladies, as I know that *our* sympathy is much valued by these noble fellows.

The letter was read aloud in the wards by the Chaplain. "It is a very feeling letter," said the men.

And so the months passed, and that fell winter which had begun with Inkerman and had dragged itself out through the long agony of the investment of Sebastopol, at last was over. In May, 1855, after six months of labour, Miss Nightingale could look with something like satisfaction at the condition of the Scutari hospitals. Had they done nothing more than survive the terrible strain which had been put upon them, it would have been a. matter for congratulation; but they had done much more than that; they had marvellously improved. The confusion and the pressure in the wards had come to an end; order reigned in them, and cleanliness; the supplies were bountiful and prompt; important sanitary works had been carried out. One simple comparison of figures was enough to reveal the extraordinary change: the rate of mortality among the cases treated had fallen from 42 per cent. to 22 per thousand. But still the indefatigable lady was not satisfied. The main problem had been solved—the physical needs of the men had been provided for; their mental and spiritual needs remained. She set up and furnished reading-rooms and recreation-rooms. She started classes and lectures. Officers were amazed to see her treating their men as if they were human beings, and assured her that she would only end by "spoiling the brutes." But that was not Miss Nightingale's opinion, and she was justified. The private soldier began to drink less, and even—though that seemed impossible—to save his pay. Miss Nightingale became a banker for the army, receiving and sending home large sums of money every month. At last, reluctantly, the Government followed suit, and established machinery of its own for the remission of money. Lord Panmure, however, remained sceptical; "it will do no good," he pronounced; "the British soldier is not a remitting animal." But, in fact, during the next six months, £71,000 was sent home.

Amid all these activities, Miss Nightingale took up the further task of inspecting the hospitals in the Crimea itself. The labour was extreme, and the conditions of life were almost intolerable. She spent whole days in the saddle, or was driven over those bleak and rocky heights in a baggage cart. Sometimes she stood for hours in the heavily falling snow, and would only reach her hut at dead of night after walking for miles through perilous ravines. Her powers of resistance seemed incredible, but at last they were exhausted. She was attacked by fever, and for a moment came very near to death. Yet she worked on; if she could not move, she could at least write; and write she did until her mind had left her; and after it had left her, in what seemed the delirious trance of death itself, she still wrote. When, after many weeks, she was strong enough to travel, she was to return to England, but she utterly refused. She would not go back, she said, before the last of the soldiers had left Scutari.

This happy moment had almost arrived, when suddenly the smouldering hostilities of the medical authorities burst out into a flame. Dr. Hall's labours had been rewarded by a K. C. B.—letters which, as Miss Nightingale told Sidney Herbert, she could only suppose to mean "Knight of the Crimean Burial-grounds"—and the honour had turned his head. He was Sir John, and he would be thwarted no longer. Disputes had lately arisen between Miss Nightingale and some of the nurses in the Crimean hospitals. The situation had been embittered by rumours of religious dissensions, for, while the Crimean nurses were Roman Catholics, many of those at Scutari were suspected of a regrettable propensity towards the tenets of Dr. Pusey. Miss Nightingale was by no means disturbed by these sectarian differences, but any suggestion that her supreme authority over all the nurses with the Army was in doubt was enough to rouse her to fury; and it appeared that Mrs. Bridgeman, the Reverend Mother in the Crimea, had ventured to call that authority in question. Sir John Hall thought that his opportunity had come, and strongly supported Mrs. Bridgeman—or, as Miss Nightingale preferred to call her, the "Reverend Brickbat." There was a violent struggle; Miss Nightingale's rage was terrible. Dr. Hall, she declared, was doing his best to "root her out of the Crimea." She would bear it no longer; the War Office was playing her false; there was only one thing to be done—Sidney Herbert must move for the production of papers in the House of Commons, so that the public might be able to judge between her and her enemies. Sidney Herbert with great difficulty calmed her down. Orders were immediately dispatched putting her supremacy beyond doubt, and the Reverend Brickbat withdrew from the scene. Sir John, however, was more tenacious. A few weeks later, Miss Nightingale and her nurses visited the Crimea for the last time, and the brilliant idea occurred to him that he could crush her by a very simple expedient—he would starve her into submission; and he actually ordered that no rations of any kind should be supplied to her. He had already tried this plan with great effect upon an unfortunate medical man whose presence in the Crimea he had considered an intrusion; but he was now to learn that such tricks were thrown away upon Miss Nightingale. With extraordinary foresight, she had brought with her a great supply of food; she succeeded in obtaining more at her own expense and by her own exertions; and thus for ten days, in that inhospitable country, she was able to feed herself and twenty-four nurses. Eventually the military authorities intervened in her favour, and Sir John had to confess that he was beaten.

It was not until July, 1856—four months after the Declaration of Peace—that Miss Nightingale left Scutari for England. Her reputation was now enormous, and the enthusiasm of the public was unbounded. The Royal approbation was expressed by the gift of a brooch, accompanied by a private letter.

You are, I know, well aware [wrote Her Majesty] of the high sense I entertain of the Christian devotion which you have displayed during this great and bloody war, and I need hardly repeat to you how warm my admiration is for your services, which are fully equal to those of my dear and brave soldiers, whose sufferings you have had the *privilege* of alleviating in so merciful a manner. I am, however, anxious of marking my feelings in a manner which I trust will be agreeable to you, and therefore send you with this letter a brooch, the form and emblems of which commemorate your great and blessed work, and which I hope you will wear as a mark of the high approbation of your Sovereign!

"It will be a very great satisfaction to me," Her Majesty added, "to make the acquaintance of one who has set so bright an example to our sex."

The brooch, which was designed by the Prince Consort, bore a St. George's cross in red enamel, and the Royal cypher surmounted by diamonds. The whole was encircled by the inscription, "Blessed are the Merciful."

iii

The name of Florence Nightingale lives in the memory of the world by virtue of the lurid and heroic adventure of the Crimea. Had she died—as she nearly did—upon her return to England, her reputation would hardly have been different; her legend would have come down to us almost as we know it today—that gentle vision of female virtue which first took shape before the adoring eyes of the sick soldiers at Scutari. Yet, as a matter of fact, she lived for more than half a century after the Crimean War; and during the greater part of that long period all the energy and all the devotion of her extraordinary nature were working at their highest pitch. What she accomplished in those years of unknown labour could, indeed, hardly have been more glorious than her Crimean triumphs; but it was certainly more important. The true history was far stranger even than the myth. In Miss Nightingale's own eyes the adventure of the Crimea was a mere incident—scarcely more than a useful stepping-stone in her career. It was the fulcrum with which she hoped to move the world; but it was only the fulcrum. For more than a generation she was to sit in secret, working her lever: and her real life began at the very moment when, in the popular imagination, it had ended.

She arrived in England in a shattered state of health. The hardships and the ceaseless effort of the last two years had undermined her nervous system; her heart was pronounced to be affected; she suffered constantly from fainting-fits and terrible attacks of utter physical prostration. The doctors declared that one thing alone would save her—a complete and prolonged rest. But that was also the one thing with which she would have nothing to do. She had never been in the habit of resting; why should she begin now? Now, when her opportunity had come at last; now, when the iron was hot, and it was time to strike? No; she had work to do; and, come what might, she would do it. The doctors protested in vain; in vain her family lamented and entreated, in vain her friends pointed out to her the madness of such a course. Madness? Mad—possessed—perhaps she was. A demoniac frenzy had seized upon her. As she lay upon her sofa, gasping, she devoured blue-books, dictated letters, and, in the intervals of her palpitations, cracked her febrile jokes. For months at a stretch she never left her bed. For years she was in daily expectation of Death. But she would not rest. At this rate, the doctors assured her, even if she did not die, she would become an invalid for life. She could not help that; there was the work to be done; and, as for rest, very likely she might rest . . . when she had done it.

Wherever she went, in London or in the country, in the hills of Derbyshire, or among the rhododendrons at Embley, she was haunted by a ghost. It was the spectre of Scutari—the hideous vision of the organisation of a military hospital. She would lay that phantom, or she would perish. The whole system of the Army Medical Department, the education of the Medical Officer, the regulations of hospital procedure . . . rest? How could she rest while these things were as they were, while, if the like necessity were to arise again, the like results would follow? And, even in peace and at home, what was the sanitary condition of the Army? The mortality in the barracks was, she found, nearly double the mortality in civil life. "You might as well take 1100 men every year out upon Salisbury Plain and shoot them," she said. After inspecting the hospitals at Chatham, she smiled grimly. "Yes, this is one more symptom of the system which, in the Crimea, put to death 16,000 men." Scutari had given her knowledge; and it had given her power too: her enormous reputation was at her back—an incalculable force. Other work, other duties, might lie before her; but the most urgent, the most obvious of all was to look to the health of the Army.

One of her very first steps was to take advantage of the invitation which Queen Victoria had sent her to the Crimea, together with the commemorative brooch. Within a few weeks of her return, she visited Balmoral, and had several interviews both with the Queen and the Prince Consort. "She put before us," wrote the Prince in his diary, "all the defects of our present military hospital system and the reforms that are needed." She related the whole story of her experiences in the East; and, in addition, she managed to have some long and confidential talks with His Royal Highness on metaphysics and religion. The impression which she created was excellent. "Sie gefällt uns sehr," noted the Prince, "ist sehr bescheiden." Her Majesty's comment was different—"Such a *head!* I wish we had her at the War Office."

But Miss Nightingale was not at the War Office, and for a very simple reason: she was a woman. Lord Panmure, however, *was* (though indeed the reason for that was not quite so simple); and it was upon Lord Panmure that the issue of Miss Nightingale's efforts for reform must primarily depend. That burly Scottish nobleman had not, in spite of his most earnest endeavours, had a very easy time of it as Secretary of State for War. He had come into office in the middle of the Sebastopol campaign, and had felt himself very well fitted for the position, since he had acquired in former days an inside knowledge of the Army—as a Captain of Hussars. It was this inside knowledge which had enabled him to inform Miss Nightingale with such authority that "the British soldier is not a remitting animal." And perhaps it was this same consciousness of a command of his subject which had impelled him to write a dispatch to Lord Raglan, blandly informing the Commander-in-Chief in the Field just how he was neglecting his duties, and pointing out to him that if he would only try he really might do a little better next time. Lord Raglan's reply, calculated as it was to make its recipient sink into the earth, did not quite have that effect upon Lord Panmure, who, whatever might have been his faults, had never been accused of being super-sensitive. However, he allowed the matter to drop; and a little later Lord Raglan died—worn out, some people said, by work and anxiety. He was succeeded by an excellent red-nosed old gentleman, General Simpson, whom nobody has ever heard of, and who took Sebastopol. But Lord Panmure's relations with him were hardly more satisfactory than his relations with Lord Raglan; for, while Lord Raglan had been too inde-pendent, poor General Simpson erred in the opposite direction, perpetually asked advice, suffered from lumbago, doubted, his nose growing daily redder and redder, whether he was fit for his post, and, by alternate mails, sent in and withdrew his resignation. Then, too, both the General and the Minister suf-fered acutely from that distressingly useful new invention, the electric telegraph. On one occasion General Simpson felt obliged actually to expostulate.

I think, my Lord [he wrote], that some telegraphic messages reach us that cannot be sent under due authority, and are perhaps unknown to you, although under the protection of your Lordship's name. For instance, I was called up last night, a dragoon having come express with a telegraphic message in these words, "Lord Panmure to Gen-eral Simpson—Captain Jarvis has been bitten by a centipede. How is he now?"

General Simpson might have put up with this, though to be sure it did seem "rather too trifling an affair to call for a dragoon to ride a couple of miles in the dark that he may knock up the Commander of the Army out of the very small allow-ance of sleep permitted him"; but what was really more than he could bear was to find "upon sending in the morning an-other mounted dragoon to inquire after Captain Jarvis, four miles off, that he never has been bitten at all, but has had a boil, from which he is fast recovering." But Lord Panmure had troubles of his own. His favourite nephew, Captain Dow-biggin, was at the front, and to one of his telegrams to the Commander-in-Chief the Minister had taken occasion to ap-pend the following carefully qualified sentence—"I recommend Dowbiggin to your notice, should you have a vacancy, and if he is fit." Unfortunately, in those early days, it was left to the discretion of the telegraphist to compress the messages which passed through his hands; so that the result was that

Lord Panmure's delicate appeal reached its destination in the laconic form of "Look after Dowb." The Headquarters Staff were at first extremely puzzled; they were at last extremely amused. The story spread; and "Look after Dowb" remained for many years the familiar formula for describing official hints in favour of deserving nephews.

And now that all this was over, now that Sebastopol had been, somehow or another, taken, now that peace was, somehow or another, made, now that the troubles of office might surely be expected to be at an end at last—here was Miss Nightingale breaking in upon the scene, with her talk about the state of the hospitals and the necessity for sanitary reform. It was most irksome; and Lord Panmure almost began to wish that he was engaged upon some more congenial occupation—discussing, perhaps, the constitution of the Free Church of Scotland—a question in which he was profoundly interested. But no; duty was paramount; and he set himself, with a sigh of resignation, to the task of doing as little of it as he possibly could.

"The Bison" his friends called him; and the name fitted both his physical demeanour and his habit of mind. That large low head seemed to have been created for butting rather than for anything else. There he stood, four-square and menacing, in the doorway of reform; and it remained to be seen whether the bulky mass, upon whose solid hide even the barbed arrows of Lord Raglan's scorn had made no mark, would prove amenable to the pressure of Miss Nightingale. Nor was he alone in the doorway. There loomed behind him the whole phalanx of professional conservatism, the stubborn supporters of the out-of-date, the worshippers and the victims of War Office routine. Among these it was only natural that Dr. Andrew Smith, the head of the Army Medical Department, should have been pre-eminent—Dr. Andrew Smith, who had assured Miss Nightingale before she left England that "nothing was wanted at Scutari." Such were her opponents; but she too was not without allies. She had gained the ear of Royalty—which was something; at any moment that she pleased she could gain the ear of the public—which was a great deal. She had a host of admirers and friends; and—to say nothing of her personal qualities—her knowledge, her tenacity, her tact—she possessed, too, one advantage which then, far more even than now, carried an immense weight—she belonged to the highest circle of society. She moved naturally among Peers and Cabinet Ministers—she was one of their own set; and in those days their set was a very narrow one. What kind of attention would such persons have paid to some middle-class woman with whom they were not acquainted, who possessed great experience of army nursing and had decided views upon hospital reform? They would have politely ignored her; but it was impossible to ignore Flo Nightingale. When she spoke, they were obliged to listen; and, when they had once begun to do that—what might not follow? She knew her power, and she used it. She supported her weightiest minutes with familiar witty little notes. The Bison began to look grave. It might be difficult—it might be damned difficult—to put down one's head against the white hand of a lady.

Of Miss Nightingale's friends, the most important was Sidney Herbert. He was a man upon whom the good fairies seemed to have showered, as he lay in his cradle, all their most enviable gifts. Well born, handsome, rich, the master of Wilton—one of those great country-houses, clothed with the glamour of a historic past, which are the peculiar glory of England—he possessed, besides all these advantages, so charming, so lively, so gentle a disposition that no one who had once come near him could ever be his enemy. He was, in fact, a man of whom it was difficult not to say that he was a perfect English gentleman. For his virtues were equal even to his good fortune. He was religious—deeply religious: "I am more and more convinced every day," he wrote, when he had been for some years a Cabinet Minister, "that in politics, as in everything else, nothing can be right which is not in accordance with the spirit of the Gospel." No one was more unselfish; he was charitable and benevolent to a remarkable degree; and he devoted the whole of his life with an unwavering conscientiousness to the public service. With such a character, with such opportunities, what high hopes must have danced before him, what radiant visions of accomplished duties, of ever-increasing usefulness, of beneficent power, of the consciousness of disinterested success! Some of those hopes and visions were, indeed, realised; but, in the end, the career of Sidney Herbert seemed to show that, with all their generosity, there was some gift or other—what was it?—some essential gift—which the good fairies had withheld, and that even the qualities of a perfect English gentleman may be no safeguard against anguish, humiliation, and defeat.

That career would certainly have been very different if he had never known Miss Nightingale. The alliance between them, which had begun with her appointment to Scutari, which had grown closer and closer while the war lasted, developed, after her return, into one of the most extraordinary of friendships. It was the friendship of a man and a woman intimately bound together by their devotion to a public cause; mutual affection, of course, played a part in it, but it was an incidental part; the whole soul of the relationship ˜as a community of work. Perhaps out of England such an intimacy could hardly have existed—an intimacy so utterly untinctured not only by passion itself but by the suspicion of it. For years Sidney Herbert saw Miss Nightingale almost daily, for long hours together, corresponding with her incessantly when they were apart; and the tongue of scandal was silent; and one of the most devoted of her admirers was his wife. But what made the connection still more remarkable was the way in which the parts that were played in it were divided between the two. The man who acts, decides, and achieves; the woman who encourages, applauds, and—from a distance—inspires:—the combination is common enough; but Miss Nightingale was neither an Aspasia nor an Egeria. In her case it is almost true to say that the rôles were reversed; the qualities of pliancy and sympathy fell to the man, those of command and initiative to the woman. There was one thing only which Miss Nightingale lacked in her equipment for public life; she had not—she never could have—the public power and authority which belong to the successful politician. That power and authority Sidney Herbert possessed; the fact was obvious, and the conclusion no less so: it was through the man that the woman must work her will. She took hold of him, taught him, shaped him, absorbed him, dominated him through and through. He did not resist—he did not wish to resist; his natural inclination lay along the same path as hers; only that terrific personality swept him forward at her own fierce pace and with her own relentless stride. Swept him—where to? Ah! Why had he ever known Miss Nightingale? If Lord Panmure was a bison, Sidney Herbert, no doubt, was a stag—a comely, gallant creature springing through the forest; but the forest is a dangerous place. One has the image of those wide eyes fascinated suddenly by something feline, something strong; there is a pause; and then the tigress has her claws in the quivering haunches; and then——!

Besides Sidney Herbert, she had other friends who, in a more restricted sphere, were hardly less essential to her. If, in her condition of bodily collapse, she were to accomplish what she was determined that she should accomplish, the attentions and the services of others would be absolutely indispensable. Helpers and servers she must have; and accordingly there was soon formed about her a little group of devoted disciples upon whose affections and energies she could implicitly rely. Devoted, indeed, these disciples were, in no ordinary sense of the term; for certainly she was no light task-mistress, and he who set out to be of use to Miss Nightingale was apt to find, before he had gone very far, that he was in truth being made use of in good earnest—to the very limit of his endurance and his capacity. Perhaps, even beyond those limits; why not? Was she asking of others more than she was giving herself? Let them look at her lying there pale and breathless on the couch; could it be said that she spared herself? Why, then, should she spare others? And it was not for her own sake that she made these claims. For her own sake, indeed! No! They all knew it! it was for the sake of the work. And so the little band, bound body and soul in that strange servitude, laboured on ungrudgingly. Among the most faithful was her "Aunt Mai," her father's sister, who from the earliest days had stood beside her, who had helped her to escape from the thraldom of family life, who had been with her at Scutari, and who now acted almost the part of a mother to her, watching over her with infinite care in all the movements and uncertainties which her state of health involved. Another constant attendant was her brother-in-law, Sir Harry Verney, whom she found particularly valuable in parliamentary affairs. Arthur Clough, the poet, also a connection by marriage, she used in other ways. Ever since he had lost his faith at the time of the Oxford Movement, Clough had passed his life in a condition of considerable uneasiness, which was increased rather than diminished by the practice of poetry. Unable to decide upon the purpose of an existence whose savour had fled together with his belief in the Resurrection, his spirits lowered still further by ill-health, and his income not all that it should be, he had determined to seek the solution of his difficulties in the United States of America.

But, even there, the solution was not forthcoming; and when, a little later, he was offered a post in a government department at home, he accepted it, came to live in London, and immediately fell under the influence of Miss Nightingale. Though the purpose of existence might be still uncertain and its nature still unsavoury, here, at any rate, under the eye of this inspired woman, was something real, something earnest: his only doubt was—could he be of any use? Certainly he could. There were a great number of miscellaneous little jobs which there was nobody handy to do. For instance, when Miss Nightingale was travelling, there were the railway-tickets to be taken; and there were proof-sheets to be corrected; and then there were parcels to be done up in brown paper, and carried to the post. Certainly he could be useful. And so, upon such occupations as these, Arthur Clough was set to work. "This that I see, is not all," he comforted himself by reflecting, "and this that I do is but little; nevertheless it is good, though there is better than it."

As time went on, her "Cabinet," as she called it, grew larger. Officials with whom her work brought her into touch and who sympathised with her objects, were pressed into her service; and old friends of the Crimean days gathered round her when they returned to England. Among these the most indefatigable was Dr. Sutherland, a sanitary expert, who for more than thirty years acted as her confidential private secretary, and surrendered to her purposes literally the whole of his life. Thus sustained and assisted, thus slaved for and adored, she prepared to beard the Bison.

Two facts soon emerged, and all that followed turned upon them. It became clear, in the first place, that that imposing mass was not immovable, and, in the second, that its movement, when it did move, would be exceeding slow. The Bison was no match for the Lady. It was in vain that he put down his head and planted his feet in the earth; he could not withstand her; the white hand forced him back. But the process was an extraordinarily gradual one. Dr. Andrew Smith and all his War Office phalanx stood behind, blocking the way; the poor Bison groaned inwardly, and cast a wistful eye towards the happy pastures of the Free Church of Scotland; then slowly, with infinite reluctance, step by step, he retreated, disputing every inch of the ground.

The first great measure, which, supported as it was by the

Queen, the Cabinet, and the united opinion of the country, it
was impossible to resist, was the appointment of a Royal Commission to report upon the health of the Army. The question
of the composition of the Commission then immediately arose;
and it was over this matter that the first hand-to-hand encounter between Lord Panmure and Miss Nightingale took
place. They met, and Miss Nightingale was victorious; Sidney
Herbert was appointed Chairman; and, in the end, the only
member of the commission opposed to her views was Dr. Andrew Smith. During the interview, Miss Nightingale made an
important discovery: she found that "the Bison was bullyable"—the hide was the hide of a Mexican buffalo, but the
spirit was the spirit of an Alderney calf. And there was one
thing above all others which the huge creature dreaded—an
appeal to public opinion. The faintest hint of such a terrible
eventuality made his heart dissolve within him; he would agree
to anything—he would cut short his grouse-shooting—he
would make a speech in the House of Lords—he would even
overrule Dr. Andrew Smith—rather than that. Miss Nightingale held the fearful threat in reserve—she would speak out
what she knew; she would publish the truth to the whole world,
and let the whole world judge between them. With supreme
skill, she kept this sword of Damocles poised above the Bison's
head, and more than once she was actually on the point of
really dropping it. For his recalcitrancy grew and grew. The
personnel of the Commission once determined upon, there was
a struggle, which lasted for six months, over the nature of its
powers. Was it to be an efficient body, armed with the right of
full inquiry and wide examination, or was it to be a polite
official contrivance for exonerating Dr. Andrew Smith? The
War Office phalanx closed its ranks, and fought tooth and
nail; but it was defeated: the Bison was bullyable.

Three months from this day [Miss Nightingale had written at last]
I publish my experience of the Crimean Campaign, and my suggestions for improvement, unless there has been a fair and tangible
pledge by that time for reform.

Who could face that?

  And, if the need came, she meant to be as good as her word.
For she had now determined, whatever might be the fate of the
Commission, to draw up her own report upon the questions at

issue. The labour involved was enormous; her health was almost desperate; but she did not flinch, and after six months of incredible industry she had put together and written with her own hand her "Notes affecting the Health, Efficiency, and Hospital Administration of the British Army." This extraordinary composition, filling more than eight hundred closely printed pages, laying down vast principles of far-reaching reform, discussing the minutest details of a multitude of controversial subjects, containing an enormous mass of information of the most varied kind—military, statistical, sanitary, architectural—was never given to the public, for the need never came; but it formed the basis of the Report of the Royal Commission; and it remains to this day the leading authority on the medical administration of armies.

Before it had been completed the struggle over the powers of the Commission had been brought to a victorious close. Lord Panmure had given way once more; he had immediately hurried to the Queen to obtain her consent; and only then, when her Majesty's initials had been irrevocably affixed to the fatal document, did he dare to tell Dr. Andrew Smith what he had done. The Commission met, and another immense load fell upon Miss Nightingale's shoulders. To-day she would, of course, have been one of the Commission herself; but at that time the idea of a woman appearing in such a capacity was unheard of; and no one even suggested the possibility of Miss Nightingale's doing so. The result was that she was obliged to remain behind the scenes throughout, to coach Sidney Herbert in private at every important juncture, and to convey to him and to her other friends upon the Commission the vast funds of her expert knowledge—so essential in the examination of witnesses—by means of innumerable consultations, letters, and memoranda. It was even doubtful whether the proprieties would admit of her giving evidence; and at last, as a compromise, her modesty only allowed her to do so in the form of written answers to written questions. At length the grand affair was finished. The Commission's Report, embodying almost word for word the suggestions of Miss Nightingale, was drawn up by Sidney Herbert. Only one question remained to be answered—would anything, after all, be done? Or would the Royal Commission, like so many other Royal Commissions before and since, turn out to have achieved nothing but the concoction of a very fat blue-book on a very high shelf?

And so the last and the deadliest struggle with the Bison began. Six months had been spent in coercing him into granting the Commission effective powers; six more months were occupied by the work of the Commission; and now yet another six were to pass in extorting from him the means whereby the recommendations of the Commission might be actually carried out. But, in the end, the thing was done. Miss Nightingale seemed indeed, during these months, to be upon the very brink of death. Accompanied by the faithful Aunt Mai, she moved from place to place—to Hampstead, to Highgate, to Derbyshire, to Malvern—in what appeared to be a last desperate effort to find health somewhere; but she carried that with her which made health impossible. Her desire for work could now scarcely be distinguished from mania. At one moment she was writing a "last letter" to Sidney Herbert; at the next she was offering to go out to India to nurse the sufferers in the Mutiny. When Dr. Sutherland wrote, imploring her to take a holiday, she raved. Rest!—

I am lying without my head, without my claws, and you all peck at me. It is *de rigueur, d'obligation,* like the saying something to one's hat, when one goes into church, to say to me all that has been said to me 110 times a day during the last three months. It is the *obbligato* on the violin, and the twelve violins all practise it together, like the clocks striking 12 o'clock at night all over London, till I say like Xavier de Maistre, *Assez, je le sais, je ne le sais que trop.* I am not a penitent; but you are like the R. C. confessor, who says what is *de rigueur. . . .*

Her wits began to turn, and there was no holding her. She worked like a slave in a mine. She began to believe, as she had begun to believe at Scutari, that none of her fellow-workers had their hearts in the business; if they had, why did they not work as she did? She could only see slackness and stupidity around her. Dr. Sutherland, of course, was grotesquely muddle-headed; and Arthur Clough incurably lazy. Even Sidney Herbert . . . oh yes, he had simplicity and candour and quickness of perception, no doubt; but he was an eclectic; and what could one hope for from a man who went away to fish in Ireland just when the Bison most needed bullying? As for the Bison himself he had fled to Scotland, where he remained buried for many months. The fate of the vital recommendation in the Commission's Report—the appointment of four

Sub-Commissions charged with the duty of determining upon the details of the proposed reforms and of putting them into execution—still hung in the balance. The Bison consented to everything; and then, on a flying visit to London, withdrew his consent and hastily returned to Scotland. Then for many weeks all business was suspended; he had gout—gout in the hands, so that he could not write. "His gout was always handy," remarked Miss Nightingale. But eventually it was clear even to the Bison that the game was up, and the inevitable surrender came.

There was, however, one point in which he triumphed over Miss Nightingale. The building of Netley Hospital had been begun, under his orders, before her return to England. Soon after her arrival she examined the plans, and found that they reproduced all the worst faults of an out-of-date and mischievous system of hospital construction. She therefore urged that the matter should be reconsidered, and in the meantime building stopped. But the Bison was obdurate; it would be very expensive, and in any case it was too late. Unable to make any impression on him, and convinced of the extreme importance of the question, she determined to appeal to a higher authority. Lord Palmerston was Prime Minister; she had known him from her childhood; he was a near neighbour of her father's in the New Forest. She went down to the New Forest, armed with the plans of the proposed hospital and all the relevant information, stayed the night at Lord Palmerston's house, and convinced him of the necessity of rebuilding Netley.

It seems to me [Lord Palmerston wrote to Lord Panmure] that at Netley all consideration of what would best tend to the comfort and recovery of the patients has been sacrificed to the vanity of the architect, whose sole object has been to make a building which should cut a dash when looked at from the Southampton river. . . . Pray, therefore, stop all further progress in the work until the matter can be duly considered.

But the Bison was not to be moved by one peremptory letter, even if it was from the Prime Minister. He put forth all his powers of procrastination, Lord Palmerston lost interest in the subject, and so the chief military hospital in England was triumphantly completed on unsanitary principles, with unventilated rooms, and with all the patients' windows facing northeast.

But now the time had come when the Bison was to trouble and to be troubled no more. A vote in the House of Commons brought about the fall of Lord Palmerston's Government, and Lord Panmure found himself at liberty to devote the rest of his life to the Free Church of Scotland. After a brief interval, Sidney Herbert became Secretary of State for War. Great was the jubilation in the Nightingale Cabinet; the day of achievement had dawned at last. The next two and a half years (1859–61) saw the introduction of the whole system of reforms for which Miss Nightingale had been struggling so fiercely—reforms which make Sidney Herbert's tenure of power at the War Office an important epoch in the history of the British Army. The four Sub-Commissions, firmly established under the immediate control of the Minister, and urged forward by the relentless perseverance of Miss Nightingale, set to work with a will. The barracks and the hospitals were remodelled; they were properly ventilated and warmed and lighted for the first time; they were given a water supply which actually supplied water, and kitchens where, strange to say, it was possible to cook. Then the great question of the Purveyor—that portentous functionary whose powers and whose lack of powers had weighed like a nightmare upon Scutari—was taken in hand, and new regulations were laid down, accurately defining his responsibilities and his duties. One Sub-Commission reorganised the medical statistics of the Army. Another established—in spite of the last convulsive efforts of the Department—an Army Medical School. Finally the Army Medical Department itself was completely reorganised; an administrative code was drawn up; and the great and novel principle was established that it was as much a part of the duty of the authorities to look after the soldier's health as to look after his sickness. Besides this, it was at last officially admitted that he had a moral and intellectual side. Coffee-rooms and reading-rooms, gymnasiums and workshops were instituted. A new era did in truth appear to have begun. Already by 1861 the mortality in the Army had decreased by one half since the days of the Crimea. It was no wonder that even vaster possibilities began now to open out before Miss Nightingale. One thing was still needed to complete and to assure her triumphs. The Army Medical Department was indeed reorganised; but the great central machine was still untouched. The War Office itself—!—If she could remould *that* nearer to her heart's desire—there indeed would be a victory! And until that final act was accomplished, how could she be certain that all the rest of her achievements might not, by some capricious turn of Fortune's wheel—a change of Ministry, perhaps, replacing Sidney Herbert by some puppet of the permanent official gang—be swept to limbo in a moment?

Meanwhile, still ravenous for more and yet more work, her activities had branched out into new directions. The army in India claimed her attention. A Sanitary Commission, appointed at her suggestion, and working under her auspices, did for our troops there what the four Sub-Commissions were doing for those at home. At the same time, these very years which saw her laying the foundations of the whole modern system of medical work in the army, saw her also beginning to bring her knowledge, her influence, and her activity into the service of the country at large. Her *Notes on Hospitals* (1859) revolutionised the theory of hospital construction and hospital management. She was immediately recognised as the leading expert upon all the questions involved; her advice flowed unceasingly and in all directions, so that there is no great hospital today which does not bear upon it the impress of her mind. Nor was this all. With the opening of the Nightingale Training School for Nurses at St. Thomas's Hospital (1860), she became the founder of modern nursing.

But a terrible crisis was now fast approaching. Sidney Herbert had consented to undertake the root and branch reform of the War Office. He had sallied forth into that tropical jungle of festooned obstructiveness, of intertwisted irresponsibilities, of crouching prejudices, of abuses grown stiff and rigid with antiquity, which for so many years to come was destined to lure reforming ministers to their doom.

The War Office [said Miss Nightingale] is a very slow office, an enormously expensive office, and one in which the Minister's intentions can be entirely negatived by all his sub-departments, and those of each of the sub-departments by every other.

It was true; and, of course, at the first rumour of a change, the old phalanx of reaction was bristling with its accustomed spears. At its head stood no longer Dr. Andrew Smith, who, some time since, had followed the Bison into outer darkness, but a yet more formidable figure, the permanent Under-Secretary himself, Sir Benjamin Hawes—Ben Hawes the Nightingale Cabinet irreverently dubbed him—a man remarkable even among civil servants for adroitness in baffling inconvenient inquiries, resource in raising false issues, and, in short, a consummate command of all the arts of officially sticking in the mud. "Our scheme will probably result in Ben Hawes's resignation," Miss Nightingale said; "and that is another of its advantages." Ben Hawes himself, however, did not quite see it in that light. He set himself to resist the wishes of the Minister by every means in his power. The struggle was long and desperate; and, as it proceeded, it gradually became evident to Miss Nightingale that something was the matter with Sidney Herbert. What was it? His health, never very strong, was, he said, in danger of collapsing under the strain of his work. But, after all, what is illness, when there is a War Office to be reorganised? Then he began to talk of retiring altogether from public life. The doctors were consulted, and declared that, above all things, what was necessary was rest. Rest! She grew seriously alarmed. Was it possible that, at the last moment, the crowning wreath of victory was to be snatched from her grasp? She was not to be put aside by doctors; they were talking nonsense; the necessary thing was not rest but the reform of the War Office; and, besides, she knew very well from her own case what one could do even when one was on the point of death. She expostulated vehemently, passionately: the goal was so near, so very near; he could not turn back now! At any rate, he could not resist Miss Nightingale. A compromise was arranged. Very reluctantly, he exchanged the turmoil of the House of Commons for the dignity of the House of Lords, and he remained at the War Office. She was delighted. "One fight more, the best and the last," she said.

For several more months the fight did indeed go on. But the strain upon him was greater even than she perhaps could realise. Besides the intestine war in his office, he had to face a constant battle in the Cabinet with Mr. Gladstone—a more redoubtable antagonist even than Ben Hawes—over the estimates. His health grew worse and worse. He was attacked by fainting-fits; and there were some days when he could only just keep himself going by gulps of brandy. Miss Nightingale spurred him forward with her encouragements and her admonitions, her zeal and her example. But at last his spirit began to sink as well as his body. He could no longer hope; he could no longer desire; it was useless, all useless; it was utterly impossible. He had failed. The dreadful moment came when the truth was forced upon him: he would never be able to reform the War Office. But a yet more dreadful moment lay behind; he must go to Miss Nightingale and tell her that he was a failure, a beaten man.

Blessed are the merciful! What strange ironic prescience had led Prince Albert, in the simplicity of his heart, to choose that motto for the Crimean brooch? The words hold a double lesson; and, alas! when she brought herself to realise at length what was indeed the fact and what there was no helping, it was not in mercy that she turned upon her old friend.

Beaten! [she exclaimed]. Can't you see that you've simply thrown away the game? And with all the winning cards in your hands! And so noble a game! Sidney Herbert beaten! And beaten by Ben Hawes! It is a worse disgrace. . . . [her full rage burst out at last] . . . a worse disgrace than the hospitals at Scutari.

He dragged himself away from her, dragged himself to Spa, hoping vainly for a return of health, and then, despairing, back again to England, to Wilton, to the majestic house standing there resplendent in the summer sunshine, among the great cedars which had lent their shade to Sir Philip Sidney, and all those familiar, darling haunts of beauty which he loved, each one of them, "as if they were persons"; and at Wilton he died. After having received the Eucharist he had become perfectly calm; then, almost unconscious, his lips were seen to be moving. Those about him bent down. "Poor Florence! Poor Florence!" they just caught. ". . . Our joint work . . . unfinished . . . tried to do . . ." and they could hear no more.

When the onward rush of a powerful spirit sweeps a weaker one to its destruction, the commonplaces of the moral judgment are better left unmade. If Miss Nightingale had been less ruthless, Sidney Herbert would not have perished; but then, she would not have been Miss Nightingale. The force that created was the force that destroyed. It was her Demon that was responsible. When the fatal news reached her, she was overcome by agony. In the revulsion of her feelings, she made a worship of the dead man's memory; and the facile instrument which had broken in her hand she spoke of for ever after as her "Master." Then, almost at the same moment, another blow fell upon her. Arthur Clough, worn out by labours very different from those of Sidney Herbert, died too: never more would he tie up her parcels. And yet a third disaster followed. The faithful Aunt Mai did not, to be sure, die; no, she did something almost worse: she left Miss Nightingale. She was growing old, and she felt that she had closer and more imperative duties with her own family. Her niece could hardly forgive her. She poured out, in one of her enormous letters, a passionate diatribe upon the faithlessness, the lack of sympathy, the stupidity, the ineptitude of women. Her doctrines had taken no hold among them; she had never known one who had *appris à apprendre;* she could not even get a woman secretary; "they don't know the names of the Cabinet Ministers —they don't know which of the Churches has Bishops and which not." As for the spirit of self-sacrifice, well—Sidney Herbert and Arthur Clough were men, and they indeed had shown their devotion; but women—! She would mount three widow's caps "for a sign." The first two would be for Clough and for her Master; but the third, "the biggest widow's cap of all"—would be for Aunt Mai. She did well to be angry; she was deserted in her hour of need; and, after all, could she be sure that even the male sex was so impeccable? There was Dr. Sutherland, bungling as usual. Perhaps even he intended to go off, one of these days, too? She gave him a look, and he shivered in his shoes. No!—she grinned sardonically; she would always have Dr. Sutherland. And then she reflected that there was one thing more that she would always have—her work.

iv

Sidney Herbert's death finally put an end to Miss Nightingale's dream of a reformed War Office. For a moment, indeed, in the first agony of her disappointment, she had wildly clutched at a straw; she had written to Mr. Gladstone to beg him to take up the burden of Sidney Herbert's work. And Mr. Gladstone had replied with a sympathetic account of the funeral.

Succeeding Secretaries of State managed between them to undo a good deal of what had been accomplished, but they could not undo it all; and for ten years more (1862–72) Miss Nightingale remained a potent influence at the War Office. After that, her direct connection with the army came to an end, and her energies began to turn more and more completely towards more general objects. Her work upon hospital reform assumed enormous proportions; she was able to improve the conditions in infirmaries and workhouses; and one of her most remarkable papers forestalls the recommendations of the Poor Law Commission of 1909. Her training school for nurses, with all that it involved in initiative, control, responsibility, and combat, would have been enough in itself to have absorbed the efforts of at least two lives of ordinary vigour. And at the same time her work in connection with India, which had begun with the Sanitary Commission on the Indian Army, spread and ramified in a multitude of directions. Her tentacles reached the India Office and succeeded in establishing a hold even upon those slippery high places. For many years it was *de rigueur* for the newly appointed Viceroy, before he left England, to pay a visit to Miss Nightingale.

After much hesitation, she had settled down in a small house in South Street, where she remained for the rest of her life. That life was a very long one; the dying woman reached her ninety-first year. Her ill-health gradually diminished; the crises of extreme danger became less frequent, and at last, altogether ceased; she remained an invalid, but an invalid of a curious character—an invalid who was too weak to walk downstairs and who worked far harder than most Cabinet Ministers. Her illness, whatever it may have been, was certainly not inconvenient. It involved seclusion; and an extraordinary, an unparalleled seclusion was, it might almost have been said, the main-spring of Miss Nightingale's life. Lying on her sofa in the little upper room in South Street she combined the intense vitality of a dominating woman of the world with the mysterious and romantic quality of a myth. She was a legend in her lifetime, and she knew it. She tasted the joys of power, like those Eastern Emperors whose autocratic rule was based upon invisibility, with the mingled satisfactions of obscurity and fame. And she found the machinery of illness hardly less effective as a barrier against the eyes of men than the ceremonial of a palace. Great statesmen and renowned generals were obliged to beg for audiences; admiring princesses from foreign countries found that they must see her at her own time, or not at all; and the ordinary mortal had no hope of ever getting beyond the downstairs sitting-room and Dr. Sutherland. For that indefatigable disciple did, indeed, never desert her. He might be impatient, he might be restless, but he remained. His "incurable looseness of thought," for so she termed it, continued at her service to the end. Once, it is true, he had actually ventured to take a holiday; but he was recalled, and he did not repeat the experiment. He was wanted downstairs. There he sat, transacting business, answering correspondence, interviewing callers, and exchanging innumerable notes with the unseen power above. Sometimes word came down that Miss Nightingale was just well enough to see one of her visitors. The fortunate man was led up, was ushered, trembling, into the shaded chamber, and, of course, could never afterwards forget the interview. Very rarely, indeed, once or twice a year, perhaps, but nobody could be quite certain, in deadly secrecy, Miss Nightingale went out for a drive in the Park. Unrecognised, the living legend flitted for a moment before the common gaze. And the precaution was necessary; for there were times when, at some public function, the rumour of her presence was spread abroad; and ladies, mistaken by the crowd for Miss Nightingale, were followed, pressed upon, and vehemently supplicated—"Let me touch your shawl,"—"Let me stroke your arm"; such was the strange adoration in the hearts of the people. That vast reserve of force lay there behind her; she could use it, if she would. But she preferred never to use it. On occasions, she might hint or threaten; she might balance the sword of Damocles over the head of the Bison; she might, by a word, by a glance, remind some refractory minister, some unpersuadable viceroy, sitting in audience with her in the little upper room, that she was something more than a mere sick woman, that she had only, so to speak, to go to the window and wave her handkerchief, for . . . dreadful things to follow. But that was enough; they understood; the myth was there—obvious, portentous, impalpable; and so it remained to the last.

With statesmen and governors at her beck and call, with her hands on a hundred strings, with mighty provinces at her feet, with foreign governments agog for her counsel, building hospitals, training nurses—she still felt that she had not enough

to do. She sighed for more worlds to conquer—more, and yet
more. She looked about her—what was there left? Of
course! Philosophy! After the world of action, the world of
thought. Having set right the health of the British Army, she
would now do the same good service for the religious convictions of mankind. She had long noticed—with regret—the
growing tendency towards free-thinking among artisans. With
regret, but not altogether with surprise: the current teaching
of Christianity was sadly to seek; nay, Christianity itself was
not without its defects. She would rectify these errors. She
would correct the mistakes of the Churches; she would point
out just where Christianity was wrong; and she would explain
to the artisans what the facts of the case really were. Before
her departure for the Crimea, she had begun this work; and
now, in the intervals of her other labours, she completed it.
Her "Suggestions for Thought to the Searchers after Truth
among the Artisans of England" (1860), unravels, in the
course of three portly volumes, the difficulties—hitherto, curiously enough, unsolved—connected with such matters as Belief
in God, the Plan of Creation, the Origin of Evil, the Future
Life, Necessity and Free Will, Law, and the Nature of Morality. The Origin of Evil, in particular, held no perplexities for
Miss Nightingale. "We cannot conceive," she remarks, "that
Omnipotent Righteousness would find satisfaction in *solitary existence*." This being so, the only question remaining to be asked
is, "What beings should we then conceive that God would
create?" Now, He cannot create perfect beings, "since, essentially, perfection is one"; if He did so, He would only be
adding to Himself. Thus the conclusion is obvious: He *must*
create *im*perfect ones. Omnipotent Righteousness, faced by the
intolerable *impasse* of a solitary existence, finds itself bound,
by the very nature of the case, to create the hospitals at Scutari. Whether this argument would have satisfied the artisans,
was never discovered, for only a very few copies of the book
were printed for private circulation. One copy was sent to
Mr. Mill, who acknowledged it in an extremely polite letter.
He felt himself obliged, however, to confess that he had not
been altogether convinced by Miss Nightingale's proof of the
existence of God. Miss Nightingale was surprised and mortified; she had thought better of Mr. Mill; for surely her proof
of the existence of God could hardly be improved upon. "A
law," she had pointed out, "implies a lawgiver." Now the Uni-

verse is full of laws—the law of gravitation, the law of the excluded middle, and many others; hence it follows that the Universe has a lawgiver—and what would Mr. Mill be satisfied with, if he was not satisfied with that?

Perhaps Mr. Mill might have asked why the argument had not been pushed to its logical conclusion. Clearly, if we are to trust the analogy of human institutions, we must remember that laws are, as a matter of fact, not dispensed by lawgivers, but passed by Act of Parliament. Miss Nightingale, however, with all her experience of public life, never stopped to consider the question whether God might not be a Limited Monarchy.

Yet her conception of God was certainly not orthodox. She felt towards Him as she might have felt towards a glorified sanitary engineer; and in some of her speculations she seems hardly to distinguish between the Deity and the Drains. As one turns over these singular pages, one has the impression that Miss Nightingale has got the Almighty too into her clutches, and that, if He is not careful, she will kill Him with overwork.

Then, suddenly, in the very midst of the ramifying generalities of her metaphysical disquisitions there is an unexpected turn, and the reader is plunged all at once into something particular, something personal, something impregnated with intense experience—a virulent invective upon the position of women in the upper ranks of society. Forgetful alike of her high argument and of the artisans, the bitter creature rails through a hundred pages of close print at the falsities of family life, the ineptitudes of marriage, the emptiness of convention, in the spirit of an Ibsen or a Samuel Butler. Her fierce pen, shaking with intimate anger, depicts in biting sentences the fearful fate of an unmarried girl in a wealthy household. It is a *cri du cœur;* and then, as suddenly, she returns once more to instruct the artisans upon the nature of Omnipotent Righteousness.

Her mind was, indeed, better qualified to dissect the concrete and distasteful fruits of actual life than to construct a coherent system of abstract philosophy. In spite of her respect for Law, she was never at home with a generalisation. Thus, though the great achievement of her life lay in the immense impetus which she gave to the scientific treatment of sickness, a true comprehension of the scientific method itself was alien to her spirit. Like most great men of action—perhaps like all

—she was simply an empiricist. She believed in what she saw, and she acted accordingly; beyond that she would not go. She had found in Scutari that fresh air and light played an effective part in the prevention of the maladies with which she had to deal; and that was enough for her; she would not inquire further; what were the general principles underlying that fact —or even whether there were any—she refused to consider. Years after the discoveries of Pasteur and Lister, she laughed at what she called the "germ-fetish." There was no such thing as "infection"; she had never seen it, therefore it did not exist. But she *had* seen the good effects of fresh air; therefore there could be no doubt about them; and therefore it was essential that the bedrooms of patients should be well ventilated. Such was her doctrine; and in those days of hermetically sealed windows it was a very valuable one. But it was a purely empirical doctrine, and thus it led to some unfortunate results. When, for instance, her influence in India was at its height, she issued orders that all hospital windows should be invariably kept open. The authorities, who knew what an open window in the hot weather meant, protested, but in vain; Miss Nightingale was incredulous. She knew nothing of the hot weather, but she did know the value of fresh air—from personal experience; the authorities were talking nonsense and the windows must be kept open all the year round. There was a great outcry from all the doctors in India, but she was firm; and for a moment it seemed possible that her terrible commands would have to be put into execution. Lord Lawrence, however, was Viceroy, and he was able to intimate to Miss Nightingale, with sufficient authority, that he himself had decided upon the question, and that his decision must stand, even against her own. Upon that, she gave way, but reluctantly and quite unconvinced; she was only puzzled by the unexpected weakness of Lord Lawrence. No doubt, if she had lived to-day, and if her experience had lain, not among cholera cases at Scutari but among yellow-fever cases in Panama, she would have declared fresh air a fetish, and would have maintained to her dying day that the only really effective way of dealing with disease was by the destruction of mosquitoes.

Yet her mind, so positive, so realistic, so ultra-practical, had its singular revulsions, its mysterious moods of mysticism and of doubt. At times, lying sleepless in the early hours, she fell into long strange agonised meditations, and then, seizing a pencil, she would commit to paper the confessions of her soul. The morbid longings of her pre-Crimean days came over her once more; she filled page after page with self-examination, self-criticism, self-surrender. "O Father," she wrote, "I submit, I resign myself, I accept with all my heart this stretching out of Thy hand to save me. . . . O how vain it is, the vanity of vanities, to live in men's thoughts instead of God's!" She was lonely, she was miserable. "Thou knowest that through all these horrible twenty years, I have been supported by the belief that I was working with Thee who wert bringing everyone, even our poor nurses, to perfection,"—and yet, after all, what was the result? Had not even she been an unprofitable servant? One night, waking suddenly, she saw, in the dim light of the night-lamp, tenebrous shapes upon the wall. The past rushed back upon her. "Am I she who once stood on that Crimean height?" she wildly asked—"'The Lady with a lamp shall stand. . . .' The lamp shows me only my utter shipwreck."

She sought consolation in the writings of the Mystics and in a correspondence with Mr. Jowett. For many years the Master of Balliol acted as her spiritual adviser. He discussed with her in a series of enormous letters the problems of religion and philosophy; he criticised her writings on those subjects with the tactful sympathy of a cleric who was also a man of the world; and he even ventured to attempt at times to instil into her rebellious nature some of his own peculiar suavity. "I sometimes think," he told her, "that you ought seriously to consider how your work may be carried on, not with less energy, but in a calmer spirit. I am not blaming the past. . . . But I want the peace of God to settle on the future." He recommended her to spend her time no longer in "conflicts with Government offices," and to take up some literary work. He urged her to "work out her notion of Divine Perfection," in a series of essays for *Frazer's Magazine*. She did so; and the result was submitted to Mr. Froude, who pronounced the second essay to be "even more pregnant than the first. I cannot tell," he said, "how sanitary, with disordered intellects, the effects of such papers will be." Mr. Carlyle, indeed, used different language, and some remarks of his about a lost lamb bleating on the mountains having been unfortunately repeated to Miss Nightingale, all Mr. Jowett's suavity was required to keep the peace. In a letter of fourteen sheets, he turned her attention from this painful topic towards a discussion of Quietism. "I don't see why," said the Master of Balliol, "active life might not become a sort of passive life too." And then, he added, "I sometimes fancy there are possibilities of human character much greater than have been realised." She found such sentiments helpful, underlining them in blue pencil; and, in return, she assisted her friend with a long series of elaborate comments upon the Dialogues of Plato, most of which he embodied in the second edition of his translation. Gradually her interest became more personal; she told him never to work again after midnight, and he obeyed her. Then she helped him to draw up a special form of daily service for the College Chapel, with selections from the Psalms, under the heads of "God the Lord, God the Judge, God the Father, and God the Friend,"—though, indeed, this project was never realised; for the Bishop of Oxford disallowed the alterations, exercising his legal powers, on the advice of Sir Travers Twiss.

Their relations became intimate. "The spirit of the twenty-third psalm and the spirit of the nineteenth psalm should be united in our lives," Mr. Jowett said. Eventually, she asked him to do her a singular favour. Would he, knowing what he did of her religious views, come to London and administer to her the Holy Sacrament? He did not hesitate, and afterwards declared that he would always regard the occasion as a solemn event in his life. He was devoted to her; though the precise nature of his feelings towards her never quite transpired. Her feelings towards him were more mixed. At first, he was "that great and good man,"—"that true saint, Mr. Jowett"; but, as time went on, some gall was mingled with the balm; the acrimony of her nature asserted itself. She felt that she gave more sympathy than she received; she was exhausted, she was annoyed, by his conversation. Her tongue, one day, could not refrain from shooting out at him. "He comes to me, and he talks to me," she said, "as if I were someone else."

v

At one time she had almost decided to end her life in retirement, as a patient at St. Thomas's Hospital. But partly owing to the persuasions of Mr. Jowett, she changed her mind; for forty-five years she remained in South Street; and in South Street she died. As old age approached, though her influence with the official world gradually diminished, her activities seemed to remain as intense and widespread as before. When hospitals were to be built, when schemes of sanitary reform were in agitation, when wars broke out, she was still the adviser of all Europe. Still, with a characteristic self-assurance, she watched from her Mayfair bedroom over the welfare of India. Still, with an indefatigable enthusiasm, she pushed forward the work, which, perhaps, was nearer to her heart, more completely her own, than all the rest—the training of nurses. In her moments of deepest depression, when her greatest achievements seemed to lose their lustre, she thought of her nurses, and was comforted. The ways of God, she found, were strange indeed. "How inefficient I was in the Crimea," she noted. "Yet He has raised up from it trained nursing."

At other times she was better satisfied. Looking back, she was amazed by the enormous change which, since her early days, had come over the whole treatment of illness, the whole conception of public and domestic health—a change in which, she knew, she had played her part. One of her Indian admirers, the Aga Khan, came to visit her. She expatiated on the marvellous advances she had lived to see in the management of hospitals, in drainage, in ventilation, in sanitary work of every kind. There was a pause; and then, "Do you think you are improving?" asked the Aga Khan. She was a little taken aback, and said, "What do you mean by 'improving'?" He replied, "Believing more in God." She saw that he had a view of God which was different from hers. "A most interesting man," she noted after the interview; "but you could never teach him sanitation."

When old age actually came, something curious happened. Destiny, having waited very patiently, played a queer trick on Miss Nightingale. The benevolence and public spirit of that long life had only been equalled by its acerbity. Her virtue had dwelt in hardness, and she had poured forth her unstinted usefulness with a bitter smile upon her lips. And now the sarcastic years brought the proud woman her punishment. She was not to die as she had lived. The sting was to be taken out of her: she was to be made soft; she was to be reduced to compliance and complacency. The change came gradually, but at last it was unmistakable. The terrible commander who had driven Sidney Herbert to his death, to whom Mr. Jowett had applied the words of Homer, ἄμοτον μεμαυῖα —raging insatiably—now accepted small compliments with gratitude, and indulged in sentimental friendships with young girls. The author of *"Notes on Nursing"*—that classical compendium of the besetting sins of the sisterhood, drawn up with the detailed acrimony, the vindictive relish, of a Swift—now spent long hours in composing sympathetic Addresses to Probationers, whom she petted and wept over in turn. And at the same time there appeared a corresponding alteration in her physical mould. The thin, angular woman, with her haughty eye and her acrid mouth, had vanished; and in her place was the rounded bulky form of a fat old lady, smiling all day long. Then something else became visible. The brain which had been steeled at Scutari was indeed, literally, growing soft. Senility—an ever more and more amiable senility—descended. Towards the end, consciousness itself grew lost in a roseate haze, and melted into nothingness. It was just then, three years before her death, when she was eighty-seven years old (1907), that those in authority bethought them that the opportune moment had come for bestowing a public honour on Florence Nightingale. She was offered the Order of Merit. That Order, whose roll contains, among other distinguished names, those of Sir Laurence Alma Tadema and Sir Edward Elgar, is remarkable chiefly for the fact that, as its title indicates, it is bestowed because its recipient deserves it, and for no other reason. Miss Nightingale's representatives accepted the honour, and her name, after a lapse of many years, once more appeared in the Press. Congratulations from all sides came pouring in. There was a universal burst of enthusiasm—a final revivification of the ancient myth. Among her other admirers, the German Emperor took this opportunity of expressing his feelings towards her. "His Majesty," wrote the German Ambassador, "having just brought to a close a most enjoyable stay in the beautiful neighbourhood of your old home near Romsey, has commanded me to present you with some flowers as a token of his esteem." Then, by Royal command, the Order of Merit was brought to South Street, and there was a little ceremony of presentation. Sir Douglas Dawson, after a short speech, stepped forward, and handed the insignia of the Order to Miss Nightingale. Propped up by pillows, she dimly recognised that some compliment was being paid her. "Too kind—too kind," she murmured; and she was not ironical.

Julian Huxley

RELIGION AND SCIENCE: OLD WINE IN NEW BOTTLES

"In la sua volontade è nostra pace."—DANTE.

"Ye are the Gods if ye did but realize it."—CARLYLE.

"THE next great task of Science is to create a religion for humanity." So says Lord Morley in one of his essays. It is a striking saying, coming as it does from one in whom thought and action have been so intertwined, one to whom reason, not dogma, is the basis of morality, achievement, not emotion, its justification.

Let those words be my encouragement; for they challenge at the outset, and to my mind rightly, two of the most persistent difficulties that confront one who tries to write of the relations between Science and Religion. The man of science too often asks what science can have to do with what he brands as utterly and wholly unscientific; the religiously-minded man demands what gain can follow from contact with the cold and inhuman attitude of pure reason. To those questions I hope that this essay will provide a partial answer. Meanwhile I shall begin with a perhaps less ultimate but more pressing question. That question is asked by many men and women of to-day, who on the one hand feel as it were instinctively that religion of some sort is necessary for life, yet on the other are unable to do violence to their intellectual selves by denying the facts that reason and scientific inquiry reveal, or by closing their eyes to them.

The question, in briefest form, is this: "What room does science leave for God?"

To the savage, all is spirit. The meanest objects are charged with influence, the commonest actions fraught with spiritual possibilities, the operations of nature one and all are brought about by spiritual powers—but powers multifarious and conflicting. "Nature can have little unity for savages. It is a Walpurgis-nacht procession, a checkered play of light and shadow, a medley of impish and elfish, friendly and inimical powers."[1]

But with ordered civilization and dispassionate observation a network of material cause and effect invaded this spiritual domain. The mysterious influences, for example, believed to be inherent in springs and running rivers became personified, and, anthropomorphized as nymphs or gods, were removed into a seclusion more remote from practical and everyday life than their unpersonified predecessors. Later, they retreated still farther from actuality into a half-believed mythology, and then passed away into the powerlessness of avowed fairy-story or literary symbolism, while the rivers, perceived as the resultant of natural forces, were more and more harnessed to man's use. So with the wind and the rain, the growth of crops, the storms of the sea. So, in due time, with the thunder and the lightning, with earthquakes, eruptions, comets, eclipses, pestilences.

This process of liberating matter from arbitrary and mysterious power, of perceiving it as orderly and endowed with regularity of natural law, of bringing it more and more beneath human control, was, on the other hand, accompanied by what may be called a combined condensation and sublimation of the spiritual forces accepted by human faith. They are built up from spirit to spirits, spirits to gods, gods to God. But now it seems as if this condensation had reached its limit, and the sublimation could only go farther by resolving the one God into an empty name or the vaguest unreality.

We look back and see the Gods of early man, and are complacently prepared to believe that they were based in error, products of mental immaturity, to be relegated to limbo without regret. But what about the present? Why should we shrink from applying the same process to the God of to-day?

Is it then to be so with every God? Is God only a personified symbol of our residuum of ignorance? Is to hold the idea of God in any form to be, as Salomon Reinach believes, in an infantile stage of human development, and must we with him define religion as "a sum of beliefs impeding the free use of human faculty"?

I think not; and I shall endeavour to justify my belief to

[1] W. James, '09, p. 21.

you, and to show that, albeit much alteration and a thorough revision of ideas is needed, the term *God* has an important scientific connotation, and further that the present stagnation of religion can be remedied if, as has happened again and again in biological evolution, the old forms become extinct or subordinate, and a new dominant type is developed along quite fresh lines.

In any case the man of science must obviously, if he face the problem at all, take up a scientific attitude of mind towards it. He cannot say that there is no such thing as religion; or try to whittle it away by explaining that it is something else —a complicated fear, or a sublimated sex-instinct, or a combination of credulity and duplicity. A thing, if it is a thing at all, is never merely something else. Nor can he submit to the pretensions of those who assert that it is too sacred to be touched, or that its certainties are greater than those of science. No—he must treat it for what it is—a fact, and a very important fact at that, in human history: and he must see whether the application of scientific method to its study—in other words, its illumination by the faculty of pure intellect —will help not only our comprehension of religion in the past, but its actual development in the future.

He can study it in various ways. He can use the method of observation and comparison, collecting and collating facts until he is able to give a connected account of the manifestations of religion and of their past history; he can study it physiologically, so to speak, to see what part it plays in the body politic, and how that part may alter with circumstances; or he may seek to investigate its essence, to discover not only how it appears and what it does, but what it *is*.

Further, he must have some general principles to lean on in his search, principles both positive and negative. He must be content to leave certain possibilities out of account because as yet he cannot see how they can be connected with his organized scheme of things; in other words, he has to be content to build slowly and imperfectly in order that he may be sure of building soundly. This is the principle which we may call positive agnosticism.

This very fact has been in the past one of the great obstacles in the way of successful treatment of religion by science. One of the attributes of man is his desire for a complete explanation, or at least a complete view, of his universe, and this has been at the bottom of much doctrine and many creeds. But before Kepler and Newton, no truly scientific account could be given of celestial phenomena; before Darwin, none of Natural History; before the recent revival in psychology, none of the mind and its workings. In the second half of the nineteenth century, for instance, science could give an adequate account of most inorganic phenomena, and, in broad outline, of evolutionary geology and biology; but mind was still refractory. Accordingly, the philosophy of science was mainly materialist. But the common man felt that mind was not the empty epiphenomenon that orthodox science would have it; and he desired a scheme of things in which mind should be more adequately explained than it could be by science at its then stage of development. *Hinc illae lacrimae.*

To-day, it is at least possible to link up, not only physics and chemistry and geology and evolutionary biology, but also anthropology and psychology, into a whole which, though far from complete, is at least organized and coherent with itself. If the seventeenth century cleared the ground for that dwelling-place of human mind which we call the scientific view of things, if the eighteenth century laid the foundations and the nineteenth built the walls, the twentieth is already fitting up some of the rooms for actual habitation.

There are certain other domains of reality which have not yet been properly investigated by science. Telepathy, for instance, and the whole mass of phenomena included broadly under the term spiritualism, are in about the same position with regard to organized scientific thought to-day as was astronomy before astrology's collapse, as was the study of electricity in the eighteenth century, or that of hypnotism in the middle of the nineteenth. What is more, the average man demands that phenomena of this order shall be included in his scheme of things. Science cannot yet do this for him; and accordingly the dwelling-place that we are building must still be incomplete; it is for those who come after to build the upper stories.

This cannot be helped. What we build, we must build firmly; on what is yet to be built, science cannot pronounce, except to say that she knows that it will be congruous with what has gone before.

What general principles, then, do we assume? We assume that the universe is composed throughout of the same matter, whose essential unity, in spite of the diversity of its so-called elements, the recent researches of physicists are revealing to us; we assume that matter behaves in the same way wherever it is found, showing the same mode of sequence of change, of cause and effect. We assume, on fairly good although indirect evidence, that there has been an evolution of the forms assumed by matter; that, in this solar system of ours, for instance, matter was once all in electronic form, that it then attained to the atomic and the molecular; that later, colloidal organic matter of a special type made its appearance, and later still, living matter arose. That the forms of life, simple at first, attained progressively to greater complexity; that mind, negligible in the lower forms, became of greater and greater importance, until it reached its present level in man.[1]

Unity, uniformity, and development are the three great principles that emerge. We know of no instance where the properties of matter change, though many where a new state of matter develops. The full properties of a molecular compound such as water, for instance, cannot be deduced at present from what we know about the properties of its constituent atoms of hydrogen and oxygen. The properties of the human mind cannot be deduced from our present knowledge of the minds of animals. New combinations and properties thus arise in time. Bergson miscalls such evolution "creative." We had better, with Lloyd Morgan, call it "emergent."

With mind, we find a gradual evolution from a state in which it is impossible to distinguish mental response from physiological reaction, up to the intensity and complexity of our own emotions and intellect. Since all material developments in evolution can be traced back step by step and shown to be specializations of one or more of the primitive properties of living matter, it is not only an economy of hypothesis, but also, in the absence of any evidence to the contrary, the proper conclusion, that mental properties also are to be traced back to the simplest and most original forms of life. What exact significance is to be attached to the term "mental properties" in such organisms, it is hard to say; we mean, however, that something of the same general nature as mind in ourselves is inherent in all life, something standing in the same relation to living matter in general as do our minds to the particular living matter of our brains.

[1] See Danysz, '21.

But there can be no reasonable doubt that living matter, in due process of time, originated from non-living; and if that be so, we must push our conclusion farther, and believe that not only living matter, but all matter, is associated with something of the same general description as mind in higher animals. We come, that is, to a monistic conclusion, in that we believe that there is only one fundamental substance, and that this possesses not only material properties, but also properties for which the word *mental* is the nearest approach. We want a new word to denote this X, this world-stuff; *matter* will not do, for that is a word which the physicists and chemists have moulded to suit themselves, and since they have not yet learned to detect or measure mental phenomena, they restrict the word "material" to mean "non-mental," and "matter" to mean that which has such "material" properties.

You will remember William of Occam's razor; "Entia non multiplicanda praeter necessitatem"; when we are monists in the sense I have just outlined, we are using that weapon to shave away a very unrestrained growth of hair which has long obscured the features of reality.

Holding to these principles, we must, until evidence to the contrary is produced, reject any explanation which proceeds by cataclysms, or by miracles; a miracle becomes (when not an illusion) simply an event which is on the one hand uncommon, and for which, on the other, there has been found no explanation. Revelation too goes by the board—save a revelation which is simply a name for the progressive increase of knowledge and insight.

Last, but not least, we do not pretend to know the Absolute. We know phenomena, and our systems, in so far as scientific, are interpretations of phenomena.

* * * * * *

Religion has been defined in a hundred different ways. It has been defined intellectually—as a creed; as myth; as a view of the universe; it has been defined emotionally as consisting in awe; in fear; in love; in mystical exaltation or communion. It has been defined from the standpoint of action—as worship; as ritual; as sacrifice; as morality. Matthew Arnold called it "morality tinged with emotion"; Salomon Reinach "a sum of scruples impeding the free use of human faculties." Jevons makes the experiencing of God the central feature; and so on and so forth. Is it possible to find any common measure for all these statements? Would it not be better to unite with those who cut the Gordian knot by writing down all religion simply as illusion? No. For their point of view is meaningless. Even illusions are, in themselves, facts to be investigated; and even illusions have a basis.

But it is not necessary to believe that it is an illusion; the knot may be untied. Ritual, Creed, Morality, Mystical Experience—all these are manifestations of religion, but not religion itself. Religion itself is the reaction between man as a personality on the one side, and, on the other, all of the universe with which he comes in contact. It is not only ritual, for you may have obviously non-religious ritual, as in a court ceremonial or a legal function: it is not merely morality, for men may practise morality, the most austere or the most *terre à terre*, uninspired by anything that could remotely be called religious: it is not belief, for we may have beliefs of all kinds, even to the most complex scientific beliefs concerning the universe, which have yet no connection with religion: it is neither communion in itself, nor ecstasy in itself, as many lovers and poets could tell you.

But because it is a reaction of the whole personality, it must involve intellectual *and* practical *and* emotional processes: and because man has the powers of abstraction and association, or rather because his mind in most cases cannot help making associations and abstractions, it follows that it will inevitably concern itself, consciously or subconsciously, with all the phenomena that it encounters, will try to bring them all into its scheme, and will try to unify them and frame concepts to deal with them as a whole.

Some men will be more concerned on the emotional, others on the intellectual, others again on the moral side: but it is impossible to separate any one of the three aspects entirely from the others.

We will begin with and treat mainly of the intellectual aspect of the problem, the credal side. For one thing, science has more direct concern with it than with the others; for another, more continuous and startling alterations have had to be made in it; and finally, the actual problem is there felt most acutely at the present moment.

What, then, is the problem? In the terms of our definition

of religion, it is in its most general terms as follows: Man has to live his life in a world in which he is confronted with forces and powers other than his own. He is a mere animalcule in comparison with the totality of these forces, his life a second in comparison with their centuries. By his mental constitution, he of necessity attempts to formulate some intelligible account of the constitution of the world and its relation to himself— or should we rather say in so far as it is in relation to himself? —and so we have a myth, a doctrine, or a creed.

At the present moment, as we have already seen, there appears to be an irreconcilable conflict between orthodox Christianity and orthodox Natural Science. The one asserts the existence of an omnipotent, omniscient, personal God— creator, ruler, and refuge. The other, by reducing ever more and more of natural phenomena to what we please to call natural laws—in other words, to orderly processes proceeding inevitably from the known constitution and properties of matter—has robbed such a God of ever more and more of his realm and possible power; until finally, with the rise of evolutionary biology and psychology, there seems to be no place any more for a God in the universe.

Stated thus, the opposition is complete. But let us return on our footsteps, and trace for one thing some of the history of religious beliefs, for another reinvestigate, from a slightly unusual standpoint, the actual knowledge of the Universe which science has given us.

Man has developed: in early stages, his physical and mental capacities developed; in later stages development has been mainly restricted to his traditions, ideas, and achievements. As part of his development, his religious ideas have altered too.

At the beginning, he appears to have no ideas of a God of Gods at all—merely of influences and powers, obviously (he would say) inherent in the forces of Nature, magically inherent in certain objects and actions—fetishes and incantations. He seems scarcely to have been conscious of himself as an individual, or of the full distinction between self and the external world.

Later, perhaps as the idea of his own personality grew, he began to ascribe a more personal existence to the forces with which he came into contact, and so to turn them more and more into beings that can properly be called Gods: polydaemonism arose and in its turn gave place to polytheism.

But while rigid custom was at first the only morality, and each external power and each human activity was regarded separately, later the rise of civilization led to a modification of custom, to a reference of action and belief to the standards of pure reason, and to an attempt at unification. Once this occurred, and equally so whether the attempt at unification had an intellectual or a moral basis, polytheism was doomed. Its downfall has been often described; the reasons for it are suggestively put by Jevons in his little book, "The Idea of God." It passes through a stage where one among the gods is pre-eminent: but finally even that does not suffice, and in its place arises a monotheistic creed.

Monotheism may start as a purely local or tribal affair—my one God against yours. It may not only start, but long continue so. Readers of Mr. Bang's collection of startling German war-sayings will remember the superbly national prayer of the Prussian pastor who addressed his God (I quote from memory) as "Du, der hoch über Cherubinen, Seraphinen, und Zeppelinen ewig trönst." (J. P. Bang, *Hurrah and Hallelujah.* London, 1916.) But this idea, too, is self-contradictory, and merges into that of one God for all men. The primitive anthropomorphism which had invested the first vague and mysterious spirits with human parts and passions, human speech and thought, also fell into gradual desuetude. It was kept up as a symbol, or because of the difficulty of describing a God except in terms human individuality, but its literal truth was deliberately denied. God became different from and more than man—omnipotent, omniscient, with no parts, with no limitations: but he retained personality—in other words, a mental or spiritual organization of the same general kind as man's, however superior in degree. With time, the divine personality became compounded more and more of man's ideals instead of his everyday thoughts and attributes. And thus and that God remains. He has created everything; he is in some sense immanent in the world, in some sense apart from it as its ruler —you take your choice according to your philosophic preferences. Beyond that, organized religious thought has not gone; and now it finds itself fronting science in an impasse.

That, very briefly and roughly, is how man's idea of God has developed. But how have man's knowledge and ideas of the natural universe developed? What has Science to say to the impasse?

Man has to deal with three great categories of phenomena—the inorganic, the organic, and the psychic. In the inorganic, chemistry first and then physics have given us a picture whose broad outlines are now familiar. There is but one type and store of energy in Nature, whether it drives a train, animates a man, radiates in heat or light, inheres in a falling stone. There is but one substance. All bodies of trees, of men, rivers and rocks, the clouds in the air and the air itself, precious stones and common clay—all can be resolved into a limited number of elements. And these elements in their turn can be resolved into combinations, differing, it appears, only quantitatively from each other, of electrical charges; so that at the last all matter is one, and becomes perhaps indistinguishable, or at least inseparable, from energy. There is no personal operator for particular happenings; the lightning and the volcano are the inevitable outcome of the material constitution of things, equally with the form and colour of a pebble and with the fact that it will drop to the ground if it is let fall. All is impersonal order and unity.

There is, however, one other great fact about the system of inorganic matter. The energy contained in it tends to be degraded, as the physicists say—in other words to become less readily available. There is available energy in moving matter. There is potential energy in all matter, dependent upon whether it can be set in motion. But if the sea were to cover the whole surface of the globe, it would be impossible to extract energy from running water as we do now, because no water would be running. So too heat is energy; but it is only available when it can flow, when there are hotter and colder bodies. The law under which transformations of energy operate has now been investigated, and it has been established that in every energy-transaction a certain modicum goes to waste as unavailable heat, so that, unless some at present unforeseen change occurs, the last state of the universe, considered as a purely physico-chemical mechanism, will be one of death, of inactivity, with all matter at a uniform low temperature and the whole stock of energy locked up and unavailable in this sea of tranquillity. True for one thing that an almost inconceivable number of millions of years must elapse before this "death of matter" is realized; and for another that we are unable to understand how such a progressive degradation could have been in operation from all eternity. We must not expect complete knowledge within a few years or a few centuries; but even if the beginning is veiled—for there is no more evidence for a "creation" than for (say) a rhythmic reversal of the direction of energy-availability—and if it is always possible that some unforeseen change in the process should occur before the whole runs down, yet it is a fact (and we are resolved to be agnostic save about facts) that, here and now, a direction is to be observed in the evolution of inorganic matter, by which natural operations are tending to become less active, and the amount of available energy is diminishing. If it continues indefinitely, first life, and later on all activity and change whatsoever will cease. There is a tendency towards death and towards unchanging inactivity.

The next great category is that of the organic, of living matter. We have to consider its origin and later history. So far as constitution goes, living matter is merely a special and highly complicated form of ordinary matter; and there can be no reasonable doubt that it has originated naturally from non-living matter.

While the *main* direction of the inorganic has been towards degradation of energy, it has shown another subsidiary direction towards the production of more and more complex forms of matter. If our general ideas are correct, there must have been a time when matter in our ordinary sense of the word did not exist—there can have been no atoms, only free electrons. From this state, there evolved one in which the various electron-systems that we call atoms first appeared; later still, atoms could join with atoms to produce molecules. Leaping over vast periods, we would come to the time when radiation had brought the temperature of the earth surface below 100 degrees centigrade; water then could form from steam and solution occur. Through solution, all soluble elements, which would otherwise remain locked in the inactivity of the solid state, are enabled to enter upon a new phase of mobility, of chemical life, as we may say. Only in water could colloid carbon compounds first be built up, and only from such substances could life originate.

Living substance, or at least much of it, must be formed of molecules containing thousands of atoms, each atom in its turn a system of circling electrons. Here already is a vast increase of complexity: it remains to be seen whether the same tendency is perpetuated later.

The evolutionary concept is to biology what the doctrine of the conservation of energy has been in the physico-chemical sciences—an indispensable preliminary to proper methods of attack. But while great stress has been laid on the various *methods* by which evolution may be supposed to have taken place—natural selection, Lamarckism, orthogenesis and the rest—biology has concerned herself comparatively little with the *form* of the process in itself. But it is here that evolution becomes of value to us in our present search; for once more we become aware of a direction. Partly from the direct evidence of palaeontology, partly from indirect evidence, but along many converging lines, we can form an idea of this direction which in broad outlines is unassailable.

During life's existence on earth—a period to be reckoned in hundreds and probably in thousands of millions of years—there has been an increase in various of its attributes. But just as in the inorganic world electrons and atoms still exist as such side by side with molecules, so also the earlier types of living matter continue to exist side by side with the later. The increase is not therefore seen uniformly in all forms at once, but is most easily observed by studying the *maximum* level attained. Size, for instance, is one of these attributes; and whereas to-day all variations are to be found between ultra-microscopic disease-germs and vast organisms like whales and elephants, there has been a gradual steadying increase (tending to a limit) in the size of the *largest* organisms existing at any one period.

If we confine ourselves for the moment to the material side, we find that the directional change in organic evolution can be reduced to this—to an increase of the control exercised by living matter over the environment, and of its independence of the environment—two reciprocal aspects of a single process. When we look more closely into the means by which this has been achieved, we shall see an increase of the maximum not only in size, but in complexity, in length of life, in efficiency of particular organs, in co-ordination of parts and general harmony, in improvement of sense-organs, and, continuing even after other tendencies have reached their limits, in brain-size and consequently in complexity of mode of reaction and behaviour.

If we turn to the psychological side, we find that there has been an increase in the intensity of mental process. This is apparent in all aspects of mind, on that of emotion equally with that of knowledge, of volition equally with that of emotion. To be an amoeba or a worm is to live a life almost without windows. Perfection of sense-organs makes it possible for life to be aware of the different types of outer events, whilst memory and, later, associative memory give the possibility of understanding their history. In higher forms volition can be maintained for longer and longer intervals, can attain greater intensity, and can fix itself upon ever more and more distant objects. With depth of feeling comes also differentiation, so that finally we find in ourselves the possibility of organizing various blends of the simple emotions into the compound emotional forms such as reverence and admiration, called *sentiments* by McDougall.

Biologically speaking, therefore, the direction observable in mental evolution is again towards increased control and increased independence; by mental and cerebral improvement there is introduced a greater accuracy and a greater range of control, as well as better adjustment between organisms and environment, than would be otherwise possible to the same bodily organs.

The direction of life may therefore be roughly summed up in the two words "more life"—more both in quantity (have not both land and air been colonized during evolution?) and also in quality. More matter has been stolen from the lifeless and embodied in the living; and the living begins to be less helpless in face of the lifeless.

The direction of living matter is thus in many ways opposed to the direction to be seen in inorganic matter; yet not only has the organic arisen from the inorganic, but its direction continues one direction already traceable before the appearance of life.[1]

Finally, we come to the psychological aspect of the universe. We have already touched on it in connection with biology, and found that in many ways at least the development of mind follows the same lines as that of living matter, and helps forward the general trend of life.

But finally a kink occurs, a critical point similar to that seen at the origin of living from non-living matter. There the attributes of living matter which mark it off from inorganic matter become dominant—its capacity for self-reproduction,

[1]See Danysz, '21.

its tendency to organization. The colloid carbon compound had been the highest known independent unit; from now on this place was taken by the organism.

In exactly the same way, in the final stages of evolution (as witnessed abundantly by fossil mammals) complexity of purely bodily organization had reached a limit, and survival, as is evidenced by increasing size of brain, came to be determined more and more by mental qualities. Finally the curve of mental development caught up with that of body, and intersected it: mind became the dominant factor in the new type of organism, and in the subsequent history of the evolutionary process. The *organism* ceased to be the highest unit, and gave place to the *person*, or self-conscious individual with organized mind.

This new critical point was reached when man arose; many authors recognize it for what it is, the beginning of a new era, by christening the subsequent geological period the Psychozoic. That period, geologically speaking, has not yet run but a tiny span; and we are no more entitled to think that we have reached or even imagined the possibilities of its future evolution than we should have been entitled to regard the possibilities of purely biological evolution as having been exhausted after the far longer period needed to give rise to a coral polyp or a jelly-fish as highest existing types of organism. Even man as a biological species is in his infancy, not to speak of other psychozoic types that may be waiting in the womb of time.

But what are the characteristics of this new phase? In the first place, mind has become self-conscious; thus the evolutionary methods of psychozoic organisms may become conscious, and they come to direct their own evolution instead of having their destinies shaped by the blind forces of natural selection.

In most respects the same direction as before is pursued, but new methods are introduced. The rate of change, of movement in that direction, is accelerated; and the possibility is given of eliminating a vast deal of waste. A watchmaker sends out very few defective watches: why? because he makes his watches on a preconceived plan. Even when an improvement in watch construction is introduced, he can draw up his plan beforehand, and at the worst, waste only time and paper, instead of metal

and far more time. Ideas do not need to be embodied before
selection can act upon them; thus an increasing amount of
evolutionary change will take place through the natural selection of ideas than through the older and far more wasteful
process, natural selection of individuals and species.

Finally, values appear upon the scene. If we could ask a wild
animal such as a fox what gave value to its life, and it could
answer us, it would doubtless say food, sleep, comfort, hunting,
sexual pleasure, and family companionship. But it cannot
answer; nor can it know the value of what it pursues, but only
appreciate the result. Strictly speaking, values do not exist for
it. However, even if we allow ourselves to speak of values in
the life of pre-human organisms, we see immediately that
wholly new values are introduced after the critical point.

Putting it summarily, we can say that, with the rise of mind
to dominance, various activities of mind come to be pursued
for their own sake, to have value in themselves. Our life is
worth living not only for the sake of eating and drinking, sleeping, athletics, and sexual pleasure. There is a value attached
to knowledge for its own sake, apart from the possible access
of control that it may bring. But this is new, a property of
man alone; not even Athena's owl will exert itself through
laborious years to understand celestial mechanics or physiology.
The highest anthropoids do not attempt to create works of
art, which for man come to have value in themselves. Natural
beauty comes to have its value too; a cow (so far as known!)
does not interrupt the business of its life to admire the sunset,
whereas men may and do. Behaviour also is implicated; with
the entry upon the scene of that practically unlimited number
of possible reactions which give us what we call free will and
choice, there comes a conviction that some modes of action are
higher than others; and so a scale of moral values comes into
being.[1]

Nor is it merely that values, in the strict sense, are created;
nor that new values come into being. But with the enlargement
of mind and its more perfect organization, there arises a new
method of appraising values, and so a new type of value
altogether. I mean of course the so-called *absolute values*.
Absolute values are never absolute in the sense of absolute completeness; they are relative to two things—to external reality

[1] See Haldane, '21; Thouless, '23.

and to our mental powers and organization.[1] They are abstractions; we generalize the value in our minds, and at the same time raise it to the highest pitch of intensity we can. An interesting point arises from this way of thinking. Apart from the guarantee of our own convictions, the observable direction of living nature is our guarantee of right: or one had better say that it is at once the guarantee and the touchstone of our convictions. But two things may be moving in the same direction, and, if one be moving much slower than the other, the slower may impede the faster; a pedestrian procession making eastward along Fleet Street will hold up the life of the city for a time, and cows walking along railways are treated as obstacles by trains proceeding in the same direction. So it comes about that much that was once progressive in organic evolution has become an obstacle or a drag to psychozoic evolution; it is *relatively* retrogressive, and, from our present standpoint, bad. To take the simplest and most fundamental example: evolution by blind natural selection was the method of progress for organisms below man. Unceasing struggle and courage was the chief factor in producing the grandeur and strength of the lion, the swiftness and grace of deer, the brilliance and lightness of the birds. But if the same end can be obtained both more quickly and more bloodlessly by new methods, then the old stands condemned. Here lies the key to the problem propounded by Huxley in his Romanes Lecture—the problem of man's relation to the rest of the cosmic process, at once sprung from it by gradual generation and separated from it by an absolute and unbridgeable chasm, at once one with it and in deadly combat with it and all its ways.

Our mode of envisaging the problem illuminates it, and shows it as inevitable and intelligible instead of insoluble and tormenting; and illuminates too many other minor problems of good and evil. But all this is a side-issue: *revenons à nos moutons.*

Unknown, or neutral, or hostile power: a movement similar in direction to the direction in which history on the whole shows

---

[1]A confusion of thought easily arises here. It may be absolutely true that 2 and 2 make 4; we may be absolutely right in certain cases to tell a lie; or may find an expression of absolute beauty in some one lovely thing. But we may grow to find that same thing aesthetically unsatisfying; we can imagine a state of society in which it would never be right to lie; while our correct knowledge of elementary arithmetic is something very partial and incomplete considered in relation to mathematical truth as a whole.

we are moving, and to that which we desire with our highest
aspirations, but operating blindly; an acceleration of that
movement by the coming of mind to biological predominance,
with certain consequent minor changes in direction by major
changes in speed and in methods. Three tendencies, but all
founded in one unity, and each arising out of the other—that
is the picture drawn for us by the present state of science. In
this sense, and in this only, can it be said that "all things work
together for righteousness."

One word on an important side-issue—the problem of evil
in man, of stagnancy and degeneration in organic evolution.
Degeneration often does occur—a reversal, in other words, of
the main tendency. But the positive fact remains that the *maximum*
level is progressively raised, and that we find that stagnation of development and even sometimes degeneration have been
factors indirectly helping on the main direction.

We must accept the positive main direction for what it is—
an external sanction of faith; confess that we do not understand the detailed working of the whole, but see in the change
of methods brought about by the rise of mind a hope that we
shall gradually learn at least to dispense with much waste and
evil and degeneration in the further course of evolution.

This main direction gives us cause for optimism. The exceptions to it temper that optimism. But the direction is there.

As we shall see later, we may either call the sum of the forces
acting in the cosmos the manifestations of God, who in this
case must be the Absolute God, and unknowable except through
these manifestations. Or we may confine the term God to its
anthropological usage, as denoting the objects of human religion, in which case we must admit that the term God as
understood by man is constituted by *man's idea of* the forces
acting in the cosmos, so that not only are these forces involved,
not only a possible Absolute God behind them, but also the
organizing power of human mind.

I wish you here to agree to my adopting the second alternative and giving the name of God to the sum of the forces acting
in the cosmos as perceived and grasped by human mind. We
can therefore now say that God is one, but that though one,
has several aspects. There is one aspect of God which is neutral
to us, in a way hostile, mere Power operating in the vastness
of the stellar universes, apprehended only as orderly, tending
in a direction which appears to be in the long run inimical. It

is to this aspect of God that Mr. Wells has given the name of the Veiled Being—a somewhat primitive term for a true idea. There is another aspect, which is the one seen operating in that sphere which comprises the whole of life upon this earth—a sphere infinitesimal in relation to the whole, yet still vast in relation to ourselves. This aspect of God is our refuge and guarantee, for here we find our assurance that our human life is a part of a whole that is not antagonistic, but moves in the same general direction as do our history and our aims. There does exist, in Matthew Arnold's words, "a power, not ourselves, that makes for righteousness." And this second aspect is not wholly separate from the first, in spite of its difference of direction; for the first is its parent, physically and temporally, and the direction of biological progress is the continuation of a line of development marked out, within the opposed inorganic direction, even from the first.

Next, there is a more immediate and more often demanded assurance that we, as individuals or as single communities in space or time, are at one with humanity as a whole. Here it is that we look to the third aspect of God, which enshrines the directive forces operating in man. These directive forces are our instincts, our needs, our values, our ideals. When those are harmonized with each other and with the outer world by reason and experience, they form a power which we can see has been directive, normative in the past, and will continue to be so in the future. It alters with man's development; but after a first rudimentary phase, its main outlines, its type of organization remain the same, for man's instincts and ideals do not greatly change, and their harmonization with each other and with experience will generally proceed in the same broad way. Although in a sense this aspect is the smallest, as comprising the smallest physical field, yet in another it is the largest, since man's ideals are in themselves unlimited, non-finite; and the values involved, to our present type of mind, appear ultimate. This third aspect of God is again historically the offspring of the second, and through the second of the first.

Matter, life, mind—this is the simplest classification of phenomena. By means of processes analogous to obtaining a resultant by the parallelogram of forces, we can obtain a resultant of material operations in general, vital operations in general, and mental operations in general, numerous and varied in direction though they be. Life is the link between the other two. Living matter is so definitely one with non-living matter, not at all obviously one with mind; yet the direction of living matter is obviously similar to that of mind, not at all obviously one with that of non-living matter.

*　*　*　*　*

It is a simple fact that the conception which man has of the universe and its relation to himself exercises important effects upon his life. A name therefore is needed for this an-thropological phenomenon. *God* is the usual name applied, and we shall retain it in default of another, premissing that the word,—like many similar general terms—"love," or "life," or "beauty," say—can be defined and applied in many ways, and that we apply it here in a particular and perhaps somewhat novel sense.

God in this sense is the universe, not as such, but so far as grasped as a whole by a mind, embodied in an idea,[1] and in con-sequence capable of influencing that mind, and through it the whole course of events. It is not grasped as a mere sum of details, but, however vaguely and imperfectly, as a single idea, unitary in spite of its complexity. Nor is it the universe in itself, but only so far as it has been thus grasped by mind. There exists no other meaning of the term which, on analysis, is found to convey anything, or at least anything scientific or comprehensible, to us. We may reason that there is an Abso-lute God behind the universe and our idea of it. But we have no proof of this statement, and such an Absolute God is, as Spencer pointed out, an Unknowable, and accordingly no con-cern of ours. That part and these aspects of the universe which have been grasped by us may prove to contain the key to many of our difficulties; meanwhile we can only be humble and admit that our idea of God, even in this restricted sense, is still ex-tremely incomplete: and in this sense there is a God far greater than our present idea and knowledge of God, only waiting to be discovered.

---

[1] It is interesting to note that a scientific treatment of the problem may force an author almost unwittingly to similar conclusions. For instance, in Jevons' book ('10) the term "God" hardly occurs at all, whereas the phrase "the idea of God" is to be found on nearly every page. If, as we are urging, God as efficient agent in the world and as reality in contact with human beings *is* outer world organized as idea, the reason for such periphrasis at once appears.

That which it is essential to establish is our way of looking at the problem. The universe does come into relation with our minds, and there, owing to the way it and our minds are organized, generates an idea which exerts an influence upon us.

The external basis of the idea of God is thus constituted by the forces operating in the universe. The universe is a unitary whole, greater and more powerful than ourselves, and its operations have resultants in certain main directions—these are phenomena which we constatate like any other phenomena. They, and that other phenomenon of our contact with the Universe and our exposure to the play of its forces, give us our objective knowledge of God. The rest of our idea of God, the inner component, depends upon the mode of action of our minds.

So far, then, we have shown that recent advance in science, particularly in our understanding of evolution, has enabled us to give a more objective account than ever before of what is involved in the concept *God*, and so to pave the way for a consensus of thought on the question.

It will be observed that there is no idea of personality implicit in this conception of God—God may or may not possess personality. It will be for us later to investigate that particular aspect of the problem.

It now remains to deal with the inner reality. Man has a wholly new type of mind. He is social and capable of speech. He generalizes, and he has a very highly developed power of association. This combination gives him a great many possibilities hitherto denied to life. In the first place, he is able to order his experiences in a totally new way, differing from the old very much as a classified card-index differs from a rough diary-record of events. The organization of his mind is elastic, capable of indefinite expansion and of specialization in any direction.

That being so, there will be always parts of his mind wholly or at least partially undeveloped; and in any case the capacities which he must employ in his everyday life, the region of his mind illuminated by the attention needed in the struggle for existence, constitute but a fraction of his mental self and its potentialities.

This brings us on to one of the most important achievements of modern psychology—the discovery and analysis of the subconscious. Impossible here to go into detail; we must content ourselves with a few broad statements. When we speak of the sub-conscious mind, we mean that in man there exist processes which appear for many reasons to be of the same nature as those of the normal mind (in that they are associated with the same parts of the nervous system, fulfil the same general biological functions, and probably operate through similar mechanisms), with the single exception that we are not conscious of them as such.[1]

The conscious mind, that which we think of as the basis of our mental individuality, as our personal being, is the result of a long process of organization. We come into the world with a set of instinctive and emotional reactions only waiting their proper stimuli to be fired off, with a capacity for learning, for amassing experience, and a capacity for modifying our instincts and our behaviour according to our experience. We incorporate experience in ourselves, and in so doing we alter the original basis of our reactions; a strongly emotional experience colours all that is closely associated with it; and so after birth we are continually making our mental microcosm not only larger but qualitatively more complex, in exactly the same way as before birth our body grew not only in size, but also in complexity of organization.

Parts of experience or of inherited tendencies may fail to become organically connected with the main parts of our minds, simply because attention has never been focussed on them, or has not attempted to bring them into relation with the rest. They are, shall we say, like bricks which might have been used in a building, but have been left lying on the ground by the workmen.

Still more remarkable are the methods by which harmony is achieved in the personal mind. It is obvious that a conflict of any sort between parts of the mind will waste energy, will prevent a clear-cut reaction being given in either direction, and so constitute a grave biological disadvantage by making us fall between two stools. If a child gets a serious fright in the dark, darkness will tend to arouse fear. But darkness also comes with evening and with the time for sleep. Two modes of reaction to darkness are therefore given, and they are self-contradictory. One part of the mind comes down its pathway towards action, and finds itself met by another which is coming along the same path in the opposite direction. If neither moves, there is a conflict; in our hypothetical case sleep is delayed;

[1]See Prince, '06 and '16; Freud, '22; Jung, '19; Rivers, '20; Brown, '22.

and if it comes, is disturbed by nightmares—the echoes of the fright—and the childish organism suffers.

Exactly similar conflicts in which fear plays a part may occur in adult life, e.g., in so-called "shell-shock"; or the sex-instinct may come into conflict with other parts of the personality.

These conflicts are resolved through one tendency or part of experience being passed into the subconscious, where it no longer can meet its opponent on the path to action. And this passage into the subconscious can be apparently automatic, unwitting, when it is called *suppression*, or performed only by voluntary effort, when it is called *repression*. In the former case, it would appear that the conflict may wholly or almost wholly cease; whereas in the second, the repressed portion of mind is perpetually striving to come to the surface again, and must thus perpetually be held down by force.

If we hold by our metaphor of the building, then in suppression, bricks which would not go well with the rest are stacked quietly in the cellars; while in repression, part of the workmen want to build a different sort of building, and have to be forcibly held down by some of the rest to prevent their doing so.

But in whatever way the subconscious may be organized it is always with us, and there will always be a remainder of our soul, or of its possibilities, which is not incorporated in our personal life at all, as well as much which is not closely organized with the main everyday personality, but is connected with it only by vague and loose bonds, approachable only by narrow pathways instead of by broad roads.

There is another process at work in the human mind which is of the utmost importance for our problem. I mean the process of sublimation. If it is not easy to give a short and clear definition of sublimation, at least the process is familiar to all. The commonest example is "falling in love," where the simple sex-instinct becomes intertwined with other instincts and with past emotional experience, and projects itself in wholly new guise upon its object. We may perhaps best say that a sublimated instinct has more and higher values attached to its satisfaction than one unsublimated. The mere satisfaction of the sexual impulse need be little more than a physiological desirability; but the satisfaction of passionate love involves every fibre of the mental organism, hopes and ideals converging with memories and instincts on to the highest pitch of being.

In such a case sublimation occurs with the normal object of the instinct. But the elasticity of man's mind permits of further complication; the instinct may be not only sublimated but attached to new objects. Through the cogs and spirals of the mind, the sexual instinct may find an outlet at higher levels, and contribute to the driving force of adventurous living, of art, or as we may see in many mystics—St. Teresa for example —of religious ecstasy.

It is as if a swift stream were falling into underground channels below the mill of our being, where it could churn and roar away to waste. But some of it is led off at a higher level, and we can learn to lead off still more; and we can make an installation of pipes whereby it can be taken up to the original level, and made to fall through new machines and do any work we may ask of it.

The mechanism of sublimation, however, deserves a few more words. Recent work in biology has shown that in low forms of animals and in early stages of high forms, the head-region is in a certain sense dominant to the rest, in that it forms first and independently; but that, once present, it exerts a formative influence upon the rest of the body, keeping the various organs in some way under control, making them different from what they would otherwise have been, and so moulding them to the part of a single and higher whole.

An extremely similar process is at work in sublimation. Ideas and ideals can be naturally dominant over others, or they can become dominant through becoming associated with primarily dominant ideas, or by receiving a larger share of attention. Attention, concentration, what you will, is one of the most remarkable mental functions. Not only can the metaphor of intense illumination of a particular field be justly used of it, but we may say that it seems to accelerate the flow of mental process through a particular channel, and so to draw into that channel the contents of other channels in connection with it, just as a rapid flow of water through a pipe sucks in water from connected pipes.

As a result of this, sublimation involves not the suppression or repression of instincts and emotional experiences, nor merely the summation of them with another instinct, but their utilization as parts of a new whole, of which the dominant instincts is like the controlling head.

When the sex-instinct is repressed, the emotional and religious life is meagre, though often violent. When the sex-instinct and the religious feeling exist side by side, without conflict but without union, you have "the natural man" of St. Paul; but when the religious ideals are dominant, and can catch up the sex-instinct into themselves, and in so doing give it a new form and a new direction, then you get one of the highest types of emotional lives. Or fear may be sublimated to reverence; or sex again to art or to philanthropy.

In every case, a new and more complicated mental activity or organ is arrived at; and the same process that we saw at work in biological evolution—the creation of ever more complex units—is thereby continued.

Then we come to the fact that man displays disharmonies of mental construction, together with an innate hankering after harmony. The most obvious disharmony is that between the instincts that are self-regarding and those that are other-regarding—between man's egotistic and his social tendencies.

It appears that man became gregarious quite late in evolutionary history. Through natural selection, sufficient "herd-instinct" was developed to ensure that men would on the whole stand by the tribe in danger, that the tribe should become a real biological unit. But it was impossible wholly to harmonize these new social instincts, even in the simplest societies, with the old, deeper-rooted, individualist tendencies; and as life became more complex and choice wider, conflict grew more and more frequent.[1]

Another obvious disharmony in modern civilized communities is the fact that sexual maturity occurs long before marriage is possible or desirable.

In all this, there is inevitably a field for all the various combinations of suppression, or repression, or sublimation.

Man's gregariousness, together with his power of speech, learning, and generalization, have led to the development of a new thing in the world—persistent and cumulative tradition. I use tradition in the broadest sense, as denoting all that owes its being to the mind of man, and is handed down, by speech or imitation or in some permanent record, from generation to generation. Language, general ideas of right and wrong, convention, invention, national feeling—all this and much more,

[1] See Trotter, '19.

constituting the more important part of the human individual's environment—is part of tradition; and tradition is preeminently and inevitably social. However individualistic we may wish to be we cannot escape modelling by this social environment.

The general effect of man's gregarious instinct is that he desires to find himself in harmony with some traditions, with the ideas that modern jargon likes to call the herd to which he belongs. The herd ideas, the traditions, may be those of a nation or of a stratum within the nation; of a whole class or of a clique; of science or of art; of a retired monasticism, or of an all-embracing world-civilization. But they are always herd ideas, and through them man is always member of some community, even though that community be tiny, or consist mainly of writers dead and gone; and he always strives to put himself in harmony with the traditions of that community.

*　　*　　*　　*　　*　　*

A long-winded introduction enough; now for the bearing of it. One of the essentials of every religion is its treatment of the subconscious, is its view and its practice as regards the relation between the personally-organized part of the mind to the remaining non-personal reservoirs. At first the non-personal part is regarded as being wholly outside the organism, and its occasional flooding up into the narrower ego is regarded as an operation of an external personality, a spirit, a God. Comparatively late, it is recognized as part of the organism, but the process by which connection is made is still regarded as divine, and called inspiration. Such ideas belong to the adolescence of the race, in precisely the same way as the discovery and acquisition of great tracts of this subconscious territory will always necessarily constitute part of the adolescence of the individual. But any developed religion must always in some way help to make these great reserves of power accessible, always teach the enlargements of the personal ego which their conquest brings about. This is one of the ways in which, to use current religious phraseology, self may be lost, and found again on a different plane.

Religion must further always provide some internal harmony, in counterpart to the harmony demanded in the unitary comprehension of external reality. The various activities and experiences of life, as they are originally given by heredity to the child, are either independent, or else antagonistic and disharmonious. There must be some means provided for bringing all of them into a true organization—in other words into a whole which, though yet single, is composed of co-operating parts. Here again the actual responses of actual religions have been many and various; but they all operate by suppression, repression, and sublimation, or by a combination of these.

It can at once be said that sublimation is the right and highest way, and that two of the criteria of religious progress are to be found in the stress laid upon sublimation, and in the enlargement and the elevation of the dominant ideas at work in the sublimating process. It is the right and highest way because through it no spiritual energy is wasted, and the age-long path of progress towards ever higher levels of complexity in organization is still continued. Among religious teachers, both Jesus and Paul laid great stress on this—on the freedom, the emancipation from the shackles of an external law made possible by the apprehension of some highest harmonizing principle and the subordination of all other ideas and desires to it. Once one can see and learn to follow such a principle, whatever one does is in a sense right, because one's desires are all subordinate to a desire for right, and to something which is right. Perhaps it would be better to say that they appear right to oneself, that the haunting, terrible sense of sin is laid to rest, and one's life liberated into free activity, one's energy made all available for achievement.

The sense of sin, if not universal at one or other period of life, is almost so, and comes from an apprehension of inner disharmony. As one would expect, selfishness and sex are its most common roots; and whenever it exists, then the necessary preliminary to any further progress of one's being is that it should be made to disappear. It can disappear, as in St. Paul's natural man, by a suppression of part of the mind or of the connection between parts, or by a failure to make certain connections, or it can be eradicated by a growth of callousness; or—and I take it that this is the proper religious solution— by discovering a clue which will harmonize the two apparently opposed sections of experience, the two antagonistic tendencies, and so resolve the problem with no loss of energy or of vital possibilities.

* * * * *

Finally, there remains to be considered the mode in which the mind may best organize the ideas of external reality given to it by its pure cognitive and intellectual faculties.

Even from the purely scientific point of view, generalization is obviously of value. When we have found unity in the outer world's apparent diversity, direction in its apparent disorderliness, we have obviously achieved a great gain. But religion appears to demand something more. If for a moment we look at the matter pragmatically, we shall find that a number of the great mystics (and a large majority of those of our own occidental type and tradition) speak of their experiences of "divine communion" as being communion with a *person*.

What does this mean? We have seen that a purely intellectual analysis gives us no handle for finding personality in God. Can we suppose that this direct intuition gives us that handle? To say so, to my mind, would be simple obscurantism. Intuition, if it shows us reality, can only show a reality capable in the long run of intellectual analysis; to deny this is to deny all our premisses. No: their intuition shows us that something akin to personality is perceived, but permits no pronouncement as to whether its resemblance to personality is given in its real nature, or introduced into it by their thought.

If we look into the history of religion, we find over and over again that man has taken something from his own mind and projected it into the external world. The magic power of fetishes, the tabus incurred by contact with certain objects, the endowment of the idea of external powers, of God, with human form, the ascription of miraculous influence to places or things—in every case there has been this projection. And there is no reason to doubt that here again there has been a similar occurrence, that man has organized his idea of external power after the pattern of a personality, and has then ascribed this type of organization to the external power itself. This projection Blake symbolized in a sentence: "Thus men forgot that All Deities reside in the Human breast."

The rival schools of psychology may disagree: but all are agreed that some modes of thinking are more primitive than others, and even in the most educated amongst us tend to persist, often in the subconscious, side by side with more developed methods that have arisen later.

The use of concrete symbols or images is the most widespread of these primitive modes of thought. It is natural that the more complex should at the first be described in terms of the less complex, that those experiences for which no proper terminology has been hammered out should be given names out of man's existing vocabulary. That is inevitable: but there is an even more fundamental process at work. It seems as if the human mind works, on its most primitive levels, by means of image-formation, and that emotions and concepts for which no simple image exist may call up symbolic images by association and indeed often dress themselves in these new clothes before they present themselves to consciousness. Some such process appears to take place in dreams (including day-dreams!) and possibly in the ordinary thought-processes of savages. More advanced modes of thought substitute the currency of an arbitrary token such as a word or a formula for the barter of images and concrete symbols; the freshness and vividness of the image is lost, but more efficient and speedier working is attained. However, in most of us the concrete image-using mode of thought is a relief from the apparently less natural and more artificial (though more efficient) operations of reason, and we relapse into it, wholly or partially, more often than we realize.

This unconscious irrational tendency to symbolism, together with the other tendency to project ideas properly attaching to the subjective world into external objects and processes—these between them account for much of the modes of expression so far found for religious belief; and, since the majority of human beings have a profound distaste for sustained or difficult thought, it is likely that they will continue to account for much in the future.

These are facts of extreme importance. The professional sceptic is at once tempted to exclaim that every such projection and illogical symbolism is illusion through and through, and must be wholly swept aside. He would be wrong. We each of us must know from our own experience the "influence" (to use a general term) which may inhere in certain things and places. True that the influence is of our own mind's making; but it is none the less real, not only as a momentary existence, but, as the term implies, as exerting a definite and often a great effect upon our lives. The lover who cherishes a ring or a lock of hair; the man who is drawn back to the haunts of his childhood or his youth; the mind refreshing itself with some loved poem or picture;—what do we have in these and innumerable other instances but a peculiarity of mind whereby it may take external objects into itself and invest them with its own emotions and ideas, in such a way that those same objects may later reflect their stored-up emotion back again into the mind? It operates by a form of association; but the actual working resembles the charging of a battery, which may subsequently discharge back. We have in it, in fact, a special faculty which, if rightly used, is of the greatest practical value. Further, the symbol, if rightly used and rightly limited, is of service to most minds in giving a more or less concrete cage for the winged, elusive, and hardly-retained creatures of abstract thought.

So too, the organization of the idea of God into a form resembling a personality appears definitely to have, at least with the majority of people belonging to what we call "Western civilization," a real value.

Biologically, the essence of real personality is first that it is organized, and secondly that on each of its many faces it can, if I may put it metaphorically, enter into action at a single point, but with its whole content of energy available behind the point. In other words, man as a personality can concentrate his mind on one particular problem of one special aspect of reality; but he is able, if need be, to summon up ever fresh reinforcements if he cannot carry the position—more facts, other ways of thinking and feeling, memories, reserves of will. In a properly organized personality, it is possible to bring the whole to bear upon any single object.

Now when the idea which man makes for himself of outer reality is organized after the same general pattern as a personality, it too will be able to act in this same sort of way.

When man in perplexity interrogates the idea he has of external reality, he is anxious to put his little individual self in harmonious relation with the whole of reality that he knows. Therefore he should organize that reality as a whole, and in such a way that it can all be brought to bear through any single point. The relation between the self and the idea of outer reality is, for any one problem, that of two pyramids touching by their points only; but the points of contact can shift as by miracle over their surfaces as the problem is changed.

But another power of personalities is their power of interpenetration. The purely material cannot do this. One portion of matter cannot occupy the same space as a second portion. It is another of the great differences between the psychozoic and all previous stages of evolution, between man and all else that we know in the universe, that the discrete units reached at this level of organization, the individual human beings, can achieve interpenetration by means of their minds. When you expound a new idea to me, and I grasp it, our minds have obviously interpenetrated. This is a simple case; but there may be an intimate union of mind with mind which is the basis of the highest spiritual achievement and the greatest happiness. If mind and matter are two properties of the same world-substance, then the rise of mind to dominance has enabled this basic substance to escape from some of the imprisoning limitations which confined it at lower levels of its development; do we not all know that despair at being boxed up, that craving for communion? Using our previous line of argument, we see that the interpenetration of personalities is right, implies a further step in progress, must be part of the basis on which future advance in evolution is to build.

But to apply this to our present point. By organizing our knowledge of outer reality after the pattern of a personality, we make it possible for it to interpenetrate our private personality. If, therefore, we have, in any true sense of the word, "found religion," it means that we shall so have organized our minds that, for flashes at least, we attain to a sense of interpenetration with the reality around us—that reality which includes not only the celestial bodies, or the rocks and waters, not only evolving life, but also other human beings, also ideas, also ideals.

This, to my mind, is what actually happens when men speak of communion with God. It is a setting, an organizing of our experiences of the universe in relation with the driving forces of our soul or mental being, so that the two are united and harmonized. There is a resolution of conflicts, an attainment of a profound serenity, a conviction that the experience is of the utmost value and importance.

Up till now, we have been defining and analysing: here we see religion in operation. It is a relation of the personality as a unit to external reality as a unit—and a relation of harmony. First, the inner structure of the mind must be organized into a harmonious unit, then our knowledge of outer reality organized similarly, and finally, in religious experience, the two must be harmonized in interpenetrating union.

Once this harmony has been achieved, it is for one thing so precious in itself that it will be sought for again; the knowledge that we have once reached the stage at which difficulties and doubts are resolved in what the philosophers would perhaps call a higher unity, but which I should prefer to call an organic harmony, is always there to fall back upon in times of discouragement; and finally the harmony is actually woven into the tissue of our mind, just as the amazing physical harmony revealed by physiology has, in the course of evolution, been woven into the structure and working of living bodies; and it can remain there as the dominant idea to which the rest of our ideas, and consequently our actions, are brought into subordinate relation. In other words, it becomes the dominant sublimating principle. Once more, however, the subordination is not forced, but free—we find that what we once thought obstacles are aids, what once seemed sin is now the willing and efficient handmaid of good. That is the fundamental fact in all genuine and valuable religious experience as such—the resolution of conflict and the losing, or enlarging as you will, of the private personality, the mere "self." You will find this set out more fully, though in different terminology, in Miss Underhill's books on mysticism, or in William James's *Varieties of Religious Experience*, or in Thouless's *Psychology of Religion*.

One side-issue. Such experience, if not absolute in the philosophical sense, is absolute for us. If I may be Irish, its absoluteness is relative to our organization and to reality as we perceive it. We cannot perceive anything fuller, more absolute—until perhaps one day, with the growth of our minds, we come to have some still richer and more complete experience. As William James was so fond of reminding the world, we have no right to assume that our minds are, much less that they must be, the highest type of mind realized in the universe—no more right than our domestic animals have, although our minds to them could only be measured by their own standards.

What is more, owing to our power of framing general concepts and ideals, and of accumulating past and future in our present, we can focus a vast deal to one point. In such experiences, whether they come through religion, or love, or art, we may say that although we are but a system of relations, we touch the Absolute—although we are mortal, we mount to the Eternal for a moment. Only, to guard against error, we must remember that it is obviously not in reality the Absolute or the Eternal that we attain to, but only the nearest approximation to them of which we are capable.

We can therefore sum up this second part of our investigation by saying that religion, to be more than mere ritual, must involve the possibility of harmonizing the parts of the soul, of wiping out the sense of sin, of sublimating instinct, of rendering the subconscious reservoirs of energy and being available for the personal self, and of organizing the ideas of external reality into a single organized mental whole—the idea of God—capable of reacting with the personal self by interpenetration.

Although he was moving to quite other conclusions, it is worth recalling James's ideas. For instance, "The line of least resistance . . . is to accept the notion . . : that there is a God, but that he is finite. . . . These, I need hardly tell you, are the terms in which common men have usually carried on their active commerce with God; and the Monistic" [sc. Absolutist] "perfections that make the notion of him so paradoxical practically and morally are the colder addition of remote professorial minds operating *in distans* upon conceptual substitutes for him alone." (James, '09, p. 311.)

I may perhaps be rebuked for trying to analyse the unanalysable, for neglecting the supreme and sufficing fact of experience of God in favour of the unprofitable and impossible task of catching the infinite in an intellectual net. There are two answers to this. One is that unanalysed experience is selfish because less communicable: with that we deal later. The other is even more important: it is this. Humanity at large is *not* content with emotional experience alone, however complete and apparently satisfying: it has always demanded an intellectual formulation of the reality with which it is in contact, as well as emotional experience of it, and so far as we can judge it will always continue to do so.

But it is further found, as matter again of general experience, that such formulations do not remain innocuous in the vacuum of pure intellect, but reverberate upon action and influence conduct. When men believe that they are surrounded with magical powers, they spend half their lives in ritual designed to affect the operations of these (wholly hypothetical)

influences. When they worship a God whom they rationalize
as man-like, they sacrifice a large proportion of their produce
on his altars, and may even kill their fellow-creatures to placate
his (again imaginary) passions. When they believe in a Divine
Revelation, they think that they possess complete enlightenment on the great problems of life and death; and they will
then cheerfully burn those who differ from them, or embark
upon the bloodiest wars in defence of this imaginary certainty.
When they worship God as absolute and as a person, they
cannot help making deductions that lead them into absurdities
of thought and of conduct: they deny or oppose ideas derived
from a study of nature, the only actual source of knowledge,
because they conflict with what they believe to be immutable
truths, but are in reality conclusions drawn from false premisses; they tend to an acquiescent and obscurantist spirit in the
belief that such moral and intellectual laziness is "doing God's
will," when that will is in reality their own personification of
cosmic direction.

Sooner or later, false thinking brings wrong conduct. Man
can perhaps get along with empirical methods and ideas which
turn out on analysis to be only symbols, provided that he does
not attempt difficult construction. He can have some sort of a
religion, which will be some sort of a help to him, even when
its so-called certitudes are only a collection of mixed metaphors,
in the same way as he can practise agriculture on a basis of
mingled empiricism and superstition. But just as he is finding
that he is only able to raise agricultural efficiency to its highest
pitch by relying on the result of scientific method, as when
he uses synthetic nitrates instead of ploughing in a leguminous
crop, or just as a power-station would be very difficult to run
if the staff had only symbolic ideas on the nature of electricity
no closer to the real than is the symbolism of most religions,
so if he does not bring scientific analysis into the intellectual
side of his religion, he cannot realize religious possibilities.
True that in a sense all knowledge and intellectual presentation is symbolic: but there is the world of difference between
the merely analogical symbolism which takes one idea or thing
as symbolic of another because there is some degree of similarity
between the two and the first is more familiar, and the scientific
symbolism which strives to find a scientific counter, so to speak,
which shall represent particular phenomena as closely as possible, and them alone.

Not only this, but religion unillumined by reason degenerates into an evil thing. Religion seems to be a natural activity and need of the average human mind. But when its more primitive components are allowed to dominate, when the instinctive and emotional in it are unchecked by reflection and rational thought, then, as history too clearly shows us, it becomes a cruel and obstructive power. To the fine mind of Lucretius, the religion that he knew was the greatest enemy:—

> *"Quae caput a caeli regionibus ostendebat*
> *Horribili super aspecta mortalibus instans."*

And he replies to the charge of impiety by pointing to the foul deeds perpetrated by religion:

> *"—Quod contra saepius illa*
> *Religio peparit scelerosa atque impia facta."*

Many another thinker and reformer has felt the same.

There are those who, like Jung, believe that religion is an illusion but also a necessity to the bulk of mankind, and therefore should be encouraged. But the broader and truer view, I believe, is the one we have adopted. We have seen that, in man, evolution has reached a new plane, on which not only have new aims and values appeared, but the possibility of new and better evolutionary methods has arisen. These new methods are only possible, however, in so far as life, in man, uses her new gifts. The progress of civilization is a constant conflict between that part of man which he shares with the beasts and that part which is his alone—between man as no more than a new kind of animal and man as a rational and spiritual being. In so far as religion is irrational, it is no more than a dog baying the moon, no higher activity than the nocturnal concerts of Howler monkeys, no more and no less moral than the nobility of birds or beasts to a strangely-marked or unusually-built member of their species, or the sense of being a trespasser so often shown by a bird that has ventured upon the nesting-territory of another. Recall the "Natural Religion" of Robert Browning's *Caliban;* on which plane did that grow? But when we have discovered its real bases, and subordinated its impulsive promptings to the control of reason and of the new, higher values in which reason must always share—then it becomes an instrument for helping in the conquest of the new regions which lie open to man as individual and as species. And in this it resembles every other human activity without exception.

In religion the danger has always been that analogy and symbolism be taken for more than they are—for scientific knowledge, or even for an absolute certainty of some still higher order—and conclusions then drawn from it. The conclusions follow with full syllogistic majesty: but their feet are of clay—their premisses are false.

If we find that this is the case to-day, we not only may but we must endeavour to make our formulation correspond more closely with reality, must not be content to take one thing in place of another, the familiar for the unfamiliar, must set about destroying the old false formulation for fear of the further harm that it will do by its hold upon man's incurable habit of drawing conclusions.

Nor does this in any way interfere with or detract from the private and unique experiences that in the long run *are* religion. They remain; but they are thus hindered from becoming draped with delusion, from leading their possessor into false courses.

We may put it in another way. Too often in the past, religious experience has been one-sided—one-or-other-sided instead of two-sided. The intellectually-inclined, the theologians, frame more or less adequate ideas of external reality, but fail in the majority of cases to set their own house in order, to organize the inner reality to react with the outer; they have theory without practice, are Dry-as-dusts. On the other hand, the emotionally-minded who are gifted besides with organizing and intuitive power, the mystics—they build up their own souls into a desired and lovely edifice, in which too they have constructed a spiritual machinery capable of viewing external realities on a new plane, under a more highly synthesized aspect; but they neglect the precise analysis of that outer reality, and so can only speak in the barest symbols and metaphors, and cannot put their hard-won knowledge into a form available for others. They have that non-communicable skill which is that of the craftsman alone as opposed to the craftsman who is also in some degree a scientist. We know good mysticism from bad, as we know good art from bad—as definitely and as personally. And we are sure that good mysticism, like good art, is somehow of supreme, transcendent

importance; but almost always it has remained like a purely
symbolic art, not having for others the value which it should
have or did have for the mystic himself, because not properly
enchained, as the French say, with stern and immutable fact.
And of the theologian we feel that he gives us the grammar,
not the spirit, that he does not help us toward the supremely
important act of experiencing, but only to understanding experience if we chance to have had it.

One word on the problem of transcendence. The mystic will
tell us that transcendence is a hall-mark of religion at its
highest. His mode of experience transcends normal experience;
things of everyday life become surcharged with new, transcendent values; he has transcended from a plane of disharmony to one of harmony. But the mystic is not alone in this.
Familiar examples are best examples: and the transcendence of
the lover's experience is so familiar that all mankind is divided
into those who have it, those who long for it, and those who
laugh at it. But the great philosopher too must mediate between the transcendent and mankind, and the true artist also,
and the moralist worthy of the name.

What goes under this technical name of transcendence,
therefore, is the product of some special psychological mechanism which may be at work in the most diverse spheres. If we
wish to substitute one technical phrase for another, we can
say that it consists in the successful attachment of what we
have called absolute value to some human activity, so as to
make it for the time at least unitary, dominant, and all-
embracing. But psychologically speaking the genesis of "absolute values" depends upon the generalizing of particular
values; the raising of them to the highest possible pitch; and
the putting of them and the rest of the mental organization
into a relation in which they are permanently or temporarily
the dominating head and front, and are connected with and
gain strength and support from all the rest of the mind.

The problem of transcendence, in other words, is not one
of divine inspiration, of wholly mysterious experience, but one
special case of the problem of sublimation; and as such it is to
be investigated by psychological science, to be understood, to
be democratized, to be made more available to all who wish
for it.

The most ardent enemies of traditional religion have often
professed the most transcendental type of morality. Some men

are pragmatic and utilitarian in regard to Truth; by others she is worshipped as fanatically as any goddess. So some men deliberately make *mariages de convenance;* to others, the transcendence of their love is such that they precipitate themselves into what can only be described as *mariages d'inconvenance.*

I have dilated upon this at some length, because those whom we may call the religious writers on religion so often lay such stress on this question of transcendence and its special value and importance. But you do not—in the long run at least—make a thing more important by giving it an imposing title; you only give it a false exclusiveness.

Transcendence is the experimental side of what we have been describing all along: it is the finding of unity in diversity, the synthesis of discord in harmony and in especial the finding of something of supreme value (and therefore dominant) which can be linked up with the whole extent of our mental being. Transcendence in religion differs from transcendence in art or love only in its objects. In love the discrepancy between the object and the ideal values hung round it is often so glaring as to provoke laughter from cynics, compassion from the rest. In art, the operations by which an artist turns a collection of mean and commonplace objects into a beautiful and single whole, a poet invests failure and death with authentic tragedy, or drags every-day to a seat in eternity, are just as transcendent as that by which the mystic converts the relation between the warring passions of his soul and the infinite catalogue of differences which he finds around him into what he can only speak of as a divine communion, all-satisfying in itself, all-important for the conduct of his life. Science can here help religion by analysing and interpreting phenomena such as transcendence, paring the false from the true, cutting down false claims, substituting the hopefulness of natural causation for the illogical vagaries of supernaturalism and incommunicability.

*　　*　　*　　*　　*

I may perhaps be allowed to close with a few more practical aspects of the problem.

Many religious ideas and practices, as man's thought clarified itself, have proved to be unserviceable, and have been thrown on the lumber-heap, or left only with the losers in the race. It is impossible for any educated man nowadays to believe in the efficacy of magic, or of animal sacrifice; to accept the first chapter of Genesis as literally true; or to believe that God has human parts and passions. But there was a time when all these could be, and were, believed.

The time is obviously coming when a great many other ideas must be cast aside in favour of new ones. If you have followed me, you will agree that it is impossible for me and those who think like me to believe in God as a person, a ruler, to continue to speak of God as a spiritual *Being* in the ordinary way. Consequently, although the value of prayer persists in so far as it is meditative and a self-purification of the mind, yet its commonly accepted petitive value must fall to the ground;[1] so must all idea of miracle and of direct inspiration; so must all that is involved in the ordinary materialist ideas of ritual, self-denial, and worship as merely propitiation or "acceptable incense"; so must all the externally-projected parts of the ideas concerning the ordaining of special priests; so must all notion of our having a complete, peculiar, or absolute knowledge of God, or of there being a divinely-appointed rule of conduct or a divinely-revealed belief.

On such matters, most advanced thinkers have been long in general agreement. But there is one very important point which, so far as I know, has been very little touched upon—chiefly, I think, because such radical thinkers have been for the most part destructive, and so have not envisaged this particular side of the question.

I hope I have been able to convince you that the scientific manner of thinking can lay the foundation for something constructive in religion: this great problem, however, remains: what sort of form or organization shall any such new-moulded religion take on itself?

We have just decided that fixed and rigid dogma is impossible, and that completeness is out of the question. Yet humanity craves for certainty and is not content to leave any factor out of the scheme of things.

To this we answer that it is here that real faith enters. We cannot know the absolute, nor have we discovered a goal for our efforts. But we have discovered a unity embracing all that we know, and a direction starting at the first moment to which our reconstructive thought can penetrate, continuing till to-day,

[1] See Turner, '16.

and showing an acceleration of speed on which we may raise
our hopes for the future.

We do not know all. For instance, I have studiously avoided
ever mentioning the word *immortality*, since I believe that
Science cannot yet profitably discuss that question. But the
discovery of unity in all that has so far been studied gives us
reasonable faith that its wings will reach out to cover all that
we shall still be enabled to learn, while the unbroken continuity
of evolutionary direction gives us the same sort of right to
believe that it will continue to-morrow and on into time as we
have to believe that apples will continue to fall to the earth.

The study of evolution may give us a further help. We have
seen how the final steps of the highest forms of animals have
been in the direction of plasticity of organization: we see it in
the rise of man from mammals, in higher as against more primitive levels of human culture, in great men as against ordinary
men. There can be no doubt that its acquisition constitutes a
step in evolutionary progress. Plasticity is needed in any new
religion. And plasticity means tolerance, means the reduction
of fixity of ritual, of convention, of dogma, of clericalism.

It is clear that, as complexity increases, need will be felt for
a finer adjustment of satisfaction to mood, a more delicate
adaptation of religion to the individual. A few types of ceremony satisfied primitive races: an elaborate system, fixed in
essence, fluctuating in detail, has grown up in modern Christianity. But the more complex the mind, the less does it like to
have to "wait till Sunday"—the less is it satisfied with the
solely biblical point of view, or the literary and musical level
of Hymns A. and M.

The less also is it satisfied with the mediation of a priest.
Priest (or Priest-King) is sole mediator in most savage tribes:
his mediation is enormously important in the Roman Catholic
Church: less so in Protestant Churches: until with the progressive raising of the spiritual and cultural level, it is perhaps
possible that he may become an obstacle instead of a help.
Mediators there must always be. They are the great ones—
prophets and poets, heroes, philosophers, musicians, artists,
and all who discover or interpret or display what for the ordinary man is hidden or difficult or rare. They mediate between
the utmost attainable by man and man in the lump. As Hegel
says of one group of these mediators, the artists, it is the function of their art to deliver to the domain of feeling and delight

of vision all that the mind may possess of essential and transcendent Being. But, with the spread of invention and the change of civilization, their mediations are becoming more and more readily accessible to all. I can get, on the whole, more satisfactory mediation from three or four feet of properly filled bookshelf than from a dozen priests. Milton will give me doctrine if I want it, but stupendously: Wordsworth will reveal nature: Shakespeare the hearts of men: Blake can put men into a mystical, Shelley into an intellectual ecstasy, while Keats and a dozen others can open universal doors of beauty. What is more, if I have had the mediation of wise parents and good teachers, or to be so fortunate as to be enthusiastic, I find that in many things I can be my own mediator, in the same way as the Protestant found that he could read his Bible and eat the holy bread and wine for himself as well or better than the priest could do it for him.

Whatever we may say or like, it is an obvious fact that much of what is essential in religious experience, which in a simpler society was only attainable in prayer and sacrifice, communal ceremony or ritual worship, is now attainable to an increasing degree through literature, music, drama, art, and is, again, as a matter of fact, so attained by an increasing number of people who do not profess a creed or belong to a church. So that, as regards the personal, individual side of religion, many of the functions of Churches will inevitably be better performed through direct contact between the individual and the mediator —philosopher, poet, artist, or whatever he be—who provides the experience.

There remains public worship and community-religion. It is clear that whereas a Church in the Middle Ages was not only Church but also Museum of curiosities, Art-gallery and Theatre, and in large measure also took the place of our press and public libraries, now it is none of these things. There is now less reason for public worship, fewer functions for it to perform. On the other hand a religion is essentially in one aspect social, and not only does the unity of nature demand a unity of religion, but such unity of religion would be of the highest importance as a bond of civilization and a guarantee of the federalist as against the solely nationalist ideal. Moreover, to many types of mind, and to almost all men in certain circumstances, the partaking in a public religious ceremony in common with others is of real importance. It is safe to say, therefore, that these ceremonies will continue, however much modified, and that for them a mediator or priest, even if but temporarily acting as such, will be needed. The problem is largely that of combining in public worship the religious effectiveness of the simple, the hallowed, and the universally familiar —such as inheres in many of the prayers, psalms, and hymns of the Church to-day—with the spontaneity and immediacy which, for instance, are to be found at a devotional meeting of the Society of Friends.

In any case, the new intellectual premises once granted, the limitations imposed on human mind once understood, the important thing is to give a greater vigour and reality to religious experience itself, whether personal and private or social and public. It is just here that Science may help, where knowledge may be power. Atonement, conversion, sense of grace, ecstasy, prayer, sacrifice—the meaning and value of these and of other religious acts and experiences can be put on a proper psychological basis, they can be shorn of excrescences, and their practice take its place in normal spiritual development. That is of the essence of any religion rooted in scientific ideas—that comprehenson should make practice easier and better worth while.

I am only too painfully aware of the omissions which such a cursory treatment of the subject inevitably involves. I have given you, I know, little but dry bones; but bones are the framework necessary before impatient life can animate a new form. If Science can construct that form, the emotions and hopes and energies of humanity will vivify and clothe it. It is with the aid of such intellectual scaffolding that the common mind of humanity in the future, inevitably rooted in scientific conceptions as it will be, must try to raise that much-desired building, a religion common to all.

In any case, I shall be more than content if I have been able to persuade you first that the term God, just as much as the terms Energy, say, or Justice, has a real meaning and scientifically-based sense. Second, that the idea of God has and will continue to have an important biological function in man as denoting an idea, organized in a particular way, of the whole of the reality with which he is in contact. Thirdly, that the physical and biological sciences, in discovering the unity of matter and energy, and the direction operating in cosmic evolution, have provided a real basis for what up till now have been only theological speculations. Fourthly, that psychological science, in revealing some of the mechanism of mind, is helping us to appreciate the value of so-called mystical experience, is laying a foundation for the proper spiritual training and development of human mind, and shows us how the idea of God may be efficacious as a dominant idea in the all-important process of sublimation. And finally that, since the scientific mode of thought is of general and not merely local or temporary validity, to build a religion on its basis is to make it possible for that religion to acquire a stability, a universality, and a practical value hitherto unattained.

We are yet at the very beginning of that task, but I cannot close better than by reminding you of another biological fact of importance, that from all analogy the human species is yet near the beginning of its evolutionary career, and that man has before him vast tracts of time to set against the vastness of his tasks.

A chapter in the history of Earth closed with the appearance of Man. In man, the *Weltstoff* had been made able to think and feel, to love beauty and truth—the cosmos had generated soul. A new chapter then began, a chapter in which we all are characters. Matter had flowered in soul. Soul has now to mould matter.

That moulding of matter by spirit is, under one aspect, Science; under another, Art; under still another, Religion. Let us be careful not to allow the moulding forces to counteract each other when they might be made to co-operate.

J. B. S. Haldane

THE LAST JUDGMENT

"Denique montibus altior omnibus ultimus ignis
Surget, inertibus ima tenentibus, astra benignis,
Flammaque libera surget ad aëra, surget ad astra,
Diruet atria, moenia, regna, suburbia, castra."

BERNARD OF CLUNY,
De Contemptu mundi, Lib. 1.

THE star on which we live had a beginning and will doubtless have an end. A great many people have predicted that end, with varying degrees of picturesqueness. The Christian account contains much that is admirable, but suffers from two cardinal defects. In the first place, it is written from the point of view of the angels and a small minority of the human race. The impartial historian of the future could legitimately demand a view of the *communiqués* of the Beast of the Book of Revelation and his adherents. For, after all, the Beast and his false prophet could work miracles of a kind, and were admittedly able propagandists. So perhaps "Another air raid on Babylon beaten off. Seventeen archangels brought down in flames" might record some of the earlier stages in the war, while "More enemy atrocities. Prophet cast into burning sulphur" would chronicle the peace terms.

But the more serious objection is perhaps to the scale of magnitudes employed. The misbehaviours of the human race might induce their creator to wipe out their planet, but hardly the entire stellar system. We may be bad, but I cannot believe that we are as bad as all that. At worst our earth is only a very small septic area in the universe, which could be sterilized without very great trouble, and conceivably is not even worth sterilizing.

I prefer *Ragnarok,* the Doom of the Reigners, which closes
the present chapter in world history acording to Norse mythology. Here mankind perish as an episode in a vaster conflict.
It is true that they misbehaved first.

> "Hart es i heimi, hordomr mikkil,
> Skeggi-aold, skalm-aold, skildir klofnir,
> Vind-aold, varg-aold, nŏr vaerold steipisk[1]

> ("Hard upon earth then, many a whoredom,
> Sword-age, axe-age, shields are cloven,
> Wind-age, wolf-age, ere world perish"),

says the Norse Sybil in the *Volospa.* But human events are a
symptom rather than a cause. The gods are to be destroyed
by the powers of darkness. Fenri, the wolf, will eat Odin, and
actually get the world between his teeth, though he will fail to
swallow it. There is a happy ending, probably due to Christian influence. Balder returns from the dead, and rules over
the descendants of two survivors of the human race. But one
episode is of considerable interest. In the middle of the fight
the sun becomes a mother, and both she and her daughter survive it. In Scandinavia, of course, the sun, who is kindly but
rather ineffective, is a female, a conception impossible to the
inhabitants of hotter climates.

Now, fission is one of the vices to which suns are subject. Indeed, something like half the "fixed" stars known to us are
double or multiple. Apparently the reason for splitting is as
follows:—A star always has a certain amount of angular momentum, or spin, due to its rotation on its axis. As it loses heat
it gets smaller, but keeps the same amount of spin. So it has
to go round faster, and finally splits in two, like a bursting
flywheel, owing to its excessive speed. The sun certainly does
not seem likely to do this, for it turns round its axis only once
in about four weeks; whereas in order to split, it would have
to do so once in less than an hour. But we can see only its outside, and last year Dr. Jeans, the president of the Royal
Astronomical Society, suggested that the sun's inside might
be rotating much faster, and that no one could say that it
would not divide to-morrow. Naturally, such an event is rather

[1] The letter ŏ was pronounced like th in then, þ like th in thin.

unlikely. The sun has gone on for several thousand million years without doing so. But it is apparently possible.

The results for the earth would be disastrous. Even if the sun's heat did not increase so greatly as to roast mankind forthwith, the earth would cease to revolve in a definite orbit, and year by year would approach the pair of suns nearer at one season, retreat from them further at another, while they themselves would gradually separate, and therefore approach nearer to the earth. Long before a collision occurred we should have come so close to one of them that, under the radiation from a sun covering perhaps a tenth of the sky, the sea would have boiled over and mankind perished.

The sun might perhaps do several other things. It might cool down, and a generation ago it seemed very plausible that it would do so within a few million years. But as we now know that the first thousand million years or so since the first ice-age recorded by geology it has not got much cooler, there is no reason to suppose that it will begin to do so for a very long time indeed. Modern physics suggests, indeed, that it will shine for at least a million million years. But before that time comes, something very strange, as we shall presently see, will have happened to our own planet.

Stars occasionally burst, expanding enormously, giving out a vast amount of heat, and then dying down again. No one knows why this occurs, but it does seem to happen to stars not at all unlike the sun. If it happened to the sun, the earth would stand as much chance of survival as a butterfly in a furnace. But these explosions are also rare. No star at all near to us has exploded during human history. If Sirius, let us say, exploded in this manner, he would send nearly as much light to the earth as does the moon, and would be visible by day. We cannot say whether this kind of ending for our world is likely or not until we know more as to why it happens to other suns than our own.

Others have suggested a comet or some stray heavenly body as a destroyer. Against this we have the fact that on all the continents nothing more than a few miles in diameter can have fallen in the last few hundred million years. The great meteor imbedded in the desert in Arizona may have formed part of a comet, and some of the scars on the moon may be due to collisions with wandering matter. But the improbability of a collision which would desolate any large part of the earth's surface is enormous, even though the Arizona meteorite would have made a considerable mess of London or New York. It has been suggested that a heavy body passing near the earth might drag it out of its orbit. The orderly and nearly circular character of the orbits of all the planets round the sun shows that they have not been greatly perturbed for a very long time, and probably since their formation. One cannot say that they will never be so perturbed, but one can assert that the odds against any such event in the next million years are more than a thousand to one.

All the possibilities that I have catalogued are essentially accidents. Some of them may happen, just as I may be killed in a railway accident; but just as my body will not go on working for ever, apart from any accidents, so the earth carries with it through space what will certainly alter its conditions profoundly, and very possibly destroy it as an abode of life. I refer to the moon.

Our Scandinavian ancestors did not neglect our satellite in their account of the twilight of the gods.

> "Austr byr in aldnar i Iarnviði
> Ok foeðir þar Fenris kindir,
> Verðr af þeim aollom einar nokkar
> Tungls tiugari, i trollz hami."

> ("Eastward in Ironwood sits the old witch
> And breeds Fenri's children,
> Of them all one shall be born
> Shaped like an ogre, who shall pitch the moon down.")

Now, here the sybil who described the future to Odin was substantially in agreement with modern astronomy. The moon will one day approach the earth so close as to be broken up, and very possibly to destroy the earth's surface features. Certain Mohammedan theologians have interpreted the first verse of the Sura called "The Moon," "The hour is come and the moon is split," as referring to the end of the world. But outside Scandinavia the prophets of doom have generally described the stars as falling out of heaven, which is an impossibility, for the same reason that a million elephants cannot fall on one fly. They are too large.

In what follows I shall attempt to describe the most probable end of our planet as it might appear to spectators on another. I have been compelled to place the catastrophe within a period of the future accessible to my imagination. For I can imagine what the human race will be like in forty million years, since forty million years ago our ancestors were certainly mammals, and probably quite definitely recognizable as monkeys. But I cannot throw my imagination forward for ten times that period. Four hundred million years ago our ancestors were fish of a very primitive type. I cannot imagine a corresponding change in our descendants.

So I have suggested the only means which, so far as I can see, would be able to speed up the catastrophe. The account given here will be broadcast to infants on the planet Venus some forty million years hence. It has been rendered very freely into English, as many of the elementary ideas of our descendants will be beyond our grasp:—

"It is now certain that human life on the earth's surface is extinct, and quite probable that no living thing whatever remains there. The following is a brief record of the events which led up to the destruction of the ancient home of our species.

"Eighteen hundred and seventy-four million years ago the sun passed very close to the giant star 318.47.19543. The tidal wave raised by it in our sun broke into an incandescent spray. The drops of this spray formed the planets, of all of which the earth rotated by far the most rapidly. The earth's year was then only very slightly shorter than now; but there were 1800 days in it, each lasting only a fifth of the time taken by a day when men appeared on earth. The liquid earth spun round for a few years as a spheroid greatly expanded at the equator and flattened at the poles by its excessive rotation. Then the tidal waves raised in it by the sun became larger and larger. Finally the crest of one of these waves flew off as the moon. At first the moon was very close to the earth, and the month was only a little longer than the day.

"As the moon raised large tides in the still liquid earth the latter was slowed down by their braking action, for all the work of raising the tides is done at the expense of the earth's rotation. But by acting as a brake on the earth, the moon was pushed forward along its course, as any brake is pushed by the wheel that it slows down. As it acquired more speed it rose gradually farther and farther away from the earth, which had now a solid crust, and the month, like the day, became longer.

When life began on the earth the moon was already distant, and during the sixteen hundred million years before man appeared it had only moved away to a moderate degree farther.

"When these distances were first measured by men the moon revolved in twenty-nine days, and the braking action of the tides amounted to twenty thousand million horse-power on the average. It is said that the effect of tidal friction in slowing down the earth's rotation, and therefore lengthening the day, was first discovered by George Darwin, a son of Charles Darwin, who gave the earliest satisfactory account of evolution. However, there is reason to believe that both these personages are among the mythical culture-heroes of early human history, like Moses, Lao-Tze, Jesus, and Newton.

"At this time the effect of tidal friction was to make each century, measured in days, just under a second shorter than the last. The friction occurred mainly in the Bering Sea between northern Asia and America. As soon as the use of heat engines was discovered, man began to oxidize the fossil vegetables to be found under the earth's surface. After a few centuries they gave out, and other sources of energy were employed. The power available from fresh water was small, from winds intermittent, and that from the sun's heat only available with ease in the tropics. The tides were therefore employed, and gradually became the main source of energy. The invention of synthetic food led to a great increase in the world's population, and after the federation of the world it settled down at about twelve thousand million. As tide engines were developed, an ever-increasing use was made of their power; and before the human race had been in existence for a million years, the tide-power utilized aggregated a million million horse-power. The braking action of the tides was increased fiftyfold, and the day began to lengthen appreciably.

"At its natural rate of slowing fifty thousand million years would have elapsed before the day became as long as the month, but it was characteristic of the dwellers on earth that they never looked more than a million years ahead, and the amount of energy available was ridiculously squandered. By the year five million the human race had reached equilibrium; it was perfectly adjusted to its environment, the life of the individual was about three thousand years; and the individuals were "happy," that is to say, they lived in accordance with instincts which were gratified. The tidal energy available was now fifty million million horse-power. Large parts of thé planet were artificially heated. The continents were remodelled, but human effort was chiefly devoted to the development of personal relationships and to art and music, that is to say, the production of objects, sounds, and patterns of events gratifying to the individual.

"Human evolution had ceased. Natural selection had been abolished, and the slow changes due to other causes were traced to their sources and prevented before very great effects had been produced. It is true that some organs found in primitive man, such as the teeth (hard, bone-like structures in the mouth), had disappeared. But largely on æsthetic grounds the human form was not allowed to vary greatly. The instinctive and traditional preferences of the individual, which were still allowed to influence mating, caused a certain standard body form to be preserved. The almost complete abolition of the pain sense which was carried out before the year five million was the most striking piece of artificial evolution accomplished. For us, who do not regard the individual as an end in itself, the value of this step is questionable.

"Scientific discovery was largely a thing of the past, and men of a scientific bent devoted themselves to the more intricate problems of mathematics, organic chemistry, or the biology of animals and plants, with little or no regard for practical results. Science and art were blended in the practice of horticulture, and the effort expended on the evolution of beautiful flowers would have served to alter the human race profoundly. But evolution is a process more pleasant to direct than to undergo.

"By the year eight million the length of the day had doubled, the moon's distance had increased by twenty per cent., and the month was a third longer than it had been when first measured. It was realized that the earth's rotation would now diminish rapidly, and a few men began to look ahead, and to suggest the colonization of other planets. The older expeditions had all been failures. The projectiles sent out from the earth had mostly been destroyed by air friction, or by meteorites in interstellar space, and those which had reached the moon intact had generally been smashed by their impact on landing. Two expeditions had landed there with oxygen supplies, successfully mapped the face of it which is turned away from the earth, and signalled their results back. But return was impossible, and their members had died on the moon. The projectiles used in the earlier expeditions were metal cylinders ten metres or less in diameter and fifty or more in length. They were dispatched from vertical metal tubes several kilometres in length, of which the lower part was imbedded below the earth, while the upper projected. In order to avoid atmospheric resistance these tubes were generally built in high mountains, so that when the projectile emerged it had relatively little air to go through. The air in the tube itself was evacuated and a lid on the top removed as the projectile arrived. It was started off by a series of mild explosions which served to give it a muzzle velocity of about five kilometres per second without causing too great a shock. When it had left the lower atmosphere it progressed on the rocket principle, being impelled forward by the explosion of charges in its tail. The empty sections of the tail were also blown backward as required. It could be turned from inside by rotating a motor, or by the crew walking round.

"On arriving in the gravitational field of another planet its fall could be slowed by the discharge downward of more of its explosive cargo, and to check the final part of its fall various types of resistance were employed, and collapsible metal rods were extruded to break the shock of landing. Nevertheless, landing was generally fatal. As is well known, different principles are now employed. In particular, on leaving the atmosphere, wings of metallic foil of a square kilometre or more in area are spread out to catch the sun's radiation pressure, and voyages are thus made on principles analogous to those employed in the ancient sailing-ships.

"The desire for individual happiness, and the fact that it was achieved on earth, made membership of such expeditions unpopular. The volunteers, who were practically committing suicide, were almost all persons whose mates had died prematurely, or whose psychology was for some reason so abnormal as to render them incapable of happiness. An expedition reached Mars successfully in the year 9,723,841, but reported that colonization was impracticable. The species dominant on that planet, which conducts its irrigation, are blind to those radiations which we perceive as light, and probably unaware of the existence of other planets; but they appear to possess senses unlike our own, and were able to annihilate this expedition and the only other which reached Mars successfully.

"Half a million years later the first successful landing was effected on Venus, but its members ultimately perished owing to the unfavourable temperature conditions and the shortage of oxygen in its atmosphere. After this such expeditions became rarer.

"In the year 17,846,151 the tide machines had done the first half of their destructive work. The day and the month were now of the same length. For millions of centuries the moon had always turned the same face to the earth, and now the earth dwellers could only see the moon from one of their hemispheres. It hung permanently in the sky above the remains of the old continent of America. The day now lasted for forty-eight of the old days, so that there were only seven and a half days in the year. As the day lengthened the climate altered enormously. The long nights were intensely cold, and the cold was generally balanced by high temperatures during the day. But there were exceptions.

"Mankind had appeared on earth during a period characterized by high mountains and recurrent ice-ages. Mountain-building had indeed almost ceased, though some ranges and many volcanoes appeared during man's early life. But four ice-ages occurred shortly before history began, and a fifth had devastated parts of the northern continents during the second hundred thousand years of history. The ice had, however, been kept within relatively narrow limits by human endeavour. After the end of this period a huge co-operative effort of the human species had destroyed the remaining ice-fields. About the year 220,000 the ice-cap of Greenland had been gradually melted by the application of tidal energy, and soon after this the Arctic Ocean had become permanently ice-free. Later the Antarctic Continent had been similarly treated. Through most of the first half of human history there was therefore no permanent ice or snow save on a few mountains. The climate throughout the earth became relatively mild and uniform, as it had been through most of the time recorded by geology.

"But as the earth's rotation slowed down, its equator contracted, causing earthquakes and mountain-building on a large scale. A good deal of land emerged from the oceans, especially the central Pacific. And with the lengthening of the nights snow began to be deposited on the uplands in fairly large amounts; near the poles the sun occasionally failed to melt i during the day, and even where it was melted the subsoil wa often permanently frozen. In spite of considerable efforts, ice-fields and giant glaciers had already appeared when the moon ceased to rise and set. Above them permanent anti-cyclones once more produced storms in the temperate regions, and rainless deserts in the tropics.

"The animals and plants only partially adapted themselves to the huge fluctuations of temperature. Practically all the undomesticated mammals, birds, and reptiles became extinct. Many of the smaller plants went through their whole life-cycle in a day, surviving only as seeds during the night. But most of the trees became extinct except when kept warm artificially.

"The human race somewhat diminished in numbers, but there was still an immense demand for power for heating and cooling purposes. The tides raised by the sun, although they only occurred fifteen times per year, were used for these ends, and the day was thus still further lengthened.

"The moon now began once more to move relative to the earth, but in the opposite direction, rising in the west and setting in the east. Very gradually at first, but then with ever-increasing speed, it began to approach the earth again, and appear larger. By the year 25,000,000 it had returned to the distance at which it was when man had first evolved, and it was realized that its end, and possibly the earth's, were only a few million years ahead. But the vast majority of mankind contemplated the death of their species with less aversion than their own, and no effective measures were taken to forestall the approaching doom.

"For the human race on earth was never greatly influenced by an envisaged future. After physiology was discovered primitive men long continued to eat and drink substances which they knew would shorten and spoil their lives. Mineral fuels were also oxidized without much forethought. The less pigmented of the primitive races exhausted the fuel under the continents on which they lived with such speed that for some centuries the planet was dominated by the yellow variety resident in eastern Asia, where mining had developed more slowly; until they too had exhausted their fuel resources. The unpigmented men appear to have foreseen this event, but did little or nothing to prevent it, even when it was clearly only a few generations ahead. Yet they had before them the history of an island in the North Atlantic on which Newton and Darwin are said to have lived, and whose inhabitants were the first to extract mineral fuel and the first to exhaust it, after which they disappeared from the stage of history, although at one time they had controlled large portions of the earth's land surface.

"On the contrary, the earth's inhabitants were often influenced in a curious way by events in the past. The early religions all attached great significance to such occurrences. If our own minds dwell more readily on the future, it is due largely to education and daily propaganda, but partly to the presence in our nuclei of genes such as H 149 and P 783 c, which determine certain features of cerebral organization that had no analogy on earth. For this reason we have undertaken the immense labour necessary to tap the central heat of our planet, rather than diminish its rotation. Even now this process involves a certain annual loss of life, and this was very much greater at first, so much so as to forbid its imitation on the earth, whose inhabitants generally valued their own lives and one another's.

"But if most men failed to look ahead, a minority felt otherwise, and expeditions to Venus became commoner. After 284 consecutive failures a landing was established, and before its members died they were able to furnish the first really precise reports as to conditions on that planet. Owing to the opaque character of our atmosphere, the light signals of the earlier expeditions had been difficult to pick up. Infra-red radiation which can penetrate our clouds was now employed.

"A few hundred thousand of the human race, from some of whom we are descended, determined that though men died, man should live for ever. It was only possible for humanity to establish itself on Venus if it were able to withstand the heat and want of oxygen there prevailing, and this could only be done by a deliberate evolution in that direction first accomplished on earth. Enough was known of the causes responsible for evolution to render the experiment possible. The human material was selected in each generation. All who were not willing were able to resign from participation, and among those whose descendants were destined for the conquest of Venus a tradition and an inheritable psychological disposition grew up such as had not been known on earth for twenty-five million years. The psychological types which had been common among the saints and soldiers of early history were revived. Confronted once more with an ideal as high as that of religion, but more rational, a task as concrete as and infinitely greater than that of the patriot, man became once more capable of self-transcendence. Those members of mankind who were once more evolving were not happy. They were out of harmony with their surroundings. Disease and crime reappeared among them. For disease is only a failure of bodily function to adjust itself to the environment, and crime a similar failure in behaviour. But disease and crime, as much as heroism and martyrdom, are part of the price which must be paid for evolution. The price is paid by the individual, and the gain is to the race. Among ourselves an individual may not consider his own interests a dozen times in his life. To our ancestors, fresh from the pursuit of individual happiness, the price must often have seemed too great, and in every generation many who have now left no descendants refused to pay it.

"The modes of behaviour which our ancestors gradually overcame, and which only recur as the rarest aberrations among ourselves, included not only such self-regarding sentiments as pride and a personal preference concerning mating. They embraced emotions such as pity (an unpleasant feeling aroused by the suffering of other individuals). In a life completely dedicated to membership of a super-organism the one is as superfluous as the other, though altruism found its place in the emotional basis of the far looser type of society prevalent on earth.

"In the course of ten thousand years a race had been evolved capable of life at one-tenth of the oxygen pressure prevalent on earth, and the body temperature had been raised by six degrees. The rise to a still higher temperature, correlated as it was with profound chemical and structural changes in the body, was a much slower process. Projectiles of a far larger size were dispatched to Venus. Of 1734, only 11 made satisfactory landings. The crews of the first two of these ultimately perished; those of the next eight were our ancestors. The organisms found on Venus were built of molecules which were mostly mirror images of those found in terrestrial bodies. Except as sources of fat they were therefore useless for food, and some of them were a serious menace. The third projectile to arrive included bacteria which had been synthesized on earth to attack l-glucose and certain other components of the organisms on Venus. Ten thousand years of laboratory work had gone to their making. With their aid the previous life on that planet was destroyed, and it became available for the use of man and the sixty terrestrial species which he had brought with him.

"The history of our planet need not be given here. After the immense efforts of the first colonizers, we have settled down as members of a super-organism with no limits to its possible progress. The evolution of the individual has been brought under complete social control, and besides enormously enhanced intellectual powers we possess two new senses. The one enables us to apprehend radiation of wave-lengths between 100 and 1200 metres, and thus places every individual at all moments of life, both asleep and awake, under the influence of the voice of the community. It is difficult to see how else we could have achieved as complete a solidarity as has been possible. We can never close our consciousness to those wave-lengths on which we are told of our nature as components of a super-organism or deity, possibly the only one in space-time, and of its past, present, and future. It appears that on earth the psychological equivalent of what is transmitted on these wave-lengths included the higher forms of art, music, and literature, the individual moral consciousness, and, in the early days of mankind, religion and patriotism. The other wave-lengths inform us of matters which are not the concern of all at all times, and we can shut them out if we so desire. Their function is not essentially different from that of instrumental radio-communication on earth. The new magnetic sense is of less importance, but is of value in flying and otherwise in view of the very opaque character of our atmosphere. It would have been almost superfluous on earth. We have also recovered the pain sense, which had become vestigial on earth, but is of value for the survival of the individual under adverse circumstances, and hence to the race. So rapid was our evolution that the crew of the last projectile to reach Venus were incapable of fertile unions with our inhabitants, and they were therefore used for experimental purposes.

"During the last few million years the moon approached the earth rather rapidly. When it became clear that the final catastrophe could not be long delayed the use of tide-power was largely discontinued, according to the signals which reached us from the earth, and wind and other sources of power were substituted. But the earth-dwellers were sceptical as to whether the approaching rupture of the moon would entail their destruction, and the spin of the earth-moon system was still used to some extent as a source of power. In the year 36,000,000 the moon was at only a fifth of its distance from the earth when history had begun. It appeared twenty-five times as large as the sun, and raised the sea-level by some 200 metres about four times a year. The effects of the tidal strain raised in it by the earth began to tell. Giant landslips were observed in the lunar mountains, and cracks occasionally opened in its surface. Earthquakes also became rather frequent on the earth.

"Finally the moon began to disintegrate. It was so near to the earth as to cover about a twentieth of the visible heavens when the first fragments of rock actually left its surface. The portion nearest to the earth, already extensively cracked, began to fly away in the form of meteorites up to a kilometre in diameter, which revolved round the earth in independent orbits. For about a thousand years this process continued gradually, and finally ceased to arouse interest on the earth. The end came quite suddenly. It was watched from Venus, but the earlier stages were also signalled from the earth. The depression in the moon's surface facing the earth suddenly opened and emitted a torrent of white-hot lava. As the moon passed round the earth it raised the temperature in the tropics to such an extent that rivers and lakes were dried up and vegetation destroyed.

"The colour changes on earth due to the flowering of the plants which were grown on it for the pleasure of the human race, and which were quite visible from our planet, no longer occurred. Dense clouds were formed and gave some protection to the earth. But above them the sea of flame on the moon increased in magnitude, and erupted in immense filaments under the earth's gravitation. Within three days the satellite had broken up into a ring of white-hot lava and dust. The last message received from the earth stated that the entire human race had retired underground, except on the Antarctic Continent, where however the ice-cap had already melted and the air temperature was 35° C. Within a day from the moon's break-up the first large fragment of it had fallen on the earth. The particles formed from it were continually jostling, and many more were subsequently driven down. Through the clouds of steam and volcanic smoke which shrouded the earth our astronomers could see but little, but later on it became clear that its tropical regions had been buried many kilometres deep under lunar fragments, and the remainder, though some traces of the former continents remain, had been submerged in the boiling ocean. It is not considered possible that any vestige of human life remains, nor can our spectroscopes detect any absorption bands of chlorophyll which would indicate the survival of plants.

"The majority of the lunar matter has formed a ring round the earth, like those of Saturn, but far denser. It is not yet in equilibrium, and fragments will continue to fall on the earth for about another thirty-five thousand years. At the end of that period the earth, which now possesses a belt of enormous mountains in its tropical regions, separated from the poles by two rings of sea, will be ready for recolonization. Preparations are being made for this event. We have largely sorted out the useful elements in the outer five kilometres or so of our planet, and it is proposed, when the earth is reoccupied, to erect artificial mountains on both planets which will extend above the Heaviside layer and enable continuous radio-communication instead of light signals to be used between the two.

"The old human race successfully cultivated individual happiness and has been destroyed by fire from heaven. This is not a cause for great regret, since happiness does not summate. The happiness of ten million individuals is not a millionfold the happiness of ten. But the unanimous co-operation of ten million individuals is something beyond their individual behaviour. It is the life of a super-organism. If, as many of the earth-dwellers hoped, the moon had broken up quietly, their species might have lasted a thousand million years instead of thirty-nine million, but their achievement would have been no greater.

"From the earth it is proposed to colonize Jupiter. It is not certain that the attempt will succeed, for the surface temperature of that planet is 130 degrees C., gravitation is three times as intense as that on Venus, and over twice that on earth, while the atmosphere contains appreciable quantities of thoron, a radio-active gas. The intense gravitation would of course destroy bodies as large as our own, but life on Jupiter will be possible for organisms built on a much smaller scale. A dwarf form of the human race about a tenth of our height, and with short stumpy legs but very thick bones, is therefore being bred. Their internal organs will also be very solidly built. They are selected by spinning them round in centrifuges which supply an artificial gravitational field, and destroy the less suitable members of each generation. Adaptation to such intense cold as that on Jupiter is impracticable, but it is proposed to send projectiles of a kilometre in length, which will contain sufficient stores of energy to last their inhabitants for some centuries, during which they may be able to develop the sources available on that planet. It is hoped that as many as one in a thousand of these projectiles may arrive safely. If Jupiter is successfully occupied the outer planets will then be attempted.

"About 250 million years hence our solar system will pass into a region of space in which stars are far denser than in our present neighbourhood. Although not more than one in ten thousand is likely to possess planets suitable for colonization, it is considered possible that we may pass near enough to one so equipped to allow an attempt at landing. If by that time the entire matter of the planet of our system is under conscious control, the attempt will stand some chance of success. Whereas the best time between the earth and Venus was one-tenth of a terrestrial year, the time taken to reach another stellar system would be measured in hundreds or thousands of years, and only a very few projectiles per million would arrive safely. But in such a case waste of life is as inevitable as in the seeding of a plant or the discharge of spermatozoa or pollen. Moreover, it is possible that under the conditions of life in the outer planets the human brain may alter in such a way as to open up possibilities inconceivable to our own minds. Our galaxy has a probable life of at least eighty million million years. Before that time has elapsed it is our ideal that all the matter in it available for life should be within the power of the heirs of the species whose original home has just been destroyed. If that ideal is even approximately fulfilled, the end of the world which we have just witnessed was an episode of entirely negligible importance. And there are other galaxies."

EPILOGUE

There are certain criteria which every attempt, however fantastic, to forestall the future should satisfy. In the first place, the future will not be as we should wish it. The Pilgrim Fathers were much happier in England under King James I

than they would be in America under President Coolidge. Most
of the great ideals of any given age are ignored by the men
of later periods. They only interest posterity in so far as they
have been embodied in art or literature. I have pictured a
human race on the earth absorbed in the pursuit of individual
happiness; on Venus mere components of a monstrous ant-
heap. My own ideal is naturally somewhere in between, and so
is that of almost every other human being alive to-day. But I
see no reason why my ideals should be realized. In the language
of religion, God's ways are not our ways; in that of science,
human ideals are the products of natural processes which do
not conform to them.

Secondly, we must use a proper time-scale. The earth has
lasted between one and eight thousand million years. Recorded
human history is a matter of about six thousand. This period
bears the same ratio to the earth's life as does a space of two
or three days to the whole of human history. I have no doubt
that in reality the future will be vastly more surprising than
anything I can imagine. But when we once realize the periods
of time which our thought can and should envisage we shall
come to see that the use, however haltingly, of our imaginations upon the possibilities of the future is a valuable spiritual
exercise.

For one of the essential elements of religion is an emotional
attitude towards the universe as a whole. As we come to realize
the tiny scale, both temporal and spatial, of the older my-
thologies, and the unimaginable vastness of the possibilities of
time and space, we must attempt to conjecture what purposes
may be developed in the universe that we are beginning to
apprehend. Our private, national, and even international aims
are restricted to a time measured in human life-spans.

"And wonder all before us lie
Deserts of vast eternity."

If it is true, as the higher religions teach, that the individual
can only achieve a good life by conforming to a plan greater
than his own, it is our duty to realize the possible magnitude
of such a plan, whether it be God's or man's. Only so can we
come to see that most good actions merely serve to stave off
the constant inroads of chaos on the human race. They are
necessary, but not sufficient. They cannot be regarded as active

co-operation in the Plan. The man who creates a new idea, whether expressed in language, art, or invention, may at least be co-operating actively. The average man cannot do this, but he must learn that the highest of his duties is to assist those who are creating, and the worst of his sins to hinder them.

I do not see how any one who has accepted the view of the universe presented by astronomy and geology can suppose that its main purpose is the preparation of a certain percentage of human souls for so much of perfection and happiness as is possible for them. This may be one of its purposes, but it can hardly be the most important. Events are taking place "for other great and glorious ends" which we can only dimly conjecture. Professor Alexander, for example, in *Space, Time, and Deity*, suggests that the end towards which "the whole creation groaneth and travaileth" is the emergence of a new kind of being which will bear the same relation to mind as do mind to life and life to matter. It is the urge towards this which finds its expression in the higher forms of religion. Without necessarily accepting such a view, one can express some of its implications in a myth. The numerical side of the myth is, I believe, correct, though whether tidal power could be utilized to the extent that I have suggested is a question for the engineers of the future.

Man's little world will end. The human mind can already envisage that end. If humanity can enlarge the scope of its will as it has enlarged the reach of its intellect, it will escape that end. If not, the judgment will have gone out against it, and man and all his works will perish eternally. Either the human race will prove that its destiny is in eternity and infinity, and that the value of the individual is negligible in comparison with that destiny, or the time will come

"When the great markets by the sea shut fast
   All that calm Sunday that goes on and on;
When even lovers find their peace at last,
   And earth is but a star, that once had shone."

Bertrand Russell

INTRODUCTION: ON THE VALUE OF SCEPTICISM

I wish to propose for the reader's favorable consideration a doctrine which may, I fear, appear wildly paradoxical and subversive. The doctrine in question is this: that it is undesirable to believe a proposition when there is no ground whatever for supposing it true. I must, of course, admit that if such an opinion became common it would completely transform our social life and our political system; since both are at present faultless, this must weigh against it. I am also aware (what is more serious) that it would tend to diminish the incomes of clairvoyants, bookmakers, bishops and others who live on the irrational hopes of those who have done nothing to deserve good fortune here or hereafter. In spite of these grave arguments, I maintain that a case can be made out for my paradox, and I shall try to set it forth.

First of all, I wish to guard myself against being thought to take up an extreme position. I am a British Whig, with a British love of compromise and moderation. A story is told of Pyrrho, the founder of Pyrrhonism (which was the old name for scepticism). He maintained that we never know enough to be sure that one course of action is wiser than another. In his youth, when he was taking his constitutional one afternoon, he saw his teacher in philosophy (from whom he had imbibed his principles) with his head stuck in a ditch, unable to get out. After contemplating him for some time, he walked on, maintaining that there was no sufficient ground for thinking he would do any good by pulling the old man out. Others, less sceptical, effected a rescue, and blamed Pyrrho for his heartlessness. But his teacher, true to his principles, praised him for his consistency. Now I do not advocate such heroic scepticism as that. I am prepared to admit the ordinary beliefs of common sense, in practice if not in theory. I am prepared to admit any well-established result of science, not as certainly true, but as sufficiently probable to afford a basis for rational action. If it is announced that there is to be an eclipse of the moon on such-and-such a date, I think it worth while to look and see whether it is taking place. Pyrrho would have thought otherwise. On this ground I feel justified in claiming that I advocate a middle position.

There are matters about which those who have investigated them are agreed; the dates of eclipses may serve as an illustration. There are other matters about which experts are not agreed. Even when the experts all agree, they may well be mistaken. Einstein's view as to the magnitude of the deflection of light by gravitation would have been rejected by all experts twenty years ago, yet it proved to be right. Nevertheless, the opinion of experts when it is unanimous, must be accepted by non-experts as more likely to be right than the opposite opinion. The scepticism that I advocate amounts only to this: (1) that when the experts are agreed, the opposite opinion cannot be held to be certain; (2) that when they are not agreed, no opinion can be regarded as certain by a non-expert; and (3) that when they all hold that no sufficient grounds for a positive opinion exist, the ordinary man would do well to suspend his judgment.

These propositions may seem mild, yet, if accepted, they would absolutely revolutionize human life.

The opinions for which people are willing to fight and persecute all belong to one of the three classes which this scepticism condemns. When there are rational grounds for an opinion, people are content to set them forth and wait for them to operate. In such cases, people do not hold their opinions with passion; they hold them calmly, and set forth their reasons quietly. The opinions that are held with passion are always those for which no good ground exists; indeed the passion is the measure of the holder's lack of rational conviction. Opinions in politics and religion are almost always held passionately. Except in China, a man is thought a poor creature unless he has strong opinions on such matters; people hate sceptics far more than they hate the passionate advocates of opinions hostile to their own. It is thought that the claims of practical life demand opinions on such questions, and that, if we become more rational, social existence would be impossible. I believe the opposite of this, and will try to make it clear why I have this belief.

Take the question of England's unemployment in the years after 1920. One party held that it was due to the wickedness of trade unions, another that it was due to the confusion on the Continent. A third party, while admitting that these causes played a part, attributed most of the trouble to the policy of the Bank of England in trying to increase the value of the pound sterling. This third party, I am given to understand, contained most of the experts, but no one else. Politicians do not find any attractions in a view which does not lend itself to party declamation, and ordinary mortals prefer views which attribute misfortune to the machinations of their enemies. Consequently people fight for and against quite irrelevant measures, while the few who have a rational opinion are not listened to because they do not minister to any one's passions. To produce converts, it would have been necessary to persuade people that the Bank of England is wicked. To convert Labor, it would have been necessary to show that the directors of the Bank of England are hostile to trade unionism; to convert the Bishop of London, it would have been necessary to show that they are "immoral." It would be thought to follow that their views on currency are mistaken.

Let us take another illustration. It is often said that socialism is contrary to human nature, and this assertion is denied by socialists with the same heat with which it is made by their opponents. The late Dr. Rivers, whose death cannot be sufficiently deplored, discussed this question in a lecture at University College, published in his posthumous book on *Pyschology and Politics*. This is the only discussion of this topic known to me that can lay claim to be scientific. It sets forth certain anthropological data which show that socialism is not contrary to human nature in Melanesia; it then points out that we do not know whether human nature is the same in Melanesia as in Europe; and it concludes that the only way of finding out whether socialism is contrary to European human nature is to try it. It is interesting that on the basis of this conclusion he was willing to become a Labor candidate. But he would certainly not have added to the heat and passion in which political controversies are usually enveloped.

I will now venture on a topic which people find even more difficult in treating dispassionately, namely, marriage customs. The bulk of the population of every country is persuaded that all marriage customs other than its own are immoral, and that those who combat this view only do so in order to justify their own loose lives. In India the remarriage of widows is traditionally regarded as a thing too horrible to contemplate. In Catholic countries divorce is thought very wicked, but some failure of conjugal fidelity is tolerated, at least in men. In America divorce is easy, but extra-conjugal relations are condemned with the utmost severity. Mohammedans believe in polygamy, which we think degrading. All these differing opinions are held with extreme vehemence, and very cruel persecutions are inflicted upon those who contravene them. Yet no one in any of the various countries makes the slightest attempt to show that the custom of his own country contributes more to human happiness than the custom of others.

When we open any scientific treatise on the subject, such as (for example) Westermarck's *History of Human Marriage*, we find an atmosphere extraordinarily different from that of popular prejudice. We find that every kind of custom has existed, many of them such as we should have supposed repugnant to human nature. We think we can understand polygamy, as a custom forced upon women by male oppressors. But what are we to say of the Tibetan custom, according to which one women has several husbands? Yet travelers in Tibet assure us that family life there is at least as harmonious as in Europe. A little of such reading must soon reduce any candid person to complete scepticism, since there seem to be no data enabling us to say that one marriage custom is better or worse than another. Almost all involve cruelty and intolerance towards offenders against the local code, but otherwise they have nothing in common. It seems that sin is geographical. From this conclusion it is only a small step to the further conclusion that the notion of "sin" is illusory, and that the cruelty habitually practiced in punishing it is unnecessary. It is just this conclusion which is so unwelcome to many minds, since the infliction of cruelty with a good conscience is a delight to moralists. That is why they invented Hell.

Nationalism is of course an extreme example of fervent belief concerning doubtful matters. I think it may be safely said that any scientific historian, writing now a history of the Great

War, is bound to make statements which, if made during the war, would have exposed him to imprisonment in every one of the belligerent countries on both sides. Again, with the exception of China, there is no country where people tolerate the truth about themselves; at ordinary times the truth is only thought ill-mannered, but in war-time it is thought criminal. Opposing systems of violent belief are built up, the falsehood of which is evident from the fact that they are only believed by those who share the same national bias. But the application of reason to these systems of belief is thought as wicked as the application of reason to religious dogmas was formerly thought. When people are challenged as to why scepticism in such matters should be wicked, the only answer is that myths help to win wars, so that a rational nation would be killed rather than kill. The view that there is something shameful in saving one's skin of wholesale slander of foreigners is one which, so far as I know, has hitherto found no supporters among professional moralists outside the ranks of the Quakers. If it is suggested that a rational nation would find ways of keeping out of war altogether, the answer is usually mere abuse.

What would be the effect of a spread of rational scepticism? Human events spring from passions, which generate systems of attendant myths. Psycho-analysts have studied the individual manifestations of this process in lunatics, certified and uncertified. A man who has suffered some humiliation invents a theory that he is King of England, and develops all kinds of ingenious explanations of the fact that he is not treated with that respect which his exalted position demands. In this case, his delusion is one with which his neighbors do not sympathize, so they lock him up. But if, instead of asserting only his own greatness, he asserts the greatness of his nation or his class or his creed, he wins hosts of adherents, and becomes a political or religious leader, even if, to the impartial outsider, his views seem just as absurd as those found in asylums. In this way a collective insanity grows up, which follows laws very similar to those of individual insanity. Every one knows that it is dangerous to dispute with a lunatic who thinks he is King of England; but as he is isolated, he can be overpowered. When a whole nation shares a delusion, its anger is of the same kind as that of an individual lunatic if its pretentions are disputed, but nothing short of war can compel it to submit to reason.

The part played by intellectual factors in human behavior is a matter as to which there is much disagreement among psychologists. There are two quite distinct questions: (1) how far are beliefs operative as causes of actions? (2) how far are beliefs derived from logical adequate evidence, or capable of being so derived? On both questions psychologists are agreed in giving a much smaller place to the intellectual factors than the plain man would give, but within this general agreement there is room for considerable differences of degree. Let us take the two questions in succession.

(1) How far are beliefs operative as causes of action? Let us not discuss the question theoretically, but let us take an ordinary day of an ordinary man's life. He begins by getting up in the morning, probably from force of habit, without the intervention of any belief. He eats his breakfast, catches his train, reads his newspaper, and goes to his office, all from force of habit. There was a time in the past when he formed these habits, and in the choice of the office, at least, belief played a part. He probably believed, at the time, that the job offered him there was as good as he was likely to get. In most men, belief plays a part in the original choice of a career, and therefore, derivatively, in all that is entailed by this choice.

At the office, if he is an underling, he may continue to act merely from habit, without active volition, and without the explicit intervention of belief. It might be thought that, if he adds up columns of figures, he believes the arithmetical rules which he employs. But that would be an error; these rules are mere habits of his body, like those of a tennis player. They were acquired in youth, not from an intellectual belief that they corresponded to the truth, but to please the school-master, just as a dog learns to sit on its hind legs and beg for food. I do not say that all education is of this sort, but certainly most learning of the three R's is.

If, however, our friend is a partner or director, he may be called upon during his day to make difficult decisions of policy. In these decisions it is probable that belief will play a part. He believes that some things will go up and others will go down, that so-and-so is a sound man, and such-and-such on the verge of bankruptcy. On these beliefs he acts. It is just because he is called upon to act on beliefs rather than mere habits that he is considered such a much greater man than a mere clerk, and is able to get so much more money—provided his beliefs are true.

In his home-life there will be much the same proportion of occasions when belief is a cause of action. At ordinary times his behavior to his wife and children will be governed by habit, or by instinct modified by habit. On great occasions— when he proposes marriage, when he decides what school to send his son to, or when he finds reason to suspect his wife of unfaithfulness—he cannot be guided wholly by habit. In proposing marriage, he may be guided by mere instinct, or he may be influenced by the belief that the lady is rich. If he is guided by instinct, he no doubt believes that the lady possesses every virtue, and this may seem to him to be a cause of his action, but in fact it is merely another effect of the instinct which alone suffices to account for his action. In choosing a school for his son, he probably proceeds in much the same way as in making difficult business decisions; here belief usually plays an important part. If evidence comes into his possession showing that his wife has been unfaithful, his behavior is likely to be merely instinctive, but the instinct is set in operation by a belief, which is the first cause of everything that follows.

Thus although beliefs are not directly responsible for more than a small part of our actions, the actions for which they are responsible are among the most important, and largely determine the general structure of our lives. In particular, our religious and political actions are associated with beliefs.

(2) I come now to our second question, which is itself twofold: (a) how far are beliefs in fact based upon evidence? (b) how far is it possible or desirable that they should be?

(a) The extent to which beliefs are based upon evidence is very much less than believers suppose. Take the kind of action which is most nearly rational: the investment of money by a rich City man. You will often find that his view (say) on the question whether the French franc will go up or down depends upon his political sympathies, and yet is so strongly held that he is prepared to risk his money on it. In bankruptcies it often appears that some sentimental factor was the original cause of ruin. Political opinions are hardly ever based upon evidence, except in the case of civil servants, who are forbidden to give utterance to them. There are of course exceptions. In the tariff reform controversy which began twenty-five years ago, most manufacturers supported the side that would increase their own incomes, showing that their opinions were really based on evidence, however little their utterances would have led one to suppose so. We have here a complication. Freudians have accustomed us to "rationalizing," *i.e.*, the process of inventing what seem to ourselves rational grounds for a decision or opinion that is in fact quite irrational. But there is, especially in English-speaking countries, a converse process which may be called "irrationalizing." A shrewd man will sum up, more or less subconsciously, the pros and cons of a question from a selfish point of view. (Unselfish considerations seldom weigh subconsciously except where one's children are concerned.) Having come to a sound egoistic decision by the help of the unconscious, a man proceeds to invent, or adopt from others, a set of high-sounding phrases showing how he is pursuing the public good at immense personal sacrifice. Anybody who believes that these phrases give his real reasons must suppose him quite incapable of judging evidence, since the supposed public good is not going to result from his action. In this case a man appears less rational than he is; what is still more curious, the irrational part of him is conscious and the rational part unconscious. It is this trait in our characters that has made the English and Americans so successful.

Shrewdness, when it is genuine, belongs more to the unconscious than to the conscious part of our nature. It is, I suppose, the main quality required for success in business. From a moral point of view, it is a humble quality, since it is always selfish; yet it suffices to keep men from the worst crimes. If the Germans had had it, they would not have adopted the unlimited submarine campaign. If the French had had it, they would not have behaved as they did in the Ruhr. If Napoleon had had it, he would not have gone to war again after the Treaty of Amiens. It may be laid down as a general rule to which there are few exceptions that, when people are mistaken as to what is to their own interest, the course that they believe to be wise is more harmful to others than the course that really is wise. Therefore anything that makes people better judges of their own interest does good. There are innumerable examples of men making fortunes because, on moral grounds, they did something which they believed to be contrary to their own interests. For instance, among early Quakers there were a number of shopkeepers who adopted the practice of asking no more for their goods than they were willing to accept, instead of bargaining with each customer, as everybody else did. They adopted this practice because they held it to be a lie to ask more than they would take. But the convenience to customers was so great that everybody came to their shops, and they grew rich. (I forget where I read this, but if my memory serves me it was in some reliable source.) The same policy *might* have been adopted from shrewdness, but in fact no one was sufficiently shrewd. Our unconscious is more malevolent than it pays us to be; therefore the people who do most completely what is in fact to their interest are those who deliberately, on moral grounds, do what they believe to be against their interest. Next to them come the people who try to think out rationally and consciously what is to their own interest, eliminating as far as possible the influence of passion. Third come the people who have instinctive shrewdness. Last of all come the people whose malevolence overbalances their shrewdness, making them pursue the ruin of others in ways that lead to their own ruin. This last class embraces 90 per cent of the population of Europe.

I may seem to have digressed somewhat from my topic, but it was necessary to disentangle unconscious reason, which is called shrewdness, from the conscious variety. The ordinary methods of education have practically no effect upon the unconscious, so that shrewdness cannot be taught by our present technique. Morality, also, except where it consists of mere habit, seems incapable of being taught by present methods; at any rate, I have never noticed any beneficent effect upon those who are exposed to frequent exhortations. Therefore on our present lines any deliberate improvement must be brought about by intellectual means. We do not know how to teach people to be shrewd or virtuous, but we do know, within limits, how to teach them to be rational: it is only necessary to reverse the practice of education authorities in every particular. We may hereafter learn to create virtue by manipulating the ductless glands and stimulating or restraining their secretions. But for the present it is easier to create rationality than virtue— meaning by "rationality" a scientific habit of mind in forecasting the effects of our actions.

(*b*) This brings me to the question: How far could or should men's actions be rational? Let us take "should" first. There are very definite limits, to my mind, within which rationality should be confined; some of the most important departments of life are ruined by the invasion of reason. Leibniz in his old age told a correspondent that he had only once asked a lady to marry him, and that was when he was fifty. "Fortunately," he added, "the lady asked time to consider. This gave me also time to consider, and I withdrew the offer." Doubtless his conduct was very rational, but I cannot say that I admire it.

Shakespeare puts "the lunatic, the lover, and the poet" together, as being "of imagination all compact." The problem is to keep the lover and the poet, without the lunatic. I will give an illustration. In 1919 I saw *The Trojan Women* acted at the Old Vic. There is an unbearably pathetic scene where Astyanax is put to death by the Greeks for fear he should grow up into a second Hector. There was hardly a dry eye in the theater, and the audience found the cruelty of the Greeks in the play hardly credible. Yet those very people who wept were, at that very moment, practicing that very cruelty on a scale which the imagination of Euripides could have never contemplated. They had lately voted (most of them) for a Government which prolonged the blockade of Germany after the armistice, and imposed the blockade of Russia. It was known that these blockades caused the death of immense numbers of children, but it was felt desirable to diminish the population of enemy countries: the children, like Astyanax, might grow up to emulate their fathers. Euripides the poet awakened the lover in the imagination of the audience; but lover and poet were forgotten at the door of the theater, and the lunatic (in the shape of the homicidal maniac) controlled the political actions of these men and women who thought themselves kind and virtuous.

Is it possible to preserve the lover and the poet without preserving the lunatic? In each of us all three exist in varying degrees. Are they so bound up together that when the one is brought under control the others perish? I do not believe it. I believe there is in each of us a certain energy which must find vent in actions not inspired by reason, but may find vent in art, in passionate love, or in passionate hate, according to circumstances. Respectability, regularity, and routine—the whole cast-iron discipline of a modern industrial society—have atrophied the artistic impulse, and imprisoned love so that it can no longer be generous and free and creative, but must be either stuffy or furtive. Control has been applied to the very things which should be free, while envy, cruelty, and hate sprawl at large with the blessing of nearly the whole bench of Bishops. Our instinctive apparatus consists of two parts—the one tending to further our own life and that of our descendants, the other tending to thwart the lives of supposed rivals. The first includes the joy of life, and love, and art, which is psychologically an offshoot of love. The second includes competition, patriotism, and war. Conventional morality does everything to suppress the first and encourage the second. True morality would do the exact opposite. Our dealings with those whom we love may be safely left to instinct; it is our dealings with those whom we hate that ought to be brought under the dominion of reason. In the modern world, those whom we effectively hate are distant groups, especially foreign nations. We conceive them abstractedly, and deceive ourselves into the belief that acts which are really embodiments of hatred are done from love of justice or some such lofty motive. Only a large measure of scepticism can tear away the veils which hide this truth from us. Having achieved that, we could begin to build a new morality, not based on envy and restriction, but on the wish for a full life and the realization that other human beings are a help and not a hindrance when once the madness of envy has been cured. This is not a Utopian hope; it was partially realized in Elizabethan England. It could be realized to-morrow if men would learn to pursue their own happiness rather than the misery of others. This is no impossibly austere morality, yet its adoption would turn our earth into a paradise.

EASTERN AND WESTERN
IDEALS OF HAPPINESS

EVERYBODY knows Wells's Time Machine, which enabled its possessor to travel backwards or forwards in time, and see for himself what the past was like and what the future will be. But people do not always realize that a great deal of the advantages of Wells's device can be secured by traveling about the world at the present day. A European who goes to New York and Chicago sees the future, the future to which Europe is likely to come if it escapes economic disaster. On the other hand, when he goes to Asia he sees the past. In India, I am told, he can see the Middle Ages; in China he can see the eighteenth century. If George Washington were to return to earth, the country which he created would puzzle him dreadfully. He would feel a little less strange in England, still less strange in France; but he would not feel really at home until he reached China. There, for the first time in his ghostly wanderings, he would find men who still believe in "life, liberty, and the pursuit of happiness," and who conceive these things more or less as Americans of the War of Independence conceived them. And I think it would not be long before he became President of the Chinese Republic.

Western civilization embraces North and South America, Europe excluding Russia, and the British self-governing dominions. In this civilization the United States leads the van; all the characteristics that distinguish the West from the East are most marked and farthest developed in America. We are accustomed to take progress for granted: to assume without hesitation that the changes which have happened during the last hundred years were unquestionably for the better, and that further changes for the better are sure to follow indefinitely. On the Continent of Europe, the war and its consequences have administered a blow to this confident belief, and men have begun to look back to the time before 1914 as a golden age, not likely to recur for centuries. In England there has been much less of this shock to optimism, and in America still less. For those of us who have been accustomed to take progress for granted, it is especially interesting to visit a country like China, which has remained where we were one hundred and fifty years ago, and to ask ourselves whether, on the balance, the changes which have happened to us have brought any real improvement.

The civilization of China, as every one knows, is based upon the teaching of Confucius, who flourished five hundred years before Christ. Like the Greeks and Romans, he did not think of human society as naturally progressive; on the contrary, he believed that in remote antiquity rulers had been wise, and the people had been happy to a degree which the degenerate present could admire but hardly achieve. This, of course, was a delusion. But the practical result was that Confucius, like other teachers of antiquity, aimed at creating a stable society, maintaining a certain level of excellence, but not always striving after new successes. In this he was more successful than any other man who ever lived. His personality has been stamped on Chinese civilization from his day to our own. During his lifetime the Chinese occupied only a small part of present-day China, and were divided into a number of warring states. During the next three hundred years they established themselves throughout what is now China proper, and founded an empire exceeding in territory and population any other that existed until the last fifty years. In spite of barbarian invasions, Mongol and Manchu dynasties, and occasional longer or shorter periods of chaos and civil war, the Confucian system survived, bringing with it art and literature and a civilized way of life. It is only in our own day, through contact with the West and with the westernized Japanese, that this system has begun to break down.

A system which has had this extraordinary power of survival must have great merits, and certainly deserves our respect and consideration. It is not a religion, as we understand the word, because it is not associated with the supernatural or with mystical beliefs. It is a purely ethical system, but its ethics, unlike those of Christianity, are not too exalted for ordinary men to practice. In essence, what Confucius teaches is something very like the old-fashioned ideal of a "gentleman" as it existed in the eighteenth century. One of his sayings will illustrate this (I quote from Lionel Giles's *Sayings of Confucius*):

The true gentleman is never contentious. If a spirit of rivalry is anywhere unavoidable, it is at a shooting-match. Yet even here he courteously salutes his opponents before taking up his position, and again when, having lost, he retires to drink the forfeit-cup. So that even when competing he remains a true gentleman.

He speaks much, as a moral teacher is bound to do, about duty and virtue and such matters, but he never exacts anything contrary to nature and the natural affections. This is shown in the following conversation:

The Duke of She addressed Confucius, saying: We have an upright man in our country. His father stole a sheep, and the son bore witness against him.—In our country, Confucius replied, uprightness is something different from this. A father hides the guilt of his son, and a son hides the guilt of his father. It is in such conduct that true uprightness is to be found.

Confucius was in all things moderate, even in virtue. He did not believe that we ought to return good for evil. He was asked on one occasion: "How do you regard the principle of returning good for evil?" And he replied: "What, then, is to be the return for good? Rather should you return justice for injustice, and good for good." The principle of returning good for evil was being taught in his day in China by the Taoists, whose teaching is much more akin to that of Christianity than is the teaching of Confucius. The founder of Taoism, Lao-Tze (supposed to have been an older contemporary of Confucius), says: "To the good I would be good; to the not-good I would also be good, in order to make them good. With the faithful I would keep faith; with the unfaithful I would also keep faith, in order that they may become faithful. Even if a man is bad, how can it be right to cast him off? Requite injury with kindness." Some of Lao-Tze's words are amazingly like parts of the Sermon on the Mount. For instance, he says:

He that humbles himself shall be preserved entire. He that bends shall be made straight. He that is empty shall be filled. He that is worn out shall be renewed. He who has little shall succeed. He who has much shall go astray.

It is characteristic of China that it was not Lao-Tze but Confucius who became the recognized national sage. Taoism has survived, but chiefly as magic and among the uneducated. Its doctrines have appeared visionary to the practical men who administered the empire, while the doctrines of Confucius were eminently calculated to avoid friction. Lao-Tze preached a doctrine of inaction: "The empire," he says, "has ever been won by letting things take their course. He who must always be doing is unfit to obtain the empire." But Chinese governors naturally preferred the Confucian maxims of self-control, benevolence, and courtesy, combined, as they were, with a great emphasis upon the good that could be done by wise government. It never occurred to the Chinese, as it has to all modern white nations, to have one system of ethics in theory and another in practice. I do not mean that they always live up to their own theories, but that they attempt to do so and are expected to do so, whereas there are large parts of the Christian ethic which are universally admitted to be too good for this wicked world.

We have, in fact, two kinds of morality side by side: one which we preach but do not practice, and another which we practice but seldom preach. Christianity, like all religions except Mormonism, is Asiatic in origin; it had in the early centuries that emphasis on individualism and other-worldliness which is characteristic of Asiatic mysticism. From this point of view, the doctrine of non-resistance was intelligible. But when Christianity became the nominal religion of energetic European princes, it was found necessary to maintain that some texts were not to be taken literally, while others, such as "render unto Cæsar the things that are Cæsar's," acquired great popularity. In our own day, under the influence of competitive industrialism, the slightest approach to non-resistance is despised, and men are expected to be able to keep their end up. In practice, our effective morality is that of material success achieved by means of a struggle; and this applies to nations as well as to individuals. Anything else seems to us soft and foolish.

The Chinese do not adopt either our theoretical or our practical ethic. They admit in theory that there are occasions when it is proper to fight, and in practice that these occasions are rare; whereas we hold in theory that there are no occasions when it is proper to fight and in practice that such occasions are very frequent. The Chinese sometimes fight, but are not a combative race, and do not greatly admire success in war or in business. Traditionally, they admire learning more than anything else; next to that, and usually in combination with it, they admire urbanity and courtesy. For ages past, administrative posts have been awarded in China on the results of competitive examinations. As there has been no hereditary aristocracy for two thousand years—with the sole exception of the family of Confucius, the head of which is a Duke—learning has drawn to itself the kind of respect which, in feudal Europe, was given to powerful nobles, as well as the respect which it inspired on its own account. The old learning, however, was very narrow, consisting merely in an uncritical study of the Chinese classics and their recognized commentators. Under the influence of the West, it has come to be known that geography, economics, geology, chemistry, and so on, are of more practical use than the moralizings of former ages. Young China—that is to say, the students who have been educated on European lines—recognize modern needs, and have perhaps hardly enough respect for the old tradition. Nevertheless, even the most modern, with few exceptions, retain the traditional virtues of moderation, politeness, and a pacific temper. Whether these virtues will survive a few more decades of Western and Japanese tuition is perhaps doubtful.

If I were to try to sum up in a phrase the main difference between the Chinese and ourselves, I should say that they, in the main, aim at enjoyment, while we, in the main, aim at power. We like power over our fellow-men, and we like power over Nature. For the sake of the former we have built up strong states, and for the sake of the latter we have built up Science. The Chinese are too lazy and too good-natured for such pursuits. To say that they are lazy is, however, only true in a certain sense. They are not lazy in the way that Russians are, that is to say, they will work hard for their living. Employers of labor find them extraordinarily industrious. But they will not work, as Americans and Western Europeans do, simply because they would be bored if they did not work, nor do they love hustle for its own sake. When they have enough to live on, they live on it, instead of trying to augment it by hard work. They have an infinite capacity for leisurely amusements—going to the theater, talking while they drink tea, admiring the Chinese art of earlier times, or walking in beautiful scenery. To our way of thinking, there is something unduly mild about such a way of spending one's life; we respect more a man who goes to his office every day, even if all that he does in his office is harmful.

Living in the East has, perhaps, a corrupting influence upon a white man, but I must confess that, since I came to know China, I have regarded laziness as one of the best qualities of which men in the mass are capable. We achieve certain things by being energetic, but it may be questioned whether, on the balance, the things that we achieve are of any value. We develop wonderful skill in manufacture, part of which we devote to making ships, automobiles, telephones, and other means of living luxuriously at high pressure, while another part is devoted to making guns, poison gases, and aeroplanes for the purpose of killing each other wholesale. We have a first-class system of administration and taxation, part of which is devoted to education, sanitation, and such useful objects, while the rest is devoted to war. In England at the present day most of the national revenue is spent on past and future wars and only the residue on useful objects. On the Continent, in most countries, the proportion is even worse. We have a police system of unexampled efficiency, part of which is devoted to the detection and prevention of crime and part to imprisoning anybody who has any new constructive political ideas. In China, until recently, they had none of these things. Industry was too inefficient to produce either automobiles or bombs; the State too inefficient to educate its own citizens or to kill those of other countries; the police too inefficient to catch either bandits or Bolsheviks. The result was that in China, compared to any white man's country, there was freedom for all, and a degree of diffused happiness which was amazing in view of the poverty of all but a tiny minority.

Comparing the actual outlook of the average Chinese with that of the average Western, two differences strike one: first, that the Chinese do not admire activity unless it serves some useful purpose; secondly, that they do not regard morality as consisting in checking our own impulses and interfering with those of others. The first of these differences has been already discussed, but the second is perhaps equally important. Professor Giles, the eminent Chinese scholar, at the end of his Gifford Lectures on "Confucianism and its Rivals," maintains that the chief obstacle to the success of Christian missions in China has been the doctrine of original sin. The traditional doctrine of orthodox Christianity—still preached by most Christian missionaries in the Far East—is that we are all born wicked, so wicked as to deserve eternal punishment. The Chinese might have no difficulty in accepting this doctrine if it applied only to white men, but when they are told that their own parents and grandparents are in hell-fire they grow indignant. Confucius taught that men are born good, and that if they become wicked, that is through the force of evil example or corrupting manners. This difference from traditional Western orthodoxy has a profound influence on the outlook of the Chinese.

Among ourselves, the people who are regarded as moral luminaries are those who forego ordinary pleasures themselves and find compensation in interfering with the pleasures of others. There is an element of the busybody in our conception of virtue: unless a man makes himself a nuisance to a great many people, we do not think he can be an exceptionally good man. This attitude comes from our notion of Sin. It leads not only to interference with freedom, but also to hypocrisy, since the conventional standard is too difficult for most people to live up to. In China this is not the case. Moral precepts are positive rather than negative. A man is expected to be respectful to his parents, kind to his children, generous to his poor relations, and courteous to all. These are not very difficult duties, but most men actually fulfill them, and the result is perhaps better than that of our higher standard, from which most people fall short.

Another result of the absence of the notion of Sin is that men are much more willing to submit their differences to argument and reason than they are in the West. Among ourselves, differences of opinion quickly become questions of "principle": each side thinks that the other side is wicked, and that any yielding to it involves sharing in its guilt. This makes our disputes bitter, and involves in practice a great readiness to appeal to force. In China, although there were military men who were ready to appeal to force, no one took them seriously, not even their own soldiers. They fought battles which were nearly bloodless, and they did much less harm than we should expect from our experience of the fiercer conflicts of the West. The great bulk of the population, including the civil administration, went about its business as though these generals and their armies did not exist. In ordinary life, disputes are usually adjusted by the friendly mediation of some third party. Compromise is the accepted principle, because it is necessary to save the face of both parties. Saving face, though in some forms it makes foreigners smile, is a most valuable national institution, making social and political life far less ruthless than it is with us.

There is one serious defect, and only one, in the Chinese system, and that is, that it does not enable China to resist more pugnacious nations. If the whole world were like China, the whole world could be happy; but so long as others are warlike and energetic, the Chinese, now that they are no longer isolated, will be compelled to copy our vices to some degree if they are to preserve their national independence. But let us not flatter ourselves that this imitation will be an improvement.

A FREE MAN'S WORSHIP[1]

To DR. FAUSTUS in his study Mephistopheles told the history of the Creation, saying:

"The endless praises of the choirs of angels had begun to grow wearisome; for, after all, did he not deserve their praise? Had he not given them endless joy? Would it not be more amusing to obtain undeserved praise, to be worshipped by beings whom he tortured? He smiled inwardly, and resolved that the great drama should be performed.

"For countless ages the hot nebula whirled aimlessly through space. At length it began to take shape, the central mass threw off planets, the planets cooled, boiling seas and burning mountains heaved and tossed, from black masses of cloud hot sheets of rain deluged the barely solid crust. And now the first germ of life grew in the depths of the ocean, and developed rapidly in the fructifying warmth into vast forest trees, huge ferns springing from the damp mould, sea monsters breeding, fighting, devouring, and passing away. And from the monsters, as the play unfolded itself, Man was born, with the power of thought, the knowledge of good and evil, and the cruel thirst for worship. And Man saw that all is passing in this mad, monstrous world, that all is struggling to snatch, at any cost, a few brief moments of life before Death's inexorable decree. And Man said: 'There is a hidden purpose, could we but fathom it, and the purpose is good; for we must reverence something, and in the visible world there is nothing worthy of reverence.' And Man stood aside from the struggle, resolving that God intended harmony to come out of chaos by human efforts. And when he followed the instincts which God had transmitted to him from his ancestry of beasts of prey, he called it Sin, and asked God to forgive him. But he doubted whether he could be justly forgiven, until he invented a divine Plan by which God's wrath was to have been appeased. And seeing the present was bad, he made it yet worse, that thereby the future might be better. And he gave God thanks for the strength that enabled him to forgo even the joys that were

[1]Reprinted from the *Independent Review*, December, 1903.

possible. And God smiled; and when he saw that Man had become perfect in renunciation and worship, he sent another sun through the sky, which crashed into Man's sun; and all returned again to nebula.

" 'Yes," he murmured, 'it was a good play; I will have it performed again.' "

Such, in outline, but even more purposeless, more void of meaning, is the world which Science presents for our belief. Amid such a world, if anywhere, our ideals henceforward must find a home. That Man is the product of causes which had no prevision of the end they were achieving; that his origin, his growth, his hopes and fears, his loves and his beliefs, are but the outcome of accidental collocations of atoms; that no fire, no heroism, no intensity of thought and feeling, can preserve an individual life beyond the grave; that all the labours of the ages, all the devotion, all the inspiration, all the noonday brightness of human genius, are destined to extinction in the vast death of the solar system, and that the whole temple of Man's achievement must inevitably be buried beneath the débris of a universe in ruins—all these things, if not quite beyond dispute, are yet so nearly certain, that no philosophy which rejects them can hope to stand. Only within the scaffolding of these truths, only on the firm foundation of unyielding despair, can the soul's habitation henceforth be safely built.

How, in such an alien and inhuman world, can so powerless a creature as Man preserve his aspirations untarnished? A strange mystery it is that Nature, omnipotent but blind, in the revolutions of her secular hurryings through the abysses of space, has brought forth at last a child, subject still to her power, but gifted with sight, with knowledge of good and evil, with the capacity of judging all the works of his unthinking Mother. In spite of Death, the mark and seal of the parental control, Man is yet free, during his brief years, to examine, to criticise, to know, and in imagination to create. To him alone, in the world with which he is acquainted, this freedom belongs; and in this lies his superiority to the resistless forces that control his outward life.

The savage, like ourselves, feels the oppression of his impotence before the powers of Nature; but having in himself nothing that he respects more than Power, he is willing to prostrate himself before his gods, without inquiring whether they are worthy of his worship. Pathetic and very terrible is the long history of cruelty and torture, of degradation and human sacrifice, endured in the hope of placating the jealous gods: surely, the trembling believer thinks, when what is most precious has been freely given, their lust for blood must be appeased, and more will not be required. The religion of Moloch —as such creeds may be generically called—is in essence the cringing submission of the slave, who dare not, even in his heart, allow the thought that his master deserves no adulation. Since the independence of ideals is not yet acknowledged, Power may be freely worshipped, and receive an unlimited respect, despite its wanton infliction of pain.

But gradually, as morality grows bolder, the claim of the ideal world begins to be felt; and worship, if it is not to cease, must be given to gods of another kind than those created by the savage. Some, though they feel the demands of the ideal, will still consciously reject them, still urging that naked Power is worthy of worship. Such is the attitude inculcated in God's answer to Job out of the whirlwind: the divine power and knowledge are paraded, but of the divine goodness there is no hint. Such also is the attitude of those who in our own day, base their morality upon the struggle for survival, maintaining that the survivors are necessarily the fittest. But others, not content with an answer so repugnant to the moral sense, will adopt the position which we have become accustomed to regard as specially religious, maintaining that, in some hidden manner, the world of fact is really harmonious with the world of ideals. Thus Man creates God, all-powerful and all-good, the mystic unity of what is and what should be.

But the world of fact, after all, is not good; and, in submitting our judgment to it, there is an element of slavishness from which our thoughts must be purged. For in all things it is well to exalt the dignity of Man, by freeing him as far as possible from the tyranny of non-human Power. When we have realised that Power is largely bad, that man, with his knowledge of good and evil, is but a helpless atom in a world which has no such knowledge, the choice is again presented to us: Shall we worship Force, or shall we worship Goodness? Shall our God exist and be evil, or shall he be recognised as the creation of our own conscience?

The answer to this question is very momentous, and affects profoundly our whole morality. The worship of Force, to which Carlyle and Nietzsche and the creed of Militarism have accustomed us, is the result of failure to maintain our own ideals against a hostile universe: it is itself a prostrate submission to evil, a sacrifice of our best to Moloch. If strength indeed is to be respected, let us respect rather the strength of those who refuse that false "recognition of facts" which fails to recognise that facts are often bad. Let us admit that, in the world we know, there are many things that would be better otherwise, and that the ideals to which we do and must adhere are not realised in the realm of matter. Let us preserve our respect for truth, for beauty, for the ideal of perfection which life does not permit us to attain, though none of these things meet with the approval of the unconscious universe. If Power is bad, as it seems to be, let us reject it from our hearts. In this lies Man's true freedom: in determination to worship only the God created by our own love of the good, to respect only the heaven which inspires the insight of our best moments. In action, in desire, we must submit perpetually to the tyranny of outside forces; but in thought, in aspiration, we are free, free from our fellowmen, free from the petty planet on which our bodies impotently crawl, free even, while we live, from the tyranny of death. Let us learn, then, that energy of faith which enables us to live constantly in the vision of the good; and let us descend, in action, into the world of fact, with that vision always before us.

When first the opposition of fact and ideal grows fully visible, a spirit of fiery revolt, of fierce hatred of the gods, seems necessary to the assertion of freedom. To defy with Promethean constancy a hostile universe, to keep its evil always in view, always actively hated, to refuse no pain that the malice of Power can invent, appears to be the duty of all who will not bow before the inevitable. But indignation is still a bondage, for it compels our thoughts to be occupied with an evil world; and in the fierceness of desire from which rebellion springs there is a kind of self-assertion which it is necessary for the wise to overcome. Indignation is a submission of our thoughts, but not of our desires; the Stoic freedom in which wisdom consists is found in the submission of our desires, but not of our thoughts. From the submission of our desires springs the virtue of resignation; from the freedom of our thoughts springs the whole world of art and philosophy, and the vision of beauty by which, at last, we half reconquer the reluctant world. But the vision of beauty is possible only to unfettered contemplation, to thoughts not weighted by the load of eager wishes; and thus Freedom comes only to those who no longer ask of life that it shall yield them any of those personal goods that are subject to the mutations of Time.

Although the necessity of renunciation is evidence of the existence of evil, yet Christianity, in preaching it, has shown a wisdom exceeding that of the Promethean philosophy of rebellion. It must be admitted that, of the things we desire, some, though they prove impossible, are yet real goods; others, however, as ardently longed for, do not form part of a fully purified ideal. The belief that what must be renounced is bad, though sometimes false, is far less often false than untamed passion supposes; and the creed of religion, by providing a reason for proving that it is never false, has been the means of purifying our hopes by the discovery of many austere truths.

But there is in resignation a further good element: even real goods, when they are unattainable, ought not to be fretfully desired. To every man comes, sooner or later, the great renunciation. For the young, there is nothing unattainable; a good thing desired with the whole force of a passionate will, and yet impossible, is to them not credible. Yet, by death, by illness, by poverty, or by the voice of duty, we must learn, each one of us, that the world was not made for us, and that, however beautiful may be the things we crave, Fate may nevertheless forbid them. It is the part of courage, when misfortune comes, to bear without repining the ruin of our hopes, to turn away our thoughts from vain regrets. This degree of submission to Power is not only just and right: it is the very gate of wisdom.

But passive renunciation is not the whole of wisdom; for not by renunciation alone can we build a temple for the worship of our own ideals. Haunting foreshadowings of the temple appear in the realm of imagination, in music, in architecture, in the untroubled kingdom of reason, and in the golden sunset magic of lyrics, where beauty shines and glows, remote from the touch of sorrow, remote from the fear of change, remote from the failures and disenchantments of the world of fact. In the contemplation of these things the vision of heaven will shape itself in our hearts, giving at once a touchstone to judge the world about us, and an inspiration by which to fashion to our needs whatever is not incapable of serving as a stone in the sacred temple.

Except for those rare spirits that are born without sin, there is a cavern of darkness to be traversed before that temple can be entered. The gate of the cavern is despair, and its floor is paved with the gravestones of abandoned hopes. There Self must die; there the eagerness, the greed of untamed desire must be slain, for only so can the soul be freed from the empire of Fate. But out of the cavern the Gate of Renunciation leads again to the daylight of wisdom, by whose radiance a new insight, a new joy, a new tenderness, shine forth to gladden the pilgrim's heart.

When, without the bitterness of impotent rebellion, we have learnt both to resign ourselves to the outward rule of Fate and to recognise that the non-human world is unworthy of our worship, it becomes possible at last so to transform and refashion the unconscious universe, so to transmute it in the crucible of imagination, that a new image of shining gold replaces the old idol of clay. In all the multiform facts of the world—in the visual shapes of trees and mountains and clouds, in the events of the life of man, even in the very omnipotence of Death—the insight of creative idealism can find the reflection of a beauty which its own thoughts first made. In this way mind asserts its subtle mastery over the thoughtless forces of Nature. The more evil the material with which it deals, the more thwarting to untrained desire, the greater is its achievement in inducing the reluctant rock to yield up its hidden treasures, the prouder its victory in compelling the opposing forces to swell the pageant of its triumph. Of all the arts, Tragedy is the proudest, the most triumphant; for it builds its shining citadel in the very centre of the enemy's country, on the very summit of his highest mountain; from its impregnable watch-towers, his camps and arsenals, his columns and forts, are all revealed; within its walls the free life continues, while the legions of Death and Pain and Despair, and all the servile captains of tyrant Fate, afford the burghers of that dauntless city new spectacles of beauty. Happy those sacred ramparts, thrice happy the dwellers on that all-seeing eminence. Honour to those brave warriors who, through countless ages of warfare, have preserved for us the priceless heritage of liberty, and have kept undefiled by sacrilegious invaders the home of the unsubdued.

But the beauty of Tragedy does but make visible a quality which, in more or less obvious shapes, is present always and everywhere in life. In the spectacle of Death, in the endurance of intolerable pain, and in the irrevocableness of a vanished past, there is a sacredness, an overpowering awe, a feeling of the vastness, the depth, the inexhaustible mystery of existence, in which, as by some strange marriage of pain, the sufferer is bound to the world by bonds of sorrow. In these moments of insight, we lose all eagerness of temporary desire, all struggling and striving for petty ends, all care for the little trivial things that, to a superficial view, make up the common life of day by day; we see, surrounding the narrow raft illumined by the flickering light of human comradeship, the dark ocean on whose rolling waves we toss for a brief hour; from the great night without, a chill blast breaks in upon our refuge; all the loneliness of humanity amid hostile forces is concentrated upon the individual soul, which must struggle alone, with what of courage it can command, against the whole weight of a universe that cares nothing for its hopes and fears. Victory, in this struggle with the powers of darkness, is the true baptism into the glorious company of heroes, the true initiation into the overmastering beauty of human existence. From that awful encounter of the soul with the outer world, enunciation, wisdom, and charity are born; and with their birth a new life begins. To take into the inmost shrine of the soul the irresistible forces whose puppets we seem to be—Death and change, the irrevocableness of the past, and the powerlessness of man before the blind hurry of the universe from vanity to vanity —to feel these things and know them is to conquer them.

This is the reason why the Past has such magical power. The beauty of its motionless and silent pictures is like the enchanted purity of late autumn, when the leaves, though one breath would make them fall, still glow against the sky in golden glory. The Past does not change or strive; like Duncan, after life's fitful fever it sleeps well; what was eager and grasping, what was petty and transitory, has faded away, the things that were beautiful and eternal shine out of it like stars in the night. Its beauty, to a soul not worthy of it, is unendurable; but to a soul which has conquered Fate it is the key of religion.

The life of Man, viewed outwardly, is but a small thing in comparison with the forces of Nature. The slave is doomed to worship Time and Fate and Death, because they are greater than anything he finds in himself, and because all his thoughts are of things which they devour. But, great as they are, to think of them greatly, to feel their passionless splendour, is greater still. And such thought makes us free men; we no longer bow before the inevitable in Oriental subjection, but we absorb it, and make it a part of ourselves. To abandon the struggle for private happiness, to expel all eagerness of temporary desire, to burn with passion for eternal things—this is emancipation, and this is the free man's worship. And this liberation is effected by a contemplation of Fate; for Fate itself is subdued by the mind which leaves nothing to be purged by the purifying fire of Time.

United with his fellow-men by the strongest of all ties, the tie of a common doom, the free man finds that a new vision is with him always, shedding over every daily task the light of love. The life of Man is a long march through the night, surrounded by invisible foes, tortured by weariness and pain, towards a goal that few can hope to reach, and where none may tarry long. One by one, as they march, our comrades vanish from our sight, seized by the silent orders of omnipotent Death. Very brief is the time in which we can help them, in which their happiness or misery is decided. Be it ours to shed sunshine on their path, to lighten their sorrows by the balm of sympathy, to give them the pure joy of a never-tiring affection, to strengthen failing courage, to instil faith in hours of despair. Let us not weigh in grudging scales their merits and demerits, but let us think only of their need—of the sorrows, the difficulties, perhaps the blindnesses, that make the misery of their lives; let us remember that they are fellow-sufferers in the same darkness, actors in the same tragedy with ourselves. And so, when their day is over, when their good and their evil have become eternal by the immortality of the past, be it ours to feel that, where they suffered, where they failed, no deed of ours was the cause; but wherever a spark of the divine fire kindled in their hearts, we were ready with encouragement, with sympathy, with brave words in which high courage glowed.

Brief and powerless is Man's life; on him and all his race the slow, sure doom falls pitiless and dark. Blind to good and evil, reckless of destruction, omnipotent matter rolls on its relentless way; for Man, condemned to-day to lose his dearest, to-morrow himself to pass through the gate of darkness, it remains only to cherish, ere yet the blow falls, the lofty thoughts that ennoble his little day; disdaining the coward terrors of the slave of Fate, to worship at the shrine that his own hands have built; undismayed by the empire of chance, to preserve a mind free from the wanton tyranny that rules his outward life; proudly defiant of the irresistible forces that tolerate, for a moment, his knowledge and his condemnation, to sustain alone, a weary but unyielding Atlas, the world that his own ideals have fashioned despite the trampling march of unconscious power.

A NIGHT AT PIETRAMALA

"What I love best in all the world," says Browning in *De Gustibus*, "is a castle, precipice-encurled, in a gash of the wind-grieved Apennine." *De Gustibus*, indeed. I take the hint and shall not argue the point. Suffice it to say that, though I like the poem, I cannot share the poet's tastes. A castle in the Apennine would come quite low in the list of the things I love. A palace in Rome, a villa just outside the gates of Siena, even a motor caravan would stand higher. For the epithet which Browning applies to the Apennine is only too appropriate. He himself, no doubt, enjoyed being grieved by the wind. I can imagine him, with bent head, tunnelling his way through one of those hellish blasts which come hooting down, in spring and winter, through the gashes between the hills. He would feel exhilarated by the effort; his struggle against the elements would elate him and he would return to his castle to write some more than ordinarily hearty pæan in praise of passion and energy—passion for passion's sake, energy admirable, not so much for its direction as for its volume. Such, I am sure, were the effects of the wind on Browning; it confirmed him in his blustering optimism. In me on the other hand, the wind of the Apennines begets nothing but neuralgia and the profoundest depression. It is not *Prospice* that I should write in the precipice-encurled castello; it is something in the style of the *City of Dreadful Night*.

That I am not exaggerating the horrors of the wind among the Apennines is proved by the fact that it has been found necessary, for the convenience and even the safety of travellers, to protect the most exposed places of the principal passes with high walls. I remember in particular one section of the main road from Florence to Bologna which is flanked for hundreds of yards by an immense parapet, like the great wall of China. The road at this point, which is between two and three thousand feet above the sea, cuts across the head of a deep and narrow valley, through which there sucks a perpetual draught. Even in summer, on halcyon days, you can hear as you pass under the lee of the wall, a melancholy wailing of the winds overhead. But on rough days in winter, in the spring and autumn, the air is full of fearful noises, as though the gates of hell had been opened and the lost souls were making holiday. What happened to travellers who passed that way before, some hundred years ago, a beneficent Grand-Ducal government built the wall, I shudder to think. They must often have been, quite literally, blown off the road.

We passed that way once in March. The Italian spring, which is not so different from the spring in other countries, was inclement that year and icy. In Florence the sun shone fitfully between huge clouds. Snow still lay in patches on Monte Morello. The breeze was nipping. "Are the passes free of snow?" we asked at the garage where we stopped to fill our petrol tank. Animated by that typically Italian desire to give an answer that will please the questioner, the garage man assured us that the road was perfectly clear. And he said it with such conviction that we imagined, as northerners would naturally imagine, that he knew. Nothing is more charming than southern courtesy, southern sympathy and the southern desire to please. The heart is touched by the kindly interest which the Italians take in your affairs; you love them for their courteous inquisitiveness; they make you at home immediately, treat you at once as a human being and do their best to please you. It is delightful. But sometimes they are really too sympathetic by half. For in order not to contradict you or give you a moment's pain by disputing the accuracy of your ideas, they will tell you what you want to hear rather than what it would be of real use to you to hear. At the same time their own self-esteem will not permit them to confess a blank ignorance; so that they will rather tell you something incorrect than tell you nothing at all. Thus, when the garage man told us that there was no snow on the road from Florence to Bologna, he said so first, because he saw that we wanted to go to Bologna and that we should have been disappointed if it had been impossible and, second, because it was pleasanter for him to say "No snow" with conviction than confess (which was the truth) that he hadn't the faintest notion whether there was snow or not.

We believed him and set out. The road rises steeply from Florence, climbs to twelve or fifteen hundred feet and then plunges down again into that long flat-bottomed valley locked in the midst of the hills, the Mugello. By the time we had reached it the sun had entirely disappeared, and the sky above us was one vast yellowish-white snowcloud. Looking at the various castelli one passes by the way, I found Browning's predilections more than ever incomprehensible.

Between Florence and Bologna there are two passes: the Futa and, five or six miles further on, the pass of Raticosa. It is near the top of the Futa that the Grand Dukes built the bulwark against the wind. It was strengthened, that day, by heaps of driven snow. Below and above, the slopes were deep in snow. In the midst of all this whiteness the road wound onwards and upwards like a muddy snake.

Under the lee of the wall we halted and took photographs of the Italian scenery. The air was calm where we stood and seemed in its stillness almost warm. But just above us, on a level with the top of the wall, was the wind. The snowflakes that it carried made its speed visible. It filled the ears with sound. I was reminded, as I stood there, of a rather ludicrous and deplorable version of *David Copperfield*, which Beerbohm Tree used sometimes to stage at His Majesty's. Tree himself acted two parts—Micawber and Peggotty; the former, I may add parenthetically, very well indeed (for he was an admirable comedian) the latter, in his more pathetic manner, with less success. But let that pass. Dressed as Peggotty, Tree never made an entrance without the wind; it was in the bluff nautical part. Every time he opened the door of his ship cottage on the sands of Yarmouth there came from the outer darkness a noise like the witches' sabbath. It never blew less than a full gale during the whole run of *David Copperfield*. Whoo-oo-oo-oo-oo—crescendo and decrescendo. In the dress circle ladies reached for their furs, men turned up the collars of their coats. It was horrible. I had hoped then that I should never hear a wind like that outside His Majesty's. And I never did till that icy March day when we paused beneath the Grand-

Ducal wall on the road from Florence to Bologna. There, for the first time, I heard nature rivalling Sir Herbert's art. A perfect site, I reflected, for the Castello Browning.

At Pietramala, which lies just under the pass of the Raticosa, we stopped at the little inn for lunch. The idlers who gathered immediately and as though by magic round our machine—for even at Pietramala, even in the snow, there were leisured car-fanciers to whom the arrival of a ten horse power Citroen was an event—lost no time in telling us that the road on the further side of the pass was blocked with wind-driven snow. We went in to our lunch feeling a little depressed —a little annoyed, too, with the garage man at Florence. The inn-keeper, however, was reassuring ; gangs of men, he told us, were to be sent out as soon as the dinner hour was over from Pietramala and the village on the other side of the pass. By four o'clock the road would be clear ; we should be in Bologna before dark. When we asked if the road by Firenzuola and Imola were open, he shook his head. For the second time that day we believed.

The inn-keeper's motives for not telling the truth were different from those that actuated the man at the garage. For the latter had lied out of misplaced politeness and pride; the inn-keeper on the contrary, lied merely out of self-interest. He wanted to make us stay the night. He was perfectly successful. At four o'clock we set out. At the top of the pass the snow lay a yard deep across the road, and there was not a shoveller to be seen. We returned. The inn-keeper was astonished: what, no shovellers? He could hardly believe it. But to-morrow morning the road would infallibly be cleared. We decided to stay the night.

I had taken with me on that journey the second volume of the *Encyclopædia Britannica*—And.-Aus. It is a capital volume from which one can derive much useful knowledge about Angiosperms, the Anglican Communion, Angling, Anthrax, Aphasia, Apples, Arrowroot, Asia, Aurora Borealis and Australia, not to mention Anthropology, Archeology, Architecture, Art, Astrology and Astronomy. I started hopefully on Animal Worship. "The bear," I learned, "enjoys a large measure of respect from all savage races that come in contact with it." From me, that evening, he got a large measure of envy. I thought of Mr. Belloc's rhyme:

> *The Polar bear is unaware*
> *Of cold that stabs us through.*
> *For why, he has a coat of hair,*
> *I would I had one too.*

For in spite of the fire, in spite of greatcoats, it was appallingly cold. "The products of the cow," I read on, and was charmed by the compendious euphemism, "are important in magic." But I got no further; it was too cold even to read. To this day I remain ignorant of the feelings of the Thlinkit Indians towards the cow, of the Kalangs towards the dog and the Siamese towards white elephants. And if I do happen to know that the Hottentot god, Cagn, is incarnated in the praying mantis, Ngo, that is due to the fact that I took the same volume with me on another tour during the summer, when the evenings were less inclement and the mind was free to devote itself to higher things than the problem of mere self-preservation.

It was cold enough in the sitting-room; but the horror only really began when we went to bed. For the bedrooms of the inn were without fireplaces; there was no possibility of heating them. In those bedrooms one could have preserved mutton indefinitely. Still dressed in all the woolly garments we possessed, we got into our stony beds. Outside the wind continued to howl among the hills. While the sheets were yet unthawed, sleep was out of the question. I lay awake listening to the noise of the wind and wondering what would be the effect of the hurricane on those flaming jets of natural gas for which Pietramala is renowned. Would the wind blow out those giant will-o'-the-wisps? Or would they burn on in spite of it? The thought of flames was comforting; I dwelt on them with a certain complaisance.

They are not uncommon, these jets of fire, among the northern Apennines. Salsomaggiore, for example, owes its coat of arms, a salamander among the flames, to its fountains of natural gas. It is in this gaseous form alone that the hydrocarbons of the Apennines make their appearance at the centre of the chain. On the outer slopes they are to be found in the more commercially useful form of petroleum, which is now extracted in small quantities from the foothills in the neighbourhood of Piacenza, Reggio and Modena. Who knows, we may yet live to see the towers of Canossa rivalled by the wooden castles of the derricks on the slopes below.

The shutters rattled, the wind howled. Decidedly, no fire could burn in the teeth of such a blast. Poor *ignes fatui!* how welcome we should have made them in this icehouse! How tenderly, like vestals, we should have cherished any flame, however fatuous!

From thinking of those flames and wishing that I had them in the room with me, I went on to wonder why it was that the gasfires of Pietramala should be so oddly familiar to me. Had I read about them? Had I recently heard them mentioned in conversation, or what? I racked my brains. And then suddenly I remembered; it was in Bence Jones's *Life and Letters of Faraday* that I had read of Pietramala.

One very wet day in the autumn of 1814 two rather queer English tourists alighted from their chaise in this squalid little village of Pietramala. One was approaching middle age, the other still a very young man. Their names were Sir Humphry Davy and Michael Faraday. They had been out of England almost exactly a year. For it was in the year 1813, just before the news of the battle of Liepzig had reached Paris, that they crossed into France. To us it seems in the natural order of things that science and religion should be national affairs, that clergymen should scream "Hurrah and Hallalujah" and chemists cheer for the flag and H_2SO_4. But it was not always so. God and the works of God were once considered international. God was the first to be nationalized; after the Reformation he once more became frankly tribal. But science and even art were still above patriotism. During the eighteenth century France and England exchanged ideas almost as freely as cannon balls. French scientific expeditions were allowed to pass in safety between the English fleets; Sterne was welcomed enthusiastically by his country's enemies. The tradition lingered on even into the eighteen hundreds. Napoleon gave medals to English men of science; and when, in 1813, Sir Humphry Davy asked for leave to travel on the continent, his request was granted at once. He was received in Paris with the highest honours, was made a member of the Institute, and in spite of the intolerable rudeness and arrogance which he habitually displayed, he was treated throughout his stay in France with the most perfect courtesy. In our

more enlightened twentieth century he would have been shot as
a spy or interned.

Restless and erratic, Davy hurried across Europe in search
of scientific truth. All was fish that came to his net. At Genoa
he made electric experiments on the torpedo fish. At Florence
he borrowed the great burning-glass of the Grand Dukes and,
with its aid, set a diamond on fire. At Rome he analysed the
pigments employed by the artists of antiquity. At Naples he
made experiments on iodine and excursions up Vesuvius. With
him went Michael Faraday as "assistant in experiments and
writing." Lady Davy, however, tried to use him as courier and
confidential servant as well. Young Faraday found the position a little trying. It was only the consciousness that he was
being given an unrivalled opportunity to educate himself that
decided him to keep his post. Sir Humphry's character might
not be entirely estimable; (indeed, Faraday was known to remark in later years that "the greatest of all his great advantages was that he had had, in Davy, a model to teach him
what he should avoid") ; but he was, undoubtedly, a mine of
scientific learning. To be with him constantly, as Faraday was,
during those eighteen months of travel, was a liberal education. Young Faraday knew it and put up with Lady D.

At Pietramala, then, they stopped in the pouring rain—and
doubtless in the howling wind as well—to look at the natural
fireworks. Specimens of the gas were bottled and taken down
to Florence for analysis. Sir Humphry concluded, correctly,
that it was a light hydrocarburet, pure.

To this desolate little village on the crest of the Apennines
Faraday devotes a couple of pages in his journal. To Florence, except in so far as it was a town where there were facili-
ties for making experiments, he gives no space at all. Faraday
paid little attention to the works of man, however beautiful. It
was the works of God that interested him. There is a magnificent consistency about him. All that he writes in his journal or letters is perfectly in character. He is always the natural
philosopher. To discover truth is his sole aim and interest. His
purpose is unalterably fixed. He never allows himself to be distracted—not by art, which he almost completely ignores; not
by politics which, in the tremendous closing scenes of the
Napoleonic drama he mentions casually once or twice, not at all
by the delights of casual social intercourse, though he always
found time for friendship—but pursues his course steadily,

perseverantly, modestly, disinterestedly and withal triumphantly as a conquering man of genius.

Outside science his great interest was religion. The battle between science and dogmatic theology, which was waged during the latter half of the nineteenth century created an impression, which still survives, that there is a certain radical incompatibility between science and religion. History shows that, as a matter of fact, no such incompatibility exists. If we read the biographies of the three most genial (in the French sense), men of science that England has produced—Sir Isaac Newton, Faraday and James Clerk Maxwell—we shall find that all three were profoundly religious. Sir Isaac devoted the greater part of a long life to the interpretation of Biblical prophecy. Faraday was an earnest and ardent Christian of the Sandemanian sect. Clerk Maxwell was a great mystic as well as a great man of science; there are letters of his which show him to have been of the company of Boehme and Swedenborg (himself, by the way, a scientific man of great distinction). There is nothing in all this that should surprise us. "An infidel astronomer is mad"; tempered, this piece of rhetoric is something like a truth. For it is certainly impossible to study nature at all closely without becoming convinced of the extraordinary strangeness and mysteriousness of the familiar world in which the mass of human beings unquestioningly pass their lives. The further our knowledge extends and the more completely we realise its implications, the more mysterious this universe is seen to be. A man must be crass and unimaginative indeed if he can study the intricacies of life, the movements of the stars, the intimate constitution of matter without feeling from time to time a sense of awe and amazement. In the ranks of the professional scientists such men undoubtedly find their place; there are unimaginative men in all professions, from that of the jockey to that of the bishop. But they are not, in general, the best at their jobs. Without imagination, without sensitiveness it is impossible to be a successful man of science. It would be difficult to find any great scientific man who had not been touched by this sense of wonder at the strangeness of things. It betrays itself in different ways according to the upbringing and temperament of those who feel it. In some, as quiet and orthodox religion; in others, unwilling to commit themselves definitely about the nature of the mystery which surrounds them, as agnosticism; in others again (Clerk Max-

well and Swedenborg are examples) the man of science is
endowed with the peculiar mental qualities of the mystic; in
yet other cases we find men possessing these same mystical
qualities, but unrefined and somehow coarse (for there are
good mystics and poor mystics just as there are good and poor
artists), and then we have, not Clerk Maxwell with his delicate
and beautiful mysticism, but Newton the interpreter of the
prophetic books. For Faraday the corollary and complement
of science was protestant Christianity. His sense of wonder, his
awe in face of the beautiful mystery of the world, expressed
itself in the terms of Sandemanian meetings and Bible reading.
He stands in the scale of mystics somewhere about half-way
between Maxwell and Newton, not very highly gifted but at
the same time not vulgarly gifted, a sort of Andrea del Sarto
between Giotto on the one hand and Caravaggio on the other.
A Cherubini between Mozart and Strauss.

That king who, in Anatole France's fable was only to be
cured of his melancholy by putting on the shirt of a happy
man, would have been well advised to apply to Faraday. A
shirt of his would have been specific against the king's malady.
For if any man was happy it was surely he. All his life long he
did, professionally, the things he desired to do. To know, to
discover the truth—that was his desire. And it is a desire whose
fulfilment does not lead to disappointment and boredom, as
does the fulfilment of almost every other human longing. For
there is no end to truth; each part of it reveals, when found,
yet other parts to be discovered. The man who desires knowledge knows no satiety, for the knowable is perpetually new.
He might live innumerable lives and never grow weary. True,
the knowable world is not everything. There is also the world
of feelings; there is also that which is humanly unknowable.
In our relation to these two worlds there is plenty of scope for
unhappiness. But Faraday was also emotionally happy. His
marriage was an unqualified success; he had good friends;
the tenor of his life was even and he did not desire more than
what he possessed. He was equally fortunate in his relation to
the unknowable. The problems of life, as they are called, never
troubled him. The religion in which he was brought up offered
a solution of them in advance; he passed through no crisis
such as that which drove Tolstoy almost to suicide. It is interesting to note that he separated the domain of science sharply
from that of religion, the knowable from the unknowable. "Not

how the world is, is the mystical, but *that* it is," says Wittgenstein. And again: "For an answer which cannot be expressed the question too cannot be expressed. The riddle does not exist. . . . The solution of the problem of life is seen in the vanishing of this problem. (Is not this the reason why men to whom after long doubting the sense of life became clear, could not then say wherein this sense consisted?)" Faraday was happy in that he never doubted, never tried to put an inexpressible question for which there is no possible answer. How the world is, he set himself to discover, with more success than attends most investigators. He did not torture his intellect with the question why or what it is. His religion offered him the explanation why; or to be more exact (for there is no explanation) it helped him to "contemplate the world *sub specie œterni*, as a limited whole." "The feeling of the world as a limited whole is the mystical feeling." Faraday had that feeling; not perhaps in its most exquisite form, but had it genuinely. His relations with the unknowable therefore were as satisfactory as his relations with what can be known.

Among the natural philosophers Faraday is by no means unique in his happiness. Indeed, as a class, I should say that men of science were happier than other men. *A priori*, and almost by definition, they ought to be. And when one reads their lives one finds that in point of fact they generally were happy. How satisfactory these lives of born men of science always are! There is an integrity about these men, a unity of purpose that to the rest of us poor distracted mortals seems wonderfully enviable and wonderfully beautiful.

If I could be born again and choose what I should be in my next existence, I should desire to be a man of science—not accidentally but by nature, inevitably a man of science. Fate might offer other alternatives—to have power or wealth, be a king or a statesman. These glittering temptations I should have small difficulty in rejecting; for my objection to the irritating turmoil of practical life is even stronger than my love of money or power, and since these cannot be obtained without plunging into practical life, I can sacrifice them cheerfully.

It is easy to make a virtue of psychological necessity. The only thing that might make me hesitate would be an offer by fate of artistic genius. But even if I could be Shakespeare, I think I should still choose to be Faraday. True, the posthumous glory of Shakespeare is greater than that of Faraday ; men still read *Macbeth* but not (even if they happen to be electricians) the *Experimental Researches in Electricity*. The work of a man of science is a creation on which others build; it has implications, it grows. If we want to know about electricity, we read what the contemporary successors and disciples of Faraday have to say about it. But *Macbeth* is a thing in itself, not a discovery on which other men can improve. There is no such thing as progress in art. Every artist begins at the beginning. The man of science, on the other hand, begins where his predecessor left off. Opinions and ideas change, under the weight of accumulated experience, from age to age. The instinctive, emotional side of man, being hereditary, remains the same. The man of science provides the experience that changes the ideas of the race ; in course of time his discoveries are superseded. The artist does not go out of date because he works with materials that do not change. Lyrics composed by a palæolithic poet would still be moving. But the views of a palæolithic astronomer would possess, for us, a merely historical and academic interest.

And yet in spite of all this I would still rather be Faraday than Shakespeare. Posthumous fame brings nobody much satisfaction this side of the grave ; and though the consciousness that one possesses a great artistic talent must be profoundly satisfying, though the free employment of it must be a source of happiness, it seems to me that the possession and employment of a scientific talent must be still more satisfying. For the artist, whose function is the apt expression and the conveyance to others of the common human emotions, must fatally pass much of his life in the emotional world of human contacts. His reflections upon the world, his personal reactions to contacts—these form the subject matter of his art. The world in which the man of science passes the professional part of his life is non-human, has nothing to do with personal relationships and emotional reactions. We are all subdued to what we work in ; and I personally would rather be subdued to intellectual contemplation than to emotion, would rather use my soul professionally for knowing than for feeling.

One of the minor disadvantages of being a great artist is the fact that the artist enjoys a considerable social prestige. Art is the subject of snobbery to a far greater extent than science. The presence of a well-known poet or painter is felt to give distinction to a dinner-party. Hostesses rarely ask one to meet bio-chemists, however distinguished. The reason for this is simple; all men and women imagine that they can appreciate the arts—and up to a point, of course, actually can—while the number who can understand the technicalities of science is remarkably small. (Vainly, alas, I wish that I myself belonged to that minority.) To this is due the enviable immunity of the men of science from the intrusion of frivolous bores. The artist, on the other hand, is one of the favourite quarries of the unemployed rich; a good specimen is worth at least an ambassador, almost an Indian prince. If the artist is a man of strong character he will find the attentions of the lion-hunters not dangerous, indeed, but profoundly exasperating. They are only dangerous to those who allow themselves to be caught. It is pleasant to be flattered; and if one likes to waste time, there is no easier way of doing so than in casual social intercourse. The artist who succumbs to social temptations loses everything: his time, his integrity, his sense of proportion, the very hope of achieving anything important. He is the more unfortunate in being exposed to them.

Towards morning when, like a mutton chop on a cold plate, I had a little thawed my bed, the phantoms of Michael Faraday and Sir Humphry Davy departed, leaving me alone with my repressed wishes. What they may have been, I don't know. But at any rate they fulfilled themselves, ideally and symbolically, in a confused nightmare of motor cars and snowdrifts.

The wind was still blowing when I woke up. We spent the forenoon shivering in the sitting-room of the inn. Every few minutes the landlord came in with fresh news about the state of affairs on the pass. Telephone messages had arrived from Florence and Bologna; an army of shovellers was being mobilized; now it was on the move; a man who had just come down from the pass had seen them at work; by two o'clock the road could not fail to be clear. After giving us each item of news, he bowed, smiled, rubbed his hands and went back to his kitchen to invent the next. He had a fertile imagination.

Fitfully, I read about the Armenian Church. But my interest was languid. I was too cold even to feel a proper enthusiasm over the discovery that "the old sacrificial hymns were probably obscene and certainly nonsensical." Remembering that phrase in subsequent summers, I have been delighted by it. How well, how pithily it describes not merely the old sacrificial hymns of pre-Christian Armenia, but a whole mass of modern art and self-styled science—the greater part of psycho-analytic literature, for example, the music of Schreker, most expressionist painting, *Ulysses*, and so on. As for the less "modern" pseudo-sciences and pseudo-art, from spiritualism to commercial fiction—these do not even possess the saving grace of obscenity; they are merely nonsensical.

The morning passed; it was time for lunch. After a meal of spaghetti and broiled goat, we felt a little stronger and a little less cold. "How are things on the pass?" we asked. But our host seemed suddenly to have lost his omniscience and with it his optimism. He did not know what was happening and he advised us to wait for a little. By five o'clock, however, all would undoubtedly be well. And the road by Firenzuola? That was hopeless; he was certain of that. He left us wondering what to do; whether to wait, whether to return to Florence—what? We were still in a state of painful uncertainty when a heaven-sent messenger in the form of a man with a horse and trap stopped at the inn door. We appealed to him. A miracle! Not only did he know the truth; he also imparted his knowledge in a plain unvarnished way. No shovellers, he assured us, were working on the pass; nor would any be sent there till the wind had changed (for when the wind was blowing in this particu-lar direction, the snow was carried back on to the road as soon as it had been taken off). The wind might change this evening, of course; but on the other hand it might only change next week. But if we wanted to go to Bologna, why hadn't we taken the Firenzuola road? Yes, why not? said the landlord, who had joined us and was listening to the conversation. Why not take the Firenzuola road? He had seen that the game was up and that there was now no further hope of getting us to stay another night. Why not? We looked at him significantly, in silence. He smiled back, imperviously good-humoured, and re-tired to compile his bill.

We set out. The sky was white and full of cloudy movement. Here and there the white mountains were scarred with black, where the precipices were too steep to allow the snow to lie. From La Casetta we slid down the break-neck road that twists down into the valley of the Santerno. Within its walls Firen-zuola was black, ancient and grim. From Firenzuola the road follows the Santerno. The river has tunnelled a winding passage through the mountains. The valley is deep and narrow; here and there road and river run between perpendicular walls of rock, banded slantwise with the lines of tilted stratification. Slowly the valley broadens out, the mountains degenerate into bare bleak downs. At the foot of the hills is the plain, narrowed here between the mountains and the sea, but expanding and expanding as one travels northwards into the immense unbroken flatness of the Po valley.

At Imola we turned into the great Via Emilia that runs in an undeviating straight line from Rimini to Piacenza. What cities are strung along that white stretched thread! Cesena, Forli, Faenza, Imola, Bologna, Reggio, Modena, Parma—bead after precious bead.

It was dark when we entered Bologna and the streets were full of maskers. It was the last day of carnival.

We nosed our way through the crowd, hooting. "Maschere!" the maskers shouted as we passed; and in our goggles and mufflers, we too seemed dressed for carnival. It was a feeble show; a few young women in dominoes, a few noisy students in fancy dress—that was all. I thought of the brilliant shows and masquerades of the past. Charming, no doubt; but one should not regret them. For shows and masquerades are symptoms of bad government. Tyrants pass all their lives at the centre of a gorgeous ballet. An oppressed populace, too poor to pay for amusements of its own, is kept in good humour by these royal theatricals, which are free of charge. And in the course of periodical Saturnalia slaves are able to sublimate their revolutionary feelings in sportive licence. If carnival has decayed, so too has oppression. And where people have pence enough to go to the cinema, there is no need for kings and popes to stage their ballets. Still, it was a very poor show; I felt they might have celebrated our arrival in Bologna a little more worthily.

SHORT STORIES

SECTION II

In the earlier section of this book which I devoted to short stories I printed the works of some of the older writers. I think they had a pleasing variety. I should like to call the reader's attention particularly to Arthur Machen's *The Inmost Light*, because he is an author too little known who writes this language of ours with great beauty. I have myself a weakness for the short story that has a precise form. I like it to have a beginning, a middle and an end. I do not want to be left in doubt about what happens. I like the author to say everything to the point that he has to say on the subject of his choice. That is the old-fashioned method. It is the one practised by that great master of the short story Guy de Maupassant. It is the one practised by Mr Rudyard Kipling in the beautiful story *Without Benefit of Clergy* which I wish I could have persuaded him to allow me to print. But I am aware that the method gives a certain tightness of effect which is sometimes disconcerting. You feel that life does not dovetail into its various parts with such neatness. In life stories straggle, they begin nowhere and tail off without a point. It gives you a sensation of airlessness when you see persons who behave so exactly according to character and incidents that fit the frame with such perfect convenience. You have just the same feeling as when you look at one of those great landscapes of the seventeenth century in which the composition has such an architectural balance, the mass of a tree corresponding with the mass of a cloud, the light and shade forming a definite pattern, and compare it with the haphazard arrangements of nature. The reason is obvious. These painters used nature as an excuse for a formal decoration. They were not interested in its fleeting beauty but in its stately grandeur. Their intention was not to portray landscape, but to create a work of art. Life for the most part escaped them; they did not care, they achieved what they aimed at. So it was also with the story writers of the older school. They arranged life to suit their purposes. They followed the patterns in their minds, they left out this and changed that, distorting facts to their advantage, according to their design; and when they attained their object produced a work of art. But in their case too life often fell by the way. Sometimes they seemed so artificial that you could not believe them, and when you do not believe a story-teller he is done. Sometimes the elegance of the design was intolerable. It is not surprising that there was a reaction. To the best of my belief it came from Russia. The great Russian writers (with the possible exception of Turgeniev) have had a very inadequate sense of form. I have a notion that most of the revolutionary changes in the arts have taken place owing to the inability of an artist, or a group of artists, to conform to the usages of his time. He has been forced to originality because he could not express himself in current terms. Cézanne tried his best to paint like Delacroix and it was only because he couldn't that he learned gradually to paint in a way that has revolutionised the whole of modern painting. I think it was because the Russians could not write the neat, rounded, well-constructed stories that the French wrote with such mastery that they developed the new technique that has had so much influence on the short-story writers of the present day. You see the beginnings of the new method in Tolstoi, but it was Chekov who brought it to perfection. It is hard to begin a story without a beginning and Chekov begins his no.differently from Guy de Maupassant. But here the resemblance ends. Incidents are told you that lead to nothing. As often as not there is no climax. Often they tail off, leaving you in the air. Sometimes they remind you of a man who thought he could build a house by laying a thousand bricks alongside of one another. You are then given the materials for a story and asked to construct it yourself. Sometimes the stories consist merely of an incident thrown at you without rhyme or reason. Sometimes they are merely the description of a character in a void. Sometimes they are no more than the noting down of a passing mood. Of course, thus liberated from the restraints of a rigid form, verisimilitude is admirably attained. This is life, you say, with its loose ends, its arbitrariness, its inconsequence. These stories seem indeed wide open to the winds of heaven; they can make the others, with their careful arrangements, their points so skilfully worked up to, seem outrageously stilted. But just as the stories of the old kind run the danger of artificiality, so these run the danger of inanity. Chekov himself did not always escape it. His followers less often still. For, as I said just now, he has had a great influence on the writers of short stories. In England especially we have never taken so keen an interest in form as the orderly and logical French. Witness the shapeless novels of the great novelists from Richardson down to the late Victorians. And the method was deceptively easy. Why, if it was merely a question of going to a hair-dresser's to get shaved, and you only had to describe the process and when the barber after cutting your chin confided in you that his girl had gone to the pictures the night before with the milkman, then anyone could write a short story. But there was a little more in it than that. The loose construction of a story by Chekov gave the imagination room to play, the vague-ness had its own significance and all that was left out de-manded from the reader an active and pleasant collaboration. But no reader gets out of a novel or a short story more than the author has put in. The reader gets so much out of Chekov's best stories because he put a great deal in.

Probably of all the modern writers who have been influenced by Chekov Katherine Mansfield is the best. I admire her delicate insight, her minute appreciation of the appearance of things and her lucid and easy English, but I cannot think that she has used the manner in her longer stories with complete success. I feel in them the want of a supporting skeleton. They remind me of great jelly-fishes, iridescent and strangely lovely as they float aimlessly about the sea, but floppy and inert. I like them page by page, but I do not quite know what they are all about, and I finish them with a slight sense of having been taken in. Her shorter stories on the other hand seem to me to have great excellence. They can do without a backbone. In them her charming gifts are admirably shewn. The reader will find the same method employed in other stories in this section and employed to my mind with uncommon felicity. I end with two compositions by Mr Harold Nicolson. I very much wanted to insert them, but did not quite know how I should describe them. They are not exactly essays, and if they are short stories they are short stories in a new manner; they pur-

port to be reminiscences, but so do many short stories; they
have the art and grace of fiction and they are written in a
conversational and urbane style that is very well suited to
fiction. If fiction is life rearranged for the purpose of pleasure
then they are very distinctly fiction. They seem to me entirely
delightful and I should have been very glad to include in this
book the whole volume from which I have been fortunately
allowed to choose two pieces.

W. S. M.

Norah Hoult

MRS. JOHNSON

Mrs. Emily Johnson opened her eyes suddenly. The clock belonging to St. Matthew's Church had begun to strike. She moistened her dry lips and started to count:

"Two, three, four, five, six. . . . not surely seven? Yes: seven."

Seven o'clock! Just fancy! She must have dozed off. It was only just after five when she had come in with a loaf of bread and quarter of margarine, and thought she would take a little rest before going out. And she had meant to be off early. A bad beginning! She must stir her pins now, and no mistake.

She threw off the blankets, and sat on the edge of the bed for a moment while her mind took stock of her body, searching to know how it felt. Her limbs were heavy and weak, and there was the same dull pain at the bottom of her back as there had been when she lay down.

"I don't feel a bit rested," she murmured. "Not a bit, I don't."

She sighed heavily, and went across to examine herself in the little wooden looking-glass that was propped on her chest of drawers. She took it off, and held it close to her eyes.

She was wearing a pink jumper of artificial silk over a magenta coloured petticoat. Her skirt she had slipped off when she lay down. Her hair, which was a peculiar grey-brown, the result of many sousings in guaranteed colour restorers and improvers, was greasy looking and part of it had come down, for Mrs. Johnson still fought shy of shingling. Her skin was a sickly yellow.

Mrs. Johnson gazed at herself with solicitude. "I do look bad," she thought. And then, not without pride, "No one could say as how I don't look bad."

But now another instinct put out its feeler and she searched the mirror for some more encouraging indication. She did not find it, and propped the mirror up again. "I look my age," she reflected with resignation as she took out hair-pins. "Leastways I look forty something though neither fair nor fat. Except," she added as an after-thought, "where I shouldn't be."

She set the kettle on the gas ring to boil. Feel better after a cup of tea, she reflected, as she had reflected many times before.

She took it hot and strong, together with a piece of bread and margarine. Towards the end of her repast she fell to considering whether she should have a good wash or no. Custom and inclination insisted, "It's not as if I hadn't washed to-day," and "After just having the 'flu, you can't be too careful." On the other hand, perhaps it freshened you up. She decided she would bathe her face and neck and leave the rest.

She did so. She even cleaned her nails, and found a pad with which subsequently she polished them. Afterwards she surveyed herself more hopefully: the tea and hot water had brought a little colour to her cheeks. She'd keep on her jumper after all. If you could only stand it there was nothing like a little bit of colour for making you look young.

She dabbed on some lip salve, both on her lips and cheeks. Not too much! The first thing was to look respectable, as of course in your way you were. And then white powder over her little chin and short broad nose. On her neck as well, to hide the creases. She had a genuine double chin to-night; that was lying in bed so long. Ah, well, it didn't show much if you remembered to hold your head well up. Now her hat pulled down; now the grey coat.

At the door in spite of her hurry she was filled with misgivings, and turned back to have another look at herself. She certainly looked very far from her real self; it had to be admitted. No one could look really well, even if they happened to be raging, tearing beauties, if they felt as ill as she did. Perhaps after all it would be better to wear a veil—not mind them being out of fashion.

With the veil attached she stared at herself keenly. Did it make her look older or younger? She wished she knew absolutely and for sure.

Still, she had had it on when she got off with that fellow in

Hyde Park last week, the Tuesday wasn't it? On the whole, perhaps, she'd stick to it. She really did feel so poorly.

She drew it up to bestow a parting lick of powder, and then, after listening a moment at the door, went softly downstairs. Yet not too softly, for though she wished to slip out unseen, she didn't want to be caught looking as if she wished to slip out unseen.

She was unfortunate, for the door of the front room opened as she reached the bottom stair, and Mrs. Lytton, the landlady, came out.

"I thought that was you, Mrs. Johnson, quiet though you was. Going out, are you?"

Mrs. Johnson licked her lips unconsciously, and then gave a propitiatory smile.

"Yes, I thought I would, Mrs. Lytton. It's a nice evening, isn't it?"

"I thought," said Mrs. Lytton staring her lodger full in the face, "you was maybe coming to pay me what you owe me."

For a brief second Mrs. Johnson thought of essaying injured dignity. But she was hopelessly outmatched, for, besides being large of bust and determined of feature and countenance, Mrs. Lytton was all dressed up. She was wearing a frock of black taffeta silk cut very low to display an expanse of pink chest, and round her neck hung three rows of pearls. It was evident, too, that her bright yellow hair had been newly waved.

Must be expecting someone, thought Mrs. Johnson. I wonder. . . . Aloud she said: "Now Mrs. Lytton, dear, you know yourself I 'aven't been able to get out for more than a week. You can't do much when you're sick in bed with the influenza, can you now?"

"Oh, I know you've been ill all right," retorted Mrs. Lytton. "Who should know it better than me that 'as 'ad to carry your meals up. You still owe me for that Bovril I got you."

"I know well how kind you've been," said Mrs. Johnson, rapidly. "And when my lad sends me the usual, you shall 'ave it all. If I don't get a bit of something from somewhere first— and I'm sure I shall—you shall 'ave that."

"Thank you for nothing, Mrs. Johnson. I know well enough when your son sends you the money, that is if he sends you it. He's missed, you know. And anyway it's not till Friday week. And you owe me three weeks' rent besides the ten bob I lent you because you was ill, or said you was, and the one and three I spent myself on the Bovril."

"*Said* I was ill," interjected Mrs. Johnson more in sorrow than in anger.

"And let me tell you straight and fair, from the horse's mouth, that I've no intention of waiting a fortnight to be paid. With one thing and another, Emily Johnson, I have put up with you till I am sick and tired. For friendship's sake. I'd not 'ave stood it from no one else. But there's reason in everything and I've my living to make, I suppose, same as everyone else. I could get more than I'm asking you for your room as you know well. Giving it away I am out of kindness."

Mrs. Johnson recognised her cue.

"Now, Rose, I've always said to everyone that there's no kinder nor more generous woman than yourself," she stated with dramatic emphasis.

"Don't Rose me! And listen. Things can't go on no longer like this. They gotta stop. D'you understand me?"

There came a knock at the hall door.

Mrs. Lytton's attention left Mrs. Johnson, and went eagerly to the other side of the door. Then she turned back to Mrs. Johnson but only to dispose of her.

"I'll see you again, Emily, when you come back, and if there's no rent or nothing coming from you you'll have to make new arrangements. I have to see a friend now about a business matter."

She stood back, and Mrs. Johnson opened the door and slipped out past the man who was standing there without a word or a look back. It would never do to appear inquisitive with Rose. And in any case she had always been one to mind her own business and not interfere with other people. "Live and let live, that's my motto," she thought with satisfaction which terminated in a touch of bitterness. "If it had only been other people's I wouldn't be where I am to-day."

She had now turned into the Camberwell Road, and the shouts of children at play, people passing hurriedly, the lights, the trams, and the coloured enticing patches made by picture palaces and public-houses began to invigorate her. She forgot the pain in her back and stepped out fairly briskly, shooting little sideways glances about her. The familiar life of the streets, the easy security it gave, warmed her blood. There were so many things and people about: surely she could hardly miss going into something lucky. She had, she thought proudly, always been one for a bit of life and excitement; and even if she wasn't as young as some of the girls, she wasn't as old as others: no, not by a long chalk she wasn't.

Inevitably her mind began to turn over other considerations. Mrs. Johnson was not one of those who never knew quite how much they carried in their pocket or bag. Circumstances made such a fine carelessness impossible. And so without any need to refresh her memory by a look her thoughts went inside her imitation leather hand-bag, and added together the silver sixpence, the penny, the halfpenny, and the farthing which lay there together. It was all she had left of the ten shillings Rose had lent her. It would be better, she decided, to walk to the Elephant and get a penny 'bus from there over Westminster Bridge. Or, would it save her more if she walked as far as Westminster, and then got a penny 'bus to the Circus? Once at the Circus she could slip into Long's, and see if there was anyone there she knew. A Guinness would do her no end of good if she only got the chance of one.

The picture of the foaming brown glass which might be awaiting her quickened her footsteps. She walked at a steady pace down the Walworth Road, taking little heed of passers-by. Experience had taught her that the busy streets of South-East London were no lucky hunting ground for her at that time in the evening. As she put it to herself, she was too refined for this side of the Bridge. And though she rarely took the recollection out of its pushed-back corner in her mind, it was in the Walworth Road, returning home with empty pockets late one night, that a man, a very low-down sort of man, had stopped suddenly in front of her and said, "Give you a bob?"

Mrs. Johnson had not come to that, as she also told herself with regard to other unpleasant incidents from time to time. Yet its effect was sufficient to make her tread the Walworth Road with special circumspection. She was above it, at least when it took its pleasures.

So she walked primly along, her fairly red lips and whitely powdered skin thrown into shadow by her veil; and if she scorned the Walworth Road it cannot be said that the Walworth Road, in busy mood just before the shops closed down, took any more notice of her.

At the Elephant she stood on the edge of the pavement for a moment undecided. She had been walking twenty-five minutes,

and the pain at her back refused to be lulled any longer. She
also felt a little dizzy in her head, and she thought petulantly
how very noisy, how much more noisy than usual, everything
was. For now the glamour had left the lights and bustle, and
what had been gay and seductive appeared only harsh and
clamorous. How hard the pavements were! Her toes felt hot
and constricted and a corn began to throb. "Them patent
shoes!" thought Mrs. Johnson with resignation. And then sorrowfully, "My poor feet!"

Meditating there upon the question of whether or no to take
the 'bus, her wandering eye perceived a young woman approaching from the right towards her.

A young woman it was, who, unlike Mrs. Johnson, attracted
a fair share of attention as she walked with airy indifference
in front of 'buses, whose drivers' heads turned to watch her
progress. For Miss Florrie Small possessed both an appearance
and a figure, and showed the latter to advantage in a tightly-
fitting costume of green velour cloth. Curves were, to a degree,
out of fashion, but they still continued to possess an attraction,
and Miss Small allowed herself a certain freedom of plump-
ness above her waist. For the rest she was careful about both
her corsets and her diet. And on this occasion her little black
felt toque with ear flaps combined smartness and becomingness
in an exceptional degree.

But what drew the eyes of many women to Miss Small was
the genuine skunk fur, large and magnificent, which hung
regally over her shoulders. Tired, shabby women, of hen-like
outline, as they pushed perambulators or plodded slowly on
weary feet, let indifferent glances drop from Miss Small's
pink, red and white countenance (for everyone made up in
these days) to her fur. Then the glances, returning to her face,
were no longer indifferent, but disapproving and even malevolent. One woman coming out with another from a public-
house observed Miss Small for a fraction, and then nudged
her companion, saying violently, "These 'ere tarts, they make
me sick, they do!"

But Miss Small was inured to stares, and even to the occasional comments of her neighbourhood. She accepted them
quite properly as a tribute to her exceptional smartness, and
had they not been forthcoming in their customary degree, she
would have hastened to the nearest public lavatory, there to
expend, if need be, even a penny at the mirror in order to

inquire after the cause. It was not that she appeared to take
any heed, for, like Mrs. Johnson, the neighbourhood of the
Elephant did not interest her professionally; but if she aroused
no attention in the Walworth Road there was little hope of her
doing so in more competitive areas.

Mrs. Johnson also observed Florrie's fur with interest, but
when she raised her eyes to the wearer's comely, if somewhat
artificial, countenance they contained only admiration and
delighted interest, modified to a close observer by a rather
uncertain appeal. As Miss Small arrived on the pavement, she
raised her veil and advanced a little towards her.

"Why, it's Florrie!" cried Mrs. Johnson in a burst of joyful surprise. "Well! Fancy running into you!"

For a second Miss Small returned Mrs. Johnson's regard
impassively. She knew the lady was apt to prove a hanger-on,
and wisdom counselled her to walk on with a nod. On the other
hand, in face of Mrs. Johnson's effusion, this would have been
tantamount to a snub, and Florrie was temperamentally averse
to snubbing people. After all, she reflected, she could easily
shake her off later. There were points of etiquette that even
Mrs. Johnson could not disregard.

"Hullo! Haven't seen you about lately," she said affably
enough.

"No, you 'aven't," said Mrs. Johnson in the tone of one
who confirms a great truth. "I've 'ad the 'flu. 'Ad it shockin'
bad! I ain't been out of bed for a week."

"You don't look too bright."

"I don't. Nor I don't feel it."

There was a short silence, while Mrs. Johnson watched Florrie, and Florrie watched for a 'bus. It turned the corner.

"I was just waiting for a 'bus up West myself," said Mrs.
Johnson. "If you don't mind my company, dear?"

"Not at all," said Florrie politely, if rather absently.

They got into the 'bus, Mrs. Johnson making a great show
of drawing back politely to let Florrie mount first. They sat
down on the left-hand side, and Florrie began to fumble in her
bag.

"Going all the way to the Circus?" said Mrs. Johnson, trying to make her voice appear indifferent.

Florrie nodded.

"I'll have a tuppenny, too," said Mrs. Johnson brightly,
surrendering her sixpence to the conductor. But as she took the

four coppers handed back, she experienced a pang. Cut into her sixpence she had, and she only meant to have a penny fare. Suppose it was an unlucky evening? Well, it couldn't be helped. And a bit of company was worth it. You never knew.

She looked sideways at Florrie. Better not say anything about her fur. She didn't seem very talkative, and it was no use giving offence. It was certainly a new one. She would have liked to know who had paid for it.

But Florrie suddenly relented. She had realised that the conductor had half anticipated that she would pay for Mrs. Johnson, and it had made her feel a little mean. After all she was in funds. She might stand the old girl a drink later.

So she asked for details of Mrs. Johnson's symptoms, and soon became really interested in the topic.

"It makes you feel so down in the dumps," said Mrs. Johnson.

"A friend of mine," replied Florrie, "once killed himself after having the 'flu."

"You don't say!"

"He did. Nice fellow he was, too, in his way. Very cheerful. Great sense of humour, you know. Always had a joke whenever you met him. He used to be in the Regent a lot with a lot of other chaps night after night. And always free with his money, you don't know! Why, he'd think nothing of taking on three girls at a time. And he wouldn't expect you to keep to beer. 'Order what you like, and how you like,' was what he'd always say. Well, after a while I missed him. He was never there. Of course I just thought that he was away or something." Florrie paused.

"Of course you would," agreed Mrs. Johnson, anxious to show her appreciation.

"So I was talking to a friend of his one evening, Jack Hulton, his name is—very like the fellow with the band, isn't it, the name I mean?—and I just happened to say, 'What's got Billy Richards these days?'—that was his name you know, Billy Richards. 'Where's Billy Richards?' I said, and he said, 'Haven't you heard?' and by the way he said it I knew there was something in the wind. 'No,' I said. 'What's up?' I said.

"Then he got telling me about it. Threw himself out of the window of an hotel or boarding-house or something in Torrington Square. At the top of the house it was. And when he was picked up he was as dead as frozen meat, poor fellow!"

"Dear, dear!" said Mrs. Johnson.

"And believe me or believe me not it was just that he'd had 'flu. Everyone said so. Had it real bad, you know. And never got over it. Moped and wouldn't go about with his friends. Though he had no money troubles at all. Very good position, I believe, in something or other. Isn't it queer what people will do when they get as low as all that?"

Mrs. Johnson agreed. The story depressed her slightly. "Well," she started, "I always fight against it myself. What I say is . . ."

"And there was someone else I knew," interrupted Florrie.

With an expression of rapt attention Mrs. Johnson gave her ear to Florrie, while her eyes occasionally wandered past through the window. They had left Trafalgar Square, and there was plenty to see.

Mrs. Johnson noticed many men unaccompanied, some walking fast making for a dinner appointment, others strolling slowly with a watchful eye. Solitary women there were, too, walking slower or a trifle faster than usual because of their recognition that it was pleasure time. Mrs. Johnson marvelled, as she never ceased to marvel, at the number of taxis there were about, returning, many of them, from the theatre, others still busy taking late arrivals. And over all the uneasy throng, passing their various ways a little more self-consciously than earlier in the day, the impassive sky stared down indifferently. It had watched men and women repeat themselves too often; or perhaps it was too far away to understand.

Mrs. Johnson felt lonely and chilled. She would have liked the evening before her to have been blotted out. Or if only it could have been all over, and she was going back to snuggle down in bed, and lose herself and her aches and pains in rest. I do need a pick-me-up, she thought self-pityingly.

"Here we are," said Florrie, breaking off from her narrative, as the 'bus drew up.

They crossed Piccadilly Circus together, going up the south side of Shaftesbury Avenue. Florrie had resumed her social air of nonchalance, but the gulf between her and Mrs. Johnson had lessened. True, the glances that came their way rested on Florrie, but the glances were casual, and both of them felt less like duchess and poor dependent and more on the equality of two members of the same overcrowded and hardworking profession.

But when Florrie had mounted the stairs leading to the lounge of the public-house that was their destination, the dividing line between them became again tightly drawn. Men, men and women together, and women alone, looking each of them up and down as they entered, classified them by professional standards. Florrie, it was evident, was a force to be reckoned with: she had smartness, she had an air, and she thus received the compliment of thoughtful appraisal. But the room passed over Mrs. Johnson in uninterested silence. She was easy to place, and her place was a low one.

Glancing round, Florrie received and returned a nod of recognition from two men sitting in the right-hand corner. But they were with two girls, and she did not choose to go over to them. She sat down at a table by the wall, facing the bar, at which one girl was already sitting. This girl was small and thin. She had applied a high colour to her sallow skin; her red mouth drooped; her brown eyes were sharp; and she appeared both sulky and on the defensive.

At Florrie she directed a suspicious glance, gathering her personality together against a rival better-dressed and better-looking than herself. Her pose endeavoured to suggest that she remained unimpressed. Mrs. Johnson she ignored after one glance.

Florrie, refreshed by the feeling of power the room had given her, expanded. "What are you going to have?" she asked Mrs. Johnson. "A Guinness?"

"Thank you very much, I will," said Mrs. Johnson. And then added, for she could not afford to leave any vestige of doubt about the matter of paying, "It's very kind of you, dear."

"Well, that's that," said Florrie, and beckoned to the waiter. He came with celerity. Florrie was a good customer.

"A couple of Guinesses, George, as quick as you like."

The waiter nodded and smiled. Before going away, he stared at the almost empty glass in front of the table's first occupant, whose name was Lily. It was a hard stare, and Lily, pretending not to notice, cursed inwardly. She had been sitting with the glass of bitter in front of her for nearly half an hour, and she knew she couldn't make it last out much longer. She gazed with an increased intensity at a man at the next table talking to two others. He had looked at her once; if he gave her the least bit more of encouragement she decided she would go over and sit at their table. It had a vacant seat, and there was no use missing the slightest opportunity. She was sick to death of walking about the streets with a headache, and being looked at as if she didn't exist.

Mrs. Johnson had also observed the waiter's look. She was sorry it was his night on, for he was a difficult person with whom to deal. She liked the other man with the long drooping dark moustache much better. He was good-natured, and had sometimes exchanged an affable word with her. But this man allowed her no grace in the way of time; and his manner always made it perfectly clear that he regarded her as an intruder. "Get off or get out" was his motto.

He returned with the glasses of stout, and Florrie deposited a shilling and a sixpence on the red wine-marked tray as she asked him some question which Mrs. Johnson was unable to overhear. He replied reassuringly.

Mrs. Johnson started to drink, darting little birdlike glances at the people around her. When the waiter returned, Lily stared at him boldly. "A Bass, please," she said in a low hoarse voice. It would be the last drink she could afford to treat herself to tonight, but perhaps it was worth waiting a little longer.

There was little conversation between the other two women. Florrie sipped her stout slowly and watched the door. Mrs. Johnson, who comprehended much of the art of living, concentrated on savouring her drink. Every time she raised her glass she experienced a thrill of satisfaction, and she followed the progress of the liquid down her throat with a tender observation. It didn't exactly warm you, but oh, how satisfying it was! Every time she placed her glass down she felt she had done much to add to her well-being. Two or three bottles a day, and, she thought, she would feel herself in no time. Self-confidence came gradually as her glass diminished, and she crossed her legs, and looked round boldly. She wished now she hadn't put the veil on when she had gone out. Men would have seen her in it when she came in, and it would certainly have given her age away.

Meanwhile Florrie became a little restless. She hated wasting time, and she knew she was not in the *milieu* to which her gifts entitled her. Sitting in a pub., a common pub., with an old hag of a finished and done-with prostitute was not suitable. But she had fixed up with Hemp to be free for him if he came along before nine. She finished off her drink in three large gulps and considered the question of ordering either another of the same or a Bass. The waiter was moving near, and, as she caught his eye, she remembered Mrs. Johnson, and hesitated.

She glanced at her companion, who in her engrossed enjoyment of her beverage had nearly come to the end of the glass without remembering that it was her bounden duty to make it stretch out to the utmost fraction of possible time. Now, however, she remembered, and raising the glass to her lips for appearance sake, set it down untouched.

Florrie noticed the action, and was moved by it. After all, she thought, the poor thing had been ill. Who could tell? She herself might one day be in Mrs. Johnson's shoes, and then she'd be thankful for any small mercy. Besides, the little bitch opposite who looked at her in such an ugly way would be impressed. It would teach her that she, Florrie Small, was not one of those who never had a few shillings in her purse. And didn't mind spending them on others.

"Have a Bass with me?" she said to Mrs. Johnson with well simulated carelessness.

Joy and surprise caught at Mrs. Johnson. What amazing luck! It was a long time since she had been treated to two drinks running. She could hardly believe it.

"Ta!" she said, her amazement making her briefer than usual. But gratitude in rich profusion flowed from her to Florrie. She looked at her with shining eyes. What a fine smart girl she was! There wasn't another one in the room to hold a candle to her. She deserved her luck with the men, her lovely fur; she did indeed. And she, Emily Johnson, didn't grudge it to her, if anyone else did.

As the waiter left them with Florrie's order, a newcomer entered, and Florrie, seeing him, jerked into animation. Her face radiated welcome, and as he came up to her she held out her hand to be shaken, and inclined her head coyly to one side in an appealing attitude. Florrie knew how to behave, as well as what was due to her. Mrs. Johnson, glancing at her unobtrusively, noted the gleam of a gold side tooth with covetousness.

She also unobtrusively took stock of Florrie's friend, and summed him up as sufficiently well off to be of importance, even though undistinguished, and not altogether at ease. He hadn't a hearty way with him, and Mrs. Johnson was inclined to be suspicious of the quiet ones. You never knew where you were with them.

After a few remarks, Florrie withdrew with him and her Bass to a table a little distance away which had just been vacated. Mrs. Johnson expected to be ignored, and she was. She was left alone with Lily.

They glanced at each other for a moment: Lily's gaze was hard and contemptuous. It was an unmistakable answer to Mrs. Johnson's vague expression of would-be friendliness. They both sat very still and aloof, slowly swallowing their ale, and watchful, at least so far as Lily was concerned, for every stray glance and every new-comer.

It was not long before Mrs. Johnson felt very much like talking to someone. She glanced at the table next to her. Two small girls, tightly costumed, tightly hatted, and made up in precisely the same way and to the same degree, were sitting there talking earnestly. One, however, was dark and more vixenish than the other, and when her friend had finished what she was saying she leaned across to her, and said as one voicing a grave problem:

"But I thought he was very fond of you."

The other girl made no answer. She turned and looked over her shoulder; then, catching Mrs. Johnson's sympathetic eye, looked through her.

"I thought he was fond of you," said the other girl again, but more urgently. Still met by silence, she sat back and raised her glass.

Mrs. Johnson's attention went to the other side of the room, where she saw a girl called Kate, very vivacious, bright of eye and flushed of cheek, sitting close to a table at which were two men, both rather grave and watchful. Kate was swinging a pretty leg, and at last she caught the eye of her neighbour. "Swing me just a little bit higher," she said gaily to him, adding, "I bet you don't mind how high."

Mrs. Johnson sighed. There was no denying some girls had the gift. She watched Kate, now engaged in conversation, with admiration till her attention was called away by the appearance of two men at her table.

They were both quite young: one had a smooth-skinned, round face, and a small dark moustache. His hair was oiled, and his eyes sharp and closely set together. He appeared to be the leading spirit of the two, but the other one, Mrs. Johnson decided, was better-looking, with nice wavy fair hair, well marked nose and jaw, and a frank boyish look. "A bit like Cecil would have seen, had he lived," reflected Mrs. Johnson, gazing at him with undisguised approval.

While they ordered whiskies she pondered on whether there was the remotest chance that she would be able to get off. Not much. She wouldn't be good enough for them. Too old! As a matter of fact she hadn't much of a chance sitting in this pub. at all. Too much light; too much competition. Still, she'd wait a bit. It was a rest.

Their conversation concerned racing matters, and Mrs. Johnson had to watch Lily's success with the dark man. "Would you like a cert. for the 3.30 to-morrow?" he had asked her.

"I know those certs," replied Lily, showing her teeth, which were white and even. She giggled and glanced coquettishly at the other young man. She also favoured him. But she took care to look quickly back at the man who had first spoken to her, and giggled again.

"Well, take it or leave it," he said. He pulled out a bit of paper and pencil and wrote something upon it. "I'm not a tipster. Am I, Frank?"

His friend shook his head.

"But I've put more money in the way of my pals than any blinking cheat of a tipster. Now then, do you want this?"

"I'm sure I'm much obliged," said Lily, accepting the slip of paper. She read it, and put it away in her hand-bag.

Mrs. Johnson felt neglected, and she also felt sociable. She decided that this was the time to force herself into action. "I'd like to get hold of a winner myself," she said, smiling at the dark young man.

He looked at her ungraciously. "A bob's my charge," he said.

Mrs. Johnson was not quarrelsome, but neither was she devoid of spirit, and the dark young man became oppressive to her.

"Didn't see *her* pay you," she said, jerking her head towards Lily. Then, alarmed at her boldness, she gave a deprecatory smile, intended to turn her remark into a joke. But the smile was a little late, and it was ignored.

"She's a friend of mine, aren't you darling?" he said, staring coolly at Mrs. Johnson while he patted Lily's arm.

Lily giggled again.

"Course you are," she said, not troubling to glance at Mrs. Johnson. "I've known you for donkey's years, haven't I?"

"But you didn't find me a donkey, did you?" he answered meaningly.

Lily went into a shriek of laughter. Pleased at his success, the young man beckoned her, and then bent and whispered in her ear. Again Lily shrieked with laughter.

Mrs. Johnson tried to catch the other young man's eye, hoping for a spark of sympathy, but failed. It was evident that, feeling somewhat uncomfortable, he was engaged in absenting his real self from the table. He was staring blankly at the wall; he hadn't bargained for women, and he was determined not to get involved.

Mrs. Johnson felt her mood change. The whole place became distasteful to her. She looked hard at the ash-tray just in front of her, fighting against a dangerous impulse to turn on Lily and shout at her.

"Some people do think they're someone," she muttered. But no one took any notice. Indeed no one heard her except the good-looking young man, and he was still determinedly engaged in not being drawn into anything.

Mrs. Johnson took a resolve. She swallowed the last drops of her Bass, carefully took out a handkerchief from her bag, and wiped her lips with exaggerated precision. The action gave her the sense of being very much a lady, and for a few seconds the reflection that she was in reality superior to everybody else in the room comforted her.

She pulled down her veil and rose, darting as she did so a look intended to convey scorn and contempt at Lily, who did not observe the gesture. Then she looked from her round the room, including the rest of its occupants in her dismissal. Which of those girls had had a devoted husband, the same as her? she asked herself. And a little public of their own with garden and field at the back. None of them. Nor ever would. Prostitutes, that's what they were, and always would be.

As she passed across the room she noticed that Florrie and her gentleman friend were very much engaged in themselves. She half paused as she passed near them, hoping for a glance of recognition, which would have warmed her. But Florrie did not look up.

Mrs. Johnson felt a little queer as she walked down the steps. She had had, she reflected, only a couple of drinks, but then her stomach had been almost empty. "Wonder if I could run to two pennyworth of chips or something?" she muttered to herself, and paused at the door to consider the question. But the cold stare of the commissionaire standing there sent her on into the street.

The lights of Wardour Street blinked heartlessly at her. Instinctively she turned into the comparative quietness of Gerrard Street, her mind going back in hostility to the place she had just left.

To herself she expressed the hope that that dirty little whore wouldn't get the young fellow; they had only come in to get a few drinks, and exchange compliments with the girls to make them feel big. As for Lily herself . . . her thoughts lingered round the girl in bitterness. Then suddenly she felt herself to be old and tired, and the hatred left her. She tried to remember the special grudge she had had against the occupants of the table, and it seemed no longer important. After all she had got two drinks out of Florrie. How much had that fur she was wearing cost?

"Let me see," she asked herself. "How much did Jim give for that fur he bought me out of his winnings at the Lewes races? A real good skunk it was."

She stood for a few minutes by the gallery entrance to the Hippodrome, her mind reconstructing the event. She had been in the field, tying the goats to a fresh bit of grass, and he had called to her. There was a parcel for her, he had said. Yes, he had had it sent by post for a surprise. And how rare and pleased he had been at seeing her in it. Everybody, or nearly everybody, who came into the bar that evening he had called behind to have a look at it. It was fourteen pounds he had given for it, and that was cost price, because he had got it through a man he knew in the trade. Poor Jim! He was generous with his money when he had it. Too generous! Better for her to-day if he'd have been the saving kind. Ah, well! What was had to be!

She looked up and down the street. She would have liked to tell someone about her husband. How good he had been to her, never denying her anything if he could help it! What would he say if he could see where she had got to to-day?

There was nobody about: the two totties who had passed her had turned into Charing Cross Road. Wait! Wasn't that a man standing on the opposite side turned in her direction? She looked back, and then turned and walked slowly towards him.

As she drew near, he crossed, making a line that led past her, but looking hard at her as he came abreast. She coughed and stood still.

No! He had sheered off. Not to his liking evidently. Not much use following; he was walking quite fast now. Mrs. Johnson sighed and walked slowly on. She ought to have gone to the Park first of all. Perhaps she would go now. But she couldn't walk all that way without a bite. She weighed the claims of 'bus fares and a snack. The latter won, for she might feel equal to walking when she had got something inside her.

She hurried across to the other side of the road, and walked rapidly along. It was cold, and she shivered. A whisky now! A whisky would be the thing to give her help in getting hold of someone. It was no good trying to be gay and enticing without food or anything. Leastways not at her age.

Withdrawing into a corner, she took two pence from her purse ready to pass over the counter. It was against her practice to let anyone see into her purse; some people were nosey; liked to see how much cash you had; some of those girls, them that hadn't been brought up at all proper, were a bit too ready with their remarks.

Now she had only threepence halfpenny left. She felt a sharp pang of regretful kindness toward those meagre brown coins. They'd be gone before the night was out, she'd be bound. And then where'd she be? Not a sou in the world! Not a bloody sou!

At the door of the café she paused, almost relinquishing her intention. Fivepence halfpenny was, after all, a lot more than threepence halfpenny. There was the farthing, which came in for loaves of bread. But the smell of hot food caught at her nostrils too alluringly to be resisted, and she went inside.

There was nobody there she knew, for the place happened to be fairly empty at the time. Two girls were at the table eating heartily, and drinking out of big cups of coffee. A man and a girl were in a corner, and there was a girl sitting by herself smoking.

Mrs. Johnson ordered her sandwich from the white-jacketed young Jew behind the counter, and thought regretfully of the chips she might have had in its stead if she had only happened to be the other side of the river. These sandwiches were the best you could get up West for their price, and held a proud position among those who were initiated; but, after all, thought

Mrs. Johnson, what she really needed was something spicy and hot. And a cup of coffee. Should she blow it all in, and order a cup? It was a difficult decision.

If she ordered a cup of coffee she would also feel entitled to a seat. Of course there was nothing actually to prevent her from sitting down with her sandwich, upon which she had liberally spread mustard; but Mrs. Johnson knew that she was in the bad books of the young Jew, and she hoped to placate him by standing. Once he had told her that you couldn't be expected to get a whole evening's rest for tuppence. "Was it," he had asked her with mock politeness, "reasonable?" And the resort was too convenient for Mrs. Johnson to wish to burn her boats entirely.

Eating as slowly as she dared, Mrs. Johnson had nearly come to the end of her sandwich when a young woman entered, quietly dressed in a grey flannel suit with a white jumper. She was pale, and though her dark eyes were lively and good natured Mrs. Johnson did not know how to place her since she sported very little make-up.

She ordered two ham sandwiches, and much to Mrs. Johnson's pleasure remained at the counter to eat them. For it was evident that she was disposed towards conversation, and not particular with whom she held it. So when Mrs. Johnson assiduously passed her the mustard, she was thanked with warmth.

"Very cold to-night," said Mrs. Johnson, encouraged.

"My God, isn't it! Cold as hell! Or I suppose hell isn't? What do you say, Tommy?"

She was addressing the Jew, who took, however, no notice. He knew Miss Agnes True, and did not care for her style.

As a retort to his silence, Agnes raised her eyebrows, and then turned down the corners of her mouth ludicrously, jerking her head back from Rosenbaum to Mrs. Johnson, who tittered, feeling that she was getting her own back to some extent. She decided she liked Agnes: not one of your stuck-up ones, she wasn't. A real nice girl. And it was plain that she had had a few drinks. That might make her generous. You never knew your luck.

For a little while Agnes was silent, concentrating upon her food. Then she turned to Mrs. Johnson again.

"I've been in the old hole. You know where I mean? Right! Got in with a chap what was as tight as an owl, and went on putting it away, too. 'Now my dear,' he says to me. 'I'm not going to ask you to take me home. I wouldn't insult you,' he says. 'But you can have as many drinks as you want.' And he meant it, too. He ordered a double Scotch straightaway. Some girls might have been too—you know what I mean—to take it. But what's the odds? That's what I say. A short life, and get through it as best you can, that's what I say."

"I wish I'd been there," said Mrs. Johnson. "I was just saying to myself that a drop of Scotch is what you want, my dear. I miss it, because you see my husband—he had a public-house of his own. And I've just had the 'flu something awful. I couldn't tell you what I feel like. It's as much as I can do just to stand up."

She raised her voice slightly in the hope that Rosenbaum would get the benefit of the last remark. Not though, she thought to herself, that his sort have any decency in them.

"You do look off it," said Agnes sympathetically. "You've come out too soon. That's what it is. You ought to have given yourself another day or two in bed."

"So I ought," said Mrs. Johnson. "I know that. But there you are. I've my living to make."

"That's right," said Agnes. "That's what it is. No time to stay at home and say your prayers. Go forth into the highways and byways and compel them to come in. That's our game. For better or for worse. For richer or for poorer. And mostly for poorer."

She laughed loudly, and not being sufficiently applauded proceeded to make her point clear.

"That's a quotation from the Bible, though you may not know it. But I know it. Oh, yes! I know my Bible. When I went to Sunday School I got the prize. Believe me or believe me not, I got a bew-ti-ful prize."

"You *are* a lively one, you are," said Mrs. Johnson.

At the sound of her voice, the Jew suddenly turned.

"Can I get you anything else, madam?" he inquired with mock politeness. Mrs. Johnson shook her head.

"Are you going to stay here all night then?" he said, changing his voice disagreeably.

"All right, all right," said Mrs. Johnson. "You're in a hurry, aren't you?"

Agnes's presence had emboldened her, and she recognised her own courage with approbation. Funny how you never feel up to yourself when you're alone, she thought.

"Wait a mo," said Agnes, cramming the last of her sandwich into her mouth, "and I'll come with you, though the perfect gentleman here is so polite and pressing to me to stay with him."

She laughed again, and Mrs. Johnson joined in her merriment. For a moment Rosenbaum took no notice, giving an attentive ear to a male customer who had just come in.

Then he turned full on Agnes, who had vexed him with her tongue before.

"Well, I must say you're one as I'd rather see your back than your face," he said, turning full on her. "You may be a nice sweet little thing, but somehow I don't seem to see it."

"Don't you insult me, you dirty Jew," said Agnes in a raised voice. "I needn't put up with anything from you, and I'm not going to. You get your living mostly from us girls, don't you; and you'd better treat us proper. I've paid you, haven't I?"

Mrs. Johnson realised that they were rousing attention from the other occupants of the café. She became a little frightened. If Rosenbaum got really offended, he might refuse to serve her again. Complain to the police or something. It would be like him.

"Get out of here, both of you," said Rosenbaum. "Get out of here, or it will be the worse for you."

"How do you mean, it will be the worse for me, you bloody Jew?" shouted Agnes. "What do you mean?"

"Come on, dear," said Mrs. Johnson. "Come on. Don't take any notice. It's beneath you."

Agnes hesitated. The temptation to have a really good row, to turn and address the whole café, to relieve herself once and for all in glorious fashion was strong. But she sensed that Rosenbaum was waiting for her next move. And he had the authorities behind him.

"All right. But you shall hear from me further," she said with dignity. She looked round the café with a thoughtful air. But it did not appear as if anyone was coming to her aid. Mrs. Johnson was already out in the street. So she shot a last arrow. "There's nothing I hate and despise more than the Jews who betrayed Our Lord, and who are responsible for every mean and dirty action under the sun," she said clearly, and went out to rejoin Mrs. Johnson.

They walked away from the door in silence, and then Agnes

said as a final comment: "The b . . . . ! The bloody b . . . . of a Jew!"

Mrs. Johnson did not reply: she only shook her head once to imply that things had come to such a pass that they were beyond her. Pulling down her veil had turned her mind to another topic. She decided to consult Agnes.

"Do you think," she said after a short interval, "that wearing this veil makes me look old?"

Agnes glanced at her without bothering to give any careful survey, and then reassured her heartily: "Old, not a bit. You look as young as ever you were."

This was not exactly what Mrs. Johnson wanted.

"But would you say," she said, pushing her veil up, "that I look better without it?"

But Agnes was in too expansive a mood to give herself to any survey of details.

"Christ!" she said. "What does it matter? If your name's up to click to-night, you'll click, veil or no veil. If it isn't, well then you won't, and that's all there is to it. Let's go and get a drink and hope for the best."

"I'd like to," said Mrs. Johnson, "but honest, dear, I'm cleaned right out."

Agnes looked at her searchingly. "I have heard that said before."

"It's the blessed truth," said Mrs. Johnson, stung into vehemence. "God strike me dead, if it isn't! 'Ere! Look!'"

Agnes looked indifferently at the opened bag thrust under her eyes. A stick of rouge, a key, a box without a lid of compressed powder, and a very dirty small powder-puff were its visible contents.

"Well, I suppose I shall have to treat you," she said. "If I wasn't on the streets already, I soon would be, what with all the things people get out of me for nothing."

Mrs. Johnson thought it wiser to be silent. Agnes was evidently in a mood when she might choose to quarrel with her at any moment. She followed her into the public-house lounge selected a little wearily. The snack she had eaten had not had the effect she hoped, for her back was hurting, and her head beginning to ache. Urgently, too, it came to her that it was time to get to business. She ought really to leave Agnes and walk about a little. She would never do any good as long as she was with someone young. But then perhaps a glass of something would pick her up.

The room they entered wore a subdued, almost dejected air. There were plenty of men, but they were men who had come to drink and talk, and only casual glances rested on Mrs. Johnson and Agnes as they sat down.

Agnes looked round searchingly. "That fellow I told you about isn't here," she said. "He said he'd come back here, and pick me up later. Much hopes of that, I don't think! Well, we'll have a bottle of the usual to keep us going."

She gave the order, and it was not till they had drunk a little that Agnes regained her former cheerfulness. "If I don't work myself off on someone to-night," she said loudly, "I shall run all the way home smiling at every man I see. And then I shall dance round my room. Why not? You get what's coming to you, and if it doesn't come, why worry?"

"That's what I say," said Mrs. Johnson. "It's no use meeting troubles half way. No use at all. And that's a fact."

She emptied her glass; and then putting it down, fortified to have a good stare round, found that it was impossible to remember the faces of anyone after she had looked away. They were far off, and didn't seem at all important. Nevertheless she had to make them important. She kept her eyes fixed for some time on a fair boyish-looking young man in a corner, who grew more and more uneasy under her half unconscious leer; and told herself that she must remember to keep a clear head. This was only her third drink: showed the way illness and starvation had affected her. Thinking of her hardships, she removed her gaze from the young man, to his great relief, and shook her head sadly as she studied the red tiled pattern of the table which glowed up at her with rich warmth.

Then, "Never mind," she told herself after a few moments. "You're as good as any of them here anyway."

She looked round again defiantly, and the young man, catching her eye, removed his regard hastily. She would have liked to find an occasion for asserting herself, for all at once it came to her that she had been far too meek with people. The way Rose had grown to ride roughshod over her lately! After all she had done for that woman in the past! When you had money and a home and a husband, people loved you. But if you were down, they'd all of them like to give you another push. If she only had Rose here now, she'd tell her what she thought of her.

Such a mean fuss over a few weeks' rent. She turned to Agnes with an idea of telling her the story of her wrongs, but the girl began to speak first.

"I tell you what!" said Agnes, with the effect of uttering a new truth. "The matter with us is that we're too refined. It's the painted bird that gets the worm every time. Much more important than being early."

Mrs. Johnson felt her mind grasp with astonishing clarity the immense significance of this utterance.

"That's right," she said, nodding her head several times. "We're too refined. Too quiet-like and decent for most of them."

"Decent's the word," interrupted Agnes. "Do you know what I was asked to do the other night? And for two pounds. Two pounds! I was supposed to make a beast of myself, if you please. Wait now, and I'll tell you the way it happened." Turning towards Mrs. Johnson, her eyes met those of a young man just coming into the room. He came towards her, and Mrs. Johnson, looking to see the cause of the delay in the narrative, saw with mixed feelings a young man standing by their table.

"Good evening, Mr. James," said Agnes, looking up with exictement flavoured by something resembling contempt in her eyes. "Or isn't it James to-night? You never know, you know. It might be one of the other holy apostles." She laughed loudly.

Mrs. Johnson reflected that Agnes was certainly a bit on. Seemed as if she cared for nobody. So flushed, too! And ordinarily she was such a pale girl.

"What's your poison?" said Mr. James, ignoring the sally, and pulling out a chair for himself.

"Just a wee drappie of the malt," said Agnes, adding absently, "as Harry Lauder says."

Mrs. Johnson looked hard at her empty glass, and then turned a fixed smile towards her companions, directed neither at Agnes nor at Mr. James, but hovering between them in the hope of winning some sort of recognition from one or the other.

Mr. James, as he called himself, pink and round faced, with thin hair already receding from his forehead, began to realise for the first time the presence of Mrs. Johnson, and glanced uneasily from her to Agnes, waiting for a cue. He didn't want to treat that elderly person, and because of her lack of attraction became suspicious. Perhaps she was the girl's mother. Perhaps he had been unwise in sitting down straight off. What he ought to have done was to sit down at another table, and wait till Agnes joined him, or the old woman sheered off. He withdrew himself a little and became thoughtful.

Agnes realised the cause of his uneasiness, and hastened to reassure him. "This lady here has just 'ad influenza. Do you know the joke, 'How did you get it?' 'I opened the window, and in flew Enza!' She has just done me the favour of having a drink with me till you turned up—for somehow I thought it might be little Jimmy's night out to-night. But she's saying that she can't keep away from her by-bye much longer, she feels so bad."

Mr. James looked at Mrs. Johnson for confirmation.

Mrs. Johnson was a little disappointed, but she admitted to herself that it was to have been expected.

"Yes, I'm just off," she said, preserving her smile, though the glow of expectancy went from her eyes, leaving them rather like that of a hurt child determined not to cry.

Mr. James understood that there was nothing to be feared from this quarter, and in his relief expanded benevolently. After all, giving the old girl a drink would only mean another eightpence, and it would look well with Agnes, who was almost the only one of her profession with whom he felt at ease. In talking of her to his chosen intimates, he would close by saying solemnly, "And to look at her you would never know she was that sort. Just a quiet-looking wholesome sort of girl, you'd think, if you didn't know her."

To which someone or other could generally be relied upon to say, "But you know different," and then there would be a burst of laughter very flattering to him. Oh, Agnes was certainly an acquisition, if she did rag you rather when there was anyone else about. So he turned to Mrs. Johnson, and said graciously, 'Have a whisky before you go. It'll do you good."

"It's most kind of you. Thank you very much, I'm sure," said Mrs. Johnson, affecting a ladylike precise voice which somehow seemed natural to her at the moment. She finished up with a little bow, thinking to herself with a gleam of pleasure, "Refined, that's what I am."

The whiskies having arrived, Mr. James decided he might dismiss Mrs. Johnson from his mind. Agnes was leaning towards him now, talking rapidly, her face close against his. He did not follow all she was saying, and laughed rather as his instinct prompted him than by the light of his own appreciation. For he considered he was well away now from the safe shore; and sometimes he felt a little thrilled by his own bravery and would glance round to see what attention he was attracting; and sometimes he felt uneasy and afraid, and his eyes grew absent as he thought of what lay in front of him. But whenever Agnes paused he nodded, looked thoughtful for a moment, smiled, and then renewed his grip on what she was saying.

Meanwhile Mrs. Johnson, sipping her whisky, watched them passively. Her mind remained tranquil, for she was not jealous of Agnes, and in so far as she thought at all, she felt glad that Agnes was evidently fixed up all right. At the back of her mind, as yet unformulated, was the realisation that her evening was running out, and that very shortly indeed she would have to try and do something about it. But she did not spoil the few precious moments in which she had a right to a comfortable seat, and was regarded with tolerance if not with approval, by taking thought. People came and went; occasionally a burst of laughter or a raised voice struck her attention; her head became heavy; and she felt further and further away from the world of struggle and discomfort.

Abruptly her pleasant coma was dispelled. "Time, gentlemen, time!" came the harsh voice of the waiter, intruding on conversation, shattering reverie, disturbing observation. To Mrs. Johnson it was the strident voice of reality shouting at her to get a move on, and remember that she had her rent to pay.

"Eleven o'clock, and I haven't spoken to a man yet," Mrs. Johnson warned herself in something of a panic. She swallowed the last of the liquor remaining in her glass, and pushing back her chair rose to her feet, frowning and determined. One predominating thought mastered her: she must get out into the street and accost someone, anyone, quick. But she remembered her manners. "Good-night, dear," she said to Agnes, who nodded and laughed, and "Good night to you," she said to Mr. James, who gave a half nod, and shuffled uneasily in his chair. She went out of the room and, a little unsteadily, down the stairs, followed by a long high laugh, over whose significance she pondered vacantly.

Coming into Leicester Square, the bright lights, as they seemed, and throngs of hurrying people, confused her. For a moment she wondered irritably if there was an accident or something, to account for so many people. And there was such a noise. Faces shot by her, gleaming with astonishing clarity, as if lit up by a powerful white light, and then in a moment vanished as if they had never been. There were two men arguing angrily outside the Empire; just past them three girls coming along arm-in-arm, their red mouths opened by laughter. Again, a placard bore down upon her suddenly and impressively, "The Wicked Shall Be Turned into Hell" it shouted at Mrs. Johnson, and passed by; while in its turn the unshaven face of a matchseller standing at the curb rose at her, and fixed her attention a few seconds owing to its aloofness. The matchseller was apart from the pushing staring talking people; he was too apart even to be a spectator. But he stayed his place like a sceneshifter who stands in the wings without a thought for the play, waiting till the end.

Crossing the road, Mrs. Johnson made her way down the short cut which leads into the Charing Cross Road. The fresh air steadied her a little, but she felt very tired and suddenly very lonely. It was because, she thought, there were so many millions of people about all talking to someone else except her alone. Outside the picture palace she paused, and laid a hand on her back.

"Christ! My back doesn't half ache," she said aloud, looking for sympathy from the commissionaire, who was impatiently awaiting the expected exit of the audience so that he could get home. Meanwhile he stared up and down, anxious not to lose any spectacle which he might add to his day's store before retiring into private life.

He was a big fellow with a fine moustache, and though he made no comment with regard to Mrs. Johnson's plaint, she continued to pause expectantly, for of a sudden she had become convinced that there existed a strong likeness between him and her dead husband. He gave her a glance at last, having failed to find anything or anybody else worthy of his attention.

"Cheer up, mother," he said consolingly, "you'll soon be dead."

"It's very strange," said Mrs. Johnson, disregarding this piece of comfort. "It's very strange indeed, but you're just the image of my husband. The absolute spit of him!"

A page-boy coming out from the cinema heard, and a grin twisted the corners of his mouth. That was a good one to tell against Big Jim. The commissionaire, aware of him, said loudly, "Well, I'm not your husband. No. Nor likely to be if I can help it. So don't get ideas."

The boy laughed loudly, and two or three people passing paused and stared with expectant grins. Mrs. Johnson felt she was being made game of, and the mixed assortment of liquor inside her lighted a spurt of indignation.

"Don't you suggest anything against my husband," she said with tones that gathered loudness. "He owned a big hotel, he did, and took more money in an hour than you do in a month: for all you stand there as if you thought you was in a beauty competition." The crowd was increased by the first arrivals from the audience, and this time the laughter was against the commissionaire, who became annoyed.

"Here, none of your lip! Move along or I'll tell the police." And then added, instinctively finding the softest place in Mrs. Johnson's armour, "You're drunk, and at your age, too!"

Mrs. Johnson did not care, even at her most irresponsible, to have the police brought into the conversation, and slowly she started to move on, saying, but not too loudly, "Don't be so free with your drinks, my fine fellow, or else if there's a law in the land, you'll be made sorry for it. Libel it is! The law of libel!"

She left him behind, and walked fairly fast. But she still continued to mutter to herself, and a few of the crowd, hoping to be provided with further entertainment, followed. Mrs. Johnson, turning suddenly, saw the white face of one of them, a young man, looming close by, and mistook his avid expression for sympathy.

"My husband was a fine man," she confided to him. "A fine big man; could have knocked down that whipper-snapper as easy as easy." She shook her head in sad reminiscence. "But he died. He died of cancer."

The thought had suddenly flashed upon her with the vividness of a great discovery, and it seemed to her as if she was recounting for the first time a fact of the utmost moment. "Yes, dear! Cancer was eating his stomach out, month after month, so as he couldn't keep a bit of food inside him; and there he was looking as yellow as a Chinaman, him that 'ad never 'ad a day's illness in his life, so that it would break your heart to see him. . . ." She stopped, for the face had vanished, the young man's prudence having conquered his curiosity.

Mrs. Johnson crossed to St. Martin's Church, and then to

Charing Cross Station, for the young man's presence had aroused her to a sense of her calling. With an effort she dismissed the pictures of her past which had occupied her mind. Better have a look at myself, she thought; and in Charing Cross Ladies' Room, she remembered, there was a full length mirror at which you could powder and have a good long view of yourself without being charged. In some of these places you would get your head eaten off if you so much as took a peep in the looking-glass without paying the attendant. It was a miserly grasping world!

Mrs. Johnson made her way into the station through the waiting-room, and proceeded downstairs. She stood in front of the mirror, and powdered her face generously while she debated within herself the question of paying out yet another penny in order to satisfy a demand of nature. She had forgotten that there was no free convenience provided here: always a catch, she told herself, somewhere. If she spent a penny, she'd only have . . . how much was it? Twopence half-penny, or twopence three farthings, to be precise. On the other hand, if she waited till she got outside and then took a risk, she might get a policeman on to her. The commissionaire's threat had brought a sense of police persecution home to her. The way they walked so silently round corners just when you thought you was safe from observation! Besides, she had always kept herself respectable in those sorts of ways: not like some she could name. But then, they'd never known any better; never been legally married and had a place of their own. She had.

Before leaving she had another long look at herself. There was no denying that she did look yellow. She turned to a smartly-dressed young woman who was standing beside her, and, moved by the craving to receive some sympathy, coughed loudly, and put her hand to her throat.

The young woman, with a broad pink face and a lot of fair hair bunched outside her ears, happened to be feeling pleased with herself, and therefore benevolently inclined. She was just about to set off in a taxi with a gentleman who was going to pay for a really smart hotel, and then some more: so meeting Mrs. Johnson's appealing eyes in the glass, she responded.

"God a bad cough, haven't you?" she said.

"Oh, terrible," replied Mrs. Johnson eagerly. "I've just had the 'flu. I've never felt like I feel now in all my life before. It's cruel, that's what it is. Have you ever felt like it, I wonder?

There's a pain that's just eating into my back, here. I feel sickish; my head aches that bad; and the soles of my poor feet make it so that I can hardly put one foot before another."

"Oh, yes, I've felt like that in my time," replied the girl, replacing a stick of rouge in her hand-bag, a beautiful expensive hand-bag it was, Mrs. Johnson noticed admiringly. "Scores of times, if it comes to that."

"Fancy that!" said Mrs. Johnson, gazing at her in a blend of admiration, wonder and appeal. Her mind worked rapidly. This girl seemed a friendly sort. No harm in trying it on.

"And the worst of it is," said Mrs. Johnson, "I haven't even got the price of my 'bus fare home. I was dying for a ——, and it's took my last penny. Now, what I'm going to do I don't really know. I'm not young and good-looking and smart like you, dearie, and it's hard to live. I suppose I shall have to walk all the way back to Camberwell, that's where I live, though I know I shall drop down in the street long before I get there."

"Nothing doing," said the girl briefly. She started to ascend the steps, and then with the thought of her own immediate lucrative future before her she repented, and pausing for a moment opened her bag. Perhaps God would see that *she* never knew want, if He saw her being generous to other people who hadn't her luck.

"Here you are," she said, going back and handing three coppers to Mrs. Johnson, who had come to meet her, after a glance round to make sure that there was no attendant watching. "That'll pay your fare home anyway. As a matter of fact I'm pretty well cleaned out myself."

"Thank you very much, dear," said Mrs. Johnson, effusive and polite to the last, though a little disappointed. "Wouldn't have hurt her to make it a tanner," she commented to herself. All dressed up as she was—pearl necklace and a beautiful cloth to her costume. Well, have to be thankful for small mercies, I suppose.

She stared at herself with mournful interest a little longer: her mind occupied with the old problem, to veil or not to veil. It looked so old-fashioned. But it did hide her wrinkles. Leave it perhaps.

At last she dragged herself away, and slowly and heavily ascended the stairs, not even pausing for a final glance at herself in the mirror in the wall at the top, for a deep weariness not to be evaded or forgotten any longer had captured her whole being. It was true what she had told her late acquaintance: she ached all down her back; her stomach was a little uneasy; her legs felt so heavy that it was a weary business dragging them up the stairs. It wasn't fair, she told herself, to expect her to try and do anything. If Rose had a heart at all, she couldn't deny her a few more nights' rest. She had fivepence halfpenny now: whatever remained from her 'bus fare she would take to Rose. "See," she would say, "this is all I have, but if it's any good to you have it. Have it!" she would say. Perhaps Rose would lend her another ten bob if she got her in the right mood.

As she left the station, keeping close to the pavement, somebody pushed into her, nearly causing her to lose her balance. She waited a moment to steady herself, and then proceeded on her way, without enough heart in her even to place in his proper category the man who had shoved her. At the end of the Strand stood crowds of people waiting for their 'buses, almost, it seemed, blocking her way on purpose, as she moved pace by pace towards Trafalgar Square. She felt blinded by voices, the jostling rush, and whimpered a little out of tiredness as she moved through.

At the doorway of a chemist's shop at the corner she paused, and stood still thinking that she might give the world a last chance to do something for her. She waited passively, now and then recollecting herself enough to turn her head and single out the approaching figure of a man walking by himself. At these moments her lips would expand in an effort of invitation which remained fixed some time after the object which had inspired it had vanished from sight.

Before very long she felt someone pause beside her. Mrs. Johnson turned hopefully. But it was a policeman who confronted her. "Now then," he said, "hadn't you better be getting along?"

Mrs. Johnson looked for a moment—which seemed to her a long while—into the red face which loomed above her. Vast and meaningless it appeared to her until gradually its significance reached her brain. Then she turned without a word, making her way mechanically across Northumberland Avenue. Arrived at the other side, she looked behind to see if he were following her. No, he had turned the other way.

It's no use, she reflected, not without satisfaction. Everybody and everything was against her. It was Friday, too, an unlucky day Friday had always been for her. Better go home while there was still a 'bus to get. It was nearly twelve, and there wouldn't be one if she waited much longer. Hadn't had any luck. But she couldn't be expected to when she was feeling as she was. No one could!

Her 'bus came, and she watched it drawing up with satisfaction. Nice friendly 'bus, that would take her home to bed. She was lucky in getting a corner seat, but, as she drew out tuppence for her ticket, a sense of the tragedy its giving up signified overcame her once more. "That's almost my last copper gone," she said aloud, looking round at the other passengers in the 'bus, and making her last bid that evening for a look or smile of sympathy, with her child's eyes half terrified, half proud. To be in such a hole!

But no one answered her. Any gaze that met hers withdrew with uneasy speed. The woman who sat next Mrs. Johnson nudged her neighbour, and exchanged with her a smile full of meaning. The man opposite gazed at his boots with great solemnity. Next to him a portly grocer thought with disgust, "Is the woman going to start begging? Here! In a 'bus! Scandalous!" And he frowned at her heavily in order that she should be discouraged from creating any such scene. And then one by one the eyes of the people who had overheard Mrs. Johnson returned to her, filled with carefully prepared impersonality. If she went on talking or addressed someone it might be amusing, the boldest thought. But be careful not to give her encouragement to pick on them.

But the flicker of life had died in Mrs. Johnson. She offered no more entertainment, but sat awaiting the time she would get out and creep home to bed. It would not be safe to risk going past her proper fare stage, she decided. She wasn't going to pay another penny, no, not if she knew it. So that meant dragging herself along the dark close-smelling Camberwell Road, which seemed to stretch itself out for ever. Sometimes she had to stop and lean against a wall to get a moment's respite. "Christ!" she would mutter at such times, and once, when she felt very exhausted, "Lord Christ!" Perhaps she had knocked herself up proper. It was disgraceful that she should have been forced to go out that evening. A fair scandal it was! And nothing had come of it. Nothing had come of it.

At last she turned the corner of her street. As she approached she thought of Rose, who might even be waiting up for her, and her steps faltered. The thing was to be very quiet going in: not let the old cat hear her. Very quietly she slipped the key into the lock and slipped in, closing the door noiselessly behind her. Holding her breath, she tiptoed upstairs, pausing ever and again to listen. But there was no sound. Rose must be asleep. Thank God for that!

Inside her little bedroom, she closed the door, and cautiously turned the key in the lock. She was in now, and she'd not be turned out again that night at least for anyone. Not if Rose came and shouted ever so. Now she was safe. There was a whole night between her and the recurrence of unpleasantness. Florrie; Lily; the face of the dark man who had been so rude; Agnes, a gay sort that girl! the good-looking fair boy; Mr. James, the big commissionaire: old beast he was; the girl who had given her threepence: dressed up tart; flickered in her confused head as she undressed. Then she dismissed them. It was all over now. The evening was over. She'd get a little rest and peace now. Feel better to-morrow perhaps.

"At least," was her last coherent thought, "I got a few drinks for nothing. Some of those girls, prostitutes though they may be, have good hearts. I will say that for them."

Osbert Sitwell

THE MACHINE BREAKS DOWN

HUGH DEARBORN was already middle-aged when I first remember him some ten years ago, but middle-aged with an unparalleled elegance, an unimpeachable style. His greying hair, his mask-like face, through which peered those witty, rather wicked eyes, his hands of carved ivory, were all made with an exquisite but rather snuff-box-like finish. This well-groomed and tailored figure, this Voltairean mask, rather too developed for the slender frame and covered with small, delicately chiselled wrinkles, formed but the very gentlemanly shell for an intense vitality out of all proportion to it—formed, in fact, the beautifully finished cabinet-gramophone case, from which sounded a wonderful but intolerable music. Not that his voice was musical, in the sense that our grandmothers used that term. It was not. His laugh never resembled a peal of church bells sounding at eventide, or a rather carelessly played xylophone, as did the elegant tremolos of various old Victorian ladies. On the contrary, his voice touching every emotion for the necessary moment, never sunk into cloying sweetness, having, rather, that enchanting trick of putting a note in the wrong, unexpected place, and then recovering, which you find in the best modern music—find originally in Rossini's *Can-Can*, that first clear gem of modern music, and then in Debussy, Ravel, and Stravinsky.

The actual manner of his conversation was perhaps less modern than its content. Artists of the spoken word vary in their methods. One, whose manner I admire most of all, talks, argues, sinks beneath the logical waters, is on the point of drowning, but as he touches the ocean bottom finds some new pearl, and swiftly brings it to the surface: his is an absolute reliance on his own brain and tongue, never afraid to risk all on an absurd argument, never fearing to sink, knowing always that he will find a new treasure. But Hugh's system is different, formal; it is as the Garden of Versailles compared with that of Hampton Court—stiff, mathematic, well ordered; his voice a terrible instrument, his art one that dies but never surrenders.

From the first Hugh Dearborn possessed a peculiar interest for me—an interest roused by some apparent contradictions in his character. Here was this exquisite shell, the fruit of fifty or sixty years of toil, but an instrument for an hour's conversation—conversation that like a flower blossoms and then dies—a mule-like art without hope of progeny. Usually the artist is led on by a desire for immortality or perhaps fired by a craving for money, but here was a real case of "Art for Art's sake." The best Hugh could hope for was an invitation to dinner, but the very perfection of his conversational techique, the very insistence and monopoly of his great art, often tended to prevent his humble end.

And this art itself, unpremeditated and yet such a technical achievement, surely could not flower on the barren air without any but purely physical preparation? Then again, after Hugh's performance of the new Symphony at the luncheon table, I once heard a rather unkind friend say to him: "Really, Hugh, you ought to put it in a book!" And this made me wonder why he had never employed these gifts in some other, more permanent, form. And how much longer, in any case, could this delicate, ageing instrument stand the ceaseless wear and tear of such a vitality?

Thus, from the first, Dearborn interested me and I collected information about him. It was certainly a mysterious life. A friend of mine, I found out, had met him originally in the garden of Walter Pater. I pictured the scene. To us children of sadder and wiser days the eighties of the last century seem a halcyon but ever so distant age; Alfred Lord Tennyson ever so much more distant than King Alfred burning the cakes; the young manhood of Mr. Arthur Balfour ever so much more remote, more legendary, than the youth of King Arthur or the Quest of the Holy Grail. A halcyon time indeed, with spring always in the warm crystal-clear air; with the laburnums, the lilacs, the lobelias and copper beeches in a perpetual riot of unsubdued and unbridled colour. There was a continual movement and sparkle in the lives of the well-to-do. Poet Laureates still wrote quite successful odes to members of the reigning family, who were then of greater interest to their subjects than professional cricket or the doped death of Miss Flossie Highfly. The county families were yet safely out of the way, secure in their distant tea-bound mansions, busy killing the beasts of the field, the birds of the air. Riches were still respectable, the rise of a millionaire was yet a romance. On the other hand, you could be poor without being thought insane, and the silver epergne was gradually retiring into the lodging-house homes of Bloomsbury. Shepheard's Hotel would soon be open in Cairo (or was it already?), and we were on the verge of an optimistic young Imperialism that would grow to a climax with Kipling and Lady Butler. And, to those who liked it, there was a pleasant stir in the world of art. Painting and prose were both stretching themselves after a long sleep that had been broken only by the short Pre-Raphaelite nightmare. This was the time of the neo-Greek: white marble mantelpieces, Alma Tadema, the prose of John Addington Symonds, the drawings of Du Maurier and Frank Miles—all were supposed, rather vaguely, to recall, to equal even, the art of Phidias. Bustles, bonnets, straight profiles and diamond myrtle-leaves were the order of the day. For the more precious there were water-lilies, almond-blossom and flowing draperies; for the very knowing, chatter about Whistler and Walter Pater.

Thus, in the garden of that old-world city, through Parnassian groves, over smooth classical lawns that glowed, as they would have said, like sad green velvet, under weeping willows which wept more gracefully than they do now, and through which there always rattled a slight fresh wind from the East, suggestive of the clattering of willow-pattern plates, wandered our young hero, in ever so clean white-flannel trousers, talented and exquisite. The old æsthete, who seldom committed himself to prophecy, leant over to my friend and said: "That young man will go far!" . . . .

From those days, alas! until the early nineteen ten's I know little of Dearborn's career. He went everywhere, knew everyone—poets, painters, the first lady who wore "bloomers," boxers, philosophers, and Channel swimmers, wasting the perfect blossom of his art on the worthy and unworthy alike. His art developed continually. His talk became something outside himself, a disembodied spirit. From a fine art it became a devouring growth, that in the end swallowed up the author of its being. He was Frankenstein, his conversation the monster . . . but a monster with charm.

To meet him was always a pleasure, to part with him the subtle torture of a thousand farewells. Perhaps Hugh himself wished to leave you, but his art forbade him. It made him linger, lead you to the longed-for terminus with a hundred little anecdotes that crucified your spirit; though regarded objectively. they were round, full, delicate, and smooth as a ripe peach. But his conversation, monstrous ectoplasm that he materialised, wound round you like a serpent, bound you with a thousand octopus-like tentacles, released you for a moment, like a cat with a mouse, and then grabbed you again, draining your blood like a vampire.

Dull people used to think it funny to say: "I wonder what he does when he is alone." Others suggested (and this was to me an interesting hypothesis) that he only existed in relation to his friends and acquaintances—his conversation but the magic rope up which clambered this fabulous spinner of words, like an Indian juggler, till, ceasing to climb it, he dissolved into the void. This perhaps might account for that lingering farewell; for when it was said, Hugh, too, would cease to exist for a while. But he was too personal, too positive for that; and, like all people of talent, as opposed to genius, he was too dated. He had little tricks, and these tricks belied his mask and proved him to be real. That manner, for instance, of wiping his eye, on entering a room, with the corner of a beautifully-folded, slightly-scented pocket-handkerchief, as one who was still laughing at some witty conversation that he had just left, did not that betray him? Was not that conversation one that he had held with Whistler, Pater, or some other already legendary figure?—was it not perhaps only a forty-year-old memory? On the other hand, it may have been a signal, like a bugle call, for focusing the attention; for Hugh, a true artist, liked to have the attention of his audience, and, if slighted, if interrupted, a strange fury gleamed from those wicked little eyes.

Like all beautiful objects, Hugh never aged, only becoming a little more worn—worn with the thin wrinkled elegance of a Chinese grotesque; but his talk became always fuller and richer. He was never silly, never dull; and again, like all *objets d'art*, though mannered, he was never really affected. Yet there was about him a quality that was sometimes a little sinister, sometimes a little sad; a mystery, certainly. But from the first, being an artist myself, I guessed that his art was a hard mistress. I have said that Hugh Dearborn knew everyone—the world, the flesh, the devil, the ass and the artist. Among his greatest friends (for his art was bilingual and surmounted all obstacles) was Henri Schmidt, the famous Parisian portrait-painter, himself a master of conversation, in an age of which he and Hugh were perhaps the only two high exponents of that art. Schmidt painted his portrait, and it is a masterpiece. Dearborn is presented to us sitting in an arm-chair, with his beautifully crinkled grey hair, his mask wrinkled and wicked, and rather over life-size, looking straight out of the picture. All his attributes are here—ring, cigarette-case, tie-pin, cane and, so to speak, the rest of the artist's equipment. This, then, was Mr. Dearborn when silence took him . . . when he was—alone! On the exquisite mask was a smile, like that Leonardo portrayed on the face of the *Gioconda*, the smile which, we are told, was caused and maintained by the music of hidden flutes—and this wonderful smile of Hugh's is as surely caused by hidden music, by the dead music of his own young voice, by remembered passages from talks with Whistler, Pater, and Oscar Wilde. This picture ranks high as a work of art, but its sadness is unbearable.

Hugh was, however, grateful to the painter for it, and many of his preambles ran: "As I was saying to an old friend of mine, who I know would interest you, especially with your real interest in, and love of, modern Art (but I expect you know him already?)—a man who really is, I think, one of the most interesting and (though perhaps I ought not to say it, for he is one of my greatest friends) amusing, but I mean really one of the most (*crescendo*) brilliant men, the painter, Henri Schmidt." . . .

The war came and went, rolling me over, submerging me as it did most of the younger generation, filling our souls with anger, rancour and hatred, with pity and love. Mr. Dearborn, unsubmerged, began to work at other things than talk for the first time in his life. He worked hard and usefully, translating various papers for the Government, being a master of languages as well as of language. The war did not break his indomitable spirit; he never grumbled, nor did he envy the younger men in the trenches, as did so many of our over-age patriots. He behaved, in fact, like what he was—a gentleman. Though there may have been little cracks in the foundation of his spirit, he appeared more elegant and gay than ever, and even took to dancing once more. After working ten arduous hours, with very little actual conversation, in a horribly improvised office, he would dine and then dance till five o'clock in the morning. His vitality was more amazing than ever. High above the coon-born music, above the vulgar, savage and sentimental strains, one could hear the floating "dying fall" of his voice. Never was anyone so gay, so young, for his age as Hugh Dearborn, but it must have been a strain even on that giant energy. He would go to bed at three o'clock, at four o'clock, at five o'clock each morning, in the highest spirits; but who can bear to think of him, as he slept alone and old, in his charming flat? But the next day at ten o'clock he would walk to his office, gay and beautifully dressed as ever, and alas! (as journalists write about royal visits) with a word for everyone.

Soon after the war I paid a visit, in search of health, to the plaster-shores of the French Riviera; and at Monte Carlo we met. Every morning at twelve o'clock, to the droning snort of a brass band, Mr. Dearborn, in white-flannel trousers (oh, how long ago was that day in the garden of Walter Pater! . . .), would descend the steps on to the pink-sugar terrace. The war had altered him, and although looking no older, he was beginning to show signs of eternal youth. But under the blue skies, in this hard, trembling light, enhanced by cacti and tropic flowers, and by this sugar-icing world, his appearance took on a new quality, his voice a new tone. He became more real, his warning voice took wing, soared out to sea like the albatross in *The Ancient Mariner*, borne in, as it were, on the crest of a returning toy-wave. His essentially aristocratic finish, and even the rather tired rasp, felt more than heard, of his voice, put the population of international profiteers to shame. It would be many years before these beaked harpies could produce an article with such a finish. . . . I saw and heard a good deal of Mr. Dearborn that spring, and grew to love his conversation. My mind would wander in it, as in a forest; I would lose my path, led away by strains of unfamiliar music, and then be pulled up suddenly by some well-known landmark—the name of Henri Schmidt, or of Durant the boxer—and in that forest I found many homely things that I little expected, and, though on the whole exotic, it was decidedly less so than the war, which at the time we conspired to consider a natural life—and much more restful.

In May I left Monte Carlo, and for nearly two years lost sight and sound of Mr. Dearborn.

Two years afterwards I was wandering about Italy with young William Erasmus, the writer. It was his first visit to the peninsula, and he was very much on the look-out for copy, though his calm, languid air, as of one dwelling on Olympian heights, was calculated to disguise the fact. But he was always watching, listening, and peering. He had, I suspect, written several Italian travel-sketches before leaving England. He was, however, a charming companion—a companion only too appreciative and receptive, his appreciation of anything amusing or interesting that was said being made even more obvious later, and in print, than at the time. Truly we must have livened up the landscape with the necessary grotesque touch, I with my fleshy Hanoverian face and big body, William, tall and thin as a young giraffe, with the small head of some extinct animal, some kind vegetarian creature that subsisted on the nibbled tops of young palm-trees in the oases— the Giant Sloth, for example! And how often, when I saw silly little jokes of mine appearing under the guise of musical or scientific articles in the weekly papers, did I wish that his character had been true to his appearance, that he had indeed resembled more nearly the Giant Sloth, instead of possessing that vast and terrible, assimilative and possessive, energy.

After leaving South Italy we visited Rome and Florence, from there exploring some of the smaller Tuscan towns. The country was in the full efflorescence of early May, only the vines were a little backward, the leaves and tendrils still looking like golden coils about to spring out and release their stored-up energy. Little hills vibrated into the distance like rings of smoke, and the foreground was full of blossom—not the impressionist drifts of colour that you find in northern Europe, but flowers of every colour, each one separate, stiff and geometrical in design, as those in an Italian primitive, or in one of the landscapes of the Douanier Rousseau. The days grew even hotter, and any sudden little blue wind that rose among the distant hills, and played for a moment in the flowering fields, bore an unimaginable load of scent.

One morning we reached the delightful small town of Lucca, finding our rooms in the chief hotel, which had been the palace of one of the noble families in the eighteenth century, when Lucca had been a rich and independent State. The hotel was full of large, lofty rooms with golden curls and network, the prevailing tones of the old paint being light blue or pink, the whole effect being more that of the French than the Italian eighteenth century. The rickety bedstead, shabby German tablecloth, and dingy modern furniture looked very remote in these chambers built as a background for gilded beds, rich brocades, and powdered wigs. The sounds of the street—shouting, snarling song, and shrilling bird-chatter of the market-place—were very faint at these patrician windows, lapping at them softly like small waves. Everything in the room was bright and quiet as in a coloured glass slide. In fact, the whole hotel had an indefinable atmosphere.

The town itself is a lovely one, with gardens and avenues of chestnuts, whose heavy leaves support their glowing, torch-like flowers on the thick battlemented walls that girdle it. We examined the churches, mostly Romanesque buildings of black and white marble, exotic as zebras, of a fabulous sculptural beauty, but seemingly less connected with the present town or its inhabitants than any pagoda whose blossom-like bells drip down their honey on the Chinese gardens. Yet none of the inhabitants seemed to feel the contradiction between their lives and their back-cloth. There the cathedral stood, like a zebra in the market-place, or like an elephant supporting a howdah—they paid no attention to it. In England these things are different. Any stranger stranded under the wide arches of York station for five minutes would guess instinctively the nature of the Minister, the Bishop's Palace, and even of the Archbishop himself. There is no need to explore. Anything queer will soon be tidied up, and, as they say, "put to right." But in Italy civilisations crowd together: marble churches of the twelfth century, brick-built Gothic palaces, gilded rooms with bellying balconies, and finally the iron bedstead and newspaper, universal symbols of modern culture, cling to each other, each the concrete form of a different view of life.

Thus we explored the town, talking. Then followed an early luncheon, after which Erasmus, who during his four and a half weeks in Italy had already become more Italian than the

Italians, even talking the language with such an exquisite
bocca Romana that the Romans were unable to grasp his
meaning, retired from that siesta which was to him the crowning proof of belonging to a cosmopolitan *intelligentsia*. He
had, however, already peered into the visitors' book for copy,
but found none—not even a resident or casual Englishman in
the hotel, which was, as he remarked, none the worse for that;
and no doubt comforting himself with thoughts of how unspoilt was this really very sophisticated small town, he retried
to rest.

The afternoon passed quickly, and the day dwindled into
the dinner-hour.

For a time we walked about the brightly-lit town, but the
cinemas were full, and we had seen *Lucia di Lammermoor* the
previous evening, so that we returned through the humming
streets to our hotel. William went to bed at ten o'clock. Half-
an-hour afterwards he called me excitedly into his room, high,
gilded, and full of dead air that magnified each sound. His
lanky pyjama-clad figure and receptive ear were pressed
ecstatically against a door—one which led into the next bedroom. "Who can it be? Who is it? Who is it?" he whispered.
And then, quite clearly, each word taking on a greater significance in this room that seemed like a gilded tomb, I heard
. . . "As I was saying only a few days ago to a man, a great
friend of mine, who has, I think, really one of the most amusing and interesting personalities—a man who, I know, would
delight you, with your knowledge and genuine appreciation of
modern art—a really witty, but, I mean to say, brilliant and
delightful man, Henri Schmidt." . . .

Thus the poor tired voice dragged on, trailing away into
the huge silence of the palace. Hour after hour the monologue
continued; sometimes the voice stumbled and there was a weak
repetition. Often the stories belonged to an earlier date, the
references to those long in their coffins, and through the weak
tones of an old man you could catch the fresher notes of an
art whose technique had not then been perfected to such a
metallic pitch. His smiling, trembling voice conjured up the
applauding laughter of other days, when he had possessed
a more appreciative audience than latterly. This, then, was
how Hugh had talked to Whistler, to Pater; this was how
. . . But now at three o'clock in the morning the voice sank
down to a slight moan. It haunted me, the stillness of the room.

What was the mystery of that beautifully-finished being, lying in that vast apartment that belonged to another age of perfected technique? Whose voices answered him in his mind, whose laughter?

Morning came to find Erasmus charmed and inquisitive, myself uneasy, not daring to break into the darkened silence of that room. No name was in the visitors' book; no one was to be seen, no voice sounded. Luncheon came, and we watched with mute inquiry.

But at about two-thirty Mr. Dearborn came downstairs, elegant and gay; his mask was rather heavy, tired, and ill-at-ease, though the detail of his appearance was as fresh as ever. But there was a curious thick dragging of his speech, an occasional twitching in the muscles of his mouth. He gave me a hearty but uncertain welcome, avoiding my name. He told me he had been rather ill, and had come here to be alone until he was better able to face the world—his world.

Then it was that I understood—realised the full tragedy of that vocal practice in the small hours. He had been pleading with his art, his Muse, his cruel mistress, to return to him, but the string was broken; she had spread her wings and left the tired old mask: the shell, though still perfect, was empty. The cabinet-gramophone case was complete and beautifully finished; but it was made for only one purpose, and there came no sound of the old music. Art is a hard mistress, mysterious in her intentions. As I left him, never, alas! to see him again, there was a slight return of his powers, and, looking at me, he said: "One spring afternoon I was in the garden of Walter Pater, walking over the lawn" . . . And then I remembered the Parnassian groves, the weeping willow-pattern trees, the exquisite and talented youth in white-flannel trousers, and the words of the old æsthete: "That young man will go far!" . . .

Michael Arlen

THE MAN WITH THE BROKEN NOSE

"Ever been to the National Gallery?" asked George Tarlyon.
It was an offensive question to ask a grown man, but I answered it.

"Ah," said Tarlyon.

"I can't help thinking," said Tarlyon, "that you did Madam Tussaud's the same afternoon. . . ."

"If you want to know, it was the Tower, St. Paul's, and the National Gallery that I did on the same afternoon. My mother took me."

"Of course, I can't compete with your mother," said Tarlyon; "but I will take you—now. Waiter—the bill, please."

It was a day in July, and we were sitting over luncheon at the Café Royal. It was very warm for the time of the year. I don't know if I have mentioned it, but I am something in the City. There was, if you remember, a slump in the City in the summer of 1922. I was in that slump. And so, with one thing and another, I sighed. . . .

"Come on," said Tarlyon firmly. "One must not neglect art. And two certainly mustn't." Poor, silly man!

We walked from the Café Royal to Trafalgar Square, which is an untidy walk on a glaring afternoon in July. And then we walked about the Gallery; we looked at paintings with that rapt look which can see All Round and Into a thing; and we stood before "Musidora Bathing Her Feet."

"What a masterpiece," Tarlyon sighed, "if only she hadn't got three legs!" I could not at first see Musidora's third leg, but after he had pointed it out to me I could see nothing else but that ghostly third leg dangling over her knee between the other two.

1363

"You see," he explained, "Gainsborough painted one leg badly, and so he painted it out and fitted another—but Musidora's third leg came back. Say what you like, there is something displeasing about a woman with an exaggerated number of legs, though some people rather like that kind of thing, saying that a woman can't have too many. . . ."

It was as we turned away, talking loftily about legs, that we were confronted by a tall and dark young man.

"Sir," he addressed Tarlyon, "I would be obliged if you would tell me in which gallery hang the pictures by Manet?"

One wondered why he didn't ask one of the many uniformed men who are strewn·about the Gallery for the purpose of being asked that kind of thing.

"You are quite sure," Tarlyon put frankly to him, "that you do not mean Monet?"

"Manet," said the dark stranger, and looked as though he meant it.

"Well, then, you're in luck," said Tarlyon; "for we, too, were just about to view the Manets. We are partial to Manet. This way."

We followed him like lambs. Tarlyon's knowledge as to where the Manets were took the form of trying every gallery in which the Manets were not. We repassed Gainsborough's three-legged lady, Tarlyon commenting. The dark stranger walked silently but firmly. He was a tall young man of slight but powerful build; his nose, which was of the patrician sort, would have been shapely had it not once been broken in such a way that for ever after it must noticeably incline to one side; and, though his appearance was that of a gentleman, he carried himself with an air of determination and assurance which would, I thought, make any conversation with him rather a business. There was any amount of back-chat in his dark eyes. His hat, which was soft and had the elegance of the well-worn, he wore cavalierly. Shoes by Lobb.

At last a picture rose before our eyes, a large picture, very blue. Now who shall describe that picture which was so blue, blue even to the grass under the soldiers' feet, the complexion of the soldiers' faces and the rifles in the soldiers' hands? Over against a blue tree stood a man, and miserably blue was his face, while the soldiers stood very stiffly with their backs to us, holding their rifles in a position which gave one no room to doubt but that they were about to shoot the solitary man for some misdemeanour. He was the loneliest looking man I have ever seen.

"Manet," said Tarlyon.

The dark young stranger was absorbed; he pulled his hat a little lower over his left eye, so that the light should not obtrude on his vision. . . .

"Come on," I whispered to Tarlyon, for we seemed to be intruding—so that I was quite startled when the stranger suddenly turned from the picture to me.

"You see, sir," he said gravely, "I know all about killing. I have killed many men. . . ."

"Army Service Corps?" inquired Tarlyon.

"No, sir," snapped the stranger. "I know nothing of your Corps. I am a Zeytounli."

"Please have patience with me," I begged the stranger. "What is a Zeytounli?"

He regarded me with those smouldering dark eyes; and I realised vividly that his nose had been broken in some argument which had cost the other man more than a broken nose.

"Zeytoun," he said, "is a fortress in Armenia. For five hundred years Zeytoun has not laid down her arms, but now she is burnt stones on the ground. The Zeytounlis, sir, are the hillmen of Armenia. I am an Armenian."

"Oh, I'm so sorry," Tarlyon murmured.

"Why?" snarled the Armenian.

"Well, you've been treated pretty badly, haven't you?" said Tarlyon. "All these massacres and things. . . ."

The stranger glared at him, and then he laughed at him. I shall remember that laugh. So will Tarlyon. Then the stranger raised a finger and, very gently, he tapped Tarlyon's shoulder.

"Listen," said he. "Your manner of speaking bores me. Turks have slain many Armenians. Wherefore Armenians have slain many Turks. You may take it from me that, by sticking to it year in and year out for five hundred years, Armenians have in a tactful way slain more Turks than Turks have slain Armenians. That is why I am proud of being Armenian. And you would oblige me, gentlemen, by informing your countrymen that we have no use for their discarded trousers, which are anyway not so good in quality as they were, but would be grateful for some guns. And you would still further oblige me by trying, in future, not to talk nonsense about Armenians.

Adieu, gentlemen. You will probably hear of me again. I am in England on public business."

He left us.

"I didn't know," I murmured, "that Armenians were like that. I have been misled about Armenians. And he speaks English very well. . . ."

"Hum," said Tarlyon thoughtfully. "But no one would say he was Armenian if he wasn't, would he?"

"Also," said I, "he is the most aggressive young man I have ever met. Manet indeed!"

"So would you be aggressive, if you had been massacred and made an atrocity of ever since you were a slip of a boy, and had spent your holidays being chased round Lake Van by roaring Turks and hairy Kurds with scimitars dripping with the blood of Circassian children."

"Oh, not Circassian!" I pleaded, for I have always been very sentimental about Circassian women; but Tarlyon insisted that they generally died young and that they were a fat race. . . .

ii

This is what actually happened, towards midnight of that very day, within a stone's-throw of Claridge's Hotel, in Brook Street, Mayfair. George Tarlyon and I had been of the same company for dinner and then bridge at a house in Brook Street. Towards midnight a gap in the bridge allowed us to slip away, which we did. Tarlyon had parked his car outside Claridge's, and thither we walked.

Now Brook Street at that hour is undecided between a state of coma and one of glittering abandon; which means that the deathly silence is every now and then shattered by rich automobiles hurling themselves and lovely ladies all covered in pearls and chrysoprase into the bosom of Grosvenor Square. Claridge's, of course, has music, so that youth may dance. But of pedestrians along Brook Street there are less than a few . . . and of young men in gents' evening wear running furiously after limousines there is a noticeable scarcity. He simply tore past us, that young man, in the middle of the road, a few yards behind a swiftly going car. The car stopped towards Grosvenor Square, and somehow the young man seemed to disappear. We were more than fifty yards away, and could not determine whether it was a man or a woman who emerged from the car and entered the house, but it looked like a fat little man. Then the car slid away. The pursuing young man had disappeared.

"He can't have been doing it for fun," said Tarlyon.

"Perhaps he's gone to have a bath," I suggested. For it was a very warm night, and running after motor-cars must have been a wet business.

"We'll see," said Tarlyon. We retraced our steps up Brook Street, and passed the house into which the occupant of the car had disappeared. It was a house like another, dark and silent; and as it stood almost at the corner we went round the corner into Grosvenor Square; at least, we were rounding the corner when a young man in a great hurry collided into us.

"Ah!" said Tarlyon.

"Sorry," said the stranger. I was right about the running —it had made his face very wet.

"So it's you!" said Tarlyon.

"Good-evening, gentlemen," said the Armenian, with a sort of furious courtesy. "If you will excuse me, I am in a hurry." He made to pass us.

"We noticed it," said Tarlyon. "In fact, we noticed nothing else."

"Damn!" snapped the Armenian. "So you saw me running?"

"So did he," I murmured, looking up Brook Street. A policeman was sauntering towards us.

"If you don't want to be asked any questions by the arm of the law," Tarlyon suggested, "you had better take a turn round the square with us."

"I won't move," the stranger muttered passionately. "I have found him at last—I won't move."

"But neither will he," I soothed him. "He's gone into the house. . . ."

"Did you see him go in?"

We nodded.

"Ah, but His Excellency is clever!" said the Armenian viciously.

We grabbed hold of him and hauled him round the square.

"Now," said Tarlyon, "what's all this Excellency nonsense?"

"*He* doesn't think it's nonsense," the young man muttered grimly.

"Look here," I said, "either this is a plot or it is not a plot. In either case you'll look rather an idiot, so——"

"You'd better confide in us," Tarlyon finished. "We, being English, have great sympathy with oppressed peoples——"

"I have noticed it," said the Armenian grimly. He was obviously a well-educated young man.

We had him walking between us, and he never even pretended that he liked our company.

"I suppose," said Tarlyon cattishly, "you've got bombs all over you."

"Sir!" snapped the Armenian.

"Sir to you," said Tarlyon.

"I was merely going to say," said the Armenian, "that in my opinion you are a fool. Do I look the kind of man to carry bombs? I favour the revolver."

"Oh, do you?" said I. Sarcastic I was, you understand.

He looked at me with those large, devilish eyes.

"And one shot," he said gently, "is always enough. . . ." I gave up.

"And where," asked Tarlyon reasonably, "does His Excellency come in?"

"He won't come in anywhere after to-night. His Excellency is going to die." And with that the Armenian suddenly stopped in his unwilling stride, and looked from one to the other of us. His broken nose made fantasy of his dark face, but I remember thinking that it must once have been a handsome enough face of its kind, for not even a broken nose made him quite ugly. He was as tall as Tarlyon, but slighter; his was a dangerous thinness. He addressed Tarlyon. He did not seem to have a very high opinion of me.

"Sir," he said—an Armenian habit, I suppose, that "sir"— "you have intruded your company on me, but I have accepted you. I have trusted you. I have treated you as gentlemen, being by nature an optimist, and I take it for granted that you will neither betray me nor try to deter me. You will understand the vigour of my purpose when I say that a young girl is concerned in this, that I have sworn a vow, and that if you were in my position you would do what I am going to do. Good-night, gentlemen. I hope we will meet again when I am less occupied with more important business."

Michael Arlen 1369

"Hold on," cried Tarlyon. "What on earth were you chasing that car for? And who the devil is His Excellency? We'd like to know, you see, so as to be able to pick him out from among the other murders in to-morrow's papers."

"Achmed Jzzit Pasha, the Young Turk," said the Armenian softly.

"Ah!" said George Tarlyon. "I see. Enver Pasha, Djemal Pasha, Talaat Pasha, and Achmed Jzzit Pasha, of the Committee of Union and Progress. I see. Talaat Pasha has already been killed, hasn't he?"

"Four of us," said the Armenian sombrely, "set out from Armenia last year, and each of us had a mission of revenge. One of us—you will remember?—shot and killed Talaat Pasha in a street in Berlin some months ago. Djemal Pasha was lately slain in Syria. Enver Pasha has fled to Bokhara. A murder has been arranged and will shortly take place in Bokhara. And I, the fourth, have at last found Achmed Jzzit, the foulest murderer of all. There is not an Armenian in the world who would not shoot Achmed Jzzit Pasha on sight if he had the chance—but Armenians who come to Western countries only too soon acquire nasty Western habits of money-grubbing and forget the glory there is in killing. But I, a Zeytounli, have never forgotten it. . . ."

"You speak English very well," I remarked. "Were you educated at an English public-school?"

"That, sir, is a matter of opinion. But even an English public-school could not make me forget that I am an Armenian, and that an Armenian's first business is to kill Turks; failing Turks, he may, of course, kill Kurds or ravish Circassian maidens——"

"Oh, not Circassians!" I pleaded.

"Well, Albanian," he allowed. "During the war I fought through the siege of Zeytoun, and then as an irregular under Andranik; and since the war I have pursued Achmed Jzzit Pasha—and to-night I have found him! He has been here in London for some months, but under an assumed name, for he knows that he is marked by the Dashnakists[1] and the Henchakists,[1] and he is afraid. It is my present business to cure him of his fear for ever." And with a wrench his arms were free of our gently restraining hands and he was off down the square.

[1] Armenian Revolutionary Societies.

But Tarlyon was swift, very swift; I panted up just as he was again "intruding himself" on the Armenian.

"You don't seem to realise," breathed Tarlyon, "that you can't enter a house in Brook Street, kill a Pasha, and get away——"

"I don't care if I get away or not," the other broke in fiercely. "Besides, my friend who killed Talaat in Berlin was acquitted. And I cannot believe that your English juries are as thick-headed as you would have me think. So will you please excuse me, sir?"

It was marvellous what venom that broken-nosed young man could put into a simple question!

"I've taken rather a fancy to you," murmured Tarlyon, "and I hate to think of your going off murdering Pashas. Come and have a drink instead, there's a good fellow."

"If I tell you," snapped the Armenian, "that there is a girl in that house, and that I must rescue that girl, then you will perhaps see your way to minding your own business."

"Has the Pasha got your girl?" I asked kindly.

"She is my sister, O fool," he said wearily. "And do you think I can allow my little sister to stay in that loathsome old creature's house one night more than I can help?"

"Collar him," said Tarlyon to me; and I grabbed the young man's other arm, though I didn't in the least want to, and again we began hauling him round the square. As I walked close to him I could feel a solid bulky thing in his hip-pocket, and I did not like the feeling.

"Now," said Tarlyon, very business-like, "what's all this about your sister?"

The Armenian almost screamed with impatience.

"Have I not told you all along that if you were in my position you would do exactly what I am going to do? Must I explain to you that my little sister was carried away by that old lecher before my eyes? Must I tell you how Zeytoun on the hill was at last shelled to dust by the batteries of two Army Corps under Achmed Jzzit Pasha, and how the Turks entered the smoking town and gave no quarter to man, woman or child? Must I, just to satisfy your wanton and asinine curiosity, ravage my heart with retailing how my father and mother were bayoneted before my eyes, and how I escaped only because those Turkish swine thought me already dead? Must I tell you how my little sister was carried away to the harem of Achmed Jzzit Pasha, who, on beholding her, swore a mighty swear that he would not rest from disembowelling Christians until he had ravished her? Did she give way? The slaying went on, day by day and night by night, so that a count of the leaves of the trees in your puny but not unattractive Green Park would make but a fraction of the number of the dead bodies that to this day lie rotting in the plain of Mush. An expert killer was Achmed Jzzit Pasha; and whether or not the natural bloodlust of the illiterate Osmanli was heightened by his oath to ravish my sister I do not know, but I do know that there has not been such a tale of dead Christians since Timur passed through the land to meet Bajazet. And that is the man who holds my sister in that house, while you detain me here with the vain questions and idiotic comments peculiar to the high-minded people of your patrician land. I followed him to Paris, but he escaped me. I found him in Bournemouth, but again I withheld my hand while I planned some way of rescuing Anaïs—fool that I was! But the idea in my head was that I must first get the girl to some place of safety—and then to come back, slay him, and pay whatever is the penalty in your country for killing a loathsome animal. But now I have realised that there is no other way of rescuing Anaïs but by killing him first. Always, wherever he goes, he keeps her locked in a room next to his, and thus it must be in this house. Bestial fancies seethe in his brain, wherefore he sleeps lightly. And while the night in dwindling, here I stand satisfying your idle curiosity. You really must excuse me now, gentlemen."

"But hold on!" cried Tarlyon. "Why kill the wretched man at all? Why not rescue your sister with the charming name and let the Pasha go on being a Pasha until he dies a horrible death by reason of those bestial fancies which you mentioned? He won't dare come after her—and I don't see much point in getting your sister back if you have got to swing for it more or less at once. Eh, Ralph?"

"Quite right," said I. "Come and have a drink instead."

"This is no time for drink," snapped the Armenian. "The night is dwindling—and how can I desist from killing him when, as I have told you, I cannot get into her room without awaking him? And it stands to reason that as soon as I see him I shall also see red, and kill—as I must, by reason of my vow and by order of the Dashnakists. As I have told you, I would have preferred to have got Anaïs out of the house first, but that seems impossible. . . ."

Tarlyon opened his mouth and closed it. I knew what was passing in Tarlyon's mind, and I thought I would let it pass, so that he might think again. But then he re-opened his mouth, and this is what he said:

"My friend and I," he said, "might perhaps consider giving you a little assistance, if in return you gave us a promise——"

"I promise nothing!"

"Drat the boy!" said Tarlyon. "What I wish to point out is that, if my friend and I help you to get your sister out of that house, you must drop this killing business. We will contrive some way of keeping His Excellency quiet while you rescue your sister—but you must give us your word of honour, or some efficient substitute, that you will not come back and murder the wretched Pasha. Now, I want no back-chat about it— either you will or you will not."

"But I am bound to the Dashnakists!" cried the Armenian; rather regretfully, I thought.

"Blast the Dashnakists!" said Tarlyon. "Yes or no?"

"I promise," said the Armenian suddenly.

My native common sense now got the better of me.

"You seem to take it for granted that we just walk into the house. How do we get in?"

"This cuts windows like a knife," said the Armenian, showing us in the palm of his hands a glittering little thing like a toy dagger. "An Argentine invention."

"The matter will be further facilitated," said Tarlyon, "by our first getting my car, which is opposite Claridge's, and driving in it to the front door. My reason for this step is that no policeman would dare suspect anything wrong in a house while a Rolls-Royce is standing outside it. Especially, Ralph, when your manly appearance is decorating the driving-seat. . . ."

"I shall be in the house," I said firmly. Not that I wanted to be—but one always says those things, and one always says them firmly.

"Perhaps that would be better," said the Armenian. "It will certainly take the two of you to keep His Excellency quiet while I break in the first locked door I see and get Anaïs. And a Rolls-Royce car is, I understand, even more impressive empty than when some one is in it—people make it seem possible."

We got the car and drove bravely to the house. We passed two policemen at the corner of Davies Street, but they were not interested in us. I must say burglary is easy when one has a large and rich car to do it from. . . .

Like all Mayfair houses, this had a tradesmen's entrance; through a little gate on the right of the few steps to the front door, down some steps, and into a little area where was the kitchen door and a window.

"Wait in the car," said the dark young man, and vanished down to the area. We heard a very faint scratching, one little wicked word, a little more scratching; and then the lights blazed up through the glass above the front door, and it was opened. The Armenian stood in the lighted doorway as though he owned the house. I admired him.

Tarlyon's first words when we were in the hall of the house were: "Give me your gun, you charming atrocity."

The Armenian surrendered his revolver without a word; he only sighed. Then he marshalled us.

"Very quiet," he whispered. "And very quick. We must try the upstairs rooms, to see which is his bedroom. One touch on the door will wake him, so you must muffle him at once, else he will rouse the servants. In the meanwhile I will find my sister; then I will take her straight out of the house, and we will await you in the car. I will blow your horn twice, to show that I am awaiting you. It will be kind of you, then, to drive us to Mr. Ritz's hotel in Piccadilly, where, perhaps, with your influence, we may get my sister a lodging for the night. But, remember, keep a tight hold on Achmed Jzzit until I blow the horn—muffle him straightway and let him not open his mouth, else he will bring the whole neighbourhood down on us. Let us begin."

We began with a bit of luck—or so it seemed. Having tiptoed up to the first landing, the very first door we touched held the lightly sleeping Pasha. We knew he was there by the howl that followed our touching the door-knob—indeed, he was a light sleeper, that man of bestial fancies! But we gave him no time to make a real noise; we leapt into the room; I switched on the light, Tarlyon leapt on bed and Pasha, I leapt after Tarlyon, and in a second we held him, making smothered howling noises under the bedclothes. We had not even had time to see if he was young or old, but the shape of him suggested that he was older than most people. His was, however, an active and restless shape. We were very gentle with him, almost too gentle, for once a distinct howl issued from somewhere under the sheets.

"Steady," said George Tarlyon to the restless shape.

"You'll throttle yourself," said George Tarlyon.

To prevent him from doing that we, with a sudden and well-concerted movement, unscrewed his head and muffled him with a handkerchief. We looked upon his face for the first time.

"You're a nasty, cruel old man," said George Tarlyon.

Achmed Jzzit Pasha looked all that the Armenian had said he was, and more. A fierce old face it was that looked murder at us. His eyes, under white, bushy eyebrows, were frantic and furious, and never for a second did he cease to struggle. I thought of that fine old Turkish warrior of the last century, the man of Plevna, Osman Pasha; this old man is of the same breed, I thought.

We had so far heard nothing of the Armenian; but that Achmed Jzzit Pasha realised that we two were only accessories was evident, for not even his struggling with us concealed the fact that he was listening, listening intently.

A slight noise, as of a drawer hastily banged, came from the next room. It was only a small noise, but it had a mighty effect on the old slayer of men. His eyes simply tore at us, his fat little body heaved frantically, he bit my finger in trying to howl—he went quite mad, that violent old Turk. I admonished him severely:

"It's only little Anaïs packing up to go away with her brother," I told him; but that old Turk knew not resignation nor repentance, and still we had gently to battle with him.

"He's an infernally long time about it," grumbled Tarlyon at last—and at that very moment the horn outside blew twice. We welcomed it.

"Now," said Tarlyon to the heaving old man, "we are about to release you. Your girl has flown, so it's too late for you to make a noise. So don't." And for form's sake he showed the revolver, though I never saw a man who looked less likely to use it. "You may not realise it," he added severely, "but we have saved your life. After the first shock has worn off you will thank two disinterested men for having saved you from the wrath of an Armenian."

With another sudden and well-concerted movement we let go. The Pasha did not make a noise. It was evident he realised that it was too late to make a noise. But in the next few seconds he revealed, for a Turk, an astonishing knowledge of the baser words and idioms of the English language. Then he leapt out of bed, a funny little creature in pink flannel pyjamas, and rushed out of the room. Breathless, we found him in the next room.

Now I have very little acquaintance with girls' bedrooms, but a glance was sufficient to show me that no girl alive could have a bedroom like that. There was no bed in it, and very little else; just a thing like a tallboy, but made of steel, or so it looked: and that, if I may say so, had certainly been ravished. . . .

Then the old man really began to howl, and we hadn't the heart to stop him. He howled himself back to the bedroom, and we followed him, looking and feeling like all the things he said we were.

"But aren't you Achmed Jzzit Pasha?" I pleaded. But the life had suddenly gone out of him; he sat on the edge of the bed.

"My name is Wagstaffe," he said weakly, "and I have the finest collection of Roman coins in the country. Or rather, I had. My son, Michael Wagstaffe, has them now—thanks to you two idiots!"

Tarlyon had an idea which took him to the window; I had the same idea, and followed him. We looked down upon the face of Brook Street, and behold! it was empty. Never was a Rolls-Royce car with lamps alight so invisible. We went back to Mr. Wagstaffe on the edge of the bed.

"We are sorry," I muttered, but he seemed not to hear us. George Tarlyon is usually a fine upstanding fellow, and some people have thought him handsome, but now he looked as though he had seen horrid spectres after dining entirely on *pâté de foie gras*.

Mr. Wagstaffe was whispering, almost to himself: "Two years ago, when I drove him out of the house, he swore that one day he would steal my coins. And now he has stolen my coins. I always knew he would keep his word, for he is a devil. And he always knew that, come what might, I would not prosecute my son for a thief. . . . My Roman coins!" And Mr. Wagstaffe wept.

We explained our position to him. We gave him a brief outline of the facts. We begged him to understand. We pointed out that if his son really had been an Armenian and if he had really been Achmed Jazzit Pasha we had undoubtedly saved his life. I couldn't help thinking that he ought to be grateful to us, but I didn't say that.

He seemed to find a little solace in our discomfiture.

"Ah, he's a clever boy, Michael," sighed Mr. Wagstaffe. "He is always on the lookout for what he calls the Mugs. I gather that you two gentlemen are Mugs—the same, perhaps, as what are known in America as Guys. But I, his father, can assure you that he is not an Armenian; nor has he ever been nearer to Armenia than the Bankruptcy Court, but he has been there twice. He calls himself the cavalier of the streets, but when he is up to any of his tricks he disguises himself as an Armenian—the disguise consisting merely of his saying he is an Armenian. It's so simple, he says, for the Mugs believe him at once, on the ground that no one would say he was an Armenian if he wasn't. I have only been back from America a week, and he must have been searching all London for me. He probably saw me at the theatre this evening, and was going to raid my house alone when you two intelligent gentlemen got in his way. But he is not a bad boy really—he's got ideas, that's what it is; and also Mugs have an irresistible fascination for him. Take your case, for instance. I have no doubt but that he will be ready to return me my coins in exchange for a cheque—though, of course, that depends on the cheque. And I can see, gentlemen, that you are eager to show your regret for breaking into my house and assaulting my person by offering to pay the cheque yourselves. I thank you; though, indeed, it is the least you can do, and an infinitely more convenient way of settling the matter than wearisome arguments in a police-court—provided, of course, that housebreaking and assault are matters for argument. I have never yet heard they were. . . ."

I giggled. I simply couldn't help it.

"That's all very well," said Tarlyon, "but what about my car?"

"What is the matter with your car?" asked Mr. Wagstaffe gently.

"There's so damn little the matter with it," snapped Tarlyon, "that it's probably half-way down the Dover road by now."

"Ah," said Mr. Wagstaffe wearily. "I see. Cars have an irresistible fascination for Michael. I see. I am sorry. Was it a good car? . . ."

"Pity," said Mr. Wagstaffe. "A great pity. He may, of course, return it. He may. You cannot, of course, compel him to, for it would be difficult for you, in your position, to put the police on him. But he may return it on his own. Michael is not a bad boy, really. He will, I am sure, communicate with me as to what I will offer for the return of my coins. I will then give him the cheque you have so kindly promised to post to me to-night, and perhaps he will soften also as regards your car and return it to you. Naturally, he will expect your cheque to approximate to the value of your car—say, half its value. Michael is something of an expert about the value of cars. That's why I said it was a pity, sir, a pity that your car was not a cheap car. But I am sure you will have no difficulty in finding a taxi-cab home. They are so abundant in Grosvenor Square that my sleep is often disturbed by them. . . ."

The rest of the story is not at all interesting. George Tarlyon's car was finally returned, and George Tarlyon is sorry that Mr. Michael Wagstaffe's nose is already broken.

Martin Armstrong

BIOGRAPHY

A STUDY IN CIRCUMSTANTIAL EVIDENCE

JOHN CAMPION followed the hotel porter up the stairs which seemed almost pitch dark after the white glare of the piazza. The porter unlocked a door, ushered Campion into a bedroom, deposited his bag upon a wooden stand, and departed, closing the door behind him.

Campion went to the window and opened the green shutters. Dazzling autumn sunshine flooded the room, and, looking out, he received the sudden impression that he was standing on the brink of a precipice, for, sheer below his window, the plain, covered with miniature vineyards, miniature fields, miniature trees, and streaked by miniature roads like chalk-lines on a slate, spread far and wide, curving at last into a wall of violet hills which rose peak above peak like wavecrests on a windy sea.

The room looked cool and spacious with its high, elaborately-painted ceiling, smooth white sheets and pillows, and a pleasing profusion of clean towels. He could detect only one fault: the servant had omitted to sweep the empty hearth into which his predecessor had thrown a quantity of tocacco-ash and several cigar-ends. He dropped into an easy-chair, feeling suddenly that he was very tired. His heart had been troubling him again in the train, and he reflected that he had been foolish to carry his bag to the station that morning.

Campion was a man of few friends. No one of his eminence ever kept himself more aloof from his contemporaries. To the public he was known by his books only: every detail of his life and habits and even his personal appearance were wrapped in complete mystery. A hatred of tobacco and a perfect irresponsiveness to music were among the characteristics of a temperament pharisaic, fastidious and cynical, which, in his work, revealed itself in a terse, mordant style, a vehicle for sharp definition, exact criticism, pungent wit, and a scepticism which delighted in playing havoc among the conventionally religious.

When he had sufficiently rested, Campion proceeded to unpack. His opened suit-case displayed perfection in the art of packing, and as he carefully removed each article from its place in the bag, he disposed it with extreme exactitude in its appointed place in drawer or cupboard. Three or four paper-backed books were placed symmetrically on a table near the bed. Between finger and thumb he lifted from the bag a bundle of long Italian cigars, sniffed them with an expression of disgusted curiosity, and placed them in a drawer. The next article to be unpacked was a Bible, newly bound in an elaborately tooled Florentine binding. Campion opened it. The inside was much used: there were pencillings here and there and on a loose sheet of paper were various references headed "Helpful Texts." With a contemptuous shrug Campion placed it in the drawer beside the cigars and removed from the bag a large, thin volume on which the title "Beethoven's Sonatas" was printed in gold. He opened the volume and glanced uncomprehendingly at the musical notation.

When all had been thus unpacked and disposed as precisely and impeccably as one of his own essays, Campion took a writing-case from a drawer and proceeded to write a letter. *I arrived here an hour ago*, he wrote, *and after four days here I shall start for England. I have already executed all your commissions. Your fifty abominable cigars are bought and have already impregnated all my linen with their disgusting stench. While in Florence I had your wife's Bible bound according to her orders with the result that it now looks as inviting as a novel by D'Annunzio. By the way, I found inside it a loose half-sheet of prescriptions (for spiritual consumption only) which I have preserved. When at Assisi yesterday I acquired a sort of Christmas Card containing a leaf from one of St. Francis's miraculous rose-trees. There is a printed guarantee to the effect that excellent results will be obtained from the leaf if used with faith. I have enclosed it in the Bible. For myself, I prefer the old-fashioned mustard-leaf which is equally efficacious with or without faith, since it produces rapid con-*

viction by certain compelling properties of its own. When in Florence I happened to pick up a volume of Beethoven's Sonatas, copiously annotated in pencil by a certain Rubinstein. The acquaintance who pointed it out to me assured me that Rubinstein was a famous pianist and that the volume was something of a curiosity. I am therefore bringing it home for Muriel on the strict understanding that she refrains from playing the contents while I am in the house. Thanks for your list of younger Italian writers. Obedient to your exhortations, I have bought a volume or two of Papini and some others. Papini's "Un Uomo Finito," which I shall finish in bed to-night, I find extremely tedious. The feverish verbosity tires and the entire lack of restraint sickens me. I have so far found no one to my taste among these younger Italians.

Having addressed and stamped this letter, Campion posted it in the hall as he went down to dinner. At dinner he found himself sharing a table with the only other Englishman in the hotel, a well-informed fellow and a good talker. Campion liked him, and after dinner they continued their conversation over coffee in the lounge. But Campion's heart was bothering him again. Clearly, he told himself, slightly scared, he ought not to have carried his bag to the station that morning. He would have to take it easy during the next few days. He rose heavily from his chair and, ordering his *café-au-lait* for ten next morning, went slowly and carefully up to bed.

In his bedroom he saw the Italian books on the table near the bed, *Un Uomo Finito* on top of the rest. The thought of them filled him with weariness and depression. He could certainly not stand any of that blustering stuff tonight, but he would have his notebook and pencil near him in case of sleeplessness. But the notebook could not be found. He did not even remember unpacking it. Campion invariably folded the notebook inside some article of clothing: he had done so that morning when packing, and at once realised that it must now be in one of the drawers, still wrapped in clothes. The first drawer that he tried to open stuck, the struggle involved in opening it irritated him, and when he got it open he did not find the notebook. These occurrences repeated themselves in the case of the second drawer and Campion, losing all patience, pursued a frenzied and unsuccessful search through both, leaving the contents in wild confusion. As they had refused to open, so both drawers refused to shut, and it was only after reproducing a stage thunderstorm that he succeeded in closing them. He undressed, feeling breathless and upset, and as he unfolded his pajamas the notebook fell out of the jacket. In stooping to pick it up he noticed that the cigar-ends still lay in the empty fire-place. How disgusting! Feeling very ill-tempered, he got into bed and switched out the light. . . .

When the waiter knocked at the door the next morning with the *café-au-lait* Campion did not reply. The waiter entered and put down the tray on the table near the bed. The English gentleman was asleep. In the twilight of the shuttered room the waiter could see the motionless hands and face and the disordered bed-clothes. He went to the window and opened the shutters. When he turned again towards the bed the waiter received a shock, for the English gentleman was not asleep, but dead. The fact was immediately, appallingly obvious. The waiter glanced hurriedly at the dressing-table, helped himself to a couple of gold studs, and left the room, locking the door behind him.

When the necessary investigations were made it was thought best that the other Englishman in the hotel should be present. It was only after a considerable search among Campion's effects that his identity was eventually established.

In England the news of Campion's death produced those results which always follow the death of an eminent writer. Monthly and weekly publications and dailies with literary pretensions printed critical articles, more or less detailed, about Campion's work. Here and there a few rare personal reminiscences appeared, and that other Englishman who had seen Campion both alive and dead in the Italian hotel where he died was pressed to contribute his experiences. So little was known of Campion himself, it was pointed out, that it became the duty of everyone who had anything to tell about the great man to tell it. The Englishman, thus exhorted, contributed his experiences. After describing his dinner and subsequent conversation with Campion, the Englishman continued as follows:

It may seem strange that one who had known Campion for not more than two hours should presume to write about his life and habits, but the fact that it was my melancholy duty to be present at the inspection of his personal belongings an hour after his death and in the room where he still lay as he had died, made it possible for me, by reason of this sudden intimate dip into his privacy, to learn a few details not perhaps generally known concerning his tastes and habits.

Like many people of artistic temperament, Campion was desperately untidy. His clothing was flung pell-mell into drawers in a disorder which one would almost have said was deliberate. As I have already stated, Campion did not smoke after our dinner together, so that I was a little surprised to discover that he was an inveterate smoker. In his bedroom, cigar-ash and several cigar-ends lay in the grate and on the table was a bundle of at least fifty Toscani.

It will surprise those familiar with his writings to learn that actually Campion was an intensely religious man.—He carried with him on his travels a Bible which gave evidence of continual use: many verses were pencil-marked and a carefully-written list of references headed "Helpful Texts" appeared on a loose sheet in the book. The Bible was evidently one of his most cherished possessions, for it had recently been rebound in an expensive Florentine binding. Enclosed in it was an illuminated card from the church of the Porziumcula, doubtless brought by him from Assisi on the day of his death.

Campion was an enthusiastic student of modern Italian literature. By his bed were found two books by Giovanni Papini, whose novel "Un Uomo Finito" he was reading at the time of his death. Inside this book, marking the page he had reached, was a long list of other Italian writers of the younger school.

No one would suspect from his books that Campion was a keen musician. Yet among his luggage he carried a volume of Beethoven's Sonatas which gave evidence, like the Bible, of much use and was, moreover, copiously annotated in pencil. Whether these notes were his own or those of a music-master, the fact remains that he had made a close study of the Sonatas of the greatest of musicians.

It is facts like these that remind us once more how rash it is to attempt to deduce too literally a writer's personality from his writings, showing us, as they do, how large a portion of an artist's character may be entirely unapparent in his art. . . .

Perhaps none of Campion's old friends ever saw this interesting fragment; at least they never publicly commented on it: and when, some years later, a well-known writer was compiling what is now the standard biography of John Campion, the details of this article, in view of the extraordinary scarcity of information relating to the man, as distinguished from the writer, proved to be of inestimable value.

THE POET
AND THE MANDRILL

In a cage outside the monkey house at the Zoo there lives the Mandrill, a beast most hideous before, having great protruding fangs and a sour, dishonest countenance: but behind he is lovely as the dawn, a wonder of rose and violet.

And one day there stood before the cage many ladies wearing stays: and there were gentlemen in silk hats, the shoulders of whose coats were padded lest they should appear as the Lord had made them. And the mandrill went to and fro in his cage, and he was very hideous: and anon he turned about, and at once he was very beautiful.

And those that looked at him exclaimed at his ugliness, but of his beauty they said not a word, for, one and all, they were proper persons.

And there came into their midst a poet. And it so happened when the mandrill turned himself backside foremost that the poet's heart leapt within him, and with a loud voice he praised the beauty of those colours, saying, "Goodness, but how exquisite, to be sure."

Then all the people gathered about the cage looked wanly upon one another as folk having a secret sorrow: and they all departed in different directions, and the poet and the mandrill were alone.

But the poet, on returning home, wrote a poem in praise of colour, lovely and radiant as a Mexican fire-opal. And the folk who had stood before the cage read the poem and were amazed: but they never knew the source of the inspiration of that poem nor that the poet was he who had grieved them at the Zoo.

William Gerhardi

THE BIG DRUM

The brass band played *Im Köpfle zwei Augle,* and it seemed
to her that the souls of these men were like notes of this music,
crying for something elusive, for something in vain. To blare
forth one's love on a brass trumpet! An earnest of one's high
endeavour fallen short through the inadequate matter of
brass; but withal in these abortive notes one felt the presence
of the heights the instrument would reach, alas, if it but could!
It touched her to the heart. She would have liked her Otto
to play the trumpet instead of the big drum. It seemed more
romantic. Otto was not a bit romantic. He was a soldier all
right, but he looked more like a man who had started life as
a shoemaker's apprentice, had grown old, and was still a shoemaker's apprentice. The band played well—a compact synthetic body—but Otto was a forlorn figure who watched the
proceedings with sustained and patient interest and was suffering by them, every now and then, to raise his drumstick
and to give a solitary, judicious "Bang!" And he—a tall
gaunt man—seemed as though he were ashamed of his small
part. And as she watched him she felt a pang of pity for
herself: wedded to him, she would be forgotten, while life,
indifferent, strode by; and no one in the world would care
whether she had her share of happiness before she died. And
the music brought this out acutely, as if along the hard stone-
paved indifference of life it dragged, dragged on excruciat-
ing its living bleeding soul. It spoke of loneliness, of laughter,
of the pathos, pity and futility of life.

She watched them. The bayonets at their side. The military badges of rank. The hard discipline. And the music
seemed to say, "Stop! What are you doing? Why are you doing this?" And thoughts flowed into her mind. Of soldiers

dreaming on a Sunday afternoon. A fierce old corporal, of whom everyone was afraid, talking to her of children and of daisies. Soldiers who, too, had dreams in long waves—of what? she did not know—but not this. And the men who stood up and blew the brass trumpets seemed to say, and the shining trumpets themselves seemed to say: "We were not born for the Army; we were born for something better—though Heaven only knows what it is!"

That was so. Undeniably so. Yet she wished it were otherwise. It helped to make allowances for Otto. Whatever else he lacked, it made her think at least he had a soul. But to be wedded for life to the big drum! She did not fancy the idea. It didn't seem a proper career. But Otto showed no sign of *wanting* to "get on"—even in the orchestra. The most exasperating thing about it all was that Otto showed no sign of even *trying!* She had asked him if he would not, in time, "move on" and take over—say, the double-bass. He did not seem to think it either feasible or necessary. Or *necessary!* He had been with the big drum for close on twelve years. "It's a good drum," he had said. And that was all.

There was no . . . "go" in him. That was it: no go. It was no use denying it. As she watched him—gaunt and spectacled —she wished Otto were more of a man and less of an old maid. The conductor, a boozer with a fat red face full of pimples, some dead and dried up, others still flourishing, was a gallant —every inch a man. He had the elasticity and suppleness and military alertness of the continental military man. She could not tell his rank from the stripes on his sleeves, but thought he must be a major. His heels were high and tipped with india-rubber, and so were straight and smart, but his trousers lacked the footstrap to keep them in position—poor dilapidated Austrian Army! How low it had sunk! Nevertheless they were tight and narrow and showed off the major's calves to advantage. He wore a pince-nez, but a rimless kind, through which gazed a pair of not altogether innocent eyes. But a man and a leader of men. While Otto had no rubber on his heels. His heels looked eaten away. He wore a pair of spectacles through which he peered from afar at his neighbour's music-stand, and at the appointed time—not one-tenth of a second too late or too early—down came the drumstick with the long-awaited "Bang!" So incidental, so contemptible was Otto's part that, in addition to handling the drum, he had to turn the pages for the man who played the cymbals. It seemed to her humiliating. It was very wrong that Otto had no music-stand of his own.

He smiled shyly, and she turned away, annoyed. The little modiste walked on, meeting the stream of people who promenaded the path surrounding the bandstand; a man on high heels, three girls with a pinched look, a famous Tyrolese basso with a long ruddy beard, a *jeune premier* with whiskers and hair like a wig, whose look appeared to imply: "Here am I." Innsbruck looked morose that Sunday morning, and the military band in the park executed music that was tattered, gross, a little common, yet compelling, even like the daily fare of life. Oh, why were there no heroes? Of course she would have loved to be dominated. That's what men were for. She was a womanly woman. From Vienna. Exalted, brimming over with life. These men of the Tyrol! And as for Otto? Why, she could have only waved her hand!

She began to wonder whether she had not really better break it off with him. If men would but realise how little was required from them. Only an outward gesture of romance: a touch sufficed, the rest would be supplied by woman's powerful imagination. Not even so much. A mere abstention from the cruder forms of clumsiness, a surface effort to conceal one's feeblest worst. A mere semblance of mastery, a glimpse of a will. In short, anything at all that would provide the least excuse for loving him as she so wished to do. A minute she stood, thinking. "A minimum. Hardly as much." There passed along the man on high heels, the three girls with the pinched look, the Tyrolese basso with the long ruddy beard, the *jeune premier* with whiskers and hair like a wig, whose look seemed to say, "Here am I"; then again the man on high heels, the three girls with the pinched look, the Tyrolese singer, and again the "jeune premier" whose look implied, "Here am I." They walked round and round as if the park were a cage and there was nothing to do but walk round—with heads bent, lifeless, sullenly resolute. And again there came along the man on high heels. "The minimum of a minimum. . . ."

The music resumed. She consulted her programme. Item 7. Potpourri from the operette *Die Fledermaus* by Johann Strauss. She returned to the stand, prepared to give her fiancé another chance. Otto's part, as before, was contemptible, more contemptible than before. He was inactive. He smiled shyly. She coloured. And, looking at him, she knew. She knew it was no use, her love could not bridge the chasm. He was despised by the rest of the band. A stick-in-the-mud. Not a man. A poor fish. Not for her. . . .

The potpourri, as if suddenly turning the corner, broke out into a resounding march, and behold, the big drum now led the way. Bang! bang! bang! bang! Clearly he whacked, never once missing the chance; and the man with the cymbals, as if one heart and brain operated their limbs, clashed the cymbals in astounding unison, the big drum pounding away, pounding away, without cease or respite. And the trumpeters smiled, as who might say: "Good old big drum! You have come into your own at last!" Bang! bang! bang! bang! The big drum had got loud and excited. And all the people standing around looked as though a great joy had come into their lives, and if they had not been a little shy of each other they would have set out and marched in step with the music, taken up *any* cause and, if only because the music implied that all men were brothers, gone forth if need be and butchered another body of brothers, to the tearing, gladdening strains of the march, (since it is not known from what rational cause men could have marched to the war). And if in the park of the neighbouring town there were just such a band with just such a drum which played this same music, the people of the neighbouring town would have marched to this music and exterminated this town. The conductor, like a driver who, having urged his horse over the hill, leans back and leaves the rest to the horse, conceded the enterprise to the drummer, as if the hard, intricate work were now over and he was taking it easy; his baton moved perfunctorily in the wake of the drum, he looked round and acknowledged the greetings of friends with gay, informal salutes of the left hand, his bland smile freely admitting to all that it was no longer himself but the drum which led them to victory. Or rather, the hard fight had already been won and these, behold, were the happy results! Bang! bang! bang! bang! Strangers passed smiles of intimate recognition, old men nodded reminiscently, small boys gazed with rapt eyes, women looked sweet and bright-eyed, ready to oblige with a kiss; while the big drum, conscious of his splendid initiative, pounded away without cease or respite.

"Wonderful! Beautiful!" said the public surrounding them. And thought:

"Noise is a good thing."

The band had described the first circle and was repeating it with added gusto and deliberation. The drum and the cymbals were pounding, pounding their due through the wholly inadequate blazing of brass. But these did not mind: "Every dog has his day"—and they followed the lead of the drum. He led them. He—Otto! Her Otto was leading them. God! Merciful Virgin! What had she done to deserve such happiness? Otto! . . . And she had doubted him, thought there was no "go" in him. No *go!* She burnt red with shame at the mere thought of it. He was all "go." And didn't he make them go, too, the whole lot of them? How he led them! Puffing, the sweat streaming down their purple faces, they blazed away till their cheeks seemed ready to burst, but Otto out-drummed them—annihilated their efforts. He—Otto! O, God! Watching him, people could hardly keep still. But that none of them stirred and all of them wanted to, added piquancy to the illusion of motion. They stood rooted—while the drum carried on for them: Bang! bang! bang! bang!

"Marvelous!" sighed the public around them.

Her Otto—cock of the walk! She could scarcely believe her eyes. Standing in front of the crowd, only a few paces from his side and raising herself on her toes ever so gently in rhythm with the music, so that by the very tininess of her movements she seemed to be sending added impetus into the band, as if indeed, she were pressing with her little feet some invisible pump, she scanned his face with tenderness, in dumb adoration. And Otto at the drum must have felt it, for, at this turn, he put new life into his thundering whacks: *Bang! bang! bang! bang!* he toiled, and the conductor, as if divining what was afoot, at that moment accelerated the pace of the march.

"Bravo, bravo!" said the people surrounding them.

There was no doubt about it. This was Art. The unerring precision. The wonderful touch. Otto! . . . . Otto, as never before, whacked the big drum, whacked it in excitement, in a frenzy, in transcending exaltation. Thundering bangs! And now she knew—what she couldn't have dreamed—she knew it by his face. Otto was a hero. A leader of men. Something fluttered in her breast, as though a bird had flown in, ready to fly out.

"Now it's all over," thought the people, "and we are going home to lunch." And everyone smiled and felt very happy and gay. A sort of prolonged accelerated thundering of the big drum, and then one tremendous BANG!

The thing was over. The conductor raised a bent hand to the peak of his cap, acknowledging the applause. The bird in her fluttered more wildly than ever. She wanted to cry out, but her throat would not obey. She clutched at her heaving breast with trembling fingers. "My love," she thought. "My king! My captain!——"

Katherine Mansfield

PICTURES

EIGHT o'clock in the morning. Miss Ada Moss lay in a black iron bedstead, staring up at the ceiling. Her room, a Bloomsbury top-floor back, smelled of soot and face powder and the paper of fried potatoes she brought in for supper the night before.

"Oh, dear," thought Miss Moss, "I am cold. I wonder why it is that I always wake up so cold in the mornings now. My knees and feet and my back—especially my back; it's like a sheet of ice. And I always was such a one for being warm in the old days. It's not as if I was skinny—I'm just the same full figure that I used to be. No, it's because I don't have a good hot dinner in the evenings."

A pageant of Good Hot Dinners passed across the ceiling, each of them accompanied by a bottle of Nourishing Stout. . . .

"Even if I were to get up now," she thought, "and have a sensible substantial breakfast . . ." A pageant of Sensible Substantial Breakfasts followed the dinners across the ceiling, shepherded by an enormous, white, uncut ham. Miss Moss shuddered and disappeared under the bedclothes. Suddenly, in bounced the landlady.

"There's a letter for you, Miss Moss."

"Oh," said Miss Moss, far too friendly, "thank you very much, Mrs. Pine. It's very good of you, I'm sure, to take the trouble."

"No trouble at all," said the landlady. "I thought perhaps it was the letter you'd been expecting."

"Why," said Miss Moss brightly, "yes, perhaps it is." She put her head on one side and smiled vaguely at the letter. "I shouldn't be surprised."

The landlady's eyes popped. "Well, I should, Miss Moss," said she, "and that's how it is. And I'll trouble you to open it, if you please. Many is the lady in my place as would have done it for you and have been within her rights. For things can't go on like this, Miss Moss, no indeed they can't. What with week in week out and first you've got it and then you haven't, and then it's another letter lost in the post or another manager down at Brighton but will be back on Tuesday for certain— I'm fair sick and tired and I won't stand it no more. Why should I, Miss Moss, I ask you, at a time like this, with prices flying up in the air and my poor dear lad in France? My sister Eliza was only saying to me yesterday—'Minnie,' she says, 'you're too soft-hearted. You could have let that room time and time again,' says she, 'and if people won't look after themselves in times like these, nobody else will,' she says. 'She may have had a College eddication and sung in West End concerts,' says she, 'but if your Lizzie says what's true,' she says, 'and she's washing her own wovens and drying them on the towel rail, it's easy to see where the finger's pointing. And it's high time you had done with it,' says she."

Miss Moss gave no sign of having heard this. She sat up in bed, tore open her letter and read:

"Dear Madam.
    Yours to hand. Am not producing at present, but have filed photo for future ref.

                                        Yours truly,
                                        BACKWASH FILM CO."

This letter seemed to afford her peculiar satisfaction; she read it through twice before replying to the landlady.

"Well, Mrs. Pine, I think you'll be sorry for what you said. This is from a manager, asking me to be there with evening dress at ten o'clock next Saturday morning."

But the landlady was too quick for her. She pounced, secured the letter.

"Oh, is it! Is it indeed!" she cried.

"Give me back that letter. Give it back to me at once, you bad, wicked woman," cried Miss Moss, who could not get out of bed because her night-dress was slit down the back. "Give me back my private letter." The landlady began slowly backing out of the room, holding the letter to her buttoned bodice.

"So it's come to this, has it?" said she. "Well, Miss Moss, if I don't get my rent at eight o'clock tonight, we'll see who's a bad, wicked woman—that's all." Here she nodded, mysteriously. "And I'll keep this letter." Here her voice rose. "It will be a pretty little bit of evidence!" And here it fell, sepulchral, "*My lady.*"

The door banged and Miss Moss was alone. She flung off the bed clothes, and sitting by the side of the bed, furious and shivering, she stared at her fat white legs with their great knots of greeny-blue veins.

"Cockroach! That's what she is. She's a cockroach!" said Miss Moss. "I could have her up for snatching my letter—I'm sure I could." Still keeping on her nightdress she began to drag on her clothes.

"Oh, if I could only pay that woman, I'd give her a piece of my mind that she wouldn't forget. I'd tell her off proper." She went over to the chest of drawers for a safety-pin, and seeing herself in the glass she gave a vague smile and shook her head. "Well, old girl," she murmured, "you're up against it this time, and no mistake." But the person in the glass made an ugly face at her.

"You silly thing," scolded Miss Moss. "Now what's the good of crying: you'll only make your nose red. No, you get dressed and go out and try your luck—that's what you've got to do."

She unhooked her vanity bag from the bedpost, rooted in it, shook it, turned it inside out.

"I'll have a nice cup of tea at an A B C to settle me before I go anywhere," she decided. "I've got one and thrippence—yes, just one and three."

Ten minutes later, a stout lady in blue serge, with a bunch of artificial "parmas" at her bosom, a black hat covered with purple pansies, white gloves, boots with white uppers, and a vanity bag containing one and three, sang in a low contralto voice:

> Sweet-heart, remember when days are forlorn
> It al-ways is dar-kest before the dawn.

But the person in the glass made a face at her, and Miss Moss went out. There were grey crabs all the way down the street slopping water over grey stone steps. With his strange, hawking cry and the jangle of the cans the milk boy went his rounds. Outside Brittweiler's Swiss House he made a splash, and an old brown cat without a tail appeared from nowhere, and began greedily and silently drinking up the spill. It gave Miss Moss a queer feeling to watch—a sinking—as you might say.

But when she came to the A B C she found the door propped open; a man went in and out carrying trays of rolls, and there was nobody inside except a waitress doing her hair and the cashier unlocking the cash-boxes. She stood in the middle of the floor but neither of them saw her.

"My boy came home last night," sang the waitress.

"Oh, I say—how topping for you!" gurgled the cashier.

"Yes, wasn't it," sang the waitress. "He brought me a sweet little brooch. Look, it's got 'Dieppe' written on it."

The cashier ran across to look and put her arm round the waitress' neck.

"Oh, I say—how topping for you."

"Yes, isn't it," said the waitress. "O-oh, he is brahn. 'Hullo,' I said, 'hullo, old mahogany.'"

"Oh, I say," gurgled the cashier, running back into her cage and nearly bumping into Miss Moss on the way. "You are a *treat!*" Then the man with the rolls came in again, swerving past her.

"Can I have a cup of tea, Miss?" she asked.

But the waitress went on doing her hair. "Oh," she sang, "we're not *open* yet." She turned round and waved her comb at the cashier.

"*Are* we, dear?"

"Oh, no," said the cashier. Miss Moss went out.

"I'll go to Charing Cross. Yes, that's what I'll do," she decided. "But I won't have a cup of tea. No, I'll have a coffee. There's more of a tonic in coffee. . . . Cheeky, those girls are! Her boy came home last night; he brought her a brooch with 'Dieppe' written on it." She began to cross the road. . . .

"Look out, Fattie; don't go to sleep!" yelled a taxi driver. She pretended not to hear.

"No, I won't go to Charing Cross," she decided. "I'll go straight to Kig and Kadgit. They're open at nine. If I get there early Mr. Kadgit may have something by the morning's post. . . . I'm very glad you turned up so early, Miss Moss. I've just heard from a manager who wants a lady to play.

. . . I think you'll just suit him. I'll give you a card to go and see him. It's three pounds a week and all found. If I were you I'd hop round as fast as I could. Lucky you turned up so early . . ."

But there was nobody at Kig and Kadgit's except the char-woman wiping over the "lino" in the passage.

"Nobody here yet, Miss," said the char.

"Oh, isn't Mr. Kadgit here?" said Miss Moss, trying to dodge the pail and brush. "Well, I'll just wait a moment, if I may."

"You can't wait in the waiting-room, Miss. I 'aven't done it yet. Mr. Kadgit's never 'ere before 'leven-thirty Saturdays. Sometimes 'e don't come at all." And the char began crawling towards her.

"Dear me—how silly of me," said Miss Moss. "I forgot it was Saturday."

"Mind your feet, *please*, Miss," said the char. And Miss Moss was outside again.

That was one thing about Beit and Bithems; it was lively. You walked into the waiting-room, into a great buzz of conversation, and there was everybody; you knew almost everybody. The early ones sat on chairs and the later ones sat on the early one's laps, while the gentlemen leaned negligently against the walls or preened themselves in front of the admiring ladies.

"Hello," said Miss Moss, very gay. "Here we are again!"

And young Mr. Clayton, playing the banjo on his walking-stick, sang: "Waiting for the Robert E. Lee."

"Mr. Bithem here yet?" asked Miss Moss, taking out an old dead powder puff and powdering her nose mauve.

"Oh, yes, dear," cried the chorus. "He's been here for ages. We've all been waiting here for more than an hour."

"Dear me!" said Miss Moss. "Anything doing, do you think?"

"Oh, a few jobs going for South Africa," said young Mr. Clayton. "Hundred and fifty a week for two years, you know."

"Oh!" cried the chorus. "You *are* weird, Mr. Clayton. Isn't he a *cure*? Isn't he a *scream*, dear? Oh, Mr. Clayton, you do make me laugh. Isn't he a *comic*?"

A dark, mournful girl touched Miss Moss on the arm.

"I just missed a lovely job yesterday," she said. "Six weeks in the provinces and then the West End. The manager said I would have it got for certain if only I'd been robust enough. He said if my figure had been fuller, the part was made for me." She stared at Miss Moss, and the dirty dark red rose under the brim of her hat looked, somehow, as though it shared the blow with her, and was crushed, too.

"Oh, dear, that was hard lines," said Miss Moss trying to appear indifferent. "What was it—if I may ask?"

But the dark, mournful girl saw through her and a gleam of spite came into her heavy eyes.

"Oh, no good to you, my dear," said she. "He wanted some one young, you know—a dark Spanish type—my style, but more figure, that was all."

The inner door opened and Mr. Bithem appeared in his shirt sleeves. He kept one hand on the door ready to whisk back again, and held up the other.

"Look here, ladies——" and then he paused, grinned his famous grin before he said—"and bhoys." The waiting-room laughed so loudly at this that he had to hold both hands up. "It's no good waiting this morning. Come back Monday; I'm expecting several calls on Monday."

Miss Moss made a desperate rush forward. "Mr. Bithem, I wonder if you've heard from . . ."

"Now let me see," said Mr. Bithem slowly, staring; he had only seen Miss Moss four times a week for the past—how many weeks? "Now, who are you?"

"Miss Ada Moss."

"Oh, yes, yes; of course, my dear. Not yet, my dear. Now I had a call for twenty-eight ladies today, but they had to be young and able to hop it a bit—see? And I had another call for sixteen—but they had to know something about sand-dancing. Look here, my dear, I'm up to the eyebrows this morning. Come back on Monday week; it's no good coming before that." He gave her a whole grin to herself and patted her fat back. "Hearts of oak, dear lady," said Mr. Bithem, "hearts of oak!"

At the North-East Film Company the crowd was all the way up the stairs. Miss Moss found herself next to a fair little baby thing about thirty in a white lace hat with cherries round it.

"What a crowd!" said she. "Anything special on?"

"Didn't you know, my dear?" said the baby, opening her

immense pale eyes. "There was a call at nine-thirty for *attractive* girls. We've all been waiting for *hours*. Have you played for this company before?" Miss Moss put her head on one side. "No, I don't think I have."

"They're a lovely company to play for," said the baby. "A friend of mine has a friend who gets thirty pounds a day. . . . Have you *arcted* much for the *fil*-lums?"

"Well, I'm not an actress by profession," confessed Miss Moss. "I'm a contralto singer. But things have been so bad lately that I've been doing a little."

"It's *like* that, isn't it, dear?" said the baby.

"I had a splendid education at the College of Music," said Miss Moss, "and I got my silver medal for singing. I've often sung at West End concerts. But I thought, for a change, I'd try my luck . . ."

"Yes, it's *like* that, isn't it, dear?" said the baby.

At that moment a beautiful typist appeared at the top of the stairs.

"Are you all waiting for the North-East call?"

"Yes!" cried the chorus.

"Well, it's all off. I've just had a 'phone through."

"But look here! What about our expenses?" shouted a voice.

The typist looked down at them, and she couldn't help laughing.

"Oh, you weren't to have been *paid*. The North-East never *pay* their crowds."

There was only a little round window at the Bitter Orange Company. No waiting-room—nobody at all except a girl, who came to the window when Miss Moss knocked, and said: "Well?"

"Can I see the producer, please?" said Miss Moss pleasantly. The girl leaned on the window-bar, half shut her eyes and seemed to go to sleep for a moment. Miss Moss smiled at her. The girl not only frowned; she seemed to smell something vaguely unpleasant; she sniffed. Suddenly she moved away, came back with a paper and thrust it at Miss Moss.

"Fill up the form!" said she. And banged the window down.

"Can you aviate—high-dive—drive a car—buck-jump—shoot?" read Miss Moss. She walked along the street asking herself those questions. There was a high, cold wind blowing; it tugged at her, slapped her face, jeered; it knew she could

not answer them. In the Square Gardens she found a little wire
basket to drop the form into. And then she sat down on one
of the benches to powder her nose. But the person in the
pocket mirror made a hideous face at her, and that was too
much for Miss Moss; she had a good cry. It cheered her wonderfully.

"Well, that's over," she sighed. "It's one comfort to be off
my feet. And my nose will soon get cool in the air. . . . It's
very nice in here. Look at the sparrows. Cheep. Cheep. How
close they come. I expect somebody feeds them. No, I've nothing for you, you cheeky little things. . . ." She looked away
from them. What was the big building opposite—the Café
de Madrid? My goodness, what a smack that little child came
down! Poor little mite! Never mind—up again. . . . By eight
o'clock to-night . . . Café de Madrid. "I could just go in
and sit there and have a coffee, that's all," thought Miss Moss.
"It's such a place for artists too. I might just have a stroke
of luck. . . . A dark handsome gentleman in a fur coat comes
in with a friend, and sits at my table, perhaps. 'No, old chap,
I've searched London for a contralto and I can't find a soul.
You see, the music is difficult; have a look at it.' " And Miss
Moss heard herself saying: "Excuse me, I happen to be a
contralto, and I have sung that part many times. . . . Extraordinary! 'Come back to my studio and I'll try your voice
now.' . . . Ten pounds a week. . . . Why should I feel nervous? It's not nervousness. Why shouldn't I go to the Café de
Madrid? I'm a respectable woman—I'm a contralto singer.
And I'm only trembling because I've had nothing to eat to-
day. . . . 'A nice little piece of evidence, my lady.' . . .
Very well, Mrs. Pine. Café de Madrid. They have concerts
there in the evenings. . . . 'Why don't they begin?' The contralto has not arrived. . . . 'Excuse me, I happen to be a
contralto; I have sung that music many times.' "

It was almost dark in the café. Men, palms, red plush seats,
white marble tables, waiters in aprons, Miss Moss walked
through them all. Hardly had she sat down when a very stout
gentleman wearing a very small hat that floated on the top of
his head like a little yacht flopped into the chair opposite
hers.

"Good evening!" said he.

Miss Moss said, in her cheerful way: "Good evening!"

"Fine evening," said the stout gentleman.

"Yes, very fine. Quite a treat, isn't it?" said she.

He crooked a sausage finger at the waiter—"Bring me a large whisky"—and turned to Miss Moss. "What's yours?"

"Well, I think I'll take a brandy if it's all the same."

Five minutes later the stout gentleman leaned across the table and blew a puff of cigar smoke full in her face.

"That's a tempting bit o' ribbon!" said he.

Miss Moss blushed until a pulse at the top of her head that she never had felt before pounded away.

"I always was one for pink," said she.

The stout gentleman considered her, drumming with her fingers on the table.

"I like 'em firm and well covered," said he.

Miss Moss, to her surprise, gave a loud snigger.

Five minutes later the stout gentleman heaved himself up. "Well, am I goin' your way, or are you comin' mine?" he asked.

"I'll come with you, if it's all the same," said Miss Moss. And she sailed after the little yacht out of the café.

PSYCHOLOGY

When she opened the door and saw him standing there she was more pleased than ever before, and he, too, as he followed her into the studio, seemed very very happy to have come.

"Not busy?"

"No. Just going to have tea."

"And you are not expecting anybody?"

"Nobody at all."

"Ah! That's good."

He laid aside his coat and hat gently, lingeringly, as though he had time and to spare for everything or as though he were taking leave of them for ever, and came over to the fire and held out his hands to the quick, leaping flame.

Just for a moment both of them stood silent in that leaping light. Still, as it were, they tasted on their smiling lips the sweet shock of their greeting. Their secret selves whispered:

"Why should we speak? Isn't this enough?"

"More than enough. I never realized until this moment . . ."

"How good it is just to be with you. . . ."

"Like this. . . ."

"It's more than enough."

But suddenly he turned and looked at her and he moved quickly away.

"Have a cigarette? I'll put the kettle on. Are you longing for tea?"

"No. Not longing."

"Well, I am."

"Oh, you." He thumped the Armenian cushion and flung on to the *sommier*. "You're a perfect little Chinee."

"Yes, I am," she laughed. "I long for tea as strong men long for wine."

She lighted the lamp under its broad orange shade, pulled the curtains and drew up the tea table. Two birds sang in the kettle; the fire fluttered. He sat up clasping his knees. It was delightful—this business of having tea—and she always had delicious things to eat—little sharp sandwiches, short sweet almond fingers, and a dark, rich cake tasting of rum—but it was an interruption. He wanted it over, the table pushed away, their two chairs drawn up to the light, and the moment came when he took out his pipe, filled it, and said, pressing the tobacco tight into the bowl: "I have been thinking over what you said last time and it seems to me . . ."

Yes, that was what he waited for and so did she. Yes, while she shook the teapot hot and dry over the spirit flame she saw those other two, him leaning back, taking his ease among the cushions, and her, curled up *en escargot* in the blue shell armchair. The picture was so clear and so minute it might have been painted on the blue teapot lid. And yet she couldn't hurry. She could almost have cried: "Give me time." She must have time in which to grow calm. She wanted time in which to free herself from all these familiar things with which she lived so vividly. For all these gay things round her were part of her—her offspring—and they knew it and made the largest, most vehement claims. But now they must go. They must be swept away, shooed away—like children, sent up the shadowy stairs, packed into bed and commanded to go to sleep—at once—without a murmur!

For the special thrilling quality of their friendship was in their complete surrender. Like two open cities in the midst of some vast plain their two minds lay open to each other. And it wasn't as if he rode into hers like a conqueror, armed to the eyebrows and seeing nothing but a gay silken flutter— nor did she enter his like a queen walking soft on petals. No, they were eager, serious travellers, absorbed in understanding what was to be seen and discovering what was hidden—making the most of this extraordinary absolute chance which made it possible for him to be utterly truthful to her and for her to be utterly sincere with him.

And the best of it was they were both of them old enough to enjoy their adventure to the full without any stupid emotional complication. Passion would have ruined everything; they quite saw that. Besides, all that sort of thing was over and done with for both of them—he was thirty-one, she was thirty—they had had their experiences, and very rich and varied they had been, but now was the time for harvest— harvest. Weren't his novels to be very big novels indeed? And her plays. Who else had her exquisite sense of real English Comedy? . . .

Carefully she cut the cake into thick little wads and he reached across for a piece.

"Do you realize how good it is," she implored. "Eat it imaginatively. Roll your eyes if you can and taste it on the breath. It's not a sandwich from the hatter's bag—it's the kind of cake that might have been mentioned in the Book of Genesis. . . . And God said: 'Let there be cake. And there was cake. And God saw that it was good.' "

"You needn't entreat me," said he. "Really you needn't. It's a queer thing but I always do notice what I eat here and never anywhere else. I suppose it comes of living alone so long and always reading when I feed . . . my habit of looking upon food as just food . . . something that's there, at certain times . . . to be devoured . . . to be . . . not there." He laughed. "That shocks you. Doesn't it?"

"To the bone," said she.

"But—look here——" He pushed away his cup and began to speak very fast. "I simply haven't got any external life at all. I don't know the names of things a bit—trees and so on— and I never notice places or furniture or what people look like. One room is just like another to me—a place to sit and read or talk in—except," and here he paused, smiled in a strange naïve way, and said, "except this studio." He looked round him and then at her; he laughed in his astonishment and pleasure. He was like a man who wakes up in a train to find that he has arrived, already, at the journey's end.

"Here's another queer thing. If I shut my eyes I can see this place down to every detail—every detail. . . . Now I come to think of it—I've never realized this consciously before. Often when I am away from here I revisit it in spirit—wander about among your red chairs, stare at the bowl of fruit on the black table—and just touch, very lightly, that marvel of a sleeping boy's head."

He looked at it as he spoke. It stood on the corner of the mantelpiece; the head to one side down-drooping, the lips parted, as though in his sleep the little boy listened to some sweet sound. . . .

"I love that little boy," he murmured. And then they both were silent.

A new silence came between them. Nothing in the least like the satisfactory pause that had followed their greetings—the "Well, here we are together again, and there's no reason why we shouldn't go on from just where we left off last time." That silence, could be contained in the circle of warm, delightful fire and lamplight. How many times hadn't they flung something into it just for the fun of watching the ripples break on the easy shores. But into this unfamiliar pool the head of the little boy sleeping his timeless sleep dropped—and the ripples flowed away, away—boundlessly far—into deep glittering darkness.

And then both of them broke it. She said: "I must make up the fire," and he said: "I have been trying a new . . ." Both of them escaped. She made up the fire and put the table back, the blue chair was wheeled forward, she curled up and he lay back among the cushions. Quickly! Quickly! They must stop it from happening again.

"Well, I read the book you left last time."

"Oh, what do you think of it?"

They were off and all was as usual. But was it? Weren't they just a little too quick, too prompt with their replies, too ready to take each other up? Was this really anything more than a wonderfully good imitation of other occasions? His heart beat; her cheek burned and the stupid thing was she could not discover where exactly they were or what exactly was happening. She hadn't time to glance back. And just as 'she had got so far it happened again. They faltered, wavered, broke down, were silent. Again they were conscious of the boundless, questioning dark. Again, there they were—two hunters, bending over their fire, but hearing suddenly from the jungle beyond a shake of wind and a loud, questioning cry. . . .

She lifted her head. "It's raining," she murmured. And her voice was like his when he had said: "I love that little boy."

Well. Why didn't they just give way to it—yield—and see what will happen then? But no. Vague and troubled though they were, they knew enough to realize their precious friendship was in danger. She was the one who would be destroyed —not they—and they'd be no party to that.

He got up, knocked out his pipe, ran his hand through his hair and said: "I have been wondering very much lately whether the novel of the future will be a psychological novel or not. How sure are you that psychology *qua* psychology has got anything to do with literature at all?"

"Do you mean you feel there's quite a chance that the mysterious non-existent creatures—the young writers of today— are trying simply to jump the psycho-analyst's claim?"

"Yes, I do. And I think it's because this generation is just wise enough to know that it is sick and to realize that its only chance of recovery is by going into its symptoms—making an exhaustive study of them—tracking them down—trying to get at the root of the trouble."

"But oh," she wailed. "What a dreadfully dismal outlook."

"Not at all," said he. "Look here . . ." On the talk went. And now it seemed they really had succeeded. She turned in her chair to look at him while she answered. Her smile said: "We have won." And he smiled back, confident: "Absolutely."

But the smile undid them. It lasted too long; it became a grin. They saw themselves as two little grinning puppets jigging away in nothingness.

"What have we been talking about?" thought he. He was so utterly bored he almost groaned.

"What a spectacle we have made of ourselves," thought she. And she saw him laboriously—oh, laboriously—laying out the grounds and herself running after, putting here a tree and there a flowery shrub and here a handful of glittering fish in a pool. They were silent this time from sheer dismay.

The clock struck six merry little pings and the fire made a soft flutter. What fools they were—heavy, stodgy, elderly— with positively upholstered minds.

And now the silence put a spell upon them like solemn music. It was anguish—anguish for her to bear it and he would die—he'd die if it were broken. . . . And yet he longed to break it. Not by speech. At any rate not by their ordinary maddening chatter. There was another way for them to speak to each other, and in the new way he wanted to murmur: "Do you feel this too? Do you understand it at all?" . . .

Instead, to his horror, he heard himself say: "I must be off; I'm meeting Brand at six."

What devil made him say that instead of the other? She jumped—simply jumped out of her chair, and he heard her crying: "You must rush, then. He's so punctual. Why didn't you say so before?

"You've hurt me; you've hurt me! We've failed!" said her secret self while she handed him his hat and stick, smiling gaily. She wouldn't give him a moment for another word, but ran along the passage and opened the big outer door.

Could they leave each other like this? How could they? He stood on the step and she just inside holding the door. It was not raining now.

"You've hurt me—hurt me," said her heart. "Why don't you go? No, don't go. Stay. No—go!" And she looked out upon the night.

She saw the beautiful fall of the steps, the dark garden ringed with glittering ivy, on the other side of the road the huge bare willows and above them the sky big and bright with stars. But of course he would see nothing of all this. He was superior to it all. He—with his wonderful "spiritual" vision!

She was right. He did see nothing at all. Misery! He'd missed it. It was too late to do anything now. Was it too late? Yes, it was. A cold snatch of hateful wind blew into the garden. Curse life! He heard her cry "au revoir" and the door slammed.

Running back into the studio she behaved so strangely. She ran up and down lifting her arms and crying: "Oh! Oh! How stupid! How imbecile! How stupid!" And then she flung herself down on the *sommier* thinking of nothing—just lying there in her rage. All was over. What was over? Oh—something was. And she'd never see him again—never. After a long long time (or perhaps ten minutes) had passed in that black gulf her bell rang a sharp quick jingle. It was he, of course. And equally, of course, she oughtn't to have paid the slightest attention to it but just let it go on ringing and ringing. She flew to answer.

On the doorstep there stood an elderly virgin, a pathetic creature who simply idolized her (heaven knows why) and had this habit of turning up and ringing the bell and then saying, when she opened the door: "My dear, send me away!" She never did. As a rule she asked her in and let her admire everything and accepted the bunch of slightly soiled looking flowers —more than graciously. But today . . .

"Oh, I am so sorry," she cried. "But I've got some one with me. We are working on some wood-cuts. I'm hopelessly busy all evening."

"It doesn't matter. It doesn't matter at all, darling," said the good friend. "I was just passing and I thought I'd leave you some violets." She fumbled down among the ribs of a large old umbrella. "I put them down here. Such a good place to keep flowers out of the wind. Here they are," she said, shaking out a little dead bunch.

For a moment she did not take the violets. But while she stood just inside, holding the door, a strange thing happened. . . . Again she saw the beautiful fall of the steps, the dark garden ringed with glittering ivy, the willows, the big bright sky. Again she felt the silence that was like a question. But this time she did not hesitate. She moved forward. Very softly and gently, as though fearful of making a ripple in that boundless pool of quiet she put her arms round her friend.

"My dear," murmured her happy friend, quite overcome by this gratitude. "They are really nothing. Just the simplest little thrippenny bunch."

But as she spoke she was enfolded—more tenderly, more beautifully embraced, held by such a sweet pressure and for so long that the poor dear's mind positively reeled and she just had the strength to quaver: "Then you really don't mind me too much?"

"Good night, my friend," whispered the other. "Come again soon."

"Oh, I will. I will."

This time she walked back to the studio slowly, and standing in the middle of the room with half-shut eyes she felt so light, so rested, as if she had woken up out of a childless sleep. Even the act of breathing was a joy. . . .

The *sommier* was very untidy. All the cushions "like furious mountains" as she said; she put them in order before going over to the writing-table.

"I have been thinking over our talk about the psychological novel," she dashed off, "it really is intensely interesting." . . . And so on and so on.

At the end she wrote: "Good night, my friend. Come again soon."

MISS BRILL

ALTHOUGH it was so brilliantly fine—the blue sky powdered with gold and great spots of light like white wine splashed over the Jardins Publiques—Miss Brill was glad that she had decided on her fur. The air was motionless, but when you opened your mouth there was just a faint chill, like a chill from a glass of iced water before you sip, and now and again a leaf came drifting—from nowhere, from the sky. Miss Brill put up her hand and touched her fur. Dear little thing! It was nice to feel it again. She had taken it out of its box that afternoon, shaken out the moth-powder, given it a good brush, and rubbed the life back into the dim little eyes. "What has been happening to me?" said the sad little eyes. Oh, how sweet it was to see them snap at her again from the red eiderdown! . . . But the nose, which was of some black composition, wasn't at all firm. It must have had a knock, somehow. Never mind—a little dab of black sealing-wax when the time came—when it was absolutely necessary. . . . Little rogue! Yes, she really felt like that about it. Little rogue biting its tail just by her left ear. She could have taken it off and laid it on her lap and stroked it. She felt a tingling in her hands and arms, but that came from walking, she supposed. And when she breathed, something light and sad—no, not sad, exactly—something gentle seemed to move in her bosom.

There were a number of people out this afternoon, far more than last Sunday. And the band sounded louder and gayer. That was because the Season had begun. For although the band played all the year round on Sundays, out of season it was never the same. It was like some one playing with only the family to listen; it didn't care how it played if there weren't any strangers present. Wasn't the conductor wearing a new coat, too? She was sure it was new. He scraped with his foot and flapped his arms like a rooster about to crow, and the bandsmen sitting in the green rotunda blew out their cheeks and glared at the music. Now there came a little "flutey" bit —very pretty!—a little chain of bright drops. She was sure it would be repeated. It was; she lifted her head and smiled.

Only two people shared her "special" seat: a fine old man in a velvet coat, his hands clasped over a huge carved walking-stick, and a big old woman, sitting upright, with a roll of knitting on her embroidered apron. They did not speak. This was disappointing, for Miss Brill always looked forward to the conversation. She had become really quite expert, she thought, at listening as though she didn't listen, at sitting in other people's lives just for a minute while they talked round her.

She glanced, sideways, at the old couple. Perhaps they would go soon. Last Sunday, too, hadn't been as interesting as usual. An Englishman and his wife, he wearing a dreadful Panama hat and she button boots. And she'd gone on the whole time about how she ought to wear spectacles; she knew she needed them; but that it was no good getting any; they'd be sure to break and they'd never keep on. And he'd been so patient. He'd suggested everything—gold rims, the kind that curved round your ears, little pads inside the bridge. No, nothing would please her. "They'll always be sliding down my nose!" Miss Brill had wanted to shake her.

The old people sat on the bench, still as statues. Never mind, there was always the crowd to watch. To and fro, in front of the flower-beds and the band rotunda, the couples and groups paraded, stopped to talk, to greet, to buy a hand-ful of flowers from the old beggar who had his tray fixed to the railings. Little children ran among them, swooping and laughing; little boys with big white silk bows under their chins, little girls, little French dolls, dressed up in velvet and lace. And sometimes a tiny staggerer came suddenly rocking into the open from under the trees, stopped, stared, as suddenly sat down "flop," until its small high-stepping mother, like a young hen, rushed scolding to its rescue. Other people sat on the benches and green chairs, but they were nearly always the same, Sunday after Sunday, and—Miss Brill had often noticed—there was something funny about nearly all of them. They were odd, silent, nearly all old, and from the way they stared they looked as though they'd just come from dark little rooms or even—even cupboards!

Behind the rotunda the slender trees with yellow leaves down drooping, and through them just a line of sea, and beyond the blue sky with gold-veined clouds.

Tum-tum-tum tiddle-um! tiddle-um! tum tiddley-um tum ta! blew the band.

Two young girls in red came by and two young soldiers in blue met them, and they laughed and paired and went off arm-in-arm. Two peasant women with funny straw hats passed, gravely, leading beautiful smoke-coloured donkeys. A cold, pale nun hurried by. A beautiful woman came along and dropped her bunch of violets, and a little boy ran after to hand them to her, and she took them and threw them away as if they'd been poisoned. Dear me! Miss Brill didn't know whether to admire that or not! And now an ermine toque and a gentleman in grey met just in front of her. He was tall, stiff, dignified, and she was wearing the ermine toque she'd bought when her hair was yellow. Now everything, her hair, her face, even her eyes, was the same colour as the shabby ermine, and her hand, in its cleaned glove, lifted to dab her lips, was a tiny yellowish paw. Oh, she was so pleased to see him—delighted! She rather thought they were going to meet that afternoon. She described where she'd been—everywhere, here, there, along by the sea. The day was so charming—didn't he agree? And wouldn't he, perhaps? . . . But he shook his head, lighted a cigarette, slowly breathed a great deep puff into her face, and, even while she was still talking and laughing, flicked the match away and walked on. The ermine toque was alone; she smiled more brightly than ever. But even the band seemed to know what she was feeling and played more softly, played tenderly, and the drum beat, "The Brute! The Brute!" over and over. What would she do? What was going to happen now? But as Miss Brill wondered, the ermine toque turned, raised her hand as though she'd seen some one else,

much nicer, just over there, and pattered away. And the band
changed again and played more quickly, more gaily than ever,
and the old couple on Miss Brill's seat got up and marched
away, and such a funny old man with long whiskers hobbled
along in time to the music and was nearly knocked over by
four girls walking abreast.

Oh, how fascinating it was! How she enjoyed it! How she
loved sitting here, watching it all! It was like a play. It was exactly like a play. Who could believe the sky at the back wasn't
painted? But it wasn't till a little brown dog trotted on solemn
and then slowly trotted off, like a little "theatre" dog—a little
dog that had been drugged, that Miss Brill discovered what
it was that made it so exciting. They were all on the stage.
They weren't only the audience, not only looking on; they
were acting. Even she had a part and came every Sunday.
No doubt somebody would have noticed if she hadn't been
there; she was part of the performance after all. How strange
she'd never thought of it like that before! And yet it explained
why she made such a point of starting from home at just the
same time each week—so as not to be late for the performance
—and it also explained why she had quite a queer, shy feeling
at telling her English pupils how she spent her Sunday afternoons. No wonder! Miss Brill nearly laughed out loud. She
was on the stage. She thought of the old invalid gentleman to
whom she read the newspaper four afternoons a week while he
slept in the garden. She had got quite used to the frail head
on the cotton pillow, the hollowed eyes, the open mouth and
the high pinched nose. If he'd been dead she mightn't have
noticed for weeks; she wouldn't have minded. But suddenly
he knew he was having the paper read to him by an actress!
"An actress!" The old head lifted; two points of light quivered in the old eyes. "An actress—are ye?" And Miss Brill
smoothed the newspaper as though it were the manuscript of
her part and said gently: "Yes, I have been an actress for a
long time."

The band had been having a rest. Now they started again.
And what they played was warm, sunny, yet there was just a
faint chill—a something, what was it?—not sadness—no, not
sadness—a something that made you want to sing. The tune
lifted, lifted, the light shone; and it seemed to Miss Brill that
in another moment all of them, all the whole company, would
begin singing. The young ones, the laughing ones who were

moving together, they would begin, and the men's voices, very resolute and brave, would join them. And then she too, she too, and the others on the benches—they would come in with a kind of accompaniment—something low, that scarcely rose or fell, something so beautiful—moving. . . . And Miss Brill's eyes filled with tears and she looked smiling at all the other members of the company. Yes, we understand, we understand, she thought—though what they understood she didn't know.

Just at that moment a boy and a girl came and sat down where the old couple had been. They were beautifully dressed; they were in love. The hero and heroine, of course, just arrived from his father's yacht. And still soundlessly singing, still with that trembling smile, Miss Brill prepared to listen.

"No, not now," said the girl. "Not here, I can't."

"But why? Because of that stupid old thing at the end there?" asked the boy. "Why does she come here at all—who wants her? Why doesn't she keep her silly old mug at home?"

"It's her fu-fur which is so funny," giggled the girl. "It's exactly like a fried whiting."

"Ah, be off with you!" said the boy in an angry whisper. Then: "Tell me, ma petite chère——"

"No, not here," said the girl. "Not *yet*."

On her way home she usually bought a slice of honey-cake at the baker's. It was her Sunday treat. Sometimes there was an almond in her slice, sometimes not. It made a great difference. If there was an almond it was like carrying home a tiny present—a surprise—something that might very well not have been there. She hurried on the almond Sundays and struck the match for the kettle in quite a dashing way.

But to-day she passed the baker's by, climbed the stairs, went into the little dark room—her room like a cupboard—and sat down on the red eiderdown. She sat there for a long time. The box that the fur came out of was on the bed. She unclasped the necklet quickly; quickly, without looking, laid it inside. But when she put the lid on she thought she heard something crying.

Harold Nicolson

THE MARQUIS DE CHAUMONT

I AM now haunted by a companion picture to Lambert Orme —the picture of Jacques de Chaumont. It is a mistake doubtless to place these two in juxtaposition, nor have I any right to suppose that others share my interest in the freaks of literary temperament. And yet Orme and de Chaumont complete each other as a piece of buhl is completed by a piece of counter-buhl. It would be a pity to separate them. Lambert began so foolishly and ended on such a note of seriousness: de Chaumont possessed such possibilities but became in the end idiotic beyond the realm of comprehension. His story, fortunately, will not be believed: but I give it none the less.

The Europeans, during the heyday of King Edward's reign, crowded to Oxford. They founded a dining club which they called "The Cosmopolitan." On alternate Saturdays they would meet for dinner at the Clarendon. The food came from Gunter's and the wines from France. One was expected to get drunk but not disgustingly drunk; and afterwards one played roulette for stakes far larger than I could possibly afford. I was passing at the time through my snobbish period, a phase which in its acute form lasted till 1911, whereafter it became endemic merely, and of late, I feel, but epidemic. At the time, however, I was deeply impressed by the Cosmopolitan. I was excited by their historic names, their Sholte dinner jackets with the emerald facings, their Cartier watches, their Fabergé cigarette cases, their faint smell of Chypre and Corona cigars; by the fact that they were all far older and more mundane than myself. The Bullingdon, of course, was the Bullingdon; but the Cosmopolitan had a slightly illict flavour about it: I took to it hesitatingly as a Newnham girl takes to Crème de Menthe.

The President of the club, if I remember rightly, was Talleyrand-Périgord. The outstanding members were Orloff, and Appony, and Econoumo and Andrea Buoncompagni, and Argenti, and Enrico Visconti Venosta, and Louis René de Gramont, and Goluchowski, and Schweinitz, and the Marquis de Chaumont. I was introduced to the latter by de Gramont, who, since he was at Balliol, was the one I knew best. De Chaumont, even at that date, was an intellectual. De Gramont was not.

I remember particularly one gala evening on which was celebrated the anniversary of the club's foundation. It must have been their only anniversary, since shortly afterwards Talleyrand, who was a German subject and as such a Rhodes Scholar, was sent away owing to flippant behaviour: for which, on arrival in Berlin, he had his ears boxed by his Emperor in front of the whole Court. Appony also left, and so did de Gramont. Visconti went and lived in a little cottage at Iffley where he studied Bergson: de Chaumont returned to Paris: the club was dissolved. But meanwhile, one warm evening towards the end of May, they celebrated their anniversary dinner. They had by then got bored with the Clarendon, and the dinner for some odd reason took place in the East Gate Hotel. I went as the guest of de Gramont: I sat between him and Enrico Visconti. The Marquis de Chaumont sat opposite. The general conversation was carried on in varying forms of English: the particular conversations were conducted in every language under the sun.

I felt a little self-conscious at first and ungainly: an unpleasant feeling that I did not properly belong. At such moments one realises one's own identity as something physically detached. I saw myself sitting there, my rather scrubby dinner-jacket, my rather wispy black tie, those two inadequate studs, that pink and bumptious face, that curly hair and nose: that voice of mine—surely there was something very unlike me about my voice? And what would Balliol say? I was, and still am, extremely sensitive to Balliol opinion. I felt somehow that the Cosmopolitan did not stand for the things that Balliol stood for: I felt that what the Balliol people criticised in me was exactly that lax strand which had led me to dinner that evening at the East Gate Hotel: as I looked and listened I felt that, for the purposes of Empire, Balliol was right every time: I felt ashamed and apprehensive. After all, it would be rather ghastly if I were seen.

The conversation by then was becomning animated; people were beginning to drink toasts and throw strawberries across the table. De Gramont rose and went and sat next Appony: de Chaumont rose and took the thus vacant chair beside me. He was a pale young man, with straight fair hair brushed backwards, and little red lips, wet and mobile. He suffered from an affection of the eyes which watered a good deal and fringed his eyelids with a slight inflammation. He had learnt English from his nurse and spoke it fluently with a strong cockney accent. He was, at the time, engaged in studying English literature: he was at the moment rather drunk.

"I 'ave discovered," he said, "the foinest loines in English literature."

"There are many fine lines in English literature."

"No, but these are really admirable. You know them doubtless? They are by Percy Shelley:

"Toime loike a dom of many-coloured glass . . ."

"It isn't 'dom,' " I interrupted, "it's dome."

"Toime like a dome . . ." he began again in a shrill recitative.

I changed the subject. "Where," I said to him, "did you learn English?" It was then that he told me about the nurse: it was then that I told him about the cockney accent. "You mean," he said, "a vulgar accent, un accent du peuple?" I said that that had in fact been my meaning. He became thoughtful at this and drank some more champagne. He then continued the conversation in French. He told me about Madame de Noailles, he recited with great fervour one of the Eblouissements. He was still reciting when, arm in arm, we walked up the High Street. In front of us reeled the other members of the club, their diamonds and their green facings flashing gaudily under the arc-lights. They sang a song in German. I tried to loiter a little behind. I observed two undergraduates leave the pavement at their approach and stand to watch them in disgusted amazement. They were still staring as de Chaumont passed them spouting Madame de Noailles, holding me firmly and affectionately by the arm. One of the undergraduates was Laurence Jones, the other was Julian Grenfell. They observed me. "For God's sake," I whispered to de Chaumont, "do shut up." He paid no attention.

We had roulette afterwards in Talleyrand's rooms above the Bullingdon. De Chaumont stopped playing roulette and sat in the window-seat, looking out upon the warm and gentle night. I went and sat beside him. "Isn't it marrvellous?" he said. "You mustn't say marrvellous, you must say marvellous." An hour later we walked back together along the Turl. "Isn't it mauvellous?" he kept repeating, "isn't it mauvellous?"

ii

In the few weeks which remained of that, his last, term at Oxford, I saw a great deal of Jacques de Chaumont. He would drop into my rooms in the evening exquisitely although simply dressed, and would speak to me at length and not without ardour of the more obscure tendencies in modern French literature. I was not fully aware at the time of the conflict which must even then have been apparent between the two directing forces of his life, a conflict which in the years that followed played havoc with his happiness and ended, in circumstances which will subsequently be related, by robbing him of a first-class chance of immortality. I realised, of course, that he had a sincere passion for literature, and that he was at the same time particularly sensitive to the advantages, such as they are, of family and position. I did not foresee, however, that his snobbishness would become as a bloated moth fretting the garment of his intellect, that the blue particles in his blood would wage eternal warfare on the red corpuscles with which, in spite of his anodyne appearance, he was unquestionably endowed. I observed, it is true, that considerations of high life assumed for him an importance which appeared, even to me, a little exaggerated. But I did not realise that these same considerations could in any circumstances become an acute mental torment, destroying his intellect as those of others have been sapped by drink, or drugs, or perversion. Yet so it was. His ancestry, his parents, his collaterals loomed in front of him in vast and menacing proportions: the side-streets in his mind were tortuous and quite interesting, but they were interrupted at frequent intervals by rigid avenues leading him back, and so inevitably, to the Rue de Varennes.

I can recollect, in the light of subsequent experience, certain symptoms which show me that his disease had already fastened upon him at the age of twenty-two. They had told him, a little unkindly perhaps, that the most exclusive club in England was not, as he had heard, the Royal Yacht Squadron but the equally Royal Automobile Club in Pall Mall. He had thereupon pulled endless strings to secure election to this institution: he had gone up to London and paid a round of calls as if seeking for admission to the Académie Française; when his efforts were crowned by triumphant success, he had some new cards printed with "Royal Automobile Club" in the bottom left-hand corner.

I can recall also a conversation which startled me at the time. Although he concentrated upon all that was best in the University life around him, yet there were moments when his watery eyes would turn northwards a little wistfully, to Blenheim, or southwards, a little wistfully, to Wytham Abbey. We dined at the latter house one evening, and it was in the dogcart returning under heavy star-twinkling trees that the conversation took place which now recurs to me. I had been saying how much, how very much, I liked Lady Abingdon.

"Is she smart?" de Chaumont asked me.

I was taken aback by this, and asked him what he meant exactly.

"Is she worldly, I mean?"

I assured him that Lady Abingdon was one of the most unworldly women I had ever known. He was silent for some time and when he spoke again it was about Mr. Walter Pater. When I got to bed I realised that by "worldly" he had meant "mondaine."

The foretaste of his final failure, of his final rejection of immortality (a rejection which interests me exceedingly and which forms the climax of this story), was given me some ten months later at Florence. I had spent February, March and April living with an Italian family at Siena in conditions of great discomfort and unremitting study. I would work the whole day without ceasing (I was making up for the time which I had lost but assuredly not wasted at Balliol), and after dinner I would walk through those narrow streets, past the incessant scream of cinema-bells, past the idling Tuscan aristocracy, and out by the great gate into the sudden hush of the surrounding hills. I would walk in this way round the looming walls, entering by another gate, stepping in again among the lights and jingle of the town. It had been a regular, a lonely and an exacting three months: I felt I deserved some relaxation: I went for four days to Florence to stay with Enrico Visconti. He lived in a villa on the hill where there was a huge and scented bath-room and fire-flies flickering in and out among the orange tubs. It was very hot, and I was a little depressed by the blatant perfection of the whole business, by the pressure of my one-and-twenty years. Visconti was charming to me and told me a great deal about Bergson and Benedetto Croce which I might not otherwise have known. And one afternoon he took me to tea with a lady, a Countess d'Orsay, who lived on the ground floor of a house on the Lung' Arno. The windows of her drawing-room were shuttered against the evening sun: it was quite dark in the room, a vague impression of people sitting in groups, of red damask and of an almost overpowering smell of narcissus. I was introduced to my hostess, and very shortly afterwards the door opened and in came de Chaumont, a very grey Homburg, and some very suède gloves, in his hand. He did not see me at first, because he was coming from the light into the dark: my own eyes by then were becoming adjusted to the obscurity and I said, "Halloa, Jacques!" He was not displeased to see me and said, " 'Ow are you? What a surprise." We sat down behind a red damask screen: Visconti, de Chaumont and myself. At the further end of the room, behind the smell of narcissus, was a group of Italians talking to each other in the shadows. De Chaumont began to ask me about Siena, and then went on to talk at length, but not without ardour, about Italian literature. I told him that I liked d'Annunzio's early poems. He said that he liked them too: did I know the sonnet which began "*Convalescente di squisiti mali*"? I said I did. Did I know the sonnet which began "*Anche a me l'oro come a Benvenuto*"? I said I didn't. He began to recite it. I thought that this, for a foreigner in an Italian house, was a rather bumptious thing to do. But he continued. He did it rather well. A hush descended on that darkened drawing-room and I became unpleasantly aware that the Italians over there were listening. De Chaumont finished—declaiming the last triumphant line with great courage and distinction. A voice—a woman's voice?—no, a man's voice, a voice like a silver bell, broke in upon us from the corner of the room. The sonnet was being repeated by

someone else and with an intonation of the utmost beauty. I
leant back in the large red sofa revelling in the languors of
that lovely voice, in the amazing finish of that lovely sonnet.
There was a hush when he had finished. Visconti whispered to
me, "It's d'Annunzio himself." I was too excited to be sorry
for de Chaumont.

D'Annunzio then recited some further poems, and notably
that splendid metrical achievement called "the rain among the
pines." I was enthralled. I crouched back among the cushions,
conscious of an emotional pressure such as I had not as yet
experienced. He finished and refused to recite again. The sun,
as it illumined the green slits of the shutters, had turned to
red. Our hostess went to them and flung them open: the room
was lightened. I could now see d'Annunzio sitting there playing with an agate paper-knife. I could not have believed that
anything not an egg could have looked so like an egg as
d'Annunzio's head. He was not very polite either to me or to
de Chaumont. I wished rather that he had remained a voice in
the dark.

We left eventually and walked along the quay. I was still
fervent with excitement. I felt somehow that de Chaumont
was unresponsive. I supposed that he was mortified by what
had indeed been an unexpected humiliation. I did not press for
an explanation. But that evening, sitting on the terrace after
dinner, I realised that his reserve arose from more curious and
recondite feelings. D'Annunzio, to his mind, was not a man of
family: in fact his name wasn't d'Annunzio at all, it was something else. He asked Visconti whether he knew the real name.
Visconti couldn't remember. "E un nome," he said, "che fa
ridere." I said that it was Gaetano something. Visconti said
he thought it was Gaetano Rapagnetta.

"Mais dans tous les cas," commented de Chaumant de-
cisively, "c'est un garçon qu'on ne peut pas voir."

Visconti, who was older than either of us, was much amused
at this, and laughed a great deal.

iii

It was several years before I again met Jacques de Chaumont. In the interval he had published two volumes of his

poems and gained thereby a not inconsiderable reputation. I
thought his verses good myself and I enjoyed reading them.
They were of the pre-war type of French poetry; at the top
of each poem there was an epigraph from Laforgue or Rimbaud or Oscar Wilde, and at the bottom a date and the names
of such places as Clarens, Coombe-Warren, Halberstadt or
Pérouse. The stage-properties which enlivened his later work,
the aquariums, cock-tail shakers and the Otis elevators, had
not as yet disclosed themselves to his Muse; these two early
volumes were all about his own extreme and ardent youth,
about greyhounds and gladioli in the manner of Madame de
Noailles. The second of the two volumes, moreover, contained
some translations from Hafiz and a rather empty sonnet to
Nijinsky.

I wrote to him about his poetry, and in return he sent me a
large photograph of himself inscribed in a handwriting that
had certainly grown larger since the Oxford days. "À Harold
Nicolson," he wrote, "cette image sage comme une image.
Jacques de Chaumont." The photograph showed him in a
smart felt hat lighting his pipe and looking upwards, as he
did so, at the photographer. It was an expensive sort of portrait and it arrived in a fawn-coloured portfolio with silk ribbons and the name of the shop embossed in gold. But in spite
of that there was something a little equivocal about it, something which I felt could not have been wholly welcome in the
rue de Varennes. It may have been the pipe, or the hat, or that
upward expression. "Jacques," I thought, "is becoming Bohemian." But that was nonsense. I looked at it again. No, there
was nothing at all Bohemian about that photograph.

He published a third volume of poetry containing a sort of
Pierrot masque which was very dull indeed. I heard that the
book had fallen flat; and shortly afterwards I heard that de
Chaumont was coming out to Constantinople in Madame de
Béthune's yacht. There were seven people on that yacht, and
by the time they reached the Bosphorus they had got considerably on each other's nerves. My chief, who was a friend of
Madame de Béthune, gave a large banquet for her the night
after her arrival. He invited all the young Turks to meet her.
There was Enver in his neat little uniform, his hands resting
patiently upon his sword-hilt, his little hair-dresser face
perked patiently above his Prussian collar. There was Djemal,

his white teeth flashing tigerish against his black beard: there was Talaat with his large gipsy eyes and his russet gipsy cheeks: there was little Djavid who spoke French fluently and who hopped about, being polite. (It is odd, when I think of it, how many of my acquaintances have been murdered, how many have been hanged.) We waited over half an hour for the Béthune party, and then the Ambassador told me that I must rearrange the dinner, as he could wait no longer. I was annoyed at this, since when seven people drop out of a dinner of thirty-five it is difficult at short notice to rearrange the places. I went into the wide corridor outside the drawing-room and began rather sulkily to draw plans upon a sheet of foolscap. The Ambassador, an impatient man for all his charm and brilliance, came out and told me to hurry up. I resumed my task feverishly and in despair; a sound of voices reached me from the central court below: I dashed aside my pencil and my paper with relief; they were all squabbling together as they came up the staircase. De Chaumont came last.

I had put him next to myself at dinner, thinking he would be pleased by this attention. He was not pleased. His eyes wandered watering around the table with an expression which no trained diplomatist can fail to recognise. He was thinking that he should have been accorded a higher place. I explained that I had put him next to myself on purpose.

"That's roight," he said, "and oim jolly well pleased to see you."

I felt that he might have said that before. We talked for a bit about old times. We then spoke of his poetry. It was a little awkward for me about that last volume which, as I have said, had fallen flat. I remarked that I had thought it a very delicate piece of work, which was strictly true. He was rather bitter about the whole business. "You see," he said, "were oi Monsieur Jacques Duval oi should not be exposed to these hattacks. But as it is, the Jews, the Freemasons, and the Socialists controive to insult me. Moy own people of course object to my publishing, at least in moy own name. Oi assure you that it is very difficult for someone with a name like moine to be taken seriously." I suggested that both Lamartine and Chateaubriand had triumphed over similar difficulties. He smiled at me pityingly and murmured something about country squires; "Ces hobereaux," he said. I realised how wide a gulf must be fixed between La Nouvelle Revue Française and the Rue de Varennes.

The next day he came to luncheon with me: we were to spend the afternoon in the bazaars. I asked Pierre de Lacretelle to come with us. It was not a successful arrangement, since Jacques insisted on talking English and Lacretelle as the day wore on became visibly annoyed. I must confess that de Chaumont on that occasion proved maddeningly superior. He arrived in a yachting cap and very white flannel trousers. He talked the whole time about people who were completely unknown to Lacretelle or myself. And he went on and on about how difficult it was for a man of family to succeed in literature. I asked him why, in such cruel circumstances, he did not change his name. He was evidently shocked by this suggestion and scarcely disguised the fact that he considered my remark ill-bred. "Soyons sérieux," he remarked as we entered the blue galleries of the bazaar.

Lacretelle, I fear, behaved rather badly. He urged de Chaumont to purchase the ugliest and most expensive objects that could be found. And he kept on saying that it was a mistake to visit the bazaars in a yachting cap as it made people raise their prices: besides, they might guess who de Chaumont really was. We said good-bye to him, a little coolly, at Galata bridge. It was then that Lacretelle exploded. He said that there were only two types of men whom he really detested. The first were the *gratins* and the second the *rastas*. De Chaumont by some strange alchemy combined both these qualities. "Et en outre," he continued, "il exagère. On n'est pas snob à ce point là. Et remarquez-le bien, c'est un fat. Il fait des bouts rimés qu'il appelle des vers: il achète des descentes de lit qu'il appelle des tapis."

During the few days that the yacht remained at Constantinople I avoided asking Lacretelle a second time to meet de Chaumont. I suggested to the latter that rather than endure the conflict between his breeding and his writing, he had better decide firmly to sacrifice the one or the other. It didn't much matter which he did. He agreed that the problem was one which imposed itself. I suggested that he might consult Madame de Béthune, who was a woman of judgment and intelligence.

"Une femme remarquable," he assented, "une femme remarquable. Mais américaine, américaine. . . ."

iv

It was Lacretelle's indignation, rather than anything that he had said or done himself, which opened my eyes to the defective in Jacques de Chaumont. At Oxford his intellectualism had detached itself as something vivid and sincere. I had taken it for granted that de Chaumont's passion for literature was the unquenchable fire of his being, and I did not consider it possible that such a flame could fizzle out under the cold water of the rue de Varennes. It did fizzle out. It is possible, of course, that had he lived in the grand siècle his two dominant inspirations might have mingled in the production of respectably sincere poetry: had it not been for the war he might even have produced some decent work in the manner of Henri de Régnier. But the war drove the gentle muse of second-rate poetry away from the colonnades and gardens and made her walk the streets. In one volume, his last volume, de Chaumont accompanied her, and there was a great deal about asphalt and the lovely legs of the Eiffel Tower and the beauties of reinforced concrete: his muse walked the pavements with the others, but she wore goloshes and was terribly afraid of being recognised: so that his fourth volume, as his third, was a failure. The promise of his juvenilia had not been fulfilled: he proclaimed that literature had gone to the Jews and Socialists: he returned to the fold of his collaterals: he read nothing except the Action Française: he began to think of marriage: he had long discussions with the Abbé Munier: he ceased even to get his clothes in London: he bought a pair of yellow dogskin gloves.

When I met him again in 1919 the effects of this degeneration were sadly apparent. He had spent the greater part of the War on the staff of General Lyautey in Morocco. On his return to Paris he was rapidly demobilised. Even as Rimbaud before him, he repudiated not only literature but his literary friends. I saw him at Foyot's, where I was dining with Lacretelle and Jean Cocteau: he sent me a note by the waiter asking me to lunch with him the next day at the Ritz: he paid no attention to my two companions.

It was with great relish that I was able the next day to tell him what an ass Cocteau had said that he was. He was rather pathetic about it. He almost convinced me that for his futile faubourg flabbiness there was something to be said. He spoke of his mother; a widow: she was getting frail and old: he was an only son: he would not wish to cause her pain. He spoke of his aunt de Maubize, of his uncle the prince, of how in France, under the third republic, it was impossible to compromise. "You see," he explained, "there are so few of us. We must keep together. We are the trustees of refoinement and distinction." I knew but little at that time of Parisian conditions and I almost believed him. I merely asked him how such people as the de Beaumonts, or Princess Marie Murat managed to reconcile their dynastic and racial duties with the enormous fun they got out of life, with the intellectual benefits they conferred on others. He smiled at me a little pityingly, making it clear that I was talking of things which only a very few people were privileged to understand. "It's moy mother," he added again. I had never seen his mother, and he was evidently in no way anxious that I should do so. I pictured her as an aged and a pathetic creature in black lace and diamonds, engrossed in religion, engrossed in Jacques. I know full well how these obligations can grow upon one, how loving hands can stretch out from the older generation to strangle the ardour of the next. How many of my friends had suffered from such infanticide, how many had cramped their style for fear of what Aunt Juliet would say at Littlehampton, or Uncle Roderick at Bath. I felt that I understood de Chaumont's point of view, I felt that on the whole he was behaving rather well.

And then, by chance, I met his mother at luncheon.

Jacques, I am glad to say, had not been invited. She was a brisk and manly little woman like a fox-terrier, and she rushed up to me jumping about and firing off little short sharp questions in a series of rapid barks. I was a friend of Jacques? He had often spoken of me. What were we to do about it? Was he in love? Did I think he would marry? Why had he chucked writing? Why had he dropped all his interesting friends? Why had he become such a bore? Et snob—enfin? She turned to a woman who was standing beside us. "C'est inconcevable, ma chère, à quel point ce garçon est devenu snob." "Ça doit être le jockey," her friend answered.

Madame de Chaumont agreed that it must be the jockey. They turned to me simultaneously—did I also think that the jockey was the cause of Jacques' inexplicable behaviour? I am not easily shocked, but I admit that at this question I blushed scarlet. I stammered something about his never having told me anything about it. I have since made frequent endeavours to remember exactly the words I used. I may have said, "He has never spoken to me about *the* jockey"; on the other hand, I may have said, "He has never spoken to me about *a* jockey." When I realised subsequently that they were referring merely to the Jockey Club; I saw how vast a difference, what a gulf between correctitude and flagrant indiscretion, stretched between the use on my part of that definite or that indefinite article. To this day I remain uncertain which of the two I employed. I remember only that I was acutely embarrassed and that everybody laughed.

v

It was about this time that the prix Goncourt was awarded to Proust for "Du coté de chez Swann." Proust began to be lionised. He would lie in bed all day in his stuffy darkened room, and in the evening he would put on his elaborate evening clothes (those white-kid gloves clasping an opera hat) and attend the receptions given to the members of the Peace Conference. He appeared there like Beethoven at the Congress of Vienna. He would flit about looking like a Goanese bridegroom. He would flit from Mr. Balfour to M. Venizelos, from Marshal Foch to M. Berthelot. He was very friendly, and ill, and amusing. He enjoyed hearing stories about the Conference. He seemed quite unaware of the early and enduring monument of his own impending fame. He drank a great deal of black coffee and stayed up very late.

On one such occasion he said that he would like to introduce me to the Marquis de Chaumont. I said that this was unnecessary since I had known de Chaumont for many years. He begged me not to be so unintelligent and so gross. Surely I must realise the pleasure it gave him to take an Englishman by the arm, to propel him across the room, to say, "Mon cher Jacques, permettez . . ." to hesitate and then to begin again, "Permettez, Monsieur, que je vous présente mon grand ami le Marquis de Chaumont." For me it would be perfectly easy. I should only have to say, "Oh! but I know de Chaumont, we were at Oxford together." And then the three of us could sit on that sofa over there and talk about the other people. "Vous voyez bien," he said, "c'est d'une simplicité. Allons-y! Ne soyez pas inintelligent!" I surrendered myself to this comedy. Proust purred like a small Siamese cat. De Chaumont, I am glad to say, was exquisitely polite. We sat on the sofa as arranged. As arranged, we talked about the other people.

After a few minutes de Chaumont rose and left us. We then talked about de Chaumont. Proust was indignant with me for regretting that so bright a talent should have been ruined by an undue deference to foreground. He did not agree with me in the least. He said that there were a great many young men who could write much better than Jacques de Chaumont, and very few young men who could show so many quarterings. It was right and fitting that Jacques should concentrate on the qualities which he possessed in so highly specialised a manner. The world was becoming too diverse: it was necessary to specialise. "Il ne fait que cultiver sa specialité! Il fait bien."

"I shall now speak to you," he said, "on the subject of elegance."

I was all attention, but fate cheated me of that discourse. We were interrupted by our hostess: Proust rose, and a few minutes later he drifted away. I leant against the window watching him. A little white face over there, those bruised eyes, that blue but shaven chin, those white gloves resting upon the opera hat. He was being universally affable. I never saw him again.

I walked away from that party with Jacques de Chaumont. I told him how excited I was by Proust, how Antoine Bibesco had promised on the following Sunday to take me to dinner with him in his bedroom. De Chaumont was not enthusiastic: "Un homme remarquable, évidemment, un homme remarquable: mais juif, juif." And that dinner never materialised. I have recently seen the letter which Proust wrote on that occasion to Antoine Bibesco. It was a letter in which he begged the latter to come alone on Sunday and not to bring me with him. The letter was quite kindly worded.

vi

A few weeks later we heard that Proust was again seriously ill. He had been working at *Pastiches et Mélanges*, and the effort had exhausted him. De Chaumont came to see me in obvious tribulation, carrying a letter in his hand. I read the letter. It was from Proust, saying that he had written a short sketch in the manner of St. Simon and would Jacques mind if he figured in it by name? The latter was embarrassed how to answer. He did not wish to offend Proust, yet on the other hand, well, really♣. . . I said that I, for my part, would have been in the seventh heaven had Proust showed any inclination to insert me in *Pastiches et Mélanges*. De Chaumont said "it moight be jolly well all roight for a foreigner, but moy mother would not loike it." I told him that I had met his mother, and was convinced that she would not mind in the least. He was only slightly disconcerted. "Then there is moy aunt, de Maubize. She 'ates Jews." I began to get a little angry at this, and told him that I doubted whether Proust would live for long, that he was the greatest living writer, that Jacques was sacrificing a free gift of immortality, and that what on earth could it matter about his aunt? He sat there turning the letter over and over in his gloved hands. Suddenly he tore it up with a gesture of decision: he flung it into one of the large brass bowls that enlivened the foyer of the Majestic.

"Non!" he said, "non pas! Ça me ratera mon Jockey."

The book appeared some months later and it contained no mention of Jacques de Chaumont. And the following year I met a member of the Jockey Club and asked him whether de Chaumont had been elected. He said that he had not been elected.

ARKETALL

THE train was waiting at Victoria Station and there remained but three minutes to the time when it was scheduled to leave. In front of the Pullman reserved for Lord Curzon clustered the photographers, holding their hooded cameras ungainlily. The station-master gazed towards the barrier. Already the two typists were ensconced in the saloon: Sir William Tyrrell in the next compartment had disappeared behind a newspaper: the red despatch boxes were piled upon the rack, and on the linoleum of the gangway Lord Curzon's armorial dressing-

case lay cheek by jowl with the fibre of Miss Petticue's portmanteau. I waited with Allen Leeper on the platform. We were
joined by Mr. Emmott of Reuter's. "Is the Marquis often as
late as this?" he inquired. "Lord Curzon," I answered, "is
never late," and as I said the words a slight stir was observable
at the barrier. Majestically, and as if he were carrying his own
howdah, Lord Curzon proceeded up the platform accompanied
by the police, paused for a moment while the cameras clicked,
smiled graciously upon the station-master, and entered the
Pullman. A whistle shrieked, a flag fluttered, the crowd stood
back from the train and began to wave expectantly. It was then
that I first saw Arketall. He was running with haste but dignity along the platform: in his left hand he held his bowler,
and in his right a green baize foot-rest. He jumped on to the
step as the train was already moving. "Crakey," said Arketall,
as he entered the saloon.

ii

Leeper and I sat opposite each other, going through the
telegrams which had been sent down to the station from the
Foreign Office. We sat there in the green morocco chairs of
the Southern Railway: the marquetry on the panels behind us
squeaked softly: the metal reading lamp chinked ever so
slightly against the glass top of the table: to our right the
houses of Purley, to our left the houses of Lewisham, passed
rapidly below us in the autumn sunshine: someone came and
told Leeper that he was wanted by Lord Curzon. I pushed the
telegrams aside and leant back in my chair. Miss Petticue was
reading the *Royal* magazine: Miss Bridges was reading her
own passport: I had ample time to study Arketall.

He sat opposite to me at the end of the saloon. A man, I
should have said, of about fifty-five; a tall man, at first impression, with a large naked face and large white bony hands. The
fine Victorian modelling of his brow and chin was marred by
a puffy weakness around the eyes and mouth: at certain angles
the thoughtful refinement of his features suggested a drawing
of Mr. Galsworthy by George Richmond: he would then shift
his position, the illusion would pass, there would be a touch of
red ink around the eyelids, a touch of violet ink about the lips:
the pallor of his cheeks, the little bleached ridges around his

mouth, would lose all suggestion of asceticism: when he leant forward in the full light of the window he had the appearance of an aged and dissolute pro-consul. His face, if he will forgive my saying so, seemed at such moments, self-indulgent. "That man," I reflected, "drinks."

I was well aware of the circumstances in which at the last moment Lord Curzon had engaged Arketall as his valet. Three days before we were due to leave for Lausanne, I had walked across to Carlton House Terrace with some papers that were urgently required. The Secretary of State was undergoing one of his recurrent attacks of phlebitis and I was taken up to his bedroom. I gave him the papers and he began to look at them, his lips, as was his wont, moving rapidly in a faint, but not unpleasant, whisper as he read the documents. My eyes wandered around the room. It was a small room with but one window which looked over the park: there was a white washing-stand, a servant's chest of drawers, and a cheap brass bedstead: the walls were papered with a simple pattern of sweet-pea, and there were some photographs and a brown wooden hair-brush upon the dressing-table: on the small mantelpiece beside me I noticed a washing-list, a bone collar-stud, and two pieces of string. It was like a single bedroom in one of the Gordon Hotels: the only luxuries were an elaborate telephone affixed to the wall beside the bed, and a large box of crystallised fruits upon a side-table. The problem of Lord Curzon's personality, which had become almost an obsession to me, was enhanced by the sight of these accessories. My eyes wandered round the room in mute surprise. They returned finally to the figure in the bed. He was no longer looking at the documents, he was looking at me. "You are observing," he said, "the simple squalor of my bedroom. I can assure you, however, that my wife's apartments are of the most unexampled magnificence." And at this his shoulders shook with that infectious laughter of his, that rich eighteenth-century amusement. "You have also," he continued, "observed the telephone. A disastrous invention, my dear Nicolson, but it has its uses. Thus if I make upon this ivory lever a slight pressure to deflect it to the right, a mere *exiguum clinamen*, the whole secrets of my household are revealed to me. I overhear. This morning, for instance, when thus switched on (I think that is the correct term) to the universe, the bell rung. A voice said, 'Is that you, Alf, and 'ow's it feeling this morning? I 'ad a devil of a time coming in with

the milk like that.' 'My dear young lady,' I answered, 'you
are singularly mistaken. You are not speaking to Mr. Alfred
Horlick, you are speaking to Lord Curzon himself.' The noises,
I may say, which greeted me from the other end indicated that
my words had produced an effect which was positively blasting.
And Horlick, an excellent valet, leaves me to-morrow."

Victim of such coincidences did Arketall sit there that morning in the Pullman with a small and incongruous bowler
perched upon his head. He became slightly uneasy at my
scrutiny: he reached for his suit-case and extracted *John o'
London's Weekly:* I returned to my telegrams. The train
skimmed tinkling and direct above the Weald of Kent.

iii

Our arrival at Dover somewhat disconcerted Arketall. It
was evident that he was proud of his competence as a travelling valet and anxious to win confidence by a brisk display of
merit. Before the train had come to a standstill he was out on
the platform, his face assuming the expression of "Leave everything to me." He was at once brushed aside by an inspector
of police and two Foreign Office messengers. A phalanx of
porters stood behind the inspector and leapt upon our baggage. The Foreign Office messengers seized the despatch boxes.
Before Arketall had realised what had happened, Lord Curzon was walking slowly towards the boat chatting to the inspector with not unconscious affability. We strolled behind.
Arketall came up to me and murmured something about passports. I waved him aside. There was a man beside the gangway
with a cinematograph, the handle of which he began to turn
gently as we approached. I glanced behind me at Arketall.
His attitude had stiffened suddenly into the processional.
"Arketall," I said to him, "you have forgotten the foot-rest."
"Crakey!" he exclaimed as he turned to run towards the train.
The other passengers were by then beginning to dribble
through the pens in which they had been herded: I leant over
the taffrail, watching the single agitation meeting the multiple
agitation: widows hurrying along searching frantically in their
reticules for those yellow tickets which would take them to
Bordighera: Arketall, in acute anxiety, breasting this fumbling
torrent with his bowler in his hand. A policeman touched me

on the shoulder: he was holding the foot-rest. "His lordship generally requires this with him on the voyage." But by then Arketall was but a distant dome-shaped head bobbing against a panic stream. The little cords that tied the awning above me were pattering against the stays in an off-shore wind: in the gap between the pier-heads a swell tumbled into foam, the inner harbour was wrinkled with scudding frowns: clearly we were in for a rough crossing. I took the foot-rest to Lord Curzon. He was sitting at his cabin table writing on loose sheets of foolscap in a huge flowing hand: his pencil dashed over the paper with incredible velocity: his lips moved: from time to time he would impatiently throw a finished sheet upon the chintz settee beside him. I adjusted the foot-rest. He groaned slightly as he moved his leg. He was much too occupied to notice my ministrations. I returned to the deck outside. A voice wailed to me from the shore: "It's gone; it's gone." Arketall flung into the words that forlorn intensity which throbs in the earlier poems of Lord Tennyson. I replied by reassuring gestures indicative that he should come on board. He was mopping his forehead with a large linen handkerchief: little white drops were still forming on it as he stood panting beside me. "Crakey," he gasped. "You had better go downstairs," I answered, "it is going to be rough." He closed one eye at me. "A little peg ay don't think." His words, at the moment, had little apparent meaning.

iv

I did not see Arketall again until we were approaching Calais. I found him talking to Sir William Tyrrell outside the cabin. "Now Ostend," he was saying, "that's another question. Nane francs a day and no questions asked." "And no questions asked," he repeated looking wistfully at the sand dunes. The inspector came up to me with a packet of passports: he said he would hand them over to the *commissaire de police* on arrival. I took them from him, desiring to solve a problem which had often assailed me, namely, whether Lord Curzon made out a passport for himself. It was there all right—"We George Nathaniel," and then his name written again in the blank spaces. That amused me, and I was still considering the curious associations evoked by such official Narcissism when we sidled up to the Calais landing-stage. The gangway was immediately opposite Lord Curzon's cabin: on the pier below stood the Consul in a top-hat, and some French officials: I went in to Lord Curzon and told him we were arriving: he was still writing hard, and paid no attention: on the settee beside him was a pile of foolscap and at least twenty envelopes stamped and addressed. A muffled jerk showed that we were already alongside. Sighing deeply Lord Curzon addressed and stamped the last envelope. "Send me that valet man," he said. I fetched Arketall, telling him to hurry as the other passengers were being kept waiting: there they were on my left secured by a cord across the deck, a serried wedge of passengers looking their part. Lord Curzon emerged genially from his cabin at the exact moment the gangway was fixed: Arketall followed with the foot-rest: he stumbled as he stepped on to the gangway and clasped the rail. "Yes, I thought he was drunk," said Sir W. Tyrrell as we followed in our correct order. Lord Curzon was being greeted by the Representative of the French Republic. He moved slowly towards the train, leaning on his ebony cane; behind him zigzagged Arketall, clasping the green baize foot-rest. "Hadn't we better warn the Marquis . . . ?" I asked. "Oh, he'll notice it soon enough." Lord Curzon had paused by the train to say a few chosen words to the Consul. Behind him stood Arketall, very rigid as to the feet, but swaying slightly with the upper part of the body, bending slowly forwards and then straightening himself with a jerk. We left for Paris.

v

The next thirty-six hours are somewhat of a blur in my memory. I can recall M. William Martin at the Gare du Nord and other top-hats raised simultaneously, and the flash and subsequent smell of magnesium wire lighting rows of white featureless faces beyond the barrier: a group of Americans pausing to stare at us, cocktail in hand, as we entered the Ritz —"Why, look, Mrs. Cameron . . ." and then the figure of Mr. Ellis, pale and courtly, standing erect beside Lord Curzon in the lift: the corridor stretching white, airless, unwindowed, the little lighted globes in the ceiling, the four detectives grouped together, a bottle of Evian and two glasses on a Saratoga trunk. I remember also a late dinner and Olivier ministering to Lord Curzon and yet not ignoring us—Olivier blending with a masterly precision the servile and the protective, the deferential and the condescending. And then the following day the familiar conference atmosphere: the crackle of Rolls-Royces upon the raked and watered gravel in front of the Affaires Etrangères: the slow ascent, maps, despatch boxes, politeness, up the wide stone staircase: the two huissiers in evening dress and silver chains, that huissier with a white nose, that other huissier whose nose is red: the first ante-room, gold and damask, the second soft-carpeted ante-room, damask and gold: the Salle de l'Horloge—green rectangles of tables, a perspective of pink rectangles of blotting-paper: M. Poincaré advancing from a group by the furthest window: the symmetry of alignment broken suddenly by papers on the green cloth, protruding edges of maps, despatch boxes with open lids, secretaries bending from behind over their employers, the interpreter sitting with his pencils and note-book by himself: the soft hum of traffic along the Quai d'Orsay.

We lunched that day with Madame Poincaré and afterwards the discussions continued: at 4 p.m. the chandeliers leapt in successive tiers to brilliance; the white and scarlet benches in the window recesses were hidden one by one as the silk curtains were drawn across them, and at five we had tea and macaroons in the large white room beyond. At nine we returned exhausted to our dinner; we were all to start for Lausanne next morning at 7.30.

We gathered sleepily at 7.5 a.m. in the hall of the Ritz: the revolving glass door was clamped open and a man in a striped apron was shaking an india-rubber mat out on to the Place Vendôme: the luggage had already preceded us, the typists were sitting in the third motor rather pinched and blue: we waited for Lord Curzon. At 7.16 a.m. he appeared from the lift escorted by Mr. Ellis. He climbed slowly into the motor, falling back on to the cushions with a sigh of pain: he beckoned to me: "I shall want my foot-rest." I dashed back into the hotel to search for Arketall. Mr. Ellis was standing by the staircase, and as I approached him I could hear something pattering above me down the stairs: at the last turning there was a bump and a sudden exclamation, and Arketall shot round and down the staircase like a bob-sleigh, landing beside me with his feet in the air and the foot-rest raised above him. "Crakey," he remarked. We had by then only eleven minutes in which to reach the Gare de Lyon. The three motors swayed and dashed

along the boulevards like fire-escapes to an incessant noise of
Claxons. Then very slowly, processionally, sleepily we walked
up through the station towards the platform. M. Poincaré in
a black silk cap with a peak was waiting, a little irritably I
thought, beside the train. There was a saloon for the French
Delegation, a saloon for the British Delegation, and separating them a satin-wood drawing-room carriage and a dining-
car. The large white clocks marked 7.29 as we entered the
train. At 7.30 we slid out into the grey morning past a stiff
line of saluting police and railway officials. Arketall was standing beside me: "Ay left me 'at behind," he remarked in sudden dismay. I had a picture of that disgraceful bowler lying
upwards on the stair carpet of the Ritz: "Tiens," they would
exclaim, "le chapeau de Lord Curzon." "You can get another,"
I answered, "at Lausanne." Miss Petticue came up to me holding a bowler. "They threw this into our motor as we were leaving the Ritz." I handed it in silence to Arketall.

vi

For the greater part of that twelve-hour journey we sat in
the drawing-room carriage discussing with our French colleagues the procedure of the impending conference: from time
to time a Frenchman would rise and retire to the back of the
train to consult M. Poincaré: from time to time Allen Leeper
or I would make our way to the front of the train to consult
Lord Curzon: outside his door Arketall sat on a spring bracket-
seat which let down on to the corridor: he would stand up when
we came, and the seat would fly up smack against the woodwork: Arketall looked shaken and unwell. Lord Curzon in his
coupé carriage reclined in a dove-coloured armchair with his
leg stretched out on the foot-rest. On the table beside him were
at least thirty envelopes stamped and addressed: he did not
appear to relish our interruptions.

Towards evening the lights were lit in that satinwood saloon.
We sat there, M. Barrère, General Weygand, Admiral Lacaze,
Sir William Tyrrell, Laroche, Massigli, Allen Leeper and myself. The discussion had by then become desultory: from time
to time a station would leap up at us from the gathering dusk,
flick past the train in a sudden rectangle of illuminated but
unfocussed shapes, be lost again in the brooding glimmer of

the Cotes d'Or. We stopped at Pontarlier and telephoned to
M. Mussolini. He answered from Locarno. He wanted us to
dine with him that night at Vevey. We pattered up and down
the platform conveying messages from M. Poincaré to Lord
Curzon, from Lord Curzon to M. Poincaré. It was agreed that
they would both proceed to Vevey, and then the train slid onwards down upon Lausanne. Lord Curzon in his dove-coloured
arm-chair was slightly petulant. He was all for dining with
M. Mussolini but would have preferred another night. "And
why Vevey?" he said. "Why indeed?" I echoed. Lord Curzon
sighed deeply and went on writing, writing. I left him and
stood in the corridor. Arketall had pulled up the blind, and as
the train jigged off to the left over some points a row of distant lights swung round to us, low lying, coruscating, white
and hard. "Evian," I said to Arketall. "Ho indeed," he answered. Ten minutes later, the train came to rest in the station of Lausanne: there was a pause and silence: the arc-
lamps on the platform threw white shapes across the corridor,
dimming our own lights, which but a few minutes before had
seemed so garish against the darkness. I returned to Lord
Curzon's compartment. "I think," he said, "that you and
Leeper had better get out here. It is quite unnecessary for you
to come on to Vevey." "Oh, but, sir . . ." I protested.
"Quite unnecessary," he repeated. I usually enjoyed an argument with Lord Curzon, but there was something in his voice
which indicated that any argument at that moment would be
misplaced. I went and told Leeper: we both seized our despatch
boxes and climbed down on to the platform. Bill Bentinck,
who had been sent on two days before to complete arrangements, came up to us, immaculate, adolescent and so reliable.
"There are four motors," he said, "and a lorry for the luggage." "The Marquis isn't coming," I informed him, "he and
M. Poincaré are going on to Vevey to dine with Mussolini.
They won't get back here till midnight." "Oh Lud," he exclaimed, "and there's a vast crowd outside and the Mayor of
Lausanne." "Lud," I echoed, and at that the slim presidential
train began to slide past us towards the night and Mussolini.
It was only then that I noticed that the platform was empty
from excess rather than from lack of public interest: behind
the barrier, behind a double row of police, stretched the expectant citizens of the Swiss Confederation. On the wide bare

desert of the platform stood Leeper in a little brown hat, myself in a little black hat, and Arketall in his recovered bowler: Miss Petticue: Miss Bridges: pitilessly the glare of forty arc-lamps beat down upon our isolation and inadequacy. We walked (with dignity I feel) towards the barrier: at our approach the magnesium wire flashed up into its own smoke and there was a stir of excitement in the crowd: somebody cheered: Arketall raised his bowler in acknowledgment: the cheers were repeated: he held his bowler raised at exactly the correct angle above his head: the Mayor advanced towards him. I intervened at that moment and explained the situation. The Mayor turned from me, a little curtly perhaps, and said something to the police inspector. The wide lane which had been kept open for us ceased suddenly to be a lane and became a crowd leaving a station: we left with it. In a few minutes we were hooting our way under the railway bridge and down to Ouchy.

vii

The hall of the Beau Rivage was crowded with hotel managers and journalists. The former bowed ingratiatingly at our entry: the latter, who had been sitting together at little tables drinking sherry, rose as a man to greet us. There was Mr. Walter, and Mr. Pirrie Gordon, and Mr. Ward Price, and Mr. Ryall. There were a great many others whom I did not know, they looked diverse and yet convivial: I like journalists in principle and was extremely sorry to disappoint them: at no moment of my life have I desired so acutely to be important. Through all this gratuitous humiliation I was conscious, however, of a thin thread somewhere within me of self-esteem. I lay idly in my bath trying to work this vaguely apprehended fibre of pleasure into the central focus of my consciousness, which seemed in its turn wholly occupied by pain: I tested myself in successive phases: the platform, solid pain: the exit from the platform, pain unrelieved: it was only when I went back to the phase in the motor that I ceased inwardly to wince. Leeper, rather tired and thinking silently about Rumania, had sat beside me; but Arketall, on the strapontin opposite, was full of talk. "Very civil," he had said. "these Swiss people. Now ay remember when ay was with a Columbian gentleman, we went to Zurich. You know Zurich, sir? Well, it was lake this . . ." Yes, Arketall at that moment had called me "sir": up to that moment he had treated me solely as a colleague. Something in the force of my personality or in Lord Curzon's absence had elevated me to a higher level of regard. I was gratified on discovering this, and lay back in my bath thinking affectionately of Lord Curzon, who at that moment must have been descending on to the platform at Vevey. Sir William Tyrrell would have to carry the foot-rest: I did so hope that, if Lord Curzon got tired, Sir William would be able to soothe him down.

We dined downstairs in the restaurant. The remainder of the Delegation had assembled by earlier trains. There was General Burnett-Stuart with a military staff, and Sir Roger Keyes with naval assistants: there was Mr. S. D. Waley of the Treasury, and Mr. Payne of the Board of Trade: our own Secretariat was under the charge of Tom Spring Rice: there was a young man of extreme elegance who looked after the maps: there was an accountant and two further lady typists, and there was Mr. McClure for the Press. Undoubtedly we were an imposing collection. M. Duca and M. Diamandy, the Rumanian representatives, were seated at a further table; they came across to us and gave us caviare out of a flat tin box. I was pleased at this, mainly for Allen Leeper's sake, since, although in general the most stimulating of companions, he is apt at moments to brood about Rumania in silent suffering: with their arrival his pang had found a voice. It was a pleasant dinner if I remember rightly, and when it was over, Leeper and I ascended to put the final touches to Lord Curzon's suite. A large drawing-room on the first floor gazing from its three high windows upon the lake: on the left a dining-room, on the right a bedroom with baths beyond. The drawing-room was sprinkled with little white arm-chairs and tables looking very occasional: there were palms and chrysanthemums in a large brass jardinière: there was a little bean-shaped bureau, and on the walls some coloured prints of ladies in green riding-habits descending the steps of Chambord, Chenonceaux and Blois. We removed these pictures and secured a larger writing-table. We sent for more flowers, and arranged some newspapers and brandy and soda upon a side table. In the bedroom next door Arketall was unpacking several trunks: I looked in on him: he was not inclined for con-

versation, but hiccoughed gently to himself as he swayed, now
over the Marquis' black suits and now over his grey. It was
by then 11.30: a telephone message came in from Vevey to
say that Lord Curzon should reach Lausanne about midnight:
we descended to the hall to await his arrival.

viii

At 12.10 there was a stir at the front door and the managers dashed to the entrance. They returned in triumph,
escorting a small brown gentleman in a brown suit and very
white shirt-cuffs. He carried a brown bowler in his left hand
and his right was thrust into his waistcoat. The iris of his
eyes was entirely surrounded by white, a phenomenon which
I had hitherto observed only in the photographs of distinguished mesmerists. He was followed by three or four other
gentlemen and two boy-scouts in black shirts. An electric
tremor ran through the assembled journalists. "Mussolini,"
they whispered in amazement. I turned to Allen Leeper.
"Really," I remarked, "that was very odd indeed." "It was,"
he answered.

Ten minutes later the glass doors again gyrated and Lord
Curzon, magnificent and smiling, stood upon the threshold.
Slowly and benignly he bowed to the managers: to the journalists he made a friendly gesture at once welcoming and dis-
missive: he proceeded to the lift. Seizing the green foot-rest
from Sir William Tyrrell, I hurried through the crowd
towards the staircase: "Tiens," exclaimed a French journalist,
indicating the foot-rest, "le trône de Bagdad." I pushed past
him and arrived on the first floor just as Lord Curzon was
leaving the lift. He paused at the doorway of his apartment
and surveyed it. "How ghastly!" he sighed. He walked
towards the window, pulled aside the yellow cretonne curtain,
and gazed across to the lights of Evian. "How positively
ghastly," he repeated. We helped him out of his large Lovat
mixture greatcoat; we propped the ebony cane against the
white wall: we pulled up the least diminutive of the sixteen
armchairs, and we placed the foot-rest in position. He sank
back, sipped at a brandy-and-soda, sighed deeply, and then
embarked on a narrative of the Vevey conference.

Ah, those Curzonian dissertations! No small thing has passed from my life now they are silenced. As if some stately procession proceeding orderly through Arcs de Triomphe along a straight wide avenue: outriders, escorts, bands; the perfection of accoutrements, the precise marshalling of detail, the sense of conscious continuity, the sense of absolute control. The voice rising at moments in almost histrionic scorn, or dropping at moments into a hush of sudden emotion; and then a flash of March sunshine, a sudden dart of eighteen-century humour, a pause while his wide shoulders rose and fell in rich amusement. And all this under a cloud of exhaustion, under a cloud of persistent pain.

The glamour of this particular discourse was somewhat dimmed for me by anxiety on behalf of Arketall. The door into the bedroom was open, and there came from it the sound of cupboards opening and shutting, the sound at intervals of a hiccough inadequately suppressed. "We had by then," Lord Curzon was saying, "reached the last point of the six which I have grouped under category A. Mussolini had as yet not fully grasped my intention; with the assistance of that dilapidated marmoset who acts as his mentor I regained my point of departure: the status of pertinenza, I explained . . ."

" 'Ic" came loudly from the adjoining room. Lord Curzon paused. My eyes met those of Allen Leeper and I motioned to him to close the door.

". . . the status of pertinenza, I explained, was in no way identical with what we regard as domicile. Poincaré, who on all such points, is exasperatingly punctilious, insisted on interrupting. He maintained . . ."

" 'Ic," said Arketall from the next room. Leeper had by then reached the doorway and closed it abruptly. "What was that?" said Lord Curzon, turning a petulant eye in my direction. "It is your servant, sir, unpacking some clothes."

"He maintained that the *droit d'établissement* . . ." The procession had re-formed and continued its stately progress: it continued until 2 a. m.: the Marquis then dismissed us: he said he had letters to write as well as a report for the Cabinet; he had by then to our certain knowledge been working without interruption for nineteen hours; and yet in the morning there was a report of eight pages for the Cabinet, and on the table in the passage twenty-two letters addressed and stamped—or, as he himself would have said "stamped and directed."

ix

Next morning there was to be a meeting to continue the conversations begun at Vevey. We arranged a large table in Lord Curzon's room and placed paper and pencils at intervals. The Marquis sat at his desk writing rapidly. Punctually at eleven both doors were flung open by Arketall. "Excellence Poyncarry," he bawled, "and General Wiggand." Lord Curzon rose genially to meet them, and conducted them to the table. They sat down and waited for M. Mussolini. General Weygand began drawing little squares and triangles on the sheet before him. M. Poincaré rose and walked up and down the room in obvious impatience, flicking his pince-nez against his thumb-nail. From time to time he would pause at one of the windows, looking at the grey fog which crept among the conifers. Lord Curzon kept on sending me with messages to the Duce urging him to come. I did not execute these missions, knowing them to be of no avail, but I had several pleasant chats in the passage with Mario Pansa, who was acting as M. Mussolini's personal secretary. From time to time I would return to Lord Curzon's room and assure them all that M. Mussolini was on his way. I would then resume my talks with Mario, whose gay Harrovian chatter relieved a situation which but for him I might have found a trifle tense. When, at 11.35, M. Mussolini actually did come, he came very quickly. Pushing Arketall aside, His Excellency shot into the room like a brown thunderbolt, stopped short, clicked his heels, bowed and exclaimed, "Je vous salue, Messieurs." They then sat down at the table, and we sat behind. The maps were spread in convenient places; the interpreter sharpened his pencil. The Vevey conversations were resumed.

That evening M. Poincaré returned to Paris, and M. Mussolini to Rome: Lord Curzon was left preëminent over a Conference consisting mostly of Ambassadors. There was M. Barrère and M. Bompard for France: and for Italy the aged Marchese Garroni: Ismet Pasha, deaf and boyish, coped with a large and resentful Turkish delegation: M. Venizelos, troubled but conciliatory, spoke for Greece: at moments, even, the mezzo-soprano of M. Tchicherine would quaver into our discussion. And as the days passed, Arketall, to my despair, entered visibly on a decline.

x

We found it difficult to induce Lord Curzon to treat the problem seriously. On the second morning Arketall, in helping his master on with his socks, had slipped and fallen. "Arketall," Lord Curzon had remonstrated, "you are either very ill or very drunk." "Both, m' Lord," Arketall had answered. Lord Curzon was so pleased with this response that his affection for Arketall became unassailable. We grew seriously uneasy. I found him one morning standing by the side-table in the dining-room pouring liqueur-brandy into a claret glass. He winked slowly at me and placed a shaky forefinger beside his nose. I was incensed at this gesture of confederacy: I told Bill Bentinck that the Marquis must again be warned. But unfortunately that morning Marchese Garroni had, in Lord Curzon's presence, mistaken Arketall for Sir Roger Keyes, had seized both his hands and had assured him in a torrent of Genoese French how great a debt, how unforgettable a debt, Italy owned to the noble and generous British Navy. Lord Curzon was so delighted by this incident that our warnings fell on even deafer ears. A catastrophe was imminent, and it came.

The Hôtel Beau Rivage at Ouchy consists of two wings joined together by a large suite of ball-rooms and dining-rooms. In the evening the natives of Lausanne and the visitors undergoing either education or treatment would gather in the foyer to listen to the band, to watch the dancing, and to observe the diplomatists and journalists passing backwards and forwards on hurried and mysterious errands. Saturday was the gala night, and on Saturdays I would generally slip down after eleven and sit there admiring the couples jerking together in the ball-room. There was an American woman of great distinction, who wore a stomacher of diamonds: there was a greedy-looking Cuban woman in a wheeled basket chair: there was Prince Nicholas of Russia, who was staying at a neighbouring pension and who danced with all the young ladies. It was a pleasant sight, and on the second Saturday I induced Lord Curzon to come and watch it. He stood there by the entrance to the ball-room leaning on his ebony cane, and smiling genially at the diverse couples who jigged and twirled before him. I observed the American lady syncopating towards us in the arms of a distinguished-looking gentleman in evening dress. I called Lord Curzon's attention to her, warning him to observe her stomacher as she passed. He glanced towards her and grasped my arm. "Surely," he said, "surely that can't be Arketall?" It was Arketall, and he recognised us at the same moment. In trying to wince away from the cold inquiry in Lord Curzon's eye, he slipped between the legs of the American lady and brought her down upon him. Lord Curzon had turned abruptly and was walking back across the foyer. I ran after him. "I think," he said, "that Arketall had better leave. He had better leave early to-morrow."

I returned to the ball-room and accompanied Arketall to his room. He was somewhat dazed by his experience and he followed me meekly. I told him that there was a train at 7.30 next morning and he had better leave by it. He plunged under the bed and began pulling out his portmanteau: it refused to move and he tugged at it viciously: three empty bottles of Benedictine and a bottle of Grand Marnier shot out into the room, followed by the trunk. Arketall sat on the floor, nodding at the empty bottles. "You must pull yourself together," I said. "You should at least assist us to minimise the scandal which your conduct has caused." "Never," he hiccoughed vaguely, "not no more."

xi

I did not witness his departure. I merely heard next morning that he had gone. While having breakfast I received a message that Lord Curzon wished to see me urgently. I found him in his dressing-gown. He was half angry and half amused. "That indefinite Arketall," he said, "has stolen my trousers." "Not all your trousers?" I asked in some confusion. "Yes, all of them, except these." Lord Curzon was wearing his evening trousers of the night before. I glanced at my watch. There was still an hour before the meeting of the Conference, but by this time Arketall must have reached Pontarlier. I ran for Bill Bentinck and told him to telephone to the frontier police: "Don't say trousers," I shouted after him, "say 'quelques effets.'" I then secured the manager and proceeded to Arketall's room. We looked in, over and under the cupboard and into the chest of drawers: I peered under the bed; there were three more bottles of Benedictine against the wall, but otherwise the space was empty. The manager and I looked at each other in despair. "C'est inénarrable," he muttered, "complètement in'é-narrable." I sat down wearily on the bed to consider our position. I jumped up again immediately and pulled back the bed-spread. Upon the crumpled bed-clothes lay a trouser-press bursting with Lord Curzon's trousers. I sent the manager to stop Bill Bentinck telephoning; myself I clasped the trouser-press and returned in triumph to Lord Curzon. He was seated at his writing-table, his pencil dashing across sheets of foolscap, his lips moving. I stood there waiting. When he had finished four or five sheets and cast them from him he turned to me indignantly. His face relaxed into a smile and then extended into that irresistible laugh of his, that endearing boyish sense of farce. "Thank you," he said, "I shall now complete my toilet. There will only be Leeper to dinner to-night, and as a reward I shall give you my celebrated imitation of Tennyson reciting 'Tears, idle tears.' "

He kept his promise. It was an amazing performance. We expressed our admiration and our gratitude. A sudden wave of depression descended upon Lord Curzon. "Ah, yes," he sighed, "ah yes. I know. All that was years ago, when I was young and could still laugh at my elders. But all young men are remorseless. You will go upstairs this evening and chaff me behind my back. You will give imitations in after life of the old buffer imitating Tennyson. And so it continues." He sighed deeply. And then he grinned. "I am sorry," he said, "for Arketall. I liked that man."

David Garnett

LADY INTO FOX

WONDERFUL or supernatural events are not so uncommon, rather they are irregular in their incidence. Thus there may be not one marvel to speak of in a century, and then often enough comes a plentiful crop of them; monsters of all sorts swarm suddenly upon the earth, comets blaze in the sky, eclipses frighten nature, meteors fall in rain, while mermaids and sirens beguile, and sea-serpents engulf every passing ship, and terrible cataclysms beset humanity.

But the strange event which I shall here relate came alone, unsupported, without companions into a hostile world, and for that very reason claimed little of the general attention of mankind. For the sudden changing of Mrs. Tebrick into a vixen is an established fact which we may attempt to account for as we will. Certainly it is in the explanation of the fact, and the reconciling of it with our general notions that we shall find most difficulty, and not in accepting for true a story which is so fully proved, and that not by one witness but by a dozen, all respectable, and with no possibility of collusion between them.

But here I will confine myself to an exact narrative of the event and all that followed on it. Yet I would not dissuade any of my readers from attempting an explanation of this seeming miracle because up till now none has been found which is entirely satisfactory. What adds to the difficulty to my mind is that the metamorphosis occurred when Mrs. Tebrick was a full-grown woman, and that it happened suddenly in so short a space of time. The sprouting of a tail, the gradual extension of hair all over the body, the slow change of the whole anatomy by a process of growth, though it would have been monstrous, would not have been so difficult to reconcile to our ordinary conceptions, particularly had it happened in a young child.

But here we have something very different. A grown lady is changed straightway into a fox. There is no explaining that away by any natural philosophy. The materialism of our age will not help us here. It is indeed *a miracle;* something from outside our world altogether; an event which we would willingly accept if we were to meet it invested with the authority of Divine Revelation in the Scriptures, but which we are not prepared to encounter almost in our time, happening in Oxfordshire amongst our neighbours.

The only things which go any way towards an explanation of it are but guesswork, and I give them more because I would not conceal anything, than because I think they are of any worth.

Mrs. Tebrick's maiden name was certainly Fox, and it is possible that such a miracle happening before, the family may have gained their name as a *soubriquet* on that account. They were an ancient family, and have had their seat at Tangley Hall time out of mind. It is also true that there was a half-tame fox once upon a time chained up at Tangley Hall in the inner yard, and I have heard many speculative wiseacres in the public-houses turn that to great account—though they could not but admit that "there was never one there in Miss Silvia's time." At first I was inclined to think that Silvia Fox, having once hunted when she was a child of ten and having been blooded, might furnish more of an explanation. It seems she took great fright or disgust at it, and vomited after it was done. But now I do not see that it has much bearing on the miracle itself, even though we know that after that she always spoke of the "poor foxes" when a hunt was stirring and never rode to hounds till after her marriage when her husband persuaded her to it.

She was married in the year 1879 to Mr. Richard Tebrick, after a short courtship, and went to live after their honeymoon at Rylands, near Stokoe, Oxon. One point indeed I have not been able to ascertain and that is how they first became acquainted. Tangley Hall is over thirty miles from Stokoe, and is extremely remote. Indeed to this day there is no proper road to it, which is all the more remarkable as it is the principal, and indeed the only, manor house for several miles around.

Whether it was from a chance meeting on the roads, or less romantic but more probable, by Mr. Tebrick becoming acquainted with her uncle, a minor canon at Oxford, and thence being invited by him to visit Tangley Hall, it is impossible to say. But however they became acquainted the marriage was a very happy one. The bride was in her twenty-third year. She was small, with remarkably small hands and feet. It is perhaps worth noting that there was nothing at all foxy or vixenish in her appearance. On the contrary, she was a more than ordinarily beautiful and agreeable woman. Her eyes were of a clear hazel but exceptionally brilliant, her hair dark, with a shade of red in it, her skin brownish, with a few dark freckles and little moles. In manner she was reserved almost to shyness, but perfectly self-possessed, and perfectly well-bred.

She had been strictly brought up by a woman of excellent principles and considerable attainments, who died a year or so before the marriage. And owing to the circumstance that her mother had been dead many years, and her father bedridden, and not altogether rational for a little while before his death, they had few visitors but her uncle. He often stopped with them a month or two at a stretch, particularly in winter, as he was fond of shooting snipe, which are plentiful in the valley there. That she did not grow up a country hoyden is to be explained by the strictness of her governess and the influence of her uncle. But perhaps living in so wild a place gave her some disposition to wildness, even in spite of her religious upbringing. Her old nurse said: "Miss Silvia was always a little wild at heart," though if this was true it was never seen by anyone else except her husband.

On one of the first days of the year 1880, in the early afternoon, husband and wife went for a walk in the copse on the little hill above Rylands. They were still at this time like lovers in their behaviour and were always together. While they were walking they heard the hounds and later the huntsman's horn in the distance. Mr. Tebrick had persuaded her to hunt on Boxing Day, but with great difficulty, and she had not enjoyed it (though of hacking she was fond enough).

Hearing the hunt, Mr. Tebrick quickened his pace so as to reach the edge of the copse, where they might get a good view of the hounds if they came that way. His wife hung back, and he, holding her hand, began almost to drag her. Before they gained the edge of the copse she suddenly snatched her hand away from his very violently and cried out, so that he instantly turned his head.

Where his wife had been the moment before was a small fox, of a very bright red. It looked at him very beseechingly, advanced towards him a pace or two, and he saw at once that his wife was looking at him from the animal's eyes. You may well think if he were aghast: and so maybe was his lady at finding herself in that shape, so they did nothing for nearly half-an-hour but stare at each other, he bewildered, she asking him with her eyes as if indeed she spoke to him: "What am I now become? Have pity on me, husband, have pity on me for I am your wife."

So that with his gazing on her and knowing her well, even in such a shape, yet asking himself at every moment: "Can it be she? Am I not dreaming?" and her beseeching and lastly fawning on him and seeming to tell him that it was she indeed, they came at last together and he took her in his arms. She lay very close to him, nestling under his coat and fell to licking his face, but never taking her eyes from his.

The husband all this while kept turning the thing in his head and gazing on her, but he could make no sense of what had happened, but only comforted himself with the hope that this was but a momentary change, and that presently she would turn back again into the wife that was one flesh with him.

One fancy that came to him, because he was so much more like a lover than a husband, was that it was his fault, and this because if anything dreadful happened he could never blame her but himself for it.

So they passed a good while, till at last the tears welled up in the poor fox's eyes and she began weeping (but quite in silence), and she trembled too as if she were in a fever. At this he could not contain his own tears, but sat down on the ground and sobbed for a great while, but between his sobs kissing her quite as if she had been a woman, and not caring in his grief that he was kissing a fox on the muzzle.

They sat thus till it was getting near dusk, when he recollected himself, and the next thing was that he must somehow hide her, and then bring her home.

He waited till it was quite dark that he might the better bring her into her own house without being seen, and buttoned her inside his topcoat, nay, even in his passion tearing open his waistcoat and his shirt that she might lie the closer to his heart. For when we are overcome with the greatest sorrow we act not like men or women but like children whose comfort in all their troubles is to press themselves against their mother's breast, or if she be not there to hold each other tight in one another's arms.

When it was dark he brought her in with infinite precautions, yet not without the dogs scenting her, after which nothing could moderate their clamour.

Having got her into the house, the next thing he thought of was to hide her from the servants. He carried her to the bedroom in his arms and then went downstairs again.

Mr. Tebrick had three servants living in the house, the cook, the parlourmaid, and an old woman who had been his wife's nurse. Besides these women there was a groom or a gardener (whichever you choose to call him), who was a single man and so lived out, lodging with a labouring family about half a mile away.

Mr. Tebrick going downstairs pitched upon the parlourmaid.

"Janet," says he, "Mrs. Tebrick and I have had some bad news, and Mrs. Tebrick was called away instantly to London and left this afternoon, and I am staying to-night to put our affairs in order. We are shutting up the house, and I must give you and Mrs. Brant a month's wages and ask you to leave to-morrow morning at seven o'clock. We shall probably go away to the Continent, and I do not know when we shall come back. Please tell the others, and now get me my tea and bring it into my study on a tray."

Janet said nothing for she was a shy girl, particularly before gentlemen, but when she entered the kitchen Mr. Tebrick heard a sudden burst of conversation with many exclamations from the cook.

When she came back with his tea, Mr. Tebrick said: "I shall not require you upstairs. Pack your own things and tell James to have the wagonette ready for you by seven o'clock to-morrow morning to take you to the station. I am busy now, but I will see you again before you go."

When she had gone Mr. Tebrick took the tray upstairs. For the first moment he thought the room was empty, and his vixen got away, for he could see no sign of her anywhere. But after a moment he saw something stirring in a corner of the room, and then behold! she came forth dragging her dressing-gown, into which she had somehow struggled.

This must surely have been a comical sight, but poor Mr. Tebrick was altogether too distressed then or at any time afterwards to divert himself at such ludicrous scenes. He only called to her softly:

"Silvia—Silvia. What do you do there?" And then in a moment saw for himself what she would be at, and began once more to blame himself heartily—because he had not guessed that his wife would not like to go naked, notwithstanding the shape she was in. Nothing would satisfy him then till he had clothed her suitably, bringing her dresses from the wardrobe for her to choose. But as might have been expected, they were too big for her now, but at last he picked out a little dressing-jacket that she was fond of wearing sometimes in the mornings. It was made of a flowered silk, trimmed with lace, and the sleeves short enough to sit very well on her now. While he tied the ribands his poor lady thanked him with gentle looks and not without some modesty and confusion. He propped her up in an armchair with some cushions, and they took tea together, she very delicately drinking from a saucer and taking bread and butter from his hands. All this showed him, or so he thought, that his wife was still herself; there was so little wildness in her demeanour and so much delicacy and decency, especially in her not wishing to run naked, that he was very much comforted, and began to fancy they could be happy enough if they could escape the world and live always alone.

From this too sanguine dream he was aroused by hearing the gardener speaking to the dogs, trying to quiet them, for ever since he had come in with his vixen they had been whining, barking and growling, and all as he knew because there was a fox within doors and they would kill it.

He started up now, calling to the gardener that he would come down to the dogs himself to quiet them, and bade the man go indoors again and leave it to him. All this he said in a dry, compelling kind of voice which made the fellow do as he was bid, though it was against his will, for he was curious. Mr. Tebrick went downstairs, and taking his gun from the rack loaded it and went out into the yard. Now there were two dogs, one a handsome Irish setter that was his wife's dog (she had brought it with her from Tangley Hall on her marriage); the other was an old fox terrier called Nelly that he had had ten years or more.

When he came out into the yard both dogs saluted him by barking and whining twice as much as they did before, the setter jumping up and down at the end of his chain in a frenzy, and Nelly shivering, wagging her tail, and looking first at her master and then at the house door, where she could smell the fox right enough.

There was a bright moon, so that Mr. Tebrick could see the dogs as clearly as could be. First he shot his wife's setter dead, and then looked about him for Nelly to give her the other barrel, but he could see her nowhere. The bitch was clean gone, till, looking to see how she had broken her chain, he found her lying hid in the back of her kennel. But that trick did not save her, for Mr. Tebrick, after trying to pull her out by her chain and finding it useless—she would not come,— thrust the muzzle of his gun into the kennel, pressed it into her body and so shot her. Afterwards, striking a match, he looked in at her to make certain she was dead. Then, leaving the dogs as they were, chained up, Mr. Tebrick went indoors again and found the gardener, who had not yet gone home, gave him a month's wages in lieu of notice and told him he had a job for him yet—to bury the two dogs and that he should do it that same night.

But by all this going on with so much strangeness and authority on his part, as it seemed to them, the servants were much troubled. Hearing the shots while he was out in the yard his wife's old nurse, or Nanny, ran up to the bedroom though she had no business there, and so opening the door saw the poor fox dressed in my lady's little jacket lying back in the cushions, and in such a reverie of woe that she heard nothing.

Old Nanny, though she was not expecting to find her mistress there, having been told that she was gone that afternoon to London, knew her instantly, and cried out:

"Oh, my poor precious! Oh, poor Miss Silvia! What dreadful change is this?" Then, seeing her mistress start and look at her, she cried out:

"But never fear, my darling, it will all come right, your old Nanny knows you, it will all come right in the end."

But though she said this she did not care to look again, and kept her eyes turned away so as not to meet the foxy slit ones of her mistress, for that was too much for her. So she hurried out soon, fearing to be found there by Mr. Tebrick, and who knows, perhaps shot, like the dogs, for knowing the secret.

Mr. Tebrick had all this time gone about paying off his servants and shooting his dogs as if he were in a dream. Now he fortified himself with two or three glasses of strong whisky and went to bed, taking his vixen into his arms, where he slept soundly. Whether she did or not is more than I or anybody else can say.

In the morning when he woke up they had the place to themselves, for on his instructions the servants had all left first thing: Janet and the cook to Oxford, where they would try and find new places, and Nanny going back to the cottage near Tangley, where her son lived, who was the pigman there.

So with that morning there began what was now to be their ordinary life together. He would get up when it was broad day, and first thing light the fire downstairs and cook the breakfast, then brush his wife, sponge her with a damp sponge, then brush her again, in all this using scent very freely to hide somewhat her rank odour. When she was dressed he carried her downstairs and they had their breakfast together, she sitting up to table with him, drinking her saucer of tea, and taking her food from his fingers, or at any rate being fed by him. She was still fond of the same food that she had been used to before her transformation, a lightly boiled egg or slice of ham, a piece of buttered toast or two, with a little quince and apple jam. While I am on the subject of her food, I should say that reading in the encyclopedia he found that foxes on the Continent are inordinately fond of grapes, and that during the autumn season they abandon their ordinary diet for them, and then grow exceedingly fat and lose their offensive odour.

This appetite for grapes is so well confirmed by Æsop, and by passages in the Scriptures, that it is strange Mr. Tebrick should not have known it. After reading this account he wrote to London for a basket of grapes to be posted to him twice a week and was rejoiced to find that the account in the encyclopedia was true in the most important of these particulars. His vixen relished them exceedingly and seemed never to tire of them, so that he increased his order first from one pound to three pounds and afterwards to five. Her odour abated so much by this means that he came not to notice it at all except sometimes in the mornings before her toilet.

What helped him most to make living with her bearable for him was that she understood him perfectly—yes, every word he said, and though she was dumb she expressed herself very fluently by looks and signs though never by the voice.

Thus he frequently conversed with her, telling her all his thoughts and hiding nothing from her, and this the more readily because he was very quick to catch her meaning and her answers.

"Puss, Puss," he would say to her, for calling her that had been a habit with him always. "Sweet Puss, some men would pity me living alone here with you after what has happened, but I would not change places while you were living with any man for the whole world. Though you are a fox I would rather live with you than any woman. I swear I would, and that too if you were changed to anything." But then, catching her grave look, he would say: "Do you think I jest on these things, my dear? I do not. I swear to you, my darling, that all my life I will be true to you, will be faithful, will respect and reverence you who are my wife. And I will do that not because of any hope that God in His mercy will see fit to restore your shape, but solely because I love you. However you may be changed, my love is not."

Then anyone seeing them would have sworn that they were lovers, so passionately did each look on the other.

Often he would swear to her that the devil might have power to work some miracles, but that he would find it beyond him to change his love for her.

These passionate speeches, however they might have struck his wife in an ordinary way, now seemed to be her chief comfort. She would come to him, put her paw in his hand and look at him with sparkling eyes shining with joy and gratitude, would pant with eagerness, jump at him and lick his face.

Now he had many little things which busied him in the house—getting his meals, setting the room straight, making the bed and so forth. When he was doing this housework it was comical to watch his vixen. Often she was as it were beside herself with vexation and distress to see him in his clumsy way doing what she could have done so much better had she been able. Then, forgetful of the decency and the decorum which she had at first imposed upon herself never to run upon all fours, she followed him everywhere, and if he did one thing wrong she stopped him and showed him the way of it. When he had forgot the hour for his meal she would come and tug his sleeve and tell him as if she spoke: "Husband, are we to have no luncheon to-day?"

This womanliness in her never failed to delight him, for it showed she was still his wife, buried as it were in the carcase of a beast but with a woman's soul. This encouraged him so much that he debated with himself whether he should not read aloud to her, as he often had done formerly. At last, since he could find no reason against it, he went to the shelf and fetched down a volume of the "History of Clarissa Harlowe," which he had begun to read aloud to her a few weeks before. He opened the volume where he had left off, with Lovelace's letter after he had spent the night waiting fruitlessly in the copse.

"Good God!

What is now to become of me?

My feet benumbed by midnight wanderings through the heaviest dews that ever fell; my wig and my linen dripping with the hoarfrost dissolving on them!

Day but just breaking . . ." etc.

While he read he was conscious of holding her attention, then after a few pages the story claimed all his, so that he read on for about half-an-hour without looking at her. When he did so he saw that she was not listening to him, but was watching something with strange eagerness. Such a fixed intent look was on her face that he was alarmed and sought the cause of it. Presently he found that her gaze was fixed on the movements of her pet dove which was in its cage hanging in the window. He spoke to her, but she seemed displeased, so he laid "Clarissa Harlowe" aside. Nor did he ever repeat the experiment of reading to her.

Yet that same evening, as he happened to be looking through his writing table drawer with Puss beside him looking over his elbow, she spied a pack of cards, and then he was forced to pick them out to please her, then draw them from their case. At last, trying first one thing, then another, he found that what she was after was to play piquet with him. They had some difficulty at first in contriving for her to hold her cards and then to play them, but this was at last overcome by his stacking them for her on a sloping board, after which she could flip them out very neatly with her claws as she wanted to play them. When they had overcome this trouble they played three games, and most heartily she seemed to enjoy them. Moreover she won all three of them. After this they often played a quiet game of piquet together, and cribbage too. I should say that in marking the points at cribbage on the board he always moved her pegs for her as well as his own, for she could not handle them or set them in the holes.

The weather, which had been damp and misty, with frequent downpours of rain, improved very much in the following week, and, as often happens in January, there were several days with the sun shining, no wind and light frosts at night, these frosts becoming more intense as the days went on till bye and bye they began to think of snow.

With this spell of fine weather it was but natural that Mr. Tebrick should think of taking his vixen out of doors. This was something he had not yet done, both because of the damp rainy weather up till then and because the mere notion of taking her out filled him with alarm. Indeed he had so many apprehensions beforehand that at one time he resolved totally against it. For his mind was filled not only with the fear that she might escape from him and run away, which he knew was groundless, but with more rational visions, such as wandering curs, traps, gins, spring guns, besides a dread of being seen with her by the neighbourhood. At last however he resolved on it, and all the more as his vixen kept asking him in the gentlest way: "Might she not go into the garden?" Yet she always listened very submissively when he told her that he was afraid if they were seen together it would excite the curiosity of their neighbours; besides this, he often told her of his fears for her on account of dogs. But one day she answered this by leading him into the hall and pointing boldly to his gun. After this he resolved to take her, though with full precautions. That is he left the house door open so that in case of need she could beat a swift retreat, then he took his gun under his arm, and lastly he had her well wrapped up in a little fur jacket lest she should take cold.

He would have carried her too, but that she delicately disengaged herself from his arms and looked at him very expressively to say that she would go by herself. For already her first horror of being seen to go upon all fours was worn off; reasoning no doubt upon it, that either she must resign herself to go that way or else stay bed-ridden all the rest of her life.

Her joy at going into the garden was inexpressible. First she ran this way, then that, though keeping always close to him, looking very sharply with ears cocked forward first at one thing, then another and then up to catch his eye.

For some time indeed she was almost dancing with delight, running round him, then forward a yard or two, then back to him and gambolling beside him as they went round the garden. But in spite of her joy she was full of fear. At every noise, a cow lowing, a cock crowing, or a ploughman in the distance hulloaing to scare the rooks, she started, her ears pricked to catch the sound, her muzzle wrinkled up and her nose twitched, and she would then press herself against his legs. They walked round the garden and down to the pond where there were ornamental waterfowl, teal, widgeon and mandarin ducks, and seeing these again gave her great pleasure. They had always been her favourites, and now she was so overjoyed to see them that she behaved with very little of her usual self-restraint. First she stared at them, then bouncing up to her husband's knee sought to kindle an equal excitement in his mind. Whilst she rested her paws on his knee she turned her head again and again towards the ducks as though she could not take her eyes off them, and then ran down before him to the water's edge.

But her appearance threw the ducks into the utmost degree of consternation. Those on shore or near the bank swam or flew to the centre of the pond, and there huddled in a bunch; and then, swimming round and round, they began such a quacking that Mr. Tebrick was nearly deafened. As I have before said, nothing in the ludicrous way that arose out of the metamorphosis of his wife (and such incidents were plentiful) ever stood a chance of being smiled at by him. So in this case, too, for realising that the silly ducks thought his wife a fox indeed and were alarmed on that account he found painful that spectacle which to others might have been amusing.

Not so his vixen, who appeared if anything more pleased than ever when she saw in what a commotion she had set them, and began cutting a thousand pretty capers. Though at first he called to her to come back and walk another way, Mr. Tebrick was overborne by her pleasure and sat down, while she frisked around him happier far than he had seen her ever since the change. First she ran up to him in a laughing way, all smiles, and then ran down again to the water's edge and began frisking and frolicking, chasing her own brush, dancing on her hind legs even, and rolling on the ground, then fell to running in circles, but all this without paying any heed to the ducks.

But they, with their necks craned out all pointing one way, swam to and fro in the middle of the pond, never stopping their quack, quack, quack, and keeping time too, for they all quacked in chorus. Presently she came further away from the pond, and he, thinking they had had enough of this sort of entertainment, laid hold of her and said to her:

"Come, Silvia, my dear, it is growing cold, and it is time we went indoors. I am sure taking the air has done you a world of good, but we must not linger any more."

She appeared then to agree with him, though she threw half a glance over her shoulder at the ducks, and they both walked soberly enough towards the house.

When they had gone about halfway she suddenly slipped round and was off. He turned quickly and saw the ducks had been following them.

So she drove them before her back into the pond, the ducks running in terror from her with their wings spread, and she not pressing them, for he saw that had she been so minded she could have caught two or three of the nearest. Then, with her brush waving above her, she came gambolling back to him so playfully that he stroked her indulgently, though he was first vexed, and then rather puzzled that his wife should amuse herself with such pranks.

But when they got within doors he picked her up in his arms, kissed her and spoke to her.

"Silvia, what a light-hearted childish creature you are. Your courage under misfortune shall be a lesson to me, but I cannot, I cannot bear to see it."

Here the tears stood suddenly in his eyes, and he lay down upon the ottoman and wept, paying no heed to her until presently he was aroused by her licking his cheek and his ear.

After tea she led him to the drawing room and scratched at the door till he opened it, for this was part of the house which he had shut up, thinking three or four rooms enough for them now, and to save the dusting of it. Then it seemed she would have him play to her on the pianoforte: she led him to it, nay, what is more, she would herself pick out the music he was to play. First it was a fugue of Handel's, then one of

Mendelssohn's Songs Without Words, and then "The Diver," and then music from Gilbert and Sullivan; but each piece of music she picked out was gayer than the last one. Thus they sat happily engrossed for perhaps an hour in the candle light until the extreme cold in that unwarmed room stopped his playing and drove them downstairs to the fire. Thus did she admirably comfort her husband when he was dispirited.

Yet next morning when he woke he was distressed when he found that she was not in the bed with him but was lying curled up at the foot of it. During breakfast she hardly listened when he spoke, and then impatiently, but sat staring at the dove.

Mr. Tebrick sat silently looking out of the window for some time, then he took out his pocketbook; in it there was a photograph of his wife taken soon after their wedding. Now he gazed and gazed upon those familiar features, and now he lifted his head and looked at the animal before him. He laughed then bitterly, the first and last time for that matter that Mr. Tebrick ever laughed at his wife's transformation, for he was not very humorous. But this laugh was sour and painful to him. Then he tore up the photograph into little pieces, and scattered them out of the window, saying to himself: "Memories will not help me here," and turning to the vixen he saw that she was still staring at the caged bird, and as he looked he saw her lick her chops.

He took the bird into the next room, then acting suddenly upon the impulse, he opened the cage door and set it free, saying as he did so:

"Go, poor bird! Fly from this wretched house while you still remember your mistress who fed you from her coral lips. You are not a fit plaything for her now. Farewell, poor bird! Farewell! Unless," he added with a melancholy smile, "you return with good tidings like Noah's dove."

But, poor gentleman, his troubles were not over yet, and indeed one may say that he ran to meet them by his constant supposing that his lady should still be the same to a tittle in her behaviour now that she was changed into a fox.

Without making any unwarrantable suppositions as to her soul or what had now become of it (though we could find a good deal to the purpose on that point in the system of Paracelsus), let us consider only how much the change in her body must needs affect her ordinary conduct. So that before we judge too harshly of this unfortunate lady, we must reflect upon the physical necessities and infirmities and appetites of her new condition, and we must magnify the fortitude of her mind which enabled her to behave with decorum, cleanliness and decency in spite of her new situation.

Thus she might have been expected to befoul her room, yet never could anyone, whether man or beast, have shown more nicety in such matters. But at luncheon Mr. Tebrick helped her to a wing of chicken, and leaving the room for a minute to fetch some water which he had forgot, found her at his return on the table crunching the very bones. He stood silent, dismayed and wounded to the heart at this sight. For we must observe that this unfortunate husband thought always of his vixen as that gentle and delicate woman she had lately been. So that whenever his vixen's conduct went beyond that which he expected in his wife he was, as it were, cut to the quick, and no kind of agony could be greater to him than to see her thus forget herself. On this account it may indeed be regretted that Mrs. Tebrick had been so exactly well-bred, and in particular that her table manners had always been scrupulous. Had she been in the habit, like a continental princess I have dined with, of taking her leg of chicken by the drumstick and gnawing the flesh, it had been far better for him now. But as her manners had been perfect, so the lapse of them was proportionately painful to him. Thus in this instance he stood as it were in silent agony till she had finished her hideous crunching of the chicken bones and had devoured every scrap. Then he spoke to her gently, taking her on to his knee, stroking her fur and fed her with a few grapes, saying to her:

"Silvia, Silvia, is it so hard for you? Try and remember the past, my darling, and by living with me we will quite forget that you are no longer a woman. Surely this affliction will pass soon, as suddenly as it came, and it will all seem to us like an evil dream."

Yet though she appeared perfectly sensible of his words and gave him sorrowful and penitent looks like her old self, that same afternoon, on taking her out, he had all the difficulty in the world to keep her from going near the ducks.

There came to him then a thought that was very disagreeable to him, namely, that he dare not trust his wife alone with any bird or she would kill it. And this was the more shocking to him to think of since it meant that he durst not trust her as much as a dog even. For we may trust dogs who are familiars, with all the household pets; nay more, we can put them upon trust with anything and know they will not touch it, not even if they be starving. But things were come to such a pass with his vixen that he dared not in his heart trust her at all. Yet she was still in many ways so much more woman than fox that he could talk to her on any subject and she would understand him, better far than the oriental women who are kept in subjection can ever understand their masters unless they converse on the most trifling household topics.

Thus she understood excellently well the importance and duties of religion. She would listen with approval in the evening when he said the Lord's Prayer, and was rigid in her observance of the Sabbath. Indeed, the next day being Sunday he, thinking no harm, proposed their usual game of piquet, but no, she would not play. Mr. Tebrick, not understanding at first what she meant, though he was usually very quick with her, he proposed it to her again, which she again refused, and this time, to show her meaning, made the sign of the cross with her paw. This exceedingly rejoiced and comforted him in his distress. He begged her pardon, and fervently thanked God for having so good a wife, who, in spite of all, knew more of her duty to God than he did. But here I must warn the reader from inferring that she was a papist because she then made the sign of the cross. She made that sign to my thinking only on compulsion because she could not express herself except in that way. For she had been brought up as a true Protestant, and that she still was one is confirmed by her objection to cards, which would have been less than nothing to her had she been a papist. Yet that evening, taking her into the drawing room so that he might play her some sacred music, he found her after some time cowering away from him in the farthest corner of the room, her ears flattened back and an expression of the greatest anguish in her eyes. When he spoke to her she licked his hand, but remained shivering for a long time at his feet and showed the clearest symptoms of terror if he so much as moved towards the piano.

On seeing this and recollecting how ill the ears of a dog can bear with our music, and how this dislike might be expected to be even greater in a fox, all of whose senses are more acute from being a wild creature, recollecting this he closed the piano and taking her in his arms, locked up the room and never went into it again. He could not help marvelling though, since it was but two days after she had herself led him there, and even picked out for him to play and sing those pieces which were her favourites.

That night she would not sleep with him, neither in the bed nor on it, so that he was forced to let her curl herself up on the floor. But neither would she sleep there, for several times she woke him by trotting around the room, and once when he had got sound asleep by springing on the bed and then off it, so that he woke with a violent start and cried out, but got no answer either, except hearing her trotting round and round the room. Presently he imagines to himself that she must want something, and so fetches her food and water, but she never so much as looks at it, but still goes on her rounds, every now and then scratching at the door.

Though he spoke to her, calling her by her name, she would pay no heed to him, or else only for the moment. At last he gave her up and said to her plainly: "The fit is on you now Silvia to be a fox, but I shall keep you close and in the morning you will recollect yourself and thank me for having kept you now."

So he lay down again, but not to sleep, only to listen to his wife running about the room and trying to get out of it. Thus he spent what was perhaps the most miserable night of his existence. In the morning she was still restless, and was reluctant to let him wash and brush her, and appeared to dislike being scented but as it were to bear with it for his sake. Ordinarily she had taken the greatest pleasure imaginable in her toilet, so that on this account, added to his sleepless night, Mr. Tebrick was utterly dejected, and it was then that he resolved to put a project into execution that would show him, so he thought, whether he had a wife or only a wild vixen in his house. But yet he was comforted that she bore at all with him, though so restlessly that he did not spare her, calling her a "bad wild fox." And then speaking to her in this manner: "Are you not ashamed, Silvia, to be such a madcap, such a wicked hoyden? You who were particular in dress. I see it was all vanity—now you have not your former advantages you think nothing of decency."

His words had some effect with her too, and with himself, so that by the time he had finished dressing her they were both in the lowest state of spirits imaginable and neither of them far from tears.

Breakfast she took soberly enough, and after that he went about getting his experiment ready, which was this. In the garden he gathered together a nosegay of snowdrops, those being all the flowers he could find, and then going into the village of Stokoe bought a Dutch rabbit (that is a black and white one) from a man there who kept them.

When he got back he took his flowers and at the same time set down the basket with the rabbit in it, with the lid open. Then he called to her: "Silvia, I have brought some flowers for you. Look, the first snowdrops."

At this she ran up very prettily, and never giving as much as one glance at the rabbit which had hopped out of its basket, she began to thank him for the flowers. Indeed she seemed indefatigable in shewing her gratitude, smelt them, stood a little way off looking at them, then thanked him again. Mr. Tebrick (and this was all part of his plan) then took a vase and went to find some water for them, but left the flowers beside her. He stopped away five minutes, timing it by his watch and listening very intently, but never heard the rabbit squeak. Yet when he went in what a horrid shambles was spread before his eyes. Blood on the carpet, blood on the armchairs and antimacassars, even a little blood spurtled on to the wall, and what was worse, Mrs. Tebrick tearing and growling over a piece of the skin and the legs, for she had eaten up all the rest of it. The poor gentleman was so heartbroken over this that he was like to have done himself an injury, and at one moment thought of getting his gun, to have shot himself and his vixen too. Indeed the extremity of his grief was such that it served him a very good turn, for he was so entirely unmanned by it that for some time he could do nothing but weep, and fell into a chair with his head in his hands, and so kept weeping and groaning.

After he had been some little while employed in this dismal way, his vixen, who had by this time bolted down the rabbit, skin, head, ears and all, came to him and putting her paws on his knees, thrust her long muzzle into his face and began licking him. But he, looking at her now with different eyes, and seeing her jaws still sprinkled with fresh blood and her claws full of the rabbit's fleck, would have none of it.

But though he beat her off four or five times even to giving her blows and kicks, she still came back to him, crawling on her belly and imploring his forgiveness with wide-open sorrowful eyes. Before he had made this rash experiment of the rabbit and the flowers, he had promised himself that if she failed in it he would have no more feeling or compassion for her than if she were in truth a wild vixen out of the woods. This resolution, though the reasons for it had seemed to him so very plain before, he now found more difficult to carry out than to decide on. At length after cursing her and beating her off for upwards of half-an-hour, he admitted to himself that he still did care for her, and even loved her dearly in spite of all, whatever pretence he affected towards her. When he had acknowledged this he looked up at her and met her eyes fixed upon him, and held out his arms to her and said:

"Oh Silvia, Silvia, would you had never done this! Would I had never tempted you in a fatal hour! Does not this butchery and eating of raw meat and rabbit's fur disgust you? Are you a monster in your soul as well as in your body? Have you forgotten what it is to be a woman?"

Meanwhile, with every word of his, she crawled a step nearer on her belly and at last climbed sorrowfully into his arms. His words then seemed to take effect on her and her eyes filled with tears and she wept most penitently in his arms, and her body shook with her sobs as if her heart were breaking. This sorrow of hers gave him the strangest mixture of pain and joy that he had ever known, for his love for her returning with a rush, he could not bear to witness her pain and yet must take pleasure in it as it fed his hopes of her one day returning to be a woman. So the more anguish of shame his vixen underwent, the greater his hopes rose, till his love and pity for her increasing equally, he was almost wishing her to be nothing more than a mere fox than to suffer so much by being half-human.

At last he looked about him somewhat dazed with so much weeping, then set his vixen down on the ottoman, and began to clean up the room with a heavy heart. He fetched a pail of water and washed out all the stains of blood, gathered up the two antimacassars and fetched clean ones from the other rooms. While he went about this work his vixen sat and watched him very contritely with her nose between her two front paws, and when he had done he brought in some luncheon for himself, though it was already late, but none for her, she having lately so infamously feasted. But water he gave her and a bunch of grapes. Afterwards she led him to the small tortoiseshell cabinet and would have him open it. When he had done so she motioned to the portable stereoscope which lay inside. Mr. Tebrick instantly fell in with her wish and after a few trials adjusted it to her vision. Thus they spent the rest of the afternoon together very happily looking through the collection of views which he had purchased, of Italy, Spain and Scotland. This diversion gave her great apparent pleasure and afforded him considerable comfort. But that night he could not prevail upon her to sleep in bed with him, and finally allowed her to sleep on a mat beside the bed where he could stretch down and touch her. So they passed the night, with his hand upon her head.

The next morning he had more of a struggle than ever to wash and dress her. Indeed at one time nothing but holding her by the scruff prevented her from getting away from him, but at last he achieved his object and she was washed, brushed, scented and dressed, although to be sure this left him better pleased than her, for she regarded her silk jacket with disfavour.

Still at breakfast she was well mannered though a trifle hasty with her food. Then his difficulties with her began for she would go out, but as he had his housework to do, he could not allow it. He brought her picture books to divert her, but she would have none of them but stayed at the door scratching it with her claws industriously till she had worn away the paint.

At first he tried coaxing her and wheedling, gave her cards to play patience and so on, but finding nothing would distract her from going out, his temper began to rise, and he told her plainly that she must wait his pleasure and that he had as much natural obstinacy as she had. But to all that he said she paid no heed whatever but only scratched the harder.

Thus he let her continue until luncheon, when she would not sit up, or eat off a plate, but first was for getting on to the table, and when that was prevented, snatched her meat and ate it under the table. To all his rebukes she turned a deaf or sullen ear, and so they each finished their meal eating little, either of them, for till she would sit at table he would give her no more, and his vexation had taken away his own appetite. In the afternoon he took her out for her airing in the garden.

She made no pretence now of enjoying the first snowdrops

or the view from the terrace. No—there was only one thing
for her now—the ducks, and she was off to them before he
could stop her. Luckily they were all swimming when she got
there (for a stream running into the pond on the far side it
was not frozen there).

When he had got down to the pond, she ran out on to the
ice, which would not bear his weight, and though he called
her and begged her to come back she would not heed him but
stayed frisking about, getting as near the ducks as she dared,
but being circumspect in venturing on to the thin ice.

Presently she turned on herself and began tearing off her
clothes, and at last by biting got off her little jacket and
taking it in her mouth stuffed it into a hole in the ice where
he could not get it. Then she ran hither and thither a stark
naked vixen, and without giving a glance to her poor husband
who stood silently now upon the bank, with despair and terror
settled in his mind. She let him stay there most of the afternoon till he was chilled through and through and worn out
with watching her. At last he reflected how she had just
stripped herself and how in the morning she struggled against
being dressed, and he thought perhaps he was too strict with
her and if he let her have her own way they could manage to
be happy somehow together even if she did eat off the floor. So
he called out to her then:

"Silvia, come now, be good, you shan't wear any more
clothes if you don't want to, and you needn't sit at table
neither, I promise. You shall do as you like in that, but you
must give up one thing, and that is you must stay with me
and not go out alone, for that is dangerous. If any dog came
on you he would kill you."

Directly he had finished speaking she came to him joyously,
began fawning on him and prancing round him so that in
spite of his vexation with her, and being cold, he could not
help stroking her.

"Oh, Silvia, are you not wilful and cunning? I see you
glory in being so, but I shall not reproach you but shall stick
to my side of the bargain, and you must stick to yours."

He built a big fire when he came back to the house and took
a glass or two of spirits also, to warm himself up, for he was
chilled to the very bone. Then, after they had dined, to cheer
himself he took another glass, and then another, and so on
till he was very merry, he thought. Then he would play with

his vixen, she encouraging him with her pretty sportiveness. He got up to catch her then and finding himself unsteady on his legs, he went down on to all fours. The long and the short of it is that by drinking he drowned all his sorrow; and then would be a beast too like his wife, though she was one through no fault of her own, and could not help it. To what lengths he went then in that drunken humour I shall not offend my readers by relating, but shall only say that he was so drunk and sottish that he had a very imperfect recollection of what had passed when he woke the next morning. There is no exception to the rule that if a man drink heavily at night the next morning will show the other side to his nature. Thus with Mr. Tebrick, for as he had been beastly, merry and a very dare-devil the night before, so on his awakening was he ashamed, melancholic and a true penitent before his Creator. The first thing he did when he came to himself was to call out to God to forgive him for his sin, then he fell into earnest prayer and continued so for half-an-hour upon his knees. Then he got up and dressed but continued very melancholy for the whole of the morning. Being in this mood you may imagine it hurt him to see his wife running about naked, but he reflected it would be a bad reformation that began with breaking faith. He had made a bargain and he would stick to it, and so he let her be, though sorely against his will.

For the same reason, that is because he would stick to his side of the bargain, he did not require her to sit up at table, but gave her her breakfast on a dish in the corner, where to tell the truth she on her side ate it all up with great daintiness and propriety. Nor did she make any attempt to go out of doors that morning, but lay curled up in an armchair before the fire dozing. After lunch he took her out, and she never so much as offered to go near the ducks, but running before him led him on to take her a longer walk. This he consented to do very much to her joy and delight. He took her through the fields by the most unfrequented ways, being much alarmed lest they should be seen by anyone. But by good luck they walked above four miles across country and saw nobody. All the way his wife kept running on ahead of him, and then back to him to lick his hand and so on, and appeared delighted at taking exercise. And though they started two or three rabbits and a hare in the course of their walk she never attempted to go after them, only giving them a look and then looking back to him, laughing at him as it were for his warning cry of "Puss! come in, no nonsense now!"

Just when they got home and were going into the porch they came face to face with an old woman. Mr. Tebrick stopped short in consternation and looked about for his vixen, but she had run forward without any shyness to greet her. Then he recognized the intruder, it was his wife's old nurse.

"What are you doing here, Mrs. Cork?" he asked her.

Mrs. Cork answered him in these words:

"Poor thing. Poor Miss Silvia! It is a shame to let her run about like a dog. It is a shame, and your own wife too. But whatever she looks like, you should trust her the same as ever. If you do she'll do her best to be a good wife to you, if you don't I shouldn't wonder if she did turn into a proper fox. I saw her, sir, before I left, and I've had no peace of mind. I couldn't sleep thinking of her. So I've come back to look after her, as I have done all her life, sir," and she stooped down and took Mrs. Tebrick by the paw.

Mr. Tebrick unlocked the door and they went in. When Mrs. Cork saw the house she exclaimed again and again: "The place was a pigstye. They couldn't live like that, a gentleman must have somebody to look after him. She would do it. He could trust her with the secret."

Had the old woman come the day before it is likely enough that Mr. Tebrick would have sent her packing. But the voice of conscience being woken in him by his drunkenness of the night before he was heartily ashamed of his own management of the business, moreover the old woman's words that "it was a shame to let her run about like a dog," moved him exceedingly. Being in this mood the truth is he welcomed her.

But we may conclude that Mrs. Tebrick was as sorry to see her old Nanny as her husband was glad. If we consider that she had been brought up strictly by her when she was a child, and was now again in her power, and that her old nurse could never be satisfied with her now whatever she did, but would always think her wicked to be a fox at all, there seems good reason for her dislike. And it is possible, too, that there may have been another cause as well, and that is jealousy. We know her husband was always trying to bring her back to be a woman, or at any rate to get her to act like one, may she not have been hoping to get him to be like a beast himself or to act like one? May she not have thought it easier to change him thus than ever to change herself back into being a woman? If we think that she had had a success of this kind only the night before, when he got drunk, can we not conclude that this was indeed the case, and then we have another good reason why the poor lady should hate to see her old nurse?

It is certain that whatever hopes Mr. Tebrick had of Mrs. Cork affecting his wife for the better were disappointed. She grew steadily wilder and after a few days so intractable with her that Mr. Tebrick again took her under his complete control.

The first morning Mrs. Cork made her a new jacket, cutting down the sleeves of a blue silk one of Mrs. Tebrick's and trimming it with swan's down, and directly she had altered it, put it on her mistress, and fetching a mirror would have her admire the fit of it. All the time she waited on Mrs. Tebrick the old woman talked to her as though she were a baby, and treated her as such, never thinking perhaps that she was either the one thing or the other, that is either a lady to whom she owed respect and who had rational powers exceeding her own, or else a wild creature on whom words were wasted. But though at first she submitted passively, Mrs. Tebrick only waited for her Nanny's back to be turned to tear up her pretty piece of handiwork into shreds, and then ran gaily about waving her brush with only a few ribands still hanging from her neck.

So it was time after time (for the old woman was used to having her own way) until Mrs. Cork would, I think, have tried punishing her if she had not been afraid of Mrs. Tebrick's row of white teeth, which she often showed her, then laughing afterwards, as if to say it was only play.

Not content with tearing off the dresses that were fitted on her, one day Silvia slipped upstairs to her wardrobe and tore down all her old dresses and made havoc with them, not sparing her wedding dress either, but tearing and ripping them all up so that there was hardly a shred or rag left big enough to dress a doll in. On this, Mr. Tebrick, who had let the old woman have most of her management to see what she could make of her, took her back under his own control.

He was sorry enough now that Mrs. Cork had disappointed him in the hopes he had had of her, to have the old woman, as it were, on his hands. True she could be useful enough in many ways to him, by doing the housework, the cooking and mending, but still he was anxious since his secret was in her keeping, and the more now that she had tried her hand with his wife and failed. For he saw that vanity had kept her mouth shut if she had won over her mistress to better ways, and her love for her would have grown by getting her own way with her. But now that she had failed she bore her mistress a grudge for not being won over, or at the best was become indifferent to the business, so that she might very readily blab.

For the moment all Mr. Tebrick could do was to keep her from going into Stokoe to the village, where she would meet all her old cronies and where there were certain to be any number of inquiries about what was going on at Rylands and so on. But as he saw that it was clearly beyond his power, however vigilant he might be, to watch over the old woman and his wife, and to prevent anyone from meeting with either of them, he began to consider what he could best do.

Since he had sent away his servants and the gardener, giving out a story of having received bad news and his wife going away to London where he would join her, their probably going out of England and so on, he knew well enough that there would be a great deal of talk in the neighbourhood.

And as he had now stayed on, contrary to what he had said, there would be further rumour. Indeed, had he known it, there was a story already going round the country that his wife had run away with Major Solmes, and that he was gone mad with grief, that he had shot his dogs and his horses and shut himself up alone in the house and would speak with no one. This story was made up by his neighbours not because they were fanciful or wanted to deceive, but like most tittle-tattle to fill a gap, as few like to confess ignorance, and if people are asked about such or such a man they must have something to say, or they suffer in everybody's opinion, are set down as dull or "out of the swim." In this way I met not long ago with someone who, after talking some little while and not knowing me or who I was, told me that David Garnett was dead, and died of being bitten by a cat after he had tormented it. He had long grown a nuisance to his friends as an exorbitant sponge upon them, and the world was well rid of him.

Hearing this story of myself diverted me at the time, but I fully believe it has served me in good stead since. For it set me on my guard as perhaps nothing else would have done, against accepting for true all floating rumour and village gossip, so that now I am by second nature a true sceptic and scarcely believe anything unless the evidence for it is conclusive. Indeed I could never have got to the bottom of this history if I had believed one tenth part of what I was told, there was so much of it that was either manifestly false or absurd, or else contradictory to the ascertained facts. It is therefore only the bare bones of the story which you will find written here, for I have rejected all the flowery embroideries which would be entertaining reading enough, I daresay, for some, but if there be any doubt of the truth of a thing it is poor sort of entertainment to read about in my opinion.

To get back to our story: Mr. Tebrick having considered how much the appetite of his neighbours would be whetted to find out the mystery by his remaining in that part of the country, determined that the best thing he could do was to remove.

After some time turning the thing over in his mind, he decided that no place would be so good for his purpose as old Nanny's cottage. It was thirty miles away from Stokoe, which in the country means as far as Timbuctoo does to us in London. Then it was near Tangley, and his lady having known it from her childhood would feel at home there, and also it was utterly remote, there being no village near it or manor house other than Tangley Hall, which was now untenanted for the greater part of the year. Nor did it mean imparting his secret to others, for there was only Mrs. Cork's son, a widower, who being out at work all day would be easily outwitted, the more so as he was stone deaf and of a slow and saturnine disposition. To be sure there was little Polly, Mrs. Cork's granddaughter, but either Mr. Tebrick forgot her altogether, or else reckoned her as a mere baby and not to be thought of as a danger.

He talked the thing over with Mrs. Cork, and they decided upon it out of hand. The truth is the old woman was beginning to regret that her love and her curiosity had ever brought her back to Rylands, since so far she had got much work and little credit by it.

When it was settled, Mr. Tebrick disposed of the remaining business he had at Rylands in the afternoon, and that was chiefly putting out his wife's riding horse into the keeping of a farmer near by, for he thought he would drive over with his own horse, and the other spare horse tandem in the dog-cart.

The next morning they locked up the house and they departed, having first secured Mrs. Tebrick in a large wicker hamper where she would be tolerably comfortable. This was for safety, for in the agitation of driving she might jump out, and on the other hand, if a dog scented her and she were loose, she might be in danger of her life. Mr. Tebrick drove with the hamper beside him on the front seat, and spoke to her gently very often.

She was overcome by the excitement of the journey and kept poking her nose first through one crevice, then through another, turning and twisting the whole time and peeping out to see what they were passing. It was a bitterly cold day, and when they had gone about fifteen miles they drew up by the roadside to rest the horses and have their own luncheon, for he dared not stop at an inn. He knew that any living creature in a hamper, even if it be only an old fowl, always draws attention; there would be several loafers most likely who would notice that he had a fox with him, and even if he left the hamper in the cart the dogs at the inn would be sure to sniff out her scent. So not to take any chances he drew up at the side of the road and rested there, though it was freezing hard and a north-east wind blowing.

He took down his precious hamper, unharnessed his two horses, covered them with rugs and gave them their corn. Then he opened the basket and let his wife out. She was quite beside herself with joy, running hither and thither, bouncing up on him, looking about her and even rolling on the ground. Mr. Tebrick took this to mean that she was glad at making this journey and rejoiced equally with her. As for Mrs. Cork, she sat motionless on the back seat of the dogcart well wrapped up, eating her sandwiches, but would not speak a word. When they had stayed there half-an-hour Mr. Tebrick harnessed the horses again, though he was so cold he could scarcely buckle the straps, and put his vixen in her basket, but seeing that she wanted to look about her, he let her tear away the osiers with her teeth till she had made a hole big enough for her to put her head out of.

They drove on again and then the snow began to come down and that in earnest, so that he began to be afraid they would never cover the ground. But just after nightfall they

got in, and he was content to leave unharnessing the horses
and baiting them to Simon, Mrs. Cork's son. His vixen was
tired by then, as well as he, and they slept together, he in the
bed and she under it, very contentedly.

The next morning he looked about him at the place and
found the thing there that he most wanted, and that was a
little walled-in garden where his wife could run in freedom
and yet be in safety.

After they had had breakfast she was wild to go out into
the snow. So they went out together, and he had never seen
such a mad creature in all his life as his wife was then. For
she ran to and fro as if she were crazy, biting at the snow
and rolling in it, and round and round in circles and rushed
back at him fiercely as if she meant to bite him. He joined her
in the frolic, and began snowballing her till she was so wild
that it was all he could do to quiet her again and bring her
indoors for luncheon. Indeed with her gambollings she tracked
the whole garden over with her feet; he could see where she
had rolled in the snow and where she had danced in it, and
looking at those prints of her feet as they went in, made his
heart ache, he knew not why.

They passed the first day at old Nanny's cottage happily
enough, without their usual bickerings, and this because of the
novelty of the snow which had diverted them. In the afternoon
he first showed his wife to little Polly, who eyed her very
curiously but hung back shyly and seemed a good deal afraid
of the fox. But Mr. Tebrick took up a book and let them get
acquainted by themselves, and presently looking up saw that
they had come together and Polly was stroking his wife, patting her and running her fingers through her fur. Presently
she began talking to the fox, and then brought her doll in to
show her so that very soon they were very good playmates
together. Watching the two gave Mr. Tebrick great delight,
and in particular when he noticed that there was something
very motherly in his vixen. She was indeed far above the child
in intelligence and restrained herself too from any hasty action.
But while she seemed to wait on Polly's pleasure yet she managed to give a twist to the game, whatever it was, that never
failed to delight the little girl. In short, in a very little while,
Polly was so taken with her new playmate that she cried when
she was parted from her and wanted her always with her. This
disposition of Mrs. Tebrick's made Mrs. Cork more agreeable

than she had been lately either to the husband or the wife.

Three days after they had come to the cottage the weather changed, and they woke up one morning to find the snow gone, and the wind in the south, and the sun shining, so that it was like the first beginning of spring.

Mr. Tebrick let his vixen out into the garden after breakfast, stayed with her awhile, and then went indoors to write some letters.

When he got out again he could see no sign of her anywhere, so that he ran about bewildered, calling to her. At last he spied a mound of fresh earth by the wall in one corner of the garden and running thither found that there was a hole freshly dug seeming to go under the wall. On this he ran out of the garden quickly till he came to the other side of the wall, but there was no hole there, so he concluded that she was not yet got through. So it proved to be, for reaching down into the hole he felt her brush with his hand, and could hear her distinctly working away with her claws. He called to her then, saying: "Silvia, Silvia, why do you do this? Are you trying to escape from me? I am your husband, and if I keep you confined it is to protect you, not to let you run into danger. Show me how I can make you happy and I will do it, but do not try to escape from me. I love you, Silvia; is it because of that that you want to fly from me to go into the world where you will be in danger of your life always? There are dogs everywhere and they all would kill you if it were not for me. Come out, Silvia, come out."

But Silvia would not listen to him, so he waited there silent. Then he spoke to her in a different way, asking her had she forgot the bargain she made with him that she would not go out alone, but now when she had all the liberty of a garden to herself would she wantonly break her word? And he asked her, were they not married? And had she not always found him a good husband to her? But she heeded this neither until presently his temper getting somewhat out of hand he cursed her obstinacy and told her if she would be a damned fox she was welcome to it, for his part he could get his own way. She had not escaped yet. He would dig her out for he still had time, and if she struggled put her in a bag.

These words brought her forth instantly and she looked at him with as much astonishment as if she knew not what could have made him angry. Yes, she even fawned on him, but in a good-natured kind of way, as if she were a very good wife putting up wonderfully with her husband's temper.

These airs of hers made the poor gentleman (so simple was he) repent his outburst and feel most ashamed.

But for all that when she was out of the hole he filled it up with great stones and beat them in with a crowbar so she should find her work at that point harder than before if she was tempted to begin it again.

In the afternoon he let her go again into the garden but sent little Polly with her to keep her company. But presently on looking out he saw his vixen had climbed up into the limbs of an old pear tree and was looking over the wall, and was not so far from it but she might jump over it if she could get a little further.

Mr. Tebrick ran out into the garden as quick as he could, and when his wife saw him it seemed she was startled and made a false spring at the wall, so that she missed reaching it and fell back heavily to the ground and lay there insensible. When Mr. Tebrick got up to her he found her head was twisted under her by her fall and the neck seemed to be broken. The shock was so great to him that for some time he could not do anything, but knelt beside her turning her limp body stupidly in his hands. At length he recognised that she was indeed dead, and beginning to consider what dreadful afflictions God had visited him with, he blasphemed horribly and called on God to strike him dead, or give his wife back to him.

"Is it not enough," he cried, adding a foul blasphemous oath, "that you should rob me of my dear wife, making her a fox, but now you must rob me of that fox too, that has been my only solace and comfort in this affliction?"

Then he burst into tears and began wringing his hands and continued there in such an extremity of grief for half-an-hour that he cared nothing, neither what he was doing, nor what would become of him in the future, but only knew that his life was ended now and he would not live any longer than he could help.

All this while the little girl Polly stood by, first staring, then asking him what had happened, and lastly crying with fear, but he never heeded her nor looked at her but only tore his hair, sometimes shouted at God, or shook his fist at Heaven. So in a fright Polly opened the door and ran out of the garden.

At length worn out, and as it were all numb with his loss, Mr. Tebrick got up and went within doors, leaving his dear fox lying near where she had fallen.

He stayed indoors only two minutes and then came out again with a razor in his hand intending to cut his own throat, for he was out of his senses in this first paroxysm of grief.

But his vixen was gone, at which he looked about for a moment bewildered, and then enraged, thinking that somebody must have taken the body.

The door of the garden being open he ran straight through it. Now this door, which had been left ajar by Polly when she ran off, opened into a little courtyard where the fowls were shut in at night; the wood-house and the privy also stood there. On the far side of it from the garden gate were two large wooden doors big enough when open to let a cart enter, and high enough to keep a man from looking over into the yard.

When Mr. Tebrick got into the yard he found his vixen leaping up at these doors, and wild with terror, but as lively as ever he saw her in his life. He ran up to her but she shrank away from him, and would then have dodged him too, but he caught hold of her. She bared her teeth at him but he paid no heed to that, only picked her straight up into his arms and took her so indoors. Yet all the while he could scarce believe his eyes to see her living, and felt her all over very carefully to find if she had not some bones broken. But no, he could find none. Indeed it was some hours before this poor silly gentleman began to suspect the truth, which was that his vixen had practised a deception upon him, and all the time he was bemoaning his loss in such heartrending terms, she was only shamming death to run away directly she was able. If it had not been that the yard gates were shut, which was a mere chance, she had got her liberty by that trick. And that this was only a trick of hers to sham dead was plain when he had thought it over. Indeed it is an old and time-honoured trick of the fox. It is in Æsop and a hundred other writers have confirmed it since. But so thoroughly had he been deceived by her, that at first he was as much overcome with joy at his wife still being alive, as he had been with grief a little while before, thinking her dead.

He took her in his arms, hugging her to him and thanking God a dozen times for her preservation. But his kissing and fondling her had very little effect now, for she did not answer him by licking or soft looks, but stayed huddled up and sullen, with her hair bristling on her neck and her ears laid back every time he touched her. At first he thought this might be because he had touched some broken bone or tender place where she had been hurt, but at last the truth came to him.

Thus he was again to suffer, and though the pain of knowing her treachery to him was nothing to the grief of losing her, yet it was more insidious and lasting. At first, from a mere nothing, this pain grew gradually until it was a torture to him. If he had been one of your stock ordinary husbands, such a one who by experience has learnt never to enquire too closely into his wife's doings, her comings or goings, and never to ask her, "How she has spent the day?" for fear he should be made the more of a fool, had Mr. Tebrick been such a one he had been luckier, and his pain would have been almost nothing. But you must consider that he had never been deceived once by his wife in the course of their married life. No, she had never told him as much as one white lie, but had always been frank, open and ingenuous as if she and her husband were not husband and wife, or indeed of opposite sexes. Yet we must rate him as very foolish, that living thus with a fox, which beast has the same reputation for deceitfulness, craft and cunning, in all countries, all ages, and amongst all races of mankind, he should expect this fox to be as candid and honest with him in all things as the country girl he had married.

His wife's sullenness and bad temper continued that day, for she cowered away from him and hid under the sofa, nor could he persuade her to come out from there. Even when it was her dinner time she stayed, refusing resolutely to be tempted out with food, and lying so quiet that he heard nothing from her for hours. At night he carried her up to the bedroom, but she was still sullen and refused to eat a morsel, though she drank a little water during the night, when she fancied he was asleep.

The next morning was the same, and by now Mr. Tebrick had been through all the agonies of wounded self-esteem, disillusionment and despair that a man can suffer. But though his emotions rose up in his heart and nearly stifled him he showed no sign of them to her, neither did he abate one jot his tenderness and consideration for his vixen. At breakfast he tempted her with a freshly killed young pullet. It hurt him to make this advance to her, for hitherto he had kept her strictly on cooked meats, but the pain of seeing her refuse it was harder still for him to bear. Added to this was now an anxiety lest she should starve herself to death rather than stay with him any longer.

All that morning he kept her close, but in the afternoon let her loose again in the garden after he had lopped the pear tree so that she could not repeat her performance of climbing.

But seeing how disgustedly she looked while he was by, never offering to run or to play as she was used, but only standing stock still with her tail between her legs, her ears flattened, and the hair bristling on her shoulders, seeing this he left her to herself out of mere humanity.

When he came out after half-an-hour he found that she was gone, but there was a fair sized hole by the wall, and she just buried all but her brush, digging desperately to get under the wall and make her escape.

He ran up to the hole, and put his arm in after her and called to her to come out, but she would not. So at first he began pulling her out by the shoulder, then his hold slipping, by the hind legs. As soon as he had drawn her forth she whipped round and snapped at his hand and bit it through near the joint of the thumb, but let it go instantly.

They stayed there for a minute facing each other, he on his knees and she facing him the picture of unrepentant wickedness and fury. Being thus on his knees, Mr. Tebrick was down on her level very nearly, and her muzzle was thrust almost into his face. Her ears lay flat on her head, her gums were bared in a silent snarl, and all her beautiful teeth threatening him that she would bite him again. Her back too was half-arched, all her hair bristling and her brush held drooping. But it was her eyes that held his, with their slit pupils looking at him with savage desperation and rage.

The blood ran very freely from his hand but he never noticed that or the pain of it either, for all his thoughts were for his wife.

"What is this, Silvia?" he said very quietly, "what is this? Why are you so savage now? If I stand between you and your freedom it is because I love you. Is it such torment to be with me?" But Silvia never stirred a muscle.

"You would not do this if you were not in anguish, poor beast, you want your freedom. I cannot keep you, I cannot hold you to vows made when you were a woman. Why, you have forgotten who I am."

The tears then began running down his cheeks, he sobbed, and said to her:

"Go—I shall not keep you. Poor beast, poor beast, I love you, I love you. Go if you want to. But if you remember me come back. I shall never keep you against your will. Go—go. But kiss me now."

He leant forward then and put his lips to her snarling fangs, but though she kept snarling she did not bite him. Then he got up quickly and went to the door of the garden that opened into a little paddock against a wood.

When he opened it she went through it like an arrow, crossed the paddock like a puff of smoke and in a moment was gone from his sight. Then, suddenly finding himself alone, Mr. Tebrick came as it were to himself and ran after her, calling her by name and shouting to her, and so went plunging into the wood, and through it for about a mile, running almost blindly.

At last when he was worn out he sat down, seeing that she had gone beyond recovery and it was already night. Then, rising, he walked slowly homewards, wearied and spent in spirit. As he went he bound up his hand that was still running with blood. His coat was torn, his hat lost, and his face scratched right across with briars. Now in cold blood he began to reflect on what he had done and to repent bitterly having set his wife free. He had betrayed her so that now, from his act, she must lead the life of a wild fox for ever, and must undergo all the rigours and hardships of the climate, and all the hazards of a hunted creature. When Mr. Tebrick got back to the cottage he found Mrs. Cork was sitting up for him. It was already late.

"What have you done with Mrs. Tebrick, sir? I missed her, and I missed you, and I have not known what to do, expecting something dreadful had happened. I have been sitting up for you half the night. And where is she now, sir?"

She accosted him so vigorously that Mr. Tebrick stood silent. At length he said: "I have let her go. She has run away."

"Poor Miss Silvia!" cried the old woman. "Poor creature! You ought to be ashamed, sir! Let her go indeed! Poor lady, is that the way for her husband to talk! It is a disgrace. But I saw it coming from the first."

The old woman was white with fury, she did not mind what

she said, but Mr. Tebrick was not listening to her. At last he looked at her and saw that she had just begun to cry, so he went out of the room and up to bed, and lay down as he was, in his clothes, utterly exhausted, and fell into a dog's sleep, starting up every now and then with horror, and then falling back with fatigue. It was late when he woke up, but cold and raw, and he felt cramped in all his limbs. As he lay he heard again the noise which had woken him—the trotting of several horses, and the voice of men riding by the house. Mr. Tebrick jumped up and ran to the window and then looked out, and the first thing that he saw was a gentleman in a pink coat riding at a walk down the lane. At this sight Mr. Tebrick waited no longer, but pulling on his boots in mad haste, ran out instantly, meaning to say that they must not hunt, and how his wife was escaped and they might kill her.

But when he found himself outside the cottage words failed him and fury took possession of him, so that he could only cry out:

"How dare you, you damned blackguard?"

And so, with a stick in his hand, he threw himself on the gentleman in the pink coat and seized his horse's rein, and catching the gentleman by the leg was trying to throw him. But really it is impossible to say what Mr. Tebrick intended by his behaviour or what he would have done, for the gentleman, finding himself suddenly assaulted in so unexpected a fashion by so strange a touzled and dishevelled figure, clubbed his hunting crop and dealt him a blow on the temple so that he fell insensible.

Another gentleman rode up at this moment and they were civil enough to dismount and carry Mr. Tebrick into the cottage, where they were met by old Nanny who kept wringing her hands and told them Mr. Tebrick's wife had run away and she was a vixen, and that was the cause that Mr. Tebrick had run out and assaulted them.

The two gentlemen could not help laughing at this, and mounting their horses rode on without delay, after telling each other that Mr. Tebrick, whoever he was, was certainly a madman, and the old woman seemed as mad as her master.

This story, however, went the rounds of the gentry in those parts and perfectly confirmed everyone in their previous opinion, namely that Mr. Tebrick was mad and his wife had run away from him. The part about her being a vixen was laughed at by the few that heard it, but was soon left out as immaterial to the story, and incredible in itself, though afterwards it came to be remembered and its significance to be understood.

When Mr. Tebrick came to himself it was past noon, and his head was aching so painfully that he could only call to mind in a confused way what had happened.

However, he sent off Mrs. Cork's son directly on one of his horses to enquire about the hunt.

At the same time he gave orders to old Nanny that she was to put out food and water for her mistress, on the chance that she might yet be in the neighbourhood.

By nightfall Simon was back with the news that the hunt had had a very long run but had lost one fox, then, drawing a covert, had chopped an old dog fox, and so ended the day's sport.

This put poor Mr. Tebrick in some hopes again, and he rose at once from his bed, and went out to the wood and began calling his wife, but was overcome with faintness, and lay down and so passed the night in the open, from mere weakness.

In the morning he got back again to the cottage but he had taken a chill, and so had to keep his bed for three or four days after.

All this time he had food put out for her every night, but though rats came to it and ate of it, there were never any prints of a fox.

At last his anxiety began working another way, that is he came to think it possible that his vixen would have gone back to Stokoe, so he had his horses harnessed in the dogcart and brought to the door and then drove over to Rylands, though he was still in a fever, and with a heavy cold upon him.

After that he lived always solitary, keeping away from his fellows and only seeing one man, called Askew, who had been brought up a jockey at Wantage, but was grown too big for his profession. He mounted this loafing fellow on one of his horses three days a week and had him follow the hunt and report to him whenever they killed, and if he could view the fox so much the better, and then he made him describe it minutely, so he should know if it were his Silvia. But he dared not trust himself to go himself, lest his passion should master him and he might commit a murder.

Every time there was a hunt in the neighbourhood he set

the gates wide open at Rylands and the house doors also, and taking his gun stood sentinel in the hope that his wife would run in if she were pressed by the hounds, and so he could save her. But only once a hunt came near, when two foxhounds that had lost the main pack strayed on to his land and he shot them instantly and buried them afterwards himself.

It was not long now to the end of the season, as it was the middle of March.

But living as he did at this time, Mr. Tebrick grew more and more to be a true misanthrope. He denied admittance to any that came to visit him, and rarely showed himself to his fellows, but went out chiefly in the early mornings before people were about, in the hope of seeing his beloved fox. Indeed it was only this hope that he would see her again that kept him alive, for he had become so careless of his own comfort in every way that he very seldom ate a proper meal, taking no more than a crust of bread with a morsel of cheese in the whole day, though sometimes he would drink half a bottle of whiskey to drown his sorrow and to get off to sleep, for sleep fled from him, and no sooner did he begin dozing but he awoke with a start thinking he had heard something. He let his beard grow too, and though he had always been very particular in his person before, he now was utterly careless of it, gave up washing himself for a week or two at a stretch, and if there was dirt under his finger nails let it stop there.

All this disorder fed a malignant pleasure in him. For by now he had come to hate his fellow men and was embittered against all human decencies and decorum. For strange to tell he never once in these months regretted his dear wife whom he had so much loved. No, all that he grieved for now was his departed vixen. He was haunted all this time not by the memory of a sweet and gentle woman, but by the recollection of an animal; a beast it is true that could sit at table and play piquet when it would, but for all that nothing really but a wild beast. His one hope now was the recovery of this beast, and of this he dreamed continually. Likewise both waking and sleeping he was visited by visions of her; her mask, her full white-tagged brush, white throat, and the thick fur in her ears all haunted him.

Every one of her foxey ways was now so absolutely precious to him that I believe that if he had known for certain she was dead, and had thoughts of marrying a second time, he would never have been happy with a woman. No, indeed, he would have been more tempted to get himself a tame fox, and would have counted that as good a marriage as he could make.

Yet this all proceeded one may say from a passion, and a true conjugal fidelity, that it would be hard to find matched in this world. And though we may think him a fool, almost a madman, we must, when we look closer, find much to respect in his extraordinary devotion. How different indeed was he from those who, if their wives go mad, shut them in madhouses and give themselves up to concubinage, and nay, what is more, there are many who extenuate such conduct too. But Mr. Tebrick was of a very different temper, and though his wife was now nothing but a hunted beast, cared for no one in the world but her.

But this devouring love ate into him like a consumption, so that by sleepless nights, and not caring for his person, in a few months he was worn to the shadow of himself. His cheeks were sunk in, his eyes hollow but excessively brilliant, and his whole body had lost flesh, so that looking at him the wonder was that he was still alive.

Now that the hunting season was over he had less anxiety for her, yet even so he was not positive that the hounds had not got her. For between the time of his setting her free, and the end of the hunting season (just after Easter), there were but three vixens killed near. Of those three one was a half-blind or wall-eyed, and one was a very grey dull-coloured beast. The third answered more to the description of his wife, but that it had not much black on the legs, whereas in her the blackness of the legs was very plain to be noticed. But yet his fear made him think that perhaps she had got mired in running and the legs being muddy were not remarked on as black.

One morning the first week in May, about four o'clock, when he was out waiting in the little copse, he sat down for a while on a tree stump, and when he looked up saw a fox coming towards him over the ploughed field. It was carrying a hare over its shoulder so that it was nearly all hidden from him. At last, when it was not twenty yards from him, it crossed over, going into the copse, when Mr. Tebrick stood up and cried out, "Silvia, Silvia, is it you?"

The fox dropped the hare out of his mouth and stood looking at him, and then our gentleman saw at the first glance that this was not his wife. For whereas Mrs. Tebrick had been of a very bright red, this was a swarthier duller beast altogether, moreover it was a good deal larger and higher at the shoulder and had a great white tag to his brush. But the fox after the first instant did not stand for his portrait you may be sure, but picked up his hare and made off like an arrow.

Then Mr. Tebrick cried out to himself: "Indeed I am crazy now! My affliction has made me lose what little reason I ever had. Here am I taking every fox I see to be my wife. My neighbours call me a madman and now I see that they are right. Look at me now, oh God! How foul a creature I am. I hate my fellows. I am thin and wasted by this consuming passion, my reason is gone and I feed myself on dreams. Recall me to my duty, bring me back to decency, let me not become a beast likewise, but restore me and forgive me, Oh my Lord."

With that he burst into scalding tears and knelt down and prayed, a thing he had not done for many weeks.

When he rose up he walked back feeling giddy and exceedingly weak, but with a contrite heart, and then washed himself thoroughly and changed his clothes, but his weakness increasing he lay down for the rest of the day, but read in the Book of Job and was much comforted.

For several days after this he lived very soberly, for his weakness continued, but every day he read in the bible, and prayed earnestly, so that his resolution was so much strengthened that he determined to overcome his folly, or his passion, if he could, and at any rate to live the rest of his life very religiously. So strong was this desire in him to amend his ways that he considered if he should not go to spread the Gospel abroad, for the Bible Society, and so spend the rest of his days.

Indeed he began a letter to his wife's uncle, the canon, and he was writing this when he was startled by hearing a fox bark.

Yet so great was this new turn he had taken that he did not rush out at once, as he would have done before, but stayed where he was and finished his letter.

Afterwards he said to himself that it was only a wild fox and sent by the devil to mock him, and that madness lay that way if he should listen. But on the other hand he could not deny to himself that it might have been his wife, and that he ought to welcome the prodigal. Thus he was torn between these two thoughts, neither of which did he completely believe. He stayed thus tormented with doubts and fears all night.

The next morning he woke suddenly with a start and on the instant heard a fox bark once more. At that he pulled on his clothes and ran out as fast as he could to the garden gate. The sun was not yet high, the dew thick everywhere, and for a minute or two everything was very silent. He looked about him eagerly but could see no fox, yet there was already joy in his heart.

Then while he looked up and down the road, he saw his vixen step out of the copse about thirty yards away. He called to her at once.

"My dearest wife! Oh, Silvia! You are come back!" and at the sound of his voice he saw her wag her tail, which set his last doubts at rest.

But then though he called her again, she stepped into the copse once more though she looked back at him over her shoulder as she went. At this he ran after her, but softly and not too fast lest he should frighten her away, and then looked about for her again and called to her when he saw her among the trees still keeping her distance from him. He followed her then, and as he approached so she retreated from him, yet always looking back at him several times.

He followed after her through the underwood up the side of the hill, when suddenly she disappeared from his sight, behind some bracken.

When he got there he could see her nowhere, but looking about him found a fox's earth, but so well hidden that he might have passed it by a thousand times and would never have found it unless he had made particular search at that spot.

But now, though he went on his hands and knees, he could see nothing of his vixen, so that he waited a little while wondering.

Presently he heard a noise of something moving in the earth, and so waited silently, then saw something which pushed itself into sight. It was a small sooty black beast, like a puppy. There came another behind it, then another and so on till there were five of them. Lastly there came his vixen pushing her litter before her, and while he looked at her silently, a prey to his confused and unhappy emotions, he saw that her eyes were shining with pride and happiness.

She picked up one of her youngsters then, in her mouth, and brought it to him and laid it in front of him, and then looked up at him very excited, or so it seemed.

Mr. Tebrick took the cub in his hands, stroked it and put it against his cheek. It was a little fellow with a smutty face and paws, with staring vacant eyes of a brilliant electric blue and a little tail like a carrot. When he was put down he took a step towards his mother and then sat down very comically.

Mr. Tebrick looked at his wife again and spoke to her, calling her a good creature. Already he was resigned and now, indeed, for the first time he thoroughly understood what had happened to her, and how far apart they were now. But looking first at one cub, then at another, and having them sprawling over his lap, he forgot himself, only watching the pretty scene, and taking pleasure in it. Now and then he would stroke his vixen and kiss her, liberties which she freely allowed him. He marvelled more than ever now at her beauty; for her gentleness with the cubs and the extreme delight she took in them seemed to him then to make her more lovely than before. Thus lying amongst them at the mouth of the earth he idled away the whole of the morning.

First he would play with one, then with another, rolling them over and tickling them, but they were too young yet to lend themselves to any other more active sport than this. Every now and then he would stroke his vixen, or look at her, and thus the time slipped away quite fast and he was surprised when she gathered her cubs together and pushed them before her into the earth, then coming back to him once or twice very humanly bid him "Good-bye and that she hoped she would see him soon again, now he had found out the way."

So admirably did she express her meaning that it would have been superfluous for her to have spoken had she been able, and Mr. Tebrick, who was used to her, got up at once and went home.

But now that he was alone, all the feelings which he had not troubled himself with when he was with her, but had, as it were, put aside till after his innocent pleasures were over, all these came swarming back to assail him in a hundred tormenting ways.

Firstly he asked himself: Was not his wife unfaithful to him, had she not prostituted herself to a beast? Could he still love her after that? But this did not trouble him so much as it might have done. For now he was convinced inwardly that she could no longer in fairness be judged as a woman, but as a fox only. And as a fox she had done no more than other foxes, indeed in having cubs and tending them with love, she had done well.

Whether in this conclusion Mr. Tebrick was in the right or not, is not for us here to consider. But I would only say to those who would censure him for a too lenient view of the religious side of the matter, that we have not seen the thing as he did, and perhaps if it were displayed before our eyes we might be led to the same conclusions.

This was, however, not a tenth part of the trouble in which Mr. Tebrick found himself. For he asked himself also: "Was he not jealous?" And looking into his heart he found that he was indeed jealous, yes, and angry too, that now he must share his vixen with wild foxes. Then he questioned himself if it were not dishonourable to do so, and whether he should not utterly forget her and follow his original intention of retiring from the world, and see her no more.

Thus he tormented himself for the rest of that day, and by evening he had resolved never to see her again.

But in the middle of the night he woke up with his head very clear, and said to himself in wonder, "Am I not a madman? I torment myself foolishly with fantastic notions. Can a man have his honour sullied by a beast? I am a man, I am immeasurably superior to the animals. Can my dignity allow of my being jealous of a beast? A thousand times no. Were I to lust after a vixen, I were a criminal indeed. I can be happy in seeing my vixen, for I love her, but she does right to be happy according to the laws of her being."

Lastly, he said to himself what was, he felt, the truth of this whole matter:

"When I am with her I am happy. But now I distort what is simple and drive myself crazy with false reasoning upon it."

Yet before he slept again he prayed, but though he had thought first to pray for guidance, in reality he prayed only that on the morrow he would see his vixen again and that God would preserve her, and her cubs too, from all dangers, and would allow him to see them often, so that he might come to love them for her sake as if he were their father, and that if this were a sin he might be forgiven, for he sinned in ignorance.

The next day or two he saw vixen and cubs again, though his visits were cut shorter, and these visits gave him such an innocent pleasure that very soon his notions of honour, duty and so on, were entirely forgotten, and his jealousy lulled asleep.

One day he tried taking with him the stereoscope and a pack of cards.

But though his Silvia was affectionate and amiable enough to let him put the stereoscope over her muzzle, yet she would not look through it, but kept turning her head to lick his hand, and it was plain to him that now she had quite forgotten the use of the instrument. It was the same too with the cards. For with them she was pleased enough, but only delighting to bite at them, and flip them about with her paws, and never considering for a moment whether they were diamonds or clubs, or hearts, or spades or whether the card was an ace or not. So it was evident that she had forgotten the nature of cards too.

Thereafter he only brought them things which she could better enjoy, that is sugar, grapes, raisins, and butcher's meat.

Bye-and-bye, as the summer wore on, the cubs came to know him, and he them, so that he was able to tell them easily apart, and then he christened them. For this purpose he brought a little bowl of water, sprinkled them as if in baptism and told them he was their godfather and gave each of them a name, calling them Sorel, Kasper, Selwyn, Esther, and Angelica.

Sorel was a clumsy little beast of a cheery and indeed puppyish disposition; Kasper was fierce, the largest of the five, even in his play he would always bite, and gave his godfather many a sharp nip as time went on. Esther was of a dark complexion, a true brunette and very sturdy; Angelica the brightest red and the most exactly like her mother; while Selwyn was the smallest cub, of a very prying, inquisitive and cunning temper, but delicate and undersized.

Thus Mr. Tebrick had a whole family now to occupy him, and, indeed, came to love them with very much of a father's love and partiality.

His favourite was Angelica (who reminded him so much of her mother in her pretty ways) because of a gentleness which was lacking in the others, even in their play. After her in his affections came Selwyn, whom he soon saw was the most intelligent of the whole litter. Indeed he was so much more quick-witted than the rest that Mr. Tebrick was led into speculating as to whether he had not inherited something of the human from his dam. Thus very early he learnt to know his name and would come when he was called, and what was stranger still, he learnt the names of his brothers and sisters before they came to do so themselves.

Besides all this he was something of a young philosopher, for though his brother Kasper tyrannized over him he put up with it all with an unruffled temper. He was not, however, above playing tricks on the others, and one day when Mr. Tebrick was by, he made believe that there was a mouse in a hole some little way off. Very soon he was joined by Sorel, and presently by Kasper and Esther When he had got them all digging, it was easy for him to slip away and then he came to his godfather with a sly look, sat down before him, and smiled and then jerked his head over towards the others and smiled again and wrinkled his brows so that Mr. Tebrick knew as well as if he had spoken that the youngster was saying, "Have I not made fools of them all?"

He was the only one that was curious about Mr. Tebrick; he made him take out his watch, put his ear to it, considered it and wrinkled up his brows in perplexity. On the next visit it was the same thing. He must see the watch again, and again think over it. But clever as he was, little Selwyn could never understand it, and if his mother remembered anything about watches it was a subject which she never attempted to explain to her children.

One day Mr. Tebrick left the earth as usual and ran down the slope to the road, when he was surprised to find a carriage waiting before his house and a coachman walking about near his gate. Mr. Tebrick went in and found that his visitor was waiting for him. It was his wife's uncle.

They shook hands, though the Rev. Canon Fox did not recognise him immediately, and Mr. Tebrick led him into the house.

The clergyman looked about him a good deal, at the dirty and disorderly rooms, and when Mr. Tebrick took him into the drawing room it was evident that it had been unused for several months, the dust lay so thickly on all the furniture.

After some conversation on indifferent topics Canon Fox said to him:

"I have called really to ask about my niece."

Mr. Tebrick was silent for some time and then said:

"She is quite happy now."

"Ah—indeed. I have heard she is not living with you any longer."

"No. She is not living with me. She is not far away. I see her every day now."

"Indeed. Where does she live?"

"In the woods with her children. I ought to tell you that she has changed her shape. She is a fox."

The Rev. Canon Fox got up; he was alarmed, and everything Mr. Tebrick said confirmed what he had been led to expect he would find at Rylands. When he was outside, however, he asked Mr. Tebrick:

"You don't have many visitors now, eh?"

"No—I never see anyone if I can avoid it. You are the first person I have spoken to for months."

"Quite right, too, my dear fellow. I quite understand—in the circumstances." Then the cleric shook him by the hand, got into his carriage and drove away.

"At any rate," he said to himself, "there will be no scandal." He was relieved also because Mr. Tebrick had said nothing about going abroad to disseminate the Gospel. Canon Fox had been alarmed by the letter, had not answered it, and thought that it was always better to let things be, and never to refer to anything unpleasant. He did not at all want to recommend Mr. Tebrick to the Bible Society if he were mad. His eccentricities would never be noticed at Stokoe. Besides that, Mr. Tebrick had said he was happy.

He was sorry for Mr. Tebrick too, and he said to himself that the queer girl, his niece, must have married him because he was the first man she had met. He reflected also that he was never likely to see her again and said aloud, when he had driven some little way:

"Not an affectionate disposition," then to his coachman: "No, that's all right. Drive on, Hopkins."

When Mr. Tebrick was alone he rejoiced exceedingly in his solitary life. He understood, or so he fancied, what it was to be happy, and that he had found complete happiness now, living from day to day, careless of the future, surrounded every morning by playful and affectionate little creatures whom he loved tenderly, and sitting beside their mother, whose simple happiness was the source of his own.

"True happiness," he said to himself, "is to be found in bestowing love; there is no such happiness as that of the mother for her babe, unless I have attained it in mine for my vixen and her children."

With these feelings he waited impatiently for the hour on the morrow when he might hasten to them once more.

When, however, he had toiled up the hillside, to the earth, taking infinite precaution not to tread down the bracken, or make a beaten path which might lead others to that secret spot, he found to his surprise that Silvia was not there and that there were no cubs to be seen either. He called to them, but it was in vain, and at last he laid himself on the mossy bank beside the earth and waited.

For a long while, as it seemed to him, he lay very still, with closed eyes, straining his ears to hear every rustle among the leaves, or any sound that might be the cubs stirring in the earth.

At last he must have dropped asleep, for he woke suddenly with all his senses alert, and opening his eyes found a full-grown fox within six feet of him sitting on its haunches like a dog and watching his face with curiosity. Mr. Tebrick saw instantly that it was not Silvia. When he moved the fox got up and shifted his eyes, but still stood his ground, and Mr. Tebrick recognised him then for the dog-fox he had seen once before carrying a hare. It was the same dark beast with a large white tag to his brush. Now the secret was out and Mr. Tebrick could see his rival before him. Here was the real father of his godchildren, who could be certain of their taking after him, and leading over again his wild and rakish life. Mr. Tebrick stared for a long time at the handsome rogue, who glanced back at him with distrust and watchfulness patent in his face, but not without defiance too, and it seemed to Mr. Tebrick as if there was also a touch of cynical humour in his look, as if he said:

"By Gad! we two have been strangely brought together!"

And to the man, at any rate, it seemed strange that they were thus linked, and he wondered if the love his rival there bare to his vixen and his cubs were the same thing in kind as his own.

"We would both of us give our lives for theirs," he said to himself as he reasoned upon it, "we both of us are happy chiefly in their company. What pride this fellow must feel to have such a wife, and such children taking after him. And has he not reason for his pride? He lives in a world where he is beset with a thousand dangers. For half the year he is hunted, everywhere dogs pursue him, men lay traps for him or menace him. He owes nothing to another."

But he did not speak, knowing that his words would only alarm the fox; then in a few minutes he saw the dog-fox look over his shoulder, and then he trotted off as lightly as a gossamer veil blown in the wind, and, in a minute or two more, back he comes with his vixen and the cubs all around him. Seeing the dog-fox thus surrounded by vixen and cubs was too much for Mr. Tebrick; in spite of all his philosophy a pang of jealousy shot through him. He could see that Silvia had been hunting with her cubs, and also that she had forgotten that he would come that morning, for she started when she saw him, and though she carelessly licked his hand, he could see that her thoughts were not with him.

Very soon she led her cubs into the earth, the dog-fox had vanished and Mr. Tebrick was again alone. He did not wait longer but went home.

Now was his peace of mind all gone, the happiness which he had flattered himself the night before he knew so well how to enjoy, seemed now but a fool's paradise in which he had been living. A hundred times this poor gentleman bit his lip, drew down his torvous brows, and stamped his foot, and cursed himself bitterly, or called his lady bitch. He could not forgive himself either, that he had not thought of the damned dog-fox before, but all the while had let the cubs frisk round him, each one a proof that a dog-fox had been at work with his vixen. Yes, jealousy was now in the wind, and every circumstance which had been a reason for his felicity the night before was now turned into a monstrous feature of his nightmare. With all this Mr. Tebrick so worked upon himself that for the time being he had lost his reason. Black was white and white black, and he was resolved that on the morrow he would dig the vile brood of foxes out and shoot them, and so free himself at last from this hellish plague.

All that night he was in this mood, and in agony, as if he had broken in the crown of a tooth and bitten on the nerve.

But as all things will have an ending so at last Mr. Tebrick, worn out and wearied by this loathed passion of jealousy, fell into an uneasy and tormented sleep.

After an hour or two the procession of confused and jumbled images which first assailed him passed away and subsided into one clear and powerful dream. His wife was with him in her own proper shape, walking as they had been on that fatal day before her transformation. Yet she was changed too, for in her face there were visible tokens of unhappiness, her face swollen with crying, pale and downcast, her hair hanging in disorder, her damp hands wringing a small handkerchief into a ball, her whole body shaken with sobs, and an air of long neglect about her person. Between her sobs she was confessing to him some crime which she had committed, but he did not catch her broken words, nor did he wish to hear them, for he was dulled by her sorrow. So they continued walking together in sadness as it were for ever, he with his arm about her waist, she turning her head to him and often casting her eyes down in distress.

At last they sat down, and he spoke, saying: "I know they are not my children, but I shall not use them barbarously because of that. You are still my wife. I swear to you they shall never be neglected. I will pay for their education."

Then he began turning over the names of schools in his mind. Eton would not do, nor Harrow, nor Winchester, nor Rugby. . . . But he could not tell why these schools would not do for these children of hers, he only knew that every school he thought of was impossible, but surely one could be found. So turning over the names of schools he sat for a long while holding his dear wife's hand, till at length, still weeping, she got up and went away and then slowly he awoke.

But even when he had opened his eyes and looked about him he was thinking of schools, saying to himself that he must send them to a private academy or even at the worst engage a tutor. "Why, yes," he said to himself, putting one foot out of bed, "that is what it must be, a tutor, though even then there will be a difficulty at first."

At those words he wondered what difficulty there would be and recollected that they were not ordinary children. No, they were foxes—mere foxes. When poor Mr. Tebrick had remembered this he was, as it were, dazed or stunned by the fact, and for a long time he could understand nothing, but at last burst into a flood of tears compassionating them and himself too. The awfulness of the fact itself, that his dear wife should have foxes instead of children, filled him with an agony of pity, and, at length, when he recollected the cause of their being foxes, that is that his wife was a fox also, his tears broke out anew, and he could bear it no longer but began calling out in his anguish, and beat his head once or twice against the wall, and then cast himself down on his bed again and wept and wept, sometimes tearing the sheets asunder with his teeth.

The whole of that day, for he was not to go to the earth till evening, he went about sorrowfully, torn by true pity for his poor vixen and her children.

At last when the time came he went again up to the earth, which he found deserted, but hearing his voice, out came Esther. But though he called the others by their names there was no answer, and something in the way the cub greeted him made him fancy she was indeed alone. She was truly rejoiced to see him, and scrambled up into his arms, and thence to his shoulder, kissing him, which was unusual in her (though natural enough in her sister Angelica). He sat down a little way from the earth fondling her, and fed her with some fish he had brought for her mother, which she ate so ravenously that he concluded she must have been short of food that day and probably alone for some time.

At last while he was sitting there Esther pricked up her ears, started up, and presently Mr. Tebrick saw his vixen come towards them. She greeted him very affectionately but it was plain had not much time to spare, for she soon started back whence she had come with Esther at her side. When they had gone about a rod the cub hung back and kept stopping and looked back to the earth, but at last turned and ran back home. But her mother was not to be fobbed off so, for she quickly overtook her child and gripping her by the scruff began to drag her along with her.

Mr. Tebrick, seeing then how matters stood, spoke to her, telling her he would carry Esther if she would lead, so after a little while Silvia gave her over, and then they set out on their strange journey.

Silvia went running on a little before while Mr. Tebrick followed after with Esther in his arms whimpering and struggling now to be free, and indeed, once she gave him a nip with her teeth. This was not so strange a thing to him now, and he knew the remedy for it, which is much the same as with others whose tempers run too high, that is a taste of it themselves. Mr. Tebrick shook her and gave her a smart little cuff after which, though she sulked, she stopped her biting.

They went thus above a mile, circling his house and crossing the highway until they gained a small covert that lay with some waste fields adjacent to it. And by this time it was so dark that it was all Mr. Tebrick could do to pick his way, for it was not always easy for him to follow where his vixen found a big enough road for herself.

But at length they came to another earth, and by the starlight Mr. Tebrick could just make out the other cubs skylarking in the shadows.

Now he was tired, but he was happy and laughed softly for joy, and presently his vixen, coming to him, put her feet upon his shoulders as he sat on the ground, and licked him, and he kissed her back on the muzzle and gathered her in his arms and rolled her in his jacket and then laughed and wept by turns in the excess of his joy.

All his jealousies of the night before were forgotten now. All his desperate sorrow of the morning and the horror of his dream were gone. What if they were foxes? Mr. Tebrick found that he could be happy with them. As the weather was hot he lay out there all the night, first playing hide and seek with them in the dark till, missing his vixen and the cubs proving obstreperous, he lay down and was soon asleep.

He was woken up soon after dawn by one of the cubs tugging at his shoelaces in play. When he sat up he saw two of the cubs standing near him on their hind legs, wrestling with each other, the other two were playing hide and seek round a tree trunk, and now Angelica let go his laces and came romping into his arms to kiss him and say "Good morning" to him, then worrying the points of his waistcoat a little shyly after the warmth of his embrace.

That moment of awakening was very sweet to him. The freshness of the morning, the scent of everything at the day's rebirth, the first beams of the sun upon a tree-top near, and a pigeon rising into the air suddenly, all delighted him. Even the rough scent of the body of the cub in his arms seemed to him delicious.

At that moment all human customs and institutions seemed

to him nothing but folly; for said he, "I would exchange all my life as a man for my happiness now, and even now I retain almost all of the ridiculous conceptions of a man. The beasts are happier and I will deserve that happiness as best I can."

After he had looked at the cubs playing merrily, how, with soft stealth, one would creep behind another to bounce out and startle him, a thought came into Mr. Tebrick's head, and that was that these cubs were innocent, they were as stainless snow, they could not sin, for God had created them to be thus and they could break none of His commandments. And he fancied also that men sin because they cannot be as the animals.

Presently he got up full of happiness, and began making his way home when suddenly he came to a full stop and asked himself: "What is going to happen to them?"

This question rooted him stockishly in a cold and deadly fear as if he had seen a snake before him. At last he shook his head and hurried on his path. Aye, indeed, what would become of his vixen and her children?

This thought put him into such a fever of apprehension that he did his best not to think of it any more, but yet it stayed with him all that day and for weeks after, at the back of his mind, so that he was not careless in his happiness as before, but as it were trying continually to escape his own thoughts.

This made him also anxious to pass all the time he could with his dear Silvia, and, therefore, he began going out to them for more of the daytime, and then he would sleep the night in the woods also as he had done that night; and so he passed several weeks, only returning to his house occasionally to get himself a fresh provision of food. But after a week or ten days at the new earth both his vixen and the cubs, too, got a new habit of roaming. For a long while back, as he knew, his vixen had been lying out alone most of the day, and now the cubs were all for doing the same thing. The earth, in short, had served its purpose and was now distasteful to them, and they would not enter it unless pressed with fear.

This new manner of their lives was an added grief to Mr. Tebrick, for sometimes he missed them for hours together, or for the whole day even, and not knowing where they might be was lonely and anxious. Yet his Silvia was thoughtful for him too and would often send Angelica or another of the cubs to fetch him to their new lair, or come herself if she could spare the time. For now they were all perfectly accustomed to his presence, and had come to look on him as their natural companion, and although he was in many ways irksome to them by scaring rabbits, yet they always rejoiced to see him when they had been parted from him. This friendliness of theirs was, you may be sure, the source of most of Mr. Tebrick's happiness at this time. Indeed he lived now for nothing but his foxes, his love for his vixen had extended itself insensibly to include her cubs, and these were now his daily payments so that he knew them as well as if they had been his own children. With Selwyn and Angelica indeed he was always happy; and they never so much as when they were with him. He was not stiff in his behaviour either, but had learnt by this time as much from his foxes as they had from him. Indeed never was there a more curious alliance than this or one with stranger effects upon both of the parties.

Mr. Tebrick now could follow after them anywhere and keep up with them too, and could go through a wood as silently as a deer. He learnt to conceal himself if ever a labourer passed by so that he was rarely seen, and never but once in their company. But what was most strange of all, he had got a way of going doubled up, often almost on all fours with his hands touching the ground every now and then, particularly when he went uphill.

He hunted with them too sometimes, chiefly by coming up and scaring rabbits towards where the cubs lay ambushed, so that the bunnies ran straight into their jaws.

He was useful to them in other ways, climbing up and robbing pigeons' nests for the eggs which they relished exceedingly, or by occasionally dispatching a hedgehog for them so they did not get the prickles in their mouths. But while on his part he thus altered his conduct, they on their side were not behindhand, but learnt a dozen human tricks from him that are ordinarily wanting in Reynard's education.

One evening he went to a cottager who had a row of skeps, and bought one of them, just as it was after the man had smothered the bees. This he carried to the foxes that they might taste the honey, for he had seen them dig out wild bees' nests often enough. The skep full was indeed a wonderful feast for them, they bit greedily into the heavy scented comb, their jaws were drowned in the sticky flood of sweetness, and they gorged themselves on it without restraint. When they had crunched up the last morsel they tore the skep in pieces, and for hours afterwards they were happily employed in licking themselves clean.

That night he slept near their lair, but they left him and went hunting. In the morning when he woke he was quite numb with cold, and faint with hunger. A white mist hung over everything and the wood smelt of autumn.

He got up and stretched his cramped limbs and then walked homewards. The summer was over and Mr. Tebrick noticed this now for the first time and was astonished. He reflected that the cubs were fast growing up, they were foxes at all points, and yet when he thought of the time when they had been sooty and had blue eyes it seemed to him only yesterday. From that he passed to thinking of the future, asking himself as he had done once before what would become of his vixen and her children. Before the winter he must tempt them into the security of his garden, and fortify it against all the dangers that threatened them.

But though he tried to allay his fear with such resolutions he remained uneasy all that day. When he went out to them that afternoon he found only his wife Silvia there and it was plain to him that she too was alarmed, but alas, poor creature, she could tell him nothing, only lick his hands and face, and turn about pricking her ears at every sound.

"Where are your children, Silvia?" he asked her several times, but she was impatient of his questions, but at last sprang into his arms, flattened herself upon his breast and kissed him gently, so that when he departed his heart was lighter because he knew that she still loved him.

That night he slept indoors, but in the morning early he was awoken by the sound of trotting horses, and running to the window saw a farmer riding by very sprucely dressed. Could they be hunting so soon, he wondered, but presently reassured himself that it could not be a hunt already.

He heard no other sound till eleven o'clock in the morning when suddenly there was the clamour of hounds giving tongue and not so far off either. At this Mr. Tebrick ran out of his house distracted and set open the gates of his garden, but with iron bars and wire at the top so the huntsmen could not follow. There was silence again; it seems the fox must have turned away, for there was no other sound of the hunt. Mr.

Tebrick was now like one helpless with fear, he dared not go out, yet could not stay still at home. There was nothing that he could do, yet he would not admit this, so he busied himself in making holes in the hedges, so that Silvia (or her cubs) could enter from whatever side she came.

At last he forced himself to go indoors and sit down and drink some tea. While he was there he fancied he heard the hounds again; it was but a faint ghostly echo of their music, yet when he ran out of the house it was already close at hand in the copse above.

Now it was that poor Mr. Tebrick made his great mistake, for hearing the hounds almost outside the gate he ran to meet them, whereas rightly he should have run back to the house. As soon as he reached the gate he saw his wife Silvia coming towards him but very tired with running and just upon her the hounds. The horror of that sight pierced him, for ever afterwards he was haunted by those hounds—their eagerness, their desperate efforts to gain on her, and their blind lust for her came at odd moments to frighten him all his life. Now he should have run back, though it was already late, but instead he cried out to her, and she ran straight through the open gate to him. What followed was all over in a flash, but it was seen by many witnesses.

The side of Mr. Tebrick's garden there is bounded by a wall, about six feet high and curving round, so that the huntsmen could see over this wall inside. One of them indeed put his horse at it very boldly, which was risking his neck, and although he got over safe was too late to be of much assistance.

His vixen had at once sprung into Mr. Tebrick's arms, and before he could turn back the hounds were upon them and had pulled them down. Then at that moment there was a scream of despair heard by all the field that had come up, which they declared afterwards was more like a woman's voice than a man's. But yet there was no clear proof whether it was Mr. Tebrick or his wife who had suddenly regained her voice. When the huntsman who had leapt the wall got to them and had whipped off the hounds Mr. Tebrick had been terribly mauled and was bleeding from twenty wounds. As for his vixen she was dead, though he was still clasping her dead body in his arms.

Mr. Tebrick was carried into the house at once and assistance sent for, but there was no doubt now about his neighbours being in the right when they called him mad.

For a long while his life was despaired of, but at last he rallied, and in the end he recovered his reason and lived to be a great age, for that matter he is still alive.

"Saki" (H. H. Munro)

LOUISE

"The tea will be quite cold, you'd better ring for some more," said the Dowager Lady Beanford.

Susan Lady Beanford was a vigorous old woman who had coquetted with imaginary ill-health for the greater part of a lifetime; Clovis Sangrail irreverently declared that she had caught a chill at the Coronation of Queen Victoria and had never let it go again. Her sister, Jane Thropplestance, who was some years her junior, was chiefly remarkable for being the most absent-minded woman in Middlesex.

"I've really been unusually clever this afternoon," she remarked gaily, as she rang for the tea. "I've called on all the people I mean to call on, and I've done all the shopping that I set out to do. I even remembered to try and match that silk for you at Harrod's, but I'd forgotten to bring the pattern with me, so it was no use. I really think that was the only important thing I forgot during the whole afternoon. Quite wonderful for me, isn't it?"

"What have you done with Louise?" asked her sister. "Didn't you take her out with you? You said you were going to."

"Good gracious," exclaimed Jane, "what *have* I done with Louise? I must have left her somewhere."

"But where?"

"That's just it. Where have I left her? I can't remember if the Carrywoods were at home or if I just left cards. If they were at home I may have left Louise there to play bridge. I'll go and telephone to Lord Carrywood and find out."

"Is that you, Lord Carrywood?" she queried over the telephone; "it's me, Jane Thropplestance. I want to know, have you seen Louise?"

"Louise," came the answer, "it's been my fate to see it three times. At first, I must admit, I wasn't impressed by it, but the

1496

music grows on one after a bit. Still, I don't think I want to see it again just at present. Were you going to offer me a seat in your box?"

"Not the opera 'Louise'—my niece, Louise Thropplestance. I thought I might have left her at your house."

"You left cards on us this afternoon, I understand, but I don't think you left a niece. The footman would have been sure to have mentioned it if you had. Is it going to be a fashion to leave nieces on people as well as cards? I hope not; some of these houses in Berkeley Square have practically no accommodations for that sort of thing."

"She's not at the Carrywoods'," announced Jane, returning to her tea; "now I come to think of it, perhaps I left her at the silk counter at Selfridge's. I may have told her to wait there a moment while I went to look at the silks in a better light, and I may easily have forgotten about her when I found I hadn't your pattern with me. In that case she's still sitting there. She wouldn't move unless she was told to; Louise has no initiative."

"You said you tried to match the silk at Harrod's," interjected the dowager.

"Did I? Perhaps it was Harrod's. I really don't remember. It was one of those places where every one is so kind and sympathetic and devoted that one almost hates to take even a reel of cotton away from such pleasant surroundings."

"I think you might have taken Louise away. I don't like the idea of her being there among a lot of strangers. Supposing some unprincipled person was to get into conversation with her."

"Impossible. Louise has no conversation. I've never discovered a single topic on which she'd anything to say beyond 'Do you think so? I dare say you're right.' I really thought her reticence about the fall of the Ribot Ministry was ridiculous, considering how much her dear mother used to visit Paris. This bread and butter is cut far too thin; it crumbles away long before you can get it to your mouth. One feels so absurd, snapping at one's food in mid-air, like a trout leaping at may-fly."

"I am rather surprised," said the dowager, "that you can sit there making a hearty tea when you've just lost a favourite niece."

"You talk as if I'd lost her in a churchyard sense, instead of having temporarily mislaid her. I'm sure to remember presently where I left her."

"You didn't visit any place of devotion, did you? If you've left her mooning about Westminster Abbey or St. Peter's, Eaton Square, without being able to give any satisfactory reason why she's there, she'll be seized under the Cat and Mouse Act and sent to Reginald McKenna."

"That would be extremely awkward," said Jane, meeting an irresolute piece of bread and butter halfway; "we hardly know the McKennas, and it would be very tiresome having to telephone to some unsympathetic private secretary, describing Louise to him and asking to have her sent back in time for dinner. Fortunately, I didn't go to any place of devotion, though I did get mixed up with a Salvation Army procession. It was quite interesting to be at close quarters with them, they're so absolutely different to what they used to be when I first remember them in the 'eighties. They used to go about then unkempt and dishevelled, in a sort of smiling rage with the world, and now they're spruce and jaunty and flamboyantly decorative, like a geranium bed with religious convictions. Laura Kettleway was going on about them in the lift of the Dover Street Tube the other day, saying what a lot of good work they did, and what a loss it would have been if they'd never existed. 'If they had never existed,' I said, 'Granville Barker would have been certain to have invented something that looked exactly like them.' If you say things like that, quite loud, in a Tube lift, they always sound like epigrams."

"I think you ought to do something about Louise," said the dowager.

"I'm trying to think whether she was with me when I called on Ada Spelvexit. I rather enjoyed myself there. Ada was trying, as usual, to ram that odious Koriatoffski woman down my throat, knowing perfectly well that I detest her, and in an unguarded moment she said: 'She's leaving her present house and going to Lower Seymour Street.' 'I dare say she will, if she stays there long enough,' I said. Ada didn't see it for about three minutes, and then she was positively uncivil. No, I am certain I didn't leave Louise there."

"If you could manage to remember where you *did* leave her, it would be more to the point than these negative assurances," said Lady Beanford; "so far, all that we know is that she is not at the Carrywoods', or Ada Spelvexit's, or Westminster Abbey."

"That narrows the search down a bit," said Jane hopefully;

"I rather fancy she must have been with me when I went to Mornay's. I know I went to Mornay's, because I remember meeting that delightful Malcolm What's-his-name there—you know whom I mean. That's the great advantage of people having unusual first names, you needn't try and remember what their other name is. Of course I know one or two other Malcolms, but none that could possibly be described as delightful. He gave me two tickets for the Happy Sunday Evenings in Sloane Square. I've probably left them at Mornay's, but still it was awfully kind of him to give them to me."

"Do you think you left Louise there?"

"I might telephone and ask. Oh, Robert, before you clear the tea-things away I wish you'd ring up Mornay's, in Regent Street, and ask if I left two theatre tickets and one niece in their shop this afternoon."

"A niece, ma'am?" asked the footman.

"Yes, Miss Louise didn't come home with me, and I'm not sure where I left her."

"Miss Louise has been upstairs all the afternoon, ma'am, reading to the second kitchenmaid, who has the neuralgia. I took up tea to Miss Louise at a quarter to five o'clock, ma'am."

"Of course, how silly of me. I remember now, I asked her to read the *Faërie Queene* to poor Emma, to try to send her to sleep. I always get some one to read the *Faërie Queene* to me when I have neuralgia, and it usually sends me to sleep. Louise doesn't seem to have been successful, but one can't say she hasn't tried. I expect after the first hour or so the kitchenmaid would rather have been left alone with her neuralgia, but of course Louise wouldn't leave off till some one told her to. Anyhow, you can ring up Mornay's, Robert, and ask whether I left two theatre tickets there. Except for your silk, Susan, those seem to be the only things I've forgotten this afternoon. Quite wonderful for me."

TOBERMORY

It was a chill, rain-washed afternoon of a late August day, that indefinite season when partridges are still in security or cold storage, and there is nothing to hunt—unless one is bounded on the north by the Bristol Channel, in which case one may lawfully gallop after fat red stags. Lady Blemley's house-party was not bounded on the north by the Bristol Channel, hence there was a full gathering of her guests round the tea-table on this particular afternoon. And, in spite of the blank-ness of the season and the triteness of the occasion, there was no trace in the company of that fatigued restlessness which means a dread of the pianola and a subdued hankering for auction bridge. The undisguised open-mouthed attention of the entire party was fixed on the homely negative personality of Mr. Cor-nelius Appin. Of all her guests, he was the one who had come to Lady Blemley with the vaguest reputation. Some one had said he was "clever," and he had got his invitation in the mod-erate expectation, on the part of his hostess, that some portion at least of his cleverness would be contributed to the general entertainment. Until tea-time that day she had been unable to discover in what direction, if any, his cleverness lay. He was neither a wit nor a croquet champion, a hypnotic force nor a begetter of amateur theatricals. Neither did his exterior sug-gest the sort of man in whom women are willing to pardon a generous measure of mental deficiency. He had subsided into mere Mr. Appin, and the Cornelius seemed a piece of trans-parent baptismal bluff. And now he was claiming to have launched on the world a discovery beside which the invention of gunpowder, of the printing-press, and of steam locomotion were inconsiderable trifles. Science had made bewildering strides in many directions during recent decades, but this thing seemed to belong to the domain of miracle rather than to scientific achievement.

"And do you really ask us to believe," Sir Wilfrid was say-ing, "that you have discovered a means for instructing animals in the art of human speech, and that dear old Tobermory has proved your first successful pupil?"

"It is a problem at which I have worked for the last seventeen years," said Mr. Appin, "but only during the last eight or nine months have I been rewarded with glimmerings of suc-cess. Of course I have experimented with thousands of animals, but latterly only with cats, those wonderful creatures which have assimilated themselves so marvellously with our civiliza-tion while retaining all their highly developed feral instincts. Here and there among cats one comes across an outstanding superior intellect, just as one does among the ruck of human beings, and when I made the acquaintance of Tobermory a week ago I saw at once that I was in contact with a 'Beyond-cat' of extraordinary intelligence. I had gone far along the road to success in recent experiments; with Tobermory, as you call him, I have reached the goal."

Mr. Appin concluded his remarkable statement in a voice which he strove to divest of a triumphant inflection. No one said "Rats," though Clovis's lips moved in a monosyllabic contortion which probably invoked those rodents of disbelief.

"And do you mean to say," asked Miss Resker, after a slight pause, "that you have taught Tobermory to say and understand easy sentences of one syllable?"

"My dear Miss Resker," said the wonder-worker patiently, "one teaches little children and savages and backward adults in that piecemeal fashion; when one has once solved the problem of making a beginning with an animal of highly developed intelligence one has no need for those halting methods. Tobermory can speak our language with perfect correctness."

This time Clovis very distinctly said, "Beyond-rats!" Sir Wilfrid was more polite, but equally sceptical.

"Hadn't we better have the cat in and judge for ourselves?" suggested Lady Blemley.

Sir Wilfrid went in search of the animal, and the company settled themselves down to the languid expectation of witnessing some more or less adroit drawing-room ventriloquism.

In a minute Sir Wilfrid was back in the room, his face white beneath its tan and his eyes dilated with excitement.

"By Gad, it's true!"

His agitation was unmistakably genuine, and his hearers started forward in a thrill of awakened interest.

Collapsing into an armchair he continued breathlessly: "I found him dozing in the smoking-room, and called out to him to come for his tea. He blinked at me in his usual way, and I said, 'Come on, Toby; don't keep us waiting'; and, by Gad! he drawled out in a most horribly natural voice that he'd come when he dashed well pleased! I nearly jumped out of my skin!"

Appin had preached to absolutely incredulous hearers; Sir Wilfrid's statement carried instant conviction. A Babel-like chorus of startled exclamation arose, amid which the scientist sat mutely enjoying the first fruit of his stupendous discovery.

In the midst of the clamour Tobermory entered the room and made his way with velvet tread and studied unconcern across to the group seated round the tea-table.

A sudden hush of awkwardness and constraint fell on the company. Somehow there seemed an element of embarrassment in addressing on equal terms a domestic cat of acknowledged dental ability.

"Will you have some milk, Tobermory?" asked Lady Blemley in a rather strained voice.

"I don't mind if I do," was the response, couched in a tone of even indifference. A shiver of suppressed excitement went through the listeners, and Lady Blemley might be excused for pouring out the saucerful of milk rather unsteadily.

"I'm afraid I've spilt a good deal of it," she said apologetically.

"After all, it's not my Axminster," was Tobermory's rejoinder.

Another silence fell on the group, and then Miss Resker, in her best district-visitor manner, asked if the human language had been difficult to learn. Tobermory looked squarely at her for a moment and then fixed his gaze serenely on the middle distance. It was obvious that boring questions lay outside his scheme of life.

"What do you think of human intelligence?" asked Mavis Pellington lamely.

"Of whose intelligence in particular?" asked Tobermory coldly.

"Oh, well, mine for instance," said Mavis, with a feeble laugh.

"You put me in an embarrassing position," said Tobermory, whose tone and attitude certainly did not suggest a shred of embarrassment. "When your inclusion in this house-party was suggested Sir Wilfrid protested that you were the most brainless woman of his acquaintance, and that there was a wide distinction between hospitality and the care of the feeble-minded. Lady Blemley replied that your lack of brain-power was the precise quality which had earned you your invitation, as you were the only person she could think of who might be idiotic enough to buy their old car. You know, the one they call 'The Envy of Sisyphus,' because it goes quite nicely up-hill if you push it."

Lady Blemley's protestations would have had greater effect

if she had not casually suggested to Mavis only that morning that the car in question would be just the thing for her down at her Devonshire home.

Major Barfield plunged in heavily to effect a diversion.

"How about your carryings-on with the tortoiseshell puss up at the stables, eh?"

The moment he had said it every one realized the blunder.

"One does not usually discuss these matters in public," said Tobermory frigidly. "From a slight observation of your ways since you've been in this house I should imagine you'd find it inconvenient if I were to shift the conversation on to your own little affairs."

The panic which ensued was not confined to the Major.

"Would you like to go and see if cook has got your dinner ready?" suggested Lady Blemley hurriedly, affecting to ignore the fact that it wanted at least two hours to Tobermory's dinner-time.

"Thanks," said Tobermory, "not quite so soon after my tea. I don't want to die of indigestion."

"Cats have nine lives, you know," said Sir Wilfrid heartily.

"Possibly," answered Tobermory; "but only one liver."

"Adelaide!" said Mrs. Cornett, "do you mean to encourage that cat to go out and gossip about us in the servants' hall?"

The panic had indeed become general. A narrow ornamental balustrade ran in front of most of the bedroom windows at the Towers, and it was recalled with dismay that this had formed a favourite promenade for Tobermory at all hours, whence he could watch the pigeons—and heaven knew what else besides. If he intended to become reminiscent in his present outspoken strain the effect would be something more than disconcerting. Mrs. Cornett, who spent much time at her toilet table, and whose complexion was reputed to be of a nomadic though punctual disposition, looked as ill at ease as the Major. Miss Scrawen, who wrote fiercely sensuous poetry and led a blameless life, merely displayed irritation; if you are methodical and virtuous in private you don't necessarily want every one to know it. Bertie van Tahn, who was so depraved at seventeen that he had long ago given up trying to be any worse, turned a dull shade of gardenia white, but he did not commit the error of dashing out of the room like Odo Finsberry, a young gentleman who was understood to be reading for the Church and who was possibly disturbed at the thought of scandals he might hear concerning other people. Clovis had the presence of mind to maintain a composed exterior; privately he was calculating how long it would take to procure a box of fancy mice through the agency of the *Exchange and Mart* as a species of hush-money.

Even in a delicate situation like the present, Agnes Resker could not endure to remain too long in the background.

"Why did I ever come down here?" she asked dramatically. Tobermory immediately accepted the opening.

"Judging by what you said to Mrs. Cornett on the croquet-lawn yesterday, you were out for food. You described the Blemleys as the dullest people to stay with that you knew, but said they were clever enough to employ a first-rate cook; otherwise they'd find it difficult to get anyone to come down a second time."

"There's not a word of truth in it! I appeal to Mrs. Cornett——" exclaimed the discomfited Agnes.

"Mrs. Cornett repeated your remark afterwards to Bertie van Tahn," continued Tobermory, "and said, 'That woman is a regular Hunger Marcher; she'd go anywhere for four square meals a day;' and Bertie van Tahn said——"

At this point the chronicle mercifully ceased. Tobermory had caught a glimpse of the big yellow Tom from the Rectory working his way through the shrubbery towards the stable wing. In a flash he had vanished through the open French window.

With the disappearance of his too brilliant pupil Cornelius Appin found himself beset by a hurricane of bitter upbraiding, anxious inquiry, and frightened entreaty. The responsibility for the situation lay with him, and he must prevent matters from becoming worse. Could Tobermory impart his dangerous gift to other cats? was the first question he had to answer. It was possible, he replied, that he might have initiated his intimate friend the stable puss into his new accomplishment, but it was unlikely that his teaching could have taken a wider range as yet.

"Then," said Mrs. Cornett, "Tobermory may be a valuable cat and a great pet; but I'm sure you'll agree, Adelaide, that both he and the stable cat must be done away with without delay."

"You don't suppose I've enjoyed the last quarter of an hour, do you?" said Lady Blemley bitterly. "My husband and

I are very fond of Tobermory—at least, we were before this horrible accomplishment was infused into him; but now, of course, the only thing is to have him destroyed as soon as possible."

"We can put some strychnine in the scraps he always gets at dinner-time," said Sir Wilfrid, "and I will go and drown the stable cat myself. The coachman will be very sore at losing his pet, but I'll say a very catching form of mange has broken out in both cats and we're afraid of it spreading to the kennels."

"But my great discovery!" expostulated Mr. Appin; "after all my years of research and experiment——"

"You can go and experiment on the shorthorns at the farm, who are under proper control," said Mrs. Cornett, "or the elephants at the Zoological Gardens. They're said to be highly intelligent, and they have this recommendation, that they don't come creeping about our bedrooms and under chairs and so forth."

An archangel ecstatically proclaiming the Millennium, and then finding that it clashed unpardonably with Henley and would have to be indefinitely postponed, could hardly have felt more crestfallen than Cornelius Appin at the reception of his wonderful achievement. Public opinion, however, was against him—in fact, had the general voice been consulted on the subject it is probable that a strong minority vote would have been in favour of including him in the strychnine diet.

Defective train arrangements and a nervous desire to see matters brought to a finish prevented an immediate dispersal of the party, but dinner that evening was not a social success. Sir Wilfrid had had rather a trying time with the stable cat and subsequently with the coachman. Agnes Resker ostentatiously limited her repast to a morsel of dry toast, which she bit as though it were a personal enemy; while Mavis Pellington maintained a vindictive silence throughout the meal. Lady Blemley kept up a flow of what she hoped was conversation, but her attention was fixed on the doorway. A plateful of carefully dosed fish scraps was in readiness on the sideboard, but sweets and savoury and dessert went their way, and no Tobermory appeared either in the dining-room or kitchen.

The sepulchral dinner was cheerful compared with the subsequent vigil in the smoking-room. Eating and drinking had at least supplied a distraction and cloak to the prevailing embarrassment. Bridge was out of the question in the general tension of nerves and tempers, and after Odo Finsberry had given a lugubrious rendering of "Melisande in the Wood" to a frigid audience, music was tacitly avoided. At eleven the servants went to bed, announcing that the small window in the pantry had been left open as usual for Tobermory's private use. The guests read steadily through the current batch of magazines, and fell gradually on the "Badminton Library" and bound volumes of *Punch*. Lady Blemley made periodic visits to the pantry, returning each time with an expression of listless depression which forestalled questioning.

At two o'clock Clovis broke the dominating silence.

"He won't turn up to-night. He's probably in the local newspaper office at the present moment, dictating the first instalment of his reminiscences. Lady What's-her-name's book won't be in it. It will be the event of the day."

Having made this contribution to the general cheerfulness, Clovis went to bed. At long intervals the various members of the house-party followed his example.

The servants taking round the early tea made a uniform announcement in reply to a uniform question. Tobermory had not returned.

Breakfast was, if anything, a more unpleasant function than dinner had been, but before its conclusion the situation was relieved. Tobermory's corpse was brought in from the shrubbery, where a gardener had just discovered it. From the bites on his throat and the yellow fur which coated his claws it was evident that he had fallen in unequal combat with the big Tom from the Rectory.

By midday most of the guests had quitted the Towers, and after lunch Lady Blemley had sufficiently recovered her spirits to write an extremely nasty letter to the Rectory about the loss of her valuable pet.

Tobermory had been Appin's one successful pupil, and he was destined to have no successor. A few weeks later an elephant in the Dresden Zoological Garden, which had shown no previous signs of irritability, broke loose and killed an Englishman who had apparently been teasing it. The victim's name was variously reported in the papers as Oppin and Eppelin, but his front name was faithfully rendered Cornelius.

"If he was trying German irregular verbs on the poor beast," said Clovis, "he deserved all he got."

ESMÉ

"ALL hunting stories are the same," said Clovis; "just as all Turf stories are the same, and all——"

"My hunting story isn't a bit like any you've ever heard," said the Baroness. "It happened quite a while ago, when I was about twenty-three. I wasn't living apart from my husband then; you see, neither of us could afford to make the other a separate allowance. In spite of everything that proverbs may say, poverty keeps together more homes than it breaks up. But we always hunted with different packs. All this has nothing to do with the story."

"We haven't arrived at the meet yet. I suppose there was a meet," said Clovis.

"Of course there was a meet," said the Baroness; "all the usual crowd were there, especially Constance Broddle. Constance is one of those strapping florid girls that go so well with autumn scenery or Christmas decorations in church. 'I feel a presentiment that something dreadful is going to happen,' she said to me; 'am I looking pale?'

"She was looking about as pale as a beetroot that has suddenly heard bad news.

" 'You're looking nicer than usual,' I said, 'but that's so easy for you.' Before she had got the right bearings of this remark we had settled down to business; hounds had found a fox lying out in some gorse-bushes."

"I knew it," said Clovis; "in every fox-hunting story that I've ever heard there's been a fox and some gorse-bushes."

"Constance and I were well mounted," continued the Baroness serenely, "and we had no difficulty in keeping ourselves in the first flight, though it was a fairly stiff run. Towards the finish, however, we must have held rather too independent a line, for we lost the hounds, and found ourselves plodding aimlessly along miles away from anywhere. It was fairly exasperating, and my temper was beginning to let itself go by inches, when on pushing our way through an accommodating hedge we were gladdened by the sight of hounds in full cry in a hollow just beneath us.

" 'There they go,' cried Constance, and then added in a gasp, 'In Heaven's name, what are they hunting?'

"It was certainly no mortal fox. It stood more than twice as high, had a short, ugly head, and an enormous thick neck.

" 'It's a hyæna,' I cried; 'it must have escaped from Lord Pabham's Park.'

"At that moment the hunted beast turned and faced its pursuers, and the hounds (there were only about six couple of them) stood round in a half-circle and looked foolish. Evidently they had broken away from the rest of the pack on the trail of this alien scent, and were not quite sure how to treat their quarry now they had got him.

"The hyæna hailed our approach with unmistakable relief and demonstrations of friendliness. It had probably been accustomed to uniform kindness from humans, while its first experience of a pack of hounds had left a bad impression. The hounds looked more than ever embarrassed as their quarry paraded its sudden intimacy with us, and the faint toot of a horn in the distance was seized on as a welcome signal for unobtrusive departure. Constance and I and the hyæna were left alone in the gathering twilight.

" 'What are we to do?' asked Constance.

" 'What a person you are for questions,' I said.

" 'Well, we can't stay here all night with a hyæna,' she retorted.

" 'I don't know what your ideas of comfort are,' I said; 'but I shouldn't think of staying here all night even without a hyæna. My home may be an unhappy one, but at least it has hot and cold water laid on, and domestic service, and other conveniences which we shouldn't find here. We had better make for that ridge of trees to the right; I imagine the Crowley road is just beyond.'

"We trotted off slowly along a faintly marked cart-track, with the beast following cheerfully at our heels.

" 'What on earth are we to do with the hyæna?' came the inevitable question.

" 'What does one generally do with hyænas?' I asked crossly.

" 'I've never had anything to do with one before,' said Constance.

" 'Well, neither have I. If we even knew its sex we might give it a name. Perhaps we might call it Esmé. That would do in either case.'

"There was still sufficient daylight for us to distinguish wayside objects, and our listless spirits gave an upward perk as we came upon a small half-naked gipsy brat picking blackberries from a low-growing bush. The sudden apparition of two horsewomen and a hyæna set it off crying, and in any case we should scarcely have gleaned any useful geographical information from that source; but there was a probability that we might strike a gipsy encampment somewhere along our route. We rode on hopefully but uneventfully for another mile or so.

" 'I wonder what that child was doing there,' said Constance presently.

" 'Picking blackberries. Obviously.'

" 'I don't like the way it cried,' pursued Constance; 'somehow its wail keeps ringing in my ears.'

"I did not chide Constance for her morbid fancies; as a matter of fact the same sensation, of being pursued by a persistent fretful wail, had been forcing itself on my rather overtired nerves. For company's sake I hulloed to Esmé, who had lagged somewhat behind. With a few springy bounds he drew up level, and then shot past us.

"The wailing accompaniment was explained. The gipsy child was firmly, and I expect painfully, held in his jaws.

" 'Merciful Heaven!' screamed Constance, 'what on earth shall we do? What are we to do?'

"I am perfectly certain that at the Last Judgment Constance will ask more questions than any of the examining Seraphs.

" 'Can't we do something?' she persisted tearfully, as Esmé cantered easily along in front of our tired horses.

"Personally I was doing everything that occurred to me at the moment. I stormed and scolded and coaxed in English and French and gamekeeper language; I made absurd, ineffectual cuts in the air with my thongless hunting-crop; I hurled my sandwich case at the brute; in fact, I really don't know what more I could have done. And still we lumbered on through the deepening dusk, with that dark uncouth shape lumbering ahead of us, and a drone of lugubrious music floating in our ears. Suddenly Esmé bounded aside into some thick bushes, where we could not follow; the wail rose to a shriek and then stopped altogether. This part of the story I always hurry over, because it is really rather horrible. When the beast joined us again, after an absence of a few minutes, there was an air of patient understanding about him, as though he knew that he had done something of which we disapproved, but which he felt to be thoroughly justifiable.

" 'How can you let that ravening beast trot by your side?' asked Constance. She was looking more than ever like an albino beetroot.

" 'In the first place, I can't prevent it,' I said; 'and in the second place, whatever else he may be, I doubt if he's ravening at the present moment.'

"Constance shuddered. 'Do you think the poor little thing suffered much?' came another of her futile questions.

" 'The indications were all that way,' I said; 'on the other hand, of course, it may have been crying from sheer temper. Children sometimes do.'

"It was nearly pitch-dark when we emerged suddenly into the high road. A flash of lights and the whir of a motor went past us at the same moment at uncomfortably close quarters. A thud and a sharp screeching yell followed a second later. The car drew up, and when I had ridden back to the spot I found a young man bending over a dark motionless mass lying by the roadside.

" 'You have killed my Esmé,' I exclaimed bitterly.

" 'I'm so awfully sorry,' said the young man; 'I keep dogs myself, so I know what you must feel about it. I'll do anything I can in reparation.'

" 'Please bury him at once,' I said; 'that much I think I may ask of you.'

" 'Bring the spade, William,' he called to the chauffeur. Evidently hasty roadside interments were contingencies that had been provided against.

"The digging of a sufficiently large grave took some little time. 'I say, what a magnificent fellow,' said the motorist as the corpse was rolled over into the trench. 'I'm afraid he must have been rather a valuable animal.'

" 'He took second in the puppy class at Birmingham last year,' I said resolutely.

"Constance snorted loudly.

" 'Don't cry, dear,' I said brokenly; 'it was all over in a moment. He couldn't have suffered much.'

" 'Look here,' said the young fellow desperately, 'you simply must let me do something by way of reparation.'

"I refused sweetly, but as he persisted I let him have my address.

"Of course, we kept our own counsel as to the earlier episodes of the evening. Lord Pabham never advertised the loss of his hyæna; when a strictly fruit-eating animal strayed from his park a year or two previously he was called upon to give compensation in eleven cases of sheep-worrying and practically to re-stock his neighbours' poultry-yards, and an escaped hyæna would have mounted up to something on the scale of a Government grant. The gipsies were equally unobtrusive over their missing offspring; I don't suppose in large encampments they really know to a child or two how many they've got."

The Baroness paused reflectively, and then continued:

"There was a sequel to the adventure, though. I got through the post a charming little diamond brooch, with the name Esmé set in a sprig of rosemary. Incidentally, too, I lost the friendship of Constance Broddle. You see, when I sold the brooch I quite properly refused to give her any share of the proceeds. I pointed out that the Esmé part of the affair was my own invention, and the hyæna part of it belonged to Lord Pabham, if it really was his hyæna, of which, of course, I've no proof."

"I refused sweetly, but as he persisted I let him have my address.

"Of course, we kept our own counsel as to the earlier episodes of the evening, Lord Pabham never advertised the loss of his hyaena; when a sheep, half-eaten animal strayed from his park a year or two previously he was called upon to give compensation in eleven cases of sheep-worrying, and practically to re-stock his neighbours' poultry-yards, and an escaped hyaena would have mounted up, to something on the scale of a Government grant. The gipsies were equally undemonstrative over their missing offspring; I don't suppose in large encampments they really know to a child or two how many they've got."

The Baroness paused reflectively, and then continued:

"There was a sequel to the adventure, though. I got through the post a charming little diamond brooch, with the name Esmé set in a spray of rosemary. Incidentally, too, I lost the friendship of Constance Broddle. You see, when I sold the brooch I quite properly refused to give her any share of the proceeds. I pointed out that the Esmé part of the affair was my own invention, and the hyaena part of it belonged to Lord Pabham, if it really was his hyaena, of which, of course, I've no proof."

NOTE

THERE must be few novelists who have not harboured a secret
wish to write a detective story. The rigidity of its conventions
makes it an exercise in ingenuity which must tempt a nimble
brain. It is a form that has its classics. I believe that the genre
was invented by Edgar Allan Poe and I do not know that any
writers have surpassed the exercises he made in it. He settled
its main lines once for all. I do not think that any of the
attempts that have since been made to ignore them have been
successful. It was certainly he who discovered the effective use
of ratiocination. His detective is the father of all the detectives
of fiction and Sherlock Holmes, though by the irony of fate
more widely known, owes much more than most people are
aware to his illustrious predecessor. But Poe wrote stories and
many of his followers have written books. They have elaborated
his technique. The space they have had at their command has
allowed them to introduce complications and so has enabled
them to delay for a longer time the delicious and thrilling
moment of discovery. But in essentials they have added little
to his wonderful tales.

I will confess to the reader that I also have wished to write a
detective story. I once thought of a very good murder, but it
was so skilfully planned that I have never been able to see how
it could be found out and the crime brought home to the
culprit. For years I have racked my brains, but I have never
found an answer to the riddle. And now I have given it up as a
bad job. Meanwhile I studied this form of fiction with care
and I came to certain conclusions which I now venture to set
before the reader. The story is the chief thing. The characters
should be natural, but it is unnecessary to go into them in any
detail. Their idiosyncrasies are only of consequence if they are
essential to the story. You do not want to know their opinions
on art, life or the immortality of the soul. Love-making is
merely tiresome and the amorous attachment of one person to

another is only opportune if it is a possible motive for an action. It is an insufficient, because too obvious, cause to lead to the unravelling of the mystery. The writing should be good, but the detective story is no place for elegances of style. Nothing should hold you up. The scene must be set, but you do not want to be bothered with descriptions of scenery. For my own part I think the detective story should deal with a murder. I am unwilling to excite myself over the robbery of a great red ruby or the theft of a secret treaty. But I do not think murder should be exaggerated. A second murder following on the first cools my ardour and a third leaves me sceptical. No, give me one corpse, a beautiful woman in evening-dress stabbed to the heart or an eminent politician with his head bashed in, and let me look forward to three hundred pages of suspense and I am happy. But the writer must play fair with me. He must give me clues which I pounce upon, but which lead to nothing, and clues which if I were quick enough (but I am not) would lead me to the discovery of the villain. He must give me a sporting chance. The culprit must be one of the principal persons brought on the scene, he must not be someone who has been so kept in the background that I cannot be expected to have thought of him, nor someone, like the plumber who had come in to repair the bathroom tap, who has nothing to do with the story. The motive for the murder must be sufficient to make it reasonable that the murderer should risk his neck for it. The interest should be held till the end and when truth is out the author should finish with the least possible delay.

The discerning reader will notice perhaps that the conventions of a good detective story are not very different from those of works of fiction whose aim is more ambitious. In them too it is very well to stick to the point, to be brief and natural, and to write as simply as possible.

Trent's Last Case follows the canon to a nicety. It is a beautiful example of technique. The characters are probable. The love interest is kept in its properly subordinate place and the reader is not made a fool of. It is the only detective story the author has written. I have often heard it lamented that he has never written another. My own opinion is that he has in this shown a singular wisdom, for when you have done a thing as perfectly as possible what on earth is the use of doing it again?

W. S. M.

E. C. Bentley

TRENT'S LAST CASE

CHAPTER I

BAD NEWS

BETWEEN what matters and what seems to matter, how should the world we know judge wisely?

When the scheming, indomitable brain of Sigsbee Manderson was scattered by a shot from an unknown hand, that world lost nothing worth a single tear; it gained something memorable in a harsh reminder of the vanity of such wealth as this dead man had piled up—without making one loyal friend to mourn him, without doing an act that could help his memory to the least honour. But when the news of his end came, it seemed to those living in the great vortices of business as if the earth too shuddered under a blow.

In all the lurid commercial history of his country there had been no figure that had so imposed itself upon the mind of the trading world. He had a niche apart in its temples. Financial giants, strong to direct and augment the forces of capital, and taking an approved toll in millions for their labour, had existed before; but in the case of Manderson there had been this singularity, that a pale halo of piratical romance, a thing especially dear to the hearts of his countrymen, had remained incongruously about his head through the years when he stood in every eye as the unquestioned guardian of stability, the stamper-out of manipulated crises, the foe of the raiding chieftains that infest the borders of Wall Street.

The fortune left by his grandfather, who had been one of those chieftains on the smaller scale of his day, had descended to him with accretion through his father, who during a long life had quietly continued to lend money and never had margined a stock. Manderson, who had at no time known what

it was to be without large sums to his hand, should have been
altogether of that newer American plutocracy which is steadied
by the tradition and habit of great wealth. But it was not so.
While his nurture and education had taught him European
ideas of a rich man's proper external circumstance; while they
had rooted in him an instinct for quiet magnificence, the larger
costliness which does not shriek of itself with a thousand
tongues; there had been handed on to him nevertheless much of
the Forty-Niner and financial buccaneer, his forebear. During
that first period of his business career which had been called his
early bad manner, he had been little more than a gambler of
genius, his hand against every man's—an infant prodigy who
brought to the enthralling pursuit of speculation a brain better endowed than any opposed to it. At St. Helena it was laid
down that war is *une belle occupation;* and so the young Manderson had found the multitudinous and complicated dog-fight
of the Stock Exchange of New York.

Then came his change. At his father's death, when Manderson was thirty years old, some new revelation of the power
and the glory of the god he served seemed to have come upon
him. With the sudden, elastic adaptability of his nation he
turned to steady labour in his father's banking business, closing his ears to the sound of the battles of the Street. In a few
years he came to control all the activity of the great firm whose
unimpeached conservatism, safety, and financial weight lifted
it like a cliff above the angry sea of the markets. All mistrust
founded on the performances of his youth had vanished. He
was quite plainly a different man. How the change came about
none could with authority say, but there was a story of certain last words spoken by his father, whom alone he had respected and perhaps loved.

He began to tower above the financial situation. Soon his
name was current in the bourses of the world. One who spoke
the name of Manderson called up a vision of all that was
broad-based and firm in the vast wealth of the United States.
He planned great combinations of capital, drew together and
centralized industries of continental scope, financed with unerring judgment the large designs of state or of private enterprise. Many a time when he "took hold" to smash a strike, or to
federate the ownership of some great field of labour, he sent
ruin upon a multitude of tiny homes; and if miners or steel-
workers or cattlemen defied him and invoked disorder, he could

be more lawless and ruthless than they. But this was done in the pursuit of legitimate business ends. Tens of thousands of the poor might curse his name, but the financier and the speculator execrated him no more. He stretched a hand to protect or to manipulate the power of wealth in every corner of the country. Forcible, cold, and unerring, in all he did he ministered to the national lust for magnitude; and a grateful country surnamed him the Colossus.

But there was an aspect of Manderson in this later period that lay long unknown and unsuspected save by a few, his secretaries and lieutenants and certain of the associates of his bygone hurling time. This little circle knew that Manderson, the pillar of sound business and stability in the markets, had his hours of nostalgia for the lively times when the Street had trembled at his name. It was, said one of them, as if Blackbeard had settled down as a decent merchant in Bristol on the spoils of the Main. Now and then the pirate would suddenly glare out, the knife in his teeth and the sulphur matches sputtering in his hatband. During such spasms of reversion to type a score of tempestuous raids upon the market had been planned on paper in the inner room of the offices of Manderson, Colefax and Company. But they were never carried out. Blackbeard would quell the mutiny of his old self within him and go soberly down to his counting-house—humming a stave or two of "Spanish Ladies," perhaps, under his breath. Manderson would allow himself the harmless satisfaction, as soon as the time for action had gone by, of pointing out to some Rupert of the markets how a *coup* worth a million to the depredator might have been made. "Seems to me," he would say almost wistfully, "the Street is getting to be a mighty dull place since I quit." By slow degrees this amiable weakness of the Colossus became known to the business world, which exulted greatly in the knowledge.

. . . .

At the news of his death panic went through the markets like a hurricane; for it came at a luckless time. Prices tottered and crashed like towers in an earthquake. For two days Wall Street was a clamorous inferno of pale despair. All over the United States, wherever speculation had its devotees, went a waft of ruin, a plague of suicide. In Europe also not a few took with their own hands lives that had become pitiably linked to the destiny of a financier whom most of them had never seen. In Paris a well-known banker walked quietly out of the Bourse and fell dead upon the broad steps among the raving crowd of Jews, a phial crushed in his hand. In Frankfort one leapt from the Cathedral top, leaving a redder stain where he struck the red tower. Men stabbed and shot and strangled themselves, drank death or breathed it as the air, because in a lonely corner of England the life had departed from one cold heart vowed to the service of greed.

The blow could not have fallen at a more disastrous moment. It came when Wall Street was in a condition of suppressed "scare"—suppressed, because for a week past the great interests known to act with or to be actually controlled by the Colossus had been desperately combating the effects of the sudden arrest of Lucas Hahn, and the exposure of his plundering of the Hahn banks. This bombshell, in its turn, had fallen at a time when the market had been "boosted" beyond its real strength. In the language of the place, a slump was due. Reports from the corn-hands had not been good, and there had been two or three railway statements which had been expected to be much better than they were. But at whatever point in the vast area of speculation the shudder of the threatened break had been felt, "the Manderson crowd" had stepped in and held the market up. All through the week the speculator's mind, as shallow as it is quick-witted, as sentimental as greedy, had seen in this the hand of the giant stretched out in protection from afar. Manderson, said the newspapers in chorus, was in hourly communication with his lieutenants in the Street. One journal was able to give in round figures the sum spent on cabling between New York and Marlstone in the past twenty-four hours; it told how a small staff of expert operators had been sent down by the Post Office authorities to Marlstone to deal with the flood of messages. Another revealed that Manderson, on the first news of the Hahn crash, had arranged to abandon his holiday and return home by the *Mauretania;* but that he soon had the situation so well in hand that he had determined to remain where he was.

All this was falsehood, more or less consciously elaborated by the "finance editors", consciously initiated and encouraged by the shrewd business men of the Manderson group, who knew that nothing could better help their plans than this illusion of hero-worship—knew also that no word had come from Manderson in answer to their messages, and that Howard B. Jeffrey, of Steel and Iron fame, was the true organizer of victory. So they fought down apprehension through four feverish days, and minds grew calmer. On Saturday, though the ground beneath the feet of Mr. Jeffrey yet rumbled now and then with Etna-mutterings of disquiet, he deemed his task almost done. The market was firm, and slowly advancing. Wall Street turned to its sleep of Sunday, worn out but thankfully at peace.

In the first trading hour of Monday a hideous rumour flew round the sixty acres of the financial district. It came into being as the lightning comes——a blink that seems to begin nowhere; though it is to be suspected that it was first whispered over the telephone——together with an urgent selling order——by some employee in the cable service. A sharp spasm convulsed the convalescent share-list. In five minutes the dull noise of the kerbstone market in Broad Street had leapt to a high note of frantic interrogation. From within the hive of the Exchange itself could be heard a droning hubbub of fear, and men rushed hatless in and out. Was it true? asked every man; and every man replied, with trembling lips, that it was a lie put out by some unscrupulous "short" interest seeking to cover itself. In another quarter-of-an-hour news came of a sudden and ruinous collapse of "Yankees" in London at the close of the Stock Exchange day. It was enough. New York had still four hours' trading in front of her. The strategy of pointing to Manderson as the saviour and warden of the markets had recoiled upon its authors with annihilating force, and Jeffrey, his ear at his private telephone, listened to the tale of disaster with a set jaw. The new Napoleon had lost his Marengo. He saw the whole financial landscape sliding and falling into chaos before him. In half-an-hour the news of the finding of Manderson's body, with the inevitable rumour that it was suicide, was printing in a dozen newspaper offices; but before a copy reached Wall Street the tornado of the panic was in full fury, and Howard B. Jeffrey and his collaborators were whirled away like leaves before its breath.

.   .   .   .

All this sprang out of nothing.

Nothing in the texture of the general life had changed. The corn had not ceased to ripen in the sun. The rivers bore their barges and gave power to a myriad engines. The flocks fattened on the pastures, the herds were unnumbered. Men laboured everywhere in the various servitudes to which they were born, and chafed not more than usual in their bonds. Bellona tossed and murmured as ever, yet still slept her uneasy sleep. To all mankind save a million or two of half-crazed gamblers, blind to all reality, the death of Manderson meant nothing; the life and work of the world went on. Weeks before he died strong hands had been in control of every wire in the huge network of commerce and industry that he had supervised. Before his corpse was buried his countrymen had made a strange discovery—that the existence of the potent engine of monopoly that went by the name of Sigsbee Manderson had not been a condition of even material prosperity. The panic blew itself out in two days, the pieces were picked up, the bankrupts withdrew out of sight; the market "recovered a normal tone".

While the brief delirium was yet subsiding there broke out a domestic scandal in England that suddenly fixed the attention of two continents. Next morning the Chicago Limited was wrecked, and the same day a notable politician was shot down in cold blood by his wife's brother in the streets of New Orleans. Within a week of its arising "the Manderson story", to the trained sense of editors throughout the Union, was "cold". The tide of American visitors pouring through Europe made eddies round the memorial or statue of many a man who had died in poverty; and never thought of their most famous plutocrat. Like the poet who died in Rome, so young and poor, a hundred years ago, he was buried far away from his own land; but for all the men and women of Manderson's people who flock round the tomb of Keats in the cemetery under the Monte Testaccio, there is not one, nor ever will be, to stand in reverence by the rich man's grave beside the little church of Marlstone.

CHAPTER II

Knocking the Town Endways

In the only comfortably furnished room in the offices of the *Record*, the telephone on Sir James Molloy's table buzzed. Sir

James made a motion with his pen, and Mr. Silver, his secretary, left his work and came over to the instrument.

"Who is that?" he said. "Who? . . . I can't hear you. . . . Oh, it's Mr. Bunner, is it? . . . Yes, but . . . I know, but he's fearfully busy this afternoon. Can't you . . . Oh, really? Well, in that case—just hold on, will you?"

He placed the receiver before Sir James. "It's Calvin Bunner, Sigsbee Manderson's right-hand man," he said concisely. "He insists on speaking to you personally. Says it is the gravest piece of news. He is talking from the house down by Bishopsbridge, so it will be necessary to speak clearly."

Sir James looked at the telephone, not affectionately, and took up the receiver. "Well?" he said in his strong voice, and listened. "Yes," he said. The next moment Mr. Silver, eagerly watching him, saw a look of amazement and horror. "Good God!" murmured Sir James. Clutching the instrument, he slowly rose to his feet, still bending ear intently. At intervals he repeated "Yes." Presently, as he listened, he glanced at the clock and spoke quickly to Mr. Silver over the top of the transmitter. "Go and hunt up Figgis and young Williams. Hurry." Mr. Silver darted from the room.

The great journalist was a tall, strong, clever Irishman of fifty, swart and black-moustached, a man of untiring business energy, well known in the world, which he understood very thoroughly, and played upon with the half-cynical competence of his race. Yet was he without a touch of the charlatan: he made no mysteries, and no pretences of knowledge, and he saw instantly through these in others. In his handsome, well-bred, well-dressed appearance there was something a little sinister when anger or intense occupation put its imprint about his eyes and brow; but when his generous nature was under no restraint he was the most cordial of men. He was managing director of the company which owned that most powerful morning paper, the *Record*, and also that most indispensable evening paper, the *Sun*, which had its offices on the other side of the street. He was, moreover, editor-in-chief of the *Record*, to which he had in the course of years attached the most variously capable personnel in the country. It was a maxim of his that where you could not get gifts, you must do the best you could with solid merit; and he employed a great deal of both. He was respected by his staff as few are respected in a profession not favourable to the growth of the sentiment of reverence.

"You're sure that's all?" asked Sir James, after a few minutes of earnest listening and questioning. "And how long has this been known? . . . Yes, of course, the police are; but the servants? Surely it's all over the place down there by now. . . . Well, we'll have a try. . . . Look here, Bunner, I'm infinitely obliged to you about this. I owe you a good turn. You know I mean what I say. Come and see me the first day you get to town. . . . All right, that's understood. Now I must act on your news. Good-bye."

Sir James hung up the receiver, and seized a railway time-table from the rack before him. After a rapid consultation of this oracle, he flung it down with a forcible word as Mr. Silver hurried into the room, followed by a hard-featured man with spectacles, and a youth with an alert eye.

"I want you to jot down some facts, Figgis," said Sir James, banishing all signs of agitation and speaking with a rapid calmness. "When you have them, put them into shape just as quick as you can for a special edition of the *Sun*." The hard-featured man nodded and glanced at the clock, which pointed to a few minutes past three; he pulled out a notebook and drew a chair up to the big writing-table. "Silver," Sir James went on, "go and tell Jones to wire our local correspondent very urgently, to drop everything and get down to Marlstone at once. He is not to say why in the telegram. There must not be an unnecessary word about this news until the *Sun* is on the streets with it—you all understand. Williams, cut across the way and tell Mr. Anthony to hold himself ready for a two-column opening that will knock the town endways. Just tell him that he must take all measures and precautions for a scoop. Say that Figgis will be over in five minutes with the facts, and that he had better let him write up the story in his private room. As you go, ask Miss Morgan to see me here at once, and tell the telephone people to see if they can get Mr. Trent on the wire for me. After seeing Mr. Anthony, return here and stand by." The alert-eyed young man vanished like a spirit.

Sir James turned instantly to Mr. Figgis, whose pencil was poised over the paper. "Sigsbee Manderson has been murdered," he began quickly and clearly, pacing the floor with his hands behind him. Mr. Figgis scratched down a line of shorthand with as much emotion as if he had been told that the day was fine—the pose of his craft. "He and his wife and two secretaries have been for the past fortnight at the house called White Gables, at Marlstone, near Bishopsbridge. He bought it four years ago. He and Mrs. Manderson have since spent a part of each summer there. Last night he went to bed about half-past eleven, just as usual. No one knows when he got up and left the house. He was not missed until this morning. About ten o'clock his body was found by a gardener. It was lying by a shed in the grounds. He was shot in the head, through the left eye. Death must have been instantaneous. The body was not robbed, but there were marks on the wrists which pointed to a struggle having taken place. Dr. Stock, of Marlstone, was at once sent for, and will conduct the post-mortem examination. The police from Bishopsbridge, who were soon on the spot, are reticent, but it is believed that they are quite without a clue to the identity of the murderer. There you are, Figgis. Mr. Anthony is expecting you. Now I must telephone him and arrange things."

Mr. Figgis looked up. "One of the ablest detectives at Scotland Yard," he suggested, "has been put in charge of the case. It's a safe statement."

"If you like," said Sir James.

"And Mrs. Manderson? Was she there?"

"Yes. What about her?"

"Prostrated by the shock," hinted the reporter, "and sees nobody. Human interest."

"I wouldn't put that in, Mr. Figgis," said a quiet voice. It belonged to Miss Morgan, a pale, graceful woman, who had silently made her appearance while the dictation was going on. "I have seen Mrs. Manderson," she proceeded, turning to Sir James. "She looks quite healthy and intelligent. Has her husband been murdered? I don't think the shock would prostrate her. She is more likely to be doing all she can to help the police."

"Something in your own style, then, Miss Morgan," he said with a momentary smile. Her imperturbable efficiency was an office proverb. "Cut it out, Figgis. Off you go! Now, madam, I expect you know what I want."

"Our Manderson biography happens to be well up to date," replied Miss Morgan, drooping her dark eyelashes as she considered the position. "I was looking over it only a few months ago. It is practically ready for to-morrow's paper. I should think the *Sun* had better use the sketch of his life they had about two years ago, when he went to Berlin and settled the potash difficulty. I remember it was a very good sketch, and they won't be able to carry much more than that. As for our paper, of course we have a great quantity of cuttings, mostly rubbish. The sub-editors shall have them as soon as they come in. Then we have two very good portraits that are our own property; the best is a drawing Mr. Trent made when they were both on the same ship somewhere. It is better than any of the photographs; but you say the public prefers a bad photograph to a good drawing. I will send them down to you at once, and you can choose. As far as I can see, the *Record* is well ahead of the situation, except that you will not be able to get a special man down there in time to be of any use for to-morrow's paper."

Sir James sighed deeply. "What are we good for, anyhow?" he inquired dejectedly of Mr. Silver, who had returned to his desk. "She even knows Bradshaw by heart."

Miss Morgan adjusted her cuffs with an air of patience. "Is there anything else?" she asked, as the telephone bell rang.

"Yes, one thing," replied Sir James, as he took up the receiver. "I want you to make a bad mistake some time, Miss Morgan—an everlasting bloomer—just to put us in countenance." She permitted herself the fraction of what would have been a charming smile as she went out.

"Anthony?" asked Sir James, and was at once deep in consultation with the editor on the other side of the road. He seldom entered the *Sun* building in person; the atmosphere of an evening paper, he would say, was all very well if you liked that kind of thing. Mr. Anthony, the Murat of Fleet Street, who delighted in riding the whirlwind and fighting a tumultuous battle against time, would say the same of a morning paper.

It was some five minutes later that a uniformed boy came in to say that Mr. Trent was on the wire. Sir James abruptly closed his talk with Mr. Anthony.

"They can put him through at once," he said to the boy.

"Hullo!" he cried into the telephone after a few moments.

A voice in the instrument replied, "Hullo be blowed! What do you want?"

"This is Molloy," said Sir James.

"I know it is," the voice said. "This is Trent. He is in the middle of painting a picture, and he has been interrupted at a critical moment. Well, I hope it's something important, that's all!"

"Trent," said Sir James impressively, "it is important. I want you to do some work for us."

"Some play, you mean," replied the voice. "Believe me, I don't want a holiday. The working fit is very strong. I am doing some really decent things. Why can't you leave a man alone?"

"Something very serious has happened."

"What?"

"Sigsbee Manderson has been murdered—shot through the brain—and they don't know who has done it. They found the body this morning. It happened at his place near Bishopsbridge." Sir James proceeded to tell the hearer, briefly and clearly, the facts that he had communicated to Mr. Figgis. "What do you think of it?" he ended.

A considering grunt was the only answer.

"Come now," urged Sir James.

"Tempter!"

"You will go down?"

There was a brief pause.

"Are you there?" said Sir James.

"Look here, Molloy," the voice broke out querulously, "the thing may be a case for me, or it may not. We can't possibly tell. It may be a mystery; it may be as simple as bread and cheese. The body not being robbed looks interesting, but he may have been outed by some wretched tramp whom he found sleeping in the grounds and tried to kick out. It's the sort of thing he would do. Such a murderer might easily have sense enough to know that to leave the money and valuables was the safest thing. I tell you frankly, I wouldn't have a hand in hanging a poor devil who had let daylight into a man like Sig Manderson as a measure of social protest."

Sir James smiled at the telephone—a smile of success. "Come, my boy, you're getting feeble. Admit you want to go and have a look at the case. You know you do. If it's anything you don't want to handle, you're free to drop it. By the by, where are you?"

"I am blown along a wandering wind," replied the voice irresolutely, "and hollow, hollow, hollow all delight."

"Can you get here within an hour?" persisted Sir James.

"I suppose I can," the voice grumbled. "How much time have I?"

"Good man! Well, there's time enough—that's just the worst of it. I've got to depend on our local correspondent for to-night. The only good train of the day went half-an-hour ago. The next is a slow one, leaving Paddington at midnight. You could have the Buster, if you like"—Sir James referred to a very fast motor car of his—"but you wouldn't get down in time to do anything to-night."

"And I'd miss my sleep. No, thanks. The train for me. I am quite fond of railway travelling, you know; I have a gift for it. I am the stoker and the stoked. I am the song the porter sings."

"What's that you say?"

"It doesn't matter," said the voice sadly. "I say," it continued, "will your people look out a hotel near the scene of action, and telegraph for a room?"

"At once," said Sir James. "Come here as soon as you can."

He replaced the receiver. As he turned to his papers again a shrill outcry burst forth in the street below. He walked to the open window. A band of excited boys was rushing down the steps of the *Sun* building and up the narrow thoroughfare toward Fleet Street. Each carried a bundle of newspapers and a large broadsheet with the simple legend:

MURDER OF

S I G S B E E

MANDERSON

Sir James smiled and rattled the money in his pockets cheerfully.

"It makes a good bill," he observed to Mr. Silver, who stood at his elbow.

Such was Manderson's epitaph.

CHAPTER III

BREAKFAST

AT ABOUT eight o'clock in the morning of the following day Mr. Nathaniel Burton Cupples stood on the verandah of the hotel at Marlstone. He was thinking about breakfast. In his case the colloquialism must be taken literally; he really was thinking about breakfast, as he thought about every conscious act of his life when time allowed deliberation. He reflected that on the preceding day the excitement and activity following upon the discovery of the dead man had disorganized his appetite and led to his taking considerably less nourishment than usual. This morning he was very hungry, having already been up and about for an hour; and he decided to allow himself a third piece of toast and an additional egg; the rest as usual. The remaining deficit must be made up at luncheon, but that could be gone into later.

So much being determined, Mr. Cupples applied himself to the enjoyment of the view for a few minutes before ordering his meal. With a connoisseur's eye he explored the beauty of the rugged coast, where a great pierced rock rose from a glassy sea, and the ordered loveliness of the vast tilted levels of pasture and tillage and woodland that sloped gently up from the cliffs toward the distant moor. Mr. Cupples delighted in landscape.

He was a man of middle height and spare figure, nearly sixty years old, by constitution rather delicate in health, but wiry and active for his age. A sparse and straggling beard and moustache did not conceal a thin but kindly mouth; his eyes were keen and pleasant; his sharp nose and narrow jaw gave him very much of a clerical air, and this impression was helped by his commonplace dark clothes and soft black hat. The whole effect of him, indeed, was priestly. He was a man of unusually conscientious, industrious, and orderly mind, with little imagination. His father's household had been used to recruit its domestic establishment by means of advertisements in which it was truthfully described as a serious family. From that fortress of gloom he had escaped with two saintly gifts somehow unspoiled: an inexhaustible kindness of heart, and a capacity for innocent gaiety which owed nothing to humour. In an earlier day and with a clerical training he might have risen to the scarlet hat. He was, in fact, a highly regarded member of the London Positivist Society, a retired banker, a widower without children. His austere but not unhappy life was spent largely among books and in museums; his profound and patiently accumulated knowledge of a number of curiously disconnected subjects which had stirred his interest at different times had given him a place in the quiet, half-lit world of professors and curators and devotees of research; at their amiable, unconvivial dinner parties he was most himself. His favourite author was Montaigne.

Just as Mr. Cupples was finishing his meal at a little table on the verandah, a big motor turned into the drive before the hotel. "Who is this?" he inquired of the waiter. "Id is der manager," said the young man listlessly. "He have been to meed a gendleman by der train."

The car drew up and the porter hurried from the entrance. Mr. Cupples uttered an exclamation of pleasure as a long, loosely-built man, much younger than himself, stepped from the car and mounted the verandah, flinging his hat on a chair. His high-boned, quixotic face wore a pleasant smile; his rough tweed clothes, his hair and short moustache were tolerably untidy.

"Cupples, by all that's miraculous!" cried the man, pouncing upon Mr. Cupples before he could rise, and seizing his outstretched hand in a hard grip. "My luck is serving me to-day," the new-comer went on spasmodically. "This is the second slice within an hour. How are you, my best of friends? And why are you here? Why sit'st thou by that ruined breakfast? Dost thou its former pride recall, or ponder how it passed away? I *am* glad to see you!"

"I was half expecting you, Trent," Mr. Cupples replied, his face wreathed in smiles. "You are looking splendid, my dear fellow. I will tell you all about it. But you cannot have had your own breakfast yet. Will you have it at my table here?"

"Rather!" said the man. "An enormous great breakfast,

too—with refined conversation and tears of recognition never dry. Will you get young Siegfried to lay a place for me while I go and wash? I shan't be three minutes." He disappeared into the hotel, and Mr. Cupples, after a moment's thought, went to the telephone in the porter's office.

He returned to find his friend already seated, pouring out tea, and showing an unaffected interest in the choice of food. "I expect this to be a hard day for me," he said, with the curious jerky utterance which seemed to be his habit. "I shan't eat again till the evening, very likely. You guess why I'm here, don't you?"

"Undoubtedly," said Mr. Cupples. "You have come down to write about the murder."

"That is rather a colourless way of stating it," the man called Trent replied, as he dissected a sole. "I should prefer to put it that I have come down in the character of avenger of blood, to hunt down the guilty, and vindicate the honour of society. That is my line of business. Families waited on at their private residences. I say, Cupples, I have made a good beginning already. Wait a bit, and I'll tell you." There was a silence, during which the new-comer ate swiftly and abstractedly, while Mr. Cupples looked on happily.

"Your manager here," said the tall man at last, "is a fellow of remarkable judgment. He is an admirer of mine. He knows more about my best cases than I do myself. The *Record* wired last night to say I was coming, and when I got out of the train at seven o'clock this morning, there he was waiting for me with a motor car the size of a hay-stack. He is beside himself with joy at having me here. It is fame." He drank a cup of tea and continued: "Almost his first words were to ask me if I would like to see the body of the murdered man—if so, he thought he could manage it for me. He is as keen as a razor. The body lies in Dr. Stock's surgery, you know, down in the village, exactly as it was when found. It's to be post-mortem'd this morning, by the way, so I was only just in time. Well, he ran me down there to the doctor's, giving me full particulars about the case all the way. I was pretty well *au fait* by the time we arrived. I suppose the manager of a place like this has some sort of a pull with the doctor. Anyhow, he made no difficulties, nor did the constable on duty, though he was careful to insist on my not giving him away in the paper."

"I saw the body before it was removed," remarked Mr.

Cupples. "I should not have said there was anything remarkable about it, except that the shot in the eye had scarcely disfigured the face at all, and caused scarcely any effusion of blood, apparently. The wrists were scratched and bruised. I expect that, with your trained faculties, you were able to remark other details of a suggestive nature."

"Other details, certainly; but I don't know that they suggest anything. They are merely odd. Take the wrists, for instance. How was it you could see bruises and scratches on them? I dare say you saw something of Manderson down here before the murder."

"Certainly," Mr. Cupples said.

"Well, did you ever see his wrists?"

Mr. Cupples reflected. "No. Now you raise the point, I am reminded that when I interviewed Manderson here he was wearing stiff cuffs, coming well down over his hands."

"He always did," said Trent. "My friend the manager says so. I pointed out to him the fact you didn't observe, that there were no cuffs visible, and that they had, indeed, been dragged up inside the coat-sleeves, as yours would be if you hurried into a coat without pulling your cuffs down. That was why you saw his wrists."

"Well, I call that suggestive," observed Mr. Cupples mildly. "You might infer, perhaps, that when he got up he hurried over his dressing."

"Yes, but did he? The manager said just what you say. 'He was always a bit of a swell in his dress,' he told me, and he drew the inference that when Manderson got up in that mysterious way, before the house was stirring, and went out into the grounds, he was in a great hurry. 'Look at his shoes,' he said to me: 'Mr. Manderson was always specially neat about his foot-wear. But those shoe-laces were tied in a hurry.' I agreed. 'And he left his false teeth in his room,' said the manager. 'Doesn't *that* prove he was flustered and hurried?' I allowed that it looked like it. But I said, 'Look here: if he was so very much pressed, why did he part his hair so carefully? That parting is a work of art. Why did he put on so much? for he had on a complete outfit of underclothing, studs in his shirt, sock-suspenders, a watch and chain, money and keys and things in his pockets.' That's what I said to the manager. He couldn't find an explanation. Can you?"

Mr. Cupples considered. "Those facts might suggest that

he was hurried only at the end of his dressing. Coat and shoes would come last."

"But not false teeth. You ask anybody who wears them. And besides, I'm told he hadn't washed at all on getting up, which in a neat man looks like his being in a violent hurry from the beginning. And here's another thing. One of his waistcoat pockets was lined with wash-leather for the reception of his gold watch. But he had put his watch into the pocket on the other side. Anybody who has settled habits can see how odd that is. The fact is, there are signs of great agitation and haste, and there are signs of exactly the opposite. For the present I am not guessing. I must reconnoitre the ground first, if I can manage to get the right side of the people of the house." Trent applied himself again to his breakfast.

Mr. Cupples smiled at him benevolently. "That is precisely the point," he said, "on which I can be of some assistance to you." Trent glanced up in surprise. "I told you I half expected you. I will explain the situation. Mrs. Manderson, who is my niece——"

"What!" Trent laid down his knife and fork with a clash. "Cupples, you are jesting with me."

"I am perfectly serious, Trent, really," returned Mr. Cupples earnestly. "Her father, John Peter Domecq, was my wife's brother. I never mentioned my niece or her marriage to you before, I suppose. To tell the truth, it has always been a painful subject to me, and I have avoided discussing it with anybody. To return to what I was about to say: last night, when I was over at the house—by the way, you can see it from here. You passed it in the car." He indicated a red roof among poplars some three hundred yards away, the only building in sight that stood separate from the tiny village in the gap below them.

"Certainly I did," said Trent. "The manager told me all about it, among other things, as he drove me in from Bishopsbridge."

"Other people here have heard of you and your performances," Mr. Cupples went on. "As I was saying, when I was over there last night, Mr. Bunner, who is one of Manderson's two secretaries, expressed a hope that the *Record* would send you down to deal with the case, as the police seemed quite at a loss. He mentioned one or two of your past successes, and Mabel—my niece—was interested when I told her afterwards.

She is bearing up wonderfully well, Trent; she has remarkable fortitude of character. She said she remembered reading your articles about the Abinger case. She has a great horror of the newspaper side of this sad business, and she had entreated me to do anything I could to keep journalists away from the place—I'm sure you can understand her feeling, Trent; it isn't really any reflection on that profession. But she said you appeared to have great powers as a detective, and she would not stand in the way of anything that might clear up the crime. Then I told her you were a personal friend of mine, and gave you a good character for tact and consideration of others' feelings; and it ended in her saying that, if you should come, she would like you to be helped in every way."

Trent leaned across the table and shook Mr. Cupples by the hand in silence. Mr. Cupples, much delighted with the way things were turning out, resumed:

"I spoke to my niece on the telephone only just now, and she is glad you are here. She asks me to say that you may make any inquiries you like, and she puts the house and grounds at your disposal. She had rather not see you herself; she is keeping to her own sitting-room. She has already been interviewed by a detective officer who is there, and she feels unequal to any more. She adds that she does not believe she could say anything that would be of the smallest use. The two secretaries and Martin, the butler (who is a most intelligent man), could tell you all you want to know, she thinks."

Trent finished his breakfast with a thoughtful brow. He filled a pipe slowly, and seated himself on the rail of the verandah. "Cupples," he said quietly, "is there anything about this business that you know and would rather not tell me?"

Mr. Cupples gave a slight start, and turned an astonished gaze on the questioner. "What do you mean?" he said.

"I mean about the Mandersons. Look here! shall I tell you a thing that strikes me about this affair at the very beginning? Here's a man suddenly and violently killed, and nobody's heart seems to be broken about it, to say the least. The manager of this hotel spoke to me about him as coolly as if he'd never set eyes on him, though I understand they've been neighbours every summer for some years. Then you talk about the thing in the coldest of blood. And Mrs. Manderson —well, you won't mind my saying that I have heard of women being more cut up about their husbands being murdered than

she seems to be. Is there something in this, Cupples, or is it my
fancy? Was there something queer about Manderson? I
travelled on the same boat with him once, but never spoke
to him. I only know his public character, which was repulsive
enough. You see, this may have a bearing on the case; that's
the only reason why I ask."

Mr. Cupples took time for thought. He fingered his sparse
beard and looked out over the sea. At last he turned to Trent.
"I see no reason," he said, "why I shouldn't tell you as between
ourselves, my dear fellow. I need not say that this must not
be referred to, however distantly. The truth is that nobody
really liked Manderson; and I think those who were nearest
to him liked him least."

"Why?" the other interjected.

"Most people found a difficulty in explaining why. In trying
to account to myself for my own sensations, I could only put
it that one felt in the man a complete absence of the sympathetic faculty. There was nothing outwardly repellent about
him. He was not ill-mannered, or vicious, or dull—indeed, he
could be remarkably interesting. But I received the impression
that there could be no human creature whom he would not
sacrifice in the pursuit of his schemes, in his task of imposing
himself and his will upon the world. Perhaps that was fanciful,
but I think not altogether so. However, the point is that Mabel,
I am sorry to say, was very unhappy. I am nearly twice your
age, my dear boy, though you always so kindly try to make
me feel as if we were contemporaries—I am getting to be an
old man, and a great many people have been good enough to
confide their matrimonial troubles to me; but I never knew
another case like my niece's and her husband's. I have known
her since she was a baby, Trent, and I know—you understand,
I think, that I do not employ that word lightly—I *know* that
she is as amiable and honourable a woman, to say nothing of
her other good gifts, as any man could wish. But Manderson,
for some time past, had made her miserable."

"What did he do?" asked Trent, as Mr. Cupples paused.

"When I put that question to Mabel, her words were that
he seemed to nurse a perpetual grievance. He maintained a
distance between them, and he would say nothing. I don't
know how it began or what was behind it, and all she would
tell me on that point was that he had no cause in the world
for his attitude. I think she knew what was in his mind, what-

ever it was; but she is full of pride. This seems to have gone on for months. At last, a week ago, she wrote to me. I am the only near relative she has. Her mother died when she was a child; and after John Peter died I was something like a father to her until she married—that was five years ago. She asked me to come and help her, and I came at once. That is why I am here now."

Mr. Cupples paused and drank some tea. Trent smoked and stared out at the hot June landscape.

"I would not go to White Gables," Mr. Cupples resumed. "You know my views, I think, upon the economic constitution of society, and the proper relationship of the capitalist to the employee, and you know, no doubt, what use that person made of his vast industrial power upon several very notorious occasions. I refer especially to the trouble in the Pennsylvania coal-fields, three years ago. I regarded him, apart from all personal dislike, in the light of a criminal and a disgrace to society. I came to this hotel, and I saw my niece here. She told me what I have more briefly told you. She said that the worry and the humiliation of it, and the strain of trying to keep up appearances before the world, were telling upon her, and she asked for my advice. I said I thought she should face him and demand an explanation of his way of treating her. But she would not do that. She had always taken the line of affecting not to notice the change in his demeanour, and nothing, I knew, would persuade her to admit to him that she was injured, once pride had led her into that course. Life is quite full, my dear Trent," said Mr. Cupples with a sigh, "of these obstinate silences and cultivated misunderstandings."

"Did she love him?" Trent inquired abruptly. Mr. Cupples did not reply at once. "Had she any love left for him?" Trent amended.

Mr. Cupples played with his tea-spoon. "I am bound to say," he answered slowly, "that I think not. But you must not misunderstand the woman, Trent. No power on earth would have persuaded her to admit that to any one—even to herself, perhaps so long as she considered herself bound to him. And I gather that, apart from this mysterious sulking of late, he had always been considerate and generous."

"You were saying that she refused to have it out with him."

"She did," replied Mr. Cupples. "And I knew by experience that it was quite useless to attempt to move a Domecq where the sense of dignity was involved. So I thought it over carefully, and next day I watched my opportunity and met Manderson as he passed by this hotel. I asked him to favour me with a few minutes' conversation, and he stepped inside the gate down there. We had held no communication of any kind since my niece's marriage, but he remembered me, of course. I put the matter to him at once and quite definitely. I told him what Mabel had confided to me. I said that I would neither approve nor condemn her action in bringing me into the business, but that she was suffering, and I considered it my right to ask how he could justify himself in placing her in such a position."

"And how did he take that?" said Trent, smiling secretly at the landscape. The picture of this mildest of men calling the formidable Manderson to account pleased him.

"Not very well," Mr. Cupples replied sadly. "In fact, far from well. I can tell you almost exactly what he said—it wasn't much. 'See here, Cupples, you don't want to butt in. My wife can look after herself. I've found that out, along with other things.' He was perfectly quiet—you know he was said never to lose control of himself—though there was a light in his eyes that would have frightened a man who was in the wrong, I dare say. But I had been thoroughly roused by his last remark, and the tone of it, which I cannot reproduce. You see," said Mr. Cupples simply, "I love my niece. She is the only child that there has been in our—in my house. Moreover, my wife brought her up as a girl, and any reflection on Mabel I could not help feeling, in the heat of the moment, as an indirect reflection upon one who is gone."

"You turned upon him," suggested Trent in a low tone. "You asked him to explain his words."

"That is precisely what I did," said Mr. Cupples. "For a moment he only stared at me, and I could see a vein on his forehead swelling—an unpleasant sight. Then he said quite quietly, 'This thing has gone far enough, I guess,' and turned to go."

"Did he mean your interview?" Trent asked thoughtfully.

"From the words alone you would think so," Mr. Cupples answered. "But the way in which he uttered them gave me a strange and very apprehensive feeling. I received the impression that the man had formed some sinister resolve. But I regret to say I had lost the power of dispassionate thought. I fell into a great rage"——Mr. Cupples's tone was mildly apologetic—"and said a number of foolish things. I reminded him that the law allowed a measure of freedom to wives who received intolerable treatment. I made some utterly irrelevant references to his public record, and expressed the view that such men as he were unfit to live. I said these things, and others as ill-considered, under the eyes, and very possibly within earshot, of half-a-dozen persons sitting on this verandah. I noticed them, in spite of my agitation, looking at me as I walked up to the hotel again after relieving my mind—for it undoubtedly did relieve it," sighed Mr. Cupples, lying back in his chair.

"And Manderson? Did he say no more?"

"Not a word. He listened to me with his eyes on my face, as quiet as before. When I stopped he smiled very slightly, and at once turned away and strolled through the gate, making for White Gables."

"And this happened——?"

"On the Sunday morning."

"Then I suppose you never saw him alive again?"

"No," said Mr. Cupples. "Or rather yes—once. It was later in the day, on the golf-course. But I did not speak to him. And next morning he was found dead."

The two regarded each other in silence for a few moments. A party of guests who had been bathing came up the steps and seated themselves, with much chattering, at a table near them. The waiter approached. Mr. Cupples rose, and, taking Trent's arm, led him to a long tennis-lawn at the side of the hotel.

"I have a reason for telling you all this," began Mr. Cupples as they paced slowly up and down.

"Trust you for that," rejoined Trent, carefully filling his pipe again. He lit it, smoked a little, and then said, "I'll try and guess what your reason is, if you like."

Mr. Cupples's face of solemnity relaxed into a slight smile. He said nothing.

"You thought it possible," said Trent meditatively—"may I say you thought it practically certain?—that I should find out for myself that there had been something deeper than a mere conjugal tiff between the Mandersons. You thought that my unwholesome imagination would begin at once to play with the idea of Mrs. Manderson having something to do with the crime. Rather than that I should lose myself in barren speculations about this, you decided to tell me exactly how matters stood, and incidentally to impress upon me, who know how excellent your judgment is, your opinion of your niece. Is that about right?"

"It is perfectly right. Listen to me, my dear fellow," said Mr. Cupples earnestly, laying his hand on the other's arm. "I am going to be very frank. I am extremely glad that Manderson is dead. I believe him to have done nothing but harm in the world as an economic factor. I know that he was making a desert of the life of one who was like my own child to me. But I am under an intolerable dread of Mabel being involved in suspicion with regard to the murder. It is horrible to me to think of her delicacy and goodness being in contact, if only for a time, with the brutalities of the law. She is not fitted for it. It would mark her deeply. Many young women of twenty-six in these days could face such an ordeal, I suppose. I have observed a sort of imitative hardness about the products of the higher education of women to-day which would carry them through anything, perhaps. I am not prepared to say it is a bad thing in the conditions of feminine life prevailing at present. Mabel, however, is not like that. She is as unlike that as she is unlike the simpering misses that used to surround me as a child. She has plenty of brains; she is full of character; her mind and her tastes are cultivated; but it is all mixed up"—Mr. Cupples waved his hands in a vague gesture—"with ideals of refinement and reservation and womanly mystery. I fear she is not a child of the age. You never knew my wife, Trent. Mabel is my wife's child."

The younger man bowed his head. They paced the length of the lawn before he asked gently, "Why did she marry him?"

"I don't know," said Mr. Cupples briefly.

"Admired him, I suppose," suggested Trent.

Mr. Cupples shrugged his shoulders. "I have been told that a woman will usually be more or less attracted by the most successful man in her circle. Of course we cannot realize how a wilful, dominating personality like his would influence a girl whose affections were not bestowed elsewhere; especially if he laid himself out to win her. It is probably an overwhelming thing to be courted by a man whose name is known all over the world. She had heard of him, of course, as a financial great power, and she had no idea—she had lived mostly among people of artistic or literary propensities—how much soulless inhumanity that might involve. For all I know, she has no adequate idea of it to this day. When I first heard of the affair the mischief was done, and I knew better than to interpose my unsought opinions. She was of age, and there was absolutely nothing against him from the conventional point of view. Then I dare say his immense wealth would cast a spell over almost any woman. Mabel had some hundreds a year of her own; just enough, perhaps, to let her realize what millions really meant. But all this is conjecture. She certainly had not wanted to marry some scores of young fellows who to my knowledge had asked her; and though I don't believe, and never did believe, that she really loved this man of forty-five, she certainly did want to marry him. But if you ask me why, I can only say I don't know."

Trent nodded, and after a few more paces looked at his watch. "You've interested me so much," he said, "that I had quite forgotten my main business. I mustn't waste my morning. I am going down the road to White Gables at once, and I dare say I shall be poking about there until midday. If you can meet me then, Cupples, I should like to talk over anything I find out with you, unless something detains me."

"I am going for a walk this morning," Mr. Cupples replied. "I meant to have luncheon at a little inn near the golf-course, The Three Tuns. You had better join me there. It's farther along the road, about a quarter of a mile beyond White Gables. You can just see the roof between those two trees. The food they give one there is very plain, but good."

"So long as they have a cask of beer," said Trent, "they are all right. We will have bread and cheese, and oh, may Heaven our simple lives prevent from luxury's contagion, weak and vile! Till then, good-bye." He strode off to recover his hat from the verandah, waved it to Mr. Cupples, and was gone.

The old gentleman, seating himself in a deck-chair on the lawn, clasped his hands behind his head and gazed up into the speckless blue sky. "He is a dear fellow," he murmured. "The best of fellows. And a terribly acute fellow. Dear me! How curious it all is!"

CHAPTER IV

HANDCUFFS IN THE AIR

A PAINTER and the son of a painter, Philip Trent had while
yet in his twenties achieved some reputation within the world
of English art. Moreover, his pictures sold. An original, forcible talent and a habit of leisurely but continuous working,
broken by fits of strong creative enthusiasm, were at the
bottom of it. His father's name had helped; a patrimony large
enough to relieve him of the perilous imputation of being a
struggling man had certainly not hindered. But his best aid
to success had been an unconscious power of getting himself
liked. Good spirits and a lively, humorous fancy will always
be popular. Trent joined to these a genuine interest in others
that gained him something deeper than popularity. His judgment of persons was penetrating, but its process was internal;
no one felt on good behaviour with a man who seemed always
to be enjoying himself. Whether he was in a mood for floods of
nonsense or applying himself vigorously to a task, his face
seldom lost its expression of contained vivacity. Apart from
a sound knowledge of his art and its history, his culture was
large and loose, dominated by a love of poetry. At thirty-two
he had not yet passed the age of laughter and adventure.

His rise to a celebrity a hundred times greater than his
proper work had won for him came of a momentary impulse.
One day he had taken up a newspaper to find it chiefly concerned with a crime of a sort curiously rare in our country—
a murder done in a railway train. The circumstances were
puzzling; two persons were under arrest upon suspicion.
Trent, to whom an interest in such affairs was a new sensation,
heard the thing discussed among his friends, and set himself
in a purposeless mood to read up the accounts given in several
journals. He became intrigued; his imagination began to
work, in a manner strange to him, upon facts; an excitement
took hold of him such as he had only known before in his
bursts of art-inspiration or of personal adventure. At the
end of the day he wrote and dispatched a long letter to the
editor of the *Record,* which he chose only because it had contained the fullest and most intelligent version of the facts.

In this letter he did very much what Poe had done in the case of the murder of Mary Rogers. With nothing but the newspapers to guide him, he drew attention to the significance of certain apparently negligible facts, and ranged the evidence in such a manner as to throw grave suspicion upon a man who had presented himself as a witness. Sir James Molloy had printed this letter in leaded type. The same evening he was able to announce in the *Sun* the arrest and full confession of the incriminated man.

Sir James, who knew all the worlds of London, had lost no time in making Trent's acquaintance. The two men got on well, for Trent possessed some secret of native tact which had the effect of almost abolishing differences of age between himself and others. The great rotary presses in the basement of the *Record* building had filled him with a new enthusiasm. He had painted there, and Sir James had bought at sight what he called a machinery-scape in the manner of Heinrich Kley.

Then a few months later came the affair known as the Ilkley mystery. Sir James had invited Trent to an emolient dinner, and thereafter offered him what seemed to the young man a fantastically large sum for his temporary services as special representative of the *Record* at Ilkley.

"You could do it," the editor had urged. "You can write good stuff, and you know how to talk to people, and I can teach you all the technicalities of a reporter's job in half an hour. And you have a head for a mystery; you have imagination and cool judgment along with it. Think how it would feel if you pulled it off!"

Trent had admitted that it would be rather a lark. He had smoked, frowned, and at last convinced himself that the only thing that held him back was fear of an unfamiliar task. To react against fear had become a fixed moral habit with him, and he had accepted Sir James's offer.

He had pulled it off. For the second time he had given the authorities a start and a beating, and his name was on all tongues. He withdrew and painted pictures. He felt no leaning towards journalism, and Sir James, who knew a good deal about art, honourably refrained—as other editors did not—from tempting him with a good salary. But in the course of a few years he had applied to him perhaps thirty times for his services in the unravelling of similar problems at home and abroad. Sometimes Trent, busy with work that held him, had refused; sometimes he had been forestalled in the discovery of the truth. But the result of his irregular connection with the *Record* had been to make his name one of the best known in England. It was characteristic of him that his name was almost the only detail of his personality known to the public. He had imposed absolute silence about himself upon the Molloy papers; and the others were not going to advertise one of Sir James's men.

The Manderson case, he told himself as he walked rapidly up the sloping road to White Gables, might turn out to be terribly simple. Cupples was a wise old boy, but it was probably impossible for him to have an impartial opinion about his niece. But it was true that the manager of the hotel, who had spoken of her beauty in terms that aroused his attention, had spoken even more emphatically of her goodness. Not an artist in words, the manager had yet conveyed a very definite idea to Trent's mind. "There isn't a child about here that don't brighten up at the sound of her voice," he had said, "nor yet a grown-up, for the matter of that. Everybody used to look forward to her coming over in the summer. I don't mean that she's one of those women that are all kind heart and nothing else. There's backbone with it, if you know what I mean— pluck—any amount of go. There's nobody in Marlstone that isn't sorry for the lady in her trouble—not but what some of us may think she's lucky at the last of it." Trent wanted very much to meet Mrs. Manderson.

He could see now, beyond a spacious lawn and shrubbery, the front of the two-storied house of dull-red brick, with the pair of great gables from which it had its name. He had had but a glimpse of it from the car that morning. A modern house, he saw; perhaps ten years old. The place was beautifully kept, with that air of opulent peace that clothes even the smallest houses of the well-to-do in an English countryside. Before it, beyond the road, the rich meadow-land ran down to the edge of the cliffs; behind it a woody landscape stretched away across a broad vale to the moors. That such a place could be the scene of a crime of violence seemed fantastic; it lay so quiet and well ordered, so eloquent of disciplined service and gentle living. Yet there beyond the house, and near the hedge that rose between the garden and the hot, white road, stood the gardener's toolshed, by which the body had been found, lying tumbled against the wooden wall.

Trent walked past the gate of the drive and along the road until he was opposite this shed. Some forty yards farther along the road turned sharply away from the house, to run between thick plantations; and just before the turn the grounds of the house ended, with a small white gate at the angle of the boundary hedge. He approached the gate, which was plainly for the use of gardeners and the service of the establishment. It swung easily on its hinges, and he passed slowly up a path that led towards the back of the house, between the outer hedge and a tall wall of rhododendrons. Through a gap in this wall a track led him to the little neatly-built erection of wood, which stood among trees that faced a corner of the front. The body had lain on the side away from the house; a servant, he thought, looking out of the nearer windows in the earlier hours of the day before, might have glanced unseeing at the hut, as she wondered what it could be like to be as rich as the master.

He examined the place carefully and ransacked the hut within, but he could note no more than the trodden appearance of the uncut grass where the body had lain. Crouching low, with keen eyes and feeling fingers, he searched the ground minutely over a wide area; but the search was fruitless.

It was interrupted by the sound—the first he had heard from the house—of the closing of the front door. Trent unbent his long legs and stepped to the edge of the drive. A man was walking quickly away from the house in the direction of the great gate.

At the noise of a footstep on the gravel, the man wheeled with nervous swiftness and looked earnestly at Trent. The sudden sight of his face was almost terrible, so white and worn it was. Yet it was a young man's face. There was not a wrinkle about the haggard blue eyes, for all their tale of strain and desperate fatigue. As the two approached each other, Trent noted with admiration the man's breadth of shoulder and lithe, strong figure. In his carriage, inelastic as weariness had made it; in his handsome, regular features; in his short, smooth, yellow hair; and in his voice as he addressed Trent, the influence of a special sort of training was confessed. "Oxford was your playground, I think, my young friend," said Trent to himself.

"If you are Mr. Trent," said the young man pleasantly, "you are expected. Mr. Cupples telephoned from the hotel. My name is Marlowe."

"You were secretary to Mr. Manderson, I believe," said Trent. He was much inclined to like young Mr. Marlowe. Though he seemed so near a physical break-down, he gave out none the less that air of clean living and inward health that is the peculiar glory of his social type at his years. But there was something in the tired eyes that was a challenge to Trent's penetration; an habitual expression, as he took it to be, of meditating and weighing things not present to their sight. It was a look too intelligent, too steady and purposeful, to be called dreamy. Trent thought he had seen such a look before somewhere. He went on to say: "It is a terrible business for all of you. I fear it has upset you completely, Mr. Marlowe."

"A little limp, that's all," replied the young man wearily. "I was driving the car all Sunday night and most of yesterday, and I didn't sleep last night after hearing the news—who would? But I have an appointment now, Mr. Trent, down at the doctor's—arranging about the inquest. I expect it'll be tomorrow. If you will go up to the house and ask for Mr. Bunner, you'll find him expecting you; he will tell you all about things and show you round. He's the other secretary; an American, and the best of fellows; he'll look after you. There's a detective here, by the way—Inspector Murch, from Scotland Yard. He came yesterday."

"Murch!" Trent exclaimed. "But he and I are old friends. How under the sun did he get here so soon?"

"I have no idea," Mr. Marlowe answered. "But he was here last evening, before I got back from Southampton, interviewing everybody, and he's been about here since eight this morning. He's in the library now—that's where the open French window is that you see at the end of the house there. Perhaps you would like to step down there and talk about things."

"I think I will," said Trent. Marlowe nodded and went on his way. The thick turf of the lawn round which the drive took its circular sweep made Trent's footsteps as noiseless as a cat's. In a few moments he was looking in through the open leaves of the window at the southward end of the house, considering with a smile a very broad back and a bent head covered with short grizzled hair. The man within was stooping over a number of papers laid out on the table.

" 'Twas ever thus," said Trent in a melancholy tone, at the first sound of which the man within turned round with startling swiftness. "From childhood's hour I've seen my fondest hopes decay. I did think I was ahead of Scotland Yard this time, and now here is the largest officer in the entire Metropolitan force already occupying the position."

The detective smiled grimly and came to the window. "I was expecting you, Mr. Trent," he said. "This is the sort of case that you like."

"Since my tastes were being considered," Trent replied, stepping into the room, "I wish they had followed up the idea by keeping my hated rival out of the business. You have got a long start, too—I know all about it." His eyes began to wander round the room. "How did you manage it? You are a quick mover, I know; the dun deer's hide on fleeter foot was never tied; but I don't see how you got here in time to be at work yesterday evening. Has Scotland Yard secretly started an aviation corps? Or is it in league with the infernal powers? In either case the Home Secretary should be called upon to make a statement."

"It's simpler than that," said Mr. Murch with professional stolidity. "I happened to be on leave with the missis at Halvey, which is only twelve miles or so along the coast. As soon as our people there heard of the murder they told me. I wired to the Chief, and was put in charge of the case at once. I bicycled over yesterday evening, and have been at it since then."

"Arising out of that reply," said Trent inattentively, "how is Mrs. Inspector Murch?"

"Never better, thank you," answered the inspector, "and frequently speaks of you and the games you used to have with our kids. But you'll excuse me saying, Mr. Trent, that you needn't trouble to talk your nonsense to me while you're using your eyes. I know your ways by now. I understand you've fallen on your feet as usual, and have the lady's permission to go over the place and make inquiries."

"Such is the fact," said Trent. "I am going to cut you out again, inspector. I owe you one for beating me over the Abinger case, you old fox. But if you really mean that you're not inclined for the social amenities just now, let us leave compliments and talk business." He stepped to the table, glanced through the papers arranged there in order, and then turned to the open roll-top desk. He looked into the drawers swiftly. "I see this has been cleared out. Well now, inspector, I suppose we play the game as before."

Trent had found himself on a number of occasions in the past thrown into the company of Inspector Murch, who stood high in the councils of the Criminal Investigation Department. He was a quiet, tactful, and very shrewd officer, a man of great courage, with a vivid history in connection with the more dangerous class of criminals. His humanity was as broad as his frame, which was large even for a policeman. Trent and he, through some obscure working of sympathy, had appreciated one another from the beginning, and had formed one of those curious friendships with which it was the younger man's delight to adorn his experience. The inspector would talk more freely to him than to any one, under the rose, and they would discuss details and possibilities of every case, to their mutual enlightenment. There were necessary rules and limits. It was understood between them that Trent made no journalistic use of any point that could only have come to him from an official source. Each of them, moreover, for the honour and prestige of the institution he represented, openly reserved the right to withhold from the other any discovery or inspiration that might come to him which he considered vital to the solution of the difficulty. Trent had insisted on carefully formulating these principles of what he called detective sportsmanship. Mr. Murch, who loved a contest, and who only stood to gain by his association with the keen intelligence of the other, entered very heartily into "the game". In these strivings for the credit of the press and of the police, victory sometimes attended the experience and method of the officer, sometimes the quicker brain and livelier imagination of Trent, his gift of instinctively recognizing the significant through all disguises.

The inspector then replied to Trent's last words with cordial agreement. Leaning on either side of the French window, with the deep peace and hazy splendour of the summer landscape before them, they reviewed the case.

Trent had taken out a thin notebook, and as they talked he began to make, with light, secure touches, a rough sketch plan of the room. It was a thing he did habitually on such occasions, and often quite idly, but now and then the habit had served him to good purpose.

This was a large, light apartment at the corner of the

house, with generous window-space in two walls. A broad table stood in the middle. As one entered by the window the roll-top desk stood just to the left of it against the wall. The inner door was in the wall to the left, at the farther end of the room; and was faced by a broad window divided into openings of the casement type. A beautifully carved old corner-cupboard rose high against the wall beyond the door, and another cupboard filled a recess beside the fire-place. Some coloured prints of Harunobu, with which Trent promised himself a better acquaintance, hung on what little wall-space was unoccupied by books. These had a very uninspiring appearance of having been bought by the yard and never taken from their shelves. Bound with a sober luxury, the great English novelists, essayists, historians, and poets stood ranged like an army struck dead in its ranks. There were a few chairs made, like the cupboard and table, of old carved oak; a modern arm-chair and a swivel office-chair before the desk. The room looked costly but very bare. Almost the only portable objects were a great porcelain bowl of a wonderful blue on the table, a clock and some cigar boxes on the mantel-shelf, and a movable telephone standard on the top of the desk.

"Seen the body?" inquired the inspector.

Trent nodded. "And the place where it lay," he said.

"First impressions of this case rather puzzle me," said the inspector. "From what I heard at Halvey I guessed it might be common robbery and murder by some tramp, though such a thing is very far from common in these parts. But as soon as I began my inquiries I came on some curious points, which by this time I dare say you've noted for yourself. The man is shot in his own grounds, quite near the house, to begin with. Yet there's not the slightest trace of any attempt at burglary. And the body wasn't robbed. In fact, it would be as plain a case of suicide as you could wish to see, if it wasn't for certain facts. Here's another thing; for a month or so past, they tell me, Manderson had been in a queer state of mind. I expect you know already that he and his wife had some trouble between them. The servants had noticed a change in his manner to her for a long time, and for the past week he had scarcely spoken to her. They say he was a changed man, moody and silent— whether on account of that or something else. The lady's maid says he looked as if something was going to arrive. It's always easy to remember that people looked like that, after something has happened to them. Still, that's what they say. There you are again, then: suicide! Now, why wasn't it suicide, Mr. Trent?"

"The facts so far as I know them are really all against it," Trent replied, sitting on the threshold of the window and clasping his knees. "First, of course, no weapon is to be found. I've searched, and you've searched, and there's no trace of any firearm anywhere within a stone's throw of where the body lay. Second, the marks on the wrists, fresh scratches and bruises, which we can only assume to have been done in a struggle with somebody. Third, who ever heard of anybody shooting himself in the eye? Then I heard from the manager of the hotel here another fact, which strikes me as the most curious detail in this affair. Manderson had dressed himself fully before going out there, but he forgot his false teeth. Now how could a suicide who dressed himself to make a decent appearance as a corpse forget his teeth?"

"That last argument hadn't struck me," admitted Mr. Murch. "There's something in it. But on the strength of the other points, which had occurred to me, I am not considering suicide. I have been looking about for ideas in this house, this morning. I expect you were thinking of doing the same."

"That is so. It is a case for ideas, it seems to me. Come, Murch, let us make an effort; let us bend our spirits to a temper of general suspicion. Let us suspect everybody in the house, to begin with. Listen: I will tell you whom I suspect. I suspect Mrs. Manderson, of course. I also suspect both the secretaries—I hear there are two, and I hardly know which of them I regard as more thoroughly open to suspicion. I suspect the butler and the lady's maid. I suspect the other domestics, and especially do I suspect the boot-boy. By the way, what domestics are there? I have more than enough suspicion to go round, whatever the size of the establishment; but as a matter of curiosity I should like to know."

"All very well to laugh," replied the inspector, "but at the first stage of affairs it's the only safe principle, and you know that as well as I do, Mr. Trent. However, I've seen enough of the people here, last night and to-day, to put a few of them out of my mind for the present at least. You will form your own conclusions. As for the establishment, there's the butler and lady's maid, cook, and three other maids, one a young girl. One chauffeur, who's away with a broken wrist. No boy."

"What about the gardener? You say nothing about that shadowy and sinister figure, the gardener. You are keeping him in the background, Murch. Play the game. Out with him— or I report you to the Rules Committee."

"The garden is attended to by a man in the village, who comes twice a week. I've talked to him. He was here last on Friday."

"Then I suspect him all the more," said Trent. "And now as to the house itself. What I propose to do, to begin with, is to sniff about a little in this room, where I am told Manderson spent a great deal of his time, and in his bedroom; especially the bedroom. But since we're in this room, let's start here. You seem to be at the same stage of the inquiry. Perhaps you've done the bedrooms already?"

The inspector nodded. "I've been over Manderson's and his wife's. Nothing to be got there, I think. His room is very simple and bare, no signs of any sort that *I* could see. Seems to have insisted on the simple life, does Manderson. Never employed a valet. The room's almost like a cell, except for the clothes and shoes. You'll find it all exactly as I found it; and they tell me that's exactly as Manderson left it, at we don't know what o'clock yesterday morning. Opens into Mrs. Manderson's bedroom—not much of the cell about that, I can tell you. I should say the lady was as fond of pretty things as most. But she cleared out of it on the morning of the discovery —told the maid she could never sleep in a room opening into her murdered husband's room. Very natural feeling in a woman, Mr. Trent. She's camping out, so to say, in one of the spare bedrooms now."

"Come, my friend," Trent was saying to himself, as he made a few notes in his little book. "Have you got your eye on Mrs. Manderson? Or haven't you? I know that colourless tone of the inspectorial voice. I wish I had seen her. Either you've got something against her and you don't want me to get hold of it; or else you've made up your mind she's innocent, but have no objection to my wasting my time over her. Well, it's all in the game; which begins to look extremely interesting as we go on." To Mr. Murch he said aloud: "Well, I'll draw the bedroom later on. What about this?"

"They call it the library," said the inspector. "Manderson used to do his writing and that in here; passed most of the time he spent indoors here. Since he and his wife ceased to hit it off together, he had taken to spending his evenings alone, and when at this house he always spent 'em in here. He was last seen alive, as far as the servants are concerned, in this room."

Trent rose and glanced again through the papers set out on the table. "Business letters and documents, mostly," said Mr. Murch. "Reports, prospectuses, and that. A few letters on private matters, nothing in them that I can see. The American secretary—Bunner his name is, and a queerer card I never saw turned—he's been through this desk with me this morning. He had got it into his head that Manderson had been receiving threatening letters, and that the murder was the outcome of that. But there's no trace of any such thing; and we looked at every blessed paper. The only unusual things we found were some packets of bank-notes to a considerable amount, and a couple of little bags of unset diamonds. I asked Mr. Bunner to put them in a safer place. It appears that Manderson had begun buying diamonds lately as a speculation—it was a new game to him, the secretary said, and it seemed to amuse him."

"What about these secretaries?" Trent inquired. "I met one called Marlowe just now outside; a nice-looking chap with singular eyes, unquestionably English. The other, it seems, is an American. What did Manderson want with an English secretary?"

"Mr. Marlowe explained to me how that was. The American was his right-hand business man, one of his office staff, who never left him. Mr. Marlowe had nothing to do with Manderson's business as a financier, knew nothing of it. His job was to look after Manderson's horses and motors and yacht and sporting arrangements and that—make himself generally useful, as you might say. He had the spending of a lot of money, I should think. The other was confined entirely to the office affairs, and I dare say he had his hands full. As for his being English, it was just a fad of Manderson's to have an English secretary. He'd had several before Mr. Marlowe."

"He showed his taste," observed Trent. "It might be more than interesting, don't you think, to be minister to the pleasures of a modern plutocrat with a large P. Only they say that Manderson's were exclusively of an innocent kind. Certainly Marlowe gives me the impression that he would be weak in the part of Petronius. But to return to the matter in hand." He looked at his notes. "You said just now that he was last seen alive here, 'so far as the servants were concerned.' That meant——?"

"He had a conversation with his wife on going to bed. But for that, the man-servant, Martin by name, last saw him in this room. I had his story last night, and very glad he was to tell it. An affair like this is meat and drink to the servants of the house."

Trent considered for some moments, gazing through the open window over the sun-flooded slopes. "Would it bore you to hear what he has to say again?" he asked at length. For reply, Mr. Murch rang the bell. A spare, clean-shaven, middle-aged man, having the servant's manner in its most distinguished form, answered it.

"This is Mr. Trent, who is authorized by Mrs. Manderson to go over the house and make inquiries," explained the detective. "He would like to hear your story." Martin bowed distantly. He recognized Trent for a gentleman. Time would show whether he was what Martin called a gentleman in every sense of the word.

"I observed you approaching the house, sir," said Martin with impassive courtesy. He spoke with a slow and measured utterance. "My instructions are to assist you in every possible way. Should you wish me to recall the circumstances of Sunday night?"

"Please," said Trent with ponderous gravity. Martin's style was making clamorous appeal to his sense of comedy. He banished with an effort all vivacity of expression from his face.

"I last saw Mr. Manderson——"

"No, not that yet," Trent checked him quietly. "Tell me all you saw of him that evening—after dinner, say. Try to recollect every little detail."

"After dinner, sir?—yes. I remember that after dinner Mr. Manderson and Mr. Marlowe walked up and down the path through the orchard, talking. If you ask me for details, it struck me they were talking about something important, because I heard Mr. Manderson say something when they came in through the back entrance. He said, as near as I can remember, 'If Harris is there, every minute is of importance. You want to start right away. And not a word to a soul.' Mr. Marlowe answered, 'Very well. I will just change out of these clothes and then I am ready'—or words to that effect. I heard

this plainly as they passed the window of my pantry. Then
Mr. Marlowe went up to his bedroom, and Mr. Manderson
entered the library and rang for me. He handed me some letters
for the postman in the morning and directed me to sit up,
as Mr. Marlowe had persuaded him to go for a drive in the
car by moonlight."

"That was curious," remarked Trent.

"I thought so, sir. But I recollected what I had heard about
'not a word to a soul,' and I concluded that this about a moonlight drive was intended to mislead."

"What time was this?"

"It would be about ten, sir, I should say. After speaking
to me, Mr. Manderson waited until Mr. Marlowe had come
down and brought round the car. He then went into the
drawing-room, where Mrs. Manderson was."

"Did that strike you as curious?"

Martin looked down his nose. "If you ask me the question,
sir," he said with reserve, "I had not known him enter that
room since we came here this year. He preferred to sit in the
library in the evenings. That evening he only remained with
Mrs. Manderson for a few minutes. Then he and Mr. Marlowe
started immediately."

"You saw them start?"

"Yes, sir. They took the direction of Bishopsbridge."

"And you saw Mr. Manderson again later?"

"After an hour or thereabouts, sir, in the library. That
would have been about a quarter past eleven, I should say;
I had noticed eleven striking from the church. I may say
I am peculiarly quick of hearing, sir."

"Mr. Manderson had rung the bell for you, I suppose.
Yes? And what passed when you answered it?"

"Mr. Manderson had put out the decanter of whisky and
a syphon and glass, sir, from the cupboard where he kept
them——"

Trent held up his hand. "While we are on that point,
Martin, I want to ask you plainly, did Mr. Manderson drink
very much? You understand this is not impertinent curiosity
on my part. I want you to tell me, because it may possibly help
in the clearing up of this case."

"Perfectly, sir," replied Martin gravely. "I have no hesitation in telling you what I have already told the inspector.
Mr. Manderson was, considering his position in life, a remark-

ably abstemious man. In my four years of service with him I never knew anything of an alcoholic nature pass his lips, except a glass or two of wine at dinner, very rarely a little at luncheon, and from time to time a whisky and soda before going to bed. He never seemed to form a habit of it. Often I used to find his glass in the morning with only a little soda water in it; sometimes he would have been having whisky with it, but never much. He never was particular about his drinks; ordinary soda was what he preferred, though I had ventured to suggest some of the natural minerals, having personally acquired a taste for them in my previous service. He used to keep them in the cupboard here, because he had a great dislike of being waited on more than was necessary. It was an under-stood thing that I never came near him after dinner unless sent for. And when he sent for anything, he liked it brought quick, and to be left alone again at once. He hated to be asked if he required anything more. Amazingly simple in his tastes, sir, Mr. Manderson was."

"Very well; and he rang for you that night about a quarter past eleven. Now can you remember exactly what he said?"

"I think I can tell you with some approach to accuracy, sir. It was not much. First he asked me if Mr. Bunner had gone to bed, and I replied that he had been gone up some time. He then said that he wanted some one to sit up until 12.30, in case an important message should come by telephone, and that Mr. Marlowe having gone to Southampton for him in the motor, he wished me to do this, and that I was to take down the message if it came, and not disturb him. He also ordered a fresh syphon of soda water. I believe that was all, sir."

"You noticed nothing unusual about him, I suppose?"

"No, sir, nothing unusual. When I answered the ring, he was seated at the desk listening at the telephone, waiting for a number, as I supposed. He gave his orders and went on listen-ing at the same time. When I returned with the syphon he was engaged in conversation over the wire."

"Do you remember anything of what he was saying?"

"Very little, sir; it was something about somebody being at some hotel—of no interest to me. I was only in the room just time enough to place the syphon on the table and with-draw. As I closed the door he was saying, 'You're sure he isn't in the hotel?' or words to that effect."

"And that was the last you saw and heard of him alive?"

"No, sir. A little later, at half-past eleven, when I had settled down in my pantry with the door ajar, and a book to pass the time, I heard Mr. Manderson go upstairs to bed. I immediately went to close the library window, and slipped the lock of the front door. I did not hear anything more."

Trent considered. "I suppose you didn't doze at all," he said tentatively, "while you were sitting up waiting for the telephone message?"

"Oh, no, sir. I am always very wakeful about that time. I'm a bad sleeper, especially in the neighbourhood of the sea, and I generally read in bed until somewhere about midnight."

"And did any message come?"

"No, sir."

"No. And I suppose you sleep with your window open, these warm nights?"

"It is never closed at night, sir."

Trent added a last note; then he looked thoughtfully through those he had taken. He rose and paced up and down the room for some moments with a downcast eye. At length he paused opposite Martin. "It all seems perfectly ordinary and simple," he said. "I just want to get a few details clear. You went to shut the windows in the library before going to bed. Which windows?"

"The French window, sir. It had been open all day. The windows opposite the door were seldom opened."

"And what about the curtains? I am wondering whether anyone outside the house could have seen into the room."

"Easily, sir, I should say, if he had got into the grounds on that side. The curtains were never drawn in hot weather. Mr. Manderson would often sit right in the doorway at nights, smoking and looking out into the darkness. But nobody could have seen him who had any business to be there."

"I see. And now tell me this. Your hearing is very acute, you say, and you heard Mr. Manderson enter the house when he came in after dinner from the garden. Did you hear him re-enter it after returning from the motor drive?"

Martin paused. "Now you mention it, sir, I remember that I did not. His ringing the bell in this room was the first I knew of his being back. I should have heard him come in, if he had come in by the front. I should have heard the door go. But he must have come in by the window." The man reflected for a moment, then added, "As a general rule, Mr. Manderson would come in by the front, hang up his hat and coat in the hall, and pass down the hall into the study. It seems likely to me that he was in a great hurry to use the telephone, so went straight across the lawn to the window—he was like that, when there was anything important to be done. He had his hat on, now I remember, and had thrown his great-coat over the end of the table. He gave his order very sharp, too, as he always did when busy. A very precipitate man indeed was Mr. Manderson; a hustler, as they say."

"Ah! he appeared to be busy. But didn't you say just now that you noticed nothing unusual about him?"

A melancholy smile flitted momentarily over Martin's face. "That observation shows that you did not know Mr. Manderson, sir, if you will pardon my saying so. His being like that was nothing unusual; quite the contrary. It took me long enough to get used to it. Either he would be sitting quite still and smoking a cigar, thinking or reading, or else he would be writing, dictating, and sending off wires all at the same time, till it almost made one dizzy to see it, sometimes for an hour or more at a stretch. As for being in a hurry over a telephone message, I may say it wasn't in him to be anything else."

Trent turned to the inspector, who met his eye with a look of answering intelligence. Not sorry to show his understanding of the line of inquiry opened by Trent, Mr. Murch for the first time put a question.

"Then you left him telephoning by the open window, with the lights on, and the drinks on the table; is that it?"

"That is so, Mr. Murch." The delicacy of the change in Martin's manner when called upon to answer the detective momentarily distracted Trent's appreciative mind. But the big man's next question brought it back to the problem at once.

"About those drinks. You say Mr. Manderson often took no whisky before going to bed. Did he have any that night?"

"I could not say. The room was put to rights in the morning by one of the maids, and the glass washed, I presume, as usual. I know that the decanter was nearly full that evening. I had refilled it a few days before, and I glanced at it when I brought the fresh syphon, just out of habit, to make sure there was a decent-looking amount."

The inspector went to the tall corner-cupboard and opened it. He took out a decanter of cut glass and set it on the table before Martin. "Was it fuller than that?" he asked quietly. "That's how I found it this morning." The decanter was more than half empty.

For the first time Martin's self-possession wavered. He took up the decanter quickly, tilted it before his eyes, and then stared amazedly at the others. He said slowly: "There's not much short of half-a-bottle gone out of this since I last set eyes on it—and that was that Sunday night."

"Nobody in the house, I suppose?" suggested Trent discreetly.

"Out of the question!" replied Martin briefly; then he added, "I beg pardon, sir, but this is a most extraordinary thing to me. Such a thing never happened in all my experience of Mr. Manderson. As for the women-servants, they never touch anything, I can answer for it; and as for me, when I want a drink I can help myself without going to the decanters." He took up the decanter again and aimlessly renewed his observation of the contents, while the inspector eyed him with a look of serene satisfaction, as a master contemplates his handiwork.

Trent turned to a fresh page of his notebook, and tapped it thoughtfully with his pencil. Then he looked up and said, "I suppose Mr. Manderson had dressed for dinner that night?"

"Certainly, sir. He had on a suit with a dress-jacket, what he used to refer to as a Tuxedo, which he usually wore when dining at home."

"And he was dressed like that when you saw him last?"

"All but the jacket, sir. When he spent the evening in the library, as usually happened, he would change it for an old shooting-jacket after dinner, a light-coloured tweed, a little too loud in pattern for English tastes, perhaps. He had it on when I saw him last. It used to hang in this cupboard here"— Martin opened the door of it as he spoke—"along with Mr. Manderson's fishing-rods and such things, so that he could slip it on after dinner without going upstairs."

"Leaving the dinner-jacket in the cupboard?"

"Yes, sir. The housemaid used to take it upstairs in the morning."

"In the morning," Trent repeated slowly. "And now that

we are speaking of the morning, will you tell me exactly what you know about that? I understand that Mr. Manderson was not missed until the body was found about ten o'clock."

"That is so, sir. Mr. Manderson would never be called, or have anything brought to him in the morning. He occupied a separate bedroom. Usually he would get up about eight and go round to the bathroom, and he would come down some time before nine. But often he would sleep till nine or ten o'clock. Mrs. Manderson was always called at seven. The maid would take in tea to her. Yesterday morning Mrs. Manderson took breakfast about eight in her sitting-room as usual, and everyone supposed that Mr. Manderson was still in bed and asleep, when Evans came rushing up to the house with the shocking intelligence."

"I see," said Trent. "And now another thing. You say you slipped the lock of the front door before going to bed. Was that all the locking-up you did?"

"To the front door, sir, yes; I slipped the lock. No more is considered necessary in these parts. But I had locked both the doors at the back, and seen to the fastenings of all the windows on the ground floor. In the morning everything was as I had left it."

"As you had left it. Now here is another point—the last, I think. Were the clothes in which the body was found the clothes that Mr. Manderson would naturally have worn that day?"

Martin rubbed his chin. "You remind me how surprised I was when I first set eyes on the body, sir. At first I couldn't make out what was unusual about the clothes, and then I saw what it was. The collar was a shape of collar Mr. Manderson never wore except with evening dress. Then I found that he had put on all the same things that he had worn the night before—large fronted shirt and all—except just the coat and waistcoat and trousers, and the brown shoes, and blue tie. As for the suit, it was one of half-a-dozen he might have worn. But for him to have simply put on all the rest just because they were there, instead of getting out the kind of shirt and things he always wore by day; well, sir, it was unprecedented. It shows, like some other things, what a hurry he must have been in when getting up."

"Of course," said Trent. "Well, I think that's all I wanted to know. You have put everything with admirable clearness,

Martin. If we want to ask any more questions later on, I suppose you will be somewhere about."

"I shall be at your disposal, sir." Martin bowed, and went out quietly.

Trent flung himself into the arm-chair and exhaled a long breath. "Martin is a great creature," he said. "He is far, far better than a play. There is none like him, none, nor will be when our summers have deceased. Straight, too; not an atom of harm in dear old Martin. Do you know, Murch, you are wrong in suspecting that man."

"I never said a word about suspecting him." The inspector was taken aback. "*You* know, Mr. Trent, he would never have told his story like that if he thought I suspected him."

"I dare say he doesn't think so. He is a wonderful creature, a great artist; but, in spite of that, he is not at all a sensitive type. It has never occurred to his mind that you, Murch, could suspect him, Martin, the complete, the accomplished. But I know it. You must understand, inspector, that I have made a special study of the psychology of officers of the law. It is a grossly neglected branch of knowledge. They are far more interesting than criminals, and not nearly so easy. All the time I was questioning him I saw handcuffs in your eye. Your lips were mutely framing the syllables of those tremendous words: 'It is my duty to tell you that anything you now say will be taken down and used in evidence against you.' Your manner would have deceived most men, but it could not deceive me."

Mr. Murch laughed heartily. Trent's nonsense never made any sort of impression on his mind, but he took it as a mark of esteem, which indeed it was; so it never failed to please him. "Well, Mr. Trent," he said, "you're perfectly right. There's no point in denying it, I have got my eye on him. Not that there's anything definite; but you know as well as I do how often servants are mixed up in affairs of this kind, and this man is such a very quiet customer. You remember the case of Lord William Russell's valet, who went in as usual, in the morning, to draw up the blinds in his master's bedroom, as quiet and starchy as you please, a few hours after he had murdered him in his bed. I've talked to all the women of the house, and I don't believe there's a morsel of harm in one of them. But Martin's not so easy set aside. I don't like his manner; I believe he's hiding something. If so, I shall find it out."

"Cease!" said Trent. "Drain not to its dregs the urn of bitter prophecy. Let us get back to facts. Have you, as a matter of evidence, anything at all to bring against Martin's story as he has told it to us?"

"Nothing whatever at present. As for his suggestion that Manderson came in by way of the window after leaving Marlowe and the car, that's right enough, I should say. I questioned the servant who swept the room next morning, and she tells me there were gravelly marks near the window, on this plain drugget that goes round the carpet. And there's a footprint in this soft new gravel just outside." The inspector took a folding rule from his pocket and with it pointed out the traces. "One of the patent shoes Manderson was wearing that night exactly fits that print; you'll find them," he added, "on the top shelf in the bedroom, near the window end, the only patents in the row. The girl who polished them in the morning picked them out for me."

Trent bent down and studied the faint marks keenly. "Good!" he said. "You have covered a lot of ground, Murch, I must say. That was excellent about the whisky; you made your point finely. I feel inclined to shout 'Encore!' It's a thing I shall have to think over."

"I thought you might have fitted it in already," said Mr. Murch. "Come, Mr. Trent, we're only at the beginning of our inquiries, but what do you say to this for a preliminary theory? There's a plan of burglary, say a couple of men in it and Martin squared. They know where the plate is, and all about the handy little bits of stuff in the drawing-room and elsewhere. They watch the house; see Manderson off to bed; Martin comes to shut the window, and leaves it ajar, accidentally on purpose. They wait till Martin goes to bed at twelve-thirty; then they just walk into the library, and begin to sample the whisky first thing. Now suppose Manderson isn't asleep, and suppose they make a noise opening the window, or however it might be. He hears it; thinks of burglars; gets up very quietly to see if anything's wrong; creeps down on them, perhaps, just as they're getting ready for work. They cut and run; he chases them down to the shed, and collars one; there's a fight; one of them loses his temper and his head, and makes a swinging job of it. Now, Mr. Trent, pick that to pieces."

"Very well," said Trent; "just to oblige you, Murch, especially as I know you don't believe a word of it. First:

no traces of any kind left by your burglar or burglars, and the window found fastened in the morning, according to Martin. Not much force in that, I allow. Next: nobody in the house hears anything of this stampede through the library, nor hears any shout from Manderson either inside the house or outside. Next: Manderson goes down without a word to anybody, though Bunner and Martin are at hand. Next: did you ever hear in your long experience of a householder getting up in the night to pounce on burglars, who dressed himself fully, with underclothing, shirt, collar and tie, trousers, waistcoat and coat, socks and hard leather shoes; and who gave the finishing touches to a somewhat dandified toilet by doing his hair, and putting on his watch and chain? Personally, I call that over-dressing the part. The only decorative detail he seems to have forgotten is his teeth."

The inspector leaned forward thinking, his large hands clasped before him. "No," he said at last. "Of course there's no help in that theory. I rather expect we have some way to go before we find out why a man gets up before the servants are awake, dresses himself fully, and is murdered within sight of his house early enough to be cold and stiff by ten in the morning."

Trent shook his head. "We can't build anything on that last consideration. I've gone into the subject with people who know. I shouldn't wonder," he added, "if the traditional notions about loss of temperature and rigour after death had occasionally brought an innocent man to the gallows, or near it. Dr. Stock has them all, I feel sure; most general practitioners of the older generation have. That Dr. Stock will make an ass of himself at the inquest, is almost as certain as that to-morrow's sun will rise. I've seen him. He will say the body must have been dead about so long, because of the degree of coldness and *rigor mortis*. I can see him nosing it all in some text book that was out of date when he was a student. Listen, Murch, and I will tell you some facts which will be a great hindrance to you in your professional career. There are many things that may hasten or retard the cooling of the body. This one was lying in the long dewy grass on the shady side of the shed. As for rigidity, if Manderson died in a struggle, or labouring under sudden emotion, his corpse might stiffen practically instantaneously; there are dozens of cases noted, particularly in cases of injury to the skull, like this one. On the other hand, the stiffening might not have begun until eight or ten hours after death. You can't hang anybody on *rigor mortis* nowadays, inspector, much as you may resent the limitation. No, what we *can* say is this. If he had been shot after the hour at which the world begins to get up and go about its business, it would have been heard, and very likely seen too. In fact, we must reason, to begin with, at any rate, on the assumption that he wasn't shot at a time when people might be awake; it isn't done in these parts. Put that time at 6.30 a.m. Manderson went up to bed at 11 p.m., and Martin sat up till 12.30. Assuming that he went to sleep at once on turning in, that leaves us something like six hours for the crime to be committed in; and that is a long time. But whenever it took place, I wish you would suggest a reason why Manderson, who was a fairly late riser, was up and dressed at or before 6.30; and why neither Martin, who sleeps lightly, nor Bunner, nor his wife heard him moving about, or letting himself out of the house. He must have been careful. He must have crept about like a cat. Do you feel as I do, Murch, about all this; that it is very, very strange and baffling?"

"That's how it looks," agreed the inspector.

"And now," said Trent, rising to his feet, "I'll leave you to your meditations, and take a look at the bedrooms. Perhaps the explanation of all this will suddenly burst upon you while I am poking about up there. But," concluded Trent in a voice of sudden exasperation, turning round in the doorway, "if you can tell me at any time, how under the sun a man who put on all those clothes could forget to put in his teeth, you may kick me from here to the nearest lunatic asylum, and hand me over as an incipient dement."

CHAPTER V
POKING ABOUT

THERE are moments in life, as one might think, when that which is within us, busy about its secret affair, lets escape into consciousness some hint of a fortunate thing ordained. Who does not know what it is to feel at times a wave of unaccountable persuasion that it is about to go well with him?—not the feverish confidence of men in danger of a blow from fate, not the persistent illusion of the optimist, but an unsought conviction, springing up like a bird from the heather, that success is at hand in some great or little thing. The general suddenly knows at dawn that the day will bring him victory; the man on the green suddenly knows that he will put down the long putt. As Trent mounted the stairway outside the library door he seemed to rise into certainty of achievement.

A host of guesses and inferences swarmed apparently unsorted through his mind; a few secret observations that he had made, and which he felt must have significance, still stood unrelated to any plausible theory of the crime; yet as he went up he seemed to know indubitably that light was going to appear.

The bedrooms lay on either side of a broad carpeted passage, lighted by a tall end window. It went the length of the house until it ran at right angles into a narrower passage, out of which the servants' rooms opened. Martin's room was the exception: it opened out of a small landing halfway to the upper floor. As Trent passed it he glanced within. A little square room, clean and commonplace. In going up the rest of the stairway he stepped with elaborate precaution against noise, hugging the wall closely and placing each foot with care; but a series of very audible creaks marked his passage.

He knew that Manderson's room was the first on the right hand when the bedroom floor was reached, and he went to it at once. He tried the latch and the lock, which worked normally, and examined the wards of the key. Then he turned to the room.

It was a small apartment, strangely bare. The plutocrat's toilet appointments were of the simplest. All remained just as it had been on the morning of the ghastly discovery in the grounds. The sheets and blankets of the unmade bed lay tumbled over a narrow wooden bedstead, and the sun shone brightly through the window upon them. It gleamed, too, upon the gold parts of the delicate work of dentistry that lay in water in a shallow bowl of glass placed on a small, plain table by the bedside. On this also stood a wrought-iron candlestick. Some clothing lay untidily over one of the two rush-bottomed chairs. Various objects on the top of a chest of drawers, which had been used as a dressing-table, lay in such disorder as a hurried man might make. Trent looked them over with a questing eye. He noted also that the occupant of the room had neither washed nor shaved. With his finger he turned over the dental plate in the bowl, and frowned again at its incomprehensible presence.

The emptiness and disarray of the little room, flooded by the sunbeams, were producing in Trent a sense of gruesomeness. His fancy called up a picture of a haggard man dressing himself in careful silence by the first light of dawn, glancing constantly at the inner door behind which his wife slept, his eyes full of some terror.

Trent shivered, and to fix his mind again on actualities opened two tall cupboards in the wall on either side of the bed. They contained clothing, a large choice of which had evidently been one of the very few conditions of comfort for the man who had slept there.

In the matter of shoes, also, Manderson had allowed himself the advantage of wealth. An extraordinary number of these, treed and carefully kept, was ranged on two long low shelves against the wall. No boots were among them. Trent, himself an amateur of good shoe-leather, now turned to these, and glanced over the collection with an appreciative eye. It was to be seen that Manderson had been inclined to pride himself on a rather small and well-formed foot. The shoes were of a distinctive shape, narrow and round-toed, beautifully made; all were evidently from the same last.

Suddenly his eyes narrowed themselves over a pair of patent-leather shoes on the upper shelf.

These were the shoes of which the inspector had already described the position to him; the shoes worn by Manderson the night before his death. They were a well-worn pair, he saw at once; he saw, too, that they had been very recently polished. Something about the uppers of these shoes had seized his attention. He bent lower and frowned over them, comparing what he saw with the appearance of the neighbouring shoes. Then he took them up and examined the line of junction of the uppers with the soles.

As he did this, Trent began unconsciously to whistle faintly, and with great precision, an air which Inspector Murch, if he had been present, would have recognized.

Most men who have the habit of self-control have also some involuntary trick which tells those who know them that they are suppressing excitement. The inspector had noted that when Trent had picked up a strong scent he whistled faintly a certain melodious passage; though the inspector could not have told you that it was in fact the opening movement of Mendelssohn's *Lied ohne Wörter* in A Major.

He turned the shoes over, made some measurements with a marked tape, and looked minutely at the bottoms. On each, in the angle between the heel and the instep, he detected a faint trace of red gravel.

Trent placed the shoes on the floor, and walked with his hands behind him to the window, out of which, still faintly whistling, he gazed with eyes that saw nothing. Once his lips opened to emit mechanically the Englishman's expletive of sudden enlightenment. At length he turned to the shelves again, and swiftly but carefully examined every one of the shoes there.

This done, he took up the garments from the chair, looked them over closely and replaced them. He turned to the wardrobe cupboards again, and hunted through them carefully. The litter on the dressing-table now engaged his attention for the second time. Then he sat down on the empty chair, took his head in his hands, and remained in that attitude, staring at the carpet, for some minutes. He rose at last and opened the inner door leading to Mrs. Manderson's room.

It was evident at a glance that the big room had been hurriedly put down from its place as the lady's bower. All the array of objects that belong to a woman's dressing-table had been removed; on bed and chairs and smaller tables there were no garments or hats, bags or boxes; no trace remained of the obstinate conspiracy of gloves and veils, handkerchiefs and ribbons, to break the captivity of the drawer. The room was like an unoccupied guest-chamber. Yet in every detail of furniture and decoration it spoke of an unconventional but exacting taste. Trent, as his expert eye noted the various perfection of colour and form amid which the ill-mated lady dreamed her dreams and thought her loneliest thoughts, knew that she had at least the resources of an artistic nature. His interest in this unknown personality grew stronger; and his brows came down heavily as he thought of the burdens laid upon it, and of the deed of which the history was now shaping itself with more and more of substance before his busy mind.

He went first to the tall French window in the middle of

the wall that faced the door, and opening it, stepped out upon a small balcony with an iron railing. He looked down on a broad stretch of lawn that began immediately beneath him, separated from the house-wall only by a narrow flower-bed, and stretched away, with an abrupt dip at the farther end, toward the orchard. The other window opened with a sash above the garden-entrance of the library. In the farther inside corner of the room was a second door giving upon the passage; the door by which the maid was wont to come in, and her mistress to go out, in the morning.

Trent, seated on the bed, quickly sketched in his notebook a plan of the room and its neighbour. The bed stood in the angle between the communicating-door and the sash-window, its head against the wall dividing the room from Manderson's. Trent stared at the pillows; then he lay down with deliberation on the bed and looked through the open door into the adjoining room.

This observation taken, he rose again and proceeded to note on his plan that on either side of the bed was a small table with a cover. Upon that farthest from the door was a graceful electric-lamp standard of copper connected by a free wire with the wall. Trent looked at it thoughtfully, then at the switches connected with the other lights in the room. They were, as usual, on the wall just within the door, and some way out of his reach as he sat on the bed. He rose, and satisfied himself that the lights were all in order. Then he turned on his heel, walked quickly into Manderson's room, and rang the bell.

"I want your help again, Martin," he said, as the butler presented himself, upright and impassive, in the doorway. "I want you to prevail upon Mrs. Manderson's maid to grant me an interview."

"Certainly, sir," said Martin.

"What sort of a woman is she? Has she her wits about her?"

"She's French, sir," replied Martin succinctly; adding after a pause: "She has not been with us long, sir, but I have formed the impression that the young woman knows as much of the world as is good for her—since you ask me."

"You think butter might possibly melt in her mouth, do you?" said Trent. "Well, I am not afraid. I want to put some questions to her."

"I will send her up immediately, sir." The butler withdrew, and Trent wandered round the little room with his hands at his back. Sooner than he had expected, a small neat figure in black appeared quietly before him.

The lady's maid, with her large brown eyes, had taken favourable notice of Trent from a window when he had crossed the lawn, and had been hoping desperately that the resolver of mysteries (whose reputation was as great below-stairs as elsewhere) would send for her. For one thing, she felt the need to make a scene; her nerves were overwrought. But her scenes were at a discount with the other domestics, and as for Mr. Murch, he had chilled her into self-control with his official manner. Trent, her glimpse of him had told her, had not the air of a policeman, and at a distance he had appeared *sympathique*.

As she entered the room, however, instinct decided for her that any approach to coquetry would be a mistake, if she sought to make a good impression at the beginning. It was with an air of amiable candour, then, that she said, "Monsieur desire to speak with me." She added helpfully, "I am called Célestine."

"Naturally," agreed Trent with businesslike calm. "Now what I want you to tell me, Célestine, is this. When you took tea to your mistress yesterday morning at seven o'clock, was the door between the two bedrooms—this door here—open?"

Célestine became intensely animated in an instant. "Oh, yes!" she said, using her favourite English idiom. "The door was open as always, monsieur, and I shut it as always. But it is necessary to explain. Listen! When I enter the room of madame from the other door in there—ah! but if monsieur will give himself the pain to enter the other room, all explains itself." She tripped across to the door, and urged Trent before her into the larger bedroom with a hand on his arm. "See! I enter the room with the tea like this. I approach the bed. Before I come quite near the bed, here is the door to my right hand—open always—so! But monsieur can perceive that I see nothing in the room of Monsieur Manderson. The door opens to the bed, not to me who approach from down there. I shut it without seeing in. It is the order. Yesterday it was as ordinary. I see nothing of the next room. Madame sleep like an angel—she see nothing. I shut the door. I place the plateau—I open the curtains—I prepare the toilette—I retire—voilà!" Célestine paused for breath and spread her hands abroad.

Trent, who had followed her movements and gesticulations

with deepening gravity, nodded his head. "I see exactly how it was now," he said. "Thank you, Célestine. So Mr. Manderson was supposed to be still in his room while your mistress was getting up, and dressing, and having breakfast in her boudoir?"

"Oui, monsieur."

"Nobody missed him, in fact," remarked Trent. "Well, Célestine, I am very much obliged to you." He reopened the door to the outer bedroom.

"It is nothing, monsieur," said Célestine, as she crossed the small room. "I hope that monsieur will catch the assassin of Monsieur Manderson. But I not regret him too much," she added with sudden and amazing violence, turning round with her hand on the knob of the outer door. She set her teeth with an audible sound, and the colour rose in her small dark face. English departed from her. "Je ne le regrette pas du tout, du tout!" she cried with a flood of words. "Madame—ah! je me jetterais au feu pour madame—une femme si charmante, si adorable! mais un homme comme monsieur—maussade, boudeur, impassible! Ah, non!—de ma vie! J'en avais pardessus la tête, de monsieur! Ah! vrai! Est-ce insupportable, tout de même, qu'il existe des types comme ça? Je vous jure que——"

"Finissez ce chahut, Célestine!" Trent broke in sharply. Célestine's tirade had brought back the memory of his student days with a rush. "En voilà une scène! C'est rasant, vous savez. Faut rentrer ça, mademoiselle. Du reste, c'est bien imprudent, croyez-moi. Hang it! have some common sense! If the inspector downstairs heard you saying that kind of thing, you would get into trouble. And don't wave your fists about so much; you might hit something. You seem," he went on more pleasantly, as Célestine grew calmer under his authoritative eye, "to be even more glad than other people that Mr. Manderson is out of the way. I could almost suspect, Célestine, that Mr. Manderson did not take as much notice of you as you thought necessary and right."

"A peine s'il m'avait regardé!" Célestine answered simply.

"Ça, c'est un comble!" observed Trent. "You are a nice young woman for a small tea-party, I don't think. A star upon your birthday burned, whose fierce, serene, red, pulseless planet never yearned in heaven, Célestine. Mademoiselle, I am busy. Bon jour. You certainly are a beauty!"

Célestine took this as a scarcely-expected compliment. The surprise restored her balance. With a sudden flash of her eyes and teeth at Trent over her shoulder, the lady's maid opened the door and swiftly disappeared.

Trent, left alone in the little bedroom, relieved his mind with two forcible descriptive terms in Célestine's language, and turned to his problem. He took the pair of shoes which he had already examined, and placed them on one of the two chairs in the room, then seated himself on the other opposite to this. With his hands in his pockets he sat with eyes fixed upon those two dumb witnesses. Now and then he whistled, almost inaudibly, a few bars. It was very still in the room. A subdued twittering came from the trees through the open window. From time to time a breeze rustled in the leaves of the thick creeper about the sill. But the man in the room, his face grown hard and sombre now with his thoughts, never moved.

So he sat for the space of half-an-hour. Then he rose quickly to his feet. He replaced the shoes on their shelf with care, and stepped out upon the landing.

Two bedroom doors faced him on the other side of the passage. He opened that which was immediately opposite, and entered a bedroom by no means austerely tidy. Some sticks and fishing-rods stood confusedly in one corner, a pile of books in another. The housemaid's hand had failed to give a look of order to the jumble of heterogeneous objects left on the dressing-table and on the mantel-shelf—pipes, penknives, pencils, keys, golf-balls, old letters, photographs, small boxes, tins, and bottles. Two fine etchings and some water-colour sketches hung on the walls; leaning against the end of the wardrobe, unhung, were a few framed engravings. A row of shoes and boots was ranged beneath the window. Trent crossed the room and studied them intently; then he measured some of them with his tape, whistling very softly. This done, he sat on the side of the bed, and his eyes roamed gloomily about the room.

The photographs on the mantel-shelf attracted him presently. He rose and examined one representing Marlowe and Manderson on horseback. Two others were views of famous peaks in the Alps. There was a faded print of three youths—one of them unmistakably his acquaintance of the haggard blue eyes—clothed in tatterdemalion soldier's gear of the sixteenth century. Another was a portrait of a majestic old lady, slightly resembling Marlowe. Trent, mechanically taking a cigarette from an open box on the mantel-shelf, lit it and stared at the photographs. Next he turned his attention to a flat leathern case that lay by the cigarette-box.

It opened easily. A small and light revolver, of beautiful workmanship, was disclosed, with a score or so of loose cartridges. On the stock were engraved the initials "J.M."

A step was heard on the stairs, and as Trent opened the breech and peered into the barrel of the weapon, Inspector Murch appeared at the open door of the room. "I was wondering——" he began; then stopped as he saw what the other was about. His intelligent eyes opened slightly. "Whose is the revolver, Mr. Trent?" he asked in a conversational tone.

"Evidently it belongs to the occupant of the room, Mr. Marlowe," replied Trent with similar lightness, pointing to the initials. "I found this lying about on the mantelpiece. It seems a handy little pistol to me, and it has been very carefully cleaned, I should say, since the last time it was used. But I know little about firearms."

"Well, I know a good deal," rejoined the inspector quietly, taking the revolver from Trent's outstretched hand. "It's a bit of a specialty with me, is firearms, as I think you know, Mr. Trent. But it don't require an expert to tell one thing." He replaced the revolver in its case on the mantel-shelf, took out one of the cartridges, and laid it on the spacious palm of one hand; then, taking a small object from his waistcoat pocket, he laid it beside the cartridge. It was a little leaden bullet, slightly battered about the nose, and having upon it some bright new scratches.

"Is that *the* one?" Trent murmured as he bent over the inspector's hand.

"That's him," replied Mr. Murch. "Lodged in the bone at the back of the skull. Dr. Stock got it out within the last hour, and handed it to the local officer, who has just sent it on to me. These bright scratches you see were made by the doctor's instruments. These other marks were made by the rifling of the barrel—a barrel like this one." He tapped the revolver. "Same make, same calibre. There is no other that marks the bullet just like this."

With the pistol in its case between them, Trent and the inspector looked into each other's eyes for some moments. Trent was the first to speak. "This mystery is all wrong," he observed. "It is insanity. The symptoms of mania are very marked. Let us see how we stand. We were not in any doubt, I believe, about Manderson having dispatched Marlowe in the car to Southampton, or about Marlowe having gone, returning late last night, many hours after the murder was committed."

"There *is* no doubt whatever about all that," said Murch, with a slight emphasis on the verb.

"And now," pursued Trent, "we are invited by this polished and insinuating firearm to believe the following line of propositions: that Marlowe never went to Southampton; that he returned to the house in the night; that he somehow, without waking Mrs. Manderson or anybody else, got Manderson to get up, dress himself, and go out into the grounds; that he then and there shot the said Manderson with his incriminating pistol; that he carefully cleaned the said pistol, returned to the house and, again without disturbing anyone, replaced it in its case in a favourable position to be found by the officers of the law; that he then withdrew and spent the rest of the day in hiding—*with* a large motor car; and that he turned up, feigning ignorance of the whole affair, at—what time was it?"

"A little after 9 p.m." The inspector still stared moodily at Trent. "As you say, Mr. Trent, that is the first theory suggested by this find, and it seems wild enough—at least it would do if it didn't fall to pieces at the very start. When the murder was done Marlowe must have been fifty to a hundred miles away. He *did* go to Southampton."

"How do you know?"

"I questioned him last night, and took down his story. He arrived in Southampton about 6.30 on the Monday morning."

"Come off!" exclaimed Trent bitterly. "What do I care about his story? What do you care about his story? I want to know how you *know* he went to Southampton."

Mr. Murch chuckled. "I thought I should take a rise out of you, Mr. Trent," he said. "Well, there's no harm in telling you. After I arrived yesterday evening, as soon as I had got the outlines of the story from Mrs. Manderson and the servants, the first thing I did was to go to the telegraph office and wire to our people in Southampton. Manderson had told his wife when he went to bed that he had changed his mind, and sent Marlowe to Southampton to get some important information from someone who was crossing by the next day's boat. It seemed right enough, but, you see, Marlowe was the only one of the household who wasn't under my hand, so to speak. He didn't return in the car until later in the evening; so before thinking the matter out any further, I wired to Southampton making certain inquiries. Early this morning I got this reply." He handed a series of telegraph slips to Trent, who read:

"Person answering description in motor answering description arrived Bedford Hotel here 6.30 this morning gave name Marlowe left car hotel garage told attendant car belonged Manderson had bath and breakfast went out heard of later at docks inquiring for passenger name Harris on Havre boat inquired repeatedly until boat left at noon next heard of at hotel where he lunched about 1.15 left soon afterwards in car company's agents inform berth was booked name Harris last week but Harris did not travel by boat Burke inspector."

"Simple and satisfactory," observed Mr. Murch as Trent, after twice reading the message, returned it to him. "His own story corroborated in every particular. He told me he hung about the dock for half-an-hour or so on the chance of Harris turning up late, then strolled back, lunched, and decided to return at once. He sent a wire to Manderson— 'Harris not turned up missed boat returning Marlowe,' which was duly delivered here in the afternoon, and placed among the dead man's letters. He motored back at a good rate, and arrived dog-tired. When he heard of Manderson's death from Martin, he nearly fainted. What with that and the being without sleep for so long, he was rather a wreck when I came to interview him last night; but he was perfectly coherent."

Trent picked up the revolver and twirled the cylinder idly for a few moments. "It was unlucky for Manderson that Marlowe left his pistol and cartridges about so carelessly," he remarked at length, as he put it back in the case. "It was throwing temptation in somebody's way, don't you think?"

Mr. Murch shook his head. "There isn't really much to lay hold of about the revolver, when you come to think. That particular make of revolver is common enough in England. It was introduced from the States. Half the people who buy a revolver to-day for self-defence or mischief provide themselves with that make, of that calibre. It is very reliable, and easily carried in the hip-pocket. There must be thousands of them in the possession of crooks and honest men. For instance," continued the inspector with an air of unconcern, "Manderson himself had one, the double of this. I found it in one of the top drawers of the desk downstairs, and it's in my overcoat pocket now."

"Aha! so you were going to keep that little detail to yourself."

"I was," said the inspector; "but as you've found one revolver, you may as well know about the other. As I say, neither of them may do us any good. The people in the house——"

Both men started, and the inspector checked his speech abruptly, as the half-closed door of the bedroom was slowly pushed open, and a man stood in the doorway. His eyes turned from the pistol in its open case to the faces of Trent and the inspector. They, who had not heard a sound to herald this entrance, simultaneously looked at his long, narrow feet. He wore rubber-soled tennis shoes.

"You must be Mr. Bunner," said Trent.

CHAPTER VI

Mr. Bunner on the Case

"Calvin c. bunner, at your service," amended the newcomer, with a touch of punctilio, as he removed an unlighted cigar from his mouth. He was used to finding Englishmen slow and ceremonious with strangers, and Trent's quick remark plainly disconcerted him a little. "You are Mr. Trent, I expect," he went on. "Mrs. Manderson was telling me a while ago. Captain, good-morning." Mr. Murch acknowledged the outlandish greeting with a nod. "I was coming up to my room, and I heard a strange voice in here, so I thought I would take a look in." Mr. Bunner laughed easily. "You thought I might have been eavesdropping, perhaps," he said. "No, sir; I heard a word or two about a pistol—this one, I guess—and that's all."

Mr. Bunner was a thin, rather short young man with a shaven, pale, bony, almost girlish face, and large, dark, intelligent eyes. His waving dark hair was parted in the middle. His lips, usually occupied with a cigar, in its absence were always half open with a curious expression as of permanent eagerness. By smoking or chewing a cigar this expression was banished, and Mr. Bunner then looked the consummately cool and sagacious Yankee that he was.

Born in Connecticut, he had gone into a broker's office on leaving college, and had attracted the notice of Manderson, whose business with his firm he had often handled. The Colossus had watched him for some time, and at length offered him the post of private secretary. Mr. Bunner was a pattern business man, trustworthy, long-headed, methodical, and accurate. Manderson could have found many men with those virtues; but he engaged Mr. Bunner because he was also swift and secret, and had besides a singular natural instinct in regard to the movements of the stock market.

Trent and the American measured one another coolly with their eyes. Both appeared satisfied with what they saw. "I was having it explained to me," said Trent pleasantly, "that my discovery of a pistol that might have shot Manderson does not amount to very much. I am told it is a favourite weapon among your people, and has become quite popular over here."

Mr. Bunner stretched out a bony hand and took the pistol from its case. "Yes, sir," he said, handling it with an air of familiarity; "the captain is right. This is what we call out home a Little Arthur, and I dare say there are duplicates of it in ten thousand hip-pockets this minute. I consider it rather too light in the hand myself," Mr. Bunner went on, mechanically feeling under the tail of his jacket, and producing an ugly-looking weapon. "Feel of that, now, Mr. Trent—it's loaded, by the way. Now this Little Arthur—Marlowe bought it just before we came over this year to please the old man. Manderson said it was ridiculous for a man to be without a pistol in the twentieth century. So he went out and bought what they offered him, I guess—never consulted me. Not but what it's a good gun," Mr. Bunner conceded, squinting along the sights. "Marlowe was poor with it at first, but I've coached him some in the last month or so, and he's practised until he is pretty good. But he never could get the habit of carrying it around. Why, it's as natural to me as wearing my pants. I have packed one for some years now, because there was always likely to be somebody laying for Manderson. And now," Mr. Bunner concluded sadly, "they got him when I wasn't around. Well, gentlemen, you must excuse me. I am going into Bishopsbridge. There is a lot to do these days, and I have to send off a bunch of cables big enough to choke a cow."

"I must be off too," said Trent. "I have an appointment at the 'Three Tuns' inn."

"Let me give you a lift in the automobile," said Mr. Bunner cordially. "I go right by that joint. Say, cap, are you coming my way too? No? Then come along, Mr. Trent, and help me get out the car. The chauffeur is out of action, and we have to do 'most everything ourselves except clean the dirt off her."

Still tirelessly talking in his measured drawl, Mr. Bunner led Trent downstairs and through the house to the garage at the back. It stood at a little distance from the house, and made a cool retreat from the blaze of the mid-day sun.

Mr. Bunner seemed to be in no hurry to get out the car. He offered Trent a cigar, which was accepted, and for the first time lit his own. Then he seated himself on the footboard of the car, his thin hands clasped between his knees, and looked keenly at the other.

"See here, Mr. Trent," he said, after a few moments. "There are some things I can tell you that may be useful to you. I know your record. You are a smart man, and I like dealing with smart men. I don't know if I have that detective sized up right, but he strikes me as a mutt. I would answer any questions he had the gumption to ask me—I have done so, in fact—but I don't feel encouraged to give him any notions of mine without his asking. See?"

Trent nodded. "That is a feeling many people have in the presence of our police," he said. "It's the official manner, I suppose. But let me tell you, Murch is anything but what you think. He is one of the shrewdest officers in Europe. He is not very quick with his mind, but he is very sure. And his experience is immense. My forte is imagination, but I assure you in police work experience outweighs it by a great deal."

"Outweighs nothing!" replied Mr. Bunner crisply. "This is no ordinary case, Mr. Trent. I will tell you one reason why. I believe the old man knew there was something coming to him. Another thing: I believe it was something he thought he couldn't dodge."

Trent pulled a crate opposite to Mr. Bunner's place on the footboard and seated himself. "This sounds like business," he said. "Tell me your ideas."

"I say what I do because of the change in the old man's manner this last few weeks. I dare say you have heard, Mr. Trent, that he was a man who always kept himself well in hand. That was so. I have always considered him the coolest and hardest head in business. That man's calm was just deadly—I never saw anything to beat it. And I knew Manderson as nobody else did. I was with him in the work he really lived for. I guess I knew him a heap better than his wife did, poor woman. I knew him better than Marlowe could—he never saw Manderson in his office when there was a big thing on. I knew him better than any of his friends."

"Had he any friends?" interjected Trent.

Mr. Bunner glanced at him sharply. "Somebody has been putting you next, I see that," he remarked. "No: properly speaking, I should say not. He had many acquaintances among the big men, people he saw 'most every day; they would even go yachting or hunting together. But I don't believe there ever was a man that Manderson opened a corner of his heart to. But what I was going to say was this. Some months ago the old man began to get like I never knew him before—gloomy and sullen, just as if he was everlastingly brooding over something bad, something that he couldn't fix. This went on without any break; it was the same down town as it was up home, he acted just as if there was something lying heavy on his mind. But it wasn't until a few weeks back that his self-restraint began to go; and let me tell you this, Mr. Trent"—the American laid his bony claw on the other's knee—"I'm the only man that knows it. With everyone else he would be just morose and dull; but when he was alone with me in his office, or anywhere where we would be working together, if the least little thing went wrong, by George! he would fly off the handle to beat the Dutch. In this library here I have seen him open a letter with something that didn't just suit him in it, and he would rip around and carry on like an Indian, saying he wished he had the man that wrote it here, he wouldn't do a thing to him, and so on, till it was just pitiful. I never saw such a change. And here's another thing. For a week before he died Manderson neglected his work, for the first time in my experience. He wouldn't answer a letter or a cable, though things looked like going all to pieces over there. I supposed that this anxiety of his, whatever it was, had got on to his nerves till they were worn out. Once I advised him to see a doctor, and he told me to go to hell. But nobody saw this side of him but me. If he was having one of these rages in the library here, for example, and Mrs. Manderson would come into the room, he would be all calm and cold again in an instant."

"And you put this down to some secret anxiety, a fear that somebody had designs on his life?" asked Trent.

The American nodded.

"I suppose," Trent resumed, "you had considered the idea of there being something wrong with his mind—a breakdown from overstrain, say. That is the first thought that your account suggests to me. Besides, it is what sometimes happens to your big business men in America, isn't it? That is the impression one gets from the newspapers."

"Don't let them slip you any of that bunk," said Mr. Bunner earnestly. "It's only the ones who have got rich too quick, and can't make good, who go crazy. Think of all our really big men—the men anywhere near Manderson's size: did you ever hear of any one of them losing his senses? They don't do it—believe *me*. I know they say every man has his loco point," Mr. Bunner added reflectively, "but that doesn't mean genuine, sure-enough craziness; it just means some personal eccentricity in a man . . . like hating cats . . . or my own weakness of not being able to touch any kind of fish-food."

"Well, what was Manderson's?"

"He was full of them—the old man. There was his objection to all the unnecessary fuss and luxury that wealthy people don't kick at much, as a general rule. He didn't have any use for expensive trifles and ornaments. He wouldn't have anybody do little things for him; he hated to have servants tag around after him unless he wanted them. And although Manderson was as careful about his clothes as any man I ever knew, and his shoes—well, sir, the amount of money he spent on shoes was sinful—in spite of that, I tell you, he never had a valet. He never liked to have anybody touch him. All his life nobody ever shaved him."

"I've heard something of that," Trent remarked. "Why was it, do you think?"

"Well," Mr. Bunner answered slowly, "it was the Manderson habit of mind, I guess; a sort of temper of general suspicion and jealousy. They say his father and grandfather were just the same. . . . Like a dog with a bone, you know, acting as if all the rest of creation was laying for a chance to steal it. He didn't really *think* the barber would start in to saw his head off; he just felt there was a possibility that he *might*, and he was taking no risks. Then again in business he was always convinced that somebody else was after his bone—which was true enough a good deal of the time; but not all the time. The consequence of that was that the old man was the most cautious and secret worker in the world of finance; and that had a lot to do with his success, too. . . . But that doesn't amount to being a lunatic, Mr. Trent; not by a long way. You ask me if Manderson was losing his mind before he died. I say I believe he was just worn out with worrying over something, and was losing his nerve."

Trent smoked thoughtfully. He wondered how much Mr. Bunner knew of the domestic difficulty in his chief's household, and decided to put out a feeler. "I understood that he had trouble with his wife."

"Sure," replied Mr. Bunner. "But do you suppose a thing like that was going to upset Sig Manderson that way? No, sir! He was a sight too big a man to be all broken up by any worry of that kind."

Trent looked half-incredulously into the eyes of the young man. But behind all their shrewdness and intensity he saw a massive innocence. Mr. Bunner really believed a serious breach between husband and wife to be a minor source of trouble for a big man.

"What *was* the trouble between them, anyhow?" Trent inquired.

"You can search me," Mr. Bunner replied briefly. He puffed at his cigar. "Marlowe and I have often talked about it, and we could never make out a solution. I had a notion at first," said Mr. Bunner in a lower voice, leaning forward, "that the old man was disappointed and vexed because he had expected a child; but Marlowe told me that the disappointment on that score was the other way around, likely as not. His idea was all right, I guess; he gathered it from something said by Mrs. Manderson's French maid."

Trent looked up at him quickly. "Célestine!" he said; and his thought was, "So that was what she was getting at!"

Mr. Bunner misunderstood his glance. "Don't you think I'm giving a man away, Mr. Trent," he said. "Marlowe isn't that kind. Célestine just took a fancy to him because he talks French like a native, and she would always be holding him up for a gossip. French servants are quite unlike English that way. And servant or no servant," added Mr. Bunner with emphasis, "I don't see how a woman could mention such a subject to a man. But the French beat me." He shook his head slowly.

"But to come back to what you were telling me just now," Trent said. "You believe that Manderson was going in terror of his life for some time. Who should threaten it? I am quite in the dark."

"Terror—I don't know," replied Mr. Bunner meditatively. "Anxiety, if you like. Or suspense—that's rather my idea of it. The old man was hard to terrify, anyway; and more than that, he wasn't taking any precautions—he was actually avoiding them. It looked more like he was asking for a quick finish —supposing there's any truth in my idea. Why, he would sit in that library window, nights, looking out into the dark, with his white shirt just a target for anybody's gun. As for who should threaten his life—well, sir," said Mr. Bunner with a faint smile, "it's certain you have not lived in the States. To take the Pennsylvania coal hold-up alone, there were thirty thousand men, with women and children to keep, who would have jumped at the chance of drilling a hole through the man who fixed it so that they must starve or give in to his terms. Thirty thousand of the toughest aliens in the country, Mr. Trent. There's a type of desperado you find in that kind of push who has been known to lay for a man for years, and kill him when he had forgotten what he did. They have been known to dynamite a man in Idaho who had done them dirt in New Jersey ten years before. Do you suppose the Atlantic is going to stop them? . . . It takes some sand, I tell you, to be a big business man in our country. No, sir: the old man knew—had always known—that there was a whole crowd of dangerous men scattered up and down the States who had it in for him. My belief is that he had somehow got to know that some of them were definitely after him at last. What licks me altogether is why he should have just laid himself open to them the way he did—why he never tried to dodge, but walked right down into the garden yesterday morning to be shot at."

Mr. Bunner ceased to speak, and for a little while both men sat with wrinkled brows, faint blue vapours rising from their cigars. Then Trent rose. "Your theory is quite fresh to me," he said. "It's perfectly rational, and it's only a question of whether it fits all the facts. I mustn't give away what I'm doing for my newspaper, Mr. Bunner, but I will say this: I have already satisfied myself that this was a premeditated crime, and an extraordinarily cunning one at that. I'm deeply obliged to you. We must talk it over again." He looked at his watch. "I have been expected for some time by my friend. Shall we make a move?"

"Two o'clock," said Mr. Bunner, consulting his own, as he got up from the footboard. "Ten a.m. in little old New York. You don't know Wall Street, Mr. Trent. Let's you and I hope we never see anything nearer hell than what's loose in the Street this minute."

CHAPTER VII

The Lady in Black

The sea broke raging upon the foot of the cliff under a good breeze; the sun flooded the land with life from a dappled blue sky. In this perfection of English weather Trent, who had slept ill, went down before eight o'clock to a pool among the rocks, the direction of which had been given him, and dived deep into clear water. Between vast gray boulders he swam out to the tossing open, forced himself some little way against a coastwise current, and then returned to his refuge battered and refreshed. Ten minutes later he was scaling the cliff again, and his mind, cleared for the moment of a heavy disgust for the affair he had in hand, was turning over his plans for the morning.

It was the day of the inquest, the day after his arrival in the place. He had carried matters not much farther after parting with the American on the road to Bishopsbridge. In the afternoon he had walked from the inn into the town, accompanied by Mr. Cupples, and had there made certain purchases at a chemist's shop, conferred privately for some time with a photographer, sent off a reply-paid telegram, and made an inquiry at the telephone exchange. He had said but little about the case to Mr. Cupples, who seemed incurious on his side, and nothing at all about the results of his investigation or the steps he was about to take. After their return from Bishopsbridge, Trent had written a long dispatch for the *Record* and sent it to be telegraphed by the proud hands of the paper's local representative. He had afterwards dined with Mr. Cupples, and had spent the rest of the evening in meditative solitude on the verandah.

This morning as he scaled the cliff he told himself that he had never taken up a case he liked so little, or which absorbed him so much. The more he contemplated it in the golden sunshine of this new day, the more evil and the more challenging it appeared. All that he suspected and all that he almost knew had occupied his questing brain for hours to the exclusion of sleep; and in this glorious light and air, though washed in body and spirit by the fierce purity of the sea, he only saw the more clearly the darkness of the guilt in which he believed, and was more bitterly repelled by the motive at which he guessed. But now at least his zeal was awake again, and the sense of the hunt quickened. He would neither slacken nor spare; here need be no compunction. In the course of the day, he hoped, his net would be complete. He had work to do in the morning; and with very vivid expectancy, though not much serious hope, he awaited the answer to the telegram which he had shot into the sky, as it were, the day before.

The path back to the hotel wound for some way along the top of the cliff, and on nearing a spot he had marked from the sea-level, where the face had fallen away long ago, he approached the edge and looked down, hoping to follow with his eyes the most delicately beautiful of all the movements of water —the wash of a light sea over broken rock. But no rock was there. A few feet below him a broad ledge stood out, a rough platform as large as a great room, thickly grown with wiry grass and walled in steeply on three sides. There, close to the verge where the cliff at last dropped sheer, a woman was sitting, her arms about her drawn-up knees, her eyes fixed on the trailing smoke of a distant liner, her face full of some dream.

This woman seemed to Trent, whose training had taught him to live in his eyes, to make the most beautiful picture he had ever seen. Her face of southern pallor, touched by the kiss of the wind with colour on the cheek, presented to him a profile of delicate regularity in which there was nothing hard; nevertheless the black brows bending down toward the point where they almost met gave her in repose a look of something like severity, strangely redeemed by the open curves of the mouth. Trent said to himself that the absurdity or otherwise of a lover writing sonnets to his mistress's eyebrow depended after all on the quality of the eyebrow. Her nose was of the straight and fine sort, exquisitely escaping the perdition of too much length, which makes a conscientious mind ashamed that it cannot help, on occasion, admiring the tip-tilted. Her hat lay pinned to the grass beside her, and the lively breeze played with her thick dark hair, blowing backward the two broad bandeaux that should have covered much of her forehead, and agitating a hundred tiny curls from the mass gathered at her nape. Everything about this lady was black, from her shoes of suède to the hat that she had discarded; lustreless black covered her to her bare throat. All she wore was fine and well put on. Dreamy and delicate of spirit as her looks declared her, it was very plain that she was long-practised as only a woman grown can be in dressing well, the oldest of the arts, and had her touch of primal joy in the excellence of the body that was so admirably curved now in the attitude of embraced knees. With the suggestion of French taste in her clothes, she made a very modern figure seated there, until one looked at her face and saw the glow and triumph of all vigorous beings that ever faced sun and wind and sea together in the prime of the year. One saw, too, a womanhood so unmixed and vigorous, so unconsciously sure of itself, as scarcely to be English, still less American.

Trent, who had halted only for a moment in the surprise of seeing the woman in black, had passed by on the cliff above her, perceiving and feeling as he went the things set down. At all times his keen vision and active brain took in and tasted details with an easy swiftness that was marvellous to men of slower chemistry; the need to stare, he held, was evidence of blindness. Now the feeling of beauty was awakened and exultant, and doubled the power of his sense. In these instants a picture was printed on his memory that would never pass away.

As he went by unheard on the turf the woman, still alone with her thoughts, suddenly moved. She unclasped her long hands from about her knees, stretched her limbs and body with feline grace, then slowly raised her head and extended her arms with open, curving fingers, as if to gather to her all the glory and overwhelming sanity of the morning. This was a gesture not to be mistaken: it was a gesture of freedom, the movement of a soul's resolution to be, to possess, to go forward, perhaps to enjoy.

So he saw her for an instant as he passed, and he did not turn. He knew suddenly who the woman must be, and it was as if a curtain of gloom were drawn between him and the splendour of the day.

During breakfast at the hotel Mr. Cupples found Trent little inclined to talk. He excused himself on the plea of a restless night. Mr. Cupples, on the other hand, was in a state of bird-like alertness. The prospect of the inquest seemed to enliven him. He entertained Trent with a disquisition upon the history of that most ancient and once busy tribunal, the coroner's court, and remarked upon the enviable freedom of its procedure from the shackles of rule and precedent. From this he passed to the case that was to come before it that morning.

"Young Bunner mentioned to me last night," he said, "when I went up there after dinner, the hypothesis which he puts forward in regard to the crime. A very remarkable young man, Trent. His meaning is occasionally obscure, but in my opinion he is gifted with a clear-headed knowledge of the world quite unusual in one of his apparent age. Indeed, his promotion by Manderson to the position of his principal lieutenant speaks for itself. He seems to have assumed with perfect confidence the control at this end of the wire, as he expresses it, of the complicated business situation caused by the death of his principal, and he has advised very wisely as to the steps I should take on Mabel's behalf, and the best course for her to pursue until effect has been given to the provisions of the will. I was accordingly less disposed than I might otherwise have been to regard his suggestion of an industrial vendetta as far-fetched. When I questioned him he was able to describe a number of cases in which attacks of one sort or another—too often successful—had been made upon the lives of persons who had incurred the hostility of powerful labour organizations. This is a terrible time in which we live, my dear boy. There is none recorded in history, I think, in which the disproportion between the material and the moral constituents of society has been so great or so menacing to the permanence of the fabric. But nowhere, in my judgment, is the prospect so dark as it is in the United States."

"I thought," said Trent listlessly, "that Puritanism was about as strong there as the money-getting craze."

"Your remark," answered Mr. Cupples, with as near an approach to humour as was possible to him, "is not in the nature of a testimonial to what you call Puritanism—a convenient rather than an accurate term; for I need not remind you that it was invented to describe an Anglican party which aimed at the purging of the services and ritual of their Church from certain elements repugnant to them. The sense of your observation, however, is none the less sound, and its truth is extremely well illustrated by the case of Manderson himself, who had, I believe, the virtues of purity, abstinence, and self-restraint in their strongest form. No, Trent, there are other and more worthy things among the moral constituents of which I spoke; and in our finite nature, the more we preoccupy ourselves with the bewildering complexity of external apparatus which science places in our hands, the less vigour have we left for the development of the holier purposes of humanity within us. Agricultural machinery has abolished the festival of the Harvest Home. Mechanical travel has abolished the inn, or all that was best in it. I need not multiply instances. The view I am expressing to you," pursued Mr. Cupples, placidly buttering a piece of toast, "is regarded as fundamentally erroneous by many of those who think generally as I do about the deeper concerns of life, but I am nevertheless firmly persuaded of its truth."

"It needs epigrammatic expression," said Trent, rising from the table. "If only it could be crystallized into some handy formula, like 'No Popery,' or 'Tax the Foreigner,' you would find multitudes to go to the stake for it. But you are planning to go to White Gables before the inquest, I think. You ought to be off, if you are to get back to the court in time. I have something to attend to there myself, so we might walk up together. I will just go and get my camera."

"By all means," Mr. Cupples answered; and they set off at once in the ever-growing warmth of the morning. The roof of White Gables, a surly patch of dull red against the dark trees, seemed to harmonize with Trent's mood; he felt heavy, sinister, and troubled. If a blow must fall that might strike down that creature radiant of beauty and life whom he had seen that morning, he did not wish it to come from his hand. An exaggerated chivalry had lived in Trent since the first teachings of his mother; but at this moment the horror of bruising anything so lovely was almost as much the artist's revulsion as the gentleman's. On the other hand, was the hunt to end in nothing? The quality of the affair was such that the thought of forbearance was an agony. There never was such a case; and he alone, he was confident, held the truth of it under his hand. At least, he determined, that day should show whether what he believed was a delusion. He would trample his compunction underfoot until he was quite sure that there was any call for it. That same morning he would know.

As they entered at the gate of the drive they saw Marlowe and the American standing in talk before the front door. In the shadow of the porch was the lady in black.

She saw them, and came gravely forward over the lawn, moving as Trent had known that she would move, erect and balanced, stepping lightly. When she welcomed him on Mr. Cupples's presentation her eyes of golden-flecked brown observed him kindly. In her pale composure, worn as the mask of distress, there was no trace of the emotion that had seemed a halo about her head on the ledge of the cliff. She spoke the appropriate commonplace in a low and even voice. After a few words to Mr. Cupples she turned her eyes on Trent again.

"I hope you will succeed," she said earnestly. "Do you think you will succeed?"

He made his mind up as the words left her lips. He said, "I believe I shall do so, Mrs. Manderson. When I have the case sufficiently complete I shall ask you to let me see you and tell you about it. It may be necessary to consult you before the facts are published."

She looked puzzled, and distress showed for an instant in her eyes. "If it is necessary, of course you shall do so," she said.

On the brink of his next speech Trent hesitated. He remembered that the lady had not wished to repeat to him the story already given to the inspector—or to be questioned at all. He was not unconscious that he desired to hear her voice and watch her face a little longer, if it might be; but the matter he had to mention really troubled his mind, it was a queer thing that fitted nowhere into the pattern within whose corners he had by this time brought the other queer things in the case. It was very possible that she could explain it away in a breath; it was unlikely that anyone else could. He summoned his resolution.

"You have been so kind," he said, "in allowing me access to the house and every opportunity of studying the case, that I am going to ask leave to put a question or two to yourself— nothing that you would rather not answer, I think. May I?"

She glanced at him wearily. "It would be stupid of me to refuse. Ask your questions, Mr. Trent."

"It's only this," said Trent hurriedly. "We know that your husband lately drew an unusually large sum of ready money from his London bankers, and was keeping it here. It is here now, in fact. Have you any idea why he should have done that?"

She opened her eyes in astonishment. "I cannot imagine," she said. "I did not know he had done so. I am very much surprised to hear it."

"Why is it surprising?"

"I thought my husband had very little money in the house. On Sunday night, just before he went out in the motor, he came into the drawing-room where I was sitting. He seemed to be irritated about something, and asked me at once if I had any notes or gold I could let him have until next day. I was surprised at that, because he was never without money; he made it a rule to carry a hundred pounds or so about him always in a note-case. I unlocked my escritoire, and gave him all I had by me. It was nearly thirty pounds."

"And he did not tell you why he wanted it?"

"No. He put it in his pocket, and then said that Mr. Marlowe had persuaded him to go for a run in the motor by moonlight, and he thought it might help him to sleep. He had been sleeping badly, as perhaps you know. Then he went off with Mr. Marlowe. I thought it odd he should need money on Sunday night, but I soon forgot about it. I never remembered it again until now."

"It was curious, certainly," said Trent, staring into the distance. Mr. Cupples began to speak to his niece of the arrangements for the inquest, and Trent moved away to where Marlowe was pacing slowly upon the lawn. The young man seemed relieved to talk about the coming business of the day. Though he still seemed tired out and nervous, he showed himself not without a quiet humour in describing the pomposities of the local police and the portentous airs of Dr. Stock. Trent turned the conversation gradually toward the problem of the crime, and all Marlowe's gravity returned.

"Bunner has told me what he thinks," he said when Trent referred to the American's theory. "I don't find myself convinced by it, because it doesn't really explain some of the oddest facts. But I have lived long enough in the United States to know that such a stroke of revenge, done in a secret, melodramatic way, is not an unlikely thing. It is quite a characteristic feature of certain sections of the labour movement there. Americans have a taste and a talent for that sort of business. Do you know *Huckleberry Finn?*"

"Do I know my own name?" exclaimed Trent.

"Well, I think the most American thing in that great American epic is Tom Sawyer's elaboration of an extremely difficult and romantic scheme, taking days to carry out, for securing the escape of the nigger Jim, which could have been managed quite easily in twenty minutes. You know how fond they are of lodges and brotherhoods. Every college club has its secret signs and handgrips. You've heard of the Know-Nothing movement in politics, I dare say, and the Ku Klux Klan. Then look at Brigham Young's penny-dreadful tyranny in Utah, with real blood. The founders of the Mormon State were of the purest Yankee stock in America; and you know what they did. It's all part of the same mental tendency. Americans make fun of it among themselves. For my part, I take it very seriously."

"It can have a very hideous side to it, certainly," said Trent, "when you get it in connection with crime—or with vice—or even mere luxury. But I have a sort of sneaking respect for the determination to make life interesting and lively in spite of civilization. To return to the matter in hand, however; has it struck you as a possibility that Manderson's mind was affected to some extent by this menace that Bunner believes in? For instance, it was rather an extraordinary thing to send you posting off like that in the middle of the night."

"About ten o'clock, to be exact," replied Marlowe. "Though, mind you, if he'd actually roused me out of my bed at midnight I shouldn't have been very much surprised. It all chimes in with what we've just been saying. Manderson had a strong streak of the national taste for dramatic proceedings. He was rather fond of his well-earned reputation for unexpected strokes and for going for his object with ruthless directness through every opposing consideration. He had decided suddenly that he wanted to have word from this man Harris——"

"Who is Harris?" interjected Trent.

"Nobody knows. Even Bunner never heard of him, and can't imagine what the business in hand was. All I know is that when I went up to London last week to attend to various things I booked a deck-cabin, at Manderson's request, for a Mr. George Harris on the boat that sailed on Monday. It seems that Manderson suddenly found he wanted news from Harris which presumably was of a character too secret for the telegraph; and there was no train that served; so I was sent off as you know."

Trent looked round to make sure that they were not overheard, then faced the other gravely. "There is one thing I may tell you," he said quietly, "that I don't think you know. Martin the butler caught a few words at the end of your conversation with Manderson in the orchard before you started with him in the car. He heard him say, 'If Harris is there, every moment is of importance.' Now, Mr. Marlowe, you know my business here. I am sent to make inquiries, and you mustn't take offence. I want to ask you if, in the face of that sentence, you will repeat that you know nothing of what the business was."

Marlowe shook his head. "I know nothing, indeed. I'm not easily offended, and your question is quite fair. What passed during that conversation I have already told the detective. Manderson plainly said to me that he could not tell me what it was all about. He simply wanted me to find Harris, tell him that he desired to know how matters stood, and bring back a letter or message from him. Harris, I was further told, might not turn up. If he did, 'every moment was of importance.' And now you know as much as I do."

"That talk took place *before* he told his wife that you were taking him for a moonlight run. Why did he conceal your errand in that way, I wonder."

The young man made a gesture of helplessness. "Why? I can guess no better than you."

"Why," muttered Trent as if to himself, gazing on the ground, "did he conceal it—from Mrs. Manderson?" He looked up at Marlowe.

"And from Martin," the other amended coolly. "He was told the same thing."

With a sudden movement of his head Trent seemed to

dismiss the subject. He drew from his breast-pocket a letter-case, and thence extracted two small leaves of clean, fresh paper.

"Just look at these two slips, Mr. Marlowe," he said. "Did you ever see them before? Have you any idea where they come from?" he added as Marlowe took one in each hand and examined them curiously.

"They seem to have been cut with a knife or scissors from a small diary for this year—from the October pages," Marlowe observed, looking them over on both sides. "I see no writing of any kind on them. Nobody here has any such diary so far as I know. What about them?"

"There may be nothing in it," Trent said dubiously. "Anyone in the house, of course, might have such a diary without your having seen it. But I didn't much expect you would be able to identify the leaves—in fact, I should have been surprised if you had."

He stopped speaking as Mrs. Manderson came towards them. "My uncle thinks we should be going now," she said.

"I think I will walk on with Mr. Bunner," Mr. Cupples said as he joined them. "There are certain business matters that must be disposed of as soon as possible. Will you come on with these two gentlemen, Mabel? We will wait for you before we reach the place."

Trent turned to her. "Mrs. Manderson will excuse me, I hope," he said. "I really came up this morning in order to look about me here for some indications I thought I might possibly find. I had not thought of attending the—the court just yet."

She looked at him with eyes of perfect candour. "Of course, Mr. Trent. Please do exactly as you wish. We are all relying upon you. If you will wait a few moments, Mr. Marlowe, I shall be ready."

She entered the house. Her uncle and the American had already strolled towards the gate.

Trent looked into the eyes of his companion. "That is a wonderful woman," he said in a lowered voice.

"You say so without knowing her," replied Marlowe in a similar tone. "She is more than that."

Trent said nothing to this. He stared out over the fields towards the sea. In the silence a noise of hobnailed haste rose on the still air. A little distance down the road a boy appeared trotting towards them from the direction of the hotel. In his hand was the orange envelope, unmistakable afar off, of a telegram. Trent watched him with an indifferent eye as he met and passed the two others. Then he turned to Marlowe. "Apropos of nothing in particular," he said, "were you at Oxford?"

"Yes," said the young man. "Why do you ask?"

"I just wondered if I was right in my guess. It's one of the things you can very often tell about a man, isn't it?"

"I suppose so," Marlowe said. "Well, each of us is marked in one way or another, perhaps. I should have said you were an artist, if I hadn't known it."

"Why? Does my hair want cutting?"

"Oh, no! It's only that you look at things and people as I've seen artists do, with an eye that moves steadily from detail to detail—rather looking them over than looking at them."

The boy came up panting. "Telegram for you, sir," he said to Trent. "Just come, sir."

Trent tore open the envelope with an apology, and his eyes lighted up so visibly as he read the slip that Marlowe's tired face softened in a smile.

"It must be good news," he murmured half to himself.

Trent turned on him a glance in which nothing could be read. "Not exactly news," he said. "It only tells me that another little guess of mine was a good one."

CHAPTER VIII
The Inquest

The coroner, who fully realized that for that one day of his life as a provincial solicitor he was living in the gaze of the world, had resolved to be worthy of the fleeting eminence. He was a large man of jovial temper, with a strong interest in the dramatic aspects of his work, and the news of Manderson's mysterious death within his jurisdiction had made him the happiest coroner in England. A respectable capacity for marshalling facts was fortified in him by a copiousness of impressive language that made juries as clay in his hands, and sometimes disguised a doubtful interpretation of the rules of evidence.

The court was held in a long, unfurnished room lately built on to the hotel, and intended to serve as a ball-room or concert-hall. A regiment of reporters was entrenched in the front seats, and those who were to be called on to give evidence occupied chairs to one side of the table behind which the coroner sat, while the jury, in double row, with plastered hair and a spurious ease of manner, flanked him on the other side. An undistinguished public filled the rest of the space, and listened, in an awed silence, to the opening solemnities. The newspaper men, well used to these, muttered among themselves. Those of them who knew Trent by sight assured the rest that he was not in the court.

The identity of the dead man was proved by his wife, the first witness called, from whom the coroner, after some inquiry into the health and circumstances of the deceased, proceeded to draw an account of the last occasion on which she had seen her husband alive. Mrs. Manderson was taken through her evidence by the coroner with the sympathy which every man felt for that dark figure of grief. She lifted her thick veil before beginning to speak, and the extreme paleness and unbroken composure of the lady produced a singular impression. This was not an impression of hardness. Interesting femininity was the first thing to be felt in her presence. She was not even enigmatic. It was only clear that the force of a powerful character was at work to master the emotions of her situation. Once or twice as she spoke she touched her eyes with her handkerchief, but her voice was low and clear to the end.

Her husband, she said, had come up to his bedroom about his usual hour for retiring on Sunday night. His room was really a dressing-room attached to her own bedroom, communicating with it by a door which was usually kept open during the night. Both dressing-room and bedroom were entered by other doors giving on the passage. Her husband had always had a preference for the greatest simplicity in his bedroom arrangements, and liked to sleep in a small room. She had not been awake when he came up, but had been half-aroused, as usually happened, when the light was switched on in her husband's room. She had spoken to him. She had no clear recollection of what she had said, as she had been very drowsy at the time; but she had remembered that he had been out for a moonlight run in the car, and she believed she had asked whether he had had a good run, and what time it was. She had asked what the time was because she felt as if she had only been a very short time asleep, and she had expected her husband to be out very late. In answer to her question he had told her it was half-past eleven, and had gone on to say that he had changed his mind about going for a run.

"Did he say why?" the coroner asked.

"Yes," replied the lady, "he did explain why. I remember very well what he said, because——" she stopped with a little appearance of confusion.

"Because——" the coroner insisted gently.

"Because my husband was not as a rule communicative about his business affairs," answered the witness, raising her chin with a faint touch of defiance. "He did not—did not think they would interest me, and as a rule referred to them as little as possible. That was why I was rather surprised when he told me that he had sent Mr. Marlowe to Southampton to bring back some important information from a man who was leaving for Paris by the next day's boat. He said that Mr. Marlowe could do it quite easily if he had no accident. He said that he had started in the car, and then walked back home a mile or so, and felt all the better for it."

"Did he say any more?"

"Nothing, as well as I remember," the witness said. "I was very sleepy, and I dropped off again in a few moments. I just remembered my husband turning his light out, and that is all. I never saw him again alive."

"And you heard nothing in the night?"

"No: I never woke until my maid brought my tea in the morning at seven o'clock. She closed the door leading to my husband's room, as she always did, and I supposed him to be still there. He always needed a great deal of sleep. He sometimes slept until quite late in the morning. I had breakfast in my sitting-room. It was about ten when I heard that my husband's body had been found." The witness dropped her head and silently waited for her dismissal.

But it was not to be yet.

"Mrs. Manderson." The coroner's voice was sympathetic, but it had a hint of firmness in it now. "The question I am going to put to you must, in these sad circumstances, be a painful one; but it is my duty to ask it. Is it the fact that your relations with your late husband had not been, for some time past, relations of mutual affection and confidence? Is it the fact that there was an estrangement between you?"

The lady drew herself up again and faced her questioner, the colour rising in her cheeks. "If that question is necessary," she said with cold distinctness, "I will answer it so that there shall be no misunderstanding. During the last few months of my husband's life his attitude towards me had given me a great deal of anxiety and sorrow. He had changed towards me; he had become very reserved, and seemed mistrustful. I saw much less of him than before; he seemed to prefer to be alone. I can give no explanation at all of the change. I tried to work against it; I did all I could with justice to my own dignity, as I thought. Something was between us, I did not know what, and he never told me. My own obstinate pride prevented me from asking what it was in so many words; I only made a point of being to him exactly as I had always been, so far as he would allow me. I suppose I shall never know now what it was." The witness, whose voice had trembled in spite of her self-control over the last few sentences, drew down her veil when she had said this, and stood erect and quiet.

One of the jury asked a question, not without obvious hesitation. "Then was there never anything of the nature of what they call Words between you and your husband, ma'am?"

"Never." The word was colourlessly spoken; but everyone felt that a crass misunderstanding of the possibilities of conduct in the case of a person like Mrs. Manderson had been visited with some severity.

Did she know, the coroner asked, of any other matter which might have been preying upon her husband's mind recently?

Mrs. Manderson knew of none whatever. The coroner intimated that her ordeal was at an end, and the veiled lady made her way to the door. The general attention, which followed her for a few moments, was now eagerly directed upon Martin, whom the coroner had proceeded to call.

It was at this moment that Trent appeared at the doorway and edged his way into the great room. But he did not look at Martin. He was observing the well-balanced figure that came quickly toward him along an opening path in the crowd, and his eye was gloomy. He started, as he stood aside from the door with a slight bow, to hear Mrs. Manderson address him by name in a low voice. He followed her a pace or two into the hall.

"I wanted to ask you," she said in a voice now weak and oddly broken, "if you would give me your arm a part of the way to the house. I could not see my uncle near the door, and I suddenly felt rather faint. . . . I shall be better in the air. . . . No, no; I cannot stay here—please, Mr. Trent!" she said, as he began to make an obvious suggestion. "I must go to the house." Her hand tightened momentarily on his arm as if, for all her weakness, she could drag him from the place; then again she leaned heavily upon it, and with that support, and with bent head, she walked slowly from the hotel and along the oak-shaded path towards White Gables.

Trent went in silence, his thoughts whirling, dancing insanely to a chorus of "Fool! fool!" All that he alone knew, all that he guessed and suspected of this affair, rushed through his brain in a rout; but the touch of her unnerved hand upon his arm never for an instant left his consciousness, filling him with an exaltation that enraged and bewildered him. He was still cursing himself furiously behind the mask of conventional solicitude that he turned to the lady when he had attended her to the house and seen her sink upon a couch in the morning-room. Raising her veil, she thanked him gravely and frankly, with a look of sincere gratitude in her eyes. She was much better now, she said, and a cup of tea would work a miracle upon her. She hoped she had not taken him away from anything important. She was ashamed of herself; she thought she could go through with it, but she had not expected those last questions. "I am glad you did not hear me," she said when he explained. "But of course you will read it all in the reports. It shook me so to have to speak of that," she added simply; "and to keep from making an exhibition of myself took it out of me. And all those staring men by the door! Thank you again for helping me when I asked you. . . . I thought I might," she ended queerly, with a little tired smile; and Trent took himself away, his hand still quivering from the cool touch of her fingers.

The testimony of the servants and of the finder of the body brought nothing new to the reporters' net. That of the police was as colourless and cryptic as is usual at the inquest stage

of affairs of the kind. Greatly to the satisfaction of Mr.
Bunner, his evidence afforded the sensation of the day, and
threw far into the background the interesting revelation of
domestic difficulty made by the dead man's wife. He told the
court in substance what he had already told Trent. The flying
pencils did not miss a word of the young American's story,
and it appeared with scarcely the omission of a sentence in
every journal of importance in Great Britain and the United
States.

Public opinion next day took no note of the faint suggestion of the possibility of suicide which the coroner, in his final
address to the jury, had thought it right to make in connection
with the lady's evidence. The weight of evidence, as the official
had indeed pointed out, was against such a theory. He had
referred with emphasis to the fact that no weapon had been
found near the body.

"This question, of course, is all-important, gentlemen," he
had said to the jury. "It is, in fact, the main issue before
you. You have seen the body for yourselves. You have just
heard the medical evidence; but I think it would be well for
me to read you my notes of it in so far as they bear on this
point, in order to refresh your memories. Dr. Stock told you
—I am going to omit all technical medical language and
repeat to you merely the plain English of his testimony—
that in his opinion death had taken place six or eight hours
previous to the finding of the body. He said that the cause of
death was a bullet wound, the bullet having entered the left
eye, which was destroyed, and made its way to the base of the
brain, which was quite shattered. The external appearance of
the wound, he said, did not support the hypothesis of its being
self-inflicted, inasmuch as there were no signs of the firearm
having been pressed against the eye, or even put very close
to it; at the same time it was not physically impossible that
the weapon should have been discharged by the deceased with
his own hand, at some small distance from the eye. Dr. Stock
also told us that it was impossible to say with certainty, from
the state of the body, whether any struggle had taken place at
the time of death; that when seen by him, at which time he
understood that it had not been moved since it was found, the
body was lying in a collapsed position such as might very well
result from the shot alone; but that the scratches and bruises
upon the wrists and the lower part of the arms had been very

recently inflicted, and were, in his opinion, marks of violence.

"In connection with this same point, the remarkable evidence given by Mr. Bunner cannot be regarded, I think, as without significance. It may have come as a surprise to some of you to hear that risks of the character described by this witness are, in his own country, commonly run by persons in the position of the deceased. On the other hand, it may have been within the knowledge of some of you that in the industrial world of America the discontent of labour often proceeds to lengths of which we in England happily know nothing. I have interrogated the witness somewhat fully upon this. At the same time, gentlemen, I am by no means suggesting that Mr. Bunner's personal conjecture as to the cause of death can fitly be adopted by you. That is emphatically not the case. What his evidence does is to raise two questions for your consideration. First, can it be said that the deceased was to any extent in the position of a threatened man—of a man more exposed to the danger of murderous attack than an ordinary person? Second, does the recent alteration in his demeanour, as described by this witness, justify the belief that his last days were overshadowed by a great anxiety? These points may legitimately be considered by you in arriving at a conclusion upon the rest of the evidence."

Thereupon the coroner, having indicated thus clearly his opinion that Mr. Bunner had hit the right nail on the head, desired the jury to consider their verdict.

CHAPTER IX

A HOT SCENT

"COME in!" called Trent.

Mr. Cupples entered his sitting-room at the hotel. It was the early evening of the day on which the coroner's jury, without leaving the box, had pronounced the expected denunciation of a person or persons unknown. Trent, with a hasty glance upward, continued his intent study of what lay in a photographic dish of enamelled metal, which he moved slowly about in the light of the window. He looked very pale, and his movements were nervous.

"Sit on the sofa," he advised. "The chairs are a job lot bought at the sale after the suppression of the Holy Inquisition in Spain. This is a pretty good negative," he went on, holding it up to the light with his head at the angle of discriminating judgment. "Washed enough now, I think. Let us leave it to dry, and get rid of all this mess."

Mr. Cupples, as the other busily cleared the table of a confusion of basins, dishes, racks, boxes, and bottles, picked up first one and then another of the objects and studied them with innocent curiosity.

"That is called hypo-eliminator," said Trent, as Mr. Cupples uncorked and smelt at one of the bottles. "Very useful when you're in a hurry with a negative. I shouldn't drink it, though, all the same. It eliminates sodium hypophosphite, but I shouldn't wonder if it would eliminate human beings too." He found a place for the last of the litter on the crowded mantel-shelf, and came to sit before Mr. Cupples on the table. "The great thing about a hotel sitting-room is that its beauty does not distract the mind from work. It is no place for the mayfly pleasures of a mind at ease. Have you ever been in this room before, Cupples? I have, hundreds of times. It has pursued me all over England for years. I should feel lost without it if, in some fantastic, far-off hotel, they were to give me some other sitting-room. Look at this table-cover; there is the ink I spilt on it when I had this room in Halifax. I burnt that hole in the carpet when I had it in Ipswich. But I see they have mended the glass over the picture of 'Silent Sympathy,' which I threw a boot at in Banbury. I do all my best work here. This afternoon, for instance, since the inquest, I have finished several excellent negatives. There is a very good dark room downstairs."

"The inquest—that reminds me," said Mr. Cupples, who knew that this sort of talk in Trent meant the excitement of action, and was wondering what he could be about. "I came in to thank you, my dear fellow, for looking after Mabel this morning. I had no idea she was going to feel ill after leaving the box; she seemed quite unmoved, and, really, she is a woman of such extraordinary self-command, I thought I could leave her to her own devices and hear out the evidence, which I thought it important I should do. It was a very fortunate thing she found a friend to assist her, and she is most grateful. She is quite herself again now."

Trent, with his hands in his pockets and a slight frown on his brow, made no reply to this. "I tell you what," he said after a short pause, "I was just getting to the really interesting part of the job when you came in. Come; would you like to see a little bit of high-class police work? It's the very same kind of work that old Murch ought to be doing at this moment. Perhaps he is; but I hope to glory he isn't." He sprang off the table and disappeared into his bedroom. Presently he came out with a large drawing-board on which a number of heterogeneous objects was ranged.

"First I must introduce you to these little things," he said, setting them out on the table. "Here is a big ivory paper-knife; here are two leaves cut out of a diary—my own diary; here is a bottle containing dentifrice; here is a little case of polished walnut. Some of these things have to be put back where they belong in somebody's bedroom at White Gables before night. That's the sort of man I am—nothing stops me. I borrowed them this very morning when everyone was down at the inquest, and I dare say some people would think it rather an odd proceeding if they knew. Now there remains one object on the board. Can you tell me, without touching it, what it is?"

"Certainly I can," said Mr. Cupples, peering at it with great interest. "It is an ordinary glass bowl. It looks like a finger-bowl. I see nothing odd about it," he added after some moments of close scrutiny.

"I can't see much myself," replied Trent, "and that is exactly where the fun comes in. Now take this little fat bottle, Cupples, and pull out the cork. Do you recognize that powder inside it? You have swallowed pounds of it in your time, I expect. They give it to babies. Grey powder is its ordinary name—mercury and chalk. It is great stuff. Now, while I hold the basin sideways over a sheet of paper, I want you to pour a little powder out of the bottle over this part of the bowl— just here. . . . Perfect! Sir Edward Henry himself could not have handled the powder better. You have done this before, Cupples, I can see. You are an old hand."

"I really am not," said Mr. Cupples seriously, as Trent returned the fallen powder to the bottle. "I assure you it is all a complete mystery to me. What did I do then?"

"I brush the powdered part of the bowl lightly with this

camel-hair brush. Now look at it again. You saw nothing odd about it before. Do you see anything now?"

Mr. Cupples peered again. "How curious!" he said. "Yes, there are two large gray finger-marks on the bowl. They were not there before."

"I am Hawkshaw the detective," observed Trent. "Would it interest you to hear a short lecture on the subject of glass finger-bowls? When you take one up with your hand you leave traces upon it, usually practically invisible, which may remain for days or months. You leave the marks of your fingers. The human hand, even when quite clean, is never quite dry, and sometimes—in moments of great anxiety, for instance, Cupples—it is very moist. It leaves a mark on any cold smooth surface it may touch. That bowl was moved by somebody with a rather moist hand quite lately." He sprinkled the powder again. "Here on the other side, you see, is the thumb-mark—very good impressions all of them." He spoke without raising his voice, but Mr. Cupples could perceive that he was ablaze with excitement as he stared at the faint gray marks. "This one should be the index finger. I need not tell a man of your knowledge of the world that the pattern of it is a single-spiral whorl, with deltas symmetrically disposed. This, the print of the second finger, is a simple loop, with a staple core and fifteen counts. I know there are fifteen, because I have just the same two prints on this negative, which I have examined in detail. Look!"—he held one of the negatives up to the light of the declining sun and demonstrated with a pencil point. "You can see they're the same. You see the bifurcation of that ridge. There it is in the other. You see that little scar near the centre. There it is in the other. There are a score of ridge-characteristics on which an expert would swear in the witness-box that the marks on that bowl and the marks I have photographed on this negative were made by the same hand."

"And where did you photograph them? What does it all mean?" asked Mr. Cupples, wide-eyed.

"I found them on the inside of the left-hand leaf of the front window in Mrs. Manderson's bedroom. As I could not bring the window with me, I photographed them, sticking a bit of black paper on the other side of the glass for the purpose. The bowl comes from Manderson's room. It is the bowl in which his false teeth were placed at night. I could bring that away, so I did."

"But those cannot be Mabel's finger-marks."

"I should think not!" said Trent with decision. "They are twice the size of any print Mrs. Manderson could make."

"Then they must be her husband's."

"Perhaps they are. Now shall we see if we can match them once more? I believe we can." Whistling faintly, and very white in the face, Trent opened another small squat bottle containing a dense black powder. "Lamp-black," he explained. "Hold a bit of paper in your hand for a second or two, and this little chap will show you the pattern of your fingers." He carefully took up with a pair of tweezers one of the leaves cut from his diary, and held it out for the other to examine. No marks appeared on the leaf. He tilted some of the powder out upon one surface of the paper, then, turning it over, upon the other; then shook the leaf gently to rid it of the loose powder. He held it out to Mr. Cupples in silence. On one side of the paper appeared unmistakably, clearly printed in black, the same two finger-prints that he had already seen on the bowl and on the photographic plate. He took up the bowl and compared them. Trent turned the paper over, and on the other side was a bold black replica of the thumb-mark that was printed gray on the glass in his hand.

"Same man, you see," Trent said with a short laugh. "I felt that it must be so, and now I know." He walked to the window and looked out. "Now I know," he repeated in a low voice, as if to himself. His tone was bitter. Mr. Cupples, understanding nothing, stared at his motionless back for a few moments.

"I am still completely in the dark," he ventured presently. "I have often heard of this finger-print business, and wondered how the police went to work about it. It is of extraordinary interest to me, but upon my life I cannot see how in this case Manderson's finger-prints are going——"

"I am very sorry, Cupples," Trent broke in upon his meditative speech with a swift return to the table. "When I began this investigation I meant to take you with me every step of the way. You mustn't think I have any doubts about your discretion if I say now that I must hold my tongue about the whole thing, at least for a time. I will tell you this: I have come upon a fact that looks too much like having very painful consequences if it is discovered by anyone else." He looked at the other with a hard and darkened face, and struck the table with his hand. "It is terrible for me here and now. Up to this moment I was hoping against hope that I was wrong about the fact. I may still be wrong in the surmise that I base upon that fact. There is only one way of finding out that is open to me, and I must nerve myself to take it." He smiled suddenly at Mr. Cupples's face of consternation. "All right—I'm not going to be tragic any more, and I'll tell you all about it when I can. Look here, I'm not half through my game with the powder-bottles yet."

He drew one of the defamed chairs to the table and sat down to test the broad ivory blade of the paper knife. Mr. Cupples, swallowing his amazement, bent forward in an attitude of deep interest and handed Trent the bottle of lamp-black.

CHAPTER X
The Wife of Dives

Mrs. Manderson stood at the window of her sitting-room at White Gables gazing out upon a wavering landscape of fine rain and mist. The weather had broken as it seldom does in that part in June. White wreathings drifted up the fields from the sullen sea; the sky was an unbroken gray deadness shedding pin-point moisture that was now and then blown against the panes with a crepitation of despair. The lady looked out on the dim and chilling prospect with a woeful face. It was a bad day for a woman bereaved, alone, and without a purpose in life.

There was a knock, and she called "Come in," drawing herself up with an unconscious gesture that always came when she realized that the weariness of the world had been gaining upon her spirit. Mr. Trent had called, the maid said; he apologized for coming at such an early hour, but hoped that Mrs. Manderson would see him on a matter of urgent importance. Mrs. Manderson would see Mr. Trent. She walked to a mirror, looked into the olive face she saw reflected there, shook her head at herself with the flicker of a grimace, and turned to the door as Trent was shown in.

His appearance, she noted, was changed. He had the jaded look of the sleepless, and a new and reserved expression, in which her quick sensibilities felt something not propitious, took the place of his half smile of fixed good-humour.

"May I come to the point at once?" he said, when she had given him her hand. "There is a train I ought to catch at Bishopsbridge at twelve o'clock, but I cannot go until I have settled this thing, which concerns you only, Mrs. Manderson. I have been working half the night and thinking the rest; and I know now what I ought to do."

"You look wretchedly tired," she said kindly. "Won't you sit down? This is a very restful chair. Of course it is about this terrible business and your work as correspondent. Please ask me anything you think I can properly tell you, Mr. Trent. I know that you won't make it worse for me than you can help in doing your duty here. If you say you must see me about something, I know it must be because, as you say, you ought to do it."

"Mrs. Manderson," said Trent, slowly measuring his words, "I won't make it worse for you than I can help. But I am bound to make it bad for you—only between ourselves, I hope. As to whether you can properly tell me what I shall ask you, you will decide that; but I tell you this on my word of honour: I shall ask you only as much as will decide me whether to publish or to withhold certain grave things that I have found out about your husband's death, things not suspected by anyone else, nor, I think, likely to be so. What I have discovered—what I believe that I have practically proved—will be a great shock to you in any case. But it may be worse for you than that; and if you give me reason to think it would be so, then I shall suppress this manuscript," he laid a long envelope on the small table beside him, "and nothing of what it has to tell shall ever be printed. It consists, I may tell you, of a short private note to my editor, followed by a long dispatch for publication in the *Record*. Now you may refuse to say anything to me. If you do refuse, my duty to my employers, as I see it, is to take this up to London with me to-day and leave it with my editor to be dealt with at his discretion. My view is, you understand, that I am not entitled to suppress it on the strength of a mere possibility that presents itself to my imagination. But if I gather from you—and I can gather it from no other person—that there is substance in that

imaginary possibility I speak of, then I have only one thing
to do as a gentleman and as one who"—he hesitated for a
phrase—"wishes you well. I shall not publish that dispatch
of mine. In some directions I decline to assist the police. Have
you followed me so far?" he asked with a touch of anxiety in
his careful coldness; for her face, but for its pallor, gave no
sign as she regarded him, her hands clasped before her, and
her shoulders drawn back in a pose of rigid calm. She looked
precisely as she had looked at the inquest.

"I understand quite well," said Mrs. Manderson in a low
voice. She drew a deep breath, and went on: "I don't know
what dreadful thing you have found out, or what the possibility that has occurred to you can be, but it was good,
it was honourable of you to come to me about it. Now will
you please tell me?"

"I cannot do that," Trent replied. "The secret is my newspaper's, if it is not yours. If I find it is yours, you shall have
my manuscript to read and destroy. Believe me," he broke
out with something of his old warmth, "I detest such mystery-
making from the bottom of my soul; but it is not I who have
made this mystery. This is the most painful hour of my life,
and you make it worse by not treating me like a hound. The
first thing I ask you to tell me," he reverted with an effort to
his colourless tone, "is this: is it true, as you stated at the
inquest, that you had no idea at all of the reason why your
late husband had changed his attitude toward you, and become
mistrustful and reserved, during the last few months of his
life?"

Mrs. Manderson's dark brows lifted and her eyes flamed;
she quickly rose from her chair. Trent got up at the same
moment, and took his envelope from the table; his manner said
that he perceived the interview to be at an end. But she held
up a hand, and there was colour in her cheeks and quick breathing in her voice as she said: "Do you know what you ask, Mr.
Trent? You ask me if I perjured myself."

"I do," he answered unmoved; and he added after a pause,
"You knew already that I had not come here to preserve the
polite fictions, Mrs. Manderson. The theory that no reputable
person, being on oath, could withhold a part of the truth
under any circumstances is a polite fiction." He still stood as
awaiting dismissal, but she was silent. She walked to the
window, and he stood miserably watching the slight movement

of her shoulders until it subsided. Then with face averted, looking out on the dismal weather, she spoke at last clearly.

"Mr. Trent," she said, "you inspire confidence in people, and I feel that things which I don't want known or talked about are safe with you. And I know you must have a very serious reason for doing what you are doing, though I don't know what it is. I suppose it would be assisting justice in some way if I told you the truth about what you asked just now. To understand that truth you ought to know about what went before—I mean about my marriage. After all, a good many people could tell you as well as I can that it was not . . . a very successful union. I was only twenty. I admired his force and courage and certainty; he was the only strong man I had ever known. But it did not take me long to find out that he cared for his business more than for me, and I think I found out even sooner that I had been deceiving myself and blinding myself, promising myself impossible things and wilfully misunderstanding my own feelings, because I was dazzled by the idea of having more money to spend than an English girl ever dreams of. I have been despising myself for that for five years. My husband's feeling for me . . . well, I cannot speak of that . . . what I want to say is that along with it there had always been a belief of his that I was the sort of woman to take a great place in society, and that I should throw myself into it with enjoyment, and become a sort of personage and do him great credit—that was his idea; and the idea remained with him after other delusions had gone. I was a part of his ambition. That was his really bitter disappointment, that I failed him as a social success. I think he was too shrewd not to have known in his heart that such a man as he was, twenty years older than I, with great business responsibilities that filled every hour of his life, and caring for nothing else—he must have felt that there was a risk of great unhappiness in marrying the sort of girl I was, brought up to music and books and unpractical ideas, always enjoying myself in my own way. But he had really reckoned on me as a wife who would do the honours of his position in the world; and I found I couldn't."

Mrs. Manderson had talked herself into a more emotional mood than she had yet shown to Trent. Her words flowed freely, and her voice had begun to ring and give play to a natural expressiveness that must hitherto have been dulled, he thought, by the shock and self-restraint of the past few days. Now she turned swiftly from the window and faced him as she went on, her beautiful face flushed and animated, her eyes gleaming, her hands moving in slight emphatic gestures, as she surrendered herself to the impulse of giving speech to things long pent up.

"The people," she said. "Oh, those people! Can you imagine what it must be for anyone who has lived in a world where there was always creative work in the background, work with some dignity about it, men and women with professions or arts to follow, with ideals and things to believe in and quarrel about, some of them wealthy, some of them quite poor; can you think what it means to step out of that into another world where you *have* to be very rich, shamefully rich, to exist at all —where money is the only thing that counts and the first thing in everybody's thoughts—where the men who make the millions are so jaded by the work, that sport is the only thing they can occupy themselves with when they have any leisure, and the men who don't have to work are even duller than the men who do, and vicious as well; and the women live for display and silly amusements and silly immoralities; do you know how awful that life is? Of course I know there are clever people, and people of taste in that set, but they're swamped and spoiled, and it's the same thing in the end; empty, empty! Oh! I suppose I'm exaggerating, and I did make friends and have some happy times; but that's how I feel after it all. The seasons in New York and London—how I hated them! And our house-parties and cruises in the yacht and the rest—the same people, the same emptiness.

"And you see, don't you, that my husband couldn't have an idea of all this. *His* life was never empty. He did not live it in society, and when he was in society he had always his business plans and difficulties to occupy his mind. He hadn't a suspicion of what I felt, and I never let him know; I couldn't, it wouldn't have been fair. I felt I must do something to justify myself as his wife, sharing his position and fortune; and the only thing I could do was to try, and try, to live up to his idea about my social qualities. . . . I did try. I acted my best. And it became harder year by year. . . . I never was what they call a popular hostess, how could I be? I was a failure; but I went on trying. . . . I used to steal holidays now and then. I used to feel as if I was not doing my part of a bargain

—it sounds horrid to put it like that, I know, but it *was* so—
when I took one of my old school-friends, who couldn't afford
to travel, away to Italy for a month or two, and we went about
cheaply all by ourselves, and were quite happy; or when I
went and made a long stay in London with some quiet people
who had known me all my life, and we all lived just as in the
old days, when we had to think twice about seats at the theatre,
and told each other about cheap dressmakers. Those and a few
other expeditions of the same sort were my best times after
I was married, and they helped me to go through with it the
rest of the time. But I felt my husband would have hated to
know how much I enjoyed every hour of those returns to the
old life.

"And in the end, in spite of everythnig I could do, he came
to know. . . . He could see through anything, I think, once
his attention was turned to it. He had always been able to
see that I was not fulfilling his idea of me as a figure in the
social world, and I suppose he thought it was my misfortune
rather than my fault. But the moment he began to see, in spite
of my pretending, that I wasn't playing my part with any
spirit, he knew the whole story; he divined how I loathed and
was weary of the luxury and the brilliancy and the masses of
money just because of the people who lived among them—
who were made so by them, I suppose. It happened last year.
I don't know just how or when. It may have been suggested
to him by some woman—for *they* all understood, of course.
He said nothing to me, and I think he tried not to change
in his manner to me at first; but such things hurt—and it
was working in both of us. I knew that he knew. After a time
we were just being polite and considerate to each other. Before he found me out we had been on a footing of—how can
I express it to you?—of intelligent companionship, I might
say. We talked without restraint of many things of the kind
we could agree or disagree about without its going very
deep . . . if you understand. And then that came to an end.
I felt that the only possible basis of our living in each other's
company was going under my feet. And at last it was gone.

"It had been like that," she ended simply, "for months before he died." She sank into the corner of a sofa by the window, as though relaxing her body after an effort. For a few
moments both were silent. Trent was hastily sorting out a tangle of impressions. He was amazed at the frankness of Mrs.

Manderson's story. He was amazed at the vigorous expressiveness in her telling of it. In this vivid being, carried away by an impulse to speak, talking with her whole personality, he had seen the real woman in a temper of activity, as he had already seen the real woman by chance in a temper of reverie and unguarded emotion. In both she was very unlike the pale, self-disciplined creature of majesty that she had been to the world. With that amazement of his went something like terror of her dark beauty, which excitement kindled into an appearance scarcely mortal in his eyes. Incongruously there rushed into his mind, occupied as it was with the affair of the moment, a little knot of ideas . . . she was unique not because of her beauty but because of its being united with intensity of nature; in England all the very beautiful women were placid, all the fiery women seemed to have burnt up the best of their beauty; that was why no beautiful woman had ever cast this sort of spell on him before; when it was a question of wit in women, he had preferred the brighter flame to the duller, without much regarding the lamp. "All this is very disputable," said his reason; and instinct answered, "Yes, except that I am under a spell"; and a deeper instinct cried out, "Away with it!" He forced his mind back to her story, and found growing swiftly in him an irrepressible conviction. It was all very fine; but it would not do.

"I feel as if I had led you into saying more than you meant to say, or than I wanted to learn," he said slowly. "But there is one brutal question which is the whole point of my inquiry." He braced his frame like one preparing for a plunge into cold waters. "Mrs. Manderson, will you assure me that your husband's change toward you had nothing to do with John Marlowe?"

And what he had dreaded came. "Oh!" she cried with a sound of anguish, her face thrown up and open hands stretched out as if for pity; and then the hands covered the burning face, and she flung herself aside among the cushions at her elbow, so that he saw nothing but her heavy crown of black hair, and her body moving with sobs that stabbed his heart, and a foot turned inward gracelessly in an abandonment of misery. Like a tall tower suddenly breaking apart she had fallen in ruins, helplessly weeping.

Trent stood up, his face white and calm. With a senseless particularity he placed his envelope exactly in the centre of the little polished table. He walked to the door, closed it noiselessly as he went out, and in a few minutes was tramping through the rain out of sight of White Gables, going nowhere, seeing nothing, his soul shaken in the fierce effort to kill and trample the raving impulse that had seized him in the presence of her shame, that clamoured to him to drag himself before her feet, to pray for pardon, to pour out words—he knew not what words, but he knew that they had been straining at his lips—to wreck his self-respect for ever, and hopelessly defeat even the crazy purpose that had almost possessed him, by drowning her wretchedness in disgust, by babbling with the tongue of infatuation to a woman with a husband not yet buried, to a woman who loved another man.

Such was the magic of her tears, quickening in a moment the thing which, as his heart had known, he must not let come to life. For Philip Trent was a young man, younger in nature even than his years, and a way of life that kept his edge keen and his spirit volcanic had prepared him very ill for the meeting that comes once in the early manhood of most of us, usually —as in his case, he told himself harshly—to no purpose but the testing of virtue and the power of the will.

CHAPTER XI
Hitherto Unpublished

My dear Molloy:—This is in case I don't find you at your office. I have found out who killed Manderson, as this dispatch will show. This was my problem; yours is to decide what use to make of it. It definitely charges an unsuspected person with having a hand in the crime, and practically accuses him of being the murderer, so I don't suppose you will publish it before his arrest, and I believe it is illegal to do so afterwards until he has been tried and found guilty. You may decide to publish it then; and you may find it possible to make some use or other before then of the facts I have given. This is your affair. Meanwhile, will you communicate with Scotland Yard, and let them see what I have written? I have done with the Manderson mystery, and I wish to God I had never touched it. Here follows my dispatch. P.T.

Marlstone, *June 16th.*

I begin this, my third and probably my final dispatch to the *Record* upon the Manderson murder, with conflicting feelings. I have a strong sense of relief, because in my two previous dispatches I was obliged, in the interests of justice, to withhold facts ascertained by me which would, if published then, have put a certain person upon his guard and possibly have led to his escape; for he is a man of no common boldness and resource. These facts I shall now set forth. But I have, I confess, no liking for the story of treachery and perverted cleverness which I have to tell. It leaves an evil taste in the mouth, a savour of something revolting in the deeper puzzle of motive underlying the puzzle of the crime itself, which I believe I have solved.

It will be remembered that in my first dispatch I described the situation as I found it on reaching this place early on Tuesday morning. I told how the body was found, and in what state; dwelt upon the complete mystery surrounding the crime, and mentioned one or two local theories about it; gave some account of the dead man's domestic surroundings; and furnished a somewhat detailed description of his movements on the evening before his death. I gave, too, a little fact which may or may not have seemed irrelevant: that a quantity of whisky much larger than Manderson habitually drank at night had disappeared from his private decanter since the last time he was seen alive. On the following day, the day after the inquest, I wired little more than an abstract of the proceedings in the coroner's court, of which a verbatim report was made at my request by other representatives of the *Record*. That day is not yet over as I write these lines; and I have now completed an investigation which has led me directly to the man who must be called upon to clear himself of the guilt of the death of Manderson.

Apart from the central mystery of Manderson's having arisen long before his usual hour to go out and meet his death, there were two minor points of oddity about this affair which, I suppose, must have occurred to thousands of those who have read the accounts in the newspapers: points apparent from the very beginning. The first of these was that, whereas the body was found at a spot not thirty yards from the house, all the people of the house declared that they had heard no cry or other noise in the night. Manderson had not been gagged; the marks on his wrists pointed to a struggle with his assailant; and there had been at least one pistol-shot. (I say at least one, because it is the fact that in murders with firearms, especially if there has been a struggle, the criminal commonly misses his victim at least once.) The odd fact seemed all the more odd to me when I learned that Martin the butler was a bad sleeper, very keen of hearing, and that his bedroom, with the window open, faced almost directly toward the shed by which the body was found.

The second odd little fact that was apparent from the out-set was Manderson's leaving his dental plate by the bedside. It appeared that he had risen and dressed himself fully, down to his necktie and watch and chain, and had gone out of doors without remembering to put in this plate, which he had carried in his mouth every day for years, and which contained all the visible teeth of the upper jaw. It had evidently not been a case of frantic hurry; and even if it had been, he would have been more likely to forget almost anything than this denture. Any-one who wears such a removable plate will agree that the put-ting it in on rising is a matter of second nature. Speaking as well as eating, to say nothing of appearances, depends upon it.

Neither of these queer details, however, seemed to lead to anything at the moment. They only awakened in me a suspicion of something lurking in the shadows, something that lent more mystery to the already mysterious question how and why and through whom Manderson met his end.

With this much of preamble I come at once to the discovery which, in the first few hours of my investigation, set me upon the path which so much ingenuity had been directed to con-cealing.

I have already described Manderson's bedroom, the rigor-ous simplicity of its furnishing, contrasted so strangely with the multitude of clothes and shoes, and the manner of its com-munication with Mrs. Manderson's room. On the upper of the two long shelves on which the shoes were ranged I found, where I had been told I should find them, the pair of patent leather shoes which Manderson had worn on the evening before his death. I had glanced over the row, not with any idea of their giving me a clue, but merely because it happens that I am a judge of shoes, and all these shoes were of the very best work-manship. But my attention was at once caught by a little pe-culiarity in this particular pair. They were the lightest kind of lace-up dress shoes, very thin in the sole, without toe-caps, and beautifully made, like all the rest. These shoes were old and well worn; but being carefully polished, and fitted, as all the shoes were, upon their trees, they looked neat enough. What caught my eye was a slight splitting of the leather in that part of the upper known as the vamp—a splitting at the point where the two laced parts of the shoe rise from the upper. It is at this point that the strain comes when a tight shoe of this sort is forced upon the foot, and it is usually guarded with a strong stitching across the bottom of the opening. In both the shoes I was examining this stitching had parted, and the leather below had given way. The splitting was a tiny affair in each case, not an eighth of an inch long, and the torn edges having come together again on the removal of the strain, there was nothing that a person who was not something of a connoisseur of shoe-leather would have noticed. Even less noticeable, and indeed not to be seen at all unless one were looking for it, was a slight straining of the stitches uniting the upper to the sole. At the toe and on the outer side of each shoe this stitching had been dragged until it was visible on a close inspection of the join.

These indications, of course, could mean only one thing—the shoes had been worn by someone for whom they were too small.

Now it was clear at a glance that Manderson was always thoroughly well shod, and careful, perhaps a little vain, of his small and narrow feet. Not one of the other shoes in the collection, as I soon ascertained, bore similar marks; they had not belonged to a man who squeezed himself into tight shoe-leather. Someone who was not Manderson had worn these shoes, and worn them recently; the edges of the tears were quite fresh.

The possibility of someone having worn them since Manderson's death was not worth considering; the body had only been found about twenty-six hours when I was examining the shoes; besides, why should anyone wear them? The possibility of someone having borrowed Manderson's shoes and spoiled them for him while he was alive seemed about as negligible. With others to choose from he would not have worn these. Besides, the only men in the place were the butler and the two secretaries. But I do not say that I gave those possibilities even as much consideration as they deserved, for my thoughts were running away with me, and I have always found it good policy, in cases of

this sort, to let them have their heads. Ever since I had got out
of the train at Marlstone early that morning I had been
steeped in details of the Manderson affair; the thing had not
once been out of my head. Suddenly the moment had come
when the dæmon wakes and begins to range.

Let me put it less fancifully. After all, it is a detail of psychology familiar enough to all whose business or inclination
brings them in contact with difficult affairs of any kind.
Swiftly and spontaneously, when chance or effort puts
one in possession of the key-fact in any system of baffling circumstances, one's ideas seem to rush to group themselves anew
in relation to that fact, so that they are suddenly rearranged
almost before one has consciously grasped the significance of
the key-fact itself. In the present instance, my brain had
scarcely formulated within itself the thought, "Somebody who
was not Manderson has been wearing these shoes," when there
flew into my mind a flock of ideas, all of the same character
and all bearing upon this new notion. It was unheard-of for
Manderson to drink much whisky at night. It was very unlike
him to be untidily dressed, as the body was when found—the
cuffs dragged up inside the sleeves, the shoes unevenly laced;
very unlike him not to wash when he rose, and to put on last
night's evening shirt and collar and underclothing; very unlike him to have his watch in the waistcoat pocket that was not
lined with leather for its reception. (In my first dispatch I
mentioned all these points, but neither I nor anyone else saw
anything significant in them when examining the body.) It
was very strange, in the existing domestic situation, that Manderson should be communicative to his wife about his doings,
especially at the time of his going to bed, when he seldom spoke
to her at all. It was extraordinary that Manderson should leave
his bedroom without his false teeth.

All these thoughts, as I say, came flocking into my mind together, drawn from various parts of my memory of the morning's inquiries and observations. They had all presented themselves, in far less time than it takes to read them as set down
here, as I was turning over the shoes, confirming my own certainty on the main point. And yet when I confronted the definite idea that had sprung up suddenly and unsupported before me—"*It was not Manderson who was in the house that
night*"—it seemed a stark absurdity at the first formulating.
It was certainly Manderson who had dined at the house and

gone out with Marlowe in the car. People had seen him at close quarters. But was it he who returned at ten? That question too seemed absurd enough. But I could not set it aside. It seemed to me as if a faint light was beginning to creep over the whole expanse of my mind, as it does over land at dawn, and that presently the sun would be rising. I set myself to think over, one by one, the points that had just occurred to me, so as to make out, if possible, why any man masquerading as Manderson should have done these things that Manderson would not have done.

I had not to cast about very long for the motive a man might have in forcing his feet into Manderson's narrow shoes. The examination of foot-marks is very well understood by the police. But not only was the man concerned to leave no foot-marks of his own: he was concerned to leave Manderson's, if any; his whole plan, if my guess was right, must have been directed to producing the belief that Manderson was in the place that night. Moreover, his plan did not turn upon leaving foot-marks. He meant to leave the shoes themselves, and he did so. The maidservant had found them outside the bedroom door, as Manderson always left his shoes, and had polished them, replacing them on the shoe-shelves later in the morning, after the body had been found.

When I came to consider in this new light the leaving of the false teeth, an explanation of what had seemed the maddest part of the affair broke upon me at once. A dental plate is not inseparable from its owner. If my guess was right, the unknown had brought the denture to the house with him, and left it in the bedroom, with the same object as he had in leaving the shoes: to make it impossible that anyone should doubt that Manderson had been in the house and had gone to bed there. This, of course, led me to the inference that *Manderson was dead before the false Manderson came to the house;* and other things confirmed this.

For instance, the clothing, to which I now turned in my review of the position. If my guess was right, the unknown in Manderson's shoes had certainly had possession of Manderson's trousers, waistcoat, and shooting jacket. They were there before my eyes in the bedroom; and Martin had seen the jacket —which nobody could have mistaken—upon the man who sat at the telephone in the library. It was now quite plain (if my guess was right) that this unmistakable garment was a cardinal feature of the unknown's plan. He knew that Martin would take him for Manderson at the first glance.

And there my thinking was interrupted by the realization of a thing that had escaped me before. So strong had been the influence of the unquestioned assumption that it was Manderson who was present that night, that neither I nor, as far as I know, anyone else had noted the point. *Martin had not seen the man's face; nor had Mrs. Manderson.*

Mrs. Manderson (judging by her evidence at the inquest, of which, as I have said, I had a full report made by the *Record* stenographers in court) had not seen the man at all. She hardly could have done, as I shall show presently. She had merely spoken with him as she lay half asleep, resuming a conversation which she had had with her living husband about an hour before. Martin, I perceived, could only have seen the man's back, as he sat crouching over the telephone; no doubt a characteristic pose was imitated there. And the man had worn his hat, Manderson's broad-brimmed hat! There is too much character in the back of a head and neck. The unknown, in fact, supposing him to have been of about Manderson's build, had had no need for any disguise, apart from the jacket and the hat and his powers of mimicry.

I paused there to contemplate the coolness and ingenuity of the man. The thing, I now began to see, was so safe and easy, provided that his mimicry was good enough, and that his nerve held. These two points assured, only some wholly unlikely accident could unmask him.

To come back to my puzzling out of the matter as I sat in the dead man's bedroom with the tell-tale shoes before me. The reason for the entrance by the window instead of by the front door will already have occurred to anyone reading this. Entering by the door, the man would almost certainly have been heard by the sharp-eared Martin in his pantry just across the hall; he might have met him face to face.

Then there was the problem of the whisky. I had not attached much importance to it; whisky will sometimes vanish in very queer ways in a household of eight or nine persons; but it had seemed strange that it should go in that way on that evening. Martin had been plainly quite dumbfounded by the fact. It seemed to me now that many a man—fresh, as this man in all likelihood was, from a bloody business, from the unclothing of a corpse, and with a desperate part still to play—would turn to that decanter as to a friend. No doubt he had a drink before sending for Martin; after making that trick with ease and success, he probably drank more.

But he had known when to stop. The worst part of the enterprise was before him: the business—clearly of such vital importance to him, for whatever reason—of shutting himself in Manderson's room and preparing a body of convincing evidence of its having been occupied by Manderson; and this with the risk—very slight, as no doubt he understood, but how unnerving!—of the woman on the other side of the half-open door awaking and somehow discovering him. True, if he kept out of her limited field of vision from the bed, she could only see him by getting up and going to the door. I found that to a person lying in her bed, which stood with its head to the wall a little beyond the door, nothing was visible through the doorway but one of the cupboards by Manderson's bedhead. Moreover, since this man knew the ways of the household, he would think it most likely that Mrs. Manderson was asleep. Another point with him, I guessed, might have been the estrangement between the husband and wife, which they had tried to cloak by keeping up, among other things, their usual practice of sleeping in connected rooms, but which was well known to all who had anything to do with them. He would hope from this that if Mrs. Manderson heard him, she would take no notice of the supposed presence of her husband.

So, pursuing my hypothesis, I followed the unknown up to the bedroom, and saw him setting about his work. And it was with a catch in my own breath that I thought of the hideous shock with which he must have heard the sound of all others he was dreading most: the drowsy voice from the adjoining room.

What Mrs. Manderson actually said, she was unable to recollect at the inquest. She thinks she asked her supposed husband whether he had had a good run in the car. And now what does the unknown do? Here, I think, we come to a supremely significant point. Not only does he—standing rigid there, as I picture him, before the dressing-table, listening to the sound of his own leaping heart—not only does he answer the lady in the voice of Manderson; he volunteers an explanatory statement. He tells her that he has, on a sudden inspiration, sent Marlowe in the car to Southampton; that he had sent him to bring back some important information from a man leaving for Paris by the steamboat that morning. Why these details from a man who had long been uncommunicative to his wife, and that upon a point scarcely likely to interest her? Why these details *about Marlowe?*

Having taken my story so far, I now put forward the following definite propositions: that between a time somewhere about ten, when the car started, and a time somewhere about eleven, Manderson was shot—probably at a considerable distance from the house, as no shot was heard; that the body was brought back, left by the shed, and stripped of its outer clothing; that at some time round about eleven o'clock a man who was not Manderson, wearing Manderson's shoes, hat, and jacket, entered the library by the garden window; that he had with him Manderson's black trousers, waistcoat, and motor-coat, the denture taken from Manderson's mouth, and the weapon with which he had been murdered; that he concealed these, rang the bell for the butler, and sat down at the telephone with his hat on and his back to the door; that he was occupied with the telephone all the time Martin was in the room; that on going up to the bedroom floor he quietly entered Marlowe's room and placed the revolver with which the crime had been committed—Marlowe's revolver—in the case on the mantelpiece from which it had been taken; and that he then went to Manderson's room, placed Manderson's shoes outside the door, threw Manderson's garments on a chair, placed the denture in the bowl by the bedside, and selected a suit of clothes, a pair of shoes, and a tie from those in the bedroom.

Here I will pause in my statement of this man's proceedings to go into a question for which the way is now sufficiently prepared:—

Who was the false Manderson?

Reviewing what was known to me, or might almost with certainty be surmised, about that person, I set down the following five conclusions:

(1) He had been in close relations with the dead man. In his acting before Martin and his speaking to Mrs. Manderson he had made no mistake.

(2) He was of a build not unlike Manderson's, especially as to height and breadth of shoulder, which mainly determine the character of the back of a seated figure when the head is concealed and the body loosely clothed. But his feet were larger, though not greatly larger, than Manderson's.

(3) He had considerable aptitude for mimicry and acting—probably some experience too.

(4) He had a minute acquaintance with the ways of the Manderson household.

(5) He was under a vital necessity of creating the belief that Manderson was alive and in that house until some time after midnight on the Sunday night.

So much I took as either certain or next door to it. It was as far as I could see. And it was far enough.

I proceed to give, in an order corresponding with the numbered paragraphs above, such relevant facts as I was able to obtain about Mr. John Marlowe, from himself and other sources:—

(1) He had been Mr. Manderson's private secretary, upon a footing of great intimacy, for nearly four years.

(2) The two men were nearly of the same height, about five feet eleven inches; both were powerfully built and heavy in the shoulder. Marlowe, who was the younger by some twenty years, was rather slighter about the body, though Manderson was a man in good physical condition. Marlowe's shoes (of which I examined several pairs) were roughly about one shoemaker's size longer and broader than Manderson's.

(3) In the afternoon of the first day of my investigation, after arriving at the results already detailed, I sent a telegram to a personal friend, a Fellow of a college at Oxford, whom I knew to be interested in theatrical matters, in these terms:

Please wire John Marlowe's record in connection with acting at Oxford some time past decade very urgent and confidential.

My friend replied in the following telegram, which reached me next morning (the morning of the inquest) :—

Marlowe was member O.U.D.S. for three years and president 19— played Bardolph Cleon and Mercutio excelled in character acting and imitations in great demand at smokers was hero of some historic hoaxes.

I had been led to send the telegram which brought this very helpful answer by seeing on the mantel-shelf in Marlowe's bedroom a photograph of himself and two others in the costume of Falstaff's three followers, with an inscription from *The Merry*

Wives, and by noting that it bore the imprint of an Oxford firm
of photographers.

(4) During his connection with Manderson, Marlowe had
lived as one of the family. No other person, apart from the
servants, had his opportunities for knowing the domestic life
of the Mandersons in detail.

(5) I ascertained beyond doubt that Marlowe arrived at a
hotel in Southampton on the Monday morning at 6.30, and
there proceeded to carry out the commission which, according
to his story, and according to the statement made to Mrs. Manderson in the bedroom by the false Manderson, had been entrusted to him by his employer. He had then returned in the
car to Marlstone, where he had shown great amazement and
horror at the news of the murder.

.   .   .   .

These, I say, are the relevant facts about Marlowe. We must
now examine fact number 5 (as set out above) in connection
with conclusion number 5 about the false Manderson.

I would first draw attention to one important fact. *The only
person who professed to have heard Manderson mention Southampton at all before he started in the car was Marlowe.* His
story—confirmed to some extent by what the butler overheard
—was that the journey was all arranged in a private talk before they set out, and he could not say, when I put the question
to him, why Manderson should have concealed his intentions
by giving out that he was going with Marlowe for a moonlight
drive. This point, however, attracted no attention. Marlowe
had an absolutely air-tight alibi in his presence at Southampton by 6.30; nobody thought of him in connection with a murder which must have been committed after 12.30—the hour at
which Martin the butler had gone to bed. But it was the Manderson who came back from the drive who went out of his way
to mention Southampton openly to two persons. *He even went
so far as to ring up a hotel at Southampton and ask questions
which bore out Marlowe's story of his errand.* This was the call
he was busy with when Martin was in the library.

Now let us consider the alibi. If Manderson was in the house
that night, and if he did not leave it until some time after
12.30, Marlowe could not by any possibility have had a direct
hand in the murder. It is a question of the distance between
Marlstone and Southampton. If he had left Marlstone in the

car at the hour when he is supposed to have done so—between 10 and 10.30—with a message from Manderson, the run would be quite an easy one to do in the time. But it would be physically impossible for the car—a 15 h. p. four-cylinder Northumberland, an average medium-power car—to get to Southampton by half-past six unless it left Marlstone by midnight at latest. Motorists who will examine the road-map and make the calculations required, as I did in Manderson's library that day, will agree that on the facts as they appeared there was absolutely no case against Marlowe.

But even if they were not as they appeared; if Manderson was dead by eleven o'clock, and if at about that time Marlowe impersonated him at White Gables; if Marlowe retired to Manderson's bedroom—how can all this be reconciled with his appearance next morning at Southampton? *He had to get out of the house, unseen and unheard, and away in the car by midnight.* And Martin, the sharp-eared Martin, was sitting up until 12.30 in his pantry, with the door open, listening for the telephone bell. Practically he was standing sentry over the foot of the staircase, the only staircase leading down from the bedroom floor.

With this difficulty we arrive at the last and crucial phase of my investigation. Having the foregoing points clearly in mind, I spent the rest of the day before the inquest in talking to various persons and in going over my story, testing it link by link. I could only find the one weakness which seemed to be involved in Martin's sitting up until 12.30; and since his having been instructed to do so was certainly a part of the plan, meant to clinch the alibi for Marlowe, I knew there must be an explanation somewhere. If I could not find that explanation, my theory was valueless. I must be able to show that at the time Martin went up to bed the man who had shut himself in Manderson's bedroom might have been many miles away on the road to Southampton.

I had, however, a pretty good idea already—as perhaps the reader of these lines has by this time, if I have made myself clear—of how the escape of the false Manderson before midnight had been contrived. But I did not want what I was now about to do to be known. If I had chanced to be discovered at work, there would have been no concealing the direction of my suspicions. I resolved not to test them on this point until the next day, during the opening proceedings at the inquest. This was to be held, I knew, at the hotel, and I reckoned upon having White Gables to myself so far as the principal inmates were concerned.

So in fact it happened. By the time the proceedings at the hotel had been begun I was hard at work at White Gables. I had a camera with me. I made search, on principles well known to and commonly practised by the police, and often enough by myself, for certain indications. Without describing my search, I may say at once that I found and was able to photograph two fresh finger-prints, very large and distinct, on the polished front of the right-hand top drawer of the chest of drawers in Manderson's bedroom; five more (among a number of smaller and less recent impressions made by other hands) on the glasses of the French window in Mrs. Manderson's room, a window which always stood open at night with a curtain before it; and three more upon the glass bowl in which Manderson's dental plate had been found lying.

I took the bowl with me from White Gables. I took also a few articles which I selected from Marlowe's bedroom, as bearing the most distinct of the innumerable finger-prints which are always to be found upon toilet articles in daily use. I already had in my possession, made upon leaves cut from my pocket diary, some excellent finger-prints of Marlowe's which he had made in my presence without knowing it. I had shown him the leaves, asking if he recognized them; and the few seconds during which he had held them in his fingers had sufficed to leave impressions which I was afterwards able to bring out.

By six o'clock in the evening, two hours after the jury had brought in their verdict against a person or persons unknown, I had completed my work, and was in a position to state that two of the five large prints made on the window-glasses, and the three on the bowl, were made by the left hand of Marlowe; that the remaining three on the window and the two on the drawer were made by his right hand.

By eight o'clock I had made at the establishment of Mr. H. T. Copper, photographer, of Bishopsbridge, and with his assistance, a dozen enlarged prints of the finger-marks of Marlowe, clearly showing the identity of those which he unknowingly made in my presence and those left upon articles in his bedroom, and those found by me as I have described, and thus establishing the facts that Marlowe was recently in Manderson's bedroom, where he had in the ordinary way no business,

and in Mrs. Manderson's room, where he had still less. I hope
it may be possible to reproduce these prints for publication
with this dispatch.

At nine o'clock I was back in my room at the hotel and sitting down to begin this manuscript. I had my story complete.

I bring it to a close by advancing these further propositions:
that on the night of the murder the impersonator of Manderson, being in Manderson's bedroom, told Mrs. Manderson, as
he had already told Martin, that Marlowe was at that moment
on his way to Southampton; that having made his dispositions
in the room, he switched off the light, and lay in the bed in his
clothes; that he waited until he was assured that Mrs. Manderson was asleep; that he then arose and stealthily crossed
Mrs. Manderson's bedroom in his stocking feet, having under
his arm the bundle of clothing and shoes for the body; that he
stepped behind the curtain, pushing the doors of a window a
little further open with his hands, strode over the iron railing
of the balcony, and let himself down until only a drop of a few
feet separated him from the soft turf of the lawn.

All this might very well have been accomplished within half-
an-hour of his entering Manderson's bedroom, which, according
to Martin, he did at about half-past eleven.

What followed your readers and the authorities may conjecture for themselves. The corpse was found next morning
clothed—rather untidily. Marlowe in the car appeared at
Southampton by half-past six.

. . . .

I bring this manuscript to an end in my sitting-room at the
hotel at Marlstone. It is four o'clock in the morning. I leave
for London by the noon train from Bishopsbridge, and immediately after arriving I shall place these pages in your hands.
I ask you to communicate the substance of them to the Criminal
Investigation Department.

PHILIP TRENT.

CHAPTER XII
EVIL DAYS

"I AM returning the cheque you sent for what I did on the
Manderson case," Trent wrote to Sir James Molloy from

Munich, whither he had gone immediately after handing in at the *Record* office a brief dispatch bringing his work on the case to an unexciting close. "What I sent you wasn't worth one-tenth of the amount; but I should have no scruple about pocketing it if I hadn't taken a fancy—never mind why—not to touch any money at all for this business. I should like you, if there is no objection, to pay for the stuff at your ordinary space-rate, and hand the money to some charity which does not devote itself to bullying people, if you know of any such. I have come to this place to see some old friends and arrange my ideas, and the idea that comes out uppermost is that for a little while I want some employment with activity in it. I find I can't paint at all: I couldn't paint a fence. Will you try me as your Own Correspondent somewhere? If you can find me a good adventure I will send you good accounts. After that I could settle down and work."

Sir James sent him instructions by telegram to proceed at once to Kurland and Livonia, where Citizen Browning was abroad again, and town and countryside blazed in revolt. It was a roving commission, and for two months Trent followed his luck. It served him not less well than usual. He was the only correspondent who saw General Dragilew killed in the street at Volmar by a girl of eighteen. He saw burnings, lynchings, fusillades, hangings; each day his soul sickened afresh at the imbecilities born of misrule. Many nights he lay down in danger. Many days he went fasting. But there was never an evening or a morning when he did not see the face of the woman whom he hopelessly loved.

He discovered in himself an unhappy pride at the lasting force of this infatuation. It interested him as a phenomenon; it amazed and enlightened him. Such a thing had not visited him before. It confirmed so much that he had found dubious in the recorded experience of men.

It was not that, at thirty-two, he could pretend to ignorance of this world of emotion. About his knowledge let it be enough to say that what he had learned had come unpursued and unpurchased, and was without intolerable memories; broken to the realities of sex, he was still troubled by its inscrutable history. He went through life full of a strange respect for certain feminine weakness and a very simple terror of certain feminine strength. He had held a rather lukewarm faith that something remained in him to be called forth, and that the voice that should call would be heard in its own time, if ever, and not through any seeking.

But he had not thought of the possibility that, if this proved true some day, the truth might come in a sinister shape. The two things that had taken him utterly by surprise in the matter of his feeling towards Mabel Manderson were the insane suddenness of its uprising in full strength and its extravagant hopelessness. Before it came, he had been much disposed to laugh at the permanence of unrequited passion as a generous boyish delusion. He knew now that he had been wrong, and he was living bitterly in the knowledge.

Before the eye of his fancy the woman always came just as she was when he had first had sight of her, with the gesture which he had surprised as he walked past unseen on the edge of the cliff; that great gesture of passionate joy in her new liberty which had told him more plainly than speech that her widowhood was a release from torment, and had confirmed with terrible force the suspicion, active in his mind before, that it was her passport to happiness with a man whom she loved. He could not with certainty name to himself the moment when he had first suspected that it might be so. The seed of the thought must have been sown, he believed, at his first meeting with Marlowe; his mind would have noted automatically that such evident strength and grace, with the sort of looks and manners that the tall young man possessed, might go far with any woman of unfixed affections. And the connection of this with what Mr. Cupples had told him of the Mandersons' married life must have formed itself in the unconscious depths of his mind. Certainly it had presented itself as an already established thing when he began, after satisfying himself of the identity of the murderer, to cast about for the motive of the crime. Motive, motive! How desperately he had sought for another, turning his back upon that grim thought, that Marlowe—obsessed by passion like himself, and privy perhaps to maddening truths about the wife's unhappiness—had taken a leaf, the guiltiest, from the book of Bothwell. But in all his investigations at the time, in all his broodings on the matter afterwards, he had been able to discover nothing that could prompt Marlowe to such a deed—nothing but that temptation, the whole strength of which he could not know, but which if it had existed must have pressed urgently upon a bold spirit in which scruple had been somehow paralyzed. If he could trust his senses at all, the young man was neither insane nor by nature evil. But that could not clear him. Murder for a woman's sake, he thought, was not a rare crime, Heaven knew! If the modern feebleness of impulse in the comfortable classes, and their respect for the modern apparatus of detection, had made it rare among them, it was yet far from impossible. It only needed a man of equal daring and intelligence, his soul drugged with the vapours of an intoxicating intrigue, to plan and perform such a deed.

A thousand times, with a heart full of anguish, he had sought to reason away the dread that Mabel Manderson had known too much of what had been intended against her husband's life. That she knew all the truth after the thing was done he could not doubt; her unforgettable collapse in his presence when the question about Marlowe was suddenly and bluntly put, had swept away his last hope that there was no love between the pair, and had seemed to him, moreover, to speak of dread of discovery. In any case, she knew the truth after reading what he had left with her; and it was certain that no public suspicion had been cast upon Marlowe since. She had destroyed his manuscript, then, and taken him at his word to keep the secret that threatened her lover's life.

But it was the monstrous thought that she might have known murder was brewing, and guiltily kept silence, that haunted Trent's mind. She might have suspected, have guessed something; was it conceivable that she was aware of the whole plot, that she connived? He could never forget that his first suspicion of Marlowe's motive in the crime had been roused by the fact that his escape was made through the lady's room. At that time, when he had not yet seen her, he had been ready enough to entertain the idea of her equal guilt and her co-operation. He had figured to himself some passionate *hystérique*, merciless as a cat in her hate and her love, a zealous abettor, perhaps even the ruling spirit in the crime.

Then he had seen her, had spoken with her, had helped her in her weakness; and such suspicions, since their first meeting, had seemed the vilest of infamy. He had seen her eyes and her mouth; he had breathed the woman's atmosphere. Trent was one of those who fancy they can scent true wickedness in the air. In her presence he had felt an inward certainty of her ultimate goodness of heart; and it was nothing against this that she had abandoned herself a moment, that day on the cliff, to the sentiment of relief at the ending of her bondage, of her years of starved sympathy and unquickened motherhood. That she had turned to Marlowe in her destitution he believed; that she had any knowledge of his deadly purpose he did not believe.

And yet, morning and evening the sickening doubts returned, and he recalled again that it was almost in her presence that Marlowe had made his preparations in the bedroom of the murdered man, that it was by the window of her own chamber that he had escaped from the house. Had he forgotten his cunning and taken the risk of telling her then? Or had he, as Trent thought more likely, still played his part with her then, and stolen off while she slept? He did not think she had known of the masquerade when she gave evidence at the inquest; it read like honest evidence. Or—the question would never be silenced, though he scorned it—had she lain expecting the footsteps in the room and the whisper that should tell her that it was done? Among the foul possibilities of human nature, was it possible that black ruthlessness and black deceit as well were hidden behind that good and straight and gentle seeming?

These thoughts would scarcely leave him when he was alone.

* * * * * * * * * * *

Trent served Sir James well, earning his pay, for six months, and then returned to Paris, where he went to work again with a better heart. His powers had returned to him, and he began to live more happily than he had expected among a tribe of strangely assorted friends, French, English, and American, artists, poets, journalists, policemen, hotel-keepers, soldiers, lawyers, business men, and others. His old faculty of sympathetic interest in his fellows won for him, just as in his student days, privileges seldom extended to the Briton. He enjoyed again the rare experience of being taken into the bosom of a Frenchman's family. He was admitted to the momentous confidence of *les jeunes,* and found them as sure that they had surprised the secrets of art and life as the departed *jeunes* of ten years before had been.

The bosom of the Frenchman's family was the same as those he had known in the past, even to the patterns of the wall-paper and movables. But the *jeunes,* he perceived with regret, were totally different from their forerunners. They were much more shallow and puerile, much less really clever. The secrets they wrested from the Universe were not such important and interesting secrets as had been wrested by the old *jeunes*. This he believed and deplored until one day he found himself seated at a restaurant next to a too well-fed man whom, in spite of the ravages of comfortable living, he recognized as one of the *jeunes* of his own period. This one had been wont to describe himself and three or four others as the Hermits of the New Parnassus. He and his school had talked outside cafés and elsewhere more than solitaries do as a rule; but then, rules were what they had vowed themselves to destroy. They proclaimed that verse, in particular, was free. The Hermit of the New Parnassus was now in the Ministry of the Interior, and already decorated: he expressed to Trent the opinion that what France needed most was a hand of iron. He was able to quote the exact price paid for certain betrayals of the country, of which Trent had not previously heard.

Thus he was brought to make the old discovery that it was he who had changed, like his friend of the Administration, and that *les jeunes* were still the same. Yet he found it hard to say what precisely he had lost that so greatly mattered; unless indeed it were so simple a thing as his high spirits.

One morning in June, as he descended the slope of the Rue des Martyrs, he saw approaching a figure that he remembered. He glanced quickly round, for the thought of meeting Mr. Bunner again was unacceptable. For some time he had recognized that his wound was healing under the spell of creative work; he thought less often of the woman he loved, and with less pain. He would not have the memory of those three days reopened.

But the straight and narrow thoroughfare offered no refuge, and the American saw him almost at once.

His unforced geniality made Trent ashamed, for he had liked the man. They sat long over a meal, and Mr. Bunner talked. Trent listened to him, now that he was in for it, with genuine pleasure, now and then contributing a question or remark. Besides liking his companion, he enjoyed his conversation, with its unending verbal surprises, for its own sake.

Mr. Bunner was, it appeared, resident in Paris as the chief Continental agent of the Manderson firm, and fully satisfied with his position and prospects. He discoursed on these for some twenty minutes. This subject at length exhausted, he went on to tell Trent, who confessed that he had been away from England for a year, that Marlowe had shortly after the death of Manderson entered his father's business, which was now again in a flourishing state, and had already come to be practically in control of it. They had kept up their intimacy, and were even now planning a holiday for the summer. Mr. Bunner spoke with generous admiration of his friend's talent for affairs. "Jack Marlowe has a natural big head," he declared, "and if he had more experience, I wouldn't want to have him up against me. He would put a crimp in me every time."

As the American's talk flowed on, Trent listened with a slowly growing perplexity. It became more and more plain that something was very wrong in his theory of the situation; there was no mention of its central figure. Presently Mr. Bunner mentioned that Marlowe was engaged to be married to an Irish girl, whose charms he celebrated with native enthusiasm.

Trent clasped his hands savagely together beneath the table. What could have happened? His ideas were sliding and shifting. At last he forced himself to put a direct question.

Mr. Bunner was not very fully informed. He knew that Mrs. Manderson had left England immediately after the settlement of her husband's affairs, and had lived for some time in Italy. She had returned not long ago to London, where she had decided not to live in the house in Mayfair, and had bought a smaller one in the Hampstead neighbourhood; also, he understood, one somewhere in the country. She was said to go but little into society. "And all the good hard dollars just waiting for some one to spraddle them around," said Mr. Bunner, with a note of pathos in his voice. "Why, she has money to burn— money to feed to the birds—and nothing doing. The old man left her more than half his wad. And think of the figure she might make in the world. She is beautiful, and she is the best woman I ever met, too. But she couldn't ever seem to get the habit of spending money the way it ought to be spent."

His words now became a soliloquy: Trent's thoughts were occupying all his attention. He pleaded business soon, and the two men parted with cordiality.

Half an hour later Trent was in his studio, swiftly and mechanically "cleaning up." He wanted to know what had happened; somehow he must find out. He could never approach herself, he knew; he would never bring back to her the shame of that last encounter with him; it was scarcely likely that he would even set eyes on her. But he must get to know! . . .

Cupples was in London, Marlowe was there. . . . And, anyhow, he was sick of Paris.

Such thoughts came and went; and below them all strained the fibres of an unseen cord that dragged mercilessly at his heart, and that he cursed bitterly in the moments when he could not deny to himself that it was there. The folly, the useless, pitiable folly of it!

In twenty-four hours his feeble roots in Paris had been torn out. He was looking over a leaden sea at the shining fortress-wall of the Dover cliffs.

.   .   .   .

But though he had instinctively picked out the lines of a set purpose from among the welter of promptings in his mind, he found it delayed at the very outset.

He had decided that he must first see Mr. Cupples, who would be in a position to tell him much more than the American knew. But Mr. Cupples was away on his travels, not expected to return for a month; and Trent had no reasonable excuse for hastening his return. Marlowe he would not confront until he had tried at least to reconnoitre the position. He constrained himself not to commit the crowning folly of seeking out Mrs. Manderson's house in Hampstead; he could not enter it, and the thought of the possibility of being seen by her lurking in its neighbourhood brought the blood to his face.

He stayed at an hotel, took a studio, and while he awaited Mr. Cupples's return attempted vainly to lose himself in work.

At the end of a week he had an idea that he acted upon with eager precipitancy. She had let fall some word at their last meeting, of a taste for music. Trent went that evening, and thenceforward regularly, to the opera. He might see her; and if, in spite of his caution, she caught sight of him, they could be blind to each other's presence—anybody might happen to go to the opera.

So he went alone each evening, passing as quickly as he might through the people in the vestibule; and each evening he came away knowing that she had not been in the house. It was a habit that yielded him a sort of satisfaction along with the guilty excitement of his search; for he too loved music, and nothing gave him so much peace while its magic endured.

One night as he entered, hurrying through the brilliant

crowd, he felt a touch on his arm. Flooded with an incredible
certainty at the touch, he turned.

It was she: so much more radiant in the absence of grief and
anxiety, in the fact that she was smiling, and in the allurement
of evening dress, that he could not speak. She, too, breathed a
little quickly, and there was a light of daring in her eyes and
cheeks as she greeted him.

Her words were few. "I wouldn't miss a note of *Tristan*,"
she said, "nor must you. Come and see me in the interval." She
gave him the number of the box.

CHAPTER XIII

ERUPTION

THE following two months were a period in Trent's life that
he has never since remembered without shuddering. He met
Mrs. Manderson half-a-dozen times, and each time her cool
friendliness, a nicely calculated mean between mere acquaintance and the first stage of intimacy, baffled and maddened him.
At the opera he had found her, to his further amazement, with
a certain Mrs. Wallace, a frisky matron whom he had known
from childhood. Mrs. Manderson, it appeared, on her return
from Italy, had somehow wandered into circles to which he belonged by nurture and disposition. It came, she said, of her
having pitched her tent in their hunting-grounds; several of
his friends were near neighbours. He had a dim but horrid
recollection of having been on that occasion unlike himself, ill
at ease, burning in the face, talking with idiot loquacity of
his adventures in the Baltic provinces, and finding from time
to time that he was addressing himself exclusively to Mrs.
Wallace. The other lady, when he joined them, had completely
lost the slight appearance of agitation with which she had
stopped him in the vestibule. She had spoken pleasantly to
him of her travels, of her settlement in London, and of people
whom they both knew.

During the last half of the opera, which he had stayed in
the box to hear, he had been conscious of nothing, as he sat

behind them, but the angle of her cheek and the mass of her hair,
the lines of her shoulder and arm, her hand upon the cushion.
The black hair had seemed at last a forest, immeasurable, path-
less and enchanted, luring him to a fatal adventure. . . . At
the end he had been pale and subdued, parting with them
rather formally.

The next time he saw her—it was at a country house where
both were guests—and the subsequent times, he had had himself in hand. He had matched her manner and had acquitted
himself, he thought, decently, considering——

Considering that he lived in an agony of bewilderment and
remorse and longing. He could make nothing, absolutely nothing, of her attitude. That she had read his manuscript and
understood the suspicion indicated in his last question to her
at White Gables was beyond the possibility of doubt. Then
how could she treat him thus amiably and frankly, as she
treated all the world of men who had done her no injury?

For it had become clear to his intuitive sense, for all the
absence of any shade of differentiation in her outward manner,
that an injury had been done, and that she had felt it. Several
times, on the rare and brief occasions when they had talked
apart, he had warning from the same sense that she was approaching this subject; and each time he had turned the conversation with the ingenuity born of fear. Two resolutions he
made. The first was that when he had completed a commissioned
work which tied him to London he would go away and stay
away. The strain was too great. He no longer burned to know
the truth; he wanted nothing to confirm his fixed internal conviction but faith, that he had blundered, that he had misread
the situation, misinterpreted her tears, written himself down a
slanderous fool. He speculated no more on Marlowe's motive
in the killing of Manderson. Mr. Cupples returned to London,
and Trent asked him nothing. He knew now that he had been
right in those words—Trent remembered them for the emphasis with which they were spoken—"So long as she considered herself bound to him . . . no power on earth could have
persuaded her." He met Mrs. Manderson at dinner at her
uncle's large and tomb-like house in Bloomsbury, and there he
conversed most of the evening with a professor of archæology
from Berlin.

His other resolution was that he would not be with her alone.
But when, a few days after, she wrote asking him to come

and see her on the following afternoon, he made no attempt to excuse himself. This was a formal challenge.

. . . .

While she celebrated the rites of tea, and for some little time thereafter, she joined with such natural ease in his slightly fevered conversation on matters of the day that he began to hope she had changed what he could not doubt had been her resolve, to corner him and speak to him gravely. She was to all appearance careless now, smiling so that he recalled, not for the first time since that night at the opera, what was written long ago of a Princess of Brunswick: "Her mouth has ten thousand charms that touch the soul." She made a tour of the beautiful room where she had received him, singling out this treasure or that from the spoils of a hundred bric-à-brac shops, laughing over her quests, discoveries, and bargainings. And when he asked if she would delight him again with a favourite piece of his which he had heard her play at another house, she consented at once.

She played with a perfection of execution and feeling that moved him now as it had moved him before. "You are a musician born," he said quietly when she had finished, and the last tremor of the music had passed away. "I knew that before I first heard you."

"I have played a great deal ever since I can remember. It has been a great comfort to me," she said simply, and half-turned to him smiling. "When did you first detect music in me? Oh, of course: I was at the opera. But that wouldn't prove much, would it?"

"No," he said abstractedly, his sense still busy with the music that had just ended. "I think I knew it the first time I saw you." Then understanding of his own words came to him, and turned him rigid. For the first time the past had been invoked.

There was a short silence. Mrs. Manderson looked at Trent, then hastily looked away. Colour began to rise in her cheeks, and she pursed her lips as if for whistling. Then with a defiant gesture of the shoulders which he remembered, she rose suddenly from the piano and placed herself in a chair opposite to him.

"That speech of yours will do as well as anything," she began slowly, looking at the point of her shoe, "to bring us to what I wanted to say. I asked you here to-day on purpose, Mr.

Trent, because I couldn't bear it any longer. Ever since the day you left me at White Gables I have been saying to myself that it didn't matter what you thought of me in that affair; that you were certainly not the kind of man to speak to others of what you believed about me, after what you had told me of your reasons for suppressing your manuscript. I asked myself how it could matter. But all the time, of course. I knew it did matter. It mattered horribly. Because what you thought was not true." She raised her eyes and met his gaze calmly. Trent, with a completely expressionless face, returned her look.

"Since I began to know you," he said, "I have ceased to think it."

"Thank you," said Mrs. Manderson; and blushed suddenly and deeply. Then, playing with a glove, she added, "But I want you to know what *was* true.

"I did not know if I should ever see you again," she went on in a lower voice, "but I felt that if I did I must speak to you about this. I thought it would not be hard to do so, because you seemed to me an understanding person; and besides, a woman who has been married isn't expected to have the same sort of difficulty as a young girl in speaking about such things when it is necessary. And then we did meet again, and I discovered that it was very difficult indeed. You made it difficult."

"How?" he asked quietly.

"I don't know," said the lady. "But yes—I do know. It was just because you treated me exactly as if you had never thought or imagined anything of that sort about me. I had always supposed that if I saw you again you would turn on me that hard, horrible sort of look you had when you asked me that last question—do you remember?—at White Gables. Instead of that you were just like any other acquaintance. You were just"— she hesitated and spread out her hands—"nice. You know. After that first time at the opera when I spoke to you I went home positively wondering if you had really recognized me. I mean, I thought you might have recognized my face without remembering who it was."

A short laugh broke from Trent in spite of himself, but he said nothing.

She smiled deprecatingly. "Well, I couldn't remember if you had spoken my name; and I thought it might be so. But the next time, at the Iretons', you did speak it, so I knew; and a dozen times during those few days I almost brought myself to tell you, but never quite. I began to feel that you wouldn't let me, that you would slip away from the subject if I approached it. Wasn't I right? Tell me, please." He nodded. "But why?" He remained silent.

"Well," she said, "I will finish what I had to say, and then you will tell me, I hope, why you had to make it so hard. When I began to understand that you wouldn't let me talk of the matter to you, it made me more determined than ever. I suppose you didn't realize that I would insist on speaking even if you were quite discouraging. I dare say I couldn't have done it if I had been guilty, as you thought. You walked into my parlour to-day, never thinking I should dare. Well, now you see."

Mrs. Manderson had lost all her air of hesitancy. She had, as she was wont to say, talked herself enthusiastic, and in the ardour of her purpose to annihilate the misunderstanding that had troubled her so long she felt herself mistress of the situation.

"I am going to tell you the story of the mistake you made," she continued, as Trent, his hands clasped between his knees, still looked at her enigmatically. "You will have to believe it, Mr. Trent; it is utterly true to life, with its confusions and hidden things and cross-purposes and perfectly natural mistakes that nobody thinks twice about taking for facts. Please understand that I don't blame you in the least, and never did, for jumping to the conclusion you did. You knew that I was estranged from my husband, and you knew what that so often means. You knew before I told you, I expect, that he had taken up an injured attitude towards me; and I was silly enough to try and explain it away. I gave you the explanation of it that I had given myself at first, before I realized the wretched truth; I told you he was disappointed in me because I couldn't take a brilliant lead in society. Well, that was true; he was so. But I could see you weren't convinced. You had guessed what it took me much longer to see, because I knew how irrational it was. Yes; my husband was jealous of John Marlowe; you divined that.

"Then I behaved like a fool when you let me see you had divined it; it was such a blow, you understand, when I had supposed all the humiliation and strain was at an end, and that his delusion had died with him. You practically asked me if my husband's secretary was not my lover, Mr. Trent—I *have* to say it, because I want you to understand why I broke down and made a scene. You took that for a confession; you thought I was guilty of that, and I think you even thought I might be a party to the crime, that I had consented. . . . That did hurt me; but perhaps you couldn't have thought anything else —I don't know."

Trent, who had not hitherto taken his eyes from her face, hung his head at the words. He did not raise it again as she continued. "But really it was simple shock and distress that made me give way, and the memory of all the misery that mad suspicion had meant to me. And when I pulled myself together again you had gone."

She rose and went to an escritoire beside the window, unlocked a drawer, and drew out a long, sealed envelope.

"This is the manuscript you left with me," she said. "I have read it through again and again. I have always wondered, as everybody does, at your cleverness in things of this kind." A faintly mischievous smile flashed upon her face, and was gone. "I thought it was splendid, Mr. Trent—I almost forgot that the story was my own, I was so interested. And I want to say now, while I have this in my hand, how much I thank you for your generous, chivalrous act in sacrificing this triumph of yours rather than put a woman's reputation in peril. If all had been as you supposed, the facts must have come out when the police took up the case you put in their hands. Believe me, I understood just what you had done, and I never ceased to be grateful even when I felt most crushed by your suspicion."

As she spoke her thanks her voice shook a little, and her eyes were bright. Trent perceived nothing of this. His head was still bent. He did not seem to hear. She put the envelope into his hand as it lay open, palm upwards, on his knee. There was a touch of gentleness about the act which made him look up.

"Can you——" he began slowly.

She raised her hand as she stood before him. "No, Mr. Trent; let me finish before you say anything. It is such an unspeakable relief to me to have broken the ice at last, and I want to end the story while I am still feeling the triumph of beginning it." She sank down into the sofa from which she had first risen. "I am telling you a thing that nobody else knows. Everybody knew, I suppose, that something had come between us, though I did everything in my power to hide it. But I don't think anyone in the world ever guessed what my husband's notion was.

People who know me don't think that sort of thing about me,
I believe. And his fancy was so ridiculously opposed to the
facts. I will tell you what the situation was. Mr. Marlowe and
I had been friendly enough since he came to us. For all his
cleverness—my husband said he had a keener brain than any
man he knew—I looked upon him as practically a boy. You
know I am a little older than he is, and he had a sort of amiable
lack of ambition that made me feel it the more. One day my
husband asked me what I thought was the best thing about
Marlowe, and not thinking much about it I said, 'His manners.' He surprised me very much by looking black at that,
and after a silence he said, 'Yes, Marlowe is a gentleman;
that's so,' not looking at me.

"Nothing was ever said about that again until about a year
ago, when I found that Mr. Marlowe had done what I always
expected he would do—fallen desperately in love with an
American girl. But to my disgust he had picked out the most
worthless girl, I do believe, of all those whom we used to meet.
She was the daughter of wealthy parents, and she did as she
liked with them; very beautiful, well educated, very good at
games—what they call a woman-athlete—and caring for nothing on earth but her own amusement. She was one of the most
unprincipled flirts I ever knew, and quite the cleverest. Every
one knew it, and Mr. Marlowe must have heard it; but she made
a complete fool of him, brain and all. I don't know how she
managed it, but I can imagine. She liked him, of course; but
it was quite plain to me that she was playing with him. The
whole affair was so idiotic, I got perfectly furious. One day
I asked him to row me in a boat on the lake—all this happened
at our house by Lake George. We had never been alone together for any length of time before. In the boat I talked to
him. I was very kind about it, I think, and he took it admirably, but he didn't believe me a bit. He had the impudence to
tell me that I misunderstood Alice's nature. When I hinted at
his prospects—I knew he had scarcely anything of his own—
he said that if she loved him he could make himself a position
in the world. I dare say that was true, with his abilities and his
friends—he is rather well connected, you know, as well as
popular. But his enlightenment came very soon after that.

"My husband helped me out of the boat when we got back.
He joked with Mr. Marlowe about something, I remember;
for through all that followed he never once changed in his man-

ner to him, and that was one reason why I took so long to realize what he thought about him and myself. But to me he was reserved and silent that evening—not angry. He was always perfectly cold and expressionless to me after he took this idea into his head. After dinner he only spoke to me once. Mr. Marlowe was telling him about some horse he had bought for the farm in Kentucky, and my husband looked at me and said, 'Marlowe may be a gentleman, but he seldom quits loser in a horse-trade.' I was surprised at that, but at that time— and even on the next occasion when he found us together—I didn't understand what was in his mind. That next time was the morning when Mr. Marlowe received a sweet little note from the girl asking for his congratulations on her engagement. It was in our New York house. He looked so wretched at breakfast that I thought he was ill, and afterwards I went to the room where he worked, and asked what was the matter. He didn't say anything, but just handed me the note, and turned away to the window. I was very glad that was all over, but terribly sorry for him too, of course. I don't remember what I said, but I remember putting my hand on his arm as he stood there staring out on the garden; and just then my husband appeared at the open door with some papers. He just glanced at us, and then turned and walked quietly back to his study. I thought that he might have heard what I was saying to comfort Mr. Marlowe, and that it was rather nice of him to slip away. Mr. Marlowe neither saw nor heard him. My husband left the house that morning for the West while I was out. Even then I did not understand. He used often to go off suddenly like that, if some business project called him.

"It was not until he returned a week later that I grasped the situation. He was looking white and strange, and as soon as he saw me he asked me where Mr. Marlowe was. Somehow the tone of his question told me everything in a flash.

"I almost gasped; I was wild with indignation. You know, Mr. Trent, I don't think I should have minded at all if anyone had thought me capable of openly breaking with my husband and leaving him for somebody else. I dare say I might have done that. But that coarse suspicion . . . a man whom he trusted . . . and the notion of concealment. It made me see scarlet. Every shred of pride in me was strung up till I quivered, and I swore to myself on the spot that I would never show by any word or sign that I was conscious of his having such a thought about me. I would behave exactly as I always had behaved, I determined—and that I did, up to the very last. Though I knew that a wall had been made between us now that could never be broken down—even if he asked my pardon and obtained it—I never once showed that I noticed any change.

"And so it went on. I never could go through such a time again. My husband showed silent and cold politeness to me always when we were alone—and that was only when it was unavoidable. He never once alluded to what was in his mind; but I felt it, and he knew that I felt it. Both of us were stubborn in our different attitudes. To Mr. Marlowe he was more friendly, if anything, than before—Heaven only knows why. I fancied he was planning some sort of revenge; but that was only a fancy. Certainly Mr. Marlowe never knew what was suspected of him. He and I remained good friends, though we never spoke of anything intimate after that disappointment of his; but I made a point of seeing no less of him than I had always done. Then we came to England and to White Gables, and after that followed—my husband's dreadful end."

She threw out her right hand in a gesture of finality. "You know about the rest—so much more than any other man," she added, and glanced up at him with a quaint expression.

Trent wondered at that look, but the wonder was only a passing shadow on his thought. Inwardly his whole being was possessed by thankfulness. All the vivacity had returned to his face. Long before the lady had ended her story he had recognized the certainty of its truth, as from the first days of their renewed acquaintance he had doubted the story that his imagination had built up at White Gables, upon foundations that seemed so good to him.

He said, "I don't know how to begin the apologies I have to make. There are no words to tell you how ashamed and disgraced I feel when I realize what a crude, cock-sure blundering at a conclusion my suspicion was. Yes, I suspected—you! I had almost forgotten that I was ever such a fool. Almost—not quite. Sometimes when I have been alone I have remembered that folly, and poured contempt on it. I have tried to imagine what the facts were. I have tried to excuse myself."

She interrupted him quickly. "What nonsense! Do be sensible, Mr. Trent. You had only seen me on two occasions in your life before you came to me with your solution of the mystery." Again the quaint expression came and was gone.

"If you talk of folly, it really is folly for a man like you to pretend to a woman like me that I had innocence written all over me in large letters—so large that you couldn't believe very strong evidence against me after seeing me twice."

"What do you mean by 'a man like me'?" he demanded with a sort of fierceness. "Do you take me for a person without any normal instincts? I don't say you impress people as a simple, transparent sort of character—what Mr. Calvin Bunner calls a case of open-work; I don't say a stranger might not think you capable of wickedness, if there was good evidence for it; but I say that a man who, after seeing you and being in your atmosphere, could associate you with the particular kind of abomination I imagined, is a fool—the kind of fool who is afraid to trust his senses. . . . As for my making it hard for you to approach the subject, as you say, it is true. It was simply moral cowardice. I understood that you wished to clear the matter up; and I was revolted at the notion of my injurious blunder being discussed. I tried to show you by my actions that it was as if it had never been. I hoped you would pardon me without any words. I can't forgive myself, and I never shall. And yet if you could know——" He stopped short, and then added quietly, "Well, will you accept all that as an apology? The very scrubbiest sackcloth made, and the grittiest ashes on the heap. . . . I didn't mean to get worked up," he ended lamely.

Mrs. Manderson laughed, and her laugh carried him away with it. He knew well by this time that sudden rush of cascading notes of mirth, the perfect expression of enjoyment; he had many times tried to amuse her merely for his delight in the sound of it.

"But I love to see you worked up," she said. "The bump with which you always come down as soon as you realize that you are up in the air at all is quite delightful. Oh, we're actually both laughing. What a triumphant end to our explanations, after all my dread of the time when I should have it out with you. And now it's all over, and you know; and we'll never speak of it any more."

"I hope not," Trent said in sincere relief. "If you're resolved to be so kind as this about it, I am not high-principled enough to insist on your blasting me with your lightnings. And now, Mrs. Manderson, I had better go. Changing the subject after this would be like playing puss-in-the-corner after an earthquake." He rose to his feet.

"You are right," she said. "But no! Wait. There is another thing—part of the same subject; and we ought to pick up all the pieces now while we are about it. Please sit down." She took the envelope containing Trent's manuscript dispatch from the table where he had laid it. "I want to speak about this."

His brows bent, and he looked at her questioningly. "So do I, if you do," he said slowly. "I want very much to know one thing."

"Tell me."

"Since my reason for suppressing that information was all a fantasy, why did you never make any use of it? When I began to realize that I had been wrong about you, I explained your silence to myself by saying that you could not bring yourself to do a thing that would put a rope round a man's neck, whatever he might have done. I can quite understand that feeling. Was that what it was? Another possibility I thought of was that you knew of something that was by way of justifying or excusing Marlowe's act. Or I thought you might have a simple horror, quite apart from humanitarian scruples, of appearing publicly in connection with a murder trial. Many important witnesses in such cases have to be practically forced into giving their evidence. They feel there is defilement in the shadow of the scaffold."

Mrs. Manderson tapped her lips with the envelope without quite concealing a smile. "You didn't think of another possibility, I suppose, Mr. Trent," she said.

"No." He looked puzzled.

"I mean the possibility of your having been wrong about Mr. Marlowe as well as about me. No, no; you needn't tell me that the chain of evidence is complete. I know it is. But evidence of what? Of Mr. Marlowe having impersonated my husband that night, and having escaped by way of my window, and built up an alibi. I have read your dispatch again and again, Mr. Trent, and I don't see that those things can be doubted."

Trent gazed at her with narrowed eyes. He said nothing to fill the brief pause that followed. Mrs. Manderson smoothed her skirt with a preoccupied air, as one collecting her ideas.

"I did not make any use of the facts found out by you," she

slowly said at last, "because it seemed to me very likely that they would be fatal to Mr. Marlowe."

"I agree with you," Trent remarked in a colourless tone.

"And," pursued the lady, looking up at him with a mild reasonableness in her eyes, "as I knew that he was innocent I was not going to expose him to that risk."

There was another little pause. Trent rubbed his chin, with an affectation of turning over the idea. Inwardly he was telling himself, somewhat feebly, that this was very right and proper; that it was quite feminine, and that he liked her to be feminine. It was permitted to her—more than permitted—to set her loyal belief in the character of a friend above the clearest demonstrations of the intellect. Nevertheless, it chafed him. He would have had her declaration of faith a little less positive in form. It was too irrational to say she "knew." In fact (he put it to himself bluntly), it was quite unlike her. If to be un-reasonable when reason led to the unpleasant was a specially feminine trait, and if Mrs. Manderson had it, she was accus-tomed to wrap it up better than any woman he had known.

"You suggest," he said at length, "that Marlowe constructed an alibi for himself, by means which only a desperate man would have attempted, to clear himself of a crime he did not commit. Did he tell you he was innocent?"

She uttered a little laugh of impatience. "So you think he has been talking me round. No, that is not so. I am merely sure he did not do it. Ah! I see you think that absurd. But see how unreasonable you are, Mr. Trent! Just now you were explain-ing to me quite sincerely that it was foolishness in you to have a certain suspicion of me after seeing me and being in my atmosphere, as you said." Trent started in his chair. She glanced at him, and went on: "Now, I and my atmosphere are much obliged to you, but we must stand up for the rights of other atmospheres. I know a great deal more about Mr. Mar-lowe's atmosphere than you know about mine even now. I saw him constantly for several years. I don't pretend to know all about him; but I do know that he is incapable of a crime of bloodshed. The idea of his planning a murder is as unthink-able to me as the idea of your picking a poor woman's pocket, Mr. Trent. I can imagine you killing a man, you know . . . if the man deserved it and had an equal chance of killing you. I could kill a person myself in some circumstances. But Mr. Marlowe was incapable of doing it, I don't care what the prov-

ocation might be. He had a temper that nothing could shake,
and he looked upon human nature with a sort of cold magnanimity that would find excuses for absolutely anything. It
wasn't a pose; you could see it was a part of him. He never put
it forward, but it was there always. It was quite irritating at
times. . . . Now and then in America, I remember, I have
heard people talking about lynching, for instance, when he was
there. He would sit quite silent and expressionless, appearing
not to listen; but you could feel disgust coming from him in
waves. He really loathed and hated physical violence. He was
a very strange man in some ways, Mr. Trent. He gave one a
feeling that he might do unexpected things—do you know that
feeling one has about some people? What part he really played
in the events of that night I have never been able to guess. But
nobody who knew anything about him could possibly believe
in his deliberately taking a man's life." Again the movement
of her head expressed finality, and she leaned back in the sofa,
calmly regarding him.

"Then," said Trent, who had followed this with earnest attention, "we are forced back on two other possibilities, which
I had not thought worth much consideration until this moment.
Accepting what you say, he might still conceivably have killed
in self-defence; or he might have done so by accident."

The lady nodded. "Of course I thought of those two explanations when I read your manuscript."

"And I suppose you felt, as I did myself, that in either of
those cases the natural thing, and obviously the safest thing,
for him to do was to make a public statement of the truth, instead of setting up a series of deceptions which would certainly
stamp him as guilty in the eyes of the law, if anything went
wrong with them."

"Yes," she said wearily, "I thought over all that until my
head ached. And I thought somebody else might have done it,
and that he was somehow screening the guilty person. But that
seemed wild. I could see no light in the mystery, and after a
while I simply left it alone. All I was clear about was that Mr.
Marlowe was not a murderer, and that if I told what you had
found out, the judge and jury would probably think he was.
I promised myself that I would speak to you about it if we
should meet again; and now I've kept my promise."

Trent, his chin resting on his hand, was staring at the carpet. The excitement of the hunt for the truth was steadily

rising in him. He had not in his own mind accepted Mrs. Manderson's account of Marlowe's character as unquestionable. But she had spoken forcibly; he could by no means set it aside, and his theory was much shaken.

"There is only one thing for it," he said, looking up. "I must see Marlowe. It worries me too much to have the thing left like this. I will get at the truth. Can you tell me," he broke off, "how he behaved after the day I left White Gables?"

"I never saw him after that," said Mrs. Manderson simply. "For some days after you went away I was ill, and didn't go out of my room. When I got down he had left and was in London, settling things with the lawyers. He did not come down to the funeral. Immediately after that I went abroad. After some weeks a letter from him reached me, saying he had concluded his business and given the solicitors all the assistance in his power. He thanked me very nicely for what he called all my kindness, and said good-bye. There was nothing in it about his plans for the future, and I thought it particularly strange that he said not a word about my husband's death. I didn't answer. Knowing what I knew, I couldn't. In those days I shuddered whenever I thought of that masquerade in the night. I never wanted to see or hear of him again."

"Then you don't know what has become of him?"

"No; but I dare say Uncle Burton—Mr. Cupples, you know —could tell you. Some time ago he told me that he had met Mr. Marlowe in London, and had some talk with him. I changed the conversation." She paused and smiled with a trace of mischief. "I rather wonder what you supposed had happened to Mr. Marlowe after you withdrew from the scene of the drama that you had put together so much to your satisfaction."

Trent flushed. "Do you really want to know?" he said.

"I ask you," she retorted quietly.

"You ask me to humiliate myself again, Mrs. Manderson. Very well. I will tell you what I thought I should most likely find when I returned to London after my travels; that you had married Marlowe and gone to live abroad."

She heard him with unmoved composure. "We certainly couldn't have lived very comfortably in England on his money and mine," she observed thoughtfully. "He had practically nothing then."

He stared at her—"gaped," she told him some time afterwards. At the moment she laughed with a little embarrassment.

"Dear me, Mr. Trent! Have I said anything dreadful? You surely must know. . . . I thought everybody understood by now. . . . I'm sure I've had to explain it often enough . . . if I marry again I lose everything that my husband left me."

The effect of this speech upon Trent was curious. For an instant his face was flooded with the emotion of surprise. As this passed away he gradually drew himself together, as he sat, into a tense attitude. He looked, she thought as she saw his knuckles grow white on the arms of the chair, like a man prepared for pain under the hand of the surgeon. But all he said, in a voice lower than his usual tone, was, "I had no idea of it."

"It is so," she said calmly, trifling with a ring on her finger. "Really, Mr. Trent, it is not such a very unusual thing. I think I am glad of it. For one thing, it has secured me—at least since it became generally known—from a good many attentions of a kind that a woman in my position has to put up with as a rule."

"No doubt," he said gravely. "And . . . the other kind?"

She looked at him questioningly. "Ah!" she laughed. "The other kind trouble me even less. I have not yet met a man silly enough to want to marry a widow with a selfish disposition, and luxurious habits and tastes, and nothing but the little my father left me."

She shook her head, and something in the gesture shattered the last remnants of Trent's self-possession.

"Haven't you, by Heaven!" he exclaimed, rising with a violent movement and advancing a step towards her. "Then I am going to show you that human passion is not always stifled by the smell of money. I am going to end the business—my business. I am going to tell you what I dare say scores of better men have wanted to tell you, but couldn't summon up what I have summoned up—the infernal cheek to do it. They were afraid of making fools of themselves. I am not. You have accustomed me to the feeling this afternoon." He laughed aloud in the rush of words, and spread out his hands. "Look at me! It is the sight of the century. It is one who says he loves you, and would ask you to give up very great wealth to stand at his side."

She was hiding her face in her hands. He heard her say brokenly, "Please . . . don't speak in that way."

He answered: "It will make a great difference to me if you

will allow me to say all I have to say before I leave you. Perhaps it is in bad taste, but I will risk that; I want to relieve my soul; it needs open confession. This is the truth. You have troubled me ever since the first time I saw you—and you did not know it—as you sat under the edge of the cliff at Marlstone, and held out your arms to the sea. It was only your beauty that filled my mind then. As I passed by you it seemed as if all the life in the place were crying out a song about you in the wind and the sunshine. And the song stayed in my ears; but even your beauty would be no more than an empty memory to me by now if that had been all. It was when I led you from the hotel there to your house, with your hand on my arm, that —what was it that happened? I only knew that your stronger magic had struck home, and that I never should forget that day, whatever the love of my life should be. Till that day I had admired as I should admire the loveliness of a still lake; but that day I felt the spell of the divinity of the lake. And next morning the waters were troubled, and she rose—the morning when I came to you with my questions, tired out with doubts that were as bitter as pain, and when I saw you without your pale, sweet mask of composure—when I saw you moved and glowing, with your eyes and your hands alive, and when you made me understand that for such a creature as you there had been emptiness and the mere waste of yourself for so long. Madness rose in me then, and my spirit was clamouring to say what I say at last now: that life would never seem a full thing again because you could not love me, that I was taken for ever in the nets of your black hair and by the incantation of your voice——"

"Oh, stop!" she cried, suddenly throwing back her head, her face flaming and her hands clutching the cushions beside her. She spoke fast and disjointedly, her breath coming quick. "You shall not talk me into forgetting common sense. What does all this mean? Oh, I do not recognize you at all—you seem another man. We are not children; have you forgotten that? You speak like a boy in love for the first time. It is foolish, unreal—I know that if you do not. I will not hear it. What has happened to you?" She was half sobbing. "How can these sentimentalities come from a man like you? Where is your self-restraint?"

"Gone!" exclaimed Trent, with an abrupt laugh. "It has got right away. I am going after it in a minute." He looked gravely down into her eyes. "I don't care so much now. I never could declare myself to you under the cloud of your great fortune. It was too heavy. There's nothing creditable in that feeling, as I look at it; as a matter of simple fact it was a form of coward-ice—fear of what you would think, and very likely say—fear of the world's comment too, I suppose. But the cloud being rolled away, I have spoken, and I don't care so much. I can face things with a quiet mind now that I have told you the truth in its own terms. You may call it sentimentality or any other nickname you like. It is quite true that it was not in-tended for a scientific statement. Since it annoys you, let it be extinguished. But please believe that it was serious to me if it was comedy to you. I have said that I love you, and honour you, and would hold you dearest of all the world. Now give me leave to go."

But she held out her hands to him.

CHAPTER XIV
Writing A Letter

"If you insist," Trent said, "I suppose you will have your way. But I had much rather write it when I am not with you. However, if I must, bring me a tablet whiter than a star, or hand of hymning angel; I mean a sheet of note-paper not stamped with your address. Don't underestimate the sacrifice I am making. I never felt like correspondence in my life."

She rewarded him.

"What shall I say?" he inquired, his pen hovering over the paper. "Shall I compare him to a summer's day? What *shall* I say?"

"Say what you want to say," she suggested helpfully.

He shook his head. "What I want to say—what I have been wanting for the past twenty-four hours to say to every man, woman, and child I met—is 'Mabel and I are betrothed, and all is gas and gaiters.' But that wouldn't be a very good open-ing for a letter of strictly formal, not to say sinister, character. I have got as far as 'Dear Mr. Marlowe.' What comes next?"

"I am sending you a manuscript," she prompted, "which I thought you might like to see."

"Do you realize?" he said, "that in that sentence there are only two words of more than one syllable? This letter is meant to impress, not to put him at his ease. We must have long words."

"I don't see why," she answered. "I know it is usual, but why is it? I have had a great many letters from lawyers and business people, and they always begin, 'with reference to our communication,' or some such mouthful, and go on like that all the way through. Yet when I see them they don't talk like that. It seems ridiculous to me."

"It is not at all ridiculous to them." Trent laid aside the pen with an appearance of relief and rose to his feet. "Let me explain. A people like our own, not very fond of using its mind, gets on in the ordinary way with a very small and simple vocabulary. Long words are abnormal, and like everything else that is abnormal, they are either very funny or tremendously solemn. Take the phrase 'intelligent anticipation,' for instance. If such a phrase had been used in any other country in Europe, it would not have attracted the slightest attention. With us it has become a proverb; we all grin when we hear it in a speech or read it in a leading article; it is considered to be one of the best things ever said. Why? Just because it consists of two long words. The idea expressed is as commonplace as cold mutton. Then there's 'terminological inexactitude.' How we all roared, and are still roaring, at that! And the whole of the joke is that the words are long. It's just the same when we want to be very serious; we mark it by turning to long words. When a solicitor can begin a sentence with, 'pursuant to the instructions communicated to our representative,' or some such gibberish, he feels that he is earning his six-and-eightpence. Don't laugh! It is perfectly true. Now Continentals haven't got that feeling. They are always bothering about ideas, and the result is that every shopkeeper or peasant has a vocabulary in daily use that is simply Greek to the vast majority of Britons. I remember some time ago I was dining with a friend of mine who is a Paris cabman. We had dinner at a dirty little restaurant opposite the central post office, a place where all the clients were cabmen or porters. Conversation was general, and it struck me that a London cabman would have felt a little out of his depth. Words like 'functionary' and 'unforgettable' and 'exterminate' and 'independence' hurtled across the table every instant. And these were just ordinary, vulgar, jolly, red-faced cabmen. Mind you," he went on hurriedly, as the lady crossed the room and took up his pen, "I merely mention this to illustrate my point. I'm not saying that cabmen ought to be intellectuals. I don't think so; I agree with Keats—happy is England, sweet her artless cabmen, enough their simple loveliness for me. But when you come to the people who make up the collective industrial brain-power of the country. . . . Why, do you know——"

"Oh, no, no, no!" cried Mrs. Manderson. "I don't know anything at the moment, except that your talking must be stopped somehow, if we are to get any farther with that letter to Mr. Marlowe. You shall not get out of it. Come!" She put the pen into his hand.

Trent looked at it with distaste. "I warn you not to discourage my talking," he said dejectedly. "Believe me, men who don't talk are even worse to live with than men who do. Oh, have a care of natures that are mute. I confess I'm shirking writing this thing. It is almost an indecency. It's mixing two moods to write the sort of letter I mean to write, and at the same time to be sitting in the same room with you."

She led him to his abandoned chair before the escritoire and pushed him gently into it. "Well, but please try. I want to see what you write, and I want it to go to him at once. You see, I would be contented enough to leave things as they are; but you say you must get at the truth, and if you must, I want it to be as soon as possible. Do it now—you know you can if you will—and I'll send it off the moment it's ready. Don't you ever feel that—the longing to get the worrying letter into the post and off your hands, so that you can't recall it if you would, and it's no use fussing any more about it?"

"I will do as you wish," he said, and turned to the paper, which he dated as from his hotel. Mrs. Manderson looked down at his bent head with a gentle light in her eyes, and made as if to place a smoothing hand upon his rather untidy crop of hair. But she did not touch it. Going in silence to the piano, she began to play very softly. It was ten minutes before Trent spoke.

"If he chooses to reply that he will say nothing?"

Mrs. Manderson looked over her shoulder. "Of course he dare not take that line. He will speak to prevent you from denouncing him."

"But I'm not going to do that anyhow. You wouldn't allow it—you said so; besides, I won't if you would. The thing's too doubtful now."

"But," she laughed, "poor Mr. Marlowe doesn't know you won't, does he?"

Trent sighed. "What extraordinary things codes of honour are!" he remarked abstractedly. "I know that there are things I should do, and never think twice about, which would make you feel disgraced if you did them—such as giving anyone who grossly insulted me a black eye, or swearing violently when I barked my shin in a dark room. And now you are calmly recommending me to bluff Marlowe by means of a tacit threat which I don't mean; a thing which hell's most abandoned fiend did never, in the drunkenness of guilt—well, anyhow, I won't do it." He resumed his writing, and the lady, with an indulgent smile, returned to playing very softly.

In a few minutes more, Trent said: "At last I am his faithfully. Do you want to see it?" She ran across the twilit room, and turned on a reading lamp beside the escritoire. Then, leaning on his shoulder, she read what follows:

DEAR MR. MARLOWE,—*You will perhaps remember that we met, under unhappy circumstances, in June of last year at Marlstone.*

On that occasion it was my duty, as representing a newspaper, to make an independent investigation of the circumstances of the death of the late Sigsbee Manderson. I did so, and I arrived at certain conclusions. You may learn from the enclosed manuscript, which was originally written as a dispatch for my newspaper, what those conclusions were. For reasons which it is not necessary to state I decided at the last moment not to make them public, nor to communicate them to you, and they are known to only two persons besides myself.

At this point Mrs. Manderson raised her eyes quickly from the letter. Her dark brows were drawn together. "Two persons?" she said with a note of inquiry.

"Your uncle is the other. I sought him out last night and told him the whole story. Have you anything against it? I always felt uneasy at keeping it from him as I did, because I had led him to expect I should tell him all I discovered, and my silence looked like mystery-making. Now it is to be cleared up finally, and there is no question of shielding you, I wanted him to know everything. He is a very shrewd adviser, too, in a way of his own; and I should like to have him with me when I see Marlowe. I have a feeling that two heads will be better than one on my side of the interview."

She sighed. "Yes, of course, uncle ought to know the truth. I hope there is nobody else at all." She pressed his hand. "I so much want all that horror buried—buried deep. I am very happy now, dear, but I shall be happier still when you have satisfied that curious mind of yours and found out everything, and stamped down the earth upon it all." She continued her reading.

Quite recently, however (the letter went on), *facts have come to my knowledge which have led me to change my decision. I do not mean that I shall publish what I discovered, but that I have determined to approach you and ask you for a private statement. If you have anything to say which would place the matter in another light, I can imagine no reason why you should withhold it.*

I expect, then, to hear from you when and where I may call upon you; unless you would prefer the interview to take place at my hotel. In either case I desire that Mr. Cupples, whom you will remember, and who has read the enclosed document, should be present also.—Faithfully yours,

PHILIP TRENT.

"What a very stiff letter!" she said. "Now I am sure you couldn't have made it any stiffer in your own rooms."

Trent slipped the letter and enclosure into a long envelope. "Yes," he said, "I think it will make him sit up suddenly. Now this thing mustn't run any risk of going wrong. It would be best to send a special messenger with orders to deliver it into his own hands. If he's away it oughtn't to be left."

She nodded. "I can arrange that. Wait here for a little."

. . . .

When Mrs. Manderson returned, he was hunting through the music cabinet, and she knelt on the carpet beside him. "Tell me something, Philip," she said.

"If it is among the few things that I know."

"When you saw uncle last night, did you tell him about—about us?"

"I did not," he answered. "I remembered you had said nothing about telling anyone. It is for you—isn't it?—to decide whether we take the world into our confidence at once or later on."

"Then will you tell him?" She looked down at her clasped hands. "I wish *you* to tell him. Perhaps if you think you will guess why. . . . There! that is settled." She lifted her eyes again to his, and for a time there was silence between them.

.   .   .   .

He leaned back at length in the deep chair. "What a world!" he said. "Mabel, will you play something on the piano that expresses mere joy, the genuine article, nothing feverish or like thorns under a pot, but joy that has decided in favour of the universe? It's a mood that can't last altogether, so we had better get all we can out of it."

She went to the instrument and struck a few chords while she thought. Then she began to work with all her soul at the theme in the last movement of the Ninth Symphony which is like the sound of the opening of the gates of Paradise.

CHAPTER XV

DOUBLE CUNNING

AN OLD oaken desk with a deep body stood by the window in a room that overlooked St. James's Park from a height. The room was large, furnished and decorated by someone who had brought taste to the work; but the hand of the bachelor lay heavily upon it. John Marlowe unlocked the desk and drew a long, stout envelope from the back of the well.

"I understand," he said to Mr. Cupples, "that you have read this."

"I read it for the first time two days ago," replied Mr. Cupples, who, seated on a sofa, was peering about the room with a benignant face. "We have discussed it fully."

Marlowe turned to Trent. "There is your manuscript," he said, laying the envelope on the table. "I have gone over it three times. I do not believe there is another man who could have got at as much of the truth as you have set down there."

Trent ignored the compliment. He sat by the table gazing stonily at the fire, his long legs twisted beneath his chair. "You mean, of course," he said, drawing the envelope towards him, "that there is more of the truth to be disclosed now. We are ready to hear you as soon as you like. I expect it will be a long story, and the longer the better, so far as I am concerned; I want to understand thoroughly. What we should both like, I think, is some preliminary account of Manderson and your relations with him. It seemed to me from the first that the character of the dead man must be somehow an element in the business."

"You were right," Marlowe answered grimly. He crossed the room and seated himself on a corner of the tall cushion-topped fender. "I will begin as you suggest."

"I ought to tell you beforehand," said Trent, looking him in the eyes, "that although I am here to listen to you, I have not as yet any reason to doubt the conclusions I have stated here." He tapped the envelope. "It is a defence that you will be putting forward—you understand that?"

"Perfectly." Marlowe was cool and in complete possession of himself, a man different indeed from the worn-out, nervous being Trent remembered at Marlstone a year and a half ago. His tall, lithe figure was held with the perfection of muscular tone. His brow was candid, his blue eyes were clear, though they still had, as he paused collecting his ideas, the look that had troubled Trent at their first meeting. Only the lines of his mouth showed that he knew himself in a position of difficulty, and meant to face it.

"Sigsbee Manderson was not a man of normal mind," Marlowe began in his quiet voice. "Most of the very rich men I met with in America had become so by virtue of abnormal greed, or abnormal industry, or abnormal personal force, or abnormal luck. None of them had remarkable intellects. Manderson delighted too in heaping up wealth; he worked incessantly at it; he was a man of dominant will; he had quite his share of luck; but what made him singular was his brain-power. In his own country they would perhaps tell you that it was his ruthlessness in pursuit of his aims that was his most striking characteristic; but there are hundreds of them who would have carried out his plans with just as little consideration for others if they could have formed the plans.

"I'm not saying Americans aren't clever; they are ten times cleverer than we are. as a nation; but I never met another who showed such a degree of sagacity and foresight, such gifts of memory and mental tenacity, such sheer force of intelligence, as there was behind everything Manderson

did in his money-making career. They called him the
'Napoleon of Wall Street' often enough in the papers; but
few people knew so well as I did how much truth there was
in the phrase. He seemed never to forget a fact that might
be of use to him, in the first place; and he did systematically
with the business facts that concerned him what Napoleon
did, as I have read, with military facts. He studied them in
special digests which were prepared for him at short intervals,
and which he always had at hand, so that he could take up his
report on coal or wheat or railways, or whatever it might
be, in any unoccupied moment. Then he could make a bolder
and cleverer plan than any man of them all. People got to
know that Manderson would never do the obvious thing, but
they got no farther; the thing he did do was almost always
a surprise, and much of his success flowed from that. The
Street got rattled, as they used to put it, when it was known
that the old man was out with his gun, and often his opponents seemed to surrender as easily as Colonel Crockett's
coon in the story. The scheme I am going to describe to you
would have occupied most men long enough. Manderson could
have plotted the whole thing, down to the last detail, while
he shaved himself.

"I used to think that his strain of Indian blood, remote
as it was, might have something to do with the cunning and
ruthlessness of the man. Strangely enough, its existence was
unknown to anyone but himself and me. It was when he asked
me to apply my taste for genealogical work to his own obscure
family history that I made the discovery that he had in him
a share of the blood of the Iroquois chief Montour and his
French wife, a terrible woman who ruled the savage politics
of the tribes of the Wilderness two hundred years ago. The
Mandersons were active in the fur trade on the Pennsylvanian
border in those days, and more than one of them married
Indian women. Other Indian blood than Montour's may have
descended to Manderson, for all I can say, through previous
and subsequent unions; some of the wives' antecedents were
quite untraceable, and there were so many generations of
pioneering before the whole country was brought under
civilization. My researches left me with the idea that there is
a very great deal of the aboriginal blood present in the
genealogical make-up of the people of America, and that it
is very widely spread. The newer families have constantly

intermarried with the older, and so many of them had a strain of the native in them—and were often rather proud of it, too, in those days. But Manderson had the idea about the disgracefulness of mixed blood, which grew much stronger, I fancy, with the rise of the negro question after the war. He was thunderstruck at what I told him, and was anxious to conceal it from every soul. Of course I never gave it away while he lived, and I don't think he supposed I would; but I have thought since that his mixed mind took a turn against me from that time onward. It happened about a year before his death."

"Had Manderson," asked Mr. Cupples, so unexpectedly that the others started, "any definable religious attitude?"

Marlowe considered a moment. "None that ever I heard of," he said. "Worship and prayer were quite unknown to him, so far as I could see, and I never heard him mention religion. I should doubt if he had any real sense of God at all, or if he was capable of knowing God through the emotions. But I understood that as a child he had a religious up-bringing with a strong moral side to it. His private life was, in the usual limited sense, blameless. He was almost ascetic in his habits, except as to smoking. I lived with him four years without ever knowing him to tell a direct verbal falsehood, constantly as he used to practise deceit in other forms. Can you understand the soul of a man who never hesitated to take steps that would have the effect of hoodwinking people, who would use every trick of the markets to mislead, and who was at the same time scrupulous never to utter a direct lie on the most insignificant matter? Manderson was like that, and he was not the only one. I suppose you might compare the state of mind to that of a soldier who is personally a truthful man, but who will stick at nothing to deceive the enemy. The rules of the game allow it; and the same may be said of business as many business men regard it. Only with them it is always war-time."

"It is a sad world," observed Mr. Cupples.

"As you say," Marlowe agreed. "Now I was saying that one could always take Manderson's word if he gave it in a definite form. The first time I ever heard him utter a down-right lie was on the night he died; and hearing it, I believe, saved me from being hanged as his murderer."

Marlowe stared at the light above his head, and Trent

moved impatiently in his chair. "Before we come to that," he said, "will you tell us exactly on what footing you were with Manderson during the years you were with him?"

"We were on very good terms from beginning to end," answered Marlowe. "Nothing like friendship—he was not a man for making friends—but the best of terms as between a trusted employee and his chief. I went to him as private secretary just after getting my degree at Oxford. I was to have gone into my father's business, where I am now, but my father suggested that I should see the world for a year or two. So I took this secretaryship, which seemed to promise a good deal of varied experience, and I had let the year or two run on to four years before the end came. The offer came to me through the last thing in the world I should have put forward as a qualification for a salaried post, and that was chess."

At the word Trent struck his hands together with a muttered exclamation. The others looked at him in surprise.

"Chess!" repeated Trent. "Do you know," he said, rising and approaching Marlowe, "what was the first thing I noted about you at our first meeting? It was your eye, Mr. Marlowe. I couldn't place it then, but I know now where I had seen your eyes before. They were in the head of no less a man than the great Nikolay Korchagin, with whom I once sat in the same railway carriage for two days. I thought I should never forget the chess eye after that, but I could not put a name to it when I saw it in you. I beg your pardon," he ended suddenly, resuming his marmoreal attitude in his chair.

"I have played the game from my childhood, and with good players," said Marlowe simply. "It is an hereditary gift, if you can call it a gift. At the University I was nearly as good as anybody there, and I gave most of my brains to that and the O.U.D.S. and playing about generally. At Oxford, as I dare say you know, inducements to amuse oneself at the expense of one's education are endless, and encouraged by the authorities. Well, one day toward the end of my last term, Dr. Munro of Queen's, whom I had never defeated, sent for me. He told me that I played a fairish game of chess. I said it was very good of him to say so. Then he said, 'They tell me you hunt, too.' I said, 'Now and then.' He asked, 'Is there anything else you can do?' 'No,' I said, not much liking the tone of the conversation—the old man generally succeeded in putting people's backs up. He grunted fiercely, and then told me that inquiries were being made on behalf of a wealthy American man of business who wanted an English secretary. Manderson was the name, he said. He seemed never to have heard it before, which was quite possible, as he never opened a newspaper and had not slept a night outside the college for thirty years. If I could rub up my spelling—as the old gentleman put it—I might have a good chance for the post, as chess and riding and an Oxford education were the only indispensable points.

"Well, I became Manderson's secretary. For a long time I liked the position greatly. When one is attached to an active American plutocrat in the prime of life one need not have many dull moments. Besides, it made me independent. My father had some serious business reverses about that time, and I was glad to be able to do without an allowance from him. At the end of the first year Manderson doubled my salary. 'It's big money,' he said, 'but I guess I don't lose.' You see, by that time I was doing a great deal more than accompany him on horseback in the morning and play chess in the evening, which was mainly what he had required. I was attending to his houses, his farm in Ohio, his shooting in Maine, his horses, his cars, and his yacht. I had become a walking railway-guide and an expert cigar-buyer. I was always learning something.

"Well, now you understand what my position was in regard to Manderson during the last two or three years of my connection with him. It was a happy life for me on the whole. I was busy, my work was varied and interesting; I had time to amuse myself too, and money to spend. At one time I made a fool of myself about a girl, and that was not a happy time; but it taught me to understand the great goodness of Mrs. Manderson." Marlowe inclined his head to Mr. Cupples as he said this. "She may choose to tell you about it. As for her husband, he had never varied in his attitude towards me, in spite of the change that came over him in the last months of his life, as you know. He treated me well and generously in his unsympathetic way, and I never had a feeling that he was less than satisfied with his bargain—that was the sort of footing we lived upon. And it was that continuance of his attitude right up to the end that made the revelation so shocking when

I was suddenly shown, on the night on which he met his end, the depth of crazy hatred of myself that was in Manderson's soul."

The eyes of Trent and Mr. Cupples met for an instant.

"You never suspected that he hated you before that time?" asked Trent; and Mr. Cupples asked at the same moment, "To what did you attribute it?"

"I never guessed until that night," answered Marlowe, "that he had the smallest ill-feeling toward me. How long it had existed I do not know. I cannot imagine why it was there. I was forced to think, when I considered the thing in those awful days after his death, that it was a case of a madman's delusion, that he believed me to be plotting against him, as they so often do. Some such insane conviction must have been at the root of it. But who can sound the abysses of a lunatic's fancy? Can you imagine the state of mind in which a man dooms himself to death with the object of delivering someone he hates to the hangman?"

Mr. Cupples moved sharply in his chair. "You say Manderson was responsible for his own death?" he asked.

Trent glanced at him with an eye of impatience, and resumed his intent watch upon the face of Marlowe. In the relief of speech it was now less pale and drawn.

"I do say so," Marlowe answered concisely, and looked his questioner in the face. Mr. Cupples nodded.

"Before we proceed to the elucidation of your statement," observed the old gentleman, in a tone of one discussing a point of abstract science, "it may be remarked that the state of mind which you attribute to Manderson——"

"Suppose we have the story first," Trent interrupted, gently laying a hand on Mr. Cupples's arm. "You were telling us," he went on, turning to Marlowe, "how things stood between you and Manderson. Now will you tell us the facts of what happened that night?"

Marlowe flushed at the barely perceptible emphasis which Trent laid upon the word "facts." He drew himself up.

"Bunner and myself dined with Mr. and Mrs. Manderson that Sunday evening," he began, speaking carefully. "It was just like other dinners at which the four of us had been together. Manderson was taciturn and gloomy, as we had latterly been accustomed to see him. We others kept a conversation going. We rose from the table, I suppose, about nine. Mrs.

Manderson went to the drawing-room, and Bunner went up to the hotel to see an acquaintance. Manderson asked me to come into the orchard behind the house, saying he wished to have a talk. We paced up and down the pathway there, out of earshot from the house, and Manderson, as he smoked his cigar, spoke to me in his cool, deliberate way. He had never seemed more sane, or more well-disposed to me. He said he wanted me to do him an important service. There was a big thing on. It was a secret affair. Bunner knew nothing of it, and the less I knew the better. He wanted me to do exactly as he directed, and not bother my head about reasons.

"This, I may say, was quite characteristic of Manderson's method of going to work. If at times he required a man to be a mere tool in his hand, he would tell him so. He had used me in the same kind of way a dozen times. I assured him he could rely on me, and said I was ready. 'Right now?' he asked. I said of course I was.

"He nodded, and said—I tell you his words as well as I can recollect them—'Well, attend to this. There is a man in England now who is in this thing with me. He was to have left to-morrow for Paris by the noon boat from Southampton to Havre. His name is George Harris—at least that's the name he is going by. Do you remember that name?' 'Yes,' I said, 'when I went up to London a week ago you asked me to book a cabin in that name on the boat that goes to-morrow. I gave you the ticket.' 'Here it is,' he said, producing it from his pocket.

" 'Now,' Manderson said to me, poking his cigar-butt at me with each sentence in a way he used to have, 'George Harris cannot leave England to-morrow. I find I shall want him where he is. And I want Bunner where *he* is. But somebody has got to go by that boat and take certain papers to Paris. Or else my plan is going to fall to pieces. Will you go?' I said, 'Certainly. I am here to obey orders.'

"He bit his cigar, and said, 'That's all right; but these are not just ordinary orders. Not the kind of thing one can ask of a man in the ordinary way of his duty to an employer. The point is this. The deal I am busy with is one in which neither myself nor anyone known to be connected with me must appear as yet. That is vital. But these people I am up against know your face as well as they know mine. If my secretary is known in certain quarters to have crossed to Paris at this time and to have interviewed certain people—and that would be known as soon as it happened—then the game is up.' He threw away his cigar-end and looked at me questioningly.

"I didn't like it much, but I liked failing Manderson at a pinch still less. I spoke lightly. I said I supposed I should have to conceal my identity, and I would do my best. I told him I used to be pretty good at make-up.

"He nodded in approval. He said, 'That's good. I judged you would not let me down.' Then he gave me my instructions. 'You take the car right now,' he said, 'and start for Southampton—there's no train that will fit in. You'll be driving all night. Barring accidents, you ought to get there by six in the morning. But whenever you arrive, drive straight to the Bedford Hotel and ask for George Harris. If he's there, tell him you are to go over instead of him, and ask him to telephone me here. It is very important he should know that at the earliest moment possible. But if he isn't there, that means he has got the instructions I wired to-day, and hasn't gone to Southampton. In that case you don't want to trouble about him any more, but just wait for the boat. You can leave the car at a garage under a fancy name—mine must not be given. See about changing your appearance—I don't care how, so you do it well. Travel by the boat as George Harris. Let on to be anything you like, but be careful, and don't talk much to anybody. When you arrive, take a room at the Hotel St. Petersbourg. You will receive a note or message there, addressed to George Harris, telling you where to take the wallet I shall give you. The wallet is locked, and you want to take good care of it. Have you got that all clear?'

"I repeated the instructions. I asked if I should return from Paris after handing over the wallet. 'As soon as you like,' he said. 'And mind this—whatever happens, don't communicate with me at any stage of the journey. If you don't get the message in Paris at once, just wait until you do—days, if necessary. But not a line of any sort to me. Understand? Now get ready as quick as you can. I'll go with you in the car a little way. Hurry.'

"That is, as far as I can remember, the exact substance of what Manderson said to me that night. I went to my room, changed into day clothes, and hastily threw a few necessaries into a kit-bag. My mind was in a whirl, not so much at the nature of the business as at the suddenness of it. I think I remember telling you the last time we met"—he turned to Trent—"that Manderson shared the national fondness for doing things in a story-book style. Other things being equal, he delighted in a bit of mystification and melodrama, and I told myself that this was Manderson all over. I hurried downstairs with my bag and rejoined him in the library. He handed me a stout leather letter-case, about eight inches by six, fastened with a strap with a lock on it. I could just squeeze it into my side-pocket. Then I went to get out the car from the garage behind the house.

"As I was bringing it round to the front a disconcerting thought struck me. I remembered that I had only a few shillings in my pocket.

"For some time past I had been keeping myself very short of cash, and for this reason—which I tell you because it is a vital point, as you will see in a minute. I was living temporarily on borrowed money. I had always been careless about money while I was with Manderson, and being a gregarious animal I had made many friends, some of them belonging to a New York set that had little to do but get rid of the large incomes given them by their parents. Still, I was very well paid, and I was too busy even to attempt to go very far with them in that amusing occupation. I was still well on the right side of the ledger until I began, merely out of curiosity, to play at speculation. It's a very old story—particularly in Wall Street. I thought it was easy; I was lucky at first; I would always be prudent—and so on. Then came the day when I went out of my depth. In one week I was separated from my roll, as Bunner expressed it when I told him; and I owed money too. I had had my lesson. Now in this pass I went to Manderson and told him what I had done and how I stood. He heard me with a very grim smile, and then, with the nearest approach to sympathy I had ever found in him, he advanced me a sum on account of my salary that would clear me. 'Don't play the markets any more,' was all he said.

"Now on that Sunday night Manderson knew that I was practically without any money in the world. He knew that Bunner knew it too. He may have known that I had even borrowed a little more from Bunner for pocket-money until my next cheque was due, which, owing to my anticipation of my salary, would not have been a large one. Bear this knowledge of Manderson's in mind.

"As soon as I had brought the car round I went into the library and stated the difficulty to Manderson.

"What followed gave me, slight as it was, my first impression of something odd being afoot. As soon as I mentioned the word 'expenses' his hand went mechanically to his left hip-pocket, where he always kept a little case containing notes to the value of about a hundred pounds in our money. This was such a rooted habit in him that I was astonished to see him check the movement suddenly. Then, to my greater amazement, he swore under his breath. I had never heard him do this before; but Bunner had told me that of late he had often shown irritation in this way when they were alone. 'Has he mislaid his notecase?' was the question that flashed through my mind. But it seemed to me that it could not affect his plan at all, and I will tell you why. The week before, when I had gone up to London to carry out various commissions, including the booking of a berth for Mr. George Harris, I had drawn a thousand pounds for Manderson from his bankers, and all, at his request, in notes of small amounts. I did not know what this unusually large sum in cash was for, but I did know that the packets of notes were in his locked desk in the library, or had been earlier in the day, when I had seen him fingering them as he sat at the desk.

"But instead of turning to the desk, Manderson stood looking at me. There was fury in his face, and it was a strange sight to see him gradually master it until his eyes grew cold again. 'Wait in the car,' he said slowly. 'I will get some money.' We both went out, and as I was getting into my overcoat in the hall I saw him enter the drawing-room, which, you remember, was on the other side of the entrance hall.

"I stepped out onto the lawn before the house and smoked a cigarette, pacing up and down. I was asking myself again and again where that thousand pounds was; whether it was in the drawing-room; and if so, why. Presently, as I passed one of the drawing-room windows, I noticed Mrs. Manderson's shadow on the thin silk curtain. She was standing at her escritoire. The window was open, and as I passed I heard her say, 'I have not quite thirty pounds here. Will that be enough?' I did not hear the answer, but next moment Manderson's shadow was mingled with hers, and I heard the chink of money. Then, as he stood by the window, and as I was moving away, these words of his came to my ears—and these at least I can repeat exactly, for astonishment stamped them on my memory—'I'm going out now. Marlowe has persuaded me to go for a moonlight run in the car. He is very urgent about it. He says it will help me to sleep, and I guess he is right.'

"I have told you that in the course of four years I had never once heard Manderson utter a direct lie about anything, great or small. I believed that I understood the man's queer, skin-deep morality, and I could have sworn that if he was firmly pressed with a question that could not be evaded he would either refuse to answer or tell the truth. But what had I just heard? No answer to any question. A voluntary statement, precise in terms, that was utterly false. The unimaginable had happened. It was almost as if someone I knew well, in a moment of closest sympathy, had suddenly struck me in the face. The blood rushed to my head, and I stood still on the grass. I stood there until I heard his step at the front door, and then I pulled myself together and stepped quickly to the car. He handed me a banker's paper bag with gold and notes in it. 'There's more than you'll want there,' he said, and I pocketed it mechanically.

"For a minute or so I stood discussing with Manderson—it was by one of those *tours de force* of which one's mind is capable under great excitement—certain points about the route of the long drive before me. I had made the run several times by day, and I believe I spoke quite calmly and naturally about it. But while I spoke my mind was seething in a flood of suddenly-born suspicion and fear. I did not know what I feared. I simply felt fear, somehow—I did not know how—connected with Manderson. My soul once opened to it, fear rushed in like an assaulting army. I felt—I knew—that something was altogether wrong and sinister, and I felt myself to be the object of it. Yet Manderson was surely no enemy of mine. Then my thoughts reached out wildly for an answer to the question why he had told that lie. And all the time the blood hammered in my ears, 'Where is that money?' Reason struggled hard to set up the suggestion that the two things were not necessarily connected. The instinct of a man in danger would not listen to it. As we started, and the car took the curve into the road, it was merely the unconscious part of me that steered and controlled it, and that made occasional empty remarks as we slid along in the moonlight. Within me was a confusion and vague alarm that was far worse than any definite terror I ever felt.

"About a mile from the house, you remember, one passed on one's left a gate, on the other side of which was the golf-course. There Manderson said he would get down, and I stopped the car. 'You've got it all clear?' he asked. With a sort of wrench I forced myself to remember and repeat the directions given me. 'That's O.K.' he said. 'Good-bye, then. Stay with that wallet.' Those were the last words I heard him speak, as the car moved gently away from him."

Marlowe rose from his chair and pressed his hands to his eyes. He was flushed with the excitement of his own narrative, and there was in his look a horror of recollection that held both listeners silent. He shook himself with a movement like a dog's, and then, his hands behind him, stood erect before the fire as he continued his tale.

"I expect you both know what the back-reflector of a motor car is."

Trent nodded quickly, his face alive with anticipation; but Mr. Cupples, who cherished a mild but obstinate prejudice against motor cars, readily confessed to ignorance.

"It is a small round or more often rectangular mirror," Marlowe explained, "rigged out from the right side of the screen in front of the driver, and adjusted in such a way that he can see, without turning round, if anything is coming up behind to pass him. It is quite an ordinary appliance, and there was one on this car. As the car moved on, and Manderson ceased speaking behind me, I saw in that mirror a thing that I wish I could forget."

Marlowe was silent for a moment, staring at the wall before him.

"Manderson's face," he said in a low tone. "He was standing in the road, looking after me, only a few yards behind, and the moonlight was full on his face. The mirror happened to catch it for an instant.

"Physical habit is a wonderful thing. I did not shift hand or foot on the controlling mechanism of the car. Indeed, I dare say it steadied me against the shock to have myself braced to the business of driving. You have read in books, no doubt, of hell looking out of a man's eyes, but perhaps you don't know what a good metaphor that is. If I had not known Manderson was there, I should not have recognized the face. It was that of a madman, distorted, hideous in the imbecility of hate, the teeth bared in a simian grin of ferocity and triumph; the eyes. . . . In the little mirror I had this glimpse of the face alone. I saw nothing of whatever gesture there may have been as that writhing white mask glared after me. And I saw it only for a flash. The car went on, gathering speed, and as it went, my brain, suddenly purged of the vapours of doubt and perplexity, was as busy as the throbbing engine before my feet. I knew.

"You say something in that manuscript of yours, Mr. Trent, about the swift automatic way in which one's ideas arrange themselves about some new illuminating thought. It is quite true. The awful intensity of ill-will that had flamed after me from those straining eyeballs had poured over my mind like a searchlight. I was thinking quite clearly now, and almost coldly, for I knew what—at least I knew whom—I had to fear, and instinct warned me that it was not a time to give room to the emotions that were fighting to possess me. The man hated me insanely. That incredible fact I suddenly knew. But the face had told me, it would have told anybody, more than that. It was a face of hatred gratified, it proclaimed some damnable triumph. It had gloated over me driving away to my fate. This too was plain to me. And to what fate?

"I stopped the car. It had gone about two hundred and fifty yards, and a sharp bend of the road hid the spot where I had set Manderson down. I lay back in the seat and thought it out. Something was to happen to me. In Paris? Probably —why else should I be sent there, with money and a ticket? But why Paris? That puzzled me, for I had no melodramatic ideas about Paris. I put the point aside for a moment. I turned to the other things that had roused my attention that evening. The lie about my 'persuading him to go for a moonlight run.' What was the intention of that? Manderson, I said to myself, will be returning without me while I am on my way to Southampton. What will he tell them about me? How account for his returning alone, and without the car? As I asked myself that sinister question there rushed into my mind the last of my difficulties: 'Where are the thousand pounds?' And in the same instant came the answer: 'The thousand pounds are in my pocket.'

"I got up and stepped from the car. My knees trembled

and I felt very sick. I saw the plot now, as I thought. The whole of the story about the papers and the necessity of their being taken to Paris was a blind. With Manderson's money about me, of which he would declare I had robbed him, I was, to all appearance, attempting to escape from England, with every precaution that guilt could suggest. He would communicate with the police at once, and would know how to put them on my track. I should be arrested in Paris, if I got so far, living under a false name, after having left the car under a false name, disguised myself, and travelled in a cabin which I had booked in advance, also under a false name. It would be plainly the crime of a man without money, and for some reason desperately in want of it. As for my account of the affair, it would be too preposterous.

"As this ghastly array of incriminating circumstances rose up before me, I dragged the stout letter-case from my pocket. In the intensity of the moment, I never entertained the faintest doubt that I was right, and that the money was there. It would easily hold the packets of notes. But as I felt it and weighed it in my hands it seemed to me there must be more than this. It was too bulky. What more was to be laid to my charge? After all, a thousand pounds was not much to tempt a man like myself to run the risk of penal servitude. In this new agitation, scarcely knowing what I did, I caught the surrounding strap in my fingers just above the fastening and tore the staple out of the lock. Those locks, you know, are pretty flimsy as a rule."

Here Marlowe paused and walked to the oaken desk before the window. Opening a drawer full of miscellaneous objects, he took out a box of odd keys, and selected a small one distinguished by a piece of pink tape.

He handed it to Trent. "I keep that by me as a sort of morbid memento. It is the key to the lock I smashed. I might have saved myself the trouble, if I had known that this key was at that moment in the left-hand side-pocket of my overcoat. Manderson must have slipped it in, either while the coat was hanging in the hall or while he sat at my side in the car. I might not have found the tiny thing there for weeks: as a matter of fact I did find it in two days after Manderson was dead, but a police search would have found it in five minutes. And then I—I with the case and its contents in my pocket, my false name and my sham spectacles and the rest of it—I should have had no explanation to offer but the highly convincing one that I didn't know the key was there."

Trent dangled the key by its tape idly. Then: "How do you know this is the key of that case?" he asked quickly.

"I tried it. As soon as I found it I went up and fitted it to the lock. I knew where I had left the thing. So do you, I think, Mr. Trent. Don't you?" There was a faint shade of mockery in Marlowe's voice.

"*Touché,*" Trent said, with a dry smile. "I found a large empty letter-case with a burst lock lying with other odds and ends on the dressing-table in Manderson's room. Your statement is that you put it there. I could make nothing of it." He closed his lips.

"There was no reason for hiding it," said Marlowe. "But to get back to my story. I burst the lock of the strap. I opened the case before one of the lamps of the car. The first thing I found in it I ought to have expected, of course, but I hadn't." He paused and glanced at Trent.

"It was——" began Trent mechanically, and then stopped himself. "Try not to bring me in any more, if you don't mind," he said, meeting the other's eye. "I have complimented you already in that document on your cleverness. You need not prove it by making the judge help you out with your evidence."

"All right," agreed Marlowe. "I couldn't resist just that much. If *you* had been in my place you would have known before I did that Manderson's little pocket-case was there. As soon as I saw it, of course, I remembered his not having had it about him when I asked for money, and his surprising anger. He had made a false step. He had already fastened his note-case up with the rest of what was to figure as my plunder, and placed it in my hands. I opened it. It contained a few notes as usual, I didn't count them.

"Tucked into the flaps of the big case in packets were the other notes, just as I had brought them from London. And with them were two small wash-leather bags, the look of which I knew well. My heart jumped sickeningly again, for this, too, was utterly unexpected. In those bags Manderson kept the diamonds in which he had been investing for some time past. I didn't open them; I could feel the tiny stones shifting under the pressure of my fingers. How many thousands of pounds' worth there were there I have no idea. We had re-

garded Manderson's diamond-buying as merely a speculative
fad. I believe now that it was the earliest movement in the
scheme for my ruin. For anyone like myself to be represented
as having robbed him, there ought to be a strong inducement
shown. That had been provided with a vengeance.

"Now, I thought, I have the whole thing plain, and I must
act. I saw instantly what I must do. I had left Manderson
about a mile from the house. It would take him twenty minutes,
fifteen if he walked fast, to get back to the house, where he
would, of course, immediately tell his story of robbery, and
probably telephone at once to the police in Bishopsbridge. I
had left him only five or six minutes ago; for all that I have
told you was as quick thinking as I ever did. It would be
easy to overtake him in the car before he neared the house.
There would be an awkward interview. I set my teeth as I
thought of it, and all my fears vanished as I began to savour
the gratification of telling him my opinion of him. There are
probably few people who ever positively looked forward to an
awkward interview with Manderson; but I was mad with
rage. My honour and my liberty had been plotted against
with detestable treachery. I did not consider what would follow the interview. That would arrange itself.

"I had started and turned the car, I was already going fast
toward White Gables, when I heard the sound of a shot in
front of me, to the right.

"Instantly I stopped the car. My first wild thought was
that Manderson was shooting at me. Then I realized that the
noise had not been close at hand. I could see nobody on the
road, though the moonlight flooded it. I had left Manderson
at a spot just round the corner that was now about a hundred
yards ahead of me. After a minute or so, I started again, and
turned the corner at a slow pace. Then I stopped again with a
jar, and for a moment I sat perfectly still.

"Manderson lay dead a few steps from me on the turf
within the gate, clearly visible to me in the moonlight."

Marlowe made another pause, and Trent, with a puckered
brow, inquired, "On the golf-course?"

"Obviously," remarked Mr. Cupples. "The eighth green
is just there." He had grown more and more interested as
Marlowe went on, and was now playing feverishly with his
thin beard.

"On the green, quite close to the flag," said Marlowe. "He

lay on his back, his arms were stretched abroad, his jacket and heavy overcoat were open; the light shone hideously on his white face and his shirt-front; it glistened on his bared teeth and one of the eyes. The other . . . you saw it. The man was certainly dead. As I sat there stunned, unable for the moment to think at all, I could even see a deep dark line of blood running down from the shattered socket to the ear. Close by lay his soft black hat, and at his feet a pistol.

"I suppose it was only a few seconds that I sat helplessly staring at the body. Then I rose and moved to it with dragging feet; for now the truth had come to me at last, and I realized the fullness of my appalling danger. It was not only my liberty or my honour that the maniac had undermined. It was death that he had planned for me; death with the degradation of the scaffold. To strike me down with certainty, he had not hesitated to end his life; a life which was, no doubt, already threatened by a melancholic impulse to self-destruction; and the last agony of the suicide had been turned, perhaps, to a devilish joy by the thought that he dragged down my life with him. For as far as I could see at the moment my situation was utterly hopeless. If it had been desperate on the assumption that Manderson meant to denounce me as a thief, what was it now that his corpse denounced me as a murderer?

"I picked up the revolver and saw, almost without emotion, that it was my own. Manderson had taken it from my room, I suppose, while I was getting out the car. At the same moment I remembered that it was by Manderson's suggestion that I had had it engraved with my initials to distinguish it from a precisely similar weapon which he had of his own.

"I bent over the body and satisfied myself that there was no life left in it. I must tell you here that I did not notice, then or afterwards, the scratches and marks on the wrists, which were taken as evidence of a struggle with an assailant. But I have no doubt that Manderson deliberately injured himself in this way before firing the shot; it was a part of his plan.

"Though I never perceived that detail, however, it was evident enough as I looked at the body that Manderson had not forgotten, in his last act on earth, to tie me tighter by putting out of court the question of suicide. He had clearly been at pains to hold the pistol at arm's length, and there was not a trace of smoke or of burning on the face. The wound was absolutely clean, and was already ceasing to bleed outwardly. I rose and paced the green, reckoning up the points in the crushing case against me.

"I was the last to be seen with Manderson. I had persuaded him—so he had lied to his wife and, as I afterwards knew, to the butler—to go with me for the drive from which he never returned. My pistol had killed him. It was true that by discovering his plot I had saved myself from heaping up further incriminating facts—flight, concealment, the possession of the treasure. But what need of them, after all? As I stood, what hope was there? What could I do?"

Marlowe came to the table and leaned forward with his hands upon it. "I want," he said very earnestly, "to try to make you understand what was in my mind when I decided to do what I did. I hope you won't be bored, because I must do it. You may both have thought I acted like a fool. But after all the police never suspected me. I walked that green for a quarter of an hour, I suppose, thinking the thing out like a game of chess. I had to think ahead and think coolly; for my safety depended on upsetting the plans of one of the longest-headed men who ever lived. And remember that, for all I knew, there were details of the scheme still hidden from me, waiting to crush me.

"Two plain courses presented themselves at once. Either of them, I thought, would certainly prove fatal. I could, in the first place, do the completely straightforward thing: take back the dead man, tell my story, hand over the notes and diamonds, and trust to the saving power of truth and innocence. I could have laughed as I thought of it. I saw myself bringing home the corpse and giving an account of myself, boggling with sheer shame over the absurdity of my wholly unsupported tale, as I brought a charge of mad hatred and fiendish treachery against a man who had never, as far as I knew, had a word to say against me. At every turn the cunning of Manderson had forestalled me. His careful concealment of such a hatred was a characteristic feature of the stratagem; only a man of his iron self-restraint could have done it. You can see for yourself how every fact in my statement would appear, in the shadow of Manderson's death, a clumsy lie. I tried to imagine myself telling such a story to the counsel for my defence. I could see the face with which he would listen to it; I could read in the lines of it his thought, that to put forward such an impudent farrago would mean merely the disappearance of any chance there might be of a commutation of the capital sentence.

"True, I had not fled. I had brought back the body; I had handed over the property. But how did that help me? It would only suggest that I had yielded to a sudden funk after killing my man, and had no nerve left to clutch at the fruits of the crime; it would suggest, perhaps, that I had not set out to kill but only to threaten, and that when I found that I had done murder the heart went out of me. Turn it which way I would, I could see no hope of escape by this plan of action.

"The second of the obvious things that I might do was to take the hint offered by the situation, and to fly at once. That too must prove fatal. There was the body. I had no time to hide it in such a way that it would not be found at the first systematic search. But whatever I should do with the body, Manderson's not returning to the house would cause uneasiness in two or three hours at most. Martin would suspect an accident to the car, and would telephone to the police. At daybreak the roads would be scoured and inquiries telegraphed in every direction. The police would act on the possibility of there being foul play. They would spread their nets with energy in such a big business as the disappearance of Manderson. Ports and railway termini would be watched. Within twenty-four hours the body would be found, and the whole country would be on the alert for me—all Europe, scarcely less; I did not believe there was a spot in Christendom where the man accused of Manderson's murder could pass unchallenged, with every newspaper crying the fact of his death into the ears of all the world. Every stranger would be suspect; every man, woman, and child would be a detective. The car, wherever I should abandon it, would put people on my track. If I had to choose between two utterly hopeless courses, I decided, I would take that of telling the preposterous truth.

"But now I cast about desperately for some tale that would seem more plausible than the truth. Could I save my neck by a lie? One after another came into my mind; I need not trouble to remember them now. Each had its own futilities and perils; but every one split upon the fact—or what would be taken for fact—that I had induced Manderson to go out with me, and the fact that he had never returned alive. Notion after notion I swiftly rejected as I paced there by the dead man, and doom seemed to settle down upon me more heavily as the moments passed. Then a strange thought came to me.

"Several times I had repeated to myself half-consciously, as a sort of refrain, the words in which I had heard Manderson tell his wife that I had induced him to go out. 'Marlowe has persuaded me to go for a moonlight run in the car. He is very urgent about it.' All at once it struck me that, without meaning to do so, I was saying this in Manderson's voice.

"As you found out for yourself, Mr. Trent, I have a natural gift of mimicry. I had imitated Manderson's voice many times so successfully as to deceive even Bunner, who had been much more in his company than his own wife. It was, you remember"—Marlowe turned to Mr. Cupples—"a strong, metallic voice, of great carrying power, so unusual as to make it a very fascinating voice to imitate, and at the same time very easy. I said the words carefully to myself again, like this—" he uttered them, and Mr. Cupples opened his eyes in amazement—"and then I struck my hand upon the low wall beside me. 'Manderson never returned alive?' I said aloud. 'But Manderson *shall* return alive!'

"In thirty seconds the bare outline of the plan was complete in my mind. I did not wait to think over details. Every instant was precious now. I lifted the body and laid it on the floor of the car, covered with a rug. I took the hat and the revolver. Not one trace remained on the green, I believe, of that night's work. As I drove back to White Gables my design took shape before me with a rapidity and ease that filled me with a wild excitement. I should escape yet! It was all so easy if I kept my pluck. Putting aside the unusual and unlikely, I should not fail. I wanted to shout, to scream!

"Nearing the house I slackened speed, and carefully reconnoitred the road. Nothing was moving. I turned the car into the open field on the other side of the road, about twenty paces short of the little door at the extreme corner of the grounds. I brought it to rest behind a stack. When, with Manderson's hat on my head and the pistol in my pocket, I had staggered with the body across the moonlit road and through that door, I left much of my apprehension behind me. With swift action and an unbroken nerve I thought I ought to succeed."

With a long sigh Marlowe threw himself into one of the deep chairs at the fireside and passed his handkerchief over his damp forehead. Each of his hearers, too, drew a deep breath, but not audibly.

"Everything else you know," he said. He took a cigarette from a box beside him and lighted it. Trent watched the very slight quiver of the hand that held the match, and privately noted that his own was at the moment not so steady.

"The shoes that betrayed me to you," pursued Marlowe after a short silence, "were painful all the time I wore them, but I never dreamed that they had given anywhere. I knew that no footstep of mine must appear by any accident in the soft ground about the hut where I laid the body, or between the hut and the house, so I took the shoes off and crammed my feet into them as soon as I was inside the little door. I left my own shoes, with my own jacket and overcoat, near the body, ready to be resumed later. I made a clear footmark on the soft gravel outside the French window, and several on the drugget round the carpet. The stripping off of the outer clothing of the body, and the dressing of it afterwards in the brown suit and shoes, and putting the things into the pockets, was a horrible business; and getting the teeth out of the mouth was worse. The head—but you don't want to hear about it. I didn't feel it much at the time. I was wriggling my own head out of a noose, you see. I wish I had thought of pulling down the cuffs, and had tied the shoes more neatly. And putting the watch in the wrong pocket was a bad mistake. It had all to be done so hurriedly.

"You were wrong, by the way, about the whisky. After one stiffish drink I had no more; but I filled up a flask that was in the cupboard and pocketed it. I had a night of peculiar anxiety and effort in front of me, and I didn't know how I should stand it. I had to take some once or twice during the drive. Speaking of that, you give rather a generous allowance of time in your document for doing that run by night. You say that to get to Southampton by half-past six in that car, under the conditions, a man must, even if he drove like a demon, have left Marlstone by twelve at latest. I had not got the body dressed in the other suit, with tie and watch-chain and so forth, until nearly ten minutes past; and then I had to get to the car and start it going. But then I don't suppose any other man would have taken the risks I did in that car at night, without a head-light. It turns me cold to think of it now.

"There's nothing much to say about what I did in the house.

I spent the time after Martin had left me in carefully thinking over the remaining steps in my plan, while I unloaded and thoroughly cleaned the revolver, using my handkerchief and a penholder from the desk. I also placed the packets of notes, the note-case, and the diamonds in the roll-top desk, which I opened and relocked with Manderson's key. When I went up-stairs it was a trying moment, for though I was safe from the eyes of Martin, as he sat in his pantry, there was a faint possibility of somebody being about on the bedroom floor. I had sometimes found the French maid wandering about there when the other servants were in bed. Bunner, I knew, was a deep sleeper. Mrs. Manderson, I had gathered from things I had heard her say, was usually asleep by eleven; I had thought it possible that her gift of sleep had helped her to retain all her beauty and vitality in spite of a marriage which we all knew was an unhappy one. Still it was uneasy work mounting the stairs, and holding myself ready to retreat to the library again at the least sound from above. But nothing happened.

"The first thing I did on reaching the corridor was to enter my room and put the revolver and cartridges back in the case. Then I turned off the light and went quietly into Manderson's room.

"What I had to do there you know. I had to take off the shoes and put them outside the door, leave Manderson's jacket, waistcoat, trousers, and black tie, after taking everything out of the pockets, select a suit and tie and shoes for the body, and place the dental plate in the bowl, which I moved from the washing-stand to the bedside, leaving those ruinous finger-marks as I did so. The marks on the drawer must have been made when I shut it after taking out the tie. Then I had to lie down in the bed and tumble it. You know all about it—all except my state of mind, which you couldn't imagine and I couldn't describe.

"The worst came when I had hardly begun my operations: the moment when Mrs. Manderson spoke from the room where I supposed her asleep. I was prepared for it happening; it was a possibility; but I nearly lost my nerve all the same. However. . . .

"By the way, I may tell you this: in the extremely unlikely contingency of Mrs. Manderson remaining awake, and so putting out of the question my escape by way of her window, I had planned simply to remain where I was a few hours, and then, not speaking to her, to leave the house quickly and quietly by the ordinary way. Martin would have been in bed by that time. I might have been heard to leave, but not seen. I should have done just as I had planned with the body, and then made the best time I could in the car to Southampton. The difference would have been that I couldn't have furnished an unquestionable alibi by turning up at the hotel at 6.30. I should have made the best of it by driving straight to the docks, and making my ostentatious inquiries there. I could in any case have got there long before the boat left at noon. I couldn't see that anybody could suspect me of the supposed murder in any case; but if anyone had, and if I hadn't arrived until ten o'clock, say, I shouldn't have been able to answer, "It is impossible for me to have got to Southampton so soon after shooting him." I should simply have had to say I was delayed by a breakdown after leaving Manderson at half-past ten, and challenged anyone to produce any fact connecting me with the crime. They couldn't have done it. The pistol, left openly in my room, might have been used by anybody, even if it could be proved that that particular pistol was used. Nobody could reasonably connect me with the shooting so long as it was believed that it was Manderson who had returned to the house. The suspicion could not, I was confident, enter anyone's mind. All the same, I wanted to introduce the element of absolute physical impossibility; I knew I should feel ten times as safe with that. So when I knew from the sound of her breathing that Mrs. Manderson was asleep again, I walked quickly across her room in my stocking feet, and was on the grass with my bundle in ten seconds. I don't think I made the least noise. The curtain before the window was of soft, thick stuff and didn't rustle, and when I pushed the glass doors farther open there was not a sound."

"Tell me," said Trent, as the other stopped to light a new cigarette, "why you took the risk of going through Mrs. Manderson's room to escape from the house. I could see when I looked into the thing on the spot why it had to be on that side of the house; there was a danger of being seen by Martin, or by some servant at a bedroom window, if you got out by a window on one of the other sides. But there were three unoccupied rooms on that side; two spare bedrooms and Mrs. Manderson's sitting-room. I should have thought it would have been safer, after you had done what was necessary to your plan in Manderson's room, to leave it quietly and escape through one of those three rooms. . . . The fact that you went through her window, you know," he added coldly, "would have suggested, if it became known, various suspicions in regard to the lady herself. I think you understand me."

Marlowe turned upon him with a glowing face. "And I think you will understand me, Mr. Trent," he said in a voice that shook a little, "when I say that if such a possibility had occurred to me then, I would have taken any risk rather than make my escape by that way. . . . Oh, well!" he went on more coolly, "I suppose that to anyone who didn't know her, the idea of her being privy to her husband's murder might not seem so indescribably fatuous. Forgive the expression." He looked attentively at the burning end of his cigarette, studiously unconscious of the red flag that flew in Trent's eyes for an instant at his words and the tone of them.

That emotion, however, was conquered at once. "Your remark is perfectly just," Trent said with answering coolness, "I can quite believe, too, that at the time you didn't think of the possibility I mentioned. But surely, apart from that, it would have been safer to do as I said; go by the window of an unoccupied room."

"Do you think so?" said Marlowe. "All I can say is, I hadn't the nerve to do it. I tell you, when I entered Manderson's room I shut the door of it on more than half my terrors. I had the problem confined before me in a closed space, with only one danger in it, and that a *known* danger: the danger of Mrs. Manderson. The thing was almost done; I had only to wait until she was certainly asleep after her few moments of waking up, for which, as I told you, I was prepared as a possibility. Barring accidents, the way was clear. But now suppose that I, carrying Manderson's clothes and shoes, had opened that door again and gone in my shirt-sleeves and socks to enter one of the empty rooms. The moonlight was flooding the corridor through the end window. Even if my face was concealed, nobody could mistake my standing figure for Manderson's. Martin might be going about the house in his silent way. Bunner might come out of his bedroom. One of the servants who were supposed to be in bed might come round the corner from the other passage—I had found Célestine prowling about quite as late as it was then. None of these things was very likely; but they were all too likely for me. They were uncertainties. Shut off from the household in Manderson's room I knew exactly what I had to face. As I lay in my clothes in Manderson's bed and listened for the almost inaudible breathing through the open door, I felt far more ease of mind, terrible as my anxiety was, than I had felt since I saw the dead body on the turf. I even congratulated myself that I had had the chance, through Mrs. Manderson's speaking to me, of tightening one of the screws in my scheme by repeating the statement about my having been sent to Southampton."

Marlowe looked at Trent, who nodded as who should say that his point was met.

"As for Southampton," pursued Marlowe, "you know what I did when I got there, I have no doubt. I had decided to take Manderson's story about the mysterious Harris and act it out on my own lines. It was a carefully prepared lie, better than anything I could improvise. I even went so far as to get through a trunk call to the hotel at Southampton from the library before starting, and ask if Harris was there. As I expected, he wasn't."

"Was that why you telephoned?" Trent inquired quickly.

"The reason for telephoning was to get myself into an attitude in which Martin couldn't see my face or anything but the jacket and hat, yet which was a natural and familiar attitude. But while I was about it, it was obviously better to make a genuine call. If I had simply pretended to be telephoning, the people at the Exchange could have told you at once that there hadn't been a call from White Gables that night."

"One of the first things I did was to make that inquiry," said Trent. "That telephone call, and the wire you sent from Southampton to the dead man to say Harris hadn't turned up, and you were returning—I particularly appreciated both those."

A constrained smile lighted Marlowe's face for a moment. "I don't know that there's anything more to tell. I returned to Marlstone, and faced your friend the detective with such nerve as I had left. The worst was when I heard you had been put on the case—no, that wasn't the worst. The worst was when I saw you walk out of the shrubbery the next day, coming away from the shed where I had laid the body. For one

ghastly moment I thought you were going to give me in charge
on the spot. Now I've told you everything, you don't look so
terrible."

He closed his eyes, and there was a short silence. Then
Trent got suddenly to his feet.

"Cross-examination?" inquired Marlowe, looking at him
gravely.

"Not at all," said Trent, stretching his long limbs. "Only
stiffness of the legs. I don't want to ask any questions. I believe what you have told us. I don't believe it simply because I
always liked your face, or because it saves awkwardness, which
are the most usual reasons for believing a person, but because
my vanity will have it that no man could lie to me steadily for
an hour without my perceiving it. Your story is an extraordinary one; but Manderson was an extraordinary man, and so
are you. You acted like a lunatic in doing what you did; but I
quite agree with you that if you had acted like a sane man you
wouldn't have had the hundredth part of a dog's chance with a
judge and jury. One thing is beyond dispute on any reading
of the affair: you are a man of courage."

The colour rushed into Marlowe's face, and he hesitated for
words. Before he could speak Mr. Cupples arose with a dry
cough.

"For my part," he said, "I never supposed you guilty for
a moment." Marlowe turned to him in grateful amazement,
Trent with an incredulous stare. "But," pursued Mr. Cupples,
holding up his hand, "there is one question which I should like
to put."

Marlowe bowed, saying nothing.

"Suppose," said Mr. Cupples, "that someone else had been
suspected of the crime and put upon trial. What would you
have done?"

"I think my duty was clear. I should have gone with my
story to the lawyers for the defence, and put myself in their
hands."

Trent laughed aloud. Now that the thing was over, his
spirits were rapidly becoming ungovernable. "I can see their
faces!" he said. "As a matter of fact, though, nobody else was
ever in danger. There wasn't a shred of evidence against anyone. I looked up Murch at the Yard this morning, and he told
me he had come round to Bunner's view, that it was a case of
revenge on the part of some American black-hand gang. So

there's the end of the Manderson case. Holy, suffering Moses! *What* an ass a man can make himself when he thinks he's being preternaturally clever!" He seized the bulky envelope from the table and stuffed it into the heart of the fire. "There's for you, old friend! For want of you the world's course will not fail. But look here! It's getting late—nearly seven, and Cupples and I have an appointment at half-past. We must go. Mr. Marlowe, good-bye." He looked into the other's eyes. "I am a man who has worked hard to put a rope round your neck. Considering the circumstances, I don't know whether you will blame me. Will you shake hands?"

CHAPTER XVI
THE LAST STRAW

"WHAT was that you said about our having an appointment at half-past seven?" asked Mr. Cupples as the two came out of the great gateway of the pile of flats. "Have we such an appointment?"

"Certainly we have," replied Trent. "You are dining with me. Only one thing can properly celebrate this occasion, and that is a dinner for which I pay. No, no! I asked you first. I have got right down to the bottom of a case that must be unique —a case that has troubled even my mind for over a year—and if that isn't a good reason for standing a dinner, I don't know what is. Cupples, we will not go to my club. This is to be a festival, and to be seen in a London club in a state of pleasurable emotion is more than enough to shatter any man's career. Besides that, the dinner there is always the same, or, at least, they always make it taste the same, I know not how. The eternal dinner at my club hath bored millions of members like me, and shall bore; but to-night let the feast be spread in vain, so far as we are concerned. We will not go where the satraps throng the hall. We will go to Sheppard's."

"Who is Sheppard?" asked Mr. Cupples mildly, as they proceeded up Victoria Street. His companion went with an unnatural lightness, and a policeman, observing his face, smiled indulgently at a look of happiness which he could only attribute to alcohol.

"Who is Sheppard?" echoed Trent with bitter emphasis. "That question, if you will pardon me for saying so, Cupples, is thoroughly characteristic of the spirit of aimless inquiry prevailing in this restless day. I suggest our dining at Sheppard's, and instantly you fold your arms and demand, in a frenzy of intellectual pride, to know who Sheppard is before you will cross the threshold of Sheppard's. I am not going to pander to the vices of the modern mind. Sheppard's is a place where one can dine. I do not know Sheppard. It never occurred to me that Sheppard existed. Probably he is a myth of totemistic origin. All I know is that you can get a bit of saddle of mutton at Sheppard's that has made many an American visitor curse the day that Christopher Columbus was born. . . . Taxi!"

A cab rolled smoothly to the kerb, and the driver received his instructions with a majestic nod.

"Another reason I have for suggesting Sheppard's," continued Trent, feverishly lighting a cigarette, "is that I am going to be married to the most wonderful woman in the world. I trust the connection of ideas is clear."

"You are going to marry Mabel!" cried Mr. Cupples. "My dear friend, what good news this is! Shake hands, Trent; this is glorious! I congratulate you both from the bottom of my heart. And may I say—I don't want to interrupt your flow of high spirits, which is very natural indeed, and I remember being just the same in similar circumstances long ago—but may I say how earnestly I have hoped for this? Mabel has seen so much unhappiness, yet she is surely a woman formed in the great purpose of humanity to be the best influence in the life of a good man. But I did not know her mind as regarded yourself. *Your* mind I have known for some time," Mr. Cupples went on, with a twinkle in his eye that would have done credit to the worldliest of creatures. "I saw it at once when you were both dining at my house, and you sat listening to Professor Peppmüller and looking at her. Some of us older fellows have our wits about us still, my dear boy."

"Mabel says she knew it before that," replied Trent, with a slightly crestfallen air. "And I thought I was acting the part of a person who was not mad about her to the life. Well, I never was any good at dissembling. I shouldn't wonder if even old Peppmüller noticed something through his double convex lenses. But however crazy I may have been as an undeclared suitor," he went on with a return to vivacity, "I am going to be much worse now. As for your congratulations, thank you a thousand times, because I know you mean them. You are the sort of uncomfortable brute who would pull a face three feet long if you thought we were making a mistake. By the way, I can't help being an ass to-night; I'm obliged to go on blithering. You must try to bear it. Perhaps it would be easier if I sang you a song—one of your old favourites. What was that song you used always to be singing? Like this, wasn't it?" He accompanied the following stave with a dexterous clog-step on the floor of the cab:

"There was an old nigger, and he had a wooden leg.
He had no tobacco, no tobacco could he beg.
Another old nigger was as cunning as a fox,
And he always had tobacco in his old tobacco-box.

Now for the chorus!

Yes, he always had tobacco in his old tobacco-box.

But you're not singing! I thought you would be making the welkin ring."

"I never sang that song in my life," protested Mr. Cupples. "I never heard it before."

"Are you sure?" inquired Trent doubtfully. "Well, I suppose I must take your word for it. It is a beautiful song, anyhow: not the whole warbling grove in concert heard can beat it. Somehow it seems to express my feelings at the present moment as nothing else could; it rises unbidden to the lips. Out of the fullness of the heart the mouth speaketh, as the Bishop of Bath and Wells said when listening to a speech of Mr. Balfour's."

"When was that?" asked Mr. Cupples.

"On the occasion," replied Trent, "of the introduction of the Compulsory Notification of Diseases of Poultry Bill, which ill-fated measure you of course remember. Hullo!" he broke off, as the cab rushed down a side street and swung round a corner into a broad and populous thoroughfare, "we're there already." The cab drew up.

"Here we are," said Trent, as he paid the man, and led Mr. Cupples into a long, panelled room set with many tables and filled with a hum of talk. "This is the house of fulfilment of

craving, this is the bower with the roses around it. I see there
are three bookmakers eating pork at my favourite table. We
will have that one in the opposite corner."

He conferred earnestly with a waiter, while Mr. Cupples, in
a pleasant meditation, warmed himself before the great fire.
"The wine here," Trent resumed, as they seated themselves,
"is almost certainly made out of grapes. What shall we drink?"

Mr. Cupples came out of his reverie. "I think," he said, "I
will have milk and soda water."

"Speak lower!" urged Trent. "The head-waiter has a weak
heart, and might hear you. Milk and soda water! Cupples, you
may think you have a strong constitution, and I don't say you
have not, but I warn you that this habit of mixing drinks has
been the death of many a robuster man than you. Be wise in
time. Fill high the bowl with Samian wine, leave soda to the
Turkish hordes. Here comes our food." He gave another order
to the waiter, who ranged the dishes before them and darted
away. Trent was, it seemed, a respected customer. "I have
sent," he said, "for wine that I know, and I hope you will try
it. If you have taken a vow, then in the name of all the teetotal
saints drink water, which stands at your elbow, but don't seek
a cheap notoriety by demanding milk and soda."

"I have never taken any pledge," said Mr. Cupples, examining his mutton with a favourable eye. "I simply don't care
about wine I bought a bottle once and drank it to see what it
was like, and it made me ill. But very likely it was bad wine.
I will taste some of yours, as it is your dinner, and I do assure
you, my dear Trent, I should like to do something unusual to
show how strongly I feel on the present occasion. I have not
been so delighted for many years. To think," he reflected aloud
as the waiter filled his glass, "of the Manderson mystery disposed of, of the innocent exculpated, and your own and Mabel's
happiness crowned—all coming upon me together! I drink to
you, my dear friend." And Mr. Cupples took a very small sip
of the wine.

"You have a great nature," said Trent, much moved. "Your
outward semblance doth belie your soul's immensity. I should
have expected as soon to see an elephant conducting at the
opera as you drinking my health. Dear Cupples! May his beak
retain ever that delicate rose-stain!—No, curse it all!" he
broke out, surprising a shade of discomfort that flitted over
his companion's face as he tasted the wine again. "I have no

business to meddle with your tastes. I apologize. You shall have
what you want, even if it causes the head-waiter to perish in
his pride."

When Mr. Cupples had been supplied with his monastic
drink, and the waiter had retired, Trent looked across the
table with significance. "In this babble of many conversations,"
he said, "we can speak as freely as if we were on a bare hillside.
The waiter is whispering soft nothings into the ear of the young
woman at the pay-desk. We are alone. What do you think of
the interview of this afternoon?" He began to dine with an
appetite.

Without pausing in the task of cutting his mutton into very
small pieces Mr. Cupples replied: "The most curious feature
of it, in my judgment, was the irony of the situation. We both
held the clue to that mad hatred of Manderson's which Marlowe found so mysterious. We knew of his jealous obsession;
which knowledge we withheld, as was very proper, if only in
consideration of Mabel's feelings. Marlowe will never know of
what he was suspected by that person. Strange! Nearly all of
us, I venture to think, move unconsciously among a network
of opinions, often quite erroneous, which other people entertain about us. I remember, for instance, discovering quite by
accident some years ago that a number of people of my acquaintance believed me to have been secretly received into the
Church of Rome. This absurd fiction was based upon the fact,
which in the eyes of many appeared conclusive, that I had expressed myself in talk as favouring the plan of a weekly abstinence from meat. Manderson's belief in regard to his secretary
probably rested upon a much slighter ground. It was Mr. Bunner, I think you said, who told you of his rooted and apparent
hereditary temper of suspicious jealousy. . . . With regard
to Marlowe's story, it appeared to me entirely straightforward,
and not, in its essential features, especially remarkable, once
we have admitted, as we surely must, that in the case of Manderson we have to deal with a more or less disordered mind."

Trent laughed loudly. "I confess," he said, "that the affair
struck me as a little unusual."

"Only in the development of the details," argued Mr. Cupples. "What is there abnormal in the essential facts? A madman conceives a crazy suspicion; he hatches a cunning plot
against his fancied injurer; it involves his own destruction.
Put thus, what is there that any man with the least knowledge

of the ways of lunatics would call remarkable? Turn now to Marlowe's proceedings. He finds himself in a perilous position from which, though he is innocent, telling the truth will not save him. Is that an unheard-of situation? He escaped by means of a bold and ingenious piece of deception. That seems to me a thing that might happen every day, and probably does so." He attacked his now unrecognizable mutton.

"I should like to know," said Trent, after an alimentary pause in the conversation, "whether there is anything that ever happened on the face of the earth that you could not represent as quite ordinary and commonplace by such a line of argument as that."

A gentle smile illuminated Mr. Cupples's face. "You must not suspect me of empty paradox," he said. "My meaning will become clearer, perhaps, if I mention some things which *do* appear to me essentially remarkable. Let me see. . . . Well, I would call the life history of the liver-fluke, which we owe to the researches of Poulton, an essentially remarkable thing."

"I am unable to argue the point," replied Trent. "Fair science may have smiled upon the liver-fluke's humble birth, but I never even heard it mentioned."

"It is not, perhaps, an appetizing subject," said Mr. Cupples thoughtfully, "and I will not pursue it. All I mean is, my dear Trent, that there are really remarkable things going on all round us if we will only see them, and we do our perceptions no credit in regarding as remarkable only those affairs which are surrounded with an accumulation of sensational detail."

Trent applauded heartily with his knife-handle on the table, as Mr. Cupples ceased and refreshed himself with milk and soda water. "I have not heard you go on like this for years," he said. "I believe you must be almost as much above yourself as I am. It is a bad case of the unrest which men miscall delight. But much as I enjoy it, I am not going to sit still and hear the Manderson affair dismissed as commonplace. You may say what you like, but the idea of impersonating Manderson in those circumstances was an extraordinarily ingenious idea."

"Ingenious—certainly!" replied Mr. Cupples. "Extraordinarily so—no! In those circumstances (your own words) it was really not strange that it should occur to a clever man. It lay almost on the surface of the situation. Marlowe was famous for his imitation of Manderson's voice; he had a talent for acting; he had a chess-player's mind; he knew the ways of the establishment intimately. I grant you that the idea was brilliantly carried out; but everything favoured it. As for the essential idea, I do not place it, as regards ingenuity, in the same class with, for example, the idea of utilizing the force of recoil in a discharged firearm to actuate the mechanism of ejecting and reloading. I do, however, admit, as I did at the outset, that in respect of details the case had unusual features. It developed a high degree of complexity."

"Did it really strike you in that way?" inquired Trent with desperate sarcasm.

"The affair became complicated," went on Mr. Cupples unmoved, "because after Marlowe's suspicions were awakened, a second subtle mind came in to interfere with the plans of the first. That sort of duel often happens in business and politics, but less frequently, I imagine, in the world of crime."

"I should say never," Trent replied; "and the reason is, that even the cleverest criminals seldom run to strategic subtlety. When they do, they don't get caught, since clever policemen have if possible less strategic subtlety than the ordinary clever criminal. But that rather deep quality seems very rarely to go with the criminal make-up. Look at Crippen. He was a very clever criminal as they go. He solved the central problem of every clandestine murder, the disposal of the body, with extreme neatness. But how far did he see through the game? The criminal and the policeman are often swift and bold tacticians, but neither of them is good for more than a quite simple plan. After all, it's a rare faculty in any walk of life."

"One disturbing reflection was left on my mind," said Mr. Cupples, who seemed to have had enough of abstractions for the moment, "by what we learned to-day. If Marlowe had suspected nothing and walked into the trap, he would almost certainly have been hanged. Now how often may not a plan to throw the guilt of murder on an innocent person have been practised successfully? There are, I imagine, numbers of cases in which the accused, being found guilty on circumstantial evidence, have died protesting their innocence. I shall never approve again of a death-sentence imposed in a case decided upon such evidence."

"I never have done so, for my part," said Trent. "To hang in such cases seems to me flying in the face of the perfectly obvious and sound principle expressed in the saying that 'you never can tell.' I agree with the American jurist who lays it down that we should not hang a yellow dog for stealing jam on circumstantial evidence, not even if he has jam all over his nose. As for attempts being made by malevolent persons to fix crimes upon innocent men, of course it is constantly happening. It's a marked feature, for instance, of all systems of rule by coercion, whether in Ireland or Russia or India or Korea; if the police cannot get hold of a man they think dangerous by fair means, they do it by foul. But there's one case in the State Trials that is peculiarly to the point, because not only was it a case of fastening a murder on innocent people, but the plotter did in effect what Manderson did; he gave up his own life in order to secure the death of his victims. Probably you have heard of the Campden Case."

Mr. Cupples confessed his ignorance and took another potato.

"John Masefield has written a very remarkably play about it," said Trent, "and if it ever comes on again in London, you should go and see it, if you like having the fan-tods. I have often seen women weeping in an undemonstrative manner at some slab of oleo-margarine sentiment in the theatre. By George! what everlasting smelling-bottle hysterics they ought to have if they saw that play decently acted! Well, the facts were that John Perry accused his mother and brother of murdering a man, and swore he had helped them to do it. He told a story full of elaborate detail, and had an answer to everything, except the curious fact that the body couldn't be found; but the judge, who was probably drunk at the time—this was in Restoration days—made nothing of that. The mother and brother denied the accusation. All three prisoners were found guilty and hanged, purely on John's evidence. Two years after, the man whom they were hanged for murdering came back to Campden. He had been kidnapped by pirates and taken to sea. His disappearance had given John his idea. The point about John is, that his including himself in the accusation, which amounted to suicide, was the thing in his evidence which convinced everybody of its truth. It was so obvious that no man would do himself to death to get somebody else hanged. Now that is exactly the answer which the prosecution would have made if Marlowe had told the truth. Not one juryman in a million would have believed in the Manderson plot."

Mr. Cupples mused upon this a few moments. "I have not your acquaintance with that branch of history," he said at length, "in fact, I have none at all. But certain recollections of my own childhood return to me in connection with this affair. We know from the things Mabel told you what may be termed the spiritual truth underlying this matter; the insane depth of jealous hatred which Manderson concealed. We can understand that he was capable of such a scheme. But as a rule it is in the task of penetrating to the spiritual truth that the administration of justice breaks down. Sometimes that truth is deliberately concealed, as in Manderson's case. Sometimes, I think, it is concealed because simple people are actually unable to express it, and nobody else divines it. When I was a lad in Edinburgh the whole country went mad about the Sandyford Place murder."

Trent nodded. "Mrs. M'Lachlan's case. She was innocent right enough."

"My parents thought so," said Mr. Cupples. "I thought so myself when I became old enough to read and understand that excessively sordid story. But the mystery of the affair was so dark, and the task of getting at the truth behind the lies told by everybody concerned proved so hopeless, that others were just as fully convinced of the innocence of old James Fleming. All Scotland took sides on the question. It was the subject of debates in Parliament. The press divided into two camps, and raged with a fury I have never seen equalled. Yet it is obvious, is it not?—for I see you have read of the case—that if the spiritual truth about that old man could have been known there would have been very little room for doubt in the matter. If what some surmised about his disposition was true, he was quite capable of murdering Jessie M'Pherson and then casting the blame on the poor feeble-minded creature who came so near to suffering the last penalty of the law."

"Even a commonplace old dotard like Fleming can be an unfathomable mystery to all the rest of the human race," said Trent, "and most of all in a court of justice. The law certainly does not shine when it comes to a case requiring much delicacy of perception. It goes wrong easily enough over the Flemings of this world. As for the people with temperaments who get mixed up in legal proceedings, they must feel as if they were in a forest of apes, whether they win or lose. Well, I dare say it's good for their sort to have their noses rubbed in reality now and again. But what would twelve red-faced realities in a jurybox have done to Marlowe? His story would, as he says, have been a great deal worse than no defence at all. It's not as if there were a single piece of evidence in support of his tale. Can't you imagine how the prosecution would tear it to rags? Can't you see the judge simply taking it in his stride when it came to the summing up? And the jury—you've served on juries, I expect—in their room, snorting with indignation over the feebleness of the lie, telling each other it was the clearest case they ever heard of, and that they'd have thought better of him if he hadn't lost his nerve at the crisis, and had cleared off with the swag as he intended. Imagine yourself on that jury, not knowing Marlowe, and trembling with indignation at the record unrolled before you—cupidity, murder, robbery, sudden cowardice, shameless, impenitent, desperate lying! Why, you and I believed him to be guilty until——"

"I beg your pardon! I beg your pardon!" interjected Mr. Cupples, laying down his knife and fork. "I was most careful, when we talked it all over the other night, to say nothing indicating such a belief. *I* was always certain that he was innocent."

"You said something of the sort at Marlowe's just now. I wondered what on earth you could mean. Certain that he was innocent! How can you be certain? You are generally more careful about terms than that, Cupples."

"I said 'certain,' " Mr. Cupples repeated firmly.

Trent shrugged his shoulders. "If you really were, after reading my manuscript and discussing the whole thing as we did," he rejoined, "then I can only say that you must have totally renounced all trust in the operations of the human reason; an attitude which, while it is bad Christianity and also infernal nonsense, is oddly enough bad positivism too, unless I misunderstand that system. Why, man——"

"Let me say a word," Mr. Cupples interposed again, folding his hands above his plate. "I assure you I am far from abandoning reason. I am certain he is innocent, and I always was certain of it, because of something that I know, and knew from the very beginning. You asked me just now to imagine myself on the jury at Marlowe's trial. That would be an unprofitable exercise of the mental powers, because I know that I should be present in another capacity. I should be in the witness-box, giving evidence for the defence. You said just now, 'If there were a single piece of evidence in support of his tale.' There is, and it is my evidence. And," he added quietly, "it is conclusive." He took up his knife and fork and went contentedly on with his dinner.

The pallor of sudden excitement had turned Trent to marble while Mr. Cupples led laboriously up to this statement. At the last word the blood rushed to his face again, and he struck the table with an unnatural laugh. "It can't be!" he exploded. "It's something you fancied, something you dreamed after one of those debauches of soda and milk. You can't really mean that all the time I was working on the case down there you knew Marlowe was innocent."

Mr. Cupples, busy with his last mouthful, nodded brightly. He made an end of eating, wiped his sparse moustache, and then leaned forward over the table. "It's very simple," he said. "I shot Manderson myself."

. . . .

"I am afraid I startled you," Trent heard the voice of Mr. Cupples say. He forced himself out of his stupefaction like a diver striking upward for the surface, and with a rigid movement raised his glass. But half of the wine splashed upon the cloth, and he put it carefully down again untasted. He drew a deep breath, which was exhaled in a laugh wholly without merriment. "Go on," he said.

"It was not murder," began Mr. Cupples, slowly measuring off inches with a fork on the edge of the table. "I will tell you the whole story. On that Sunday night I was taking my before-bedtime constitutional, having set out from the hotel about a quarter past ten. I went along the field path that runs behind White Gables, cutting off the great curve of the road, and came out on the road nearly opposite that gate that is just by the eighth hole on the golf-course. Then I turned in there, meaning to walk along the turf to the edge of the cliff, and go back that way. I had only gone a few steps when I heard the car coming, and then I heard it stop near the gate. I saw Manderson at once. Do you remember my telling you I had seen him once alive after our quarrel in front of the hotel? Well, this was the time. You asked me if I had, and I did not care to tell a falsehood."

A slight groan came from Trent. He drank a little wine, and said stonily, "Go on, please."

"It was, as you know," pursued Mr. Cupples, "a moonlight night, but I was in shadow under the trees by the stone wall, and anyhow they could not suppose there was anyone near them. I heard all that passed just as Marlowe has narrated it to us, and I saw the car go off towards Bishopsbridge. I did not see Manderson's face as it went, because his back was to me, but he shook the back of his left hand at the car with extraordinary violence, greatly to my amazement. Then I waited for him to go back to White Gables, as I did not want to meet him again. But he did not go. He opened the gate through which I had just passed, and he stood there on the turf of the green, quite still. His head was bent, his arms hung at his sides, and he looked somehow—rigid. For a few moments he remained in this tense attitude, then all of a sudden his right arm moved swiftly, and his hand was at the pocket of his overcoat. I saw his face raised in the moonlight, the teeth bared, and the eyes glittering, and all at once I knew that the man was not sane. Almost as quickly as that flashed across my mind, something else flashed in the moonlight. He held the pistol before him, pointing at his breast.

"Now I may say here I shall always be doubtful whether Manderson really meant to kill himself then. Marlowe naturally thinks so, knowing nothing of my intervention. But I think it quite likely he only meant to wound himself, and to charge Marlowe with attempted murder and robbery.

"At that moment, however, I assumed it was suicide. Before I knew what I was doing I had leapt out of the shadows and seized his arm. He shook me off with a furious snarling noise, giving me a terrific blow in the chest, and presenting the revolver at my head. But I seized his wrists before he could fire, and clung with all my strength—you remember how bruised and scratched they were. I knew I was fighting for my own life now, for murder was in his eyes. We struggled like two beasts, without an articulate word, I holding his pistol-hand down and keeping a grip on the other. I never dreamed that I had the strength for such an encounter. Then, with a perfectly instinctive movement—I never knew I meant to do it—I flung away his free hand and clutched like lightning at the weapon, tearing it from his fingers. By a miracle it did not go off. I darted back a few steps, he sprang at my throat like a wild cat, and I fired blindly in his face. He would have been about a yard away, I suppose. His knees gave way instantly, and he fell in a heap on the turf.

"I flung the pistol down and bent over him. The heart's

action ceased under my hand. I knelt there staring, struck motionless; and I don't know how long it was before I heard the noise of the car returning.

"Trent, all the time that Marlowe paced that green, with the moonlight on his white and working face, I was within a few yards of him, crouching in the shadow of the furze by the ninth tee. I dared not show myself. I was thinking. My public quarrel with Manderson the same morning was, I suspected, the talk of the hotel. I assure you that every horrible possibility of the situation for me had rushed across my mind the moment I saw Manderson fall. I became cunning. I knew what I must do. I must get back to the hotel as fast as I could, get in somehow unperceived, and play a part to save myself. I must never tell a word to anyone. Of course I was assuming that Marlowe would tell everyone how he had found the body. I knew he would suppose it was suicide; I thought everyone would suppose so.

"When Marlowe began at last to lift the body, I stole away down the wall and got out into the road by the club-house, where he could not see me. I felt perfectly cool and collected. I crossed the road, climbed the fence, and ran across the meadow to pick up the field path I had come by that runs to the hotel behind White Gables. I got back to the hotel very much out of breath."

"Out of breath," repeated Trent mechanically, still staring at his companion as if hypnotized.

"I had had a sharp run," Mr. Cupples reminded him. "Well, approaching the hotel from the back I could see into the writing-room through the open window. There was nobody in there, so I climbed over the sill, walked to the bell and rang it, and then sat down to write a letter I had meant to write the next day. I saw by the clock that it was a little past eleven. When the waiter answered the bell I asked for a glass of milk and a postage stamp. Soon afterwards I went up to bed. But I could not sleep."

Mr. Cupples, having nothing more to say, ceased speaking. He looked in mild surprise at Trent, who now sat silent, supporting his bent head in his hands.

"He could not sleep," murmured Trent at last in a hollow tone. "A frequent result of over-exertion during the day. Nothing to be alarmed about." He was silent again, then looked up with a pale face. "Cupples, I am cured. I will never touch a crime-mystery again. The Manderson affair shall be Philip

Trent's last case. His high-blown pride at length breaks under him." Trent's smile suddenly returned. "I could have borne everything but that last revelation of the impotence of human reason. Cupples, I have absolutely nothing left to say, except this: you have beaten me. I drink your health in a spirit of self-abasement. And *you* shall pay for the dinner."